APA Handbook of
Research Methods
in Psychology

APA Handbooks in Psychology® Series

APA Addiction Syndrome Handbook—two volumes
    Howard J. Shaffer, Editor-in-Chief
APA Educational Psychology Handbook—three volumes
    Karen R. Harris, Steve Graham, and Tim Urdan, Editors-in-Chief
APA Handbook of Adolescent and Young Adult Development—one volume
    Lisa J. Crockett, Gustavo Carlo, and John E. Schulenberg, Editors
APA Handbook of Behavior Analysis—two volumes
    Gregory J. Madden, Editor-in-Chief
APA Handbook of Career Intervention—two volumes
    Paul J. Hartung, Mark L. Savickas, and W. Bruce Walsh, Editors-in-Chief
APA Handbook of Clinical Geropsychology—two volumes
    Peter A. Lichtenberg and Benjamin T. Mast, Editors-in-Chief
APA Handbook of Clinical Psychology—five volumes
    John C. Norcross, Gary R. VandenBos, and Donald K. Freedheim, Editors-in-Chief
APA Handbook of Community Psychology—two volumes
    Meg A. Bond, Irma Serrano-García, and Christopher B. Keys, Editors-in-Chief
APA Handbook of Comparative Psychology—two volumes
    Josep Call, Editor-in-Chief
APA Handbook of Consumer Psychology—one volume
    Lynn R. Kahle, Editor-in-Chief
APA Handbook of Contemporary Family Psychology—three volumes
    Barbara H. Fiese, Editor-in-Chief
APA Handbook of Counseling Psychology—two volumes
    Nadya A. Fouad, Editor-in-Chief
APA Handbook of Dementia—one volume
    Glenn E. Smith, Editor-in-Chief
APA Handbook of Ethics in Psychology—two volumes
    Samuel J. Knapp, Editor-in-Chief
APA Handbook of Forensic Neuropsychology—one volume
    Shane S. Bush, Editor-in-Chief
APA Handbook of Forensic Psychology—two volumes
    Brian L. Cutler and Patricia A. Zapf, Editors-in-Chief
APA Handbook of Giftedness and Talent—one volume
    Steven I. Pfeiffer, Editor-in-Chief
APA Handbook of Human Systems Integration—one volume
    Deborah A. Boehm-Davis, Francis T. Durso, and John D. Lee, Editors-in-Chief
APA Handbook of Industrial and Organizational Psychology—three volumes
    Sheldon Zedeck, Editor-in-Chief
APA Handbook of Intellectual and Developmental Disabilities—two volumes
    Laraine Masters Glidden, Editor-in-Chief
APA Handbook of Men and Masculinities—one volume
    Y. Joel Wong and Stephen R. Wester, Editors-in-Chief
APA Handbook of Multicultural Psychology—two volumes
    Frederick T. L. Leong, Editor-in-Chief

APA Handbook of Neuropsychology—two volumes
    Gregory G. Brown, Tricia Z. King, Kathleen Y. Haaland, and Bruce Crosson, Editors
APA Handbook of Nonverbal Communication—one volume
    David Matsumoto, Hyisung Hwang, and Mark Frank, Editors-in-Chief
APA Handbook of Personality and Social Psychology—four volumes
    Mario Mikulincer and Phillip R. Shaver, Editors-in-Chief
APA Handbook of Psychology and Juvenile Justice—one volume
    Kirk Heilbrun, Editor-in-Chief
APA Handbook of Psychology, Religion, and Spirituality—two volumes
    Kenneth I. Pargament, Editor-in-Chief
APA Handbook of the Psychology of Women—two volumes
    Cheryl B. Travis and Jacquelyn W. White, Editors-in-Chief
APA Handbook of Psychopathology—two volumes
    James N. Butcher, Editor-in-Chief
APA Handbook of Psychopharmacology—one volume
    Suzette M. Evans, Editor-in-Chief
APA Handbook of Research Methods in Psychology, Second Edition—three volumes
    Harris Cooper, Editor-in-Chief
APA Handbook of Sexuality and Psychology—two volumes
    Deborah L. Tolman and Lisa M. Diamond, Editors-in-Chief
APA Handbook of Sport and Exercise Psychology—two volumes
    Mark H. Anshel, Editor-in-Chief
APA Handbook of Testing and Assessment in Psychology—three volumes
    Kurt F. Geisinger, Editor-in-Chief
APA Handbook of Trauma Psychology—two volumes
    Steven N. Gold, Editor-in-Chief

APA Handbooks in Psychology

APA Handbook of
Research Methods in Psychology

SECOND EDITION

VOLUME 3

Data Analysis and Research Publication

Harris Cooper, *Editor-in-Chief*

Marc N. Coutanche, Linda M. McMullen, A. T. Panter, David Rindskopf, and Kenneth J. Sher, *Associate Editors*

AMERICAN PSYCHOLOGICAL ASSOCIATION

Copyright © 2023 by the American Psychological Association. All rights reserved. Except as permitted under the United States Copyright Act of 1976, no part of this publication may be reproduced or distributed in any form or by any means, including, but not limited to, the process of scanning and digitization, or stored in a database or retrieval system, without the prior written permission of the publisher.

The opinions and statements published are the responsibility of the authors and editors, and such opinions and statements do not necessarily represent the policies of the American Psychological Association.

Published by
American Psychological Association
750 First Street, NE
Washington, DC 20002
https://www.apa.org

Order Department
https://www.apa.org/pubs/books
order@apa.org

Typeset in Berkeley by Circle Graphics, Inc., Reisterstown, MD

Printer: Sheridan Books, Chelsea, MI
Cover Designer: Mark Karis

Library of Congress Cataloging-in-Publication Data

Names: Cooper, Harris M., editor. | American Psychological Association, issuer.
Title: APA handbook of research methods in psychology / editor-in-Chief
  Harris Cooper; associate editors Marc N. Coutanche, Linda M. McMullen,
  A.T. Panter, David Rindskopf, and Kenneth J. Sher
Description: Second Edition. | Washington, DC : American Psychological
  Association, [2023-] | Series: APA handbooks in psychology | Revised
  edition of APA handbook of research methods in psychology, c2012. |
  Includes bibliographical references and index. | Contents: v. 1.
  Foundations, planning, measures, and psychometrics--v. 2. Research designs:
  quantitative, qualitative, neuropsychological, and biological--v. 3. Data analysis
  and research publication |
Identifiers: LCCN 2022020492 (print) | LCCN 2022020493 (ebook) |
  ISBN 9781433837135 (v. 1 ; hardcover) | ISBN 9781433841330 (v. 2 ; hardcover) |
  ISBN 9781433841354 (v. 3 ; hardcover) | ISBN 9781433841323 (v. 1 ; ebook) |
  ISBN 9781433841347 (v. 2 ; ebook) | ISBN 9781433841361 (v. 3 ; ebook)
Subjects: LCSH: Psychology--Research--Methodology--Handbooks, manuals, etc. |
  Psychology--Research--Handbooks, manuals, etc.
Classification: LCC BF76.5 .A73 2023 (print) | LCC BF76.5 (ebook) |
  DDC 150.72/1--dc23/eng/20220802
LC record available at https://lccn.loc.gov/2022020492
LC ebook record available at https://lccn.loc.gov/2022020493

https://doi.org/10.1037/0000320-000

Printed in the United States of America

10 9 8 7 6 5 4 3 2 1

Contents

Volume 3: Data Analysis and Research Publication

Editorial Board xi
Contributors xiii

Part I. Quantitative Data Analysis 1

Section 1. Preparing Data for Analysis 3

Chapter 1. Methods for Dealing With Bad Data and Inadequate Models:
    Distributions, Linear Models, and Beyond. 5
    Rand R. Wilcox and Guillaume A. Rousselet
Chapter 2. Maximum Likelihood and Multiple Imputation Missing Data Handling:
    How They Work, and How to Make Them Work in Practice 27
    Timothy Hayes and Craig K. Enders
Chapter 3. Exploratory Data Analysis. 53
    Paul F. Velleman and David C. Hoaglin

Section 2. Describing Data 75

Chapter 4. Graphic Displays of Data. 77
    Leland Wilkinson
Chapter 5. Estimating and Visualizing Interactions in Moderated Multiple
    Regression. 111
    Connor J. McCabe and Kevin M. King
Chapter 6. Effect-Size Estimation 129
    Michael Borenstein
Chapter 7. Measures of Clinically Significant Change. 147
    Russell J. Bailey, Benjamin M. Ogles, and Michael J. Lambert

Section 3. Methods With Single Outcomes 167

Chapter 8. Analysis of Variance and the General Linear Model 169
    James Jaccard and Ai Bo
Chapter 9. Generalized Linear Models 201
    David Rindskopf
Chapter 10. Multilevel Modeling for Psychologists 219
    John B. Nezlek

Section 4. Methods With Outcomes Measured Over Time 243

Chapter 11. Longitudinal Data Analysis 245
    Andrew K. Littlefield
Chapter 12. Event History Analysis 269
    Fetene B. Tekle and Jeroen K. Vermunt
Chapter 13. Latent State–Trait Models 297
    Rolf Steyer, Christian Geiser, and Christiane Loßnitzer
Chapter 14. Latent Variable Modeling of Continuous Growth 317
    David A. Cole, Jeffrey A. Ciesla, and Qimin Liu
Chapter 15. Dynamical Systems and Differential Equation Models of Change 337
    Steven M. Boker and Robert G. Moulder
Chapter 16. A Multivariate Growth Curve Model for Three-Level Data 351
    Patrick J. Curran, Chris L. Strauss, Ethan M. McCormick,
    and James S. McGinley

Section 5. Multivariate Methods 377

Chapter 17. Exploratory Factor Analysis and Confirmatory Factor Analysis 379
    Keith F. Widaman and Jonathan Lee Helm
Chapter 18. Latent Class and Latent Profile Models 411
    Brian P. Flaherty, Liying Wang, and Cara J. Kiff
Chapter 19. Decision Trees and Ensemble Methods in the Behavioral Sciences 429
    Kevin J. Grimm, Ross Jacobucci, and John J. McArdle

Section 6. Dyadic and Social Network Data 449

Chapter 20. Using the Social Relations Model to Understand Interpersonal
    Perception and Behavior 451
    P. Niels Christensen, Deborah A. Kashy, and Katelin E. Leahy
Chapter 21. Dyadic Data Analysis. 465
    Richard Gonzalez and Dale Griffin

Section 7. Using Data Collected by Others 479

Chapter 22. The Data of Others: New and Old Faces of Archival Research 481
    Sophie Pychlau and David T. Wagner
Chapter 23. Social Network Analysis in Psychology: Recent Breakthroughs
    in Methods and Theories. 501
    *Wei Wang, Tobias Stark, James D. Westaby, Adam K. Parr,
    and Daniel A. Newman*
Chapter 24. Meta-Analysis 539
    Jeffrey C. Valentine, Therese D. Pigott, and Joseph Morris

Part II. Publishing and the Publication Process 561

Chapter 25. Research Data Management and Sharing 563
    Katherine G. Akers and John A. Borghi
Chapter 26. Questionable Practices in Statistical Analysis. 579
    Rex B. Kline
Chapter 27. Ethical Issues in Manuscript Preparation and Authorship 597
    Jennifer Crocker

Index 617

Editorial Board

EDITOR-IN-CHIEF

Harris Cooper, PhD, Hugo L. Blomquist Professor, Emeritus, Department of Psychology and Neuroscience, Duke University, Durham, NC, United States

ASSOCIATE EDITORS

Marc N. Coutanche, PhD, Associate Professor of Psychology, and Research Scientist in the Learning Research and Development Center, University of Pittsburgh, Pittsburgh, PA, United States

Linda M. McMullen, PhD, Professor Emerita, Department of Psychology, University of Saskatchewan, Saskatoon, SK, Canada

A. T. Panter, PhD, Senior Associate Dean for Undergraduate Education, College of Arts and Sciences, and Professor, L. L. Thurstone Psychometric Laboratory, The University of North Carolina at Chapel Hill, Chapel Hill, NC, United States

David Rindskopf, PhD, Distinguished Professor of Educational Psychology and Psychology, City University of New York Graduate Center, New York, NY, United States

Kenneth J. Sher, PhD, Chancellor's Professor, Curators' Distinguished Professor of Psychological Sciences, Emeritus, Department of Psychological Sciences, University of Missouri, Columbia, MO, United States

Contributors

Katherine G. Akers, PhD, Shiffman Medical Library, Wayne State University, Detroit, MI, United States

Russell J. Bailey, PhD, Department of Behavioral Science, Utah Valley University, Orem, UT, United States

Ai Bo, PhD, Helen Bader School of Social Welfare, University of Wisconsin-Milwaukee, Milwaukee, WI, United States

Steven M. Boker, PhD, Department of Psychology, University of Virginia, Charlottesville, VA, United States

Michael Borenstein, PhD, Biostat, Inc., Englewood, NJ, United States

John A. Borghi, PhD, Lane Medical Library, Stanford University School of Medicine, Stanford, CA, United States

P. Niels Christensen, PhD, Department of Psychology, Radford University, Radford, VA, United States

Jeffrey A. Ciesla, PhD, Department of Psychological Sciences, Kent State University, Kent, OH, United States

David A. Cole, PhD, Department of Psychology and Human Development, Vanderbilt University, Nashville, TN, United States

Jennifer Crocker, PhD, Department of Psychology, The Ohio State University, Columbus, OH, United States

Patrick J. Curran, PhD, Department of Psychology, The University of North Carolina at Chapel Hill, Chapel Hill, NC, United States

Craig K. Enders, PhD, Department of Psychology, University of California Los Angeles, Los Angeles, CA, United States

Brian P. Flaherty, PhD, Department of Psychology, University of Washington, Seattle, WA, United States

Christian Geiser, PhD, QuantFish LLC, Ronceverte, West Virginia, United States

Richard Gonzalez, PhD, Department of Psychology, University of Michigan, Ann Arbor, MI, United States

Dale Griffin, PhD, Marketing and Behavioural Science Division, UBC Sauder School of Business, The University of British Columbia, Vancouver, BC, Canada

Kevin J. Grimm, PhD, Department of Psychology, Arizona State University, Tempe, AZ, United States

Timothy Hayes, PhD, Department of Psychology, Florida International University, Miami, FL, United States

Jonathan Lee Helm, PhD, Department of Psychology, San Diego State University, San Diego, CA, United States

David C. Hoaglin, PhD, Department of Population and Quantitative Health Sciences, UMass Chan Medical School, Worcester, MA, United States

James Jaccard, PhD, Silver School of Social Work, New York University, New York, NY, United States

Ross Jacobucci, PhD, Department of Psychology, University of Notre Dame, Notre Dame, IN, United States

Deborah A. Kashy, PhD, Department of Psychology, Michigan State University, East Lansing, MI, United States

Cara J. Kiff, PhD, Private Practice, Los Angeles, CA, United States

Kevin M. King, PhD, Department of Psychology, University of Washington, Seattle, WA, United States

Rex B. Kline, PhD, Department of Psychology, Concordia University, Montréal, QC, Canada

Michael J. Lambert, PhD, Department of Psychology, Brigham Young University, Provo, UT, United States (retired)

Katelin E. Leahy, MA, Department of Psychology, Michigan State University, East Lansing, MI, United States

Andrew K. Littlefield, PhD, Department of Psychological Sciences, Texas Tech University, Lubbock, TX, United States

Qimin Liu, PhD candidate, Psychological Sciences, Vanderbilt University, Nashville, TN, United States

Christiane Loßnitzer, Dipl-Psych, Institute for Psychoanalysis Stuttgart-Tübingen, Tübingen, Germany

John J. McArdle, PhD, Deceased

Connor J. McCabe, PhD, Department of Psychiatry and Behavioral Sciences, University of Washington School of Medicine, Seattle, WA, United States

Ethan M. McCormick, PhD, Lifespan Cognitive Dynamics Lab, Donders Institute for Brain, Cognition, and Behaviour, Radboud University, Nijmegen, The Netherlands

James S. McGinley, PhD, Vector Psychometric Group, LLC, Chapel Hill, NC, United States

Joseph Morris, MPH, School of Public Health, Georgia State University, Atlanta, GA, United States

Robert G. Moulder, PhD, Institute of Cognitive Science, University of Colorado Boulder, Boulder, CO, United States

Daniel A. Newman, PhD, Department of Psychology, University of Illinois Urbana-Champaign, Urbana, IL, United States

John B. Nezlek, PhD, Institute of Psychology, SWPS University of Social Sciences and Humanities, Warsaw, Poland; Department of Psychological Sciences, College of William and Mary, Williamsburg, VA, United States

Benjamin M. Ogles, PhD, Department of Psychology, Brigham Young University, Provo, UT, United States

Adam K. Parr, PhD, Teachers College, Columbia University, New York, NY, United States

Therese D. Pigott, PhD, School of Public Health and the College of Education and Human Development, Georgia State University, Atlanta, GA, United States

Sophie Pychlau, PhD candidate, Department of Management, Lundquist College of Business, University of Oregon, Eugene, OR, United States

David Rindskopf, PhD, City University of New York Graduate Center, New York, NY, United States

Guillaume A. Rousselet, PhD, Centre for Cognitive Neuroimaging, School of Psychology and Neuroscience, University of Glasgow, Glasgow, Scotland

Tobias Stark, PhD, Department of Interdisciplinary Social Science and European Research Centre on Migration and Ethnic Relations, Utrecht University, Utrecht, The Netherlands

Rolf Steyer, PhD, Department of Psychology, University of Jena, Jena, Germany

Chris L. Strauss, MA, Department of Psychology, The University of North Carolina at Chapel Hill, Chapel Hill, NC, United States

Fetene B. Tekle, PhD, Janssen Pharmaceutica NV (J&J), Beerse, Belgium

Jeffrey C. Valentine, PhD, Department of Counseling and Human Development, University of Louisville, Louisville, KY, United States

Paul F. Velleman, PhD, Department of Statistical and Data Sciences (Emeritus), Cornell University, Ithaca, NY, United States

Jeroen K. Vermunt, PhD, Department of Methodology, Tilburg University, Tilburg, The Netherlands

David T. Wagner, PhD, Department of Management, Lundquist College of Business, University of Oregon, Eugene, OR, United States

Liying Wang, MS, Department of Psychology, University of Washington, Seattle, WA, United States

Wei Wang, PhD, Department of Psychology, City University of New York Graduate Center, New York, NY, United States

James D. Westaby, PhD, Teachers College, Columbia University, New York, NY, United States

Keith F. Widaman, PhD, Graduate School of Education, University of California, Riverside, Riverside, CA, United States

Rand R. Wilcox, PhD, Department of Psychology, University of Southern California, Los Angeles, CA, United States

Leland Wilkinson, PhD, Deceased

Part I

QUANTITATIVE DATA ANALYSIS

SECTION 1

PREPARING DATA FOR ANALYSIS

Chapter 1

METHODS FOR DEALING WITH BAD DATA AND INADEQUATE MODELS: DISTRIBUTIONS, LINEAR MODELS, AND BEYOND

Rand R. Wilcox and Guillaume A. Rousselet

A fundamental goal is making inferences about a population of individuals based on a sample of participants. For example, based on some measure of depressive symptoms, what is the average score among all adults? How does the typical male compare with the typical female? As another example, what can be said about the cognitive functioning of children given some measure of aggression in the home? In the first example, not all adults can be measured, which raises the issue of what can be gleaned about the population of all adults based on a sample of n participants. In the second example, taking measures on all households is impossible. What inferences are reasonable based on a sample of n households?

Inferential methods are based on assumptions. One of the more commonly made assumptions is that data reflect a random sample from the population of interest. There are a few inferential methods where this assumption suffices. But typically additional assumptions are required. They include assumptions about how the probabilities associated with all possible outcomes might be modeled. Often assumptions are made about the nature of the population. For example, classic inferential methods assume that when comparing groups, the groups have a common unknown variance. A similar assumption, to be described, is made when dealing with regression. Standard regression methods assume that a linear model can be used to model the typical value of some dependent variable Y, such as the cognitive functioning of children, based on some explanatory variable X, such as a measure of aggression in the home. That is, it is assumed that given X, the typical value for Y is given by

$$Y = \beta_0 + \beta_1 X, \qquad (1.1)$$

where β_0 and β_1 are the population intercept and slope, respectively, that characterize the population of interest.

There are classic methods for comparing groups and studying associations that are routinely taught and used. Based on hundreds of journal articles published during the last 50 years, these methods work well when comparing groups that do not differ in any manner or when dealing with regression when in fact there is no association. If groups differ or there is an association, they might continue to perform well, but under general conditions this is not the case. One reason can be bad data. Here, the notion of bad data is taken to mean data that have a serious negative impact on the intended goal of some statistical method. Bad data might be due to erroneous measures, but it can also refer to valid measures that are not consistent with the underlying assumptions of a particular technique.

https://doi.org/10.1037/0000320-001
APA Handbook of Research Methods in Psychology, Second Edition: Vol. 3. Data Analysis and Research Publication, H. Cooper (Editor-in-Chief)
Copyright © 2023 by the American Psychological Association. All rights reserved.

Closely related to the notion of bad data are inadequate models. That is, a statistical method might be based on assumptions that poorly reflect the population under study. The result is that important differences among groups can be missed. Moreover, characterizations of how groups compare, such as certain measures of effect size, can grossly underestimate the extent the groups differ for the bulk of the participants. As for regression, there are various ways important associations among variables can be missed or poorly characterized. Recent years have seen many improved methods for dealing with known concerns. Moreover, it is well established that these more modern methods can provide a deeper and more nuanced understanding of data. Describing these concerns and how they might be addressed in technically sound manners are the main goals in this chapter. The final section describes books, journal articles, and software aimed at taking advantage of the modern robust methods mentioned here.

Before continuing, there is one more introductory remark that is vitally important. There is now a general awareness that outliers, meaning unusually large or small values, can be a serious practical concern. They can destroy the likelihood of discovering important differences among groups when using any method based on the means as we will illustrate. They can have a highly detrimental impact on measures of effect size based on the means and variances. Roughly, they can mask important differences among the bulk of the participants. Outliers can also be devastating when dealing with regression and Pearson's correlation.

When comparing groups, a seemingly simple solution is to remove the outliers and proceed using some well-known inferential method based on means. From a technical point of view, however, this results in a highly invalid method, regardless of how large the sample size might be, for reasons to be explained and illustrated. There are well-developed methods for dealing with outliers in a technically sound manner (e.g., Staudte & Sheather, 1990; Wilcox, 2022). Currently, however, these methods remain relatively unknown among nonstatisticians. Details about how to detect and deal with outliers are described later in this chapter.

NORMAL DISTRIBUTIONS

Consider some random variable X. For example, X might be some measure of anxiety. A common approach to making inferences about a population of individuals is to assume that some family of distributions can be used to model the probabilities associated with X. Numerous inferential methods are based on the assumption that the probabilities associated with the possible outcomes are given by a normal distribution. It is informative to review how the normal distribution was derived.

Suppose a random sample of n participants yields a sample mean $\bar{X}$. Now imagine that the study is repeated many times, each with n participants, yielding sample means $\bar{X}_1, \bar{X}_2, \bar{X}_3, \ldots$ There are differences among these sample means (see Figure 1.1D). Gauss assumed that the variation of these sample means is smaller than the variation of any other measure of central tendency that might be used such as the median or a trimmed mean. He then showed that by implication, the raw data are being randomly sampled from a normal distribution that has the probability density function

$$f(x) = \frac{1}{\sigma\sqrt{2\pi}} \exp\left[-\frac{(x-\mu)^2}{2\sigma^2}\right], \quad (1.2)$$

where $-\infty \leq x \leq \infty$, μ is the population mean, and σ is the population standard deviation. That is, a normal distribution means that for any value x between $-\infty$ and ∞, the probability of getting a value less than or equal to x is greater than 0 albeit possibly very small. If, for example, intelligence quotient (IQ) scores are assumed to have a normal distribution, this means that getting an IQ score less than or equal to -10 is greater than zero when normality is assumed, which is of course impossible. In practical terms, distributions are never exactly normal. The issue is whether they provide a sufficiently accurate

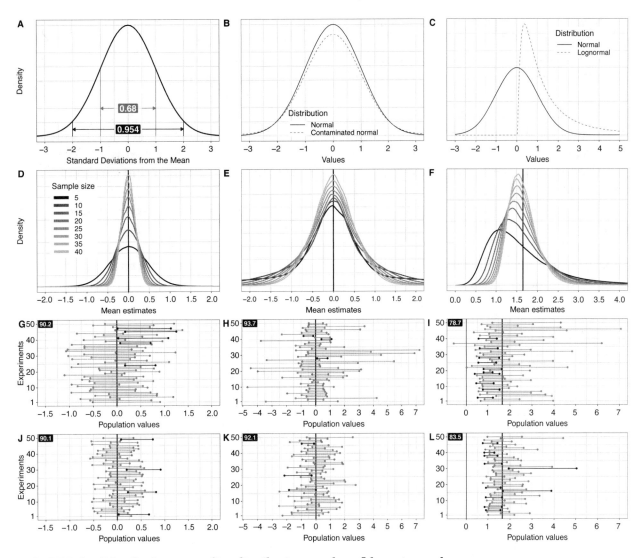

FIGURE 1.1. Distributions, sampling distributions, and confidence intervals.

approximation of the true probabilities when analyzing data. For some purposes the answer is "yes," but for others the answer is an emphatic "no" as will be illustrated. Interestingly, the assumption that the sample mean has the smallest variation of any estimator was known to be false over two centuries ago. In modern terminology, Laplace showed that as we move toward a distribution where outliers are likely to occur, at some point the median has a smaller amount of variation than the mean (Hand, 1998). This is illustrated ahead in conjunction with what is called a *mixed normal distribution*.

Normal distributions are bell-shaped and symmetric about the population mean. Moreover, they have several convenient features that greatly simplify technical issues when developing methods for making inference about a population. One is that regardless of what the mean and standard deviation happen to be, the probability that a randomly sampled observation is within one standard deviation on the mean is 0.68. The probability that a randomly sampled observation is within two standard deviations on the mean is 0.954. These properties are depicted in Figure 1.1A. All the illustrations and examples in this chapter can be reproduced using free R code (R Core Team, 2020; Wilcox & Rousselet, 2021). Each column corresponds to different population distributions, which are illustrated in the first row: A, normal population; B, contaminated normal distribution; C, shifted lognormal distribution. In B and C, the same normal distribution from A is illustrated for comparison. Rows D–F are the sampling distributions of the mean from 50,000 experiments. Rows G–L are the 90% confidence intervals from 50 experiments. The inserts in the upper left corners indicate the actual coverage of the confidence intervals, based on 100,000 simulated experiments. The gray confidence intervals include the population value, the black ones do not. For graphs G–I, $n = 10$; and for graphs J–L, $n = 30$.

Another convenient property is that if X has a normal distribution,

$$Z = \frac{X - \mu}{\sigma} \quad (1.3)$$

has a standard normal distribution meaning a normal distribution with mean 0 and standard deviation 1. A third important feature is that random sampling from a normal distribution implies that the sample mean, $\bar{X}$, also has a normal distribution with mean μ and standard deviation $\sigma/\sqrt{n}$. (The standard deviation of $\bar{X}$, typically labeled the standard error of $\bar{X}$, is equal to $\sigma/\sqrt{n}$ assuming only random sampling.) This in turn means that

$$Z = \frac{\bar{X} - \mu}{\sigma/\sqrt{n}} \quad (1.4)$$

has a standard normal distribution. Let c denote the $1 - \alpha/2$ quantile of a standard normal distribution. That is, $P(Z \leq c) = 1 - \alpha/2$. A little algebra shows that

$$P\left(\bar{X} - c\frac{\sigma}{\sqrt{n}} \leq \mu \leq \bar{X} + c\frac{\sigma}{\sqrt{n}}\right) = 1 - \alpha, \quad (1.5)$$

a result covered in the typical introductory statistics course. That is, the interval

$$\left(\bar{X} - c\frac{\sigma}{\sqrt{n}}, \bar{X} + c\frac{\sigma}{\sqrt{n}}\right) \quad (1.6)$$

contains the unknown population mean with probability $1 - \alpha$. Equation 1.6 is called a $1 - \alpha$ *confidence interval for the population mean*. Here, probability is being viewed in terms of relative frequencies over millions (and, in theory, infinitely many) trials or studies. If a study is repeated many times, there is some variation in the resulting confidence intervals. Imagine that the goal is to compute a $1 - \alpha = 0.95$ confidence interval. Over many studies, Equation 1.6 will contain the true population mean 95% of the time assuming random sampling from a normal distribution.

In practice, the population variance is rarely known, but given a random sample, $X_1, \ldots, X_n$, it can be estimated with the sample variance

$$\frac{1}{n-1}\sum(X_i - \bar{X})^2. \quad (1.7)$$

A confidence interval can be computed if the distribution of

$$T = \frac{\bar{X} - \mu}{s/\sqrt{n}} \quad (1.8)$$

can be determined. Still assuming normality, the distribution of T can be derived and is generally known as *Student's t distribution*. Its quantiles depend on the sample size, more precisely the degrees of freedom, $\nu = n - 1$. If t is the 0.975 quantile, then

$$\left(\bar{X} - t\frac{s}{\sqrt{n}}, \bar{X} + t\frac{s}{\sqrt{n}}\right) \quad (1.9)$$

is a 0.95 confidence interval for the population. An issue here is understanding the impact of bad data on the accuracy of this confidence interval. A related issue is the impact of nonnormality, that is, an incorrect probability model.

One final property of normal distributions is worth mentioning. In general, the sample mean and variance are dependent. This result is not too surprising because the sample mean plays a role when computing the sample variance. But under normality, they are independent, which plays a fundamental role when deriving the distribution of T. The dependence between $\bar{X}$ and s helps explain why certain practical concerns arise when using T.

HYPOTHESIS TESTING VERSUS DECISION MAKING

Basic hypothesis testing methods are routinely taught and used. The most basic features are important here because they provide perspectives on why bad data and inadequate models can be a serious practical concern. Consequently, some of these basic features are summarized here.

In the simplest case, a speculation is made about the value of the population mean, which is typically labeled μ_0. This speculation is called the *null hypothesis* and is commonly written as

$$H_0 : \mu = \mu_0. \tag{1.10}$$

Rejecting this hypothesis when in fact it is true is called *a Type I error*, or *false positive*. Imagine that this hypothesis is rejected when $|T| \geq t$, where t is the $1 - \alpha/2$ quantile of a Student's t distribution. Then assuming normality, the probability of a Type I error is α. Lakens et al. (2018) discuss the important issue of choosing and justifying a value for α.

Suppose a study is conducted based on a sample size of 25 participants. Then for $\alpha = 0.05$, $t_{0.975} = 2.064$ and for $\alpha = 0.01$, $t_{0.995} = 2.797$. Now, suppose it is reported that $|T| > 2.064$. That is, Equation 1.10 is rejected when $\alpha = 0.05$. But based on this result alone, it is unknown whether one would again reject when $\alpha = 0.01$. The p value is the smallest value for α that results in rejecting the null hypothesis. That is, it reflects how cautious one can be about committing a Type I error and still reject.

A concern about p values is that often they are misinterpreted (e.g., Cassidy et al., 2019; Kmetz, 2019; Wasserstein et al., 2019). For example, a small p value does not indicate whether $\mu - \mu_0$ is large. More broadly, it is not a good measure of effect size. Instead, a small p value can be treated as a warning signal that there is something odd with a model (Greenland et al., 2016). Also, a small p value does not indicate the probability of rejecting again if a study is replicated. This is a power issue. Power, or true positive, the probability of rejecting when the null hypothesis is false, is a function of $\mu - \mu_0$, σ and the sample size, n. That is, power depends on the unknown difference between the true and hypothesized value, as well as the standard error of the mean.

One more comment should be made. Tukey (1991) argued that testing for exact equality is nonsensical. For the situation at hand, his argument was that surely the actual population mean differs from the hypothesized value at some decimal place. Jones and Tukey (2000) argued that Tukey's three-decision rule should be used. If, for example, the hypothesis given by (10) is rejected and $\bar{X} < \mu_0$, decide that $\mu < \mu_0$. If the hypothesis is rejected and $\bar{X} > \mu_0$, decide that $\mu > \mu_0$. Otherwise, make no decision. In this context, a p value reflects the strength of the empirical evidence that a decision can be made. This view is consistent with an interpretation suggested by R. A. Fisher (Biau et al., 2010). However, a p value does not reflect the probability that a correct decision has been made. In essence, the components of hypothesis testing remain, but the intended goal is to determine the extent making a decision is reasonable. From this point of view, power corresponds to the probability of making a decision.

NONNORMAL DISTRIBUTIONS

There are at least two fundamental types of nonnormal distributions that can create serious practical concerns when using any method based on means. The first has to do with what are called *heavy-tailed distributions*. To illustrate what this means, consider two populations of individuals. The first has a standard normal distribution meaning that the mean is 0 and the variance is 1. The second also has a normal distribution with mean 0 but standard deviation $\sigma = 10$. Further imagine that when randomly sampling a participant, there is a 0.9 probability of choosing someone from the first population and a 0.1 probability of choosing someone from the second population. This is an example of a contaminated or mixed normal distribution that was discussed at length by Tukey (1960). Figure 1.1B shows the standard normal distribution and the mixed normal just described. As can be seen, the distributions appear to be very similar and indeed they are, based on various metrics for measuring the difference between two distributions (e.g., Wilcox, 2022). However, while the standard normal has variance 1, the mixed normal has variance 10.9. Tukey is illustrating that the population variance is highly sensitive to the tails of a distribution. In fact, there is a formal proof that an arbitrarily small shift away from a normal distribution can result in an arbitrary large increase in the population variance (e.g., Staudte & Sheather, 1990). In practical terms, a small shift away from a normal distribution might destroy the power of any method based on means.

The mixed normal is said to be a heavy-tailed distribution because its tails lie above the tails of a normal distribution. Samples from heavy-tailed distributions tend to have outliers. Outliers inflate the variance of the sampling distributions (the standard error), which means that estimates are more variable across experiments (Figure 1.1E). Outliers also inflate the sample variance as well, which can result in poor power when using standard methods based on the mean, as well as inaccurate confidence intervals (Figure 1.1H and K). Of course, power might remain reasonably high when dealing with a nonnormal distribution. However, outlier detection techniques described below often find outliers.

Skewed distributions also are a serious concern when using any method based on means. They can result in a poor indication of the typical response (Figure 1.1C and F). Moreover, they can result in inaccurate confidence intervals (Figure 1.1I and L) and poor control over the Type I error probability when using the mean. The seriousness of a skewed distribution is a function of the sample size, the degree of skewness and the likelihood of encountering outliers. Skewed distributions with heavy tails (outliers are common) are especially serious in terms of Type I errors and power as will be illustrated.

DETECTING OUTLIERS

There are at least four serious concerns about outliers. First, outliers can destroy power when using any method based on means as previously noted. A second concern is that the sample mean can poorly reflect the typical response. A third concern is that when using measures of effect size based on the mean and variance, outliers can mask a large effect size among the bulk of the participants. Each of these concerns will be described in more detail. The immediate goal is to describe a fourth concern: methods for detecting outliers, based on the mean and variance, can be highly unsatisfactory. These methods suffer from what is called *masking*: the very presence of outliers can cause them to be missed, which is a well-known result in the statistics literature (e.g., Rousseeuw & Leroy, 1987).

Properties of normal distributions suggest a simple and seemingly natural way of detecting outliers: declare a value an outlier if it is more than two standard deviations from the mean. More formally, declare the value X an outlier if

$$\frac{|\bar{X} - X|}{s} > 2. \qquad (1.11)$$

In fairness, using Equation 1.11 to detect outliers performs well in certain situations, but alternative methods are substantially better at avoiding masking. Notice that outliers can inflate the sample mean. The problem is that outliers have more of an impact on the sample standard deviation s. As an illustration, consider the integers $1, 2, \ldots, 20$. Next, suppose the value 100 is added, which is clearly unusual. In this case, Equation 1.11 works well, and 100 is declared an outlier. But if the value 200 is added, 100 is no longer declared an outlier. That is, the value 200 masked the presence of the other outlier, 100. What is needed is a measure of variation that is reasonably insensitive to outliers.

There are two simple methods aimed at achieving this goal. The first is to use a boxplot rule. Let $Q1$ and $Q3$ denote the lower and upper quartiles respectively. The boxplot rule declares X an outlier if

$$X < Q1 - 1.5(Q3 - Q1) \quad (1.12)$$

or if

$$X > Q3 + 1.5(Q3 - Q1). \quad (1.13)$$

Two outliers can ruin the method based on Equation 1.11. But the boxplot rule can handle situations where about 25% of the data are outliers. Presumably this suffices in most cases, but there are exceptions.

An alternative approach is the *MAD-median rule*. MAD refers to the median absolute deviation measure of variation, which is the median of $|X_1 - M|, \ldots, |X_n - M|$, where M is the median. Now X is declared an outlier if

$$\frac{|X - M|}{MAD/0.6745} > 2.24. \quad (1.14)$$

(When dealing with a normal distribution, MAD/0.6745 estimates the standard deviation.) The MAD-median rule can deal with situations where nearly half of the data are outliers. It is a special case of a method derived by Rousseeuw and van Zomeren (1990) aimed at detecting outliers when dealing with multivariate data.

Regarding the boxplot rule, there are issues regarding how the quartiles should be estimated. Frigge et al. (1989) derived results supporting the use of what are called the *ideal fourths*. Also, Carling (2000) derived a modification of the boxplot rule that might be worth considering.

When dealing with multivariate data, methods for detecting outliers are needed that consider the overall structure of the data. For example, it is not unusual for someone to have heart disease, or for someone else to be young, but it is unusual to be both young and have heart disease. Numerous methods for dealing with this issue have been proposed (Hubert et al., 2008; Rousseeuw & Leroy, 1987; Wilcox, 2022), but the details go well beyond the scope of this chapter. No single method dominates, but two that perform relatively well are a *projection method* and a so-called *minimum generalized variance method*. These methods play a crucial role when dealing with regression.

Dealing With Outliers When Testing Hypotheses

When testing hypotheses based on means, a tempting strategy is to simply remove outliers and estimate the standard errors of the sample means using the remaining data. But as previously noted, from a technical point of view, this approach is highly unsatisfactory. The reason is that the expression for the standard error of the mean is derived assuming that the data are uncorrelated. Even with a random sample, if the extreme values are removed, the remaining data are now correlated. For example, if 20 values are randomly sampled from a standard normal distribution and put in ascending order, Pearson's correlation between the two middle values (the values used to compute the median) is approximately 0.94. The result is that the estimate of the standard error after outliers are removed can be highly inaccurate regardless of how large the sample size might be. A consequence is inaccurate confidence intervals and poor control over the Type I error probability regardless of how large the sample size might be. There are theoretical results indicating how to deal with this issue, some of which are described here.

Broadly, a strategy for avoiding the deleterious impact of outliers is to use a measure of central tendency that is insensitive to outliers. Certainly, the best-known measure that has this property is the median. After putting data in ascending order, it trims all but one or two values. Consider, for example, the mixed normal distribution in Figure 1.1. Based on a random sample of size $n = 50$, the standard error of the mean is 0.46. In contrast, the standard error of the median is 0.19. A confidence interval for the median can be computed assuming random sampling only (e.g., Hettmansperger & McKean, 2011). An appeal of this method is that it avoids any concerns about violating the normality assumption or dealing with skewed distributions.

Although the median can have a smaller standard error than the mean, the reality is that often it has a larger standard error than alternative measures because it trims too many values. There are two basic ways of dealing with this issue. The first is to use a compromised amount of trimming. For example, trim the 20% smallest and largest values. This 20% trimmed mean has been studied extensively (Wilcox, 2022). Tukey and McLaughlin (1963) were the first to derive a correct estimate of the standard error. Under normality, their method performs nearly as well as Student's *t* test in terms of power when using 20% trimming. Theory and simulations indicate that it improves on methods based on means, in terms of achieving accurate confidence intervals, when dealing with skewed distributions (Wilcox, 2017b, 2022). For an extensive comparison of the mean, 20% trimmed mean, and median, see Wilcox and Rousselet (2018).

Another way of dealing with outliers is to remove any values flagged as an outlier based on the MAD-median rule. There are several measures of central tendency that are closely related to this approach. Currently, the best way of computing confidence intervals for these measures is with a percentile bootstrap described later in this chapter. It might seem that this approach is preferable to using a trimmed mean, but this issue is not simple. For an extensive discussion of this issue see Wilcox (2022).

Theoretical results (e.g., Staudte & Sheather, 1990; Wilcox, 2022) indicate how to estimate standard errors when extreme values are removed. An appropriate method depends on how extreme values are treated. When working with trimmed means, data are first *Winsorized*. Winsorizing data means that rather than trim the 20% smallest values, set them equal to the smallest value not trimmed. Similarly, the largest 20% are set equal to the largest value not trimmed. For instance, the observations 5, 8, 12, 16, and 19 would become 8, 8, 12, 16, and 16 after being Winsorized. Then compute the sample variance based on these Winsorized values, yielding s_w^2. The squared standard error of the 20% trimmed mean is estimated with

$$\frac{s_w^2}{0.36n}. \qquad (1.15)$$

When outliers are removed using something like the MAD-median rule, deriving an expression for the standard error is substantially more complicated (e.g., Huber & Ronchetti, 2009). However, in terms of testing hypotheses, a relatively simple strategy is available: use a percentile bootstrap method, which we describe in the next section.

DEALING WITH SKEWED DISTRIBUTIONS: WHY TRANSFORMATIONS CAN BE UNSATISFACTORY AND WHAT TO DO INSTEAD

When using methods based on means, skewed distributions are a much more serious concern than once thought. An early suggestion was to transform the data. For example, use the logarithms of the data. There are situations where this approach yields data that look more like a normal distribution. But by modern standards this is a relatively ineffective approach. First, transformed data often remain skewed. Second, this approach does not deal with outliers in a satisfactory manner (e.g., Doksum & Wong, 1983; Rasmussen, 1989). That is, one still needs to use a measure of central tendency that is insensitive to outliers. A transformation might reduce the number of outliers, but the number of outliers can remain about the same (as illustrated in the upcoming paragraphs), and situations are encountered where the number of outliers increases. Grayson (2004) argued that a transformation can transform the construct being measured. For instance, if the goal is to make inferences about the mean, a transformation can alter this goal.

Data stemming from a study dealing with self-awareness (Dana, 1990) are used to illustrate this last point. Interested readers can reproduce our calculations using R code (Wilcox & Rousselet, 2021). A portion of the study measured the time participants could keep a portion of an apparatus in contact with a specified target. The mean, 20% trimmed mean, and median are 448, 283, and 262, respectively. Now, suppose the data are log transformed. Computing the mean of the transformed data, then transforming back to the original scale (by raising 10 to the power of the estimate just computed), yields 283, which corresponds to the 20% trimmed mean in this case. In effect, inferences based on the transformed data are aimed at making inferences about something other than the mean of the untransformed data without necessarily dealing with issues related to outliers. A simple and effective alternative to transformations is to use methods that are relatively insensitive to outliers. Nevertheless, transformations can be useful in other situations. For instance, they can be used to characterize an important difference between an ordinal and disordinal interaction in a two-by-two ANOVA design (Wagenmakers et al., 2012).

PLOTS

There is a vast array of plots that can provide a deeper understanding of data. A variety of methods are discussed and illustrated by Rousselet et al. (2017) when comparing two groups. For a broader range of plots, see, for example, the R packages ggplot2 (Wickham, 2016) and plotly (Sievert, 2020). We used ggplot2 to create all the figures in this chapter. Here, a few of the more basic plots are described, and some of their relative merits are discussed.

The first is a Q-Q plot. A particular version plots the quantiles of the observed data versus the quantiles of a corresponding normal distribution. If the data represent a random sample from a normal distribution, the resulting Q-Q plot will have, approximately, a straight line. Figure 1.2A shows Q-Q plots based on 200 observations. In the left panel sampling is from a standard normal distribution; in the middle panel sampling is from the mixed normal in Figure 1.1B; in the right panel sampling is from the skewed distribution in Figure 1.1C. Each column shows the same sample of $n = 200$ observations represented in different ways. Sampling was from the same distributions as in Figure 1.1: normal, contaminated normal, and lognormal. Row A contains Q-Q plots, row B the boxplots, row C, the histograms, and row D contains the kernel density plots.

Note the points that are separated and appear to deviate from the plot of the bulk of the points. Often such points are taken to be outliers, but using a Q-Q plot as an outlier detection method can result in masking. Data stemming from a study dealing with the sexual attitudes of undergraduate students are used to illustrate this point (Pedersen et al., 2002). One portion of the study asked 105 undergraduate males how many sexual partners they want over the next 30 years. The mean and median are 64.9 and 1, respectively. One student responded 6,000, and two others responded 150. The next largest response was 45. Figure 1.3A shows the Q-Q plot, which indicates one outlier: 6,000. But the boxplot rule indicates that there are 12 outliers and the MAD-median rule indicates that there are 33 outliers. Figure 1.3B shows the Q-Q plot when the one extreme outlier is removed. More outliers are detected but still fewer than indicated by the boxplot rule and MAD-median rule. This might suggest that one could keep removing points until the Q-Q plot indicates no outliers, but this approach can be highly unsatisfactory as well. Figure 1.3C shows the Q-Q plot when responses greater than 6 are ignored. This might suggest that values greater than 2 but less than 6 are outliers, but based on all the data, the boxplot rule and the MAD-median rule suggest that this is not the case. This an example of swamping: declaring points outliers when in fact they are not that unusual.

Now consider Figure 1.3D, which shows the Q-Q plot of the cortisol awakening response of 328 older adults who were participants in an intervention program aimed at improving their physical and emotional wellbeing. The cortisol awakening response (CAR) is the difference between cortisol levels upon awakening and measured again 30 to 45 minutes later. Past studies have found associations between CAR and measures of stress. The Q-Q plot suggests there are about 10 to 12 outliers, but the MAD-median rule indicates that there are 24. (Shifting the data so that all values are greater than 0, and then log transforming the data, the number of outliers is still 24.) Generally, it is suggested that when checking whether there are any outliers, use a

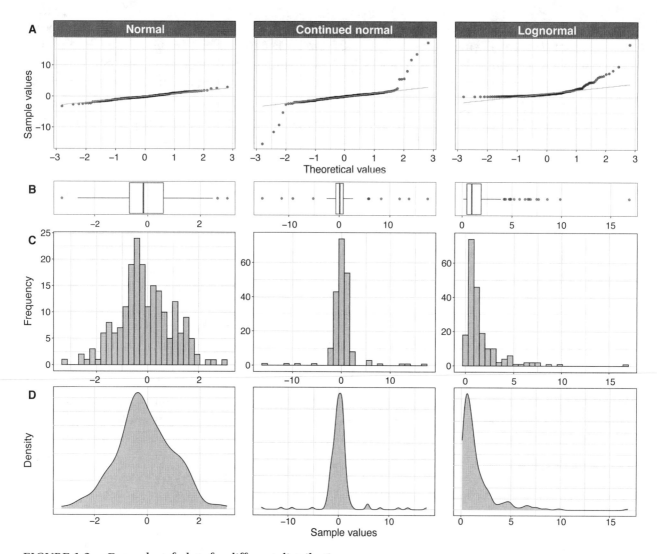

FIGURE 1.2. Examples of plots for different distributions.

method designed specifically for this purpose. Such methods have been studied in terms of masking and swamping. The likelihood of masking and swamping is difficult to study when using a Q-Q plot simply because there is no specified decision rule beyond looking at the plot.

Four other basic plots should be mentioned. The first is a boxplot as illustrated in Figure 1.2B. The box extends from the first quartile (Q1) to the third quartile (Q3). The thicker line inside the box indicates the median, the second quartile. The left horizontal line starts at Q1 and ends at Q1 − 1.5x(Q3 − Q1); the right horizontal line starts at Q3 and ends at Q3 + 1.5x(Q3 − Q1). Observations outside these extreme values are flagged as outliers and marked as disks, providing a visual representation of the boxplot rule in Equations 1.12 and 1.13.

Histograms are another commonly used method, three examples of which are shown in Figure 1.2C. The histogram creates bins, and the height of a rectangle is used to indicate the frequency of values in the bin. It is sometimes suggested that histograms can be used to detect outliers, but it can be highly unsatisfactory for this purpose. In Figure 1.2C, the histogram of the lognormal sample suggests a few outliers among the large values, which is confirmed based on a boxplot rule; however, the boxplot rule suggests the presence of many more outliers. Again, it is suggested that methods designed specifically for detecting outliers should be used.

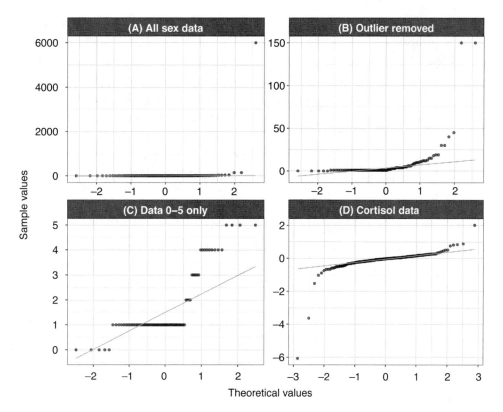

FIGURE 1.3. Q-Q plots can suffer from masking. (A–C) Number of desired sexual partners in 105 undergraduate males. (D) Cortisol response in 328 older adults.

(See Figure 1.5D as examples of *kernel density plots*, which are essentially smoothed histograms. In kernel density plots, the y-axis units are meaningless, and the area under the curve sums to 1, so these plots are useful to assess the relative frequency of different values.)

When dealing with situations where a relatively small number of values are possible, it can be more informative to plot the relative frequencies of every possible value, as illustrated in Figure 1.4. The data in that figure deal with the degree to which smokers experience negative emotional responses (e.g., anger, irritation) upon being exposed to antismoking warnings on cigarette packets. The possible responses were the integers between 0 and 16, inclusive. One group was

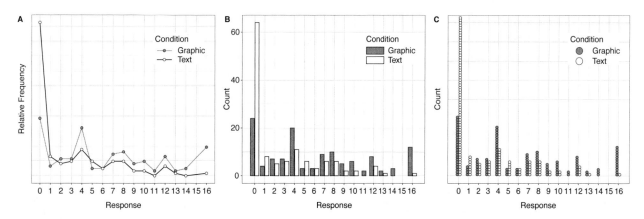

FIGURE 1.4. Plots of a small number of possible values. (A) Plot of relative frequencies. (B) Plot of counts. (C) Plot of count by stacking dots corresponding to individual observations. There is one dot per observation.

given text only. The other group was given text plus graphics. Both groups have sample size 125. Comparing means, 20% trimmed means and medians, all three *p* values were less than 0.001. However, the plot reveals that the most pronounced difference occurs for the response zero.

HETEROSCEDASTICITY PLUS MORE COMMENTS ON SKEWED DISTRIBUTIONS

When comparing two or more independent groups, classic methods based on means assume homoscedasticity: The groups have a common population variance even when the means differ. It has long been known that when there is heteroscedasticity, meaning that two or more groups have different variances, homoscedastic methods can be highly unsatisfactory (e.g., Brown & Forsythe, 1974; Dunnett, 1980; Pratt, 1964). Numerous methods have been proposed for dealing with this issue. When using a homoscedastic method to compare means, there are general conditions where an incorrect estimate of the standard error is used regardless of how large the sample size might be (Cressie & Whitford, 1986). To complicate matters, when distributions differ in skewness, even heteroscedastic methods can be unsatisfactory (e.g., Wilcox, 2022).

A natural and commonly used strategy is to test the hypothesis that there is homoscedasticity. The idea is that if the test fails to reject, use a method that assumes homoscedasticity. However, Wilcox (2022, Section 5.2) lists six published papers that do not support this approach. The basic problem is that methods for comparing variances do not have enough power to detect situations where it is beneficial to abandon the homoscedasticity assumption.

Instead of trying to detect homoscedasticity violations, it is better to use heteroscedastic methods by default. Yuen (1974) derived such a heteroscedastic method for comparing the trimmed means of two independent groups. Extensions to more than two groups are covered in Wilcox (2022). Theory and simulations indicate that concerns about differences in skewness, in terms of Type I errors, decrease as the amount of trimming increases. But even with 20% trimming, situations are encountered where the control over the Type I error probability can be rather unsatisfactory using Yuen's method when the sample sizes are small. A way of improving the control over the Type I error probability is to switch to a bootstrap method, the basics of which are described next.

BOOTSTRAP METHODS

There is a vast literature dealing with bootstrap techniques (e.g., Efron & Tibshirani, 1993). The main point here is that there are two basic versions that have practical value for a wide range of situations. The first is called a *percentile bootstrap*; for a primer using the R programming language (R Core Team, 2020), see Rousselet et al. (2017). To convey the basic idea, consider the goal of comparing two independent groups based on some measure of central tendency. For convenience, the focus is on the population medians, which are denoted by θ_1 and θ_2 and estimated with the sample medians M_1 and M_2, respectively. The sample sizes are denoted by n_1 and n_2. Basically, the percentile bootstrap method performs a simulation on the observed data to get an estimate of the distribution of $D = M_1 - M_2$, the distribution of the difference between the sample medians. This results in a confidence interval for $\theta_1 - \theta_2$ as well as a *p* value when testing $H_0: \theta_1 = \theta_2$ (Liu & Singh, 1997).

To elaborate, imagine that n_1 values are sampled with replacement from the first group and that n_2 values are sampled with replacement from the second group. Compute the difference between the resulting medians and label the result D^*. Repeat this process many times. For illustrative purposes, assume this is done 1,000 times yielding 1,000 D^* values. Put these 1,000 values in ascending order yielding $D^*_{(1)} \leq \cdots \leq D^*_{(1,000)}$. Then the middle 95% of these values are between $D^*_{(26)}$ and $D^*_{(975)}$ inclusive. A 0.95 confidence interval for $\theta_1 - \theta_2$ is $(D^*_{(26)}, D^*_{(975)})$. As for a *p* value, suppose *B* bootstrap samples are used, and let *A* denote the number of D^* values less than 0. Let $p^* = A/B$.

Then a (generalized) p value is $2p^*$ or $1 - 2p^*$, whichever is smaller.

This percentile bootstrap method performs very well when using a 20% trimmed mean. However, when comparing medians and there are ties (duplicated values), a slight modification is needed. Let C denote the number of times $D^* = 0$. Now $p^* = (A + 0.5C)/B$. Currently, this is the only known method that continues to perform reasonably well in simulations when there are tied values (Wilcox, 2006).

Generally, a percentile bootstrap method works well when dealing with estimators that are reasonably insensitive to outliers. However, when comparing means, it is unsatisfactory (Becher, 1993). Better is a *bootstrap-t method*. Bootstrap samples are generated as before, only now the goal is to estimate the sampling distribution of the test statistic when the null hypothesis is true. For notational convenience, let $q_1 = s_1^2/n_1$ and $q_2 = s_2^2/n_2$. A heteroscedastic test statistic for comparing means is

$$W = \frac{\bar{X}_1 - \bar{X}_2}{\sqrt{q_1 + q_2}}. \quad (1.16)$$

Typically, a critical value is determined via Welch's (1938) method, which uses a critical value based on Student's t distribution with degrees of freedom estimated based on q_1 and q_2 (this is the default in the t test function in R). The bootstrap-t method begins by shifting each group to have a mean of 0. That is, the data are shifted so that the null hypothesis is true. Then bootstrap samples are generated based on the shifted data, W is computed based on the resulting bootstrap values yielding W^*, and this process is repeated many times. Again, suppose this is done $B = 1{,}000$ times and the W^* values are put in ascending order yielding $W^*_{(1)} \leq \cdots \leq W^*_{(1{,}000)}$. When testing at the 0.05 level, reject if $W \leq W^*_{(26)}$ or if $W \geq W^*_{(976)}$. A confidence interval can be computed as well. This is called an *equal-tailed bootstrap-t method* (method BT). A closely related approach is to compute a critical value based on $|W|$ instead. This yields what is called the *symmetric bootstrap-t approach* (method SB). These bootstrap methods are readily adapted to the one-sample case where the goal is to test Equation 1.10, and are available in many R packages (e.g., Table 1 in Rousselet et al., 2017).

Bootstrap methods are nonparametric, meaning that it is not assumed that data are sampled from a parametric family of distributions such as the family of normal distributions. But bootstrap methods are not distribution free. A distribution-free method means that assuming random sampling only, the actual Type I error probability can be determined exactly. Broadly, there are situations where the bootstrap-t improves on nonbootstrap methods when the focus is on means. But concerns remain regarding the ability to control the Type I error probability or computing reasonably accurate confidence interval. For example, when testing Equation 1.10 at the 0.05 level with a sample size of $n = 20$, the actual level of Student's t test is 0.14 when dealing a skewed, light-tailed (lognormal) distribution (the same distribution illustrated in Figure 1.1C). Using methods BT and SB, the actual levels are 0.078 and 0.093, respectively. Increasing the sample size to $n = 100$, the actual level of Student's t test is 0.083 while for BT and SB the actual level is 0.058 for both. However, when dealing with a skewed, heavy-tailed distribution, the actual levels of all three methods can exceed 0.15. For symmetric, heavy-tailed distributions, the actual level of Student's t test is less than the nominal level. For the mixed normal distribution, again with $n = 100$, the actual level of Student's t test is 0.041. For BT and SB, the actual levels are 0.092 and 0.018, respectively. Also, switching to a bootstrap method does not alter the fact that power can be relatively low when using means. It is the combination of the percentile bootstrap method with estimators that are relatively insensitive to outliers that perform reasonably well for a broad range of situations.

ROBUST METHOD: WHAT DOES THIS MEAN?

Traditionally, the term *robust* is generally associated with methods that perform reasonably well in terms of controlling the Type I error probability.

In the statistics literature, such methods are said to be *level robust*. But for the last 50 years, the term *robust* has taken on a broader meaning. Roughly, a method is characterized as not robust if a small change in a distribution can alter its properties substantially. For example, if a small departure from a normal distribution can destroy power, the method is not robust. From this point of view, inferential methods based on the means and variances are not robust. The notion of robustness extends to population parameters. For example, there is a formal proof that an arbitrarily small change in a distribution can make the population variance arbitrarily large. The same is true for the population mean. There are three mathematical methods for characterizing whether a parameter is robust. The population mean and variance do not satisfy any of them. The same is true for Pearson's correlation. The population median and the trimmed mean are robust. There is now a well-developed mathematical foundation for developing and characterizing robust methods (Hampel et al., 1986; Huber & Ronchetti, 2009; Staudte & Sheather, 1990). The catalyst for these methods was Tukey's paper on the mixed normal. These mathematical results have played a crucial role in the development of the many robust methods summarized in Wilcox (2022).

A simple way of characterizing the robustness of estimators is with the smallest proportion of values that must be altered to make it arbitrarily large or small. This proportion is called the *breakdown point of an estimator*. The breakdown point of the median is about 0.5, the highest possible value. That is, the median is insensitive to outliers even when the number of outliers is unusually large. The breakdown point of the 20% trimmed mean is 0.2. Typically, this suffices in terms of dealing with the negative impact of outliers, but exceptions do occur. The breakdown point of the mean is only $1/n$. The sample variance has a breakdown point of only $1/n$ as well.

The mixed normal distribution in Figure 1.1 is often used to illustrate the potential impact of a small departure from a normal distribution. Consider, for example, the two normal distributions in the left panel of Figure 1.5. The variance for both distributions is one. The first has a mean of 0 and the second has a mean equal to 1. When using Student's t with a common sample size of 25, and when testing at the 0.05 level, power is 0.93. The power of Yuen's method based on a 20% trimmed mean is 0.89. However, for the distributions in the right panel, the power of Student's t is only 0.28. The reason is that mixed normal distributions are being compared, which have variance 10.9. In contrast, using Yuen's method, power is 0.80. The point is that the choice of method can make a substantial difference, which raises concerns about using a single perspective regarding how groups compare.

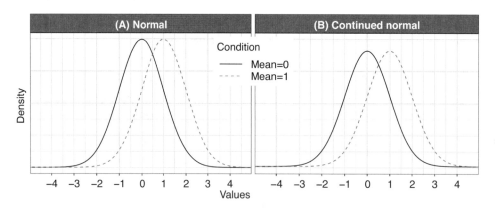

FIGURE 1.5. Comparisons of two independent distributions. (A) Two normal distributions, both with variance 1. One has a mean of 0, the other a mean of 1. (B) Two mixed normal distributions, with the same means as the distributions in A, but both with variances of 10.9.

RANK-BASED METHODS

A common suggestion is to use a rank-based method when dealing with nonnormal distributions. Roughly, rank-based techniques convert the observed data to ranks: the smallest value gets a rank of 1, the next smallest a rank of 2, and so on. Because ranks are used, the impact of outliers is mitigated. For example, if the smallest value is 5, its rank is 1. If this value is reset to −100,000, its rank is still 1. Classic rank-based methods (e.g., Wilcoxon-Mann-Whitney test, Friedman's test, the Kruskal-Wallis test) are sometimes characterized as methods for comparing medians. There are conditions where they do indeed to compare medians, but, in general, this is not the case. Given the goal of comparing medians, it is better to use a method that directly estimates the population median. A more precise description of these classic methods is that they test the hypothesis that groups have identical distributions.

Let X and Y denote two independent variables and let $p = P(X < Y)$, the probability that a randomly sampled observation from the first group is less than a randomly sampled observation from the second group. The Wilcoxon-Mann-Whitney test is based on an estimate of p. However, it is not a good method for computing a confidence interval for p or testing the hypothesis that $p = 0.5$. The reason is that the standard error of the estimate of p was derived assuming the distributions are identical. For example, even when the null hypothesis is true, there can be a high probability of rejecting when the groups have different variances. Numerous methods have been derived for dealing with this issue. Currently, the methods derived by Cliff (1996) and Brunner and Munzel (2000) perform relatively well. Also see Ruscio and Mullen (2012). These methods can yield inaccurate confidence intervals when p is close to 0 or 1. A slight generalization of Cliff's method corrects this problem (Wilcox, 2022).

EFFECT SIZE

Effect size refers broadly to quantitative methods that characterize how two or more groups compare or the extent to which some null hypothesis is false.

There are two points here. First, measures of effect size based on means and variances are not robust. Consider for example the commonly used measure of effect size

$$\delta = \frac{\mu_1 - \mu_2}{\sigma}, \quad (1.17)$$

where μ_1 and μ_2 are the population means of two independent groups and by assumption the groups have a common standard deviation, σ. This was a natural approach when first proposed. For the distributions in the left panel in Figure 1.5, $\delta = 1$, which is often characterized as being relatively large (e.g., Cohen, 1988). However, in the right panel $\delta = 0.3$, which is often characterized as being relatively small. Put another way, outliers have the potential of masking a large effect among the bulk of the participants. The second major point is that there are now several robust methods that allow heteroscedasticity (e.g., Wilcox, 2022). Some of these methods employ the general strategy of replacing the numerator and denominator in Equation 1.17 with robust alternatives.

For instance, for two independent groups, let $N = n_1 + n_2$ be the total sample size and let $q = n_1/N$. One possibility when using a 20% trimmed mean is

$$\hat{\eta} = \frac{\overline{X}_{t1} - \overline{X}_{t2}}{\hat{\varsigma}}, \quad (1.18)$$

where

$$\hat{\varsigma}^2 = \frac{(1-q)s_{1wN}^2 + qs_{2wN}^2}{q(1-q)},$$

and for the jth group $s_{jwN}^2 = s_{jw}^2/0.642$. For normal distributions, s_{jwN}^2 estimates the population variance of the jth group. This measure of effect size is a simple generalization of the measure of effect size derived by Kulinskaya et al. (2008, p. 177) and represents a robust, heteroscedastic analog of Cohen's D.

Another perspective consists in considering the distribution of D, the difference between a randomly sampled participant from each group. This approach contains, as a special case,

$p = P(X < Y)$ previously discussed. To provide an alternative perspective, let θ_D denote the median of the typical difference and consider the hypothesis

$$H_0: \theta_D = 0.$$

Suppose the observed data are shifted so that the median of the typical difference is 0. This shifted data represents an estimate of the distribution of D when H_0 is true.

Note that θ_D corresponds to the Qth quantile of this shifted data. If H_0 is true, θ_D corresponds to the 0.5 quantile of the shifted data. A nonparametric measure of effect size is Q, the quantile of θ_D based on the shifted data. Consider two normal distributions having a common variance and following Cohen (1988), suppose $\delta = 0.2$, 0.5, and 0.8 are considered small, medium, and large effect sizes, respectively. The corresponding values for Q are 0.55, 0.64, and 0.71. A confidence interval for Q can be computed using a basic percentile bootstrap method.

Yet another approach is to use what is called *explanatory power*. Roughly, it is the variation in measures of central tendency divided by the variation in the groups. This approach represents a generalization of Pearson's correlation. More details can be found in Wilcox (2017a, 2022).

REGRESSION

As previously indicated, a basic goal is to estimate the typical value of some dependent variable Y, given a value for some explanatory variable X. A standard way of doing this is to assume that given a value for X, the typical value of Y can be determined by the straight line given by Equation 1.1. Based on this model, common goals are making inferences about the slope, β_1, and the intercept, β_0. Typically, estimates of β_1 and β_0 are based on the least squares method. Let b_1 and b_0 be some choice for the slope and intercept, and let $\hat{Y} = b_0 + b_1 X$ be the resulting estimate of Y given X. The least squares method chooses b_1 and b_0 to be the values that minimize

$$\sum (Y - \hat{Y})^2,$$

the sum being taken over the n pairs of observations that are available. A concern is that this approach gives too much weight to extreme values. In other words, outliers can result in a very poor fit to the bulk of the points, as well as a relatively large standard error, leading to low power.

Inferences about the slope and intercept are based on four assumptions. The first is random sampling. The second is that given a value for X, Y has a normal distribution. Imagine, for example, the goal is to determine the typical level of depressive symptoms (Y) given the age of a participant. The assumption is that the measure of the depressive symptoms has a normal distribution for participants age 50, age 60, and generally for any age that is relevant.

The third assumption is homoscedasticity. Consider again the goal of determining the typical measure of depressive symptoms given the age of a participant. Among the participants age 50, there will be some variation in the Y values. The same is true for any other age. Homoscedasticity means that for any two ages, the variance of Y is the same. Independence implies homoscedasticity. But if there is an association, there is no reason to assume homoscedasticity. If in fact there is heteroscedasticity (the variances differ at different ages), homoscedastic methods are using an incorrect estimate of the standard error that can result in poor power or inaccurate confidence intervals, regardless of the sample size. A seemingly natural strategy is to test the homoscedasticity assumption. But it is unknown how to ensure that the power of any test is sufficiently high to detect a situation where the homoscedasticity assumption should not be used. Another strategy is to transform the data to achieve homoscedasticity (e.g., Montgomery et al., 2012). But there is a simpler approach: Use a method that allows heteroscedasticity. There are several ways this can be done that work nearly as well as homoscedastic methods when the homoscedasticity assumption is true (e.g., Wilcox, 2017a, 2022).

Still assuming the linear model given by Equation 1.1 is true, there are two types of outliers that can have a serious negative impact when making inferences about the slope or intercept

(Figure 1.6B). The first is called a *regression outlier*, meaning a point that is unusually far from the regression line. Such outliers can inflate the standard error, which in turn can mean low power. Simply discarding these outliers and using some conventional method for estimating the standard error is technically unsound. It can yield a highly inaccurate estimate, which in turn yields inaccurate confidence intervals regardless of the sample size. Currently, the best way to deal with this issue is to use a robust regression estimator in conjunction with a percentile bootstrap method. There are many robust regression estimators (e.g., Wilcox, 2022). As usual, no single estimator dominates, but one that performs relatively well is the Theil-Sen estimator. First, compute the slope for every pair of points in the data. The Theil-Sen estimator is the median of all such slopes. It is not being suggested, however, that all other robust regression estimators should be excluded from consideration: The relative merits of other techniques are described and illustrated in other places (e.g., Wilcox, 2022).

The other type of outlier that is a practical concern is called a *bad leverage point*. Consider a situation where for the bulk of the participants the slope is 1. A bad leverage point is a point where the value of the independent variable, X, is an outlier that results in an estimate of the slope that deviates substantially from 1. A *good leverage point* is a leverage point that is reasonably consistent with the regression line for the bulk of the participants. Leverage points reduce the standard error of a regression estimator, but they

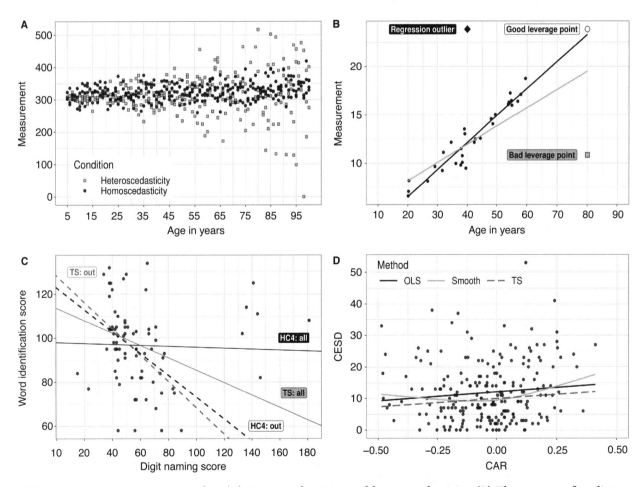

FIGURE 1.6. Regression examples. (A) Homoscedasticity and heteroscedasticity. (B) Three types of outliers. (C) Robust regression example. HC4 is a heteroscedastic method. TS is the Theil-Sen robust method. For each method, two lines are illustrated: with (all) or without (out) leverage points. (D) Linear regression and smooth regression. CAR = cortisol awakening response; CESD = Center for Epidemiological Studies Depression; OLS = ordinary least squares.

can result in a poor fit to the bulk of the data. In contrast to regression outliers, removing bad leverage points and estimating the standard error using some conventional method is technically sound. It is prudent to always check on the impact of removing any bad leverage points, even when using a robust estimator.

This last point is illustrated with data dealing with predicting reading abilities in children (Figure 1.6C). Here, a measure of speeded naming for digits is used to predict the typical measure of the ability to identify words. The sample size is $n = 81$. Using least squares regression, the estimate of the slope is -0.021 and a 0.95 confidence interval, using a heteroscedastic (HC4) method, is $(-0.198, 0.155)$. The p value when testing $H_0: \beta_1 = 0$ is 0.810. Removing the leverage points, now the estimate of the slope is -0.497, the 0.95 confidence interval is $(-0.851, -0.144)$ and the p value is 0.006. Switching to a robust (Theil-Sen) estimator, again with leverage points removed, the estimate of the slope is -0.6, the 0.95 confidence interval is $(-1, -0.222)$ and the p value is 0.008. That is, even after removing leverage points, a robust regression estimator might indicate a stronger association compared to the least squares estimate. If the leverage points are retained, the Theil-Sen estimate of the slope is -0.28 and the p value is 0.035.

The fourth basic assumption is that Equation 1.1 provides an adequate model for determining the typical value of Y given a value for X. A more flexible approach is fitting a polynomial model. This approach might suffice, but experience with nonparametric regression estimators, called *smoothers*, strongly indicate that exceptions occur more often than might be expected. By taking advantage of smoothers, interesting associations might be detected that would otherwise be missed.

Smoothers are an attempt to estimate a regression line in a flexible manner without specifying a particular parametric model such as Equation 1.1. There is a substantial literature dealing with smoothers (e.g., Harrell, 2006; Wilcox, 2022). Suppose the goal is to estimate the typical value of Y when $X = 8$. Roughly, smoothers focus on X values close to 8; the closer to 8 they happen to be, the more weight they are given. Values for X that are sufficiently far from 8 are ignored. Here, for brevity, the focus is on the *running interval smoother* in Wilcox (2022). The running interval smoother is convenient because it can be used to estimate any measure of central tendency given X. When dealing with more than one predictor, a relatively well-known approach is the generalized additive model (Hastie & Tibshirani, 1990). An advantage of the running interval smoother is that it provides a more flexible approach to dealing with interactions.

Figure 1.6D provides an illustration based on the CAR measure and a measure of depression symptoms based on the Center for Epidemiologic Studies Depression Scale (CESD). Using least squares, the slope is estimated to be 5.7. Testing $H_0: \beta_1 = 0$, with HC4 estimate of the standard error and leverage points removed, the slope is 5.7 and the p value is 0.167. With leverage points retained, the slope is estimated to be 1.34 and the p value is 0.168. Using a robust (Theil-Sen) estimator with leverage points removed, the slope is 5.3 and the p value is 0.242. However, look at Figure 1.6D, which shows the plot based on the running interval smoother when estimating the 20% trimmed mean of CESD, given a value for CAR. The plot suggests that for CAR negative (cortisol increase after awakening), there is slight negative association, but for CAR greater than 0, there is a positive association. For CAR less than 0, no significant result is found when testing $H_0: \beta_1 = 0$ using the least squares when leverage points are retained (slope = 0.75, $p = 0.861$). With the leverage points removed slope = -7.91 and the p value is 0.235. For the Theil-Sen estimator, slope = -4.36 and $p = 0.275$ with leverage points. With leverage removed, slope = 0 and $p = 0.609$. But for CAR greater than or equal to 0, with leverage points removed, the slopes are positive: the least squares estimate of the is slope of 32 and a p value of 0.009), and Theil-Sen yields a slope of 28.7 and a p value of 0.022).

An alternative approach is to replace X with X^a with the goal of getting a straight regression line, where a is to be determined. However, the half-slope ratio method for choosing *a* (e.g., Wilcox, 2022) indicates that no such *a* exists for the situation at hand. Yet another strategy is to use the logarithms of the data (e.g., Andersen, 2012; Montgomery et al., 2012). This approach can indeed straighten a regression line, but it is important to not assume this is the case.

Taking logs of the data used in the upper left panel of Figure 1.6D, the running interval smoother indicates a bend that is a bit less severe than the bend using the untransformed data. That is, transforming the data is no guarantee that it will yield a sufficiently straight regression line. (The smallest CAR value is −6, so 7 was added to each value so that logs of the data can be used.) Again, comparing the slopes for CAR less than 0 versus greater than 0, the *p* value is 0.01. Moreover, a projection method indicates that there are outliers after transforming the data that might be affecting the plot. A plot of the regression line indicates that the distinct bend remains. The analyses just described were repeated, where now the dependent variable is a measure of life satisfaction. Again, there is a distinct bend close to CAR = 0.

CONCLUDING REMARKS

Recent years have seen many new and improved methods for detecting and dealing with bad data as well as inadequate models. There are many such methods beyond those mentioned here that have the potential to provide a deeper and more nuanced understanding of data. A cursory glance at these advances might seem overwhelming for those unfamiliar with this literature. Various journal articles have been written with the goal of providing a guide to modern methods (e.g., Field & Wilcox, 2017; Wilcox & Keselman, 2003; Wilcox & Rousselet, 2018). For books that cover both classic methods as well as modern robust methods, see Wilcox (2017a, 2017b). For a book that provides a more extensive coverage of robust methods, see Wilcox (2022).

Notice that different methods are sensitive to different features of the data. For example, when comparing two skewed distributions, comparing means is not the same as comparing 20% trimmed means or medians. Multiple methods are usually needed to get a deep understanding of our data. However, this raises the issue of controlling the probability of one or more Type I errors when multiple tests are performed. There are methods for achieving this goal (e.g., Wilcox, 2022). Another possibility is to first focus on an exploratory study. This could be followed by a confirmatory study aimed at replicating any interesting results stemming from the exploratory study.

As for software, there are numerous R packages that provide easy access to both classic and modern robust methods. All of the examples described here were performed via the R package WRS. Readers may access an RMarkdown notebook that reproduces all the calculations, and the figures used in this chapter at the link provided in Wilcox and Rousselet (2021). Detailed descriptions of how to use these functions can be found in Wilcox (2017a, 2017b, 2022). For many situations, a single command is all that is needed once the data are read into R. For MATLAB functions designed to deal with correlations, see Pernet et al. (2013).

A perpetual problem is that often basic training does not take into account relevant advances in the statistics literature. This is unfortunate given the cost and time needed to acquire data. Hopefully, this chapter helps address this concern.

References

Andersen, R. (2012). Methods for detecting badly behaved data: Distributions, linear models, and beyond. In H. Cooper, P. M. Camic, D. L. Long, A. T. Panter, D. Rindskopf, & K. J. Sher (Eds.), *APA handbook of research methods in psychology, Vol. 3. Data analysis and research publication* (pp. 5–26). American Psychological Association. https://doi.org/10.1037/13621-001

Becher, H. (1993). Bootstrap hypothesis testing procedures. *Biometrics, 49*(4), 1268–1272. https://doi.org/10.2307/2532271

Biau, D. J., Jolles, B. M., & Porcher, R. (2010). P value and the theory of hypothesis testing: An explanation for new researchers. *Clinical Orthopaedics and Related Research, 468*(3), 885–892. https://doi.org/10.1007/s11999-009-1164-4

Brown, M. B., & Forsythe, A. (1974). The small sample behavior of some statistics which test the equality of several means. *Technometrics*, *16*(1), 129–132. https://doi.org/10.1080/00401706.1974.10489158

Brunner, E., & Munzel, U. (2000). The nonparametric Behrens-Fisher problem: Asymptotic theory and small-sample approximation. *Biometrical Journal. Biometrische Zeitschrift*, *42*(1), 17–25. https://doi.org/10.1002/(SICI)1521-4036(200001)42:1<17::AID-BIMJ17>3.0.CO;2-U

Carling, K. (2000). Resistant outlier rules and the non-Gaussian case. *Computational Statistics & Data Analysis*, *33*(3), 249–258. https://doi.org/10.1016/S0167-9473(99)00057-2

Cassidy, S. A., Dimova, R., Giguère, B., Spence, J. R., & Stanley, D. J. (2019). Failing grade: 89% of introduction-to-psychology textbooks that define or explain statistical significance do so incorrectly. *Advances in Methods and Practices in Psychological Science*, *2*(3), 233–239. https://doi.org/10.1177/2515245919858072

Cliff, N. (1996). *Ordinal methods for behavioral data analysis*. Erlbaum.

Cohen, J. (1988). *Statistical power analysis for the behavioral sciences* (2nd ed.). Academic Press.

Cressie, N. A. C., & Whitford, H. J. (1986). How to use the two sample t-test. *Biometrical Journal*, *28*(2), 131–148. https://doi.org/10.1002/bimj.4710280202

Dana, E. (1990). *Salience of the self and salience of standards: Attempts to match self to standard* [Unpublished doctoral dissertation]. University of Southern California.

Doksum, K. A., & Wong, C.-W. (1983). Statistical tests based on transformed data. *Journal of the American Statistical Association*, *78*(382), 411–417.

Dunnett, C. W. (1980). Pairwise multiple comparisons in the unequal variance case. *Journal of the American Statistical Association*, *75*(372), 789–795. https://doi.org/10.1080/01621459.1980.10477551

Efron, B., & Tibshirani, R. J. (1993). *An Introduction to the bootstrap*. Chapman & Hall.

Field, A. P., & Wilcox, R. R. (2017). Robust statistical methods: A primer for clinical psychology and experimental psychopathology researchers. *Behaviour Research and Therapy*, *98*, 19–38. https://doi.org/10.1016/j.brat.2017.05.013

Frigge, M., Hoaglin, D. C., & Iglewicz, B. (1989). Some implementations of the Boxplot. *The American Statistician*, *43*(1), 50–54.

Grayson, D. (2004). Some myths and legends in quantitative psychology. *Understanding Statistics*, *3*(2), 101–134. https://doi.org/10.1207/s15328031us0302_3

Greenland, S., Senn, S. J., Rothman, K. J., Carlin, J. B., Poole, C., Goodman, S. N., & Altman, D. G. (2016). Statistical tests, P values, confidence intervals, and power: A guide to misinterpretations. *European Journal of Epidemiology*, *31*(4), 337–350. https://doi.org/10.1007/s10654-016-0149-3

Hampel, F. R., Ronchetti, E. M., Rousseeuw, P. J., & Stahel, W. A. (1986). *Robust statistics*. Wiley.

Hand, A. (1998). *A history of mathematical statistics from 1750 to 1930*. Wiley.

Harrell, F. E. (2006). *Regression modeling strategies: With applications to linear models, logistic regression, and survival analysis* (2nd ed.). Springer.

Hastie, T. J., & Tibshirani, R. J. (1990). *Generalized additive models*. Chapman and Hall.

Hettmansperger, T. P., & McKean, J. W. (2011). *Robust nonparametric statistical methods* (2nd ed.). Arnold.

Huber, P. J., & Ronchetti, E. (2009). *Robust statistics* (2nd ed.). Wiley. https://doi.org/10.1002/9780470434697

Hubert, M., Rousseeuw, P. J., & van Aelst, S. (2008). High-breakdown robust Multivariate methods. *Statistical Science*, *23*(1), 92–119. https://doi.org/10.1214/088342307000000087

Jones, L. V., & Tukey, J. W. (2000). A sensible formulation of the significance test. *Psychological Methods*, *5*(4), 411–414. https://doi.org/10.1037/1082-989X.5.4.411

Kmetz, J. L. (2019). Correcting corrupt research: Recommendations for the profession to stop misuse of p-values. *American Statistician*, *73*(Suppl. 1), 36–45. https://doi.org/10.1080/00031305.2018.1518271

Kulinskaya, E., Morgenthaler, S., & Staudte, R. (2008). *Meta analysis: A guide to calibrating and combining statistical evidence*. Wiley.

Lakens, D., Adolfi, F. G., Albers, C. J., Anvari, F., Apps, M. A. J., Argamon, S. E., Baguley, T., Becker, R. B., Benning, S. D., Buchanan, E. M., Caldwell, A. R., Van Calster, B., Carlsson, R., Chen, S.-C., Chung, B., Colling, L. J., Collins, G. S., Crook, Z., . . . Zwaan, R. A. (2018). Justify your alpha. *Nature Human Behaviour*, *2*(3), 168–171. https://doi.org/10.1038/s41562-018-0311-x

Liu, R. G., & Singh, K. (1997). Notions of limiting p values based on data depth and bootstrap. *Journal of the American Statistical Association*, *92*(437), 266–277. https://doi.org/10.2307/2291471

Montgomery, D. C., Peck, E. A., & Vining, G. G. (2012). *Introduction to linear regression analysis* (5th ed.). Wiley.

Pedersen, W. C., Miller, L. C., Putcha-Bhagavatula, A. D., & Yang, Y. (2002). Evolved sex differences in the number of partners desired? The long and the short of it. *Psychological Science, 13*(2), 157–161. https://doi.org/10.1111/1467-9280.00428

Pernet, C. R., Wilcox, R., & Rousselet, G. A. (2013). Robust correlation analyses: A Matlab toolbox for psychology research. *Frontiers in Quantitative Psychology and Measurement.* https://doi.org/10.3389/fpsyg.2012.00606

Pratt, J. W. (1964). Robustness of some procedures for the two-sample location problem. *Journal of the American Statistical Association, 59*(307), 665–680. https://doi.org/10.2307/2283092

R Core Team. (2020). *R: A language and environment for statistical computing* [Computer software]. R Foundation for Statistical Computing. https://www.R-project.org/

Rasmussen, J. L. (1989). Data transformation, type I error rate and power. *British Journal of Mathematical & Statistical Psychology, 42*(2), 203–213. https://doi.org/10.1111/j.2044-8317.1989.tb00910.x

Rousseeuw, P. J., & Leroy, A. M. (1987). *Robust regression & outlier detection.* Wiley. https://doi.org/10.1002/0471725382

Rousseeuw, P. J., & van Zomeren, B. C. (1990). Unmasking multivariate outliers and leverage points. *Journal of the American Statistical Association, 85*(411), 633–639. https://doi.org/10.1080/01621459.1990.10474920

Rousselet, G. A., Pernet, C. R., & Wilcox, R. R. (2017). Beyond differences in means: Robust graphical methods to compare two groups in neuroscience. *The European Journal of Neuroscience, 46*(2), 1738–1748. https://doi.org/10.1111/ejn.13610

Ruscio, J., & Mullen, T. (2012). Confidence intervals for the probability of superiority effect size measure and the area under a receiver operating characteristic curve. *Multivariate Behavioral Research, 47*(2), 201–223. https://doi.org/10.1080/00273171.2012.658329

Sievert, C. (2020). *Interactive web-based data visualization with R, plotly, and shiny.* Chapman and Hall/CRC. https://doi.org/10.1201/9780429447273

Staudte, R. G., & Sheather, S. J. (1990). *Robust estimation and testing.* Wiley. https://doi.org/10.1002/9781118165485

Tukey, J. W. (1960). A survey of sampling from contaminated normal distributions. In I. Olkin, S. Ghurye, W. Hoeffding, W. Madow, & H. Mann (Eds.), *Contributions to probability and statistics* (pp. 448–485). Stanford University Press.

Tukey, J. W. (1991). The philosophy of multiple comparisons. *Statistical Science, 6*(1), 100–116. https://doi.org/10.1214/ss/1177011945

Tukey, J. W., & McLaughlin, D. H. (1963). Less vulnerable confidence and significance procedures for location based on a single sample: Trimming/Winsorization 1. *Sankhya A, 25*(3), 331–352. https://www.jstor.org/stable/25049278

Wagenmakers, E.-J., Krypotos, A.-M., Criss, A. H., & Iverson, G. (2012). On the interpretation of removable interactions: A survey of the field 33 years after Loftus. *Memory & Cognition, 40*(2), 145–160. https://doi.org/10.3758/s13421-011-0158-0

Wasserstein, R. L., Schirm, A. L., & Lazar, N. A. (2019). Moving to a world beyond "$p < 0.05$." *American Statistician, 73*(Suppl. 1), 1–19. https://doi.org/10.1080/00031305.2019.1583913

Welch, B. L. (1938). The significance of the difference between two means when the population variances are unequal. *Biometrika, 29*(3-4), 350–362. https://doi.org/10.1093/biomet/29.3-4.350

Wickham, H. (2016). *ggplot2: Elegant graphics for data analysis.* Springer-Verlag. https://ggplot2.tidyverse.org

Wilcox, R. R. (2006). Comparing medians. *Computational Statistics & Data Analysis, 51*(3), 1934–1943. https://doi.org/10.1016/j.csda.2005.12.008

Wilcox, R. R. (2017a). *Modern statistics for the social and behavioral sciences: A practical introduction* (2nd ed.). Chapman & Hall/CRC Press. https://doi.org/10.1201/9781315154480

Wilcox, R. R. (2017b). *Understanding and applying basic statistical methods using R.* Wiley.

Wilcox, R. R. (2022). *Introduction to robust estimation and hypothesis testing* (5th ed.). Academic Press.

Wilcox, R. R., & Keselman, H. J. (2003). Modern robust data analysis methods: Measures of central tendency. *Psychological Methods, 8*(3), 254–274. https://doi.org/10.1037/1082-989X.8.3.254

Wilcox, R. R., & Rousselet, G. A. (2018). A guide to robust statistical methods in neuroscience. *Current Protocols in Neuroscience, 82*(1), 8.42.1–8.42.30. https://doi.org/10.1002/cpns.41

Wilcox, R. R., & Rousselet, G. A. (2021). Methods for dealing with bad data and inadequate models: Distributions, linear models, and beyond (reproducibility package). figshare. https://doi.org/10.6084/m9.figshare.14866035

Yuen, K. K. (1974). The two-sample trimmed *t* for unequal population variances. *Biometrika, 61*(1), 165–170. https://doi.org/10.2307/2334299

CHAPTER 2

MAXIMUM LIKELIHOOD AND MULTIPLE IMPUTATION MISSING DATA HANDLING: HOW THEY WORK, AND HOW TO MAKE THEM WORK IN PRACTICE

Timothy Hayes and Craig K. Enders

The goal of this chapter is to provide an overview of maximum likelihood estimation and multiple imputation, two major missing data handling strategies with strong support from the methodological literature. The theoretical and computational underpinnings of these methods were mostly developed in the 1970s and 1980s (Dempster et al., 1977; Rubin, 1976, 1987), and both became a practical reality in the 1990s, when multiple imputation methods came online (Schafer, 1997) and structural equation modeling software packages began implementing maximum likelihood missing data estimators (Arbuckle, 1996). Both approaches have developed since then, and several important developments have appeared in the methodology literature since the first edition of this handbook.

Many missing data methods have been proposed and investigated in the literature, and there is now broad awareness that older approaches like deleting incomplete data records or filling in missing data with a single prediction (e.g., mean imputation, regression imputation) are seriously flawed. For example, the American Psychological Association's Task Force on Statistical Inference characterized deletion as "among the worst methods available for practical applications" (Wilkinson & Task Force on Statistical Inference, American Psychological Association, Science Directorate, 1999, p. 598). Because descriptions of these older methods abound in the literature, we focus strictly on the two major missing data handling frameworks that have broad theoretical and empirical support: maximum likelihood estimation and multiple imputation.

To set the stage for the material that follows, imagine a researcher who has collected data for a particular study and decided in advance on an analysis model (or set of models) that they intend to run—say, a linear regression analysis—but, upon sitting down to analyze the data, finds themselves confronted with missing values on one or more variables in their intended model. If the researcher is aware that discarding cases will lead to inaccurate model results (e.g., estimated regression coefficients that may be too large or too small, potentially inflated Type I or Type II error rates), they must now think carefully about what should be done instead. At the broadest level, our goal in this chapter is to help empower researchers facing this prototypical dilemma to make informed choices about how to use and configure modern missing data handling approaches in a manner tailored to the unique features of their intended analyses. A major theme of this chapter is that because each analysis one intends to run may involve different sets of variables containing missing data potentially

https://doi.org/10.1037/0000320-002
APA Handbook of Research Methods in Psychology, Second Edition: Vol. 3. Data Analysis and Research Publication, H. Cooper (Editor-in-Chief)
Copyright © 2023 by the American Psychological Association. All rights reserved.

attributable to different causes and because each analysis may, further, contain unique features (e.g., interactions, categorical predictors, outcomes) that require specialized approaches to estimation, a one-size-fits-all approach to missing data handling is rarely appropriate; instead, missing data handling must generally be customized to the needs of each specific analysis.

To help researchers understand how to choose missing data handling methods appropriate for their intended analyses, we begin with a detailed review of the mechanisms that might generate missing data on the variables in a given model. We then provide overviews of missing data handling in the maximum likelihood and multiple imputation frameworks, describe the foundations of these methods as well as more recent extensions, and apply both methods to an illustrative example using simulated data based on a study of $N = 300$ chronic pain patients. Following this, we provide a brief overview of models for data that are missing not at random and close with a set of recommendations for reporting the results of one's missing data analyses.

MISSING DATA MECHANISMS

The manner in which missing data affect the accuracy and precision of one's model estimates depends on the reason why the data are missing. Broadly, scores on a given variable could be missing for purely haphazard reasons unrelated to the data, they could be missing systematically due to scores that are observed in the data, or they could be missing systematically due to the unseen values themselves (Little & Rubin, 1987; Rubin, 1976, 1987). Each of these *missing data mechanisms* (Rubin, 1976) carries distinct implications for how best to handle missing data as well as the potential consequences of mishandling it.

To build an intuition for these concepts, consider a researcher interested in understanding the relationship between levels of self-reported chronic pain (measured with a trichotomous indicator coded: -1 = low pain, 0 = moderate pain, $+1$ = severe pain) and levels of psychosocial disability due to pain (a construct capturing pain's impact on emotional behaviors such as psychological autonomy and communication, emotional stability, and so on) in a sample of chronic pain patients. Now, imagine that not all chronic pain patients in the sample choose to report their psychosocial disability scores. As summarized in Table 2.1, the missing data mechanism that applies in this case depends on whether the probability of missing data on disability (y) is systematically related to the patients' chronic pain levels (x) and whether, within each level of chronic pain, the probability of missing data is related to the unseen values of disability (y). The combinations of these two scenarios in the four cells define three missing data processes or mechanisms: missing completely at random, missing (conditionally) at random, and missing not at random (with focused and diffuse subtypes).

Correspondingly, the four panels of Figure 2.1 use simulated data to illustrate how the conditional distributions of the disability scores within each level of chronic pain might appear under each missing data mechanism from Table 2.1. Observed scores are shown as circles and missing (unseen) values are asterisks. Before proceeding, it is important to emphasize that in Figure 2.1 we present the distributions of missing values alongside the observed values for purely pedagogical reasons: to illustrate the underlying missing data theory by providing a "God's-eye view" of how

TABLE 2.1

Rubin's (1976) Missing Data Mechanisms for a Simple Regression of y on x Classified by Whether or Not the Missing Data Are Observed at Random and Missing at Random

Question 2: Is the probability of missing data on y equal for all possible values of y after conditioning on x?	Question 1: Is the probability of missing data on y equal for all possible observed values of x?	
	Yes	No
Yes	MCAR	MAR
No	Focused MNAR	Diffuse MNAR

Note. MCAR = missing completely at random; MAR = missing at random; MNAR = missing not at random.

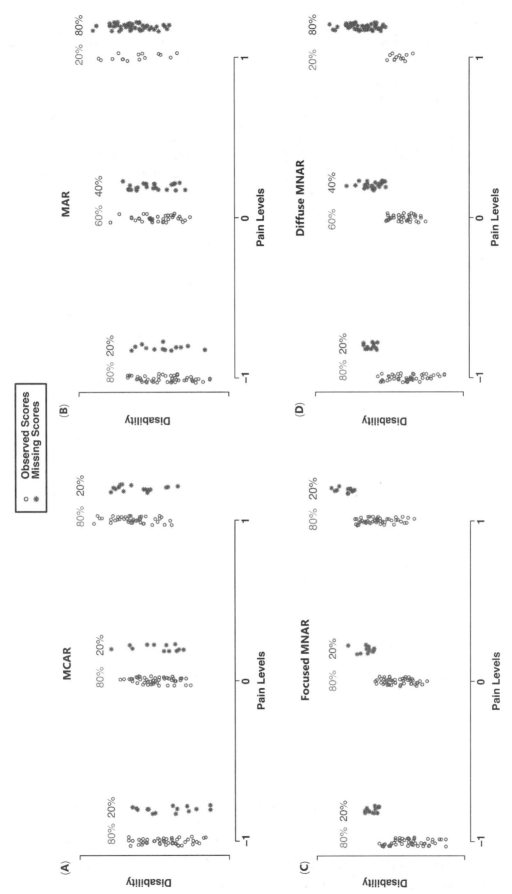

FIGURE 2.1. Missing data mechanisms illustrated using simulated data on chronic pain and psychosocial disability. MCAR = missing completely at random; MAR = missing at random; MNAR = missing not at random.

the distributions of unseen values might appear under each missing data mechanism if they could be observed. With real data, however, one would only have access to the observed values (circles) and would never know the distributions of the would-be scores (asterisks) that participants might have reported if their data were not missing.

Returning to the chronic pain scenario, what if the patients who opt not to report their disability scores are a random subsample of patients with respect to both their pain levels and their disability levels—as would occur, for example, if a glitch in the survey software used to collect data caused the software to randomly crash when assessing disability levels? Figure 2.1A shows the conditional distributions of both observed (circles) and missing (asterisks) disability scores within each level of chronic pain in this type of scenario. Here, we see that the percentage of patients opting not report their disability scores is equal for all observed pain levels (missing values are random with respect to x), and the distributions of the observed and unseen values are roughly the same (i.e., have the same center and spread) within each level of chronic pain. Because in this situation the probability of missing data is random with respect to both the observed and missing values, the pattern of missing data is, in essence, as random as it could ever possibly be—hence, the designation *missing completely at random* (MCAR, e.g., Little & Rubin, 1987; Rubin, 1987). This condition is reflected in the upper left of Table 2.1.

By contrast, what if individuals experiencing higher levels of chronic pain were systematically less likely to report their levels of disability (e.g., because their pain levels interfered with their ability to participate)? Figure 2.1B depicts such a scenario. Here, the percentages of missing scores on disability (presented above each distribution of asterisks) are systematically higher at higher levels of chronic pain (i.e., missing values are no longer random with respect to x), but the distributions of the observed and unseen values are once again roughly the same within each level of chronic pain (i.e., missing y values are randomly distributed after conditioning on x). Although such a mechanism can no longer be said to be completely random, the missing data are said to be *missing at random* (MAR) because the unseen (missing) y-values (disability scores) remain randomly distributed within each level of x (chronic pain). This condition is designated in the upper right of Table 2.1.

Typical applications of the maximum likelihood and multiple imputation methods described below operate under the assumption that all missing data are MAR. Importantly, under a MAR mechanism, the observed data distributions (circles) act as reasonable proxies for what the complete data distributions (circles + asterisks) would have been, and inferences based on the observed data should yield accurate estimates. In line with this idea, maximum likelihood missing data handling utilizes all of the observed data to help identify the optimal parameter estimates, and multiple imputation uses the conditional distributions of the observed data as the basis for filling in the missing values. We describe these methods in detail in later sections.

Finally, consider next what would happen if patients with higher levels of disability (y) were less likely to report their disability scores than those with lower levels of disability, as depicted in Figure 2.1C and D. As the bottom row of Table 2.1 implies, any time that the probability of missing data is unequal across values of y, the data are considered *missing not at random* (MNAR; see Little & Rubin, 1987; Rubin, 1976). Following Gomer and Yuan (2021), the exact type of MNAR mechanism depends on whether the probability of missingness is also related to the observed values of x. The scenario depicted in Figure 2.1C, in which the probability of missing data is systematically related only to the unseen scores on y (disability) but not to the observed values of x (pain), is called a *focused MNAR mechanism*, whereas the scenario depicted in Figure 2.1D, in which the probability of missing data is systematically related to both the unseen scores on y (disability) and the observed values of x (pain,) is called a *diffuse MNAR mechanism*. Whether focused or diffuse, under an MNAR mechanism the observed data distributions (circles) do not act as reasonable proxies for what the complete data distributions (circles + asterisks) would have been, and inferences based exclusively on these observed distributions are no longer be guaranteed to yield accurate results. We briefly discuss approaches to handling MNAR missing data later in the chapter.

Auxiliary Variables

In the previous section, we followed an example in which a researcher was interested in the relationship between chronic pain (x) and disability (y), and we considered the consequences that might result when missing disability scores (y) were generated by a completely random process, a systematic process related to the observed values of chronic pain (x), or a systematic process related to the unseen values of disability (y) itself (or a combination of both). But what would happen if missing data were caused by a variable *other* than pain or disability—that is, a measured variable in the data that isn't part of the main analysis plan?

Continuing with the bivariate example depicted in Figure 2.1, what if stress was correlated with both pain and disability and was also the cause of missing data, such that individuals with higher levels of stress were less likely to report their disability scores than individuals with moderate or low levels of stress? In such a scenario, the probability of reporting one's disability score would be completely random within levels of stress (that is, the missing data would be MAR, if one conditioned on stress), but it would not necessarily be so within levels of chronic pain. Although pain and stress may be correlated, because they are not perfectly correlated, the conditional distributions of disability within levels of stress are not identical to the conditional distributions within levels of pain depicted in Figure 2.1B. For this reason, the probability of missing data on disability within each level of chronic pain does not necessarily remain equal across all values of disability, as required by a MAR process (i.e., Question 2 in Table 2.1).

Omitting an important determinant of missingness that is also correlated with the main analysis variables leads to what may be termed an *MNAR-by-omission process* (see Collins et al., 2001, for a detailed discussion of this topic; see also Enders, 2022, Chapter 1, for this terminology). Applied to our bivariate example, omitting the stress scores from the analysis requires the relation between pain severity and disability to absorb the entire influence of the stress scores on missingness. Depending on the magnitude of the correlations, the net result is that the analysis partially rather than fully conditions on the determinants of missingness. Because the distinction between MAR and MNAR data is defined in terms of the probability of observing each value of y after conditioning on x, it follows that this *MNAR-by-omission* mechanism is more severe to the extent that the missing data cause (e.g., stress) is highly correlated with the residuals of y (disability) after conditioning on x (chronic pain; see Collins et al., 2001; Raykov & West, 2016)—in effect, there is more information about the distribution of missing values being omitted from the analysis, leading to greater misspecification and nonresponse bias.

In order to avoid preventable MNAR-by-omission mechanisms and increase the plausibility that the data are MAR, researchers must decide which *auxiliary variables* (e.g., demographic variables, participants' responses to additional psychological questionnaires) from outside of the substantive model of interest should ultimately be included to aid missing data estimation, raising an important question as to how one can best approach this task (Collins et al., 2001). Ideally, plausible determinants of missing data (e.g., stress in the bivariate example) could be identified through a combination of substantive theory, practical experience, and data exploration. As noted previously, the goal is to identify variables that both predict missingness and have salient correlations (or more accurately, semipartial or residual correlations) with the incomplete analysis variables.

Although a variety of statistical approaches might potentially be applied to this task, one particularly useful search strategy is to include auxiliary variables that exhibit at least moderate (e.g., $|r| = .3$) correlations with the residuals of each incomplete variable (i.e., external variables with moderate semipartial correlations). To help accomplish this, Raykov and West (2016) developed a latent variable approach to estimating these correlations within the *structural equation modeling* (SEM) framework. As a simpler alternative to this method, users could first estimate the matrix of bivariate correlations between the substantive model variables and candidate auxiliary variables using a modern approach to missing data handling such as the maximum likelihood or multiple imputation procedures described below and then scan these bivariate correlations for entries greater than .3 in absolute value. Screening based on correlations is an effective strategy for identifying auxiliary variables because strong predictors of missingness (i.e., variables on which participants with and without missing values differ) are only capable of introducing nonresponse bias if they are also correlated with the analysis variables.

MAXIMUM LIKELIHOOD ESTIMATION

The goal of *maximum likelihood* (ML) *estimation* is to identify the model parameter values most likely responsible for producing the data. The missing data handling aspect of maximum likelihood happens behind the scenes as a part of the same process. Importantly, ML estimation does not discard incomplete data records nor does it impute them. Rather, when confronted with missing values, maximum likelihood uses the normal curve to deduce the missing parts of the data as an optimization algorithm iterates to a solution.[1] The resulting parameter values are those with maximum support from (or best fit to) the observed data. To understand how this procedure accommodates missing data, it is first necessary to understand a bit about how ML estimation works in the context of complete data, beginning with what exactly is meant by the concept of a *likelihood*, a quantity that essentially functions as a measure of fit between a person's data and a set of model parameters.

Likelihoods are closely related to probabilities. One way of understanding probabilities is as the relative frequencies with which one would expect to observe a set of events or score values over many repeated trials (e.g., Hoel, 1984, p. 8). For example, if one flipped a fair coin many times, one would expect roughly half of those flips to come up heads, assuming that the true population proportion was .50. The idea of a likelihood inverts this logic by asking what population parameters could most plausibly have generated the observed data (i.e., given an observed sample of 50 heads and 50 tails from 100 flips, what population proportion of heads is most likely to have generated it?).

These same principles can be applied to continuous statistical distributions such as the normal curve displayed in Figure 2.2A. The relative probability of obtaining a particular score from a normal distribution with a known mean and standard deviation can be calculated using the *univariate normal density function*. More formally, the probability density, p_i, that individual i's score in a data set, y_i, was obtained from a univariate normal distribution with mean μ and standard deviation σ, may be written:

$$p_i(y_i|\mu, \sigma^2) = \text{constant} \times \exp\left(-.5 \times \frac{(y_i - \mu)^2}{\sigma^2}\right)$$
$$= \text{constant} \times \exp(-.5(z_i^2)), \quad (2.1)$$

where exp( ) indicates the exponential function and "constant" represents a collection of terms that ensure that the area of the normal density curve sums (integrates) to 1. Because these constant terms do not change with new input to the function, they can be ignored in order to simplify our present discussion. Importantly the vertical pipe in the notation $p_i(y_i|\mu, \sigma^2)$ makes clear that Equation 2.1 returns the relative probability of a given score, y_i, conditional or dependent on a known mean and variance, μ and σ^2. Visually, the probability density, p_i is the height of the normal distribution at a particular value of y_i. The bottom row of the expression makes clear that the term in the exponent contains a squared z-score. In Equation 2.1, smaller squared z-scores

---

[1] Technically, the estimator marginalizes over the missing values.

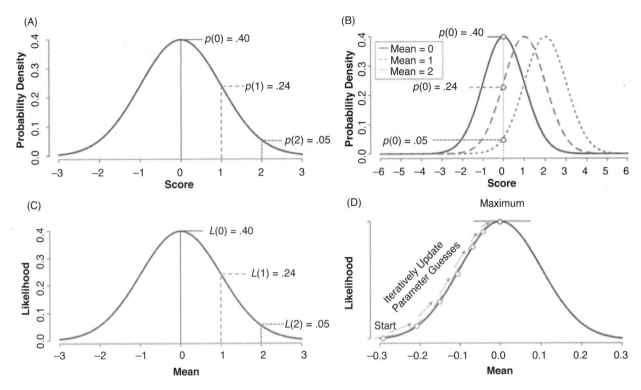

FIGURE 2.2. Illustrations of univariate normal density curves and univariate normal likelihood functions.

associated with scores closer to the mean result in larger probability densities than those of larger squared z-scores further from the center.

To illustrate, Figure 2.2A graphs the density function from Equation 2.1 applied to scores from a standard normal distribution. Panel A shows the probability densities associated with three different scores in a standard normal distribution: a score at the mean (0), one standard deviation (SD) above the mean (1), and two standard deviations above the mean (2). As the figure shows, in the context of a standard normal distribution, the relative probability of obtaining a score at the mean, $p(0) = .40$, is roughly twice as large (i.e., twice as high in vertical elevation) as the relative probability associated with obtaining a score one SD above the mean, $p(1) = .24$, and it is eight times larger than the relative probability associated with obtaining a score two SDs above the mean, $p(2) = .05$.

To move from probability densities toward the idea of likelihoods, Figure 2.2B shows the probability densities associated with drawing a score of approximately 0 from three hypothetical normal curves with the same variance ($\sigma^2 = 1$) but different means. Panel B highlights that a score of 0 has a high relative probability of being drawn from a distribution with mean 0, $p(0) = .40$, a comparatively lower relative probability of being drawn from a distribution with mean 1, $p(0) = .24$, and a very low relative probability of being drawn from a distribution with mean 2, $p(0) = .05$. Although these statements concern relative probabilities rather than likelihoods, we might utilize the knowledge that drawing a score approximately equal to 0 is a far more probable outcome for some population means than for others: as noted previously, a likelihood reverses this logic and asks, what population mean is most likely to have produced the data on hand (i.e., a particular score of 0). Based on this single observation, we can infer that $\mu = 0$ is most likely responsible for the datum.

A univariate normal likelihood has the same formula as Equation 2.1. The key difference is that after obtaining a sample of data, the y values become known, and the parameters become unknowns. Symbolically, we can write this as

$L_i(\mu, \sigma^2|y_i)$. To illustrate, Figure 2.2C graphs the likelihood of different parameter values based on a single observed data point, $y_i = 0$. Because the parameters and data have switched roles, the horizontal axis now lists the unknown parameter values instead of hypothetical score values. Importantly, the meaning of the vertical coordinates has also changed; the likelihood is no longer a relative probability but an index of support for different parameter values. Panel C shows that a score of $y_i = 0$ has the most support for a population mean of 0 and decreasing support for a mean of 1 and 2.

Shifting from individual scores to an entire data set, the overall likelihood, L, for a sample of N individuals can be calculated as the product of the individual likelihoods. The resulting graph would look like Figure 2.2C, but the vertical coordinates would represent the entire sample's support for different unknown parameter values. Note that, in practice, ML optimization algorithms work with the natural logarithm of the overall likelihood in order to turn the product of probabilities into a more mathematically tractable sum. The purpose of our discussion of ML estimation here is to provide readers with a broad conceptual overview of the logic of the method, however, so we omit that detail here (for further information on the details of ML, readers are encouraged to consult Eliason, 1993).

In practice, ML estimation is typically implemented using *iterative optimization algorithms*. Iterative optimization algorithms begin with a blunt guess—a *starting value*—for a proposed parameter estimate and iteratively improve upon this guess until finding the estimate(s) that maximize the likelihood of producing the observed data (i.e., the parameter values that have the most support from the data). This process is visualized in Figure 2.2D for a sample of $N = 100$ standard normal observations, with circles representing sequential iterative updates and tangent lines representing the slope of the curve at each guess. The flat tangent line at the peak of the likelihood function is a mathematical indication that the optimizer has found the optimal estimate for the data.

Building up to a bivariate analysis example, it turns out that the univariate normal density function of Equation 2.1 is all that is needed to estimate a linear regression model with complete data. To understand how this is so, examine Figure 2.3, which depicts a hypothetical bivariate scatterplot from the regression of disability on chronic pain levels. The normal curves convey the distributions of the disability scores at the three

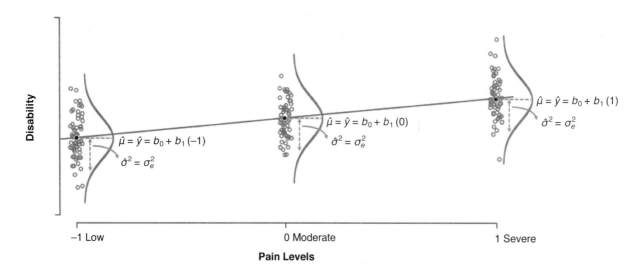

FIGURE 2.3. Regression of psychosocial disability on chronic pain with superimposed conditional normal distributions.

different pain levels. The regression line cuts through these distributions at their (conditional) means, which are just the predicted scores shown as black dots. As the annotations in the figure imply, one way of understanding the regression of disability on pain levels is to view the analysis as attempting to estimate a single regression intercept, single regression slope, and single estimated residual variance that best capture the conditional means ($\hat{y}$ values) and constant (residual) variance of the conditional distributions of disability for individuals with each level of self-reported pain. With this in mind, we can use ML estimation to estimate a bivariate regression model by setting $\mu = \hat{y}_i$ and $\sigma^2 = \sigma_e^2$ in Equation 2.1 as follows:

$$L_i = \text{constant} \times \exp\left(-.5 \times \frac{[y_i - (b_0 + b_1 X_1)]^2}{\sigma_e^2}\right)$$

$$= \text{constant} \times \exp\left(-.5 \times \frac{(y_i - \hat{y}_i)^2}{\sigma_e^2}\right)$$

$$= \text{constant} \times \exp(-.5(z_i^2)). \quad (2.2)$$

Following the earlier example, the likelihood represents a single score's support for the three unknown parameter values in the equation (b_0, b_1, and σ_e^2), and the entire sample's support for different parameter values combines N individual likelihoods. Although there are now multiple parameters, the iterative optimization algorithm updates each parameter one at a time following the same process depicted in Figure 2.2D. Note that, although both x_i and y_i appear in Equation 2.2, it is only the univariate distribution of y_i that determines the likelihood; the predictor values, x_i, are simply considered to be fixed constants used to define the conditional mean of each y_i. Applied to Figure 2.3, the analysis makes no assumptions about the distribution of pain severity nor does it make any attempt to estimate the parameters of such a distribution.

Moving to missing data, how can we compute Equation 2.2 if either x_i or y_i is missing? The fundamental idea behind *full information maximum likelihood* (FIML, Arbuckle, 1996) estimation procedures is to utilize all available data on all model variables to inform the final model estimates. However, to do so requires switching from a univariate estimation procedure whose only goal is to estimate the parameters associated with y_i to a *multivariate* estimation procedure that also considers the parameters of x_i as estimated quantities in the analysis (i.e., instead of treating the predictor values as fixed, x is also assigned a distribution). We can accomplish this by first incorporating the observed values of both the predictors and outcome(s) into a multivariate normal density function, and then quantifying their support for a set of proposed parameters by rewriting this density as a *multivariate normal likelihood function*:

$$L_i(\mathbf{\mu}, \mathbf{\Sigma} | \mathbf{y}_i)$$

$$= \text{constant} \times \exp\left[-.5 \times (\mathbf{y}_i - \mathbf{\mu})' \mathbf{\Sigma}^{-1} (\mathbf{y}_i - \mathbf{\mu})\right]$$

$$= \text{constant} \times \exp(-.5(z_i^2)), \quad (2.3)$$

where "constant" again indicates a collection of terms that can be ignored for our present purposes, $\mathbf{y}_i$ is a vector of scores on k multivariate outcomes for person i, $\mathbf{\mu}$ is a vector of k model-implied means, and $\mathbf{\Sigma}$ is a $k \times k$ model-implied variance–covariance matrix corresponding to the same multivariate outcomes. In the bottom expression, the z_i^2 is a shorthand notation that now represents the *Mahalanobis distance* for case i—a multivariate analog of a squared z-score quantifying the standardized distance of an individual's scores on the outcomes in $\mathbf{y}_i$ from the center of the proposed multivariate normal distribution. Conceptually, the equation works exactly the same as before. That is, each likelihood is essentially a vertical coordinate that measures the scores' support for a particular combination of unknown parameter values. The goal of estimation is to find the parameter values that maximize fit to the data.

The simple regression model can be readily extended to a multivariate estimation framework by setting $\mathbf{y}_i' = [x_i \quad y_i]'$ and by populating $\mathbf{\mu}$ and $\mathbf{\Sigma}$ with predicted parameter values derived from the regression model—obtained using algebraic mean and covariance expectations (e.g., Bollen, 1989, pp. 21–36)—such that the squared z-score from Equation 2.3, the Mahalanobis distance, becomes

$$z_i^2 = (y_i - \mu)' \Sigma^{-1} (y_i - \mu)$$

$$= \left(\begin{bmatrix} x_i \\ y_i \end{bmatrix} - \begin{bmatrix} \mu_x \\ b_0 + b_1 \mu_x \end{bmatrix} \right)' \begin{bmatrix} \sigma_x^2 & b_1 \sigma_x^2 \\ b_1 \sigma_x^2 & b_1^2 \sigma_x^2 + \sigma_e^2 \end{bmatrix}^{-1}$$

$$\left(\begin{bmatrix} x_i \\ y_i \end{bmatrix} - \begin{bmatrix} \mu_x \\ b_0 + b_1 \mu_x \end{bmatrix} \right). \quad (2.4)$$

In the context of this model, an iterative optimization procedure would search for estimates of the unknown regression parameters, b_0, b_1, σ_e^2, μ_x, and σ_x^2 that maximize the overall sample likelihood or fit to the data.

To extend such a multivariate model to handle missing data, the FIML function (Arbuckle, 1996) strategically alters Equation 2.3 as follows:

$$L_i^{FIML}(\mu_i, \Sigma_i | y_i)$$

$$= \text{constant} \times \exp\left[-.5 \times (y_i - \mu_i)' \Sigma_i^{-1} (y_i - \mu_i) \right]. \quad (2.5)$$

The crucial elements of Equation 2.5 are the i subscripts added to μ and $\hat{\Sigma}$, implying that the likelihood for the ith individual is calculated with a mean vector and covariance matrix subsetted to contain elements corresponding to only those variables on which individual i has complete data. For example, if an individual has observed data on y but not x, Equation 2.5 calculates the individual's likelihood by ignoring all quantities related to x and setting $y_i = [y_i]$, $\mu_i = [b_0 + b_1 \mu_x]$, and $\Sigma_i = [b_1^2 \sigma_x^2 + \sigma_e^2]$. Conversely, if an individual has observed data on x but not y, Equation 2.7 calculates the individual's likelihood by ignoring all quantities related to y and setting $y_i = [x_i]$, $\mu_i = [\mu_x]$, and $\Sigma_i = [\sigma_x^2]$. Finally, individuals with complete data on both x and y have matrices y_i, μ_i, and Σ_i defined as in Equation 2.4. In this way, FIML incorporates all observed values on every variable into the estimation process.

Importantly, FIML estimation does not discard incomplete data records nor does it impute them. Although it isn't obvious from the equations, maximum likelihood uses the normal curve to deduce the missing parts of the data as the optimization algorithm iterates to a solution. To illustrate, reconsider Figure 2.3. Intuitively, knowing an individual's pain level provides important information about disability, as an individual with high pain is much more likely to have a higher rather than lower disability score. In a similar vein, knowing an individual's disability score also carries information about their pain. Although the missing values are never filled in, maximum likelihood can nevertheless be viewed as an "implicit imputation" routine (Widaman, 2006) in the sense that it intuits the missing parts of the data based on the observed scores.

Incorporating Auxiliary Variables in an FIML Analysis

Revisiting earlier ideas, recall that an MNAR-by-omission process occurs when the analysis or imputation procedure fails to condition on a correlate of missingness that also correlates with the residuals of the analysis variables. Because FIML estimates may become biased when missing data on an outcome or predictor variable are MNAR, researchers are well-advised to guard against this possibility by introducing auxiliary variables pertinent to both predictors and outcomes with missing data. Note that auxiliary variables can themselves have missing values (see Enders, 2008), although their utility diminishes if their values are missing with the analysis variables.

Because FIML handles missing data directly as a part of the model estimation process, auxiliary variables that lie outside of one's substantive analysis model of interest must be incorporated into this model in some way. One intuitive possibility would be to specify all auxiliary variables as additional exogenous covariates in the substantive model—for example, adding stress as an explicit predictor in the regression of disability on pain. However, doing so would

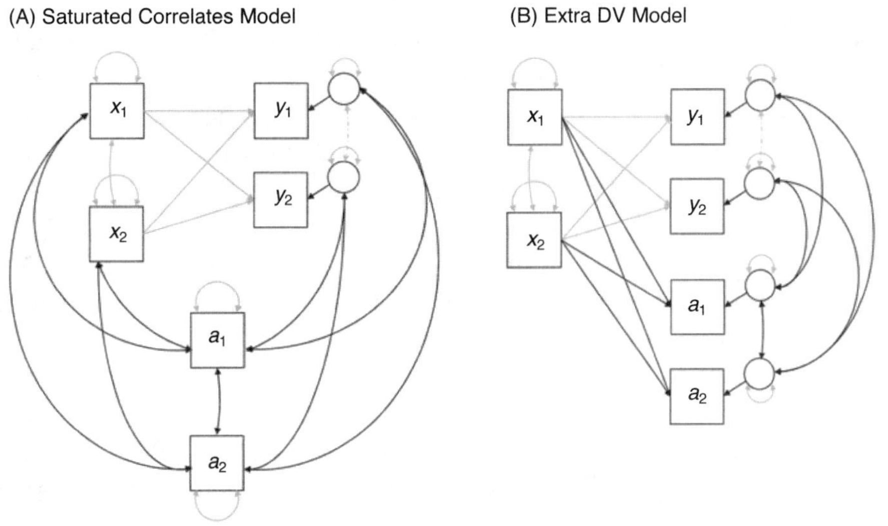

(A) Saturated Correlates Model   (B) Extra DV Model

FIGURE 2.4. Graham's (2003) models for incorporating auxiliary variables into a full information maximum likelihood analysis.

convert this bivariate regression into a multiple regression, changing the meaning of the coefficients. In this new model, the *partial* regression coefficient for pain would reflect the influence of pain on disability after removing overlapping variance between stress and pain rather than the intended bivariate regression coefficient reflecting the total influence of pain on disability.

To avoid this undesirable side effect, Graham (2003) proposed that auxiliary variables in an FIML-estimated SEM could be specified as *saturated correlates*—free-floating variables in one's model specified to covary with (a) all predictors in the model, (b) the residuals of all outcomes, and (c) each other. Figure 2.4A shows a path diagram[2] of a substantive model involving two predictor variables (x_1 and x_2) and two outcome variables (y_1 and y_2), with the focal model parameters drawn in light gray, and two auxiliary variables (a_1 and a_2) specified as saturated correlates. Because the auxiliary variables in a saturated correlates model are related to all other model variables via two-headed arrows (i.e., correlations or residual correlations, depicted using solid black lines), they are able to assist missing data estimation in all parts of the model without altering the meaning of the partial regression coefficients.

Alternatively, Graham (2003) suggested that one might specify all auxiliary variables as *extra dependent variables* (extra DVs)—additional outcomes regressed on the predictors, with their residuals covarying with one another and with the residuals of the outcome variables. Mirroring Figure 2.4A, Figure 2.4B shows a path diagram of the same model with the auxiliary variables reconfigured as extra DVs. The diagrammatic conventions of Figure 2.4B are the same as those of Figure 2.4A, with the exception that black one-headed arrows are now used to indicate the regressions of the auxiliary variables on the predictors. The logic of this method is analogous to the logic of the saturated correlates approach: the extra variables pass their information to every other variable but, because the auxiliary variables are modeled as additional outcomes rather than covariates, the meaning of all partial regression coefficients associated with the focal analysis (the gray arrows in Figure 2.4) will once again remain intact.

---

[2]In conventional path diagrammatic notation, rectangles indicate observed (manifest) variables, circles indicate unobserved (latent) residuals, two-headed arrows indicate variances when attached to a single rectangle or circle and covariances when connecting two rectangles or circles, and one-headed arrows connect regression predictors to outcomes.

In sum, both of Graham's (2003) models provide conceptually straightforward strategies for incorporating auxiliary variables into one's model when using FIML estimation with missing data. The saturated correlates and extra DV approaches do come with some limitations, however. Importantly, including more than a few auxiliary variables in these models can result in matrices with an improper structure and, thus, an increased probability of convergence failures (Savalei & Bentler, 2009). One possible solution is to include one or two auxiliary variables with the highest correlation (or residual correlation) with the incomplete variables. In practice, it is often difficult to find more than one or two extra variables that meaningfully increase explained variance, so there is often little benefit to including large numbers of auxiliary variables. A second solution, proposed by Howard et al. (2015), is to first select a large number auxiliary variables for inclusion, then utilize principal components analysis to extract a smaller subset of components that, in turn, function as auxiliary variables. Their simulations show that even a single principal component score is an effective surrogate for a large number of auxiliary variables.

Maximum Likelihood: Recent Developments

Maximum likelihood analyses have evolved considerably in recent years. The estimators that were widely available when the first edition of this handbook was published were generally limited to multivariate normal data (e.g., Equation 2.3). This is still a common (and very reasonable) assumption for missing data analyses, but flexible estimation routines that accommodate mixtures of categorical and continuous variables are now widely available (Lüdtke et al., 2020; Muthén et al., 2016).

Estimators for mixed response types generally deploy a so-called *factored regression strategy* that breaks the overall likelihood function into a set of component likelihoods (Ibrahim, 1990). To illustrate its simplest incarnation, reconsider the bivariate normal example from Equation 2.3. Factored regression models use the probability chain rule to convert the bivariate distribution into the product of two or more univariate distributions, each of which corresponds to a regression model. Using generic notation, the factorization for the bivariate regression analysis is

$$f(Y, X) = f(Y|X) \times f(X), \qquad (2.6)$$

where each "f of something" represents a probability distribution (or likelihood) induced by a regression model; the leftmost term represents the multivariate distribution of the variables from Equation 2.3, the first term after the equals sign corresponds to the focal regression model (the linear regression model depicted in Figure 2.3), and the rightmost term is a supporting (empty) regression for the incomplete predictor. By avoiding the multivariate distribution on the left and working with the univariate distributions on the right, we can mix and match distributions that honor the metrics of the data. For example, reconsider the linear regression depicted in Figure 2.3. Suppose instead that the three pain levels represented qualitative rather than quantitative differences among participants. Mixtures of categorical and numeric variables are at odds with a multivariate normal distribution, but the factored approach readily accommodates this by specifying $f(X)$ as a logistic regression.

Factorizing a multivariate distribution into component univariate models also paves the way for estimating interactions and nonlinear effects with missing data (Lüdtke et al., 2020; Robitzsch & Luedtke, 2021). For example, consider the following moderated multiple regression analysis where the influence of depression varies by sex (0 = female, 1 = male) to influence psychosocial disability:

$$\begin{aligned}DISABILITY_i = b_0 &+ b_1(DEPRESSION_i) \\ &+ b_2(SEVERE\ PAIN_i) + b_3(MALE_i) \\ &+ b_4(DEPRESSION_i)(MALE_i) + e_i.\end{aligned}$$
(2.7)

Note that, in line with the example data presented later in the chapter, SEVERE PAIN refers to a binary indicator where 0 = no/little/moderate pain and where 1 = severe pain. Using generic notation, the factored regression specification for the model is

$$f(DISABILITY|DEPRESSION, SEVERE\ PAIN,$$
$$MALE, DEPRESSION \times MALE)$$
$$\times f(DEPRESSION|SEVERE\ PAIN, MALE)$$
$$\times f(SEVERE\ PAIN|MALE) \times f(MALE), \quad (2.8)$$

where the first term corresponds to the moderated regression analysis, and the remaining terms are supporting regression models for the predictors. Two points are worth noting. First, two of the predictors are binary, and their supporting models would be logistic regressions, as previously noted. Second, the focal analysis involves the product of two variables, but the product term itself is not a unique variable (i.e., it does not get predicted by other regressors). Factored regression models are an important recent innovation, as classic estimators based on multivariate normality are known to introduce bias when applied to models with interactions and other types nonlinear effects (e.g., so-called *just-another-variable approaches*; Cham et al., 2017). The analysis examples illustrate the factor regression approach.

MULTIPLE IMPUTATION

To review, maximum likelihood is a direct estimator that incorporates missing data handling into each analysis in a single step. Because maximum likelihood addresses both the missing data model and the substantive analysis model simultaneously, users must choose the maximum likelihood estimator that best captures the important features of both models, for example, relying on the multivariate normal likelihood function of Equation 2.5 to handle simple scenarios in which all analysis variables and auxiliary variables are continuous and all relationships in the model are linear (no-moderated) but switching to the factored likelihood of Equation 2.8 to handle more complex scenarios in which key model variables are categorical, key relationships in the model are nonlinear (e.g., moderated), or both. In this way, maximum likelihood estimation proceeds on an analysis-by-analysis basis, tailoring the estimation approach to the specific features of each model. Importantly, because maximum likelihood integrates missing data handling into the estimation of the substantive model, auxiliary variables must be actively incorporated into the substantive analysis model as saturated correlates, extra DVs, or additional terms in a factored likelihood.

In contrast to maximum likelihood, multiple imputation is a two-stage procedure that separates missing data handling from the analysis. The first stage creates multiple copies of the data (e.g., at least 20), each containing different estimates of the missing values. A typical imputation routine uses the estimated model parameters to compute predicted values of the missing data that are augmented with random noise to preserve variation. Having created a set of filled-in data sets, the second stage consists of analyzing each data set and using "Rubin's rules" (Little & Rubin, 1987; Rubin, 1987) to combine estimates and standard errors into a single package of results. These pooled point estimates and standard errors average over many plausible values for the missing data.

Separating missing data imputation from data analysis can be a benefit or an Achilles heel. On the one hand, because numerous auxiliary variables—both continuous or categorical—can be easily included as predictors in the initial imputation stage, these variables are no longer required to be incorporated into the analysis model as somewhat awkward saturated correlates or extra DVs. On the other hand, this separation also creates the possibility that the model charged with constructing the imputations contradicts or is somehow incompatible with the second-stage analysis model (Bartlett et al., 2015; Meng, 1994). For example, this could happen because the first-stage imputation model omits one of the analysis variables (all analysis model variables must be included in the imputation model, regardless of whether they are complete or incomplete, in order to preserve their correlational structure in the resulting imputations), incorrectly specifies an incomplete variable's distribution, or fails to preserve a structural feature of the data such as clustering or grouping. The importance of these issues cannot be overstated: an incorrectly specified imputation model that does not preserve the key features of an intended analysis can actually inject bias into one's results, potentially compounding existing bias caused by missing data or even creating bias where none previously existed.

For this reason, we find it useful to distinguish imputation methods according to the similarity between the imputation and analysis models. When the analysis model(s) one intends to run are relatively straightforward, it is sometimes possible to create a single, general set of multiple imputations that serve a variety of different analytic goals. For example, a researcher could use a multivariate regression model (or a series of univariate regressions) for imputation and then fit any number of subsequent linear regression models to the filled-in data sets, so long as these models do not feature interactions or polynomial terms that add complexity to the analysis. Although this option does not have a common name, Enders (2022) used the phrase "agnostic imputation" to convey that imputations aren't tailored to one specific analytic goal. Common examples of agnostic imputation approaches include the popular joint model (Schafer, 1997) and fully conditional specification frameworks (Raghunathan et al., 2001; Van Buuren et al., 2006).

By contrast, when the analysis model(s) one intends to estimate are more complex, it is best to apply the same models at both stages in order to tailor the imputations to the unique features of each specific analysis. For example, a researcher could use a moderated regression approach to create imputations that accurately reflect the nonlinearity caused by the product term(s), and the second stage analysis would be an identical moderated regression model. The literature has described this option using numerous labels, including the sequential specification, model-based imputation, fully Bayesian imputation, and substantive model-compatible multiple imputation (Bartlett et al., 2015; Enders et al., 2020; Lüdtke et al., 2020; Zhang & Wang, 2017).

By classifying procedures according to the alignment between the imputation and analysis models, our goal is to emphasize that an analysis model's composition—in particular, whether it includes nonlinear effects such as interactions, polynomial terms, or random effects—determines the type of imputation strategy that works best. A tailored, model-based approach is preferable for analyses that feature these types of nonlinearities, whereas agnostic imputation schemes are well suited for descriptive summaries and additive models that do not include such terms. It is also perfectly acceptable to mix and match these two approaches within a given project as needed, and it is similarly acceptable to use some combination of maximum likelihood estimation and multiple imputation.

Stage 1. Creating Imputed Data Sets

Digging a bit deeper into the mechanics, most multiple imputation procedures use Bayesian estimation and Markov chain Monte Carlo (MCMC) algorithms for the initial imputation stage. These algorithms iterate between two steps: update the parameter estimates conditional on the filled-in data, then update the missing values conditional on the new parameter estimates. To illustrate, suppose it is of interest to estimate a bivariate association between pain levels and psychosocial disability. To simplify the notation, we generically refer to these variables as y and x, respectively. For now, assume that y (disability) has missing values and x (pain) is complete.

Agnostic imputation is appropriate for this model because the analysis does not involve interactive or nonlinear effects. A typical agnostic imputation scheme would use linear regression such as the one depicted in Figure 2.3 as the first-stage imputation model, and the supporting MCMC algorithm would repeatedly alternate between estimating the regression model parameters and imputing the data. Focusing on the imputation step, each missing data point is replaced by an estimate that equals the sum of a predicted value and a normally distributed random noise term. Using generic notation, the following equation defines the imputations

$$y_{i(\text{Imp})} = b_0 + b_1 x_i + \dot{e}_i = \hat{y}_{i(\text{Imp})} + \dot{e}_i, \quad (2.9)$$

where $y_{i(\text{Imp})}$ is the imputation generated for the ith observation on incomplete variable y_i (e.g., disability), x_i is a complete variable (e.g., pain), b_0 and b_1 are regression coefficients updated to reflect the current iteration of the MCMC algorithm, $\hat{y}_{i(\text{Imp})}$ is the predicted value of y_i given an individual's observed x_i score, and $\dot{e}_i$ is a synthetic residual term (i.e., a random number) sampled from a normal distribution, the spread of which depends on the estimated residual variance.

To illustrate, Figure 2.3 can be reconstrued as depicting the distributions of plausible disability imputations at three values of pain. The black dots on the regression line are the predicted values and the spread of the normal curves reflects the estimated residual variation (i.e., the variation of the $\dot{e}_i$ terms). Candidate imputations fall exactly on vertical lines, but Figure 2.3 uses horizontal jitter to improve visibility of the circles in high-density portions of the distribution.

The MCMC algorithm imputes missing values by selecting circles from each distribution at random, depending on one's pain level. This agnostic imputation procedure can easily be extended to multivariate missing data (e.g., estimating the correlations among three incomplete variables, such as pain, disability, and depression) by using a round robin sequence of linear regression models, each of which features an incomplete variable regressed on all other variables (complete or previously imputed; see van Buuren et al., 2006, for a description of this *fully conditional specification* [FCS] procedure).

As a second example, suppose the analysis model is the moderated regression from Equation 2.7. An agnostic imputation scheme is no longer appropriate for this analysis (Bartlett et al., 2015), as the presence of a product term requires a model-based approach that tailors imputation to this specific analysis. In fact, model-based imputation invokes the same factored regression specification shown in Equation 2.8; in lieu of the round robin scheme described in the previous paragraph, imputation uses a collection of equations that consists of the focal analysis variable and supporting regression models for each incomplete predictor. Although the basic idea is still the same—imputation equals a predicted value plus noise—model-based imputation is more complex because the distribution of imputations can depend on more than one regression equation.

The MCMC algorithm repeats the two-step estimation procedure (update the parameters, then update the imputations) for many computational cycles. A typical application saves a relatively small number of complete data sets—a common recommendation is to use $M = 20$ data sets (Graham et al., 2007)—from a much longer MCMC process consisting of hundreds or even thousands of computational cycles. One way to do this is to save each imputed data set from the final iteration of a unique MCMC process or chain. In order to ensure that the MCMC algorithm produces accurate, representative imputations, it is critical to determine an appropriate total number of iterations T (also called the *burn-in period*), as the MCMC algorithm must iterate long enough to escape its dependence on random starting values and converge to a steady state. To determine this number, T, researchers must assess one or more MCMC *convergence diagnostics*. Although graphical displays such as trace plots (Schafer, 1997) might be used for this purpose, the potential scale reduction factor (a measure capturing the similarity of MCMC chains initiated from different random starting values; Gelman & Rubin, 1992) is especially useful because simple rules of thumb nearly always produce acceptable results (e.g., determine the number of iterations required for the index to drop below 1.05, then set T to that value).

Stage 2. Analyzing Imputations and Pooling Estimates

The product of the first stage is a set of M filled-in data sets. Although it might seem reasonable to do so, averaging the filled-in values themselves is inappropriate; the correct procedure is to analyze each filled-in data set separately and combine multiple sets of estimates and standard errors into one package of results. Repeating an analysis many times sounds tedious, but most software packages have built-in routines that automate this process.

Rubin (1987) provided the rules or equations for pooling estimates and standard errors. The multiple imputation point estimate is simply the arithmetic average of the M estimates

$$\bar{\theta} = \frac{1}{M}\sum_{m=1}^{M}\hat{\theta}_m, \qquad (2.10)$$

where $\hat{\theta}_m$ is a parameter value from data set m, and $\bar{\theta}$ is the average estimate. Pooling standard errors is a bit more complicated because a simple average of the complete-data standard errors would overstate precision. The correct pooling expression is

$$SE_{\hat{\theta}} = \sqrt{\text{mean}(SE^2) + \text{var}(\hat{\theta}_m) + \frac{\text{var}(\hat{\theta}_m)}{M}}$$
$$= \sqrt{V_W + V_B + SE_{\hat{\theta}}^2}, \qquad (2.11)$$

where the first term under the radical represents the average squared standard error (the within-imputation sampling variance, V_W), the second term depends on the variance of the M parameter estimates around their average (the between-imputation variance, V_B), and the final term represents the squared standard error of the pooled estimate ($SE_{\hat{\theta}}^2$). Conceptually, the first term estimates the sampling error of a complete-data analysis, and the next two terms are essentially correction factors that inflate the standard error to compensate for uncertainty due to the imputations–that is, additional uncertainty (sampling variability) in the parameter estimates caused by missing data. We note that this additional missing data uncertainty is also reflected in FIML standard errors, though their calculation is not as straightforward.

Because different variables in an analysis (e.g., the predictors and outcome in the regression of Equation 2.7) may be more or less affected by missing data, it follows that their associated standard errors may be correspondingly influenced by different degrees of missing data uncertainty. To quantify the degree of this influence, it is useful to divide the second and third terms under the radical in Equation 2.11 by the entire quantity under the radical to calculate a useful R^2-like quantity known as the *fraction of missing information* (FMI, Rubin, 1987), which gives proportional impact of missing data on the squared standard error. For example, FMI = .20 means that variation due to missing data accounts for 20% of the squared standard error.

In addition to using the FMI to quantify missing data uncertainty in each standard error in a single model, it can also be useful to examine changes in the FMI values that result from adding one or more auxiliary variables to an initial model. To understand why, consider that if an auxiliary variable correlates highly with a certain variable in the substantive analysis model and also contains comparatively more complete data than that variable (e.g., because the auxiliary variable was collected at baseline, before later measurements were affected by participant dropout), the complete values of this auxiliary variable, to some extent, act as proxies for the unseen values of the analysis variable, contributing information to the analysis that might serve to reduce missing data uncertainty (Collins et al., 2001). The success of an auxiliary variable (or set of auxiliary variables) in reducing missing data uncertainty in parameter standard errors is naturally captured by decreased FMI values.[3] Although there is no firm rule regarding how steep a decrease in FMI values must be in order to be considered meaningful, reporting information about which auxiliary variables seem useful for repairing parameter standard errors and recovering lost power can help alert researchers working in the same sub-

---

[3] We note, however, that it may require pooling the results of many imputed data sets to achieve stable enough FMI values to compare across analyses (e.g., von Hippel, 2018, for a primer on the number of imputations needed in multiple imputation analyses).

stantive area to the possible benefits of including these auxiliary variables in their future research. We note that the FMI can also be calculated using FIML estimation, although this option is not available in all software packages (for details, see Savalei & Rhemtulla, 2012). We report these diagnostics in the upcoming analysis examples, where available.

FULL INFORMATION MAXIMUM LIKELIHOOD AND MULTIPLE IMPUTATION DATA ANALYSIS EXAMPLES

To illustrate maximum likelihood and multiple imputation, we present illustrative analyses using synthetic data based on a real study of 300 chronic pain sufferers. The data set includes a number of psychological correlates of chronic pain. The focal variables for the analyses are a gender dummy code (0 = female, 1 = male), a binary severe pain indicator (0 = no, little, or moderate pain, 1 = severe pain), a depression composite, and a scale measuring psychosocial disability. We also considered four self-report auxiliary variables: perceived control over pain, pain interference with daily life activities, anxiety, and stress.

All data and analysis scripts are available for download at https://case.fiu.edu/about/directory/profiles/hayes-timothy.html. We provide scripts for all multiple imputation examples using Blimp software (Enders & Keller, 2021) for the imputation step and Mplus 8 (Muthén & Muthén, 2017) for the analysis and pooling steps as well as R scripts (R Core Team, 2021) for all FIML examples using the lavaan package (Rosseel, 2012) for analyses requiring multivariate normal likelihood functions and the mdmb package (Robitzsch & Luedtke, 2021) for analyses requiring factored likelihood functions. This list of software packages is far from exhaustive, and the software choices used in our supplemental materials represent only one configuration among a dizzying number possible. Because the software landscape is ever-shifting, with new software packages constantly being developed and existing packages frequently releasing updated functionality and syntax, we do not focus on detailed descriptions of software here, referring readers instead to the supplemental materials (see also Grund et al., 2021; Hayes, 2019; Lüdtke et al., 2020; Rosseel, 2012).

Table 2.2 displays descriptive statistics for these variables, computed by analyzing and pooling 100 imputed data sets. The bolded entries in Table 2.2 indicate correlations between auxiliary variables and model variables greater than $|r| = .30$. Because all four auxiliary variables correlated with at least one substantive model variable at or above this level, we included all four auxiliary variables as extra DVs in the FIML analyses and as additional variables in the imputation models. Table 2.2 also reports *covariance coverage* information for all variables: the main diagonal provides the percentage of observed data for each variable, whereas the off-diagonals in the upper triangle provides the percentage of data present for each pair of variables. As described below, in our experience, covariance coverage tables provide a quick and convenient way for readers to assess the prevalence of missing values in a given data set.

The first analysis example compares FIML estimation to multiple imputation in the following linear regression model:

$$DISABILITY_i = b_0 + b_1(DEPRESSION_i)$$
$$+ b_2(SEVERE\ PAIN_i)$$
$$+ b_3(MALE_i) + e_i. \quad (2.12)$$

Agnostic imputation is appropriate for this analysis because the model does not feature interactive or nonlinear terms. In the first section of Table 2.3 we present a side-by-side comparison of results from this linear regression analysis using (a) standard multivariate normal FIML estimation, (b) the factored FIML estimation procedure that treats each binary predictor more appropriately with its own logistic regression submodel (for more information, see Lüdtke et al., 2020), and (c) the agnostic FCS imputation method described two sections earlier, with dichotomous variables imputed using latent probit imputation methods.

Note that all three missing data handling methods incorporated the same model variables

TABLE 2.2

Pooled Descriptive Statistics by Sex

			Bivariate correlations (lower triangle) and covariance coverage (upper triangle)						
	M	*SD*	1	2	3	4	5	6	7
			Males						
1. Depression	15.29	6.59	91%	77%	65%	91%	91%	91%	91%
2. Severe pain	0.40	0.49	.36	86%	62%	86%	86%	86%	86%
3. Disability	22.35	4.73	.22	.17	72%	72%	72%	72%	72%
4. Anxiety	12.06	4.82	**.57**	.18	**.34**	100%	100%	100%	100%
5. Stress	4.14	1.76	**.54**	.21	.26	.69	100%	100%	100%
6. Control	20.33	5.58	**−.35**	−.21	**−.48**	−.30	−.16	100%	100%
7. Interfere	27.92	8.53	**.30**	**.36**	**.40**	.28	.20	−.45	100%
			Females						
1. Depression	13.85	5.66	88%	77%	63%	88%	88%	88%	88%
2. Severe pain	0.19	0.39	.07	85%	60%	85%	85%	85%	85%
3. Disability	21.80	4.97	.46	.28	71%	71%	71%	71%	71%
4. Anxiety	11.19	4.37	**.59**	−.02	.27	100%	100%	100%	100%
5. Stress	3.73	1.82	**.53**	.11	**.30**	.69	100%	100%	100%
6. Control	21.03	5.11	**−.30**	−.03	−.29	−.30	−.36	100%	100%
7. Interfere	27.15	8.75	**.36**	.25	.24	.23	.19	−.36	100%

Note. Descriptive statistics were pooled across $M = 100$ multiply imputed data sets, with imputations generated separately for males and females. For each group, entries in the lower triangle of the correlation matrix represent bivariate correlations, whereas entries on the main diagonal and upper triangle indicate covariance coverage (percentage of data present). Bolded values indicate correlations between auxiliary variables and model variables exceeding values of $|r| = .30$.

TABLE 2.3

Estimates and Standard Errors From Linear and Moderated Regression Model by Estimation Method

	Linear regression								Moderated regression				
	FIML: Multivariate normal			FIML: Factored		Agnostic multiple imputation			FIML: Factored		Model-based multiple imputation		
Parameter	Est.	SE	FMI	Est.	SE	Est.	SE	FMI	Est.	SE	Est.	SE	FMI
Intercept	17.91***	0.90	.44	17.93***	0.90	17.98***	0.86	.38	21.38***	0.41	21.55***	0.43	.30
Depression	0.25***	0.06	.45	0.25***	0.06	0.26***	0.06	.40	0.40***	0.07	0.41***	0.08	.44
Severe Pain	1.92*	0.76	.40	1.85*	0.75	1.85*	0.82	.45	1.89**	0.73	1.88*	0.74	.40
Male	−0.30	0.62	.27	−0.30	0.62	−0.31	0.63	.27	−0.10	0.61	−0.20	0.63	.30
Depression × Male	—	—	—	—	—	—	—	—	−0.30**	0.11	−0.30**	0.10	.34
Residual Variance	19.3***	2.14	0.46	19.34***	—	19.90***	2.30	.50	18.31***	—	19.10***	2.22	.50
R^2	.16	—	—	.16	—	.16**	0.05	.45	.20	—	.20***	.06	.47

Note. FIML = full information maximum likelihood, FMI = fraction of missing information. Listwise and multivariate normal FIML estimation were conducted using the lavaan package in R (Rosseel, 2012), which returns estimates of the FMI upon request, facilitating comparison with the FMI values returned by the multiple imputation analysis in Mplus (L. K. Muthén & Muthén, 2017). Factored likelihood estimation was conducted using R package mdmb (Robitzsch & Luedtke, 2021). Multiple imputations were generated using Blimp software (Enders & Keller, 2021) and subsequently analyzed and pooled using Mplus version 8.6 (L. K. Muthén & Muthén, 2017). Both agnostic and model-based imputation methods were used to impute, analyze, and pool $M = 100$ data sets.
* = $p < .05$, ** = $p < .01$, *** = $p < .001$.

and auxiliary variables. Additionally, the factored FIML and agnostic multiple imputation methods used comparable procedures to treat all dichotomous variables appropriately. Because it has long been known that FIML and multiple imputation converge on similar solutions when the same input data is used for both (see Collins et al., 2001, pp. 336–338 and Table 1), it comes as no surprise that the results of all three methods are near-identical. In fact, despite ignoring the correct scaling of the dichotomous predictors in the model, the results produced by multivariate normal FIML estimation in this analysis were even comparable to the other methods. This finding mirrors simulation results from Muthén et al. (2016).

The second analysis example compares FIML estimation to multiple imputation in the moderated regression model from Equation 2.7. Because the analysis model includes an incomplete interaction effect, standard multivariate normal FIML estimation and agnostic imputation routines are no longer appropriate. Instead, a tailored approach is necessary for this situation. Thus, in the second section of Table 2.3, we present a side-by-side comparison of results from this moderated regression model using (a) the factored FIML estimation procedure from Equation 2.8 and (b) the model-compatible imputation method described above, with dichotomous variables once again treated appropriately using either logistic regression (ML) or latent probit methods (imputation). Because these methods incorporated the same model variables and auxiliary variables (e.g., they employed comparable strategies both to address the scaling of the dichotomous predictors and the presence of the product term in the moderated regression analysis), it is again unsurprising that their resulting estimates, standard errors, and patterns of significance are nearly indistinguishable.

METHODS FOR MNAR MISSING DATA

In contrast to a missing-at-random mechanism, in which the unseen scores are unrelated to the probability of missingness after conditioning on or controlling for the observed data, an MNAR mechanism is one where the unseen scores still carry information about missingness even after conditioning on the observed data. When this is true, the analysis model must include an additional component that describes the occurrence of missing data. The two major modeling approaches for MNAR mechanisms—selection models and pattern mixture models—do just that, albeit in different ways. A selection model includes an additional regression equation with a binary missing data indicator (0 = observed, 1 = missing) as the dependent variable, whereas a pattern mixture model uses that missing data indicator as a predictor.

To illustrate the two models, reconsider the simple regression model where x predicts y (see Figure 2.3), and suppose that the unseen values of y determine whether the outcome is missing (e.g., the individuals with the highest disability levels opt not to report their scores, as in the MNAR mechanisms of Figure 2.1C and D). We also need a dummy variable M_y that codes whether Y is missing. Figure 2.5A shows the selection model as a path diagram. Notice that the composition of the diagram resembles a single-mediator model where the analysis variables predict missingness via direct and indirect effects.

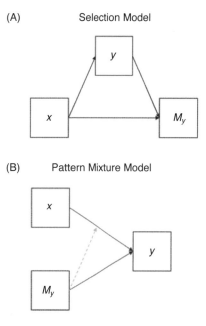

FIGURE 2.5. Conceptual diagrams of missing not at random missing data approaches.

In contrast, a pattern mixture model resembles a moderated process where M_y defines qualitatively different subgroups with unique parameter values. Figure 2.5B shows the path diagram; the arrow connecting M_y to Y is an intercept difference, and the dashed line indicates that x's slope differs between groups.

MNAR analyses require strict, unverifiable assumptions (e.g., a correct missingness model with the right configuration of effects), and simple misspecifications can produce biased estimates. Consequently, methodologists often suggest using these models as part of a sensitivity analysis that explores different missingness assumptions. A simple example is one where the researcher augments the main MAR analysis with one or more selection or pattern mixture models. An online supplemental document can present side-by-side comparisons of two or more sets of analysis results, with any discrepant estimates noted in the main body of the manuscript.

REPORTING THE RESULTS OF A MISSING DATA ANALYSIS

Although many of the principles summarized in this chapter have been known in the methodological literature for decades, misconceptions about missing data remain prevalent (van Ginkel et al., 2020), and surveys of the published literature have repeatedly found missing data reporting practices to be woefully inadequate (e.g., Jeličić et al., 2009; Nicholson et al., 2017). As a result, researchers aspiring to learn good reporting practices may find themselves without trustworthy examples to refer to, left to simply do their best to describe missing data analyses to an audience of readers (and reviewers) whose knowledge of the topic may be incomplete or even misguided. To help researchers navigate this landscape, in this section we provide several broad recommendations for missing data reporting.

The first thing researchers must report is descriptive statistics for all variables in the sample, including the prevalence of missing data on all model variables. With this in mind, our first recommendation is to use a modern method like FIML or multiple imputation to appropriately deal with missing data when estimating and reporting descriptive statistics, including all auxiliary variables deemed useful to estimation. We highlight this recommendation because, in our experience, many researchers use modern missing data handling methods only when estimating their main analysis models, often using specialized software, but return to their favorite general software package to estimate descriptive statistics using default deletion settings (e.g., using FIML in Mplus to estimate an SEM but computing descriptive statistics using listwise deletion in SPSS). This is unfortunate, because descriptive statistics based on marginal (unconditional) distributions tend to be even more severely affected by missing data than regression coefficients based on conditional distributions like those shown in Figure 2.1. In this way, modern missing data handling methods are just as crucial (if not more) for estimating descriptive statistics as they are for estimating more complex analysis models.

Our second recommendation is to report the prevalence of missing data by including covariance coverage (a matrix with the proportion of complete data for each variable or variable pair) in the upper triangle of the reported correlation matrix, as we have in Table 2.2. This provides readers with a compact yet comprehensive overview of the pattern of missing data affecting each model variable and pair of variables. If the proportion of missing data for a particular model variable or pair of variables is high, we recommend reminding readers of the general principle that *the greater the percentage of missing data affecting a particular variable or analysis model, the greater the need to address missing data using a modern method*. Citing quantitative simulation studies demonstrating the accuracy of FIML and multiple imputation under a variety of missing data rates (e.g., Collins et al., 2001, who showed across four studies that FIML and multiple imputation provide unbiased—and equivalent—results even under 50% missing data)[4]

---

[4] It might also be useful to point out that planned missing data designs, such as the popular *three form design*, intentionally produce extremely high missing data rates, (e.g., close to 70% between some variable pairs; see Graham et al., 2006).

can help to counter, or to preempt, the commonly held misconception that there is some amount of missing data that is simply too much for modern methods to handle (e.g., "it is dangerous to impute a variable with 50% missing values . . .").

Our next major recommendation is to provide theoretical justification for the missing data mechanism(s) one believes to be affecting each substantive model. This recommendation stems from the reality that, although one could plausibly rule out an MCAR (or focused MNAR) mechanism by finding any evidence at all that the observed variables in one's data set predict the probability of missingness on a given variable (e.g., in a *t* test of missing vs. nonmissing cases or a logistic regression analysis predicting a missing data indicator), analogous statistical procedures for ruling out a MAR (or MCAR) mechanism by finding evidence that the conditional distributions of observed and unseen values differ systematically from one another (as in Figure 2.1C and D) are undefined without access to the missing scores (the asterisks in Figure 2.1). As such, the MAR mechanism assumed by standard FIML and multiple imputation methods can neither be proven (or shown) nor ruled out using real data but must instead be argued for on the basis of theory.

When initially considering which missing data mechanisms seem theoretically plausible, we recommend starting with the assumption that when participants decline to answer a certain question or decide to skip a particular testing session, they generally do so for a reason, making a pure MCAR mechanism highly unlikely. It is also unlikely that one's intended analysis model already contains all missing data causes necessary on which to condition in order to meet the MAR assumption. Instead, it seems most reasonable to begin with the assumption that the missing data on all model variables are at least MNAR by omission at the outset, requiring the identification of the auxiliary variables required to make the data MAR (e.g., using the bivariate or semipartial correlation approaches described earlier). Reporting information about any auxiliary variables identified is crucial to helping future researchers know which measures they should consider including in their study designs.

In some lucky cases, a combination of substantive theory and practical judgment can rule out an MNAR mechanism. For example, attrition in a study of infants' spatial skills could only occur if the infants' parents or caregivers declined to return them to the study, making it straightforward to rule out the infants' unseen scores as a potential source of MNAR missingness. In other cases, however, the distinction may not be so clear. Take, for example, the missing psychosocial disability data described earlier, which could plausibly have been caused (a) by the patients' scores on external variable(s) like pain or stress, as in Figure 2.1B, (b) by patients' unseen disability scores, as in Figure 2.1C, or (c) by a combination of both, as in Figure 2.1D. In such cases, it may be necessary to conduct a sensitivity analysis, as described earlier, estimating a variety of MAR and MNAR models and comparing their results. If the pattern of results remains similar across these analyses, then the consequences of assuming a particular mechanism may make little difference. But if the results of these competing analyses differ, it may be useful to present all model results side-by-side so that readers can compare the effects of making different missing data assumptions. Although this side-by-side approach sacrifices the parsimony of choosing and displaying only one final model, it increases transparency and preserves a more detailed account of the models' possible results in the published record.

Next, we recommend providing the details of the missing data handling methods applied to each substantive analysis of interest, including all software packages used (along with their version numbers) and any specific settings invoked in the process. Because different analysis models may contain unique features (e.g., categorical predictors, product terms, or multilevel random effects) that require special consideration and because the variables included in different models may be acted upon by different missing data mechanisms (requiring different auxiliary variables), it follows that *missing data handling strategies should generally be tailored to, and reported with respect to, each specific analysis model one intends to run.* When using FIML estimation, researchers should report how they incorporated auxiliary variables into the model (as saturated correlates? extra dependent variables?), how they incorporated incomplete predictors into the likelihood function,[5] as well as any special estimation procedures required to address specific features of the substantive model (e.g., using the factored FIML approach described earlier to address interactions).

When using multiple imputation, researchers should report exactly what variables were included in each imputation model. At a minimum, this should include all variables from the substantive model, regardless of whether the variables are complete or missing (leaving a variable out of the imputation model results in imputations that assume its correlation with all other model variables is 0) along with any auxiliary variables identified earlier. It is also critical to report any special imputation procedures used to accommodate particular features of a substantive model, for example, using model-based imputation methods to generate imputations appropriate for a moderation analysis, as described above. Following this, one should report how many imputed data sets were analyzed and pooled (as stated earlier, 20 imputed data sets is a good general rule, but more are better, if computational time allows).

Additionally, one should report convergence information for any imputation models run. For example, one might report that "an initial diagnostic run indicated that the worst (highest) potential scale reduction factor across all model parameters dropped below 1.05 after approximately 2,000 iterations, suggesting converge of the MCMC chains." Although this could seem like nuts-and-bolts technical information not worth including in a published paper, we believe that providing this information is important because it serves to subtly combat a widely held misconception that one can multiply impute one's data without assessing convergence, simply trusting one's default software settings. This misconception is especially troubling because default settings in software packages are often dramatically insufficient (e.g., the SPSS multiple imputation routine uses only five iterations, when hundreds or thousands may be necessary).

Finally, when using multiple imputation to address missing data, it is sometimes necessary to address readers' (or reviewers'[6]) potential unease with this approach by clearly and succinctly explaining how the method works and rebutting possible misconceptions. Toward this end, one might assure readers that although the notion of filling in missing values may seem to conjure images of fraudsters purposefully editing values in a data file in order to make an analysis appear significant, the synthetic values generated in a multiple imputation analysis are driven by the data, not by the researcher, with no guarantee that they will lead to flattering model results (e.g., if the correlation between a pair of variables in the data is 0, the correlation between imputed values generated for these variables is also 0). It can also be helpful to remind readers that resorting to listwise deletion methods to avoid imputing missing values will necessarily result in discarding potentially large amounts of real data provided by participants who responded to some—but not all—measures. Viewed in this way, multiple imputation, like FIML, is as much—if not more—about preserving and using all observed values in a data set as it is about filling in missing values. In fact, despite their surface-level differences (e.g., explicitly filling in missing values with imputations generated from a multivariate normal distribution vs. implicitly assuming a multivariate normal distribution is likely to have

---

[5]Although we have not emphasized specific software commands in this chapter, we note that one can freely estimate the distributions of predictor variables and incorporate them into the multivariate normal likelihood function of Equation 2.3 by declaring all exogenous variable means and variances in the MODEL statement in Mplus, or by setting the argument fixed.x = FALSE in the lavaan() function in lavaan and explicitly referencing all exogenous means, variances, and covariances in the lavaan model syntax.

[6]In some cases, when concerns are raised during the review process, this clarifying information may be most appropriate to include in a response to peer reviewers. In other cases, however, as when one believes that readers in their subfield are broadly unfamiliar with these methods, it may be appropriate to include this information in the main document.

produced the unseen values), both multiple imputation and FIML estimation are based on the same underlying assumptions and are well-known to produce near-identical results under the same input (as shown by Collins et al., 2001, and as reflected in the results of our analysis examples presented earlier).

In sum, although far from exhaustive, we hope that this brief list of reporting recommendations helps researchers think through how best to describe the results of their missing data analyses to readers who may vary in their levels of familiarity and comfort with these analyses. Because expertise in missing data analysis among one's readers cannot be taken for granted, we recommend that researchers err on the side of reporting too much information rather than too little; all else being equal, it seems better to describe each and every step in a missing data analysis thoroughly than to risk incorrectly assuming that some details can be treated as "common knowledge" and left unsaid. Providing such clear and detailed descriptions of each missing data analysis not only helps readers understand and, hopefully, accept the need for these analyses in a particular study but also provides them with a template for reporting such analyses in their own future work.

SUMMARY

The goal of this chapter was to provide an overview of maximum likelihood estimation and multiple imputation, two major missing data handling strategies with strong support from the methodological literature. Both approaches have developed since the first edition of this handbook, and the types of analyses that researchers can perform are broader than ever. Given the same data and assumptions, maximum likelihood and multiple imputation usually produce indistinguishable results, so the choice of method often boils down to practical considerations and personal preference—the analysis examples illustrated this conclusion. In truth, the most important consideration isn't which method to use, but rather the composition of the analysis model. In general, any analysis that features an incomplete interaction term, curvilinear effect, random slope, or other type of nonlinearity requires newer factored regression methods, whereas "classic" versions of maximum likelihood and multiple imputation are well suited for analyses that do not have these special features. Models with mixtures of categorical and numeric variables are a second example where factored regression specifications are useful, and multiple imputation is generally more flexible for these types of problems.

In closing, we note that this tailored, analysis-by-analysis approach to thinking about missing data handling also implies an important underlying principle: *The fundamental goal of the missing data handling approaches discussed throughout this chapter is to accurately and appropriately adjust the results of a target analysis for the likely influences of missing data.* That is, although the problems caused by missing data may originate in the form of missing scores in one's data file, these problems ultimately manifest themselves in the form of potentially distorted, untrustworthy estimates in one's statistical models, and it is these estimates—not the missing scores, themselves—whose accuracy is at stake in a missing data analysis. This suggests, for example, that an "impute first, decide the analysis later" approach is rarely viable[7] and is never wise, as such an approach is fundamentally backwards: the synthetic values generated in a multiple imputation analysis are not intended to function individually as perfect proxies for participants' missing raw scores[8] but, rather, to function together to adjust the estimates of a specific statistical analysis model that one intends to fit to the filled-in data. Thus, to paraphrase a well-known idiom (Covey, 1989), researchers are well-advised to "begin with the

---

[7]Except in the luckiest cases, for example, when a single set of agnostic multiple imputations might serve the goals of multiple subsequent analyses. We note that it is this scenario that is assumed by the current default imputation settings in SPSS, potentially leading users to infer that a single set of imputations should serve the goals of any conceivable analysis.

[8]Indeed, perfectly estimating participants' individual true scores is well-known to be a statistically intractable problem even with complete data (e.g., Steiger & Schönemann, 1978).

analysis in mind," treating the specific features of each substantive model as the "true north" that guides all subsequent missing data handling decisions. By approaching the task in this way, we believe that researchers will be able to confidently identify the most appropriate methods for addressing missing data in every analysis of interest.

References

Arbuckle, J. N. (1996). Full information estimation in the presence of incomplete data. In G. A. Marcoulides, & R. E. Schumacker (Eds.), *Advanced structural equation modeling* (pp. 243–277). Lawrence Erlbaum Associates. Inc.

Bartlett, J. W., Seaman, S. R., White, I. R., & Carpenter, J. R. (2015). Multiple imputation of covariates by substantive-model compatible fully conditional specification. *Statistical Methods in Medical Research*, 24(4), 462–487. https://doi.org/10.1177/0962280214521348

Bollen, K. A. (1989). *Structural equations with latent variables*. Wiley. https://doi.org/10.1002/9781118619179

Cham, H., Reshetnyak, E., Rosenfeld, B., & Breitbart, W. (2017). Full information maximum likelihood estimation for latent variable interactions with incomplete indicators. *Multivariate Behavioral Research*, 52(1), 12–30. https://doi.org/10.1080/00273171.2016.1245600

Collins, L. M., Schafer, J. L., & Kam, C. M. (2001). A comparison of inclusive and restrictive strategies in modern missing data procedures. *Psychological Methods*, 6(4), 330–351. https://doi.org/10.1037/1082-989X.6.4.330

Covey, S. R. (1989). *The seven habits of highly effective people*. Simon & Schuster.

Dempster, A. P., Laird, N. M., & Rubin, D. B. (1977). Maximum likelihood from incomplete data via the EM algorithm. *Journal of the Royal Statistical Society. Series B. Methodological*, 39(1), 1–22. https://doi.org/10.1111/j.2517-6161.1977.tb01600.x

Eliason, S. R. (1993). *Maximum likelihood estimation: Logic and practice*. SAGE.

Enders, C. K. (2008). A note on the use of missing auxiliary variables in full information maximum likelihood-based structural equation models. *Structural Equation Modeling*, 15(3), 434–448. https://doi.org/10.1080/10705510802154307

Enders, C. K. (2022). *Applied missing data analysis* (2nd ed.). Guilford Press.

Enders, C. K., Du, H., & Keller, B. T. (2020). A model-based imputation procedure for multilevel regression models with random coefficients, interaction effects, and nonlinear terms. *Psychological Methods*, 25(1), 88–112. https://doi.org/10.1037/met0000228

Enders, C. K., & Keller, B. T. (2021). *Blimp user's manual* (Version 3) [Computer software]. Applied Missing Data. https://www.appliedmissingdata.com/multilevel-imputation.html

Gelman, A., & Rubin, D. B. (1992). Inference from iterative simulation using multiple sequences. *Statistical Science*, 7(4), 457–472. https://doi.org/10.1214/ss/1177011136

Gomer, B., & Yuan, K.-H. (2021). Subtypes of the missing not at random missing data mechanism. *Psychological Methods*, 26(5), 559–598. https://doi.org/10.1037/met0000377

Graham, J. W. (2003). Adding missing-data-relevant variables to FIML-based structural equation models. *Structural Equation Modeling*, 10(1), 80–100. https://doi.org/10.1207/S15328007SEM1001_4

Graham, J. W., Olchowski, A. E., & Gilreath, T. D. (2007). How many imputations are really needed? Some practical clarifications of multiple imputation theory. *Prevention Science*, 8(3), 206–213. https://doi.org/10.1007/s11121-007-0070-9

Graham, J. W., Taylor, B. J., Olchowski, A. E., & Cumsille, P. E. (2006). Planned missing data designs in psychological research. *Psychological Methods*, 11(4), 323–343. https://doi.org/10.1037/1082-989X.11.4.323

Grund, S., Lüdtke, O., & Robitzsch, A. (2021). Multiple imputation of missing data in multilevel models with the R package mdmb: A flexible sequential modeling approach. *Behavior Research Methods*, 53(6), 2631–2649. https://doi.org/10.3758/s13428-020-01530-0

Hayes, T. (2019). Flexible, free software for multilevel multiple imputation: A review of blimp and jomo. *Journal of Educational and Behavioral Statistics*, 44(5), 625–641. https://doi.org/10.3102/1076998619858624

Hoel, P. G. (1984). *An introduction to mathematical statistics* (5th ed.). Wiley.

Howard, W. J., Rhemtulla, M., & Little, T. D. (2015). Using principal components as auxiliary variables in missing data estimation. *Multivariate Behavioral Research*, 50(3), 285–299. https://doi.org/10.1080/00273171.2014.999267

Ibrahim, J. G. (1990). Incomplete data in generalized linear models. *Journal of the American Statistical Association*, 85(411), 765–769. https://doi.org/10.1080/01621459.1990.10474938

Jeličić, H., Phelps, E., & Lerner, R. M. (2009). Use of missing data methods in longitudinal studies: The persistence of bad practices in developmental psychology. *Developmental Psychology, 45*(4), 1195–1199. https://doi.org/10.1037/a0015665

Little, R. J. A., & Rubin, D. B. (1987). *Statistical analysis with missing data*. Wiley.

Lüdtke, O., Robitzsch, A., & West, S. G. (2020). Regression models involving nonlinear effects with missing data: A sequential modeling approach using Bayesian estimation. *Psychological Methods, 25*(2), 157–181. https://doi.org/10.1037/met0000233

Meng, X. (1994). Multiple-imputation inferences with uncongenial sources of input. *Statistical Science, 9*(4), 538–558.

Muthén, B. O., Muthén, L. K., & Asparouhov, T. (2016). *Regression and mediation analysis using Mplus*. Muthén & Muthén.

Muthén, L. K., & Muthén, B. (2017). *Mplus user's guide* (8th ed.). Muthén & Muthén.

Nicholson, J. S., Deboeck, P. R., & Howard, W. (2017). Attrition in developmental psychology: A review of modern missing data reporting and practices. *International Journal of Behavioral Development, 41*(1), 143–153. https://doi.org/10.1177/0165025415618275

R Core Team. (2021). *R: A language and environment for statistical computing*. R Foundation for Statistical Computing. https://r-project.org/

Raghunathan, T. E., Lepkowski, J. M., Van Hoewyk, J., & Solenberger, P. (2001). A multivariate technique for multiply imputing missing values using a sequence of regression models. *Survey Methodology, 27*(1), 85–95.

Raykov, T., & West, B. T. (2016). On enhancing plausibility of the missing at random assumption in incomplete data analyses via evaluation of response-auxiliary variable correlations. *Structural Equation Modeling, 23*(1), 45–53. https://doi.org/10.1080/10705511.2014.937848

Robitzsch, A., & Luedtke, O. (2021). *Package 'mdmb'* (R package version 1.5–8) [Computer software]. https://cran.r-project.org/package=mdmb

Rosseel, Y. (2012). lavaan: An R package for structural equation modeling. *Journal of Statistical Software, 48*(2), 1–36. https://doi.org/10.18637/jss.v048.i02

Rubin, D. B. (1976). Inference and missing data. *Biometrika, 63*(3), 581–592. https://doi.org/10.1093/biomet/63.3.581

Rubin, D. B. (1987). *Multiple imputation for nonresponse in surveys*. Wiley. https://doi.org/10.1002/9780470316696

Savalei, V., & Bentler, P. M. (2009). A two-stage approach to missing data: Theory and application to auxiliary variables. *Structural Equation Modeling, 16*(3), 477–497. https://doi.org/10.1080/10705510903008238

Savalei, V., & Rhemtulla, M. (2012). On obtaining estimates of the fraction of missing information from full information maximum likelihood. *Structural Equation Modeling, 19*(3), 477–494. https://doi.org/10.1080/10705511.2012.687669

Schafer, J. L. (1997). *Analysis of incomplete multivariate data*. Chapman & Hall. https://doi.org/10.1201/9781439821862

Steiger, J. H., & Schönemann, P. H. (1978). A history of factor indeterminacy. In S. Shye (Ed.), *Theory construction and data analysis in the behavioural sciences* (pp. 136–178). Jossey-Bass Publishers.

Van Buuren, S., Brand, J. P. L., Groothuis-Oudshoorn, C. G. M., & Rubin, D. B. (2006). Fully conditional specification in multivariate imputation. *Journal of Statistical Computation and Simulation, 76*(12), 1049–1064. https://doi.org/10.1080/10629360600810434

van Ginkel, J. R., Linting, M., Rippe, R. C. A., & van der Voort, A. (2020). Rebutting existing misconceptions about multiple imputation as a method for handling missing data. *Journal of Personality Assessment, 102*(3), 297–308. https://doi.org/10.1080/00223891.2018.1530680

von Hippel, P. T. (2018). How many imputations do you need? A two-stage calculation using a quadratic rule. *Sociological Methods & Research, 49*(3), 699–718. https://doi.org/10.1177/0049124117747303

Widaman, K. F. (2006). III. Missing data: What to do with or without them. *Monographs of the Society for Research in Child Development, 71*(3), 42–64. https://doi.org/10.1111/j.1540-5834.2006.00404.x

Wilkinson, L., & Task Force on Statistical Inference, American Psychological Association, Science Directorate. (1999). Statistical methods in psychology journals: Guidelines and explanations. *American Psychologist, 54*(8), 594–604. https://doi.org/10.1037/0003-066X.54.8.594

Zhang, Q., & Wang, L. (2017). Moderation analysis with missing data in the predictors. *Psychological Methods, 22*(4), 649–666. https://doi.org/10.1037/met0000104

Chapter 3

EXPLORATORY DATA ANALYSIS

Paul F. Velleman and David C. Hoaglin

Exploratory data analysis (EDA), pioneered by John W. Tukey (1915–2000), introduces a variety of innovative techniques and combines them with five important principles of data analysis: display, re-expression, residuals, resistance, and iteration. Many of the techniques that Tukey pioneered have become familiar: stem-and-leaf display, five-number summary, boxplot, and a rule for flagging potential outliers in batches of data. Computing methods have extended EDA to larger data sets and higher dimensions, and diagnostic statistics have extended the EDA approach to include more traditional statistical methods.

Although its innovative methods have received much attention, the principal contribution of EDA is philosophical. EDA advocates exploring data for patterns and relations without requiring prior hypotheses. The principle of *resistance* calls for identifying extraordinary cases and then setting them aside or downweighting them. *Re-expression* uses mathematical transformations to simplify patterns in data. EDA suggests that analyses are more scientifically useful and productive when data have been transformed to agree better with basic assumptions. *Residuals* come from summarizing the patterns found so far and subtracting that summary from the data, to reveal departures and additional patterns. EDA often works with residuals to refine or extend models fitted to data. Frequent use of graphical *displays* maintains contact with data, residuals, and summaries, and it often reveals unexpected behavior. EDA approaches do not terminate with a hypothesis test. Effective data analysis is *iterative*, finding and summarizing patterns and then probing more deeply.

These approaches stand in contrast to the formalistic scientific method paradigm of first stating a hypothesis based on prior theory, then collecting data, and finally applying a statistical test of the hypothesis. Proponents of the EDA philosophy maintain that the EDA approach is more likely to discover new and interesting patterns and relations, in much the same way that science has traditionally made progress. Exploratory analyses can incorporate methods of statistical inference, but use them more as indicators of the strength of a relation or the fit of a model than as confirmation of a hypothesis.

EDA attitudes also contrast with analyses that approach very large data sets ("big data") in highly algorithmic ways. Many of those analyses pursue, with considerable success, a different objective: prediction. Efron (2020), in a thought-provoking address, referred to "pure prediction algorithms." The processes of EDA more clearly resemble Efron's notion of estimation. EDA's processes can be adapted and applied, iteratively, to "big data"; the analyst should play a central role in the iterations (e.g., to have the best chance of detecting potential outliers and the need for re-expression).

Unsupervised learning algorithms, widely applied to large and complex data, can be sensitive to outliers and the choice (or omission) of re-expression. Discussions of such "data science" methods frequently mention EDA, but actual analyses often skip this important first step. Although Tukey illustrated EDA methods for small data sets, the EDA philosophy applies equally well to arbitrarily large data sets.

In this chapter, we elucidate the EDA approach, illustrating it with examples. We hope to convince the reader that this approach should be a standard part of anyone's analysis of data. For many experienced data analysts, an EDA approach forms the main ingredient of their analyses, with only the occasional "seasoning" of formal hypothesis testing.

WOES OF TRADITIONAL STATISTICS

The discipline of statistics offers a wide variety of ways to formulate and test hypotheses. All, however, rely on assumptions about the pattern of behavior in the data and about the distribution of variations around that pattern. For example, fitting a simple regression line is appropriate when the relation of y to x resembles a straight line and the fluctuations around a line all have the same variance. Methods that compare groups may require that the groups share the same variance. The basic model in a two-factor analysis of variance (ANOVA) expresses the response as an additive combination of the contributions of the two factors and assumes that the error variance is the same for all treatment levels. In logistic regression, the individual outcomes are usually assumed to follow binomial distributions, whose success probabilities (in the logit scale) follow the pattern specified in the linear predictor. Virtually every standard method makes the tacit assumption that the underlying data are homogeneous—that is, that they are all consistent measurements of the same things about the same kinds of individuals for whom the same model, analysis, or comparison is appropriate.

These assumptions are frequently violated by otherwise perfectly ordinary data. Often, to check, we need only make an appropriate display. As the famous philosopher (and baseball Hall of Famer) Yogi Berra said, "You can learn a lot by looking."

Ironically, although statistics software makes displaying data simple, it also abets the tendency to rush to a hypothesis test without pausing for displays. The traditional approach to statistics has an even more fundamental weakness. By focusing on testing hypotheses, we fail to ask the far more fundamental and important question of our data: "Is anything going on that I didn't expect?" Isaac Asimov is commonly credited[1] with saying, "The most exciting phrase to hear in science, the one that heralds new discoveries, is not 'Eureka!' but 'That's funny . . .'"

EDA increases our chance of a "That's funny . . ." insight about our data—and those are the events that lead to new theories and breakthroughs. For example, Leonard Mlodinow, in his 2008 book *The Drunkard's Walk,* tells the story of the "That's funny . . ." moment that led Daniel Kahneman to begin his revolutionary research with Amos Tversky into the psychology of how humans misperceive random events—work that led to his 2002 Nobel Prize in Economics. As a junior professor of psychology at Hebrew University, Kahneman was lecturing to a group of flight trainers. The trainers insisted that when they chastised a flyer for a poor maneuver, the flyer improved, but when they complimented a good one, the flyer usually did worse the next time. The trainers had concluded that negative reinforcement worked and positive reinforcement did not. Kahneman knew that psychology had shown otherwise. Rather than ignoring this observation as just a strange aberration, he searched for the explanation. His insight that the often-counterintuitive result known as *regression to the mean* was responsible for

---

[1] This is commonly, and plausibly, credited to Asimov, but we have not found a reference.

the trainers' misperception started him on his research path.

EDAs incorporate techniques, such as boxplots and stem-and-leaf displays, and also commonly use such traditional methods as least squares regression, ANOVA, analysis of covariance (ANCOVA), and logistic regression. So EDA should be viewed primarily as an enhancement of, rather than a replacement for, traditional methods. By using both wisely, you will learn more from your data.

EXPLORING

The tradition of the scientific method requires researchers to follow a straight and narrow path: theory first, then hypothesis, then data collection, and finally statistical tests of the stated hypothesis (and no others).

Exploring often requires that we leave the beaten path. But it does not require us to travel without a compass—or a GPS. The challenge is less to know where we are than to see where we are going. In this chapter, we present guidelines and best practices to help you make progress without wandering aimlessly. Our guiding principles are display, re-expression, resistance, residuals, and iteration.

Lacking a map, we need to take frequent sightings. We make many displays of the data, and we continue to do so all along the way. We are not trying—or even hoping—to confirm that the required assumptions for a hypothesis test have been met. We are looking for new territory to explore. Like all explorers, we are seeking—and expecting—the unexpected. Fortunately, displays are particularly good tools for this task. Appropriate displays readily show outliers, unexpected clumps and clusters, and patterns of relation that we might not have anticipated.

Nor are we obliged to follow steep or thorny paths when gentler, clearer ones are available. We re-express data to more easily summarize and compare them and fit models that describe relations. It is easier and more scientifically useful to fit a simple linear model to the logarithm of a variable than to fit an exponential model to the original data. Speed (reciprocal time) is often a more useful variable than duration.

Resistant methods protect against undue influence by outlying cases or even small clusters of cases. Some statistics, such as the median, are inherently resistant. Others, such as least squares regression, can be made resistant by diagnostics that identify potentially influential cases so they can be dealt with separately.

Whenever we fit a model to data, it is wise to examine the residuals—the differences between the model and the data. EDA suggests displays such as quantile–quantile plots, partial regression plots, and partial boxplots that are particularly well suited to understanding what residuals tell us about our data and models. In the names of these displays, *partial* refers to the removal (*partialing out*) of the contributions of the other predictors or factors.

EDA anticipates that what we learn from examining the residuals will lead us to improve our understanding and our models. We may decide to re-express variables to mitigate violations of assumptions revealed only in the residuals, set aside outliers identified in the residuals, or introduce additional variables suggested by the residuals.

DISPLAYS AND SOME OF WHAT THEY REVEAL

Every data analysis should begin with graphs. Of course, this idea is not unique to EDA. Every introductory statistics text starts with data displays (see Chapter 4, this volume). But often, displays of the data appear only in the introductory chapters, and the figures in the chapters on statistical inference show only normal or *t*-distribution curves. EDA teaches that we should make graphs early and often.

Some data displays are taught in every statistics class. We look at histograms to get a picture of how the data are distributed and to check for multiple modes and outliers. We look at scatterplots to see how one variable changes in relation to another, focusing on the direction, form, and strength of that relation.

To illustrate, consider a standard test of manual dexterity, which records the time it takes subjects to invert 16 cylinders with one hand (Aaron & Jansen, 2003). This test can form the basis for studying crossover training: whether training one limb can benefit the other and what underlying mental processes might support the benefit. Gogola et al. (2010) studied the performance of 175 subjects ranging in age from 4 to 16. A histogram of their times (Figure 3.1) is skewed to the right and suggests that two subjects had unusually long times.

Modes

Histograms such as the one in Figure 3.1 may be the most common display for examining the distribution of a variable. Exploratory analyses often start with histograms. But EDA teaches that histograms can be a call to action. Histograms offer the opportunity to detect *inhomogeneity* in the data. All statistical methods make the tacit assumption that the data are homogeneous—that is, that we are dealing with measurements of the same thing made on members of a coherent population. Without homogeneity, it is difficult to imagine what—or whom—a summary of the data would be about.

One clue that the data may not be homogeneous is the presence of two or more modes in a histogram. For example, the same researchers also measured the dexterity of patients who had had surgery, using a variety of measures. One of these measures, the Jebsen Large Heavy Object Test (Jebsen et al., 1969), records the time (in seconds) to lift and move a weighted can. In the histogram of the times for 34 subjects, shown in Figure 3.2, the mode around 9 seconds consists of patients who had had surgery on both limbs, who may differ from other patients in important ways.

Outliers

A related issue is the identification and treatment of outliers. Values that stray far from the rest of the data, or that stand apart from important patterns in the data, demand our attention. They may be particularly informative by clarifying the limits of our data or pointing out special cases, or they may be errors in need of correction or removal. Regardless of the reason, they should not be allowed to distort subsequent analyses of the data. EDA teaches that if we cannot correct an outlier, we should set it aside or use methods that are immune to its effects.

The argument that outliers should be prevented from subverting a data analysis reflects the philosophical foundations of EDA. Some analysts are reluctant to set aside any legitimately recorded values, fearing that doing so could bias subsequent analyses. But standard statistical methods are notoriously sensitive to outlying values and are likely to be invalid when applied to data that include outliers. Data containing outliers are, almost by definition, not homogeneous.

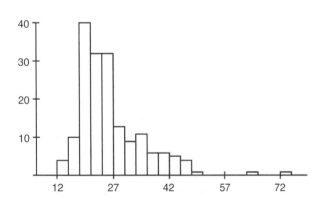

FIGURE 3.1. Histogram of the times (in seconds) of 175 subjects on a test of manual dexterity.

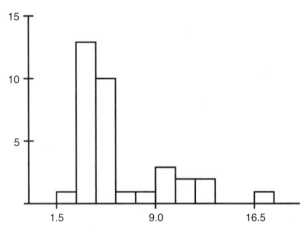

FIGURE 3.2. Times (in seconds) on the Jebsen Large Heavy Object Test for 34 subjects who had had surgery.

So statistical models intended for homogeneous data are likely to strike a clumsy compromise between the outliers and the rest of the data rather than describe patterns and relations in the bulk of the data.

Boxplots

One tool that can be helpful in nominating extreme values for consideration as outliers is the boxplot, introduced by John Tukey in his pathbreaking 1977 book, *Exploratory Data Analysis*. The standard boxplot uses a rule to identify possible outliers (as *outside* or, if extreme enough, *far outside*) and plot them individually. Hoaglin et al. (1986) studied the rule's performance, and Hoaglin and Iglewicz (1987) refined it.

A boxplot of the task times for the 175 normal subjects, shown in Figure 3.3, identifies five task times as outside and two as far out. The records for these subjects should be examined for possible explanations of their particularly slow performance.

The boxplot's outlier nomination rules should not be taken as a *definition* of outliers. The decision to treat a case as an outlier is a judgment call that the data analyst must make. But boxplots can help by directing attention to cases that deserve consideration as outliers. The standard boxplot calls attention to outside observations fairly often. Hoaglin et al. (1986) found that in well-behaved (i.e., Gaussian) data, the percentage of samples that contain one or more outside observations varies between 33% and 14% for $5 \leq n \leq 20$. The corresponding percentage for far outside lies between 1% and 5%.

Boxplots are also helpful for comparing groups. Because they show the median and quartiles of each group, they make it easy to compare centers and spreads (as interquartile ranges) among groups. Because they suppress details of the distributions, they minimize distractions that can make it difficult to compare several histograms.

Figure 3.4 shows the results of repeated dexterity trials by the same 175 subjects. Except for a few high values, times decreased from Trial 1 to Trial 3 as subjects practiced the task, but times stabilized after Trial 3. Because boxplots isolate outliers, we can more easily ignore their influence when judging the performance pattern of most of the subjects.

Stem-and-Leaf Displays

John Tukey also introduced (in the late 1960s) the stem-and-leaf display, which offers a histogram's view of distribution shape while preserving the individual data values. Each digit to the right of the vertical line represents a data value (e.g., 12 seconds and 14 seconds on the first line).

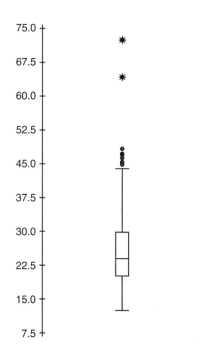

FIGURE 3.3. Boxplot of the times (in seconds) of the 175 normal subjects on the test of manual dexterity.

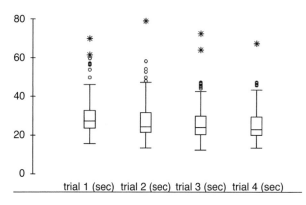

FIGURE 3.4. Boxplots of the times (in seconds) of the 175 normal subjects on four consecutive dexterity tests.

```
1|24
1|67888999999
2|0000111123344
2|555555666677889
3|0023333
3|5567889
4|0012
4|57
5|
5|
6|4
6|
7|2
```

FIGURE 3.5. Stem-and-leaf display of the task times (in seconds) for 63 subjects.

A stem-and-leaf display of some of the dexterity times (Figure 3.5) shows individual values as well as the overall distribution shape. Stem-and-leaf displays are particularly useful as pencil-and-paper tools for a quick look at modest collections of data values.

Two-Variable Relations

The EDA approach guides consideration of relations between pairs of variables. Of course, we start with a display. Now we look at the overall *direction*, *shape*, and *strength* of the relation. The scatterplot of dexterity task time versus age in Figure 3.6 shows a negative direction with older subjects taking less time, a curved shape, and a reasonably consistent pattern.

Because exploratory analyses rely on displays, they often push common methods a bit farther. For example, points in scatterplots can be assigned colors or symbols according to values of a third categorical variable. The symbols in Figure 3.6 record whether the tested hand was the subject's dominant (×) or nondominant (o) hand.

If the form of the relation were straight, then lines fitted separately to each group could be compared. That is not feasible with a curved plot such as this one. Modern statistics software often supports the ability to "touch" a point in a plot to ask for its identity—a valuable tool for identifying and understanding outliers and subgroups in the data.

Other Displays

Other displays and display methods are less common or depend on computers. Normal probability plots provide a better way to compare a variable's distribution with the normal than does a histogram with a normal curve overlaid. One drawback of such histograms is related to Winsor's principle: All distributions are normal in the middle (Tukey, 1960). Although the principle is clearly not universally true, it does correctly—and memorably—advise us to focus attention on the tails of a distribution.

A scatterplot matrix (called a SPLOM by some programs) lays out an array of scatterplots in the same pattern as correlations in a correlation table. *Plot brushing* highlights the same cases in each plot simultaneously as the viewer passes a rectangular "brush" over any one of them, displaying relations among several variables. An alternative approach for displaying three variables together is an animated *rotating plot*, offered in several statistics programs. Some programs, such as Data Desk (Velleman, 2004), can display data that have up to nine dimensions.

Another approach, a parallel-coordinate plot (Inselberg, 2009), displays high-dimensional data by assigning the coordinates to parallel lines and connecting the data of each case. For the four trials of the dexterity experiment seen in the boxplots of Figure 3.4, the lines in Figure 3.7 connect the times for each subject. Here we can trace the performance of individual subjects—for example, the outlying slow performances were by the same subjects.

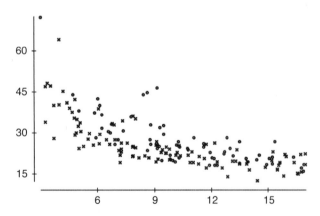

FIGURE 3.6. Scatterplot of task time (in seconds) versus age (in years). The plotting symbol distinguishes the dominant hand (×) from the nondominant hand (o).

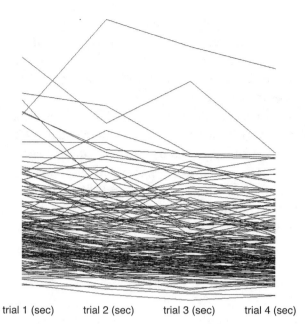

FIGURE 3.7. Parallel-coordinate plot of the times (in seconds) of the 175 normal subjects on four consecutive dexterity trials.

RE-EXPRESSION

One of the most versatile techniques in the data analyst's toolkit, re-expression applies the same mathematical function (e.g., logarithm, square root) to each data value of a variable. This transformation smoothly changes the relative positions of the data, with the aim of simplifying the analysis.

Some researchers mistakenly believe that transforming the data is wrong, that the analysis must work with the data in their original scale. Those who hold this view often fail to find important features of their data. In fact, many measures in science and social science involve a transformation. Some of these are familiar in everyday experience (Hoaglin, 1988).

- Reports of earthquakes usually give the magnitude on the Richter scale, which expresses the strength of the earthquake's motion in logarithmic units (base 10).
- Measurements of the intensity of sounds customarily produce results in decibels. The fundamental quantity actually measured, however, is sound pressure (usually in dynes per square centimeter), and the "sound pressure level" (in decibels) is related logarithmically to sound pressure.
- Although ratings of automobiles' fuel economy are usually given in miles per gallon in the United States, these often come from measurements that determine the number of gallons used on a standard test course. Thus, the familiar miles-per-gallon figures result from a reciprocal transformation. In fact, throughout the rest of the world, fuel use is reported in units of liters per 100 km—the reciprocal (gasoline volume per distance) of miles per gallon. (The constant that relates metric to old British units does not affect the distribution.)

EDA teaches that we should always consider whether an alternative form of a variable might allow a simpler model or description. This aspect of EDA draws on more than 70 years of work in statistics (Bartlett, 1947; Box & Cox, 1964; Emerson, 1983; Emerson & Stoto, 1983; Kruskal, 1968; Tukey, 1957). A wisely chosen re-expression offers a variety of benefits.

1. The distribution of data and residuals can be made more symmetric and more nearly normal.
2. The variances of several groups to be compared can be made more nearly equal.
3. The relation between two variables can be made more nearly linear.
4. The variation of points around a regression line can be made more nearly equal across the span of the data.
5. A linear relation between two variables can be made more nearly parallel for groups of values in the data.
6. The appropriateness of an additive model relating a response to two or more factors can be improved (and the need for interaction terms reduced or removed).

In traditional terms, the symmetry achieved by Benefit 1 is necessary for the mean to summarize the center of the distribution. Normality is expected for t tests, and normal fluctuations are assumed for linear models such as regression and ANOVA. The equality of variance among groups (Benefit 2) is assumed by ANOVA and ANCOVA models as well as for a pooled *t* test. Linearity (Benefit 3) is fundamental to regression methods, which also require the residuals to have constant variance everywhere (Benefit 4) for common inference methods. Both the use of dummy variables in regression and the generalization of that idea to ANCOVAs require that linear models for subgroups be parallel (Benefit 5). And the ANOVA model calls for additivity (Benefit 6).

One remarkable insight noted by the authors is that re-expressions that improve one aspect of the data often improve several—or even all—of the others.

A Re-expression Example

The dexterity experiment offers a good example. Many task-based measures of performance record the time for a subject to complete a task. These include the classic mouse-running maze tasks as well as cognitive function tests, such as the Trail Making test (Reitan, 1958) and the Stroop test (Stroop, 1935).

Thinking about re-expression encourages us to consider constraints on the distribution of the data values. For *time per task*, it is not possible to get a value below some lower limit—certainly not less than 0. But there is no upper limit. Indeed, some subjects may not be able to complete some tasks at all. (The dexterity measure is used in cognitive-based training of postsurgery patients who have suffered severe hand or arm injuries, some of whom cannot complete the task in any reasonable time. In addition, mice under sufficiently stressful conditions may give up on solving a maze.) These constraints introduce two problems for data analysis. First, the distribution of values is almost certain to be skewed to the high end—and the stem-and-leaf, histogram, and boxplot in Figures 3.1, 3.3, 3.4, and 3.5 show the expected skewness. And, second, we must cope with *infinities* for subjects who do not complete the task at all.

Researchers have often ignored skewness, hoping it would not be severe enough to invalidate statistics applied to the data. A variety of ad hoc methods have been suggested for the infinities, including just substituting "some large value" and omitting them from the data. Neither ignoring the data nor assigning some large value is suitable, because either approach can severely distort statistical analyses. Some authors have suggested that nonparametric methods would be more appropriate because they are insensitive to both skewness and outlier problems. But these methods often restrict what we can see in the data.

EDA suggests that by reconsidering the way the data are recorded, we may gain additional insights and understanding. And, along the way, we can obtain simpler models for how the data behave. For the dexterity results, EDA-trained analysts would immediately think of looking at the *reciprocal* of the recorded times. These values have units of *tasks per second*—a measure of speed rather than duration. To make the units easier to deal with, we might multiply by 60 to obtain *tasks per minute*. A scale change or a shift in values from adding or subtracting a constant has no effect on the pattern of the values.

The reciprocal addresses both of the problems we noted. Infinities become a speed of zero tasks per second. And re-expressing data as $1/x$ has the effect of pulling in the high tail relative to the low one. For example, Figure 3.8 shows the histogram and boxplot of the speeds that correspond to the durations in Figures 3.1 and 3.3. The boxplot looks much more symmetric, and one data value

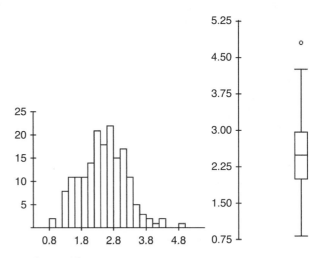

FIGURE 3.8. Histogram and boxplot of the speeds (in reciprocal seconds) of the 175 normal subjects on the test of manual dexterity.

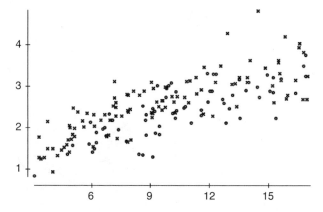

FIGURE 3.9. Scatterplot of speed (in reciprocal seconds) versus age (in years). The plotting symbol distinguishes the dominant hand (×) from the nondominant hand (o).

is outside at the upper end—a 14-year-old whose speed was 5 tasks per minute.

As most discussions of re-expression have noted, appropriate re-expression can improve the relations among variables as well as their individual distributions. Figure 3.9 shows the scatterplot of speed versus age, with symbols assigned according to hand as in Figure 3.6.

Now the relation is nicely linear—suitable for a regression model. The slope has changed from negative to positive, corresponding to the change in the meaning of the response variable. Durations are shorter for older subjects, so speed improves with age. The variation in speed is roughly constant across the age range.

Occam

William of Occam (c. 1288–c. 1348) is known for asserting that the simpler explanation that accounts for the facts is generally better. Years of experience in consulting and data analysis, along with the advice of prominent statisticians who have amassed far more experience, have convinced us that this is excellent guidance for analyzing data. Simpler models are not only easier to understand and explain but also are more likely to lead to future advances.

We often choose a re-expression such as the logarithm or square root because it works to simplify the analysis. Appropriate re-expression has merit for this reason alone. Models built to fit appropriately re-expressed data are both easier to understand and more likely to lead to further advances.

The cynical (but quite correct) view is that proper re-expression and data exploration are more likely to answer the most important question a researcher can ask: "What should my next grant proposal be about?" For the clinician, an analysis of appropriately re-expressed data is likely to give simpler diagnostic rules and guidelines.

For example, in Figure 3.10 the original scale (time) does not make it easy to summarize the effect of dominant versus nondominant hand. In the reciprocal scale (speed), the patterns for the two hands are linear and parallel, offering the summary that the dominant hand is about 0.3 tasks per minute faster at any of the ages studied.

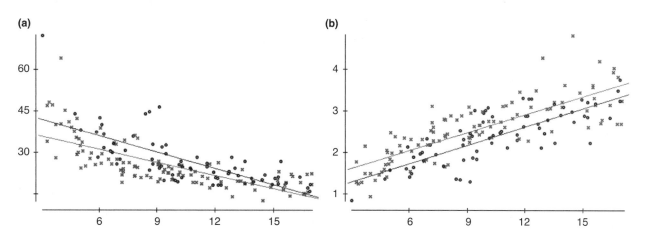

FIGURE 3.10. Scatterplots with separate regression lines for dominant (×) and nondominant (o) hands. (a) Time (in seconds) versus age (in years). (b) Speed (in reciprocal seconds) versus age (in years). The dominant hand takes less time (lower line in the left plot) and is, correspondingly, faster (upper line in the right plot).

EXTENDING THE ANALYSIS

One purpose of the dexterity trials was to investigate the phenomenon of crossover training. As we have seen, subjects improve with training up to about the third session. Researchers wanted to investigate whether performance in one hand is improved by training the other hand. The question is of importance to cognitive researchers because it addresses issues of how learning takes place. It is of clinical importance to therapists, who do not want to tire out an injured limb by training and wonder whether training the other, uninjured limb would be an appropriate protocol.

In Figure 3.11 the boxplots show that, overall, training the opposite hand does lead to improvement. A parallel-coordinate plot of the speeds in the tested hand before and after training the other hand shows the individual improvements and would support investigating, for example, whether handedness matters.

DATA ANALYSIS ETHICS

We set outliers aside for special consideration and re-express to improve the ability of models to fit the data. Both of these practices can improve the p values of hypothesis tests. Are we cheating?

This question cuts to the core of the difference in philosophy between EDA and the way traditional statistical inference is often used in psychology. Those who look to statistical methods to guard against the misuse of data may be scandalized by our proposal that a scientist should be free to seek the most appropriate re-expression and should focus on modeling the main body of the data and not the occasional extraordinary case. We reject the idea that statistical methods can or should serve as enforcers of honest data analysis. The goal should be truth about the world. Truth is, of course, a challenging goal, and one that we may rarely, if ever, attain. Nevertheless, it should be our guiding principle. (Philosophers call such a goal a *regulative ideal*.)

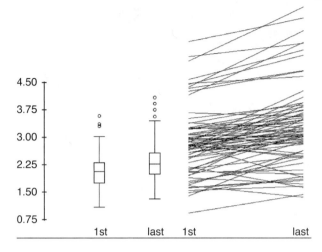

FIGURE 3.11. Boxplots and parallel-coordinate plot of speeds (in reciprocal seconds) before and after training the opposite hand.

Methods alone can never approach this ideal. It requires the honest efforts of the scientists and social scientists who do the research and analysis. In short, if a researcher wants to cheat, no amount of standardized statistical practice can stop it. Indeed, it may be easier to hide misconduct by following so-called *standard practice* and reporting only the usual summary statistics. We should not constrain honest researchers in an attempt to restrain less honest ones. Moreover, we should teach the ethics of honest research as a fundamental part of the education of researchers in all fields (Velleman, 2008).

Even honest researchers share the well-known human tendency to imagine patterns in data. In a provocative essay, Diaconis (1985) examined this aspect of EDA and discussed a variety of remedies:

- publish without p values
- try to quantify and correct for the distortion
- try it out on fresh data
- borrow strength[2]
- cross-validate
- bootstrap the exploration

He placed EDA in the context of theories of data analysis and concluded that "the new exploratory

---

[2]*Borrowing strength* is a general term that refers to seeking support for estimating values and, especially, variances from other parts of the data or other sources. When we fit a regression, we borrow strength from all the data (and the assumption that a linear model is appropriate) to enable more precise estimates and predictions for individual values.

MEASUREMENT SCALES

One tradition in psychology categorizes measurement scales as nominal, ordinal, interval, or ratio. The work in measurement arose from a debate about whether psychology could be a true science when many measurements made by psychologists were not comparable to those made by physicists. Although the argument for psychology as a science has largely been won, it has led some to suggest that the measurement scale of a variable should constrain the appropriate analysis methods. Often, for example, this line of reasoning has been used to argue in favor of nonparametric methods.

But this approach misunderstands measurement scales in many situations. Velleman and Wilkinson (1993), for example, noted that the measurement scale of a variable is not a property of the variable itself but rather a property of how it is used. They offer a number of examples of common variables that may be viewed as having one measurement scale in one context and a different scale in another.

A little thought reveals many common examples. Playing card suits appear to be nominal but are ordered in bridge. Playing card values can be ratio scaled in some games (casino), ordinal in others (poker), and nominal in still others (Go Fish). Velleman and Wilkinson (1993) offered the example of the consecutive numbers on tickets for a door prize handed out as attendees arrive at a meeting. These are nominal when selecting the winner but could be used (in interval scale) to count the number of attendees or (in ordinal scale) to record the order of their arrival.

We approach measurement scales by exploring data without any assumptions but then asking whether the best models and descriptions found for the data can be supported by the ways in which the data were measured. Surprisingly often, we have discovered a richness in data that was not evident at first. In short, EDAs deemphasize measurement scales—at least, until the final summary of the analysis.

Kinds of Data

Although it rejects measurement scale as a constraint, EDA does categorize data by types to offer guidance for re-expression. Mosteller and Tukey (1977, Chapter 5) suggested the categories and recommended re-expressions in Table 3.1.

REGRESSION

The EDA approach extends beyond elementary data summaries. Analyses that use multiple regression or ANOVA should consider the benefits of re-expression and of removing outliers.

TABLE 3.1

Summary of Re-expressions Suggested for Various Types of Data

Type of data	Suggested re-expressions
Amounts	Nonnegative real values. Logarithms are a good first guess. Natural and base-10 logs differ only by a constant multiplier, but base-10 logs are usually easier to interpret. (Times and rates are examples of amounts although, as we have noted, rates—because they are ratios—often benefit from a reciprocal transformation.)
Counts	Nonnegative integer values whose units are "number of. . . ." Square roots and logs are a good place to start.
Balances	Real values that may be positive or negative. Often these arise as a difference between two amounts (and then re-expressing those amounts may be helpful). Balances often need no re-expression.
Counted fractions	Fractions of a whole such as percentages (100 × number counted in a group/total group size). Special re-expressions that acknowledge the boundaries of these data at both ends, such as the logit, may be helpful.
Ranks	Integer values recording order. Treat like a counted fraction.
Grades	Ordered groups such as Freshman/First-Year, Sophomore, Junior, Senior. Little need to re-express.
Names	Nominal data. If the data simply name individuals, re-expression offers no advantage.

Most statistics programs compute diagnostic statistics that can help identify both influential cases and unexpected patterns. We recommend examining the following:

- Leverage. The leverage of any case in a simple or multiple regression is the amount by which that case's predicted value would change if the dependent value of the case were changed by one unit and the regression recomputed. Cases with particularly large leverage can dominate the fitting of a regression model.
- Studentized residuals. The standard deviation of the sampling distribution of a regression residual depends on the case's leverage. Cases near the multivariate mean of the x's have smaller variance than those far from the center of the data. Studentized residuals adjust for this. A scatterplot of the studentized residuals versus the predicted values has had the linear effects of the predictors removed and is adjusted for differences in the underlying variation of the prediction errors. Consequently, it displays any underlying patterns more clearly and vividly. This makes it an effective tool for assessing whether the relation of the response variable to the predictors is linear (and, thus, whether the regression model is appropriate).
- Difference in fits (DFFITS). The DFFITS statistic for each case shows the impact of omitting that case on the corresponding predicted value. This leave-out-one diagnostic combines leverage and studentized residual in a single measure.
- DFBETAS. When the *coefficients* of predictor variables are of interest, the DFBETAS statistics provide a suitably scaled measure of the change in each coefficient associated with omitting each case.

Most statistics packages have options to report all four of these statistics for a regression analysis. Each can be used to identify cases that may deserve special attention because of their undue influence on the regression model or because they deviate sharply from the pattern fitted by the regression model.

Diagnostic plots can be especially helpful for exploring multiple-regression models. Displays of residuals are commonly offered by all statistics software and should be examined for the same features that one would look for in a single variable. In a multiple regression, it is common to make a scatterplot of the residuals against the predicted values. Displays of studentized residuals are more useful because of their stabilized standard deviations.

When a coefficient is of interest, it is important to interpret it correctly: The coefficient for a particular predictor indicates how the dependent variable changes in response to change in that predictor after adjusting for the linear effects of the other predictor variables (in the data at hand). In general, no simpler language is satisfactory. We often read (even in textbooks) that a regression coefficient estimates the amount of change in the dependent variable when its predictor changes by one unit and all other predictors are held fixed. It is straightforward to show mathematically that such an interpretation is incorrect—unless the data have been collected in a way that explicitly holds the other predictors fixed (e.g., in a well-controlled experiment, to which we turn next). More important, EDA offers displays that help to interpret regression coefficients correctly.

One particularly useful exploratory display, offered by most modern statistics programs, is the *partial regression plot*. This scatterplot displays the relation between the response variable and any selected predictor variable after adjusting for simultaneous linear change in the other predictor variables. The plot, thus, displays exactly what the coefficient of the selected predictor means. Specifically, the plot has a least-squares slope equal to the coefficient of the selected predictor in the multiple regression model, and it has the same least-squares residuals as the full multiple regression. It is an excellent tool for understanding how consistently the selected predictor fits the response (by judging the variation in the residuals) and for diagnosing unusual behavior in the data that may affect that particular coefficient (Cook & Weisberg, 1982; Velleman & Welsch, 1981).

TABLE 3.2

Analysis of Variance Table for Difference Limen

Source	df	Sum of squares	Mean square	F ratio	p value
Constant	1	276799	276799	46.296	0.0024
Date	1	115.629	115.629	1.6582	0.1985
Rate	3	51077.6	17025.9	244.16	≤ 0.0001
Weight	6	1913.63	318.939	4.5737	0.0002
Sight	1	11816.3	11816.3	1.9763	0.2325
Sex	1	31543.7	31543.7	5.2758	0.0832
Subject (Sight × Sex)	4	23915.6	5978.89	85.740	≤ 0.0001
Sight × Sex	1	14136.8	14136.8	2.3644	0.1989
Error	430	29985.3	69.7332		
Total	447	164504			

ANALYSIS OF VARIANCE

The term *analysis of variance* customarily describes analyses of data that involve two or more factors and have one or more observations for each possible combination of the levels (or versions) of all the factors. Beyond such *factorial designs*, a wide variety of designs use balanced subsets of the possible combinations.

EDA emphasizes analyzing the data first and only later summarizing the contributions of various sources of variability (Hoaglin et al., 1991). Natural initial steps include looking at the data and considering the possibility of re-expression. We illustrate these ideas in the context of a classical set of data from a difference limen experiment for which a variety of illustrative analyses have been published on several occasions (Green & Tukey, 1960; E. G. Johnson & Tukey, 1987; P. O. Johnson, 1946; P. O. Johnson & Tsao, 1944).

The experiment involved eight subjects, "two persons in each cell of a 2 × 2 design for male versus female and sighted versus [congenitally] blind." Subjects were asked to detect a change in the weight pulling on a ring. The controlled treatments consisted of

two *Dates* (1, 2), four *Rates*
(50, 100, 150, and 200 grams per 30 seconds), and seven (initial) *Weights* (100, 150, 200, 250, 300, 350, and 400 grams). The experimental procedure involved attaching a pail by a lever system to a ring on the subject's finger. One of the seven initial *Weights* was placed into the pail, and then water was allowed to flow into the pail at one of four constant *Rates* until the subject reported a change in pull on the finger. The intended response, the difference limen (*DL*), was measured by the amount of water added [up to the] time of report. Five determinations were made for each of the 28 *Rate × Weight* combinations, and the average of these values was used as the response. The entire experiment was conducted, for each person, at each of two *Dates*, one week apart. (E. G. Johnson & Tukey, 1987, p. 174)[3]

The design calls for an analysis predicting *DL* from *Date, Rate, Weight, Sight, Sex,* and *Subject* (nested within the combination of *Sight* and *Sex*). That ANOVA is shown in Table 3.2.[4]

EDA teaches that we should always examine the residuals in an analysis because subtracting

---

[3] In this quotation, we have added italics and initial capitals to names of factors for consistency with usage in this chapter.
[4] Our results do not exactly match those of P. O. Johnson and Tsao (1944) or those of Green and Tukey (1960). P. O. Johnson (1946) used these data to illustrate complex ANOVA calculations and found a model with all interaction terms but without a *Subject* term. Green and Tukey followed a path closer to the one we are about to discuss. All of the previous authors had to perform these rather daunting calculations by hand, so errors may have crept in.

a summary of the patterns found so far is likely to reveal additional patterns or further evidence about the current summary. Plotting the residuals from the ANOVA of Table 3.2 against the predicted values (Figure 3.12) reveals that *DL* as originally measured does not satisfy the assumptions of ANOVA. In particular, it is clear that the variance of the response is not constant across the values of the factors studied. The pattern resembles a fan, opening to the right (larger residuals tend to belong to larger predicted values) and shows some curvature.

Green and Tukey (1960) discussed the importance of the scale used for the response variable:

> We want to choose a scale that will yield the simplest relations with the independent variables. By simplest relations we mean, for example, fewer important interactions, and larger main effects relative to the error variance. A change of variable that nearly removes a particular main effect also usually leads to very revealing results. Secondarily, we would like the dependent variable to have approximately homogeneous variance within cells of the design. (p. 128)

When variance increases with predicted value (as in Figure 3.12), functions such as the square root, logarithm, and reciprocal are likely to help.

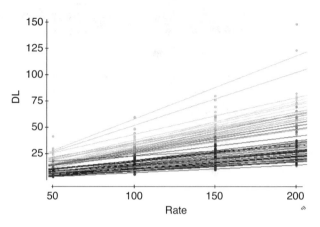

FIGURE 3.13. Difference limen (DL) plotted against *Rate*. Lines are least squares fits for each *Subject* × *Weight* × *Date* combination.

For these data, the units of the variables suggest an alternative way to address the first goal mentioned by Green and Tukey (1960). The *Difference Limen* is measured in grams. The *Rate* factor is measured in grams per 30 seconds. If we plot the *DL* against *Rate* and add lines to the plot for each *Subject* × *Weight* × *Date* combination, we obtain Figure 3.13.

But if we reformulate *Rate* as *Time* (in seconds) until the subject declares a felt change, we obtain Figure 3.14. (The calculation is *Seconds* = (*DL*/*Rate*) × 30.) The fact that response *Time* is virtually constant for the four rates of increase (for each combination of *Subject*, *Weight*, and *Date*) suggests that one can get whatever difference limen

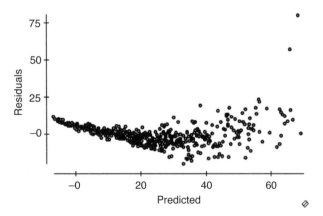

FIGURE 3.12. Residuals from the analysis of variance for *DL* (Difference Limen) on *Date*, *Weight*, *Rate*, *Sight*, *Sex*, and *Subject* (*Sight* × *Sex*) show nonlinearity and a fan shape that calls for re-expression or reformulation.

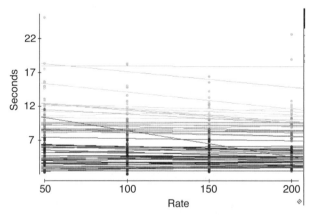

FIGURE 3.14. Response in seconds is almost constant versus *Rate* for each *Subject* × *Weight* × *Date* combination.

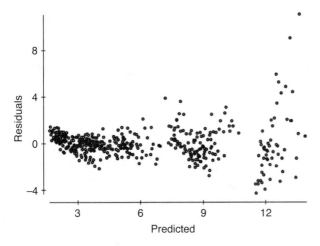

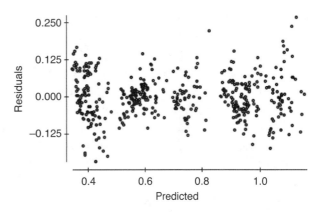

FIGURE 3.15. Plot of residuals versus predicted values for the ANOVA of *Seconds* on *Date*, *Weight*, *Rate*, *Sight*, *Sex*, and *Subject* (within *Sight* × *Sex*).

FIGURE 3.16. Plot of residuals versus predicted values for the analysis of variance of Log_{10} *Seconds* on *Date*, *Weight*, *Rate*, *Sight*, *Sex*, and *Subject* (within *Sight* × *Sex*).

one wants by choosing the *Rate* appropriately. That observation argues strongly that converting the average *DL* to an average *Time* (in seconds) will produce a simpler analysis. P. O. Johnson and Tsao (1944) found this relation (as an interaction in their analysis of average *DL*). Green and Tukey found it and made the argument for using *Time* as the response that we recount here. Technically, this type of change is sometimes called *reformulation* rather than re-expression because it does not involve applying a simple mathematical function to each data value. When available, it is another useful technique in the analyst's toolkit.

Although the summary is simpler for the data in seconds, the residual plot in Figure 3.15 still shows a bend, increasing spread from left to right, and possible subgroups. An analysis of Log_{10} *Seconds* yields the residual plot in Figure 3.16. This pattern is more like what we hope for: roughly flat, with similar variation in the residuals across the range of predicted values and no bends. The overall pattern in Figure 3.16 is horizontal and homoscedastic. The residuals form clusters. Further checking shows that each subject is a cluster, although some subjects' clusters overlap. The ANOVA table presented in Table 3.3 shows significant effects for *Date* and *Weight*. Because this ANOVA treats *Subject* as a random factor (and the other factors as fixed), we do not focus on the significance of the effects for the individual

TABLE 3.3

Analysis of Variance Table for Log_{10} Seconds

Source	df	Sum of squares	Mean square	F ratio	p value
Constant	1	223.836	223.836	80.238	0.0009
Date	1	0.093378	0.093378	17.592	≤ 0.0001
Rate	3	0.012418	0.004139	0.77983	0.5057
Weight	6	0.332250	0.055375	10.433	≤ 0.0001
Sight	1	3.79149	3.79149	1.3591	0.3085
Sex	1	7.70730	7.70730	2.7628	0.1718
Subject (Sight × Sex)	4	11.1586	2.78964	525.56	≤ 0.0001
Sight × Sex	1	3.40870	3.40870	1.2219	0.3310
Error	430	2.28240	0.005308		
Total	447	28.7865			

subjects; the *p* value for *Subject* arises from comparing the *Subject* mean square against the residual mean square. Although they have much larger mean squares than *Date* and *Weight* (and *Rate*), *Sight*, *Sex*, and *Sight* × *Sex* are far from significant because the denominator for their F ratios is the *Subject* (*Sight* × *Sex*) mean square. Green and Tukey (1960) discussed choices between fixed and random for the various factors and the reasons for them.

From an EDA perspective, the analysis does not end with an ANOVA table. The customary next step examines the individual values for each line in the table: the main effects for *Date*, *Rate*, *Weight*, *Sight*, and *Sex*; the interaction effects for *Sight* × *Sex*; the effects for *Subject* (nested within *Sight* × *Sex*); and the residuals. Figure 3.17 shows dot plots of the various effects and a boxplot of the residuals; we chose the order because the residuals provide the denominator for *Weight*, *Rate*, and *Date* and the *Subject* effects provide the denominator for *Sight*, *Sex*, and *Sight* × *Sex*. Because each set of effects sums to 0 (in two ways for *Sight* × *Sex*), the effects for the lines other than *Weight* and *Rate* consist of positive and negative values with the same magnitude. Such a display makes it easy to compare the sizes of the effects for the various parts of the model.

The variation among the residuals and among the *Subject* effects dominates the display. The effects for *Date* appear small alongside the residuals, but each of those effects represents a mean of 224 observations. On the other hand, the effects for *Sight*, *Sex*, and *Sight* × *Sex* do not seem much smaller than the *Subject* effects, but each *Subject* effect represents a mean of 56 observations. Relative to the variation in the *Subject* effects, the effects for *Sight*, *Sex*, and *Sight* × *Sex* are not large enough to reach significance.

Of the two experimental factors, different *Weights* have noticeable effects, although they are not very large compared with the variation in the residuals. By contrast, differing *Rates* have little effect at all.

As Figure 3.18 shows, the effects for *Weight* are systematically related to the level of weight. Subjects were able to more quickly discern a change when the initial weight was small than when it was larger—a result consistent with Weber's law but not a particularly exciting outcome for so complex an experiment.

Exploratory ANOVA can go further (Hoaglin et al., 1991), but we stop here for this chapter. The choice to reformulate the response as seconds and then re-express it as log-seconds may seem specific to this analysis and difficult to generalize,

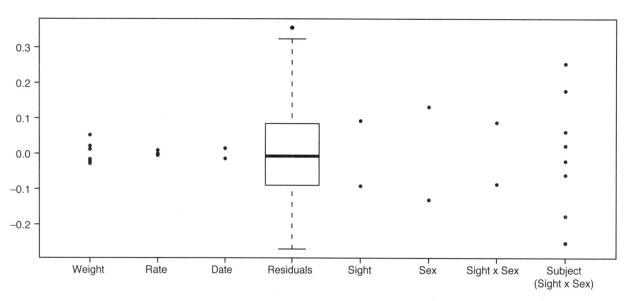

FIGURE 3.17. Effects and residuals for the analysis of variance of Log_{10} Seconds on Date, Weight, Rate, Sight, Sex, and Subject (within Sight × Sex).

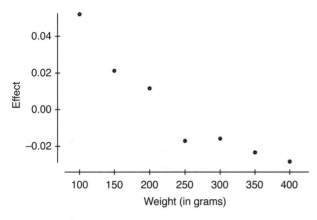

FIGURE 3.18. The effects of *Weight* generally fall consistently with increasing weight.

but other analyses present similar opportunities. And for re-expression, EDA has specific techniques for letting the data guide the choice (Emerson, 1983; Emerson & Stoto, 1983).

THE EDA PROCESS

Data exploration is a diagnostic procedure. The data analyst attempts to detect and characterize any aspect of the data that may help in understanding the underlying pathologies. Diagnosis requires an open mind and a willingness to expect the unexpected. Checklists have proved helpful in clinical medicine (e.g., Gawande, 2010). In that spirit, we offer a data exploration and diagnosis checklist. As with many checklists for complex processes, this one is divided into shorter, focused checklists for each of the large steps of analysis.

Checklist I. Display the Data

A. **Look at the distributions of the variables with a stem-and-leaf display, histogram, or dot plot.**
   1. Be alert for multiple modes
      a) Consider splitting data into subgroups
   2. Be alert for outliers
      a) Identify, understand, correct (if possible), or set aside
   3. Check for skewness
      a) Consider re-expression to improve symmetry

B. **Compare groups with boxplots.**
   1. Check for skewness within groups
      a) Consider re-expression to improve symmetry
   2. Check that groups have similar spreads
      a) Consider re-expression to promote constant spread (spread-vs.-level plot)
   3. Check for outliers
      a) Identify, understand, correct (if possible), or set aside

C. **Consider bivariate relations with scatterplots.**
   1. Check for approximate straightness
      a) Consider re-expression to improve straightness
      b) Usually re-expressing y is preferred, as it is likely also to make the variability of y more nearly constant across the range of x
   2. Check for constant variance of y for all x values (homoscedasticity)
      a) Consider re-expressing y, especially if larger values of y are more variable
   3. Check for local clusters, parallel trends, or other evidence of subgroups
      a) Consider splitting the data into subgroups
   4. Check for outliers
      a) Consider both y-direction outliers and x-direction high-leverage points
         i) The influence of a case depends on both
         ii) Identify, understand, correct (if appropriate), or consider setting aside or treating specially

D. **Consider multivariate relations with scatterplot matrices and rotating plots.**
   1. Check for approximate straightness
      a) Consider re-expression to improve linearity
      b) Scatterplot matrices make it easy to notice variables that would benefit from re-expression in several bivariate relationships; re-express those variables first
   2. Check for local clusters, parallel trends, or other evidence of subgroups
      a) In rotating plots, rotate so that the main trend is perpendicular to the screen to look for subgroups

    b) In scatterplot matrices, use plot brushing to identify clusters in one scatterplot and check whether they stand out in other scatterplots
    c) Consider splitting the data into subgroups
 3. Check for outliers
    a) In scatterplot matrices, select points that stand away from the other data to see whether they may be unusual in other scatterplots; they may be outliers in a multivariate sense
    b) Be alert for points that may be multivariate outliers but are not unusual on any univariate or bivariate display
       i) Diagnostic statistics are available to help with this (see the discussion of regression)

If the exploratory displays in the first checklist suggest that it is appropriate to summarize variables or model their behavior, then use Checklists II through V, depending on the number and structure of the variables.

Checklist II. Summarize and Describe Individual Variables

A. **Summarize individual variables with resistant measures.**
   1. Median
   2. Quartiles
      a) Several definitions of quartiles are in use, but it matters little which you use
   3. Q-spread (interquartile range)
   4. Extremes (minimum and maximum)
B. **Summarize individual variables with traditional maximum-likelihood methods.**
   1. Mean
   2. Standard deviation
   3. Confidence interval
      a) But check displays to be sure assumptions are plausible

Checklist III. Compare Multiple Groups

A. **Use ANOVA to compare group means.**
   1. Consider the form of the response variable
      a) Use spread-vs.-level plot to check for need to re-express
   b) Plot residuals against predicted values and look for violations of homoscedasticity and for curvature
 2. Check residuals for outliers

Checklist IV. Summarize and Describe Relations Between Pairs of Quantitative Variables

A. **Use resistant smoothing to reveal general trends.**
B. **Fit linear models with least squares regression and check diagnostic displays and statistics.**
   1. Plot studentized residuals vs. predicted values; check for the following:
      a) Curvature
         i) If so, go back to Checklist I.D.1, consider re-expression, and fit again
      b) Subgroups, especially parallel patterns
         i) Parallel patterns suggest an analysis-of-covariance approach or the introduction of indicator variables and a multiple regression
      c) Outliers and high-leverage points
         i) Consider correcting, omitting, or treating specially; one possibility introduces an indicator variable for each errant case

Checklist V. Summarize Multivariate Relations Involving a Single Quantitative Response Variable and Multiple Potential Quantitative Predictors

A. **Fit a least squares multiple regression and compute and examine the residuals.**
   1. Plot studentized residuals against predicted values
      a) Look for bends—consider re-expressing y
      b) Look for heteroscedasticity—consider re-expressing y
      c) Look for parallel patterns—consider indicator variables for groups
      d) Look for outliers—consider correcting, setting aside, or treating specially (e.g., with an indicator variable for each)
   2. Examine leverage and influence measures; identify influential cases

a) Histograms and stem-and-leaf displays help to identify extreme values; boxplots can do that conveniently for large numbers of values; leverages are not likely to be normally distributed because they are bounded by 0 and 1
b) Set aside influential cases and repeat the analysis to assess their true influence on your conclusions
3. Examine partial regression plots—especially for coefficients that are of particular interest
    a) Check as for simple regressions in Checklist IV

Regression model building is an exploration of several aspects at once. We simultaneously seek effective functional forms to model the data and appropriate variables with which to build our models. Along the way, we identify extraordinary cases and prevent them from dominating our decisions. There is no fixed path. You may choose to examine a response variable plotted against each factor or predictor before moving on to models with multiple factors and predictors. The most important aspect of the EDA approach is that the human analyst is intimately involved at each step, using discipline-based knowledge to guide decisions. For example, one path for building a multiple regression model might go according to Checklist VI.

Checklist VI. Build a Multiple Regression Model in Interactive Steps

A. Choose a promising predictor variable and fit a simple (y vs. x) regression. Look at plots and diagnostics as in Checklist V. Use the information from displays of this relation to reconsider the form of the model, possible re-expressions of the variables, isolation of possible outliers, and whether the selected predictor should be replaced with an alternative predictor.

B. Consider the relations between the residuals and remaining available predictors. Be alert to opportunities for re-expression and the possibility that other cases should be isolated as outliers. Select one or more of the available predictors (after possible re-expression and outlier deletion) to add to the model. Diagnose as in Checklist V.
 1. Isolate extraordinary cases by assigning individual indicator variables to them and including those in the model
C. Iterate. At each iteration it may be appropriate to proceed stepwise—that is, introduce one predictor at a time or introduce collections of conceptually related predictors together. The most important idea is to continually monitor and diagnose the developing model, exploring for unanticipated relations, clusters, outliers, and violations of assumptions.

Designed experiments are likely sources of data with a quantitative response and two categorical factors. In such cases the factors are defined and controlled. However, this form of data can also arise from observational studies, where the factors may be observed and not under control.

Checklist VII. Summarize Multivariate Relations of a Single Quantitative Response Variable and Two Categorical Factors

A. Median polish.
B. Look for re-expressions to improve additivity.
 1. Use the diagnostic plot for a two-way table to suggest a function for re-expression[5]
C. Plot residuals. If they are reasonably symmetric and not heavy-tailed, consider fitting the ANOVA model (i.e., summarize by means).
 1. Diagnose ANOVA residuals as in Checklist VI; check for heteroscedasticity and curvature
 2. Diagnose possible outliers

---

[5]Emerson and Hoaglin (1983) and Emerson (1983) discussed the diagnostic plot for a two-way table and its background. The plot is a graphical descendant of Tukey's (1949) one degree of freedom for nonadditivity.

Checklist VIII. Summarize Multivariate Relations of a Single Quantitative Response Variable and Multiple Categorical Factors

A. If data come from a designed experiment, explore the ANOVA corresponding to the design.
   1. Examine boxplots of the residuals at each level of each factor and possibly for combinations of factors
      a) Look for outliers—treat them as before
      b) Look for skewness—consider re-expressing y
   2. Explore for evidence of nonadditivity
B. Data from designed experiments can be explored in much the same way as for multiple regression. EDA supports the idea that factors and interactions can be included or removed from a developing model. At each step, the residuals should be checked, and unanticipated clusters, outliers, nonlinearity, or (for analyses of covariances) lack of parallelism should be addressed.

These EDA principles and approaches extend naturally to more complex situations. The general rules are to make displays of individual variables first and deal with any special issues. Then check any models for the data by similarly examining residuals to see whether they reveal anything worthy of special attention. Always be alert to the opportunity to re-express variables to simplify the models or to better satisfy model assumptions. Be willing to isolate outliers and influential cases by setting them aside or by fitting special terms just for them.

COMPETING MODELS

When we explore data with many variables, it is often productive to entertain multiple, competing models, developing each, comparing results, and learning from one to inform the others. This strategy might lead simply to offering multiple alternative models for the data. Or it might develop into a Darwinian competition among the models: less useful or successful forms lose out to the more successful ones—a "Survival of the Best Fit."

When researchers apply statistics primarily to test hypotheses, they often have a sense of completion. We have stated and tested the hypotheses, reached conclusions about them, and can move on to other topics. EDA does not adopt that attitude. It never reaches a natural stopping place. As with the larger corpus of science, an EDA is never done. New data or new understanding may lead us to modify or develop an analysis further. Of course, you can reach a point at which everyone involved agrees that there is little gain from doing more with the data you have. But experience has shown that, even then, a new idea or suggestion can reopen the question.

References

Aaron, D. H., & Jansen, C. W. S. (2003). Development of the functional dexterity test (FDT): Construction, validity, reliability, and normative data. *Journal of Hand Therapy*, 16(1), 12–21. https://doi.org/10.1016/S0894-1130(03)80019-4

Bartlett, M. S. (1947). The use of transformations. *Biometrics*, 3(1), 39–52. https://doi.org/10.2307/3001536

Box, G. E. P., & Cox, D. R. (1964). An analysis of transformations. *Journal of the Royal Statistical Society. Series B. Methodological*, 26(2), 211–243. https://doi.org/10.1111/j.2517-6161.1964.tb00553.x

Cook, R. D., & Weisberg, S. (1982). *Residuals and influence in regression*. Chapman & Hall.

Diaconis, P. (1985). Theories of data analysis: From magical thinking through classical statistics. In D. C. Hoaglin, F. Mosteller, & J. W. Tukey (Eds.), *Exploring data tables, trends, and shapes* (pp. 1–36). Wiley.

Efron, B. (2020). Prediction, estimation, and attribution. *Journal of the American Statistical Association*, 115(530), 636–655. https://doi.org/10.1080/01621459.2020.1762613

Emerson, J. D. (1983). Mathematical aspects of transformation. In D. C. Hoaglin, F. Mosteller, & J. W. Tukey (Eds.), *Understanding robust and exploratory data analysis* (pp. 247–282). Wiley.

Emerson, J. D., & Hoaglin, D. C. (1983). Analysis of two-way tables by medians. In D. C. Hoaglin, F. Mosteller, & J. W. Tukey (Eds.), *Understanding robust and exploratory data analysis* (pp. 166–210). Wiley.

Emerson, J. D., & Stoto, M. A. (1983). Transforming data. In D. C. Hoaglin, F. Mosteller, & J. W. Tukey (Eds.), *Understanding robust and exploratory data analysis* (pp. 97–128). Wiley.

Gawande, A. (2010). *The checklist manifesto.* Metropolitan Books.

Gogola, G. R., Lacy, B., Morse, A., Aaron, D., & Velleman, P. F. (2010, June). *Hand dexterity values for 3 to 17 year-old typically developing children* [Paper presentation]. Eighth Triennial Congress of the International Federation of Societies for Hand Therapy, Orlando, FL, United States.

Green, B. F., Jr., & Tukey, J. W. (1960). Complex analyses of variance: General problems. *Psychometrika, 25*(2), 127–152. https://doi.org/10.1007/BF02288577

Hoaglin, D. C. (1988). Transformations in everyday experience. *Chance, 1*(4), 40–45.

Hoaglin, D. C., & Iglewicz, B. (1987). Fine-tuning some resistant rules for outlier labeling. *Journal of the American Statistical Association, 82*(400), 1147–1149. https://doi.org/10.1080/01621459.1987.10478551

Hoaglin, D. C., Iglewicz, B., & Tukey, J. W. (1986). Performance of some resistant rules for outlier labeling. *Journal of the American Statistical Association, 81*(396), 991–999. https://doi.org/10.1080/01621459.1986.10478363

Hoaglin, D. C., Mosteller, F., & Tukey, J. W. (Eds.). (1991). *Fundamentals of exploratory analysis of variance.* Wiley. https://doi.org/10.1002/9780470316832

Inselberg, A. (2009). *Parallel coordinates: Visual multidimensional geometry and its applications.* Springer. https://doi.org/10.1007/978-0-387-68628-8

Jebsen, R. H., Taylor, N., Trieschmann, R. B., Trotter, M. J., & Howard, L. A. (1969). An objective and standardized test of hand function. *Archives of Physical Medicine and Rehabilitation, 50*(6), 311–319.

Johnson, E. G., & Tukey, J. W. (1987). Graphical exploratory analysis of variance illustrated on a splitting of the Johnson and Tsao data. In C. L. Mallows (Ed.), *Design, data, and analysis by some friends of Cuthbert Daniel* (pp. 171–244). Wiley.

Johnson, P. O. (1946). *Statistical methods in research.* Prentice Hall.

Johnson, P. O., & Tsao, F. (1944). Factorial design in the determination of differential limen values. *Psychometrika, 9*(2), 107–144. https://doi.org/10.1007/BF02288717

Kruskal, J. B. (1968). Statistical analysis: Transformations of data. In D. L. Sills (Ed.), *International encyclopedia of the social sciences* (Vol. 15, pp. 182–193). Macmillan & The Free Press.

Mlodinow, L. (2008). *The drunkard's walk.* Pantheon Books.

Mosteller, F., & Tukey, J. W. (1977). *Data analysis and regression.* Addison-Wesley.

Reitan, R. M. (1958). Validity of the Trail Making Test as an indicator of organic brain damage. *Perceptual and Motor Skills, 8*(3), 271–276. https://doi.org/10.2466/pms.1958.8.3.271

Stroop, J. R. (1935). Studies of interference in serial verbal reactions. *Journal of Experimental Psychology, 18*(6), 643–662. https://doi.org/10.1037/h0054651

Tukey, J. W. (1949). One degree of freedom for non-additivity. *Biometrics, 5*(3), 232–242. https://doi.org/10.2307/3001938

Tukey, J. W. (1957). On the comparative anatomy of transformations. *Annals of Mathematical Statistics, 28*(3), 602–632. https://doi.org/10.1214/aoms/1177706875

Tukey, J. W. (1960). A survey of sampling from contaminated distributions. In I. Olkin, S. G. Ghurye, W. Hoeffding, W. G. Madow, & H. B. Mann (Eds.), *Contributions to probability and statistics: Essays in honor of Harold Hotelling* (pp. 448–485). Stanford University Press.

Tukey, J. W. (1977). *Exploratory data analysis.* Addison-Wesley.

Velleman, P. F. (2004). *Data desk.* Data Description.

Velleman, P. F. (2008). Truth, damn truth, and statistics. *Journal of Statistics Education: An International Journal on the Teaching and Learning of Statistics, 16*(2). https://doi.org/10.1080/10691898.2008.11889565

Velleman, P. F., & Welsch, R. E. (1981). Efficient computing of regression diagnostics. *The American Statistician, 35*, 234–242. https://doi.org/10.2307/2683296

Velleman, P. F., & Wilkinson, L. (1993). Nominal, ordinal, interval, and ratio typologies are misleading. *The American Statistician, 47*, 65–72. https://doi.org/10.2307/2684788

SECTION 2
DESCRIBING DATA

CHAPTER 4

GRAPHIC DISPLAYS OF DATA

Leland Wilkinson

The results of a survey by Cleveland (1984) on the use of graphics in scientific articles are shown in Figure 4.1. The horizontal axis represents the percentage of total page area devoted to graphics in 47 articles sampled from the 1980 to 1981 volumes of selected science journals. The circles represent Cleveland's individual measurements, and the box-and-whisker schematics divide each set of circles into quartiles. There are significant differences among disciplines in the use of graphs. Moreover, as Cleveland noted, the substantial differences among disciplines remain when the measure is number of graphs per article instead of page area.

This pattern of graphics usage appears not to have changed in the decades following Cleveland's (1984) study. Best et al. (2001) found similar results in a more recent survey. Furthermore, they found differences in graphics usage among subdisciplines of psychology, with the "hard" scientists using more graphics than the "soft" scientists. These results appear paradoxical. Why would "soft" scientists, who eschew mathematics, tend to avoid graphics (even simple charts, illustrations, or diagrams)? Why would "hard" scientists turn to graphs when equations, algorithms, and tables are sufficient support for their findings?

We might speculate that social scientists have always had an aversion toward graphics. On the contrary, Funkhouser (1937), Beniger and Robyn (1978), Fienberg (1979), Stigler (1983), Tufte (1983, 1990, 1997), Collins (1993), Wainer (1997), Wainer and Spence (1997), Wainer and Velleman (2001), and Wainer (2009) demonstrated that social scientists were among the earliest, most enthusiastic, and most inventive users of graphics in scientific publications. If anything, "hard" scientists were latecomers to the graphics field. The beautiful reproductions in Playfair (2005) reveal, in a wealth of figures, probably the first instances of bar, line, pie, and stacked area charts.

We might also imagine that social scientists think the use of graphics is evidence of sloppy thinking: Numbers are precise, and graphics are fuzzy. It is no easier to lie with graphics than with statistics, however (Huff, 1954; Monmonier, 1996). And it is a simple calculation to show that the typical printed journal figure (assuming a width of 3 inches) permits approximately 4 digits of precision in its resolution—more than typical data analyzed by psychologists. And if social scientists are prejudiced against graphics, why do they use them so often in their talks?

We might also think that software to do the kind of graphics needed by social scientists (as opposed to business people) is lacking. On the contrary, there is a plethora of such software. As we shall see, almost every major statistics package has comprehensive graphics capabilities,

https://doi.org/10.1037/0000320-004
APA Handbook of Research Methods in Psychology, Second Edition: Vol. 3. Data Analysis and Research Publication, H. Cooper (Editor-in-Chief)
Copyright © 2023 by the American Psychological Association. All rights reserved.

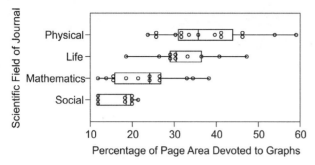

FIGURE 4.1. Dot–boxplot of results in Cleveland (1984) on the use of graphics in scientific journals. The horizontal axis represents the percentage of total page area devoted to graphics in 47 articles sampled from the 1980–1981 volumes of selected science journals.

and there are several good charting packages for producing the kind of technical graphics featured in this chapter.

We might also think that publishers make the use of graphics in articles inordinately expensive. Unfortunately, there is some truth to this idea. Some journal publishers (especially in the social sciences and humanities) have failed to keep up with new technology and continue to imagine that embedding graphics in articles is more expensive than setting type. These publishers still require authors to submit double-spaced, plain-text manuscripts, with figures separated from the text. This manuscript format dates from the time of manual typewriters, when production assistants used rubber cement to layout figures for photo-offset printing. Publishers used a simple formula to calculate book and journal prices; they multiplied cost-of-goods-sold by 7. Nowadays, while publishers have automated their production process (using software like Quark Express or Adobe InDesign), they continue to use the multiply-by-7 rule. Consequently, the publisher's expense of arranging figures and text by hand in Quark or Adobe is multiplied by a factor of 7. This is why some publishers ask authors to keep figures to a minimum. Other publishers, using different tools, welcome figures and do not charge extra for them. I discuss these technologies later in this chapter.

It should be evident by this point that I advocate new policies and present new ideas in this chapter rather than summarize conventional thinking about graphics usage. The reason for this approach is simple: Much conventional wisdom on the production and usage of graphics in scientific publications is wrong. I support this assertion through citations to the psychological and statistical literature and to commercial production technology. Moreover, I try to expose the subjectivity in popular writing on graphics usage as well as the long-standing tendency of "graphics gurus" to ignore scientific research on graphical communication. I express my own opinions, nonetheless. There is nothing wrong with aesthetic prescriptions based on reasonable rules and clean design, as long as these opinions are not disguised as facts.

The point of view in this chapter differs somewhat from other chapters in this handbook. As I mentioned, some of the assertions in this chapter are subjective, so I decided to use the first-person in order to prevent a false impression of scientific objectivity. More importantly, there are four groups I am trying to influence in this chapter: (a) researchers who are publishing, (b) editors and reviewers, (c) publishers, and (d) software developers. Because I have been fortunate in the last 50 years to teach in graduate departments of psychology, statistics, and computer science, I have been exposed to developments in each field that affect practices in the others. I have also witnessed the isolation in these communities; few researchers have the time to read the literature outside their fields. This chapter is an attempt to call on all three disciplines.

The remainder of this chapter consists of three parts. The next section presents guidelines based on aesthetics and on cognitive science. The third section offers exemplars—suggested graphics for displaying one or more variables embedded in models frequently employed by psychologists and other researchers. The brief final section surveys software for producing scientific graphics on computers.

GUIDELINES

Charts are maps of abstract worlds. The word *chart* and the word *cartography* have the same root (Latin *charta*, a piece of paper or papyrus).

We map the globe in order to orient ourselves in the world. Graphical worlds transcend geography. We graph abstractions in order to orient ourselves in abstract worlds. As Pinker (1997) argued, abstract reasoning is built on metaphors for reality. We manipulate abstractions by making them analogous to concrete objects.

Many useful guidelines for making charts and scientific graphics understandable, therefore, can be derived from the regularities of the perceived physical world. As with well-designed computer interfaces, well-designed graphics are generally consistent with these perceived regularities:

- Dense objects (mountains or histograms) rest on a base.
- Members of a group (birds in a flock or points in a cloud) are near each other.
- Paths through space (geographic or abstract) are connected.
- We think of images as having a natural orientation with a top and a bottom.
- We interpret red as hot and blue as cool.
- We perceive pale-blue objects as more distant than bright-green ones.

Violating commonsense reasoning leads to confusion. The designer who ignores these regularities interferes with the primary purpose of a graphic: to convey truthfully a structured message through the visual system.

Regularity in the physical world is not the same as perceived regularity of the physical world, of course. In some cases, graphics can compensate for our biases. For example, Stevens (1985) and others demonstrated that our psychometric function for stimulus intensity is nonlinear. If we wish to convey magnitude via certain stimulus modes (area, volume, brightness, and so on), we might want to arrange for a nonlinear mapping from the data to the representation—similar to the way engineers design nonlinear inputs to controls that pilots expect to process linearly.

In proposing guidelines for chart construction, we must keep in mind our communication goals. Popular writers frequently overlook this caveat when they develop their lists of design rules. Over the centuries of their history, various charts have emphasized *communication* (e.g., Snow's map of cholera deaths in London, reproduced in Tufte, 1983), *persuasion* (Fletcher's map of the distribution of ignorance in 19th century England and Wales, reproduced in Wainer, 1997), and artistic *design* (e.g., Playfair's chart of imports and exports of England to and from North America, reproduced in Tufte, 1983). These criteria are not exclusive, of course. Some charts incorporate all three (e.g., Minard's famous map–chart of Napoleon's troop losses in the Russian campaign, reproduced in Tufte, 1983).

Not surprisingly, modern critics of graphics have tended to align themselves along these same dimensions. Communicators (e.g., Cleveland, 1984; Kosslyn, 1994) have conducted experiments to determine rules that improve the transfer of information from chart-maker to chart-viewer. Persuaders (e.g., Holmes, 1991) have evaluated charts on the basis of their emotional impact. Designers (e.g., Herdeg, 1981) have looked for elegance and simplicity. Others (e.g., Tufte, 1983) have adopted the criteria of the communicator and the methods of the designer. None of these approaches can claim exclusive validity. Since scientists are more interested in rules that foster accurate communication of replicable results, however, I will focus on communication.

Evaluating graphical communication has been the province of psychology in the subdisciplines of human factors, ergonomics, and applied cognitive science. For almost a century, human-factors psychologists have developed methods and criteria for evaluating graphics. Military psychologists, for example, have conducted randomized experiments to test the effectiveness of aircraft cockpit displays.

Psychologists gave less attention to the perception of statistical graphics until a statistician, William Cleveland, published a series of experiments designed to identify aspects of charts that helped or hindered accurate decoding of quantitative data (Cleveland & McGill, 1984). Beniger and Robyn (1978) cited a number of statisticians' informal studies of the effectiveness of popular charts in the 1920's, but these did not induce many psychologists to study the topic more formally.

Cleveland used paper-and-pencil tests containing simple graphical elements—points, lines, angles, areas, colors—generated randomly by a computer. His subjects gave magnitude estimates of the values generating the instances of each element. From these estimates, he derived and analyzed error rates. One can quibble with his methodology, but the results are intriguing and stimulated subsequent studies by psychologists to test them further.

Figure 4.2 summarizes the main result of Cleveland's experiments. The top of the figure (BEST) represents elements that resulted in fewer errors and the bottom (WORST) represents those with more.

Cleveland's hierarchy gives us a start in designing effective displays. There are exceptions to these rules, however. A chart is more than the sum of its parts; elements interact in the perceptual mix of a chart. These interactions can suppress or enhance errors. Thus, it is dangerous to extrapolate from Cleveland's findings to the evaluation of complex charts.

Interactions in the perceptual mix immediately suggest Gestalt effects. There is reasonable evidence that similarity, proximity, closure, figure-ground, and configural effects apply to the perception of statistical graphics (Coren & Girgus, 1978; Garner, 1981; Klippel et al., 2004). For example, Cleveland et al. (1982) found that the relation between the size of a scatterplot cloud and the size of a surrounding frame affects the judgment of correlation by both novice and expert viewers. Their result is most likely due to a figure-ground effect: Small clouds surrounded by large, white frames are perceived as more correlated. There is a confound in this study, however. The size of the plotting symbols was allowed to vary with the size of the cloud. In unpublished research with a graduate student, I found that the effect disappears when the darkness of the cloud is attenuated by reducing the size of the plotting symbols. The conclusion of Cleveland et al. (1982) should be modified to say that small, *dark* clouds surrounded by large, white frames are perceived as more correlated.

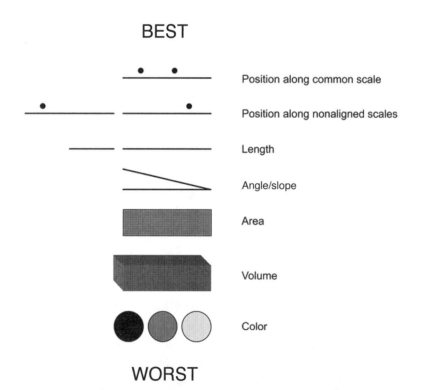

FIGURE 4.2. Hierarchy of graphic elements derived from Cleveland and McGill (1984) and other studies by Cleveland.

This modified result is consistent with Gestalt principles of figure-ground and proximity. Doherty and Anderson (2009) discussed this and other effects in the perception of correlation in scatterplots.

Another caution against generalizing from Cleveland's findings arises from the absence of consideration of cognitive processes in the derivation of the hierarchy. Cleveland deliberately ignored cognition in his studies, preferring instead to concentrate on perception. Because his methods are consistent with those of magnitude scaling and his stimuli are similar to ones used by the psychophysicists, his results are fairly consistent with the psychophysical literature on power-function exponents for graphic stimuli (Stevens, 1961). If we remove annotation, text, legends, and axes from a graph, leaving only a single type of element (e.g., points, lines, areas), then Cleveland's hierarchy would probably be consistent with the patterns of responding.

Cognition introduces strong biases. Images, icons, text, and other symbolic aspects of a graphic affect higher level visual processing in strange ways. For example, features such as physical or political boundaries drawn as lines between two cities on a map can cause overestimation of Euclidean distance between them when viewing the map (Tversky, 1993; Tversky et al., 2000). Similarly, connecting paths drawn between two cities can induce underestimation of distance (Klippel et al., 2004). The Cleveland rules are too simple for capturing these contextual effects. Kosslyn (1994), Heiser et al. (2003), Tversky (2005), and Tversky et al. (2007) are good sources for understanding how these processes affect graphical information processing in general.

Another important and frequently ignored role of cognition involves memory for graphs. Wilkinson and McConathy (1990) found that the Cleveland hierarchy is not always consistent in accounting for subjects' errors in magnitude estimation of the Cleveland elements under recall. This result is consistent with the finding that graphic elements are not stored as photographic images (Kosslyn, 1994). Line elements, for example, are encoded through simple prototypes (mountains, camel humps, snakes) that can distort global shape. For thematic elements in maps, Tversky (1981) and McNamara et al. (1984) found substantial distortions in memory when judging distance and other relations.

Many writers have prescribed general rules for effective graphical communication. The following guidelines are derived from Bertin (1967, 1981), Tufte (1983), Lewandowsky and Spence (1989), Cleveland (1993, 1994, 1995), Kosslyn (1994), Lewandowsky (1999), Robbins (2005), Ware (2008), and Few (2009). Some guidelines are based on my own opinions; I will make clear when I disagree with the other writers.

All the graphics in this article are in black-and-white because the publisher requested that I restrict my examples to monochrome. My last book (Wilkinson, 2005) is entirely in color, and I am a strong believer in the use of color in scientific graphics. Nevertheless, this restriction has forced me to examine more closely the many issues involved in producing black-and-white graphics. For clear scientific communication, lack of color is not as much of a handicap as it first seems. In many cases, it is an asset.

I use the term *gurus* to denote those who write books, blogs, or other informal publications on graphics usage. I use the term without pejorative implication. I intend this term to be more inclusive than the term *experts* because gurus include writers who have no formal training or expertise in psychology, statistics, or design; these writers nevertheless express strong opinions on proper usage and we at least ought to pay attention to what they are saying. I paraphrase gurus in italics without attribution because these ubiquitous statements share forms derived from common but unknown mythical sources (analogous to the Q unknown common source for the Synoptic Gospels). The following prescriptions are not ordered by importance.

Avoid Clutter

Do not clutter the data region inside the plotting frame delimited by axes. Tufte (1983) informally defined a data–ink ratio and urged us to maximize it by removing irrelevant detail. At the limit, this exhortation is nonsense, of course: The ultimate graph would contain no ink. And some of Tufte's examples (reducing Tukey's box plot to a dot and two lines) are extreme. But this exhortation has value as long as we do not remove redundant features that can reinforce an accurate perception. Most writers agree that one should avoid ornate textures (especially stripes and screens), gratuitous colors, excessive tick marks and grid lines, ornate fonts, and unnecessary embellishment.

The use of gratuitous clutter has been termed *chartjunk* (Tufte, 1983). Graphics gurus like to lampoon chartjunk: *Markings and visual elements are chartjunk if they go beyond the minimum set of visuals necessary to communicate the information.*

The scientific evidence suggests the gurus are wrong. Carswell (1992) and Gillan and Richman (1994) found mixed results for the relation of the data-ink ratio to performance. Gillan and Sorensen (2009) found that decorative backgrounds in charts can actually *enhance* processing. And it is not clear that viewers prefer lower data–ink ratios (Inbar et al., 2007; Norman, 2007).

So, the case against chartjunk has to rest on aesthetics. My opinion is to avoid it because it is unnecessary and incompatible with the look-and-feel of a scientific journal. Claims that chartjunk graphs in *USA Today* (or other popular media) are misleading, however, have relatively little scientific support.

Exploit Redundancy

Redundancy is not clutter. While worthless from a game theory point of view, redundancy aids selective attention in a viewing task by providing a richer relevant feature set. And while irrelevant (orthogonal to signal) cues indeed interfere with reaction times and accuracy (Stroop, 1935), redundant relevant cues (coincident with signal) do not generally hurt performance (Backs & Walrath, 1995). Mapping a variable to both color and shape, for example, is not necessarily a bad idea. Placing numbers on bars to denote their magnitude is not a bad thing, despite the admonitions of some gurus. If the exact magnitude of a line slope is focal to the research context (as in psychophysical response functions), it can help to place a number indicating its value next to the line. Such annotations inside the frame of a graphic, if used sparingly, can improve communication.

Use 3-D Sparingly

In most applications, one or more panels of 2-D graphs is preferable to one panel of 3-D graphs. Psychologists are accustomed to this practice, because they conventionally represent two-way analysis-of-variance interactions with several lines in a single frame rather than attempting a 3-D plot of the response surface. The exception to this 3-D proscription is (a) when a surface is relatively coherent, (b) the audience is accustomed to reading surface graphs, and (c) 2-D paneling would create a messy graph. Figure 4.3 is an example. This graphic depicts the time performance of a statistical classifier. The point of the figure is to show that for higher levels of N

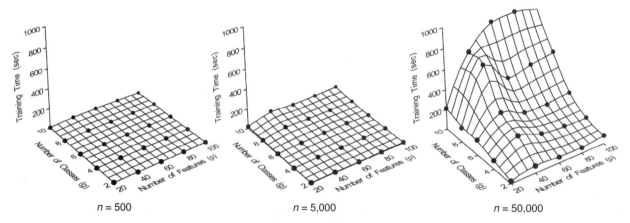

FIGURE 4.3. 3-D plot of classifier performance derived from a figure in Wilkinson (2018).

(number of cases), the surface based on two other variables is not exponentially increasing. It would be difficult to convey this structure in separate 2-D plots because the contours would be messy. Three-dimensional plots can work well for smooth functional surfaces. Needless to say, 3-D bar and pie graphics have no place in a scientific journal (Rangecroft, 2003).

There is considerable controversy over pseudo 3-D (2½-D) and drop-shadow effects. Gurus tend to lampoon those who use them, saying they interfere with veridical perception: *My pet peeve is adding shading to figures. Creating charts with drop shadows or pseudo 3-D is a bad idea. These gimmicks ruin the clarity of the chart.*

The research record does not support this contention. Spence (1990, 2004) drew a distinction between *apparent* and *effective* dimensionality and found that properly drawn pseudo 3-D bar charts (apparent dimensionality of three and effective dimensionality of two) do not impair processing. As with chartjunk, however, my opinion is not to use these embellishments, because they are aesthetically inappropriate for a scientific journal.

Avoid Visual Illusions

One reason to avoid 3-D graphics is because the projections used to display them in 2-D can lead to visual illusions. Black-and-white perspective projections lack texture and color depth cues and, thus, tend to flatten images. Isometric (axis-parallel) projections, used in front-top-side engineering drawings, are used in some graphing software. These projections lead to illusions such as the Necker cube. Psychologists are well aware of this topic. Other readers can consult Coren and Girgus (1978) and Gregory (2009).

Limit Categories

When I designed the new graphics system in SPSS, I ran into trouble with the marketing department. The marketers insisted on placing no limit on the number of categories allowed in a legend. Against my advice, the programmers were forced to devise a multicolumn legend to accommodate larger numbers of categories. When they ran out of colors and textures, the programmers were forced to cycle through the same set more than once! I mentioned Miller's (1956) magic number seven but to no avail. In fact, the number of colors or textures or shapes easily processed in a graph is somewhat less than seven. There is a large literature relevant to this area. The aspects that determine processing involve Miller's estimate of working-memory chunking capacity, the discriminability of an ordered set of colors or shapes in the visual system, and the psycho-physical power function for the stimulus dimension (color or shape). The relations are complex, but the result is simple: A graphic that uses many more than four categories of a color or shape is unlikely to be processed accurately.

If you need to represent a large number of categories, do not try to do it with symbols or colors. Instead, consider using position on an axis (sorted on a reasonable feature dimension) to order the categories (see Figure 4.13 for an example). If you have no choice but to represent categories in a scatterplot, consider aggregating categories into a manageable number. Wasting legend space on rarely occurring categories means that viewers will ignore them or be unable to locate them in the first place.

Transform

When I programmed the graphics system in SYSTAT, I made a simple rule for determining default frame limits: set each axis range to an interval that encloses *all* values of the variable plotted. For example, imagine superimposing a scatterplot on top of a bar chart of the same variables. In SYSTAT, the default axis chosen for each plot is the same, so the points fall appropriately on top of the bars that summarize them.

I soon heard from a few users that they did not like this feature. Upon closer examination, I discovered that they were creating bar charts on the means of variables within groups and the tops of their bars fell near the bottom of the frame. They did not like seeing all the white space above the bars.

The left panel of Figure 4.4 shows what was happening. The plot shows the number of

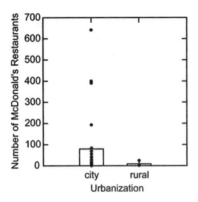 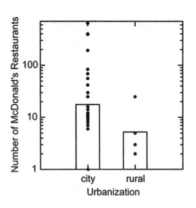 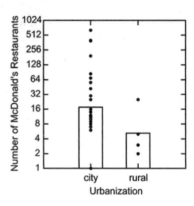

FIGURE 4.4. The effect of transformations on the height of bars. Data are based on the number of McDonald's restaurants in each of 57 countries as of 1990.

McDonald's restaurants in each of 57 countries as of 1990. I have superimposed the data to show where the means of the raw data (represented by the tops of the bars) fall. In effect, users making this type of plot are computing means on highly skewed distributions—not a good idea. As an alternative, the middle panel shows the graphic after a log transformation of the counts. Now the bars fall in the middle of the frame, and the means of the logs are a reasonable summary of the counts in each group. Correcting the statistics solves the aesthetic problem. Wilkinson (2005) discussed this problem in more detail and provided examples where supposed outliers in a graph are not outliers when the data are appropriately transformed.

Interestingly, we usually square-root counts (to symmetrize Poisson distributions). The highly skewed distribution of McDonald's restaurants responds better to logging. There is a remaining issue, however. Most people have difficulty comprehending the magnitudes of decimal logs. They fail to understand, for example, that a unit increase on the Richter scale indicates an earthquake with a tenfold increase in energy. Or, they do not realize that decibels increase by a factor of 10. For many, doublings are easier to understand. The right panel of Figure 4.4 shows the same plot computed on a base-2 log scale. An added benefit is that base-2 logs produce more tick marks, yielding a finer description of the distribution. Finally, we should note that the middle and right plots are identical except for the scale. This congruence highlights the fact that statistics (t tests, F tests, etc.) don't care which base we use for logs.

Sort

Sorting a categorical variable is an inescapable step toward creating a statistical graphic. It is inescapable because any ordering of categorical axis or legend implies a sort. Bertin (1967) offered numerous examples showing the value of simple and multivariate data sorts. Some gurus advise against sorting alphabetically. This is nonsense. Sorting alphabetically is meaningful if the organizing principle is alphabetical (e.g., words, names, brands) and viewers need to look up individual items rather than detect trends. In cases where this is disputable, a good compromise is to panel two or more graphics with different sort orders on the same categories. Figure 4.5 contains two panels showing confusions among Morse Code signals using data in Rothkopf (1957).

There are several types of sorts relevant to graphics. A *lexical* sort uses a lexical ordering of strings ("0," "1," "10," "2," "3," "4," "5," "6," "7," "8," "9"). A *numerical* sort uses a numerical ordering ("0," "1," "2," "3," "4," "5," "6," "7," "8," "9," "10"). Most computer languages have a default lexical sort order, so users must take care when sorting categories denoted by numerals. A *nested* sort orders multiple variables (A, B within A, C within B within A, . . .). Nested sorts can use lexical or some other ordering. An example of a lexical nested sort

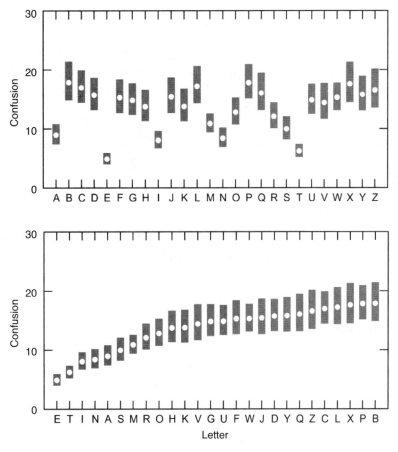

FIGURE 4.5. Confusions among Morse code signals using data in Rothkopf (1957).

for two variables is ({"Female," "Young"}, {"Male," "Old"}, {"Male," "Young"}).

A useful type of sort for graphics is to order categories by frequency or by some other numerical variable. The classical example of this type of ordering is the so-called Pareto chart (Juran, 1951). Sorting benefits many types of multivariate graphics, including icons, parallel coordinate plots, and scatterplot matrices (SPLOMs). There are many published papers in the informational visualization community on this topic (particularly IEEE InfoVis conference papers). Almost all of them use a simple ordering algorithm: Compute the principal components on a correlation matrix of the variables and order the variables according to their loadings on the first principal component. Alternatively, one can use multidimensional dimensional scaling (MDS) to determine a nonlinear seriation.

Orient

We are accustomed to seeing graphics in a canonical orientation (bottom/top, left/right). There are exceptions (e.g., Hebrew and Mandarin readers), but the following simple rule should be followed in English language journals: Order categories from top to bottom and continue from bottom to top. This ordering is followed almost universally for tables (top to bottom, left to right) and for XY plots (bottom to top, left to right). The rare exceptions are notable for their obtuseness. For example, computer pixel displays index top to bottom and left to right; this indexing scheme was devised to allow simple linear addressing of raster-scan frame buffers, but it has caused graphics programmers endless grief navigating from graphics-world to display-world. The mathematical transformation is trivial, but the mental transformation is counterintuitive.

Anchor

Graphics need an origin and other reference points to anchor absolute and comparative judgments. The origin of a graph frame is conventionally in the lower left corner (unless axes are crossed). For paneled graphics, the global origin is at the bottom left of all the panes, and local origins for each pane are at its bottom left. This overall structure allows panes to be nested within panes. Tufte calls paneled graphics *small multiples*, but this is too flat a description. Paneled graphics are *nested tables* of graphics.

The Trellis plot (Becker et al., 1996) is close to Tufte's idea. The visual distinction between a one-way layout and a multiway layout is embedded in the strip labels attached to the cells; a one-way table has one strip label per cell and multiway tables have more. Figure 4.6 compares this design to an alternative that is based on the classic analysis of variance (ANOVA) table. The two panels contain plots of the miles-per-gallon of selected cars versus their weights. The scatterplots are arranged in a two-way table of number of gears by number of cylinders. The top panel was produced using the Trellis facility in the R Lattice package. The bottom panel was produced by SYSTAT. The strip labels in the Trellis plot steal plotting area from the scatterplots (forcing them to be nonsquare) and add complexity. The scales and tick labels are arranged in an alternating pattern around the Trellis panel, making it difficult to decode values.

The SYSTAT panel, called a *multiplot*, employs a simple scheme for arranging axes. Tabular variables go on the left and top, just as they do in conventional table layouts. Continuous variables go on the right and bottom, with a smaller typeface to distinguish them from the tabular variables. The continuous variable axis labels are repeated to facilitate lookup; repetition also helps the viewer to see that these are not one big axis. I have also made the tabular variables boldface to emphasize this distinction. This layout scheme allows us to display higher order factorials and nested designs that are not easily discernible in a Trellis layout. Visually decoding the design is assisted by anchoring the factorial structure at the margins of the table, exactly the way analysis of variance tables are conventionally arranged.

There are advantages to both displays. The Trellis facilitates a bottom-up scan of its graphical contents; after a remarkable cell is located, the viewer discerns the values of the table (factor) variables by looking at the strip labels. The multiplot facilitates a top-down scan; the viewer looks for trends across factors, and after locating simple or interaction effects, she examines individual cells for deviations from expected effects. The success of Trellis indicates that different people have different scanning strategies. Overall, neither form can be considered superior for all purposes. I should mention that the SYSTAT design can be implemented in R with some custom programming. I urge R developers to produce a macro for this plot design so that psychologists can use R to make a display more in keeping with the customary ANOVA layout used in journals.

A second type of anchoring is important for decoding values in a frame. Figure 4.7 illustrates two ways of displaying tick marks on an axis. The panel on the left was produced by the default tick mark algorithm in R. The panel on the right was produced by SYSTAT. The floating ticks in the left panel impair positional judgments because the frame cannot be used to anchor the scales at round numbers or integers; positions of the elements have to be referenced against individual tick marks.

The motivation for floating ticks was the finding by Cleveland et al. (1982) that I discussed earlier. In order to keep the frame filled, the designers picked a frame size to minimize white space and then added tick marks wherever nice round values occur. By contrast, the ticking algorithm on the right panel draws a compromise between filling the frame and anchoring nice numbers at the corners. By enlarging the set of nice numbers for scale values, it is possible to fill the frame and anchor the corners at the same time. This algorithm is more consistent with tick spacing in graphics produced by psychologists, engineers, scientists, and mathematicians. The R Project needs to fix this defect.

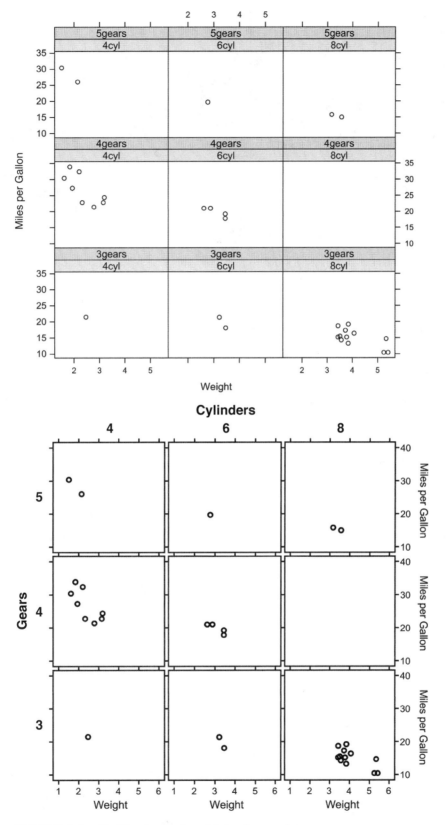

FIGURE 4.6. Trellis plot and multiplot for car data.

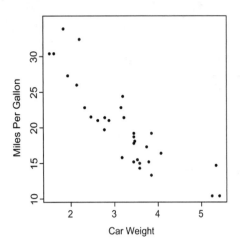
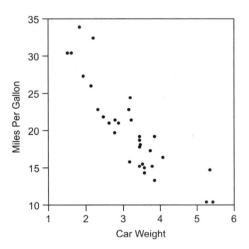

FIGURE 4.7. Tick mark placement in R and SYSTAT.

A third type of anchoring is facilitated by grid lines. As Tufte and others have argued, grid lines—especially dashed grid lines—can clutter a graphic. Carr (1994) developed a solution to this problem. Instead of drawing grid lines as black dashes against a white background, Carr drew white gridlines against a light gray frame background. Figure 4.8 shows an example. There is a bonus in this approach: frames stand out from the rest of an article's text and white space. I would advocate a faint gray background as a default mode for published statistical graphics in the future, whether or not grid lines are used.

Annotate

The importance of annotation hardly needs mentioning. Captions, titles, legends, and other annotations help make a graphic communicate a message without dependence on the article text. Authors need to keep in mind that readers sometimes skip text (and even abstracts) and look at figures to decide whether to read in more detail. One detail that is often overlooked, however, involves legends. Computer programs routinely produce legends, but it is sometimes better to annotate directly on graphic elements. Figure 4.9 shows an example. A conventional legend would distinguish each curve in this plot by using

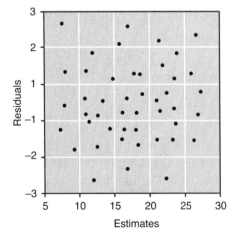

FIGURE 4.8. Residual plot with gray background and white gridlines.

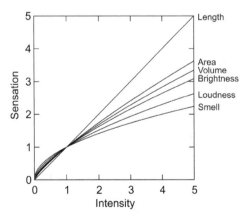

FIGURE 4.9. Psychophysical power functions with annotation next to curves as an alternative to a legend.

different types of dashed lines or lines of different colors. Much simpler and more easily decodable is to label each line with its own annotation, as in Figure 4.9. When there is room in a frame, try to consider this type of annotation rather than a separate legend, which forces scanning from two different locations.

EXEMPLARS

We now turn to examples for specific problems. This section is organized by type of model (univariate, multivariate) and type of variable (continuous, categorical). I also discuss specific problems researchers encounter in graphing scientific data, such as huge data sets. As with other figures in this chapter, I include only what I regard as the best approach to the problem. It is easier to lampoon poorly designed graphics and harder to offer exemplars. When offering exemplars, however, I do not mean to imply that there are no examples that might be better.

One Variable

The simplest graphics involve only one variable. These graphics are often omitted in articles, perhaps because scientists want to get to models as quickly as possible. The distributions of variables affect models, however, so a well-documented article should provide a simple display of the data. For multivariate analyses, the one-dimensional plots in this section can be paneled in a space-conserving display.

Categorical variable. Figure 4.10 shows a simple display representing values on one categorical variable. The data are from 1,606 respondents to the 1993 General Social Survey (Davis et al., 1993). Respondents were asked, "How many sex partners have you had in the last 12 months?" Those reporting more than four partners (some reported up to 100) were consolidated into the last category. There were 1,466 responses in the resulting six categories.

This bar graphic is conventional and appropriate for these data. Bars are most suited for displaying either magnitudes referenced against

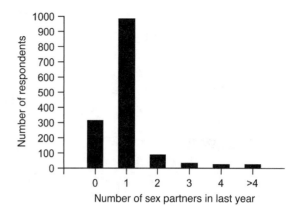

FIGURE 4.10. Bar graphic of data from the General Social Survey. The variable is the reported number of sexual partners in the past year.

zero (anchored bars, as in this figure) or a range of values on a continuous scale (range bars, as in Figure 4.12). I have omitted a bounding box from the frame of this plot; it is optional and not harmful. The plot might be improved by using a bounding box and gray background with white grid lines so that the heights of the bars are easier to assess.

Much has been made of the requirement that bars be anchored at zero. There is no canon law requiring this, but it is often a good idea. If the data are not on a so-called absolute scale, it is probably better to consider a dot plot, as in Figure 4.13. If our goal is to represent counts or incomes or reaction times, however, a bar is a reasonable graphical element.

Suppose we want to represent the proportion of each subgroup in our total sample. Figure 4.11 shows how to do this: a pie chart. Gurus wax apoplectic over pie charts.

- *Pie charts are bad! They are ugly and provide the reader no visual assistance in comparing categories.*
- *We all know that pie charts are bad.*
- *Pie charts are hopeless.*
- *Warning! Pie charts are generally not recommended for visualizing information!*

The scientific evidence to the contrary is unambiguous, however. Pie charts are better than bar charts for representing proportions of

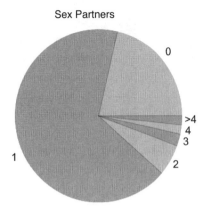

FIGURE 4.11. Pie chart of the same data used in Figure 4.10 but displayed as proportions of total responses found within each category.

wholes (Simkin & Hastie, 1987; Spence, 2005; Spence & Lewandowsky, 1991). The gurus' animosity toward pie charts may be based on pie charts' ubiquity and frequent abuses (3-D pies, pies of means or medians). Unfortunately, gurus have been given a boost by Cleveland's hierarchy (Figure 4.2). Gurus mistakenly assume that the perception of pie slices involves a judgment of angle, which is low on Cleveland's hierarchy. As the research shows, however, the process is more complex; both angle and area interact to overcome the bias of each. Gurus sometimes construct strawman examples to show that a bar chart with nearly equal-height bars can reveal slight differences that a pie chart with nearly equal-area slices conceals. This misses the point, however; comparative and absolute judgment are not the same thing; bars are good for one, pies for the other.

So, what are the real pitfalls in using pies? First of all, pie slices are usually colored. Unfortunately, colors, particularly bright colors, affect judgments of area. Coloring a slice red, for example, tends to make the slice appear larger (Cleveland & McGill, 1983). I have ameliorated this bias in Figure 4.11 by choosing two alternating shades of light gray to increase the contrast between adjacent slices.

Second, pies are not good for representing many categories—whether sorted or unsorted—because the eye resolves tiny angles downward toward zero. In such a case, it is probably better to revert to a bar chart with a percentage scale, sorting the bars by percentage. Figure 4.12 shows the gold medal counts for various countries in the 2004 Summer Olympics. The data are sorted by proportions with a range-bar format originally due to Juran (1951). This is a good substitute for a pie when there are many categories. Unlike a divided bar graph (which is really a pie chart in rectangular coordinates), this range-bar form allows one to see both the cumulative distribution and the contributions to the whole for each category.

My general advice on pies is: Do not be bullied out of using a pie chart for proportion-of-whole data with a few categories. Cite the references I mentioned if an editor or reviewer argues with you.

There is another alternative to bars for categorical data: dot plots. Anchoring bars at zero

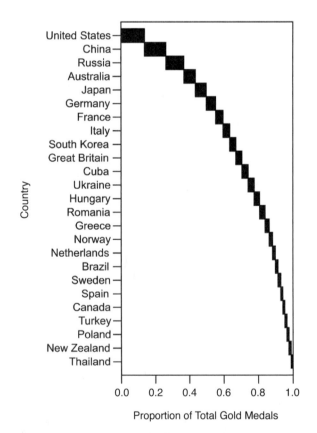

FIGURE 4.12. Gold medal counts for various countries in the 2004 Summer Olympics.

can sacrifice resolution when no data values exist near zero; this creates tall bars of nearly equal height even when data vary significantly across bars (Chambers et al., 1983). Also, there are times when we need to display confidence intervals or standard errors. The bar chart with error bars, used in many scientific journals, is not a good way to handle the problem. Solid bars cover the lower half of error bars. Hollow bars allow us to see the error bars, but this type of graphic pairs a symmetric element (error bar) with an asymmetric element (anchored bar), in an awkward display.

Dots are preferable to bars in such cases. Figure 4.13 shows an example using the Olympic data. The dots are sorted by frequency and confidence intervals are shown for each country using an algorithm in Wilkinson (2006).

Some users and computer programs apply line or area elements to categorical variables. Popular examples are line graphics of means in analysis of variance, or area graphics of profiles across categories. These elements should generally be avoided with categorical data. Spacings between categories (even ordered categories) are not fixed, so slopes of line segments or profiles between categories are meaningless.

Continuous variable. Figure 4.14 shows five ways of representing a continuous variable. None of these is preferable to the other; each has a particular purpose. The data are per-capita consumption of spirits for each of the 50 U.S. states (Bureau of the Census, 1986). The two graphics on the left are traditional densities. On the top is a histogram. Histogram bars look like ordinary bars, but they measure areas rather than intervals, and they rest on a continuous scale rather than on a set of categories.

Most histogram programs and statistical textbooks produce incorrect or suboptimal histograms. The problems with them are as follows. (a) They use the wrong number of bars. The statistical literature provides clear guidelines on this, but they have been largely ignored by software developers (Scott, 1979; Wand, 1997). (b) They do not deal properly with integer or granular data. Instead of detecting granularity, programs tend to use a formula based on sample size for determining the number of bars. They should also be paying attention to the number of discrete values in the data. For much psychological data, where values fall on Likert scales, ordinary histogram programs are inadequate; users have to fiddle with sensitive parameters to get nice-looking histograms. (c) They do not locate bars at appropriate tick marks on the base scale. A primary purpose of a histogram is to assess the density of data within meaningful sub-regions of the range of a variable. If a computer program locates the limits of a bar at fractional values on a Likert scale variable, this purpose is defeated. (d) They place tick marks in the middle of bars. This is nonsensical. Histogram bars partition a scale into intervals; tick marks need to demarcate these intervals by locating the endpoints.

Below the histogram in Figure 4.14 is a kernel density. In contrast to histograms, where we wish

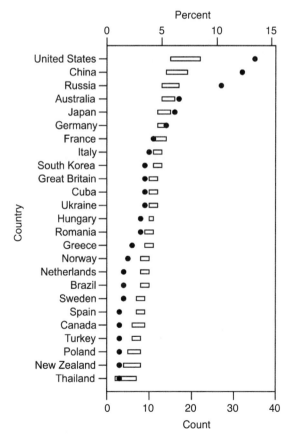

FIGURE 4.13. Modified Pareto chart of gold medal counts used in Figure 4.12. Bars are used to represent confidence intervals.

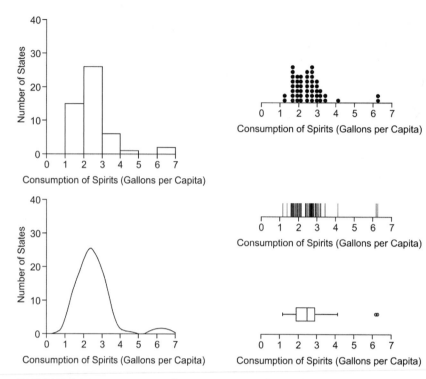

FIGURE 4.14. Five ways of representing a density. Data are per capita consumption of spirits for each of the 50 U.S. states.

to inspect density within discrete intervals, we use a kernel density to estimate the shape of a population density. Silverman (1986) and Scott (1992) explained the details. Kernel densities overcome a serious flaw in histograms—they do not depend on a choice of cutpoints. If the intervals of a histogram are shifted to the left or right on the base scale, the shape of that histogram can change dramatically. Kernel densities *are* relatively sensitive to a parameter called *bandwidth* (analogous to the width of histogram bars); but there is well-understood statistical theory for dealing with this problem, and some simple guidelines that work quite well. Kernel density software generally uses these guidelines for its default settings.

Note that the scale for the kernel density and the histogram are identical in Figure 4.13. That is not coincidental. SYSTAT uses the histogram algorithm to determine the tick marks and scale for kernel densities and all other densities, including the ones on the right panels of Figure 4.13. This makes it easy to overlay densities, including mathematical densities such as the normal curve or chi-square. Constructing a density scale this way should be the default for any statistical graphics program.

Histograms are more useful than kernels when we are interested in displaying frequencies within intervals, especially when the intervals themselves are bounded by meaningful, round units. We see from the histogram in Figure 4.14 that 26 states have an average spirits consumption between 2 and 3 gallons a year. Kernels are more useful than histograms when we are looking for a smooth estimate of a continuous distribution. We see from the kernel density in Figure 4.14 that the distribution is bimodal, with a few states having extremely high consumption. We do notice that in the histogram as well, but need to remember that other cutpoints and locations could mask that feature in a histogram. It is a well-known defect of the ordinary histogram that its shape changes when bar locations (centers of bars) are moved on the scale.

The densities on the right panel are useful for displaying distributions in less space. Each can be embedded in a categorical-by-continuous variable display, as in Figure 4.14. On the top is a dot histogram (Wilkinson, 2005). This display represents each observation with a dot located at its scale value. If several values coincide on the scale, the dots are stacked vertically. This display is most suited for small samples, when each value is to be displayed. It is not well-suited for large samples; consider a histogram or kernel density instead. Many programs for dot plots compute them incorrectly. They simply create a histogram and replace the bars with dots stacked to the heights of the bars. The whole point of a dot plot is to place each dot (or tower of dots) at the location given by its data value (or neighborhood value). Placing dots at the center of intervals defeats its purpose and makes the data appear granular instead of appropriately irregular.

The next lower graphic is a stripe plot (Chambers et al., 1983). A vertical stripe occurs at each data value. This display can handle more cases than the dot plot, although it is not suitable for large data sets.

The bottom graphic on the right of Figure 4.14 is a box plot, or schematic plot (Tukey, 1977). As Tufte (1983) noted, Tukey's plot is based on an earlier display that represented the quartiles of a distribution. In that earlier plot, the whiskers cover the range, and the box covers the midrange. Tukey improved on this design by scaling the whiskers to allow for extreme values. The display in Figure 4.14 shows how important this feature can be. Two states (Nevada and New Hampshire) have unusually large values, possibly due to gambling and cheap liquor in one convenient location. Some gurus think that box plots can be used to identify outliers. This opinion is incorrect because the formulas Tukey used for calculating outside values do not involve the sample size (n). Consequently, box plots of large batches, regardless of their distribution, contain many outliers. For this reason, Tukey called these outside values, not outliers.

Recall that Figure 4.1 combines dot and box plots in one frame. This combination is felicitous for small samples because the dots reveal bimodality and local features, while the boxes reveal the quartiles. This so-called *dot-box plot*

can be produced by a single command in SYSTAT or by overlaying multiple plots in a package such as R.

Two Variables

This section covers categorical and continuous variables in their various combinations. I address each combination in a separate subsection.

Categorical variables. Figure 4.15 shows five ways of representing two categorical variables crossed with each other. The data are from the 1993 General Social Survey used in Figure 4.10. The additional variable is general happiness, as measured by the response to the question, "Taken all together, how would you say things are these days—would you say that you are very happy, pretty happy, or not too happy?"

The upper left plot shows a heatmap of happiness against number of sexual partners. The darkness scale represents the proportion of respondents within each happiness category. This plot is simply a table. Directly below is another table containing the actual cell counts. I have conditioned the darkness of the numerals on the row totals. This usage is potentially misleading unless the dependency on row totals is made clear in the caption. This is always an issue with displaying tables of percentages or proportions (of row, column, or total counts). I have provided this example to show that tables of numerals are in fact graphics. With modern publishing capabilities, we can use shading to represent the magnitude of residuals, probabilities, or other statistics.

The graphic at the top right is a mosaic plot (Friendly, 1994, 2002; Hartigan & Kleiner, 1981), a relative of the treemap (Shneiderman, 1992). This graphic uses area to indicate the relative frequency of each category combination. As Cleveland's research and Figure 4.9 show, however, the judgment of area involves a psychometric function with an exponent considerably less than 1. More problematic is the judgment of *rectangle* areas; there is a large literature in psychology showing that rectangle judgments are multidimensional. Mosaics are also potentially confusing because

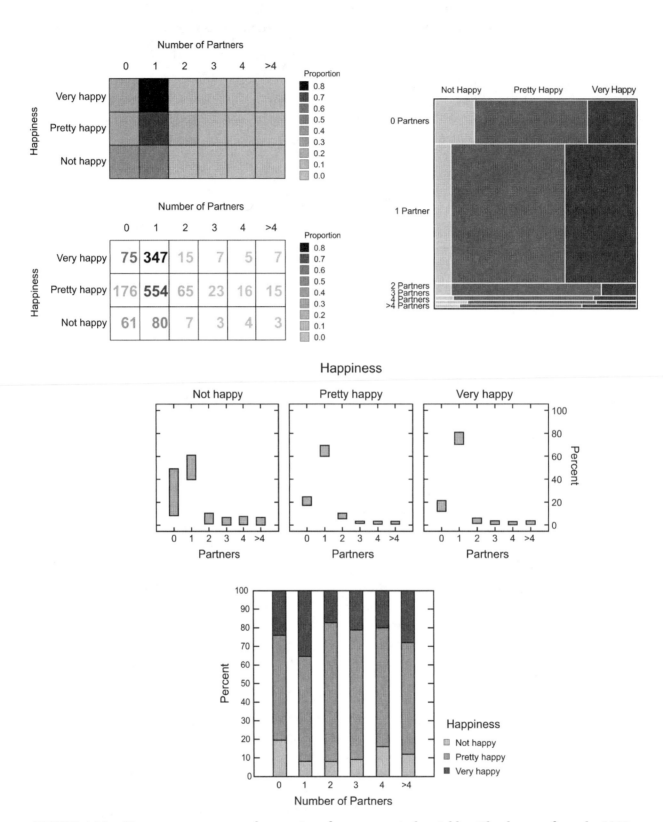

FIGURE 4.15. Five ways to represent the crossing of two categorical variables. The data are from the 1993 General Social Survey used in Figure 4.10. The additional variable is general happiness, as measured by the response to the question "Taken all together, how would you say things are these days—would you say that you are very happy, pretty happy, or not too happy?"

the rows and columns do not align as they do in an ordinary table. Despite the passionate following mosaics and treemaps have among some statistical computing and visualization experts, the rest of the world appears to find them confusing. When they are in color, as is the custom, the potential for confusion is even greater.

The graphic in the middle row of Figure 4.15 is my favorite of this group. This graphic features confidence intervals on the percentages within each happiness group. There is no need to use area or brightness to represent additional variables. The correlation in partner patterns across the happiness levels is readily apparent. This plot also illustrates another point. Confidence intervals on proportions or percentages are asymmetric. It seems to me that there is no need to display the actual cell percent. The intervals keep our eyes from focusing on points and encourages us to think of ranges. I have argued elsewhere that confidence intervals should be primary and point estimates secondary in many statistical summaries (Wilkinson et al., 1999).

The bottom panel shows a multiple divided bar chart. This layout has the same problems as the single divided bar chart, which is worse than the pie chart for most applications. It is a popular display, but I do not recommend it.

Continuous variables. Figure 4.16 shows the usual way of representing two continuous variables crossed with each other: the *scatterplot*. The data are per-capita consumption of spirits for each of the 50 US states, used in Figure 4.14 (Bureau of the Census, 1986). The additional variable is number of deaths from chronic liver disease and cirrhosis per 100,000 people by state. I have enhanced this scatterplot in a number of ways. The bordering box plots help us to assess the marginal distributions of the variables and highlight the Nevada and New Hampshire outliers; there are outliers for consumption but not for deaths. The smoother shows the conditional mode of deaths (estimated mode of deaths given consumption). This was computed through kernel regression (Scott, 1992). This smoother limits itself to areas where there is a concentration

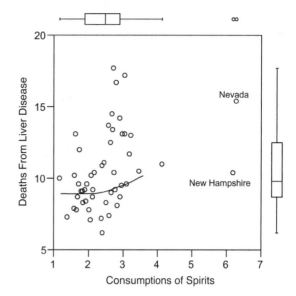

FIGURE 4.16. Scatterplot with bordered boxplots. The data are per capita consumption of spirits for each of the 50 U.S. states, used in Figure 4.14. The additional variable is number of deaths from chronic liver disease and cirrhosis per 100,000 people by state.

of points, so it provides a conservative estimate of trend. We can see a suggestion of a positive relationship between aggregate consumption and deaths.

Time series data require special treatment. Figure 4.17 shows four examples. The data are numbers of U.S. patents issued in the century from 1880 to 1980 (Wilkinson et al., 1996). The top panel shows a line element. Lines are most useful when a series is relatively smooth. The next panel shows a point element with a superimposed *loess* smoother (Cleveland & Devlin, 1988). Points are best when supplemented with a smoother; they tend to obscure time order if used alone, unless the series is especially smooth. The third panel contains spikes. These are vertical lines used to reveal deviation from a constant level. Here they are used to display the residuals from the *loess* smooth. The lowest panel shows an area chart for the raw series. This highlights trend but prevents the use of confidence intervals and other enhancements to the plot. Cleveland (1994) discussed other graphical representations for time series data. This landmark book is still the best reference for learning how to plot time series.

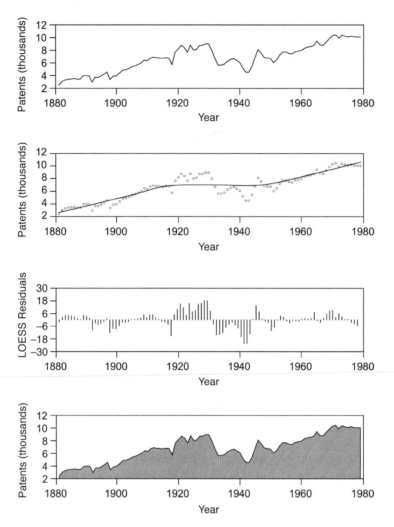

FIGURE 4.17. Four types of display of time series. The data are numbers of U.S. patents issued in the century from 1880 to 1980.

Figure 4.18 shows four ways of representing a categorical variable crossed with a continuous variable. The data are based on 80 graduate students over a 10-year period in a U.S. psychology department (Wilkinson, 2005). Graduate Record Examination Advanced Psychology Test scores are plotted against whether or not the students eventually received their PhD.

The upper left graphic employs a dot for the mean and a range bar to represent a 95% confidence interval on the mean. The bars do not overlap, which suggests that the advanced test can help identify those who achieve a PhD. (Interestingly, neither the verbal nor quantitative test scores predicted graduation in this sample.)

The lower left graphic is a notched box plot (McGill et al., 1978). This is a variation on the box plot that not only conveys more of the important data landmarks than the classic confidence interval plot but also provides an approximate confidence interval of its own. If the data are independent samples from identically distributed populations that are lumpy in the middle (approximately normal in their interquartile range), then comparing the notches yields an approximate 95% test of the null hypothesis that the true medians in the population are equal. In this example, the notches do not overlap, reinforcing what we concluded from the confidence intervals on the means. Because it relies on the median instead of the mean, the notched box plot

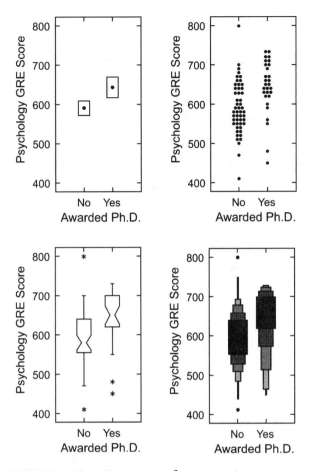

FIGURE 4.18. Four ways of representing a categorical variable crossed with a continuous variable. The data are based on 80 graduate students over a 10-year period in a U.S. psychology department. Graduate Record Examination Advanced Psychology Test scores are plotted against whether the students eventually received their doctorate.

procedure is more robust against outliers. Note also that the box plot highlights outliers in both groups. The other two types of display do not.

The lower right graphic is a *letter-value box plot* (Hofmann et al., 2006). This is a variation on the box plot that uses more of the letter values (successive splits of the data batch). The box plot uses 2 letter values (median and hinge), while this plot uses many more. The letter-value box plot is useful for large samples, where there is more information to be mined in the tails of the distribution.

The upper right graphic is a dot plot (Wilkinson, 1999a). Used frequently in the medical literature, this plot shows every data point. In a small sample (e.g., clinical case study), a dot plot can be useful for readers who wish to consider every data value. It is of little use in making graphical inferences on group differences, however. It is best to think of dot plots as one-dimensional scatterplots.

Three Variables

Figure 4.19 shows a triple crossing of categorical variables. The data are from the 1993 General Social Survey used in Figures 4.3 and 4.5. The additional variable is gender (observed by the interviewer, not reported by the respondent). We ask whether the relationship between reported happiness and number of sexual partners differs by gender.

The top plot in the figure shows a paneled graphic. The format is similar to a Trellis display (Becker et al., 1996), but the labeling of the paneling variables (happiness and gender) is placed outside the plotting area to improve readability.

The middle plot collapses happiness into a legend in order to reduce the number of panels. This is a popular method for saving space, particularly when representing factorial layouts in ANOVA and other designs. It is a favorite of statistical computer programs as well, but it has several problems. First, the line segments used to highlight trends have slopes that depend on the particular spacing and arrangement of partner categories. Unless we employ an external scaling procedure to determine the spacing of the partners categories, we have scant justification for using these lines. Second, the collapsing introduces a symbol choice problem. It is difficult to find symbols that are easily distinguishable for more than a few categories. The symbols collide, as well, at the upper end of the horizontal scales. Using different types of dashed lines does not ameliorate the problem; we have the same dearth of choices as for symbols.

The bottom plot introduces an even less attractive alternative. Clustered bar charts are used widely, but they have several defects. First, it is difficult to discern separate patterns for the categories. One needs to focus on one set of bars

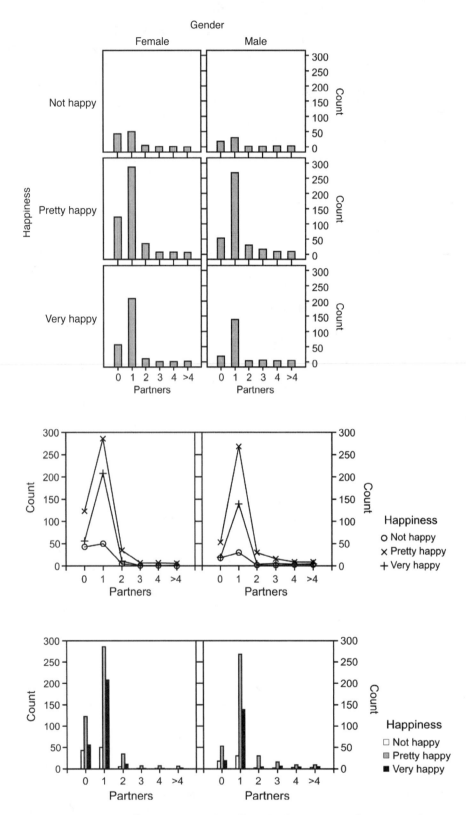

FIGURE 4.19. Different ways to handle a triple crossing of categorical variables. The data are from the 1993 General Social Survey used in Figures 4.3 and 4.5. The additional variable is gender.

to do this, but there is visual interference from the other bars in each cluster. Second, these bars can become quite thin with more than a few categories. Decoding this graphic is problematic. Some programs do this type of interleaving for multiple-group histograms. That practice is even worse, because densities are misleadingly segmented. Back-to-back histograms or bars (as in an age–sex pyramid) is useful for two categories but is not easily extended to more.

Three continuous variables usually force us into 3-D (see Figure 4.3), but there are alternatives. One alternative is to contour. Figure 4.20 shows a graphic of death rates against birth rates per 100,000 population for 27 selected countries in a 1990 UN databank (Wilkinson, 1999b). The third dimension is the kernel density estimate. The plot reveals two concentrations of countries. Industrialized countries, to the left, have relatively low death rates and moderate birth rates. Developing countries, toward the upper right, have high death rates and extraordinarily high birth rates. The curve in the middle of the contours (a *loess* smooth) shows that the overall relation between death and birth rates is curvilinear. This is one of my favorite data sets because it elicits thinking about several issues: (a) the proper scaling of the axes (a 2-to-1 aspect ratio because of the common rate scale); (b) the need for a nonlinear smoother (linear regression would be inappropriate for this distribution); (c) the use of annotation (the zero-population-growth line divides the frame into two meaningful regions); and (d) the use of contours (the kernel density estimate highlights the nonnormality of the joint distribution and emphasizes the bimodal clusters). Plotting this data set with default values in the typical statistical package would generate visual nonsense.

Many Variables

There is no single effective way to display many variables, but several methods, including projection and paneling, work fairly well. Some of the best methods are the simplest, including the examples in this section. One relatively simple approach is to project from higher-dimensional space into a 2-D space via principal components or multidimensional scaling. Psychologists have done this for decades, when they graph the first two dimensions of a factor or components analysis.

There is one paneling method, invented by Hartigan (1975), that has many uses. Figure 4.21 shows a SPLOM of five continuous and categorical variables. The data are from Chartrand (1997), based on a national survey of attitudes toward psychological counseling. There were 3,035 respondents to the survey. The variables in the SPLOM are age, gender, income, number

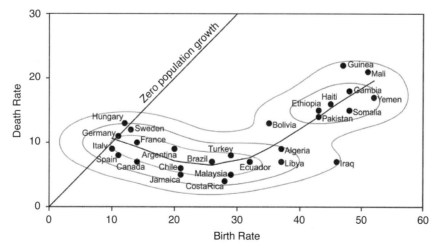

FIGURE 4.20. Plot of death rates against birth rates per 100,000 population for 27 selected countries in a 1990 United Nations data bank. Contours represent level curves of a kernel density.

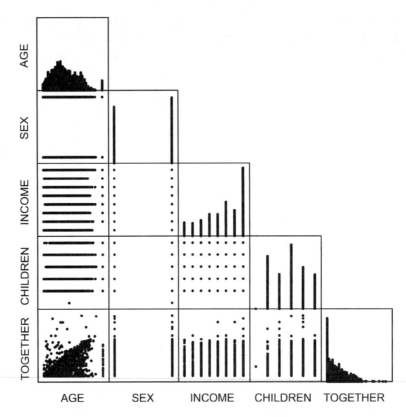

FIGURE 4.21. Scatterplot matrix (SPLOM) of survey data from Chartrand (1997) measuring attitudes toward psychological counseling.

of children, and number of years together with one's partner in a current relationship.

This SPLOM pairs every variable against every other. Usually, SPLOMs are symmetric like this one, so only half of the panels are displayed. Rectangular SPLOMs plot one set of variables against another. Scales are usually unnecessary because the display is intended to show joint distributions rather that specific values. This is especially true when more than a few variables are displayed.

SPLOMs usually involve only continuous variables. This example shows why this limitation is unnecessary. By using dot plots on the diagonals and scatterplots off the diagonals, we are able to discern the distributions of categories as well as continua. We see several anomalies, including the single value at the bottom of the children-age panel and the group of extreme values (missing value codes) at the high end of the age scale. One anomaly is more subtle, but the graphic leads

us to it. The together-age plot at the lower left corner has an unusual shape.

A clean triangular bivariate distribution like this suggests a logical implication. In this case, we would expect the reported duration of a relationship to be less than the age of the respondent. There appear to be some respondents above the main diagonal in this panel who are ghosts or, alternatively, have made a serious error in judging their age or the duration of their relationship (assuming both scales are the same). This curiosity was not detected in the preliminary data cleaning performed by the polling organization. Sometimes we need graphical methods to reveal anomalies.

Sometimes, also, we need different coordinate systems to represent a table and reveal graphical patterns. In *The Grammar of Graphics* (hereafter *GG*, Wilkinson, 2005), I show examples of tables in various coordinate systems in the chapter called Coordinates and in the chapter called Facets. In those chapters, I show why Tufte's small multiples terminology is too limited. I use the term *facets* to indicate that a table is formally a product of sets (an idea borrowed from Louis Guttman). The layout of a table can be performed in rectangular, polar, or other coordinate systems. Figure 4.22 is an example. There are two facets in this graphic—the month of the year and the compass orientation. Each is intrinsically circular, so the display naturally requires a nested polar layout. The elements inside the circular frames are histograms of wind direction (sometimes called *wind roses*) in a 24-hour period. A similar table might be used to represent circadian rhythms in an organism over a single year or a circumplex nested within a circumplex (Wiggins, 1982).

Nonrectangular Data Sets

I have covered rectangular data sets (cases by variables) in all the examples so far. Recently, there has been an explosion of interest in other forms of data. This trend has been facilitated by computer programs designed for analyzing social network, text, weblink, and other relational data. Some of the most beautiful examples of network graphics have been produced in Katy Börner's lab at Indiana (http://ella.slis.indiana.edu/~katy/gallery/index.html), Tamara Munzner's lab at University of British Columbia (https://www.cs.ubc.ca/~tmm/papers.html), the Marcotte LGL Project at University of Texas at Austin (https://lgl.sourceforge.net/#gallery), and the Tree of Life Project at Berkeley (https://ucjeps.berkeley.edu/TreeofLife/).

The algorithms used to lay out vertex-edge graphs are largely ad hoc. The most widely used ones are based on a derivation of the MDS algorithm, invented by psychologists in the 1960s and reinvented by engineers 25 years later. The so-called *force-directed* (Fruchterman & Reingold, 1991) or *springs* (Kamada & Kawai, 1989) methods have well-known drawbacks, but they are widely available in open-source software and frequently produce attractive results. As Newman (2003) noted, however, that there is no reason to assume that this algorithm would reveal anything uniquely useful about the network.

Graph layouts are often cluttered, with edges and nodes filling the display frame. The result is often described as a "hairball." An alternative approach is to use MDS directly and display only nodes. Figure 4.23 presents a *word cloud* of the top 50 words in *Moby Dick*. I filtered stop words (*a, the, and, . . .*) from the text and computed a node-edge graph of the 50 most frequent words. Edges in this graph were assigned to any pair of words if both occurred within a sliding window (*n*-gram) of seven words. From this graph, I computed a 50-by-50 matrix of the pairwise geodesic distances (shortest paths through the *n*-gram graph) between words. I computed the MDS on this geodesic distance matrix. In Figure 4.23, the sizes of the words are proportional to their frequency in the novel. To display more than 50 words, one can use transparency to keep words from obscuring other words.

Until recently, there have been few ways to visualize relations between sets of objects. The Venn diagram is over a century old, but computing one on sets of real data has been problematic.

A statistical method for fitting Venn and Euler (more than three sets) diagrams is available, called *venneuler*, is available in R (CRAN). Figure 4.24

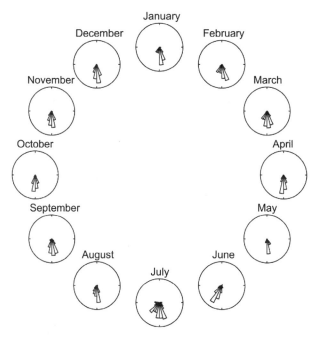

FIGURE 4.22. Circular plot of wind roses from geophysical data.

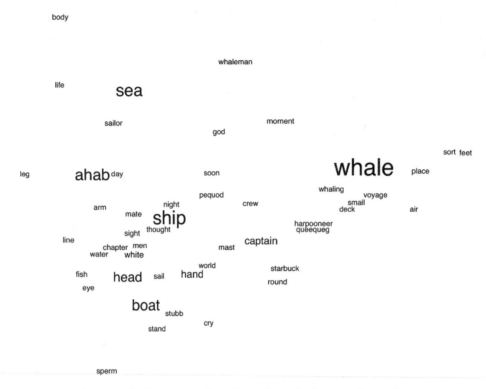

FIGURE 4.23. Multidimensional scaling of words from *Moby Dick*. Distances were computed from cooccurrences in a seven-word window moving through the text.

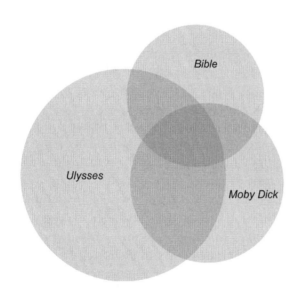

FIGURE 4.24. Venn diagram of shared words in three different books—James Joyce's *Ulysses*, the King James translation of the Bible, and *Moby Dick*. Size of circles is proportional to count of unique words in each work.

shows a Venn diagram of the shared words in *Ulysses*, *Moby Dick*, and the King James translation of the Bible. The sizes of the circles are proportional to the number of unique words (omitting stop words) in each book. The algorithm devised to fit this model is similar to MDS, but it is based on the areas of 2^n possible circle intersections rather than the distances between $n(n-1)/2$ objects. This algorithm has applications in psychology and bioinformatics. For example, it can be used to fit a Venn/Euler diagram to the correlation matrix of regression coefficient estimates in linear or logistic regression to reveal multicollinearity—a common textbook example (Cohen et al., 2003).

Uncertainty

There are two common methods for representing error in a graphic. The first is sharp: Error bounds are represented by clear edges, points, or lines. The second is fuzzy: Error is represented by blurring an estimate. Figure 4.25 shows a conventional sharp way of representing error in a graphic. The

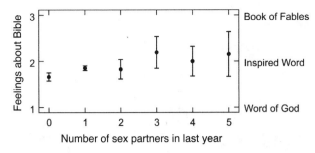

FIGURE 4.25. Plot of 95% confidence intervals. The data are from the 1993 General Social Survey used in Figure 4.3. The additional variable is feelings about the Bible, as measured by the response to the question "Which of these statements comes closest to describing your feelings about the Bible?" The responses coded are 1 (Word of God), 2 (inspired word), and 3 (book of fables).

data are from the 1993 General Social Survey used in Figure 4.3. The additional variable is feelings about the Bible, as measured by the response to the question, "Which of these statements comes closest to describing your feelings about the Bible?" The responses coded are 1 (Word of God), 2 (Inspired Word), and 3 (Book of Fables). We assume that the dependent variable is continuous (biblical absolutism vs. relativism) even though the responses are integers.

The upper plot shows error bars representing 95% confidence intervals on the means by category. Error bars are also used to represent one standard deviation or one standard error. It is important to make clear in accompanying titles or notes which type is used.

Figure 4.26 shows one way to represent error by fuzziness. The data are from Gonnelli et al. (1996). They represent concentration of bone alkaline phosphatase (BAP) in a sample of women of different ages. The authors fit a linear regression (shown in the upper left panel) to argue that BAP levels increase with age.

A modal regression in the upper right panel indicates that there is a discontinuity in this relationship at age 45 or so, corresponding most likely to the onset of menopause. Accordingly, I fit separate linear regressions to the two subgroups split at age 45 (third panel). These regressions appear to be sensitive to outliers, however,

so I fit linear models using robust regression with t weighting (fourth panel). This fit indicates that a plausible model for predicting BAP from age involves level differences but no slope differences.

It is not easy to compute confidence intervals on the robust linear fits, so I resorted to bootstrapping to provide an estimate of error. The bottom panel shows the result of 20 bootstrap robust fits displayed as faint dashed lines. The nonoverlapping envelopes of the fits indicate that the level-change model is reasonable. I show many more examples of representing error in the chapter called Uncertainty in the Grammar of Graphics.

Big Data

Suppose we wish to visualize an N-by-p matrix of real numbers where N and p are quite large. Unlike when N and p are moderate, we face several difficulties with large N and p.

- We don't have enough memory to allow responsive interaction.
- Our display algorithms do not scale (Keim, 2000).
- The curse of dimensionality means that distances between N fixed points in high dimensional spaces (as p becomes large) tend toward a constant.
- We cannot send big data "over the wire" in client-server environments. Browser memory limits capacity but so does transmission speed.
- Plotting many points on display devices (even megapixel or 4K) produces a big opaque spot. We can use kernels, alpha-channel rendering, binning, and other methods to mitigate overlaps, but this impedes brushing and linking gestures.
- Projections often violate metric axioms—points close together in higher dimensional space may be far apart in lower dimensional projections. Conversely, points far apart in higher dimensional space may be close together in a projection (Luo et al., 2021).

There are some practical approaches to alleviating these difficulties, none of which is altogether sufficient. Next, I take a look at the related problems of large N and large p.

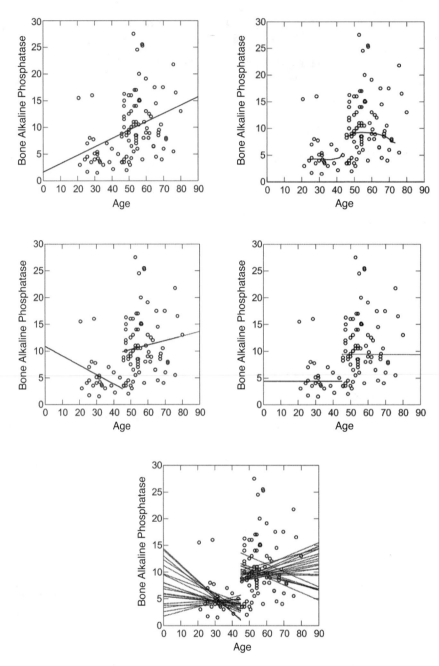

FIGURE 4.26. Using fuzziness to depict error. The data are from Gonnelli et al. (1998). They represent concentration of bone alkaline phosphatase in a sample of women of different ages.

Large N

We can aggregate rows (points) to reduce the number we have to plot. That is what we do with elements like summary bars and lines. That is also why some companies claiming to visualize big data restrict their big data plots to bars or lines. For points, however, we must aggregate differently. Histograms are easy to do in one dimension and scatterplots can be 2-D histogrammed. We simply bin the values into a 2-D mesh and then plot the mesh as a scatterplot or 3-D surface. Alternatively, we can create hexagonal instead of square bins (Carr et al., 1987). In higher dimensions we can use an N-dimensional aggregation algorithm presented in Wilkinson (2018). This algorithm is available in the R Package called data.table.

Some gurus advocate simple random sampling for exploratory data analysis (EDA) on deep (large-N) data matrices. This approach is inappropriate for EDA. First, outliers are unlikely to be sampled (which is why they are outliers in the first place); in EDA, we are often concerned with identifying outliers before we move to formal modeling. Second, for reasons similar to the outlier problem, features that are not salient are lost in simple random samples. In short, samples appropriate for EDA are not necessarily appropriate for probabilistic modeling. Wilkinson and Luo (2020) describe this problem in more detail.

Large p

Data sets with many columns present more formidable issues. The standard approach for handling this problem is to compute the first few principal components (through an singular value decomposition or Hotelling's classical method on the covariance matrix) and apply standard visualization methods to the components. If N is also large, we can reduce rows through aggregation.

This approach works suitably for analyzing joint structures that are based on angles between variables in higher-dimensional space. The principal component analysis, singular value decomposition, or eigendecomposition does not preserve distances between points in the original space, however. We cannot be sure that points that are closer together in high-dimensional space are close in the projected space. Conversely, points close in the projected space may not be relatively close in the higher dimensional space.

Figure 4.27 gives an example based on some data provided by H2O.ai. We performed a kmeans clustering on the data set after normalizing the columns to unit [0, 1] intervals. Next, we projected the points into two dimensions using the nonlinear mapping called UMAP (McInnes et al., 2020). By definition, points in a kmeans cluster are computed to be closer to the centroid of that cluster than to the centroid of any other cluster. Surprisingly, the UMAP projection splits the two clusters. Part of this splitting is due to the tendency of nonlinear mapping to weight small

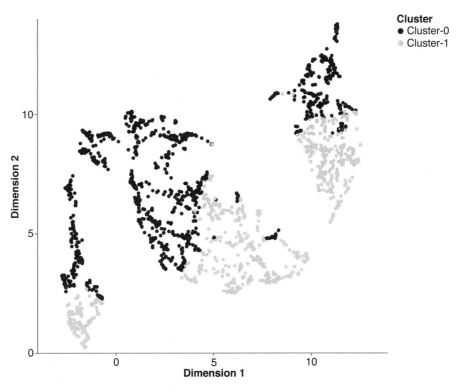

FIGURE 4.27. UMAP (SPLOM [scatterplot matrix]) projection of k means clustering of selected variables from the U.S. Census adult data set.

distances higher than large, but a similar effect nevertheless happens with other projection methods. Wilkinson and Luo (2020) described this problem in more detail.

SOFTWARE

The graphical software field changes so rapidly that I do not provide published references to packages. It is easy to Google or Bing or DuckDuckGo the names of these packages to learn more about them.

Programming Systems

Sophisticated graphics require programming systems. The best programmable graphics systems are SAS, SPSS, SYSTAT, Mathematica, ggplot2, and Python Graphics. The last two packages are free (open source). Some of these packages have menus for drawing graphics, but one must use their scripting capabilities to produce many of the graphics in this article. The ggplot2 system is growing more rapidly in this area than the others. Hadley Wickham developed this package, based on *GG*. This package greatly simplifies the production of tabular and complex graphics. The graphics in this chapter were produced using SYSTAT and Advisor (an analytic and graphics program I wrote in Java).

For Java programmers, Prefuse is a library of graphing classes that can be used to do a wide range of visualizations. More recently, Mike Bostock built another system called D3 (Data Driven Documents) that affords Javascript/HTML programmers fine control of graphics features. D3 is probably more advanced than most researchers can handle, but it is still one of the most effective toolkits for implementing interactive graphics. The vega-lite toolkit implements *GG* architecture on top of D3. The ant-vis/G2 product is a native Javascript *GG* package with unparalleled extensions and a large team based in China.

Menu Systems

The best menu-driven graphics systems for producing the type of graphics featured in this chapter are eCharts and Microsoft PowerBI. Tableau Software and Power BI offer menu-driven business graphing systems that may not always serve the needs of the scientific research community. Because Tableau's architecture is based on *GG*, it is capable of producing an enormous number of different graphics, including many in this chapter.

Production

For layout and final production of graphics files, I recommend Adobe products. I used them for some minor editing of the graphics in this chapter. There have been other easier-to-use editing packages, but they have gone out of business, unfortunately. The primary advantage of Adobe Illustrator is its graphics file processing capability. Adobe is one of the few, if only, programs that can handle transparency in Encapsulated PostScript files (EPS). Since Adobe is the originator of PDF and EPS files, it maintains control over file standards. In my experience, Illustrator handles different variants of Windows Metafiles (WMF) and Extended Windows Metafiles (EMF) more flexibly than Microsoft's own applications.

All the graphics files for this chapter were printed from vector (as opposed to bitmap) files. Vector files are resolution-independent, so they can be typeset at the highest resolution of printers' Linotronic machines (over 2500 dots per inch). I used EPS, but some publishers have switched to PDF for graphics files because it is more portable and supports transparency. Web publishers are increasingly turning to another vector format, Scalable Vector Graphics (SVG), because those files can be printed or displayed on the web at maximum resolution.

Never use bitmap file formats such as TIFF, PNG, JPEG, GIF, PCT or BMP for production publishing unless you want all your typefaces and graphics to look as if you photocopied them through a screen door. If you try to make the resolution of bitmap files fine enough for hard-copy publication, they will balloon into huge files for each graphic, even after file compression.

For typesetting, I recommend learning LaTeX if a journal allows it. LaTeX is free and supports indexing, citations, bibliographies, and cross-referencing—all things that are difficult to do in Word or other word processors. For APA (American Psychological Association) publications, use Microsoft Word. I used Open Office (Neo Office on the Macintosh) to process the original manuscript and Apple Pages and Microsoft Word for revisions.

References

Backs, R. W., & Walrath, L. C. (1995). Ocular measures of redundancy gain during visual search of colour symbolic displays. *Ergonomics, 38*(9), 1831–1840. https://doi.org/10.1080/00140139508925230

Becker, R. A., Cleveland, W. S., & Shyu, M.-J. (1996). The design and control of Trellis display. *Journal of Computational and Graphical Statistics, 5*(2), 123–155.

Beniger, J. R., & Robyn, D. L. (1978). Quantitative graphics in statistics: A brief history. *The American Statistician, 32*(1), 1–11.

Bertin, J. (1981). *Graphics and graphic information–processing* (W. J. Berg & H. Wainer, Trans.). Walter de Gruyter. (Original work published 1981) https://doi.org/10.1515/9783110854688

Bertin, J. (1983). *Semiology of graphics* (W. J. Berg & H. Wainer, Trans.). University of Wisconsin Press. (Original work published 1967)

Best, L. A., Smith, L. D., & Stubbs, D. A. (2001). Graph use in psychology and other sciences. *Behavioural Processes, 54*(1-3), 155–165. https://doi.org/10.1016/S0376-6357(01)00156-5

Bureau of the Census. (1986). *State and metropolitan area data book*. US Government Printing Office.

Carr, D. B. (1995). Using gray in plots. *Statistical Computing & Graphics Newsletter, 5*(2), 11–14.

Carr, D. B., Littlefield, R. J., Nicholson, W. L., & Littlefield, J. S. (1987). Scatterplot matrix techniques for large N. *Journal of the American Statistical Association, 82*(398), 424–436.

Carswell, C. M. (1992). Choosing specifiers: An evaluation of the basic tasks model of graphical perception. *Human Factors, 34*(5), 535–554. https://doi.org/10.1177/001872089203400503

Chambers, J. M., Cleveland, W. S., Kleiner, B., & Tukey, P. A. (1983). *Graphical methods for data analysis*. Wadsworth Publishing.

Chartrand, J. M. (1997). *National sample survey* [Unpublished raw data].

Cleveland, W. S. (1984). Graphs in scientific publications. *The American Statistician, 38*(4), 261–269. https://doi.org/10.2307/2683400

Cleveland, W. S. (1993). A model for studying display methods of statistical graphics (with discussion). *Journal of Computational and Graphical Statistics, 2*(4), 323–343. https://doi.org/10.2307/1390686

Cleveland, W. S. (1994). *The elements of graphing data* (Rev. ed.). Hobart Press.

Cleveland, W. S. (1995). *Visualizing data*. Hobart Press.

Cleveland, W. S., & Devlin, S. (1988). Locally weighted regression analysis by local fitting. *Journal of the American Statistical Association, 83*(403), 596–610. https://doi.org/10.1080/01621459.1988.10478639

Cleveland, W. S., Diaconis, P., & McGill, R. (1982). Variables on scatterplots look more highly correlated when the scales are increased. *Science, 216*(4550), 1138–1141. https://doi.org/10.1126/science.216.4550.1138

Cleveland, W. S., & McGill, R. (1983). A color-caused optical illusion on a statistical graph. *The American Statistician, 37*(2), 101–105.

Cleveland, W. S., & McGill, R. (1984). Graphical perception: Theory, experimentation, and application to the development of graphical methods. *Journal of the American Statistical Association, 79*(387), 531–554. https://doi.org/10.1080/01621459.1984.10478080

Cohen, J., Cohen, P., West, S., & Aiken, L. S. (2003). *Applied multiple regression/correlation analysis for the behavioral sciences*. Erlbaum.

Collins, B. M. (1993). Data visualization: Has it all been seen before? In R. A. Earnshaw & D. Watson (Eds.), *Animation and scientific visualization: Tools and applications* (pp. 3–28). Academic Press.

Coren, S., & Girgus, J. S. (1978). *Seeing is deceiving: The psychology of visual illusions*. Erlbaum.

Davis, J. A., Smith, T. W., & Marsden, P. V. (1993). *The general social survey*. National Opinion Research Center.

Doherty, M. E., & Anderson, R. B. (2009). Variation in scatterplot displays. *Behavior Research Methods, 41*(1), 55–60. https://doi.org/10.3758/BRM.41.1.55

Few, S. (2009). *Now you see it: Simple visualization techniques for quantitative analysis*. Analytics Press.

Fienberg, S. (1979). Graphical methods in statistics. *The American Statistician, 33*(4), 165–178.

Friendly, M. (1994). Mosaic displays for n-way contingency tables. *Journal of the American Statistical Association, 89*(425), 190–200. https://doi.org/10.1080/01621459.1994.10476460

Friendly, M. (2002). A brief history of the mosaic display. *Journal of Computational and Graphical Statistics, 11*(1), 89–107. https://doi.org/10.1198/106186002317375631

Fruchterman, T. M. J., & Reingold, E. M. (1991). Graph drawing by force-directed placement. *Software, Practice & Experience*, *21*(11), 1129–1164. https://doi.org/10.1002/spe.4380211102

Funkhouser, H. G. (1937). Historical development of the graphical representation of statistical data. *Osiris*, *3*, 269–404. https://doi.org/10.1086/368480

Garner, W. R. (1981). The analysis of unanalyzed perceptions. In M. Kubovy & J. R. Pomerantz (Eds.), *Perceptual organization* (pp. 119–139). Erlbaum.

Gillan, D. J., & Richman, E. H. (1994). Minimalism and the syntax of graphs. *Human Factors*, *36*(4), 619–644. https://doi.org/10.1177/001872089403600405

Gillan, D. J., & Sorensen, D. (2009, October 1). Effects of graph backgrounds on visual search. In *Proceedings of the Human Factors and Ergonomics Society 53rd Annual Meeting* (pp. 1096–1100).

Gonnelli, S., Cepollaro, C., Montagnani, A., Monaci, G., Campagna, M. S., Franci, M. B., & Gennari, C. (1996). Bone alkaline phosphatase measured with a new immunoradiometric assay in patients with metabolic bone diseases. *European Journal of Clinical Investigation*, *26*(5), 391–396. https://doi.org/10.1046/j.1365-2362.1996.142304.x

Gregory, R. L. (2009). *Seeing through illusions*. Oxford University Press.

Hartigan, J. A. (1975). Printer graphics for clustering. *Journal of Statistical Computation and Simulation*, *4*(3), 187–213. https://doi.org/10.1080/00949657508810123

Hartigan, J. A., & Kleiner, B. (1981). Mosaics for contingency tables. In *Computer science and statistics: Proceedings of the 13th Symposium on the Interface* (pp. 268–273).

Heiser, J., Tversky, B., Agrawala, M., & Hanrahan, P. (2003). Cognitive design principles for visualizations: Revealing and instantiating. In *Proceedings of the Cognitive Science Society Meetings* (pp. 545–550).

Herdeg, W. (1981). *Graphis diagrams: The graphic visualization of abstract data*. Graphis Press.

Hofmann, H., Kafadar, K., & Wickham, H. (2006). *Letter-value box plots—Adjusting box plots for large data sets* (Technical Report 10). Department of Statistics, Iowa State University.

Holmes, N. (1991). *Designer's guide to creating charts and diagrams*. Watson-Guptill Publications.

Huff, D. (1954). *How to lie with statistics*. W. W. Norton & Company.

Inbar, O., Tractinsky, N., & Meyer, J. (2007). Minimalism in information visualization: Attitudes towards maximizing the data-ink ratio. In *Proceedings of the 14th European Conference on Cognitive Ergonomics* (pp. 185–188). ACM Press.

Juran, J. M. (1951). The economics of quality. In J. M. Juran (Ed.), *Quality control handbook* (pp. 1–41). McGraw-Hill.

Kamada, T., & Kawai, S. (1989). An algorithm for drawing general undirected graphs. *Information Processing Letters*, *31*(1), 7–15. https://doi.org/10.1016/0020-0190(89)90102-6

Keim, D. A. (2000). Designing pixel-oriented visualization techniques: Theory and applications. *IEEE Transactions on Visualization and Computer Graphics*, *6*(1), 59–78. https://doi.org/10.1109/2945.841121

Klippel, A., Knuf, L., Hommel, B., & Freksa, C. (2004). Perceptually induced distortions in cognitive maps. In C. Freksa, M. Knauff, B. Krieg-Brückner, B. Nebel, & T. Barkowsky (Eds.), *Spatial cognition* (pp. 204–213). Springer Verlag.

Kosslyn, S. M. (1994). *Elements of graph design*. W. H. Freeman.

Lewandowsky, S. (1999). Statistical graphs and maps: Higher level cognitive processes. In M. G. Sirken, D. J. Herrmann, S. Schechter, N. Schwarz, J. M. Tanur, & R. Tourangeau (Eds.), *Cognition and survey research* (pp. 349–362). Wiley.

Lewandowsky, S., & Spence, I. (1989). The perception of statistical graphs. *Sociological Methods & Research*, *18*(2-3), 200–242. https://doi.org/10.1177/0049124189018002002

Luo, H., Patania, A., Kim, J., & Vejdemo-Johansson, M. (2021). Generalized penalty for circular coordinate representation. *Foundations of Data Science*, *3*(4), 729–767. https://doi.org/10.3934/fods.2021024

McGill, R., Tukey, J. W., & Larsen, W. A. (1978). Variations of box plots. *The American Statistician*, *32*(1), 12–16. https://doi.org/10.2307/2683468

McInnes, L., Healy, L., & Melville, J. (2020). UMAP: Uniform manifold approximation and projection for dimension reduction. *arXiv*. https://doi.org/10.48550/arXiv.1802.03426

McNamara, T. P., Ratcliff, R., & McKoon, G. (1984). The mental representation of knowledge acquired from maps. *Journal of Experimental Psychology: Learning, Memory, and Cognition*, *10*(4), 723–732. https://doi.org/10.1037/0278-7393.10.4.723

Miller, G. A. (1956). The magical number seven plus or minus two: Some limits on our capacity for processing information. *Psychological Review*, *63*(2), 81–97. https://doi.org/10.1037/h0043158

Monmonier, M. (1996). *How to lie with maps*. University of Chicago Press. https://doi.org/10.7208/chicago/9780226029009.001.0001

Newman, M. E. J. (2003). The function and structure of complex networks. *SIAM Review*, *45*(2), 167–256. https://doi.org/10.1137/S003614450342480

Norman, D. A. (2007). Simplicity is highly overrated. *Interaction*, *14*(2), 40–41. https://doi.org/10.1145/1229863.1229885

Pinker, S. (1997). *How the mind works*. W. W. Norton & Company.

Playfair, W. (2005). *The commercial and political atlas and statistical breviary*. Cambridge University Press. (Original work published 1786)

Rangecroft, M. (2003). As easy as pie. *Behaviour & Information Technology*, *22*(6), 421–426. https://doi.org/10.1080/01449290310001615437

Robbins, N. B. (2005). *Creating more effective graphs*. Wiley.

Rothkopf, E. Z. (1957). A measure of stimulus similarity and errors in some paired-associate learning tasks. *Journal of Experimental Psychology*, *53*(2), 94–101. https://doi.org/10.1037/h0041867

Scott, D. W. (1979). On optimal and data-based histograms. *Biometrika*, *66*(3), 605–610. https://doi.org/10.1093/biomet/66.3.605

Scott, D. W. (1992). *Multivariate density estimation: Theory, practice, and visualization*. Wiley. https://doi.org/10.1002/9780470316849

Shneiderman, B. (1992). Tree visualization with tree-maps: A 2-d space-filling approach. *ACM Transactions on Graphics*, *11*(1), 92–99. https://doi.org/10.1145/102377.115768

Silverman, B. W. (1986). *Density estimation for statistics and data analysis*. Chapman & Hall.

Simkin, D., & Hastie, R. (1987). An information processing analysis of graph perception. *Journal of the American Statistical Association*, *82*(398), 454–465. https://doi.org/10.1080/01621459.1987.10478448

Spence, I. (1990). Visual psychophysics of simple graphical elements. *Journal of Experimental Psychology: Human Perception and Performance*, *16*(4), 683–692. https://doi.org/10.1037/0096-1523.16.4.683

Spence, I. (2004). The apparent and effective dimensionality of representations of objects. *Human Factors*, *46*(4), 738–747. https://doi.org/10.1518/hfes.46.4.738.56809

Spence, I. (2005). No humble pie: The origins and usage of a statistical chart. *Journal of Educational and Behavioral Statistics*, *30*(4), 353–368. https://doi.org/10.3102/10769986030004353

Spence, I., & Lewandowsky, S. (1991). Displaying proportions and percentages. *Applied Cognitive Psychology*, *5*(1), 61–77. https://doi.org/10.1002/acp.2350050106

Stevens, S. S. (1961). To honor Fechner and repeal his law: A power function, not a log function, describes the operating characteristic of a sensory system. *Science*, *133*(3446), 80–86. https://doi.org/10.1126/science.133.3446.80

Stevens, S. S. (1985). *Psychophysics: Introduction to its perceptual, neural, and social prospects*. Transaction Books.

Stigler, S. (1983). *The history of statistics*. Harvard University Press.

Stroop, J. R. (1935). Studies of interference in serial verbal reactions. *Journal of Experimental Psychology*, *18*(6), 643–662. https://doi.org/10.1037/h0054651

Tufte, E. R. (1983). *The visual display of quantitative information*. Graphics Press.

Tufte, E. R. (1990). *Envisioning data*. Graphics Press.

Tufte, E. R. (1997). *Visual explanations*. Graphics Press.

Tukey, J. W. (1977). *Exploratory data analysis*. Addison-Wesley.

Tversky, B. (1981). Distortions in memory for maps. *Cognitive Psychology*, *13*(3), 407–433. https://doi.org/10.1016/0010-0285(81)90016-5

Tversky, B. (1993). Cognitive maps, cognitive collages, and spatial mental models. In U. A. Frank & I. Campari (Eds.), *Spatial information theory: A theoretical basis for GIS—Proceedings of COSIT '93* (pp. 14–24). Springer Verlag.

Tversky, B. (2005). Prolegomenon to scientific visualizations. In J. K. Gilbert (Ed.), *Visualizations in science education* (pp. 29–42). Kluwer Publishing.

Tversky, B., Agrawala, M., Heiser, J., Lee, P., Hanrahan, P., Doantam, P., Stolte, C., & Daniel, M.-P. (2007). Cognitive design principles for generating visualizations. In G. Allen (Ed.), *Applied spatial cognition: From research to cognitive technology* (pp. 53–73). Lawrence Erlbaum.

Tversky, B., Zacks, J., Lee, P. U., & Heiser, J. (2000). Lines, blobs, crosses, and arrows: Diagrammatic communication with schematic figures. In M. Anderson, P. Cheng, & V. Haarslev (Eds.), *Theory and application of diagrams* (pp. 221–230). Springer-Verlag. https://doi.org/10.1007/3-540-44590-0_21

Wainer, H. (1997). *Visual revelations: Graphical tales of fate and deception from Napoleon Bonaparte to Ross Perot*. Springer-Verlag.

Wainer, H. (2009). *Picturing the uncertain world*. Princeton University Press. https://doi.org/10.1515/9781400832897

Wainer, H., & Spence, I. (1997). Who was Playfair? *Chance*, *10*(1), 35–37. https://doi.org/10.1080/09332480.1997.10554796

Wainer, H., & Velleman, P. F. (2001). Statistical graphics: Mapping the pathways of science. *Annual Review of Psychology*, *52*(1), 305–335. https://doi.org/10.1146/annurev.psych.52.1.305

Wand, M. P. (1997). Data-based choice of histogram bin width. *The American Statistician*, *51*(1), 59–64.

Ware, C. (2008). *Visual thinking for design*. Morgan Kaufman.

Wiggins, J. S. (1982). Circumplex models of interpersonal behavior in clinical psychology. In P. C. Kendall & J. N. Butcher (Eds.), *Handbook of research methods in clinical psychology* (pp. 183–221). Wiley.

Wilkinson, L. (1999a). Dot plots. *The American Statistician*, *53*(3), 276–281.

Wilkinson, L. (1999b). Statistical methods in psychology journals: Guidelines and explanations. *American Psychologist*, *54*(8), 594–604. https://doi.org/10.1037/0003-066X.54.8.594

Wilkinson, L. (2005). *The grammar of graphics* (2nd ed.). Springer-Verlag.

Wilkinson, L. (2006). Revising the Pareto chart. *The American Statistician*, *60*(4), 332–334. https://doi.org/10.1198/000313006X152243

Wilkinson, L. (2009). *SYSTAT, Version 13* [Computer software]. Systat Software.

Wilkinson, L. (2018). Visualizing big data outliers through distributed aggregation. *IEEE Transactions on Visualization and Computer Graphics*, *24*(1), 256–266. https://doi.org/10.1109/TVCG.2017.2744685

Wilkinson, L., Anand, A., & Dang, T. N. (2012). Substantial improvements in the set-covering projection classifier CHIRP (composite hypercubes on iterated random projections). *ACM Transactions on Knowledge Discovery from Data*, *6*(4), 1–18. https://doi.org/10.1145/2382577.2382583

Wilkinson, L., Blank, G., & Gruber, C. (1996). *Desktop data analysis with SYSTAT*. Prentice-Hall.

Wilkinson, L., & Luo, H. (2020). A distance-preserving matrix sketch. *arXiv:2009.03979*. https://doi.org/10.48550/arXiv.2009.03979

Wilkinson, L., & McConathy, D. (1990). Memory for graphs. In *Proceedings of the Section on Statistical Graphics of the American Statistical Association* (pp. 25–32).

Wilkinson, L., & Task Force on Statistical Inference, American Psychological Association, Science Directorate. (1999). Statistical methods in psychology journals: Guidelines and explanations. *American Psychologist*, *54*(8), 594–604. https://doi.org/10.1037/0003-066X.54.8.594

CHAPTER 5

ESTIMATING AND VISUALIZING INTERACTIONS IN MODERATED MULTIPLE REGRESSION

Connor J. McCabe and Kevin M. King

Interactions quantify how the effect of an independent variable on a dependent variable differs across levels of one (or more) other variable(s). Tests of interactions are ubiquitous in psychological science, as many hypotheses of psychological phenomena seek to identify *moderated effects* that characterize for whom, when, or in which contexts an effect is present (vs. absent) or stronger (vs. weaker) compared with other conditions. To clarify terminology, we consider *interactions* as the *statistical quantity* determining the degree to which the effect of one variable on an outcome is conditioned by others. We consider the term *moderation* as a reference to the *quality* of this effect that is formulated as a specific research hypothesis. For instance, in educational research, one may hypothesize a moderated effect that girls have an educational advantage in school achievement for language subject courses compared with boys (Voyer & Voyer, 2014), then test a Gender × Subject interaction to provide evidence of this hypothesis. In developmental psychology, researchers propose that although children with difficult temperament may be at higher risk for poorer health outcomes, they may be at no greater risk compared with nonvulnerable peers under the care of highly skilled caregivers (Monroe & Simons, 1991). Examining a Caregiving × Temperament interaction addresses the hypothesis that effective caregiving buffers the effect of difficult temperament on poorer health. All of these examples represent *moderation hypotheses*, with interactions being a formal statistical means of testing them. The estimate and precision of an interaction effect, used in tandem with probing and graphing tools, allow researchers to evaluate empirical support for such hypotheses.

This chapter focuses on testing, probing, and visualizing interaction effects in moderated multiple regression (MMR) models. Although several analytic traditions have provided parallel treatments for interaction effects, we focus on MMR because it subsumes many of these other traditions, such as those based in analysis of variance (ANOVA; Cohen, 1968), while laying the groundwork for more advanced methods of analysis (e.g., multilevel models, generalized linear models). Within this flexible MMR framework, this chapter aims to review foundational approaches for testing, probing, and visualizing interaction effects; to highlight pitfalls and rectify misconceptions commonly encountered in interaction analysis; and to provide an update on state-of-the-science approaches in evaluating these effects. We hope that this chapter will serve as a foundation for understanding and pursuing moderation hypotheses within and beyond the linear regression context.

https://doi.org/10.1037/0000320-005
APA Handbook of Research Methods in Psychology, Second Edition: Vol. 3. Data Analysis and Research Publication, H. Cooper (Editor-in-Chief)
Copyright © 2023 by the American Psychological Association. All rights reserved.

ESTIMATING AND PROBING INTERACTIONS IN MMR

We describe, in this section, the fundamentals of the MMR and how interactions may be estimated and probed within this model.

Overview

We begin with a prototypical MMR model in which we have measured a focal independent variable X, a second moderator variable Z, and an outcome variable Y. For simplicity, assume all variables are continuous, and each predictor is linearly associated with the outcome. Suppose we have a moderation hypothesis that Z enhances the effect of X on Y. This scenario represented in an MMR equation is as follows:

$$y_i = b_0 + b_1 x_i + b_2 z_i + b_{12} x_i z_i + e_i. \quad (5.1)$$

Equation 5.1 represents the linear prediction of an outcome for individual i (y_i) as a function of four regressors: the intercept, the values of their predictors x_i and z_i, and the product of these predictors.

The intercept term (b_0) describes the value of y_i at the origin (i.e., when all independent variables are at 0). The coefficients b_1 and b_2 are called *lower-order* effects; as we describe in more detail below, these represent the effects of x_i and z_i on y_i, respectively, when the other variable involved in the interaction takes the value of 0. In this linear case, the product term coefficient b_{12}, the *higher-order* effect in this equation, quantifies the interaction between x_i and z_i on y_i. This coefficient describes how the effect of one regressor on y_i involved in the interaction changes for any single unit increase in the other. In other words, b_{12} may be interpreted directly as the amount that the slope of x_i changes for a one unit change in z_i, and vice versa. Note that the term e_i represents the residual error—that is, the distance between the individual's predicted value of y_i based on this equation, compared to the observed value of y_i.

Simple Slopes

Computationally, there is no distinction in an MMR as to which variable is the focal variable and which is the moderating variable. Nonetheless, analysts often have theoretical reason to select which variable serves as the moderator of the other. Therefore, analysts may rearrange the terms in Equation 5.1 to clarify how z_i moderates (i.e., modifies, conditions, or changes) the effect of x_i on y_i:

$$y_i = b_0 + b_2 z_i + (b_1 + b_{12} z_i) x_i + e_i. \quad (5.2)$$

We can see above that the effect of x_i on y_i is captured by the expression $(b_1 + b_{12} z_i) x_i$. The presence of z_i in Equation 5.2 indicates that the effect of x_i on y_i is, therefore, dependent on the value of z_i. For instance, b_1 represents the effect of x_i on y_i strictly when $z_i = 0$; $b_1 + b_{12}$ is this effect when $z_i = 1$; and so on. Each of these equations is known as a *simple slope* because they describe the "simple" effect of x_i on y_i at a particular point of interest along the moderator z_i.

Calculation of the standard errors (SEs) for a simple slope at a given value of z_i involves taking the square root of its variance, computed using the general variance formula for the sum of two random variables. This is done as follows (see Aiken & West, 1991, and Bauer & Curran, 2005):

$$SE(b_1 + b_{12} z_i | z_i) = \sqrt{\mathrm{var}(b_1) + 2 z_i * \mathrm{cov}(b_1, b_{12}) + z_i^2 * \mathrm{var}(b_{12})}, \quad (5.3)$$

where var(b_1) and var(b_{12}) refer to the variances of the lower order coefficients for x_i and the product term coefficient, respectively, while cov(b_1, b_{12}) refers to the covariance of these quantities. Each of these quantities are available in the variance–covariance matrix of the regression coefficients based on an estimated MMR, which can be readily extracted from output provided in modern statistical software programs (e.g., by applying the *vcov* function to an estimated linear model (*lm*) object in the base R package). Finally, using the simple slope estimate and its standard error, the analyst can compute a confidence interval and/or a *t* value to perform statistical significance testing on this simple slope. For instance, a t value can be readily computed by dividing $b_1 + b_{12}z_i$ for a given z_i by its standard error, which can be evaluated against a standard t distribution to determine a corresponding p value,

$$t = \frac{b_1 + b_{12}z_i \mid z_i}{SE(b_1 + b_{12}z_i \mid z_i)}. \tag{5.4}$$

Forms of Interaction

Interactions can take one of several forms depending on the strength and signs of the product and lower-order terms (Table 5.1). First, illustrated in Equation 5.1 and 5.2 above, an interaction can be *synergistic*, in which higher levels of the moderating variable enhance the effect of the focal variable on the outcome. Common examples in published research include assessing whether the cooccurrence of impulsive traits (e.g., sensation seeking and impulsivity) produces multiplicative risk for problem health behaviors (McCabe et al., 2015; Meisel et al., 2019), or assessing whether psychotherapy treatment may be particularly effective for certain demographic groups or conditions compared to others (e.g., Schneider et al., 2015). Interactions can also take the form of a *buffering* effect, in which the

TABLE 5.1

Forms of Interaction

Form	Description	Coefficient signs	Ordinal example	Disordinal example
Synergistic	X, Z, and X × Z are associated with Y in the same direction	b_X: + b_Z: + b_{XZ}: +; b_X: − b_Z: − b_{XZ}: −		
Buffering	X (or Z) is associated in the same direction with Y as X × Z, but Z (or X) is in the opposite direction	b_X: + b_Z: − b_{XZ}: + or −; b_X: − b_Z: + b_{XZ}: + or −		
Antagonistic	X and Z are associated with Y in the same direction, but X × Z is in the opposite direction	b_X: + b_Z: + b_{XZ}: −; b_X: − b_Z: − b_{XZ}: +		

strength of the relation between the focal and outcome variables lessens as the moderator increases. For example, numerous studies have demonstrated that the presence of social support may mitigate the impact of environmental stressors on psychopathology risk (Kessler et al., 1985).

Finally, interactions can be *antagonistic* when both the focal and moderator variables are associated with the outcome in the same direction, yet the interaction itself is in the opposite direction. This scenario indicates that the presence of the focal or moderator variable is associated with change in the outcome, yet their effect on producing change in an outcome is largely redundant (we find the phrase "one is enough" a helpful heuristic). For instance, assume we predicted success in graduate school as a function of motivation, ability, and their interaction (e.g., Cohen et al., 2014). An antagonistic interaction would demonstrate that being exceptionally motivated or capable is enough to succeed in graduate school; yet, being motivated and capable adds little to success if a student is already exceptional in one of these regards.

Ordinal and Disordinal Interactions

For each of these forms, an interaction can be ordinal or disordinal in nature. An *ordinal* interaction indicates that the rank order of an outcome stays largely consistent across all levels of the two interacting variables (e.g., third column of Table 5.1). However, cases in which the rank order of an outcome changes across levels of the focal variable are known as *disordinal*, or *crossover*, interactions (e.g., fourth column of Table 5.1). Visually, disordinal interactions are distinguishable in a simple slopes plot by whether the slopes displayed intersect at some level of the *x*-axis variable. The value of the focal variable at which this change happens is known as the crossover point (denoted *co* below) and can be computed as follows:

$$x_{co} = -\frac{b_2}{b_{12}}. \quad (5.5)$$

We note that for any two simple slopes that are not exactly parallel (i.e., the interaction effect is not precisely zero), *all* interactions are disordinal interactions at an infinite range of the focal variable. Therefore, providing evidence of a disordinal effect requires careful consideration of whether this crossover point reflects a meaningful value of the focal predictor. Computationally, methods for generating confidence intervals for the crossover point (Lee et al., 2015; Widaman et al., 2012) provide statistical tests for distinguishing whether this point lies within a plausible range of the focal variable. Graphically, we advise that researchers generate simple slopes plots that accurately represent the range of the observed data and include the observed data underlying these effects to support whether a disordinal interaction is truly reflected in the data at-hand. One must remember that the interpretation of interaction forms is heavily dependent on where the bulk of the data lies along the range of each variable. Thus, as we discuss in greater detail later in this chapter, it is critical to plot interactions against the observed data, consider the ranges of each variable displayed, and temper one's interpretation to the range of the data that the models cover well.

INTERACTION ANALYSIS EXAMPLES

In this section, we provide several examples of interaction analysis based on the type of variables involved in the interaction, such as those involving continuous, binary, and/or multicategorical variables. Although we present these examples separately, we emphasize that the fundamental concepts that underlie testing and probing interactions are synonymous across all variable types in MMR. For instance, if categorical variables are coded in such a way that represent the primary comparison(s) of interest, pick-a-point methods for probing interaction effects involving categorical variables are identical to continuous variable scenarios. As we describe below, the distinction is only that an interaction is probed at two specific levels (i.e., categories), rather than at select points along a continuous moderator. Nonetheless, several considerations should be made given the nature of each variable type, and we, thus, introduce them in independent sections.

A Note on Effects Coding

Throughout our categorical variable interaction examples, we use *dummy variable coding*. Dummy coding produces a model with a readily interpretable intercept, simplifies the algebra involved in probing interactions considerably, and in our experience, is especially helpful for teaching the fundamentals of categorical variable interactions relative to other options. Nonetheless, we note that several coding schemes are possible, including weighted and unweighted effects coding, contrast coding, and many others, such that effects coding may be a distinct topic unto itself. We advise readers to reference Chapter 8 of Cohen et al. (2014) for a thorough treatment of the topic or Chapter 8 of this volume for more detail. Although a critical topic in multiple regression analysis broadly, the fundamental nature of an interaction changes little (if at all) across different coding choices.

Example 1. Continuous Variable Interactions

Assume we are interested in predicting subjective well-being as a function of sleep, exercise, and their interaction. In this hypothetical example, we may have a moderation hypothesis that although sleep and exercise each support well-being in themselves, those who sleep more perform better during their exercise routines, therefore, benefiting more from exercise when well-rested. In more typical moderation language, we may equivalently state that sleep enhances the health benefits of exercise on subjective well-being. Note that our moderation hypothesis speaks to the effect we expect for each lower order term, as well as the specific form of interaction: Sleep and exercise generally improve well-being, but the combination of their effects contributes to better well-being above and beyond their independent effects (i.e., a *synergistic* effect).

Assume sleep is measured as the average number of hours one sleeps per night, exercise is measured as the average number of days of moderate exercise completed in a month, and that all regressors have been centered at their sample means of 7 hours of sleep and 10 days per month of exercise, respectively (more described on this later). Assuming further that subjective well-being is measured as a normally distributed variable with a mean of 100 and a standard deviation of 10, results of a regression analysis may provide us with the following:

$$wellbeing = 100 + 1.2 * exercise + 1.5 * sleep \\ + 0.8 * exercise * sleep. \quad (5.6)$$

Rearranging terms provides clarity for the effect of our focal exercise variable,

$$wellbeing = 100 + 1.5 * sleep \\ + (1.2 + 0.8 * sleep) * exercise. \quad (5.7)$$

In Equations 5.6 and 5.7, the interaction coefficient (0.8) describes how many additional units of well-being are gained from exercising for each additional hour of sleep, above and beyond the influence of exercise and sleep alone. Because this coefficient is difficult to interpret directly, we may enter in hypothetical values of our moderator variable to this equation to provide a more straightforward description of what these results imply in the population. This procedure is known as *probing* an interaction effect using the pick-a-point method (Aiken & West, 1991) and is carried out by constructing simple slopes for the focal variable across interesting values of the moderator.

For instance, entering the value of 0 for sleep in this equation simplifies it to $100 + 1.2 * exercise$. This shows that when sleep is at 0, the mean of well-being increases by 1.2 units as exercise increases by one day per month. Importantly, because we have mean-centered our variables, we can equivalently state that each additional day of moderate exercise increases well-being by 1.2 points when an individual has average amounts (i.e., 7 hours) of sleep. We may construct additional simple slopes by selecting other values of sleep hours to describe more precisely how exercise affects well-being among individuals reporting different levels of sleep. For instance, we can describe this effect when sleep is one unit *lower* than the mean (i.e., 6 hours) with the equation 98.5 + 0.8 * *exercise*, one unit *higher* (i.e., 8 hours) with the equation 101.5 + 2.0 * *exercise*, and so on. Figure 5.1 provides a graphical depiction of these simple slopes, which we describe in more detail in the visualization section of this chapter.

Example 2. Interactions Involving Dichotomous Variables

Interactions involving dichotomous variables are those in which one regressor is a nominal variable with two categories. We start with a hypothetical example testing sex differences in the relation between social support and major depression. Although studies have shown an inverse relation between social support and depression across sexes, theory and supporting work has suggested that those assigned female sex at birth may be more sensitized to the harmful effects of low social support than those assigned male at birth (e.g., Kendler et al., 2005). Therefore, one may have the hypothesis that the relation between low social support and depression is stronger among females than males. We may pursue this hypothesis by testing a Sex × Social Support interaction.

Assume depression was measured as a T score ($M = 50$, $SD = 10$), social support was a standard normal variable ($M = 0$, $SD = 1$), and 58% of the sample reported sex assigned at birth as female. Given the response categories "female" and "male" in our sex variable are not numerical quantities, we employ a dummy coding scheme that represents these two categories. To dummy code our sex variable, we create a new variable in our data set called "female," wherein males are represented by the value of "0" and females represented by "1." Note that we have assigned males the value of 0 because our moderation hypothesis primarily concerns the effects among females compared to a male reference group; thus, a unit increase in this variable denotes the difference between females relative to males. Further, we have called this variable "female" rather than "sex" to denote intuitively which of these two sexes is represented by "1." As we have done in our continuous variable example, we may then estimate an MMR model by regressing depression on social support, female, and their product:

$$Depression = 48 - 1 * support + 4 * female \\ - 2 * support * female. \quad (5.8)$$

Interpreting and probing Equation 5.8 follows nearly identically from our continuous variable example above. However, we must note that our categorical moderator can only assume one of

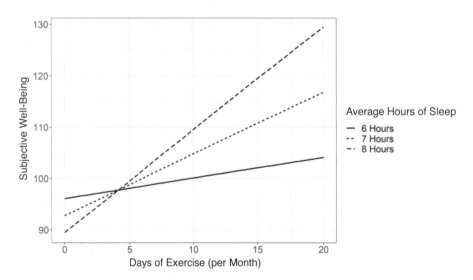

FIGURE 5.1. Example of a simple slopes plot illustrating a synergistic exercise × sleep interaction.

two values, and that 0 now has a specific meaning given our use of dummy variable coding. For instance, we can represent the simple slope of social support on depression separately for males and females by probing this interaction via simple slopes at 0 and 1, respectively:

$$Depression_{males} = 48 - 1 * support$$
$$Depression_{females} = 52 - 3 * support. \quad (5.9)$$

Note that this is analogous to generating simple slopes equations at moderator values described in our continuous variable example above; the only difference is that the points at which we generate the simple slopes represent each sex category (0 or "males" and 1 or "females") rather than select levels of a continuous moderator.

Equations 5.8 and 5.9 describe the differences in depression between males and females as well as how sex moderates the effect of social support. For instance, we reiterate that the intercept reflects the value of depression when all regressors are at 0; however, because our coding scheme has assigned 0 to males, we can state more precisely that our intercept in Equation 5.8 ($b_0 = 48$) is the mean of depression for males in the sample. Relatedly, the lower order coefficient on social support ($b_{support} = -1$) represents the effect strictly when "female" is 0. In other words, this effect denotes that every (standardized) unit increase in social support decreases depression by one unit among males. The coefficient for our "female" variable indicates how much depression changes for a unit change in this variable, when social support is held at its mean. Because a one-unit change in female indicates a categorical shift from male to female, this is synonymous with the *mean difference* between males and females: the mean depression score in the sample for females was four units higher compared with males (i.e., the intercept in the simple slope for females). Finally, the product term ($b_{support*female} = -2$) and signs of each lower-order coefficient suggest a *buffering* interaction effect: The protective effect for each standard deviation increase in social support is two units higher among females (–3; slope in bottom line of Equation 5.9) compared with males (–1; slope in top line of Equation 5.9), and, therefore, supports our initial moderation hypothesis.

Example 3. Interactions Involving Multicategorical Variables

Interaction effects may be pursued in the context of multicategorical variable interactions, defined as nominal variables containing three or more categories. Common examples in the psychological literature include race/ethnicity (e.g., U.S. Census categories of White, Black or African American, Asian American, American Indian/Alaska Native, and Native Hawaiian/Pacific Islander), gender identity (e.g., cisgender, transgender, or nonbinary), or age group (e.g., childhood, adolescence, and adulthood), among many others. Compared to those involving binary or continuous variables, the distinguishing feature of multinomial variable interactions is that the interaction effect must be tested as a set of product terms rather than as a single coefficient. This stems directly from the fact that a multicategorical variable with k categories must be represented in a regression model with $k-1$ coded variables in order to be quantified numerically within a regression model (Cohen et al., 2014). Therefore, as we detail below, interactions involving a multicategorical variable with k categories must be tested as a set of at least $k-1$ product terms. We review strictly the fundamentals of this topic in this chapter; for an excellent tutorial devoted to describing how to test, interpret, and display multicategorical interactions at length, we strongly recommend Hayes and Montoya (2017) for additional reading.

Assume an analyst wished to compare differences in anxiety across three treatment conditions (Treatment 1 [T_1], Treatment 2 [T_2], and a control condition), as well as test moderation of these differences by a binary biological sex variable (dummy coded such that 1 = female as in the preceding section). We may begin by estimating a purely additive model in which we regress anxiety on dummy-coded sex and treatment condition variables. Taking the control condition and male sex as reference groups, this model is represented as

$$Anxiety = b_0 + b_1 T_1 + b_2 T_2 + b_3 female. \quad (5.10)$$

This regression provides estimates describing the difference in anxiety between the control condition and Treatment 1 (b_1), the control condition and Treatment 2 (b_2), and between females compared to males. Extending from the binary example from the preceding section, we may interpret b_0 as the level of anxiety at the intersection of our reference categories denoted by 0—that is, among males in the control group. Building from this model, we may perform an omnibus test of the Treatment × Sex interaction by comparing this model with an MMR that contains the products $T_1 *$ female and $T_2 *$ female, as follows:

$$Anxiety = b_0 + b_1 T_1 + b_2 T_2 + b_3 female \\ + b_{13} T_1 * female + b_{23} T_2 * female. \quad (5.11)$$

Equation 5.10 can be considered a constrained version of Equation 5.11 in which the terms b_{13} and b_{23} are each taken to be 0.

We can evaluate evidence of a Treatment × Sex interaction by comparing model fit of Equation 5.11 relative to Equation 5.10. Namely, a significant improvement in fit resulting from the inclusion of b_{13} and b_{23} suggests that variance in the outcome is explained by the inclusion of these terms, above and beyond the strictly additive effects present in Equation 5.10. This can be computed by differencing the squared multiple correlation value in Equation 5.10 (R_1^2) relative to Equation 5.11 (R_2^2; i.e., I $R^2 = R_2^2 - R_1^2$). This difference value can then be converted to an F ratio to perform significance testing on this effect,

$$F = \frac{df_{resid.} \Delta R^2}{(k-1)(1-R_2^2)}, \quad (5.12)$$

where $df_{resid.}$ refers to the residual degrees of from the MMR in Equation 5.11 (Hayes & Montoya, 2017).

Once the omnibus test of the interaction is performed, the analyst may probe this effect in an analogous fashion to the methods described in the preceding sections. Namely, our use of dummy coding means that the terms b_{13} and b_{23} each quantify respective sex differences in the relation between Treatment 1 and Treatment 2 and anxiety, each compared with those in the control condition. Thus, these terms can be evaluated directly to describe the nature of the interaction effect for each specific treatment condition relative to the control condition. We note that although sex differences between Treatment 1 and Treatment 2 are not provided directly, we can readily change the dummy coding scheme utilized (e.g., by designating Treatment 1 as the reference group) and repeating the steps above to generate these quantities. Doing so does not change any fundamental aspect of the magnitude of the omnibus interaction effect, nor does it affect the performance of the model itself (e.g., R_1^2 and R_2^2 remain unchanged).

THE JOHNSON–NEYMAN TECHNIQUE

When a moderator is continuous, a practical limitation of the pick-a-point approach is that only a select number of moderator levels can be feasibly described. As such, representing an interaction at only several select values of a moderator limits the full exploration of an interaction effect. Particularly in situations in which a moderator variable is skewed or a sample size is especially large, failing to describe an interaction effect across its full moderator range may result in relevant effects missed within the data (i.e., a Type II error). The Johnson–Neyman (J-N) technique is a tool for addressing this concern analytically (Johnson & Fay, 1950; Potthoff, 1964). This technique provides an estimate of the range of the moderator variable at which a focal variable is significantly associated with the outcome.

Several tools for J-N analyses are available in standard statistical software, including statistical packages in R (e.g., the *interactions* package; Long, 2019), web applications (e.g., interActive; McCabe et al., 2018), or through the PROCESS macro available in SPSS and SAS (Hayes, 2013; Hayes & Matthes, 2009). Despite the ready availability of these tools, we (McCabe et al., 2018) and others (Finsaas & Goldstein, 2021) have noted that exceedingly few studies testing a continuous moderator provide results from these analyses in practice. We suspect that because this technique is presented as more mathematically complex than the pick-a-point method, analysts may be hesitant to learn and apply it in psychological science. We hope that this section makes clear that, in effect, this is approach is simply an extension of the pick-a-point method that can be accomplished with minimal mathematical background; the distinction is only that an interaction is probed across all feasible levels of a moderator, rather than at only select values.

A mathematical understanding of the J-N technique can be built from Equations 5.3 and 5.4 above that describes the standard error and t value corresponding with a given simple slope effect. In these equations, the analyst chooses a particular value of z_i in this equation, solves for t, and determines whether a simple slope is statistically different from zero based on this value. The J-N technique is strictly "working backwards" from Equations 5.3 and 5.4 (Preacher et al., 2006): Rather than solving for t, we determine z_i value(s) for which t is beyond some critical value (because α is typically assumed to be 0.05 in much psychological research, the critical value selected is usually ±1.96). For instance, assuming a critical t value of ±1.96, we can rearrange Equation 5.4 above to yield

$$1.96^2 * SE(b_1 + b_3 z_i | z_i)^2 - (b_1 + b_3 z_i | z_i)^2 = 0. \qquad (5.13)$$

The quadratic formula can then be used to determine the values of z_i that resolve this equality (Bauer & Curran, 2005).

Alternatively, we can accomplish the goals of the J-N technique by computing the estimates and standard errors of slopes manually across a range of feasible moderator values. This method obviates the need for algebra that may be less familiar to applied scientists and may be especially approachable for analysts with some familiarity with computer programming (e.g., writing *for* loops or R functions). For instance, assume we pursued the Exercise × Sleep interaction described in Example 1 using a sample of $N = 300$ participants. Assume an MMR produced the estimates $b_{exercise} = 1.19$ and $b_{exercise*sleep} = 0.97$, as well as variances and covariances of

$var(b_{exercise}) = 0.013$, $cov(b_{exercise}, b_{exercise*sleep}) = -0.001$, and $var(b_{exercise*sleep}) = 0.016$. Using this information, we can then compute the simple slope of exercise, as well as its standard error and t value, across a hypothetical range of our sleep moderator. Given sleep ranges from 5 to 9 hours in the sample, we may choose a sequence of hypotheticals that range from 5 to 9 hours in increments of 0.5 hours. We note that if a greater level of nuance in our moderator values is desired, we can set this increment at a smaller number (e.g., 0.01 hours) to better approximate the algebraic results of the J-N technique (if loops or functions are used, this can be done trivially with essentially no discernible consequences in computation time). Computing and tabling these results may produce those shown in Table 5.2.

Based on these values, we observe that the levels of the moderator where the simple slopes are statistically nonzero are at 5 and 6.5 hours of sleep (bolded), such that the regions of significance range from below 5 hours to above 6.5 hours. The signs of these slopes indicate that exercise may be *negatively* associated with well-being at 5 hours of sleep or less and *positively* associated

TABLE 5.2

Conditional Effects of Exercise on Well-Being Across Levels of Sleep

Sleep value	Exercise slope	SE	t value	95% CI
5.0	**−0.682**	**0.278**	**−2.455**	**[−1.228, −0.135]**
5.5	−0.194	0.222	−0.877	[−0.630, 0.242]
6.0	0.293	0.170	1.720	[−0.042, 0.629]
6.5	**0.781**	**0.130**	**5.989**	**[0.524, 1.037]**
7.0	1.268	0.114	11.151	[1.044, 1.492]
7.5	1.756	0.130	13.518	[1.500, 2.011]
8.0	2.243	0.170	13.219	[1.909, 2.577]
8.5	2.731	0.221	12.371	[2.296, 3.165]
9.0	3.218	0.277	11.625	[2.673, 3.763]

Note. Bold rows indicate the lower bound sleep values where the slope of exercise on well-being is statistically significant. That is, sleep hours of less than 5.0 and greater than 6.5 are levels of sleep where exercise is significantly associated with well-being. Italicized rows indicate levels of sleep at which the slopes are not significantly different from zero.

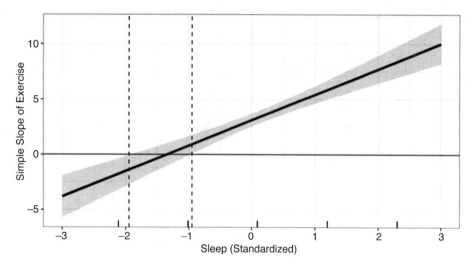

FIGURE 5.2. Marginal effects plot demonstrating the range of simple slopes of exercise across levels of sleep. Figure was created using the interActive application. Adapted from "Improving Present Practices in the Visual Display of Interactions," by C. J. McCabe, D. S. Kim, and K. M. King, 2018, *Advances in Methods and Practices in Psychological Science*, 1(2), p. 154 (https://doi.org/10.1177/2515245917746792). Copyright 2018 by SAGE. Adapted with permission.

at 6.5 hours of sleep or greater—a potentially critical insight that may have been missed if only select values were used.

Importantly, interpreting the practical significance of these slopes relies on a careful understanding of the distribution of the data. For instance, noting that only 4.3% ($n = 13$) report 5 hours of sleep in the sample and 67.3% ($n = 202$) report greater than 6.5 hours, we may have greater confidence in the positive slope estimates provided by these analyses. For this reason, we strongly advise that analysts report proportions of observed data within the regions of significance when reporting the results of J-N analyses and supplement these results with simple slopes displayed at moderator values representative of each region of significance. Displaying these effects in a marginal effects plot may also add clarity and communicate precision in these simple slopes (Figure 5.2).

PLOTTING INTERACTIONS

As we have shown, interpreting an interaction effect in lay terms may not be necessarily easy or straightforward (Dawson, 2014; Preacher et al., 2006) because it requires algebra to probe these effects via simple slopes. Instead, graphical displays provide visually efficient means of communicating the strength of evidence for an interaction effect, without unduly burdening readers with the task of unpacking these effects themselves. Additionally, in providing additional elements beyond the simple slopes estimates, such as observed data points, confidence regions, and all quantities of interest, plots can provide a clearer depiction of how confident we may be in these effects given the data at-hand (McCabe et al., 2018).

Three-Dimensional Surfaces

One method of displaying continuous variable interactions is by plotting the regression surface using a three-dimensional (3-D) plot. The utility in 3-D plots is that an axis can be devoted to each variable involved in the interaction, allowing a comprehensive representation of the interaction effect across all possible levels of the focal and moderating variables. By contrast, plotting simple slopes represents the interaction effect at only select levels of the moderator, relegates information about these levels to the legend of a two-dimensional figure, and requires the analyst make potentially arbitrary decisions on which slopes best communicate the interaction effect (Finsaas & Goldstein, 2021).

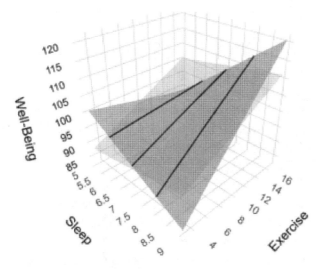

FIGURE 5.3. Three-dimensional (3D) plot illustrating an Exercise × Sleep interaction described in Example 1. This figure was created through adapted code provided from "Do Simple Slopes Follow-Up Tests Lead Us Astray? Advancements in the Visualization and Reporting of Interactions," by M. C. Finsaas and B. L. Goldstein, 2021, *Psychological Methods*, 26(1), 38–60 (https://doi.org/10.1037/met0000266). Copyright 2021 by the American Psychological Association. An online interactive version of this plot is available at https://rpubs.com/connorjmccabe/ch5_3Dplot_Example1.

A 3-D plot of Example 1 is displayed in Figure 5.3, and an interactive version of this plot can be found at https://rpubs.com/connorjmccabe/ch5_3Dplot_Example1. In this plot, we have overlayed a regression plane (lighter gray plane) for this model assuming no interaction present in this data (i.e., $b_{exercise*sleep}$ is 0). We can see from this figure that the interaction effect introduces curvature in the regression surface relative to the strictly additive model. Intuitively, the strength of the interaction effect is reflected by how much "bend" in the regression surface is introduced by the presence of an interaction, such that the greater the curvature, the stronger the interaction effect. We can also see from this curved surface that the simple slopes we show in Figure 5.1 are a sampling of effects shown along this surface (e.g., the three black lines in this plot are exactly those provided in Figure 5.1). As demonstrated in Figure 5.3, 3-D plots can provide a comprehensive means of plotting continuous variable interaction effects. Regardless of whether these plots are provided in printed publication, we advocate their use in fully exploring the data space of continuous variable interactions (e.g., see Finsaas & Goldstein, 2021, for resources in constructing and interpreting these plots).

SIMPLE SLOPES PLOTS

Whereas 3D figures benefit from displaying a large quantity of information regarding an interaction effect, they are often difficult to interpret directly due to the inherent challenge in processing information across a complex three-dimensional surface. Though particularly helpful as a dynamic interactive display (e.g., Finsaas & Goldstein, 2021), 3-D plots lend themselves somewhat poorly to static media, such as in printed manuscripts, and may become crowded and difficult to interpret when numerous elements are contained within the display. As such, an alternative is to plot simple slopes effects at only select values of the moderating variable (e.g., see Figure 5.1 and plots in Table 5.1 for simple examples), wherein visual differences in the slopes of these lines aid readers in judging the strength of the interaction effect (Cleveland & McGill, 1987). When constructed thoughtfully, such displays can efficiently and effectively communicate the nature of an interaction, with minimal loss of data integrity and scientific inference.

To ensure that an interaction is fully explored, accurately communicated, and appropriately specified given the data at-hand, we advise incorporating several graphical elements in the construction of these simple slopes figures (King et al., 2000; McCabe et al., 2018; Tufte, 2001). First, noting that only a limited number of values of the moderator can be specified when constructing these plots, analysts should select values that are theoretically interesting and meaningful. We advise that analysts also label these values clearly in the figure and show as many relevant levels of the moderator as is feasible to display. For instance, it is exceedingly common in psychological science for continuous variable interaction plots to include only two simple slopes, shown at 1 *SD* above and below the mean of a moderating variable. Moreover, theses slopes are often labeled ambiguously as "Low" and "High" and are displayed across "Low" and "High" ranges of the focal (x-axis) variable (Figure 5.4). However, the choice of displaying simple slopes at these select values is arbitrary and may in fact represent the data poorly or incompletely if the focal and/or moderating variable is distributed nonnormally (e.g., substantially skewed or multimodal) or the sample size is large. As such, we recommend that analysts display the interaction effect at all quantities of interest—that is, across the full observed range of the focal variable and across multiple thoughtfully chosen levels of the moderator.

Second, we advise that plots include some *measure of uncertainty* in the simple slope estimates. Providing uncertainty estimates, such as error bars or confidence regions, provides a visual depiction of how precisely each effect was estimated, as well as a visual indicator of whether a given simple slope is significantly different from zero. This is critical because factors such as sample size or variance of the MMR estimates can affect the precision of simple slopes. It is feasible, for instance, that two independent samples produce identical simple slope estimates, yet may suggest different inferences depending strictly on sample characteristics (e.g., sample size; see Figure 3 of McCabe et al., 2018). We note that including measures of uncertainty in simple slopes plots is consistent with newer statistical perspectives encouraging the use of confidence intervals in describing statistical quantities (Cumming, 2014); given simple slopes plots are visual depictions of such quantities, we (and others; Brambor et al., 2006) advocate for their inclusion in all visual displays of interactions.

Third, simple slopes plots should display the observed data on which the model estimates are based. Although observed data aid in determining whether an interaction effect is appropriately specified and sensible (Tay et al., 2016), we note that many simple slopes plots published to-date do not provide these quantities, perhaps due to the graphical difficulty in representing values across both the focal and moderator variables simultaneously. Analysts may resolve this by displaying simple slopes across small multiple (i.e., trellis) plots, wherein each multiple represents some select range of the moderating variable (Figure 5.5, produced using the interActive application). These plots also allow additional graphical elements (e.g., confidence regions) to be included without sacrificing interpretability of the figure. Alternatively, information regarding

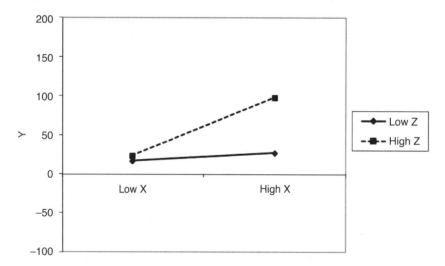

FIGURE 5.4. A prototypical simple slopes plot providing little clarity regarding specific X and Z values plotted, and minimal quantities of interest. Adapted from "Improving Present Practices in the Visual Display of Interactions," by C. J. McCabe, D. S. Kim, and K. M. King, 2018, *Advances in Methods and Practices in Psychological Science*, 1(2), p. 151 (https://doi.org/10.1177/2515245917746792). Copyright 2018 by Sage. Adapted with permission.

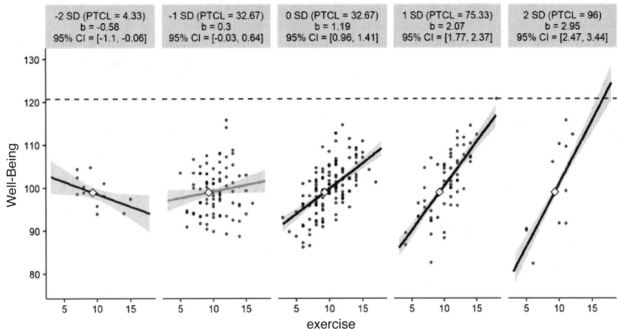

FIGURE 5.5. Small multiple displays of a continuous variable interaction that contains several elements essential to graphical integrity. This figure was generated using the interActive application. Adapted from "Improving Present Practices in the Visual Display of Interactions," by C. J. McCabe, D. S. Kim, and K. M. King, 2018, *Advances in Methods and Practices in Psychological Science*, 1(2), p. 156 (https://doi.org/10.1177/2515245917746792). Copyright 2018 by Sage. Adapted with permission.

the moderator level can be assigned to the color and/or size of each data point (e.g., Hallgren et al., 2019). This approach may be preferable in situations where multiple plots are suboptimal or it is feasible to show all graphical elements within a single plot (e.g., when a moderator is dichotomous).

PITFALLS, MISCONCEPTIONS, AND FUTURE DIRECTIONS

In this section, we clarify several common misconceptions we have seen commonly in the psychological literature regarding interactions. We then provide a brief introduction to interaction analysis in the context of more advanced statistical models.

Centering: What It Does (and Does Not) Accomplish

Centering in MMR involves subtracting some value c from each observation of a variable. Though the variance of this rescaled variable remains unchanged, the value of 0 for this variable is now c. In the context of interactions involving continuous variables, this procedure provides a useful means of facilitating the interpretation of coefficients produced by an MMR. For instance, it is both common (and highly recommended) practice for researchers to center continuous predictors involved in an interaction at their sample mean prior to analyzing an interaction. Rescaling the moderator variable (z_i) from Equation 5.1, we can accomplish this by performing the following:

$$y_i = b_0 + b_1 x_i + b_2(z_i - \bar{z}) + b_{12} x_i (z_i - \bar{z}) + e_i. \tag{5.14}$$

Recall that regression coefficients can be interpreted as how much an outcome changes for a one-unit change regressor, when all regressors are at 0. Because we have transformed z such that its mean equals 0, the lower order coefficients provided by this model can now be interpreted as estimates when z is at its sample mean. The utility in centering variables is that for many variables in psychology, the value of zero has little meaning, or is outside the observed range of the data. By centering a variable around a more meaningful value (such as the mean), the analyst can better ensure that lower order coefficients produced in a regression output are sensible given the data at-hand.

Nonetheless, several myths exist regarding what centering does (and does not) accomplish (see Dalal & Zickar, 2012, for an excellent treatment of this topic). Most commonly, we have found that researchers believe that mean-centering reduces (essential) collinearity between an interaction and its lower order terms, such that centering improves the performance of an MMR. This is not true. It is helpful to recall that an MMR estimates a curved regression surface (see Figure 5.3) and that the estimates provided in a regression output describe the linear effects present along this surface at the specific instance when all regressors are at 0. When recentering a variable, the analyst is strictly changing the points along this surface at which estimates are presented, with no consequence to the estimated surface itself (i.e., centering does not change the estimate of the interaction). This point can be further observed in comparing fit statistics (e.g., R^2) between centered and noncentered MMR models. If centering changed the fundamental performance of the model, these statistical quantities would change as well (for instance, we encourage analysts compare centered and uncentered regression outputs in their own work). When centering in MMR, nothing is fundamentally altered about the model itself. Rather, rescaling our variable(s) aids in making our regression coefficients more readily interpretable.

Polynomial Effects

We have observed that across several graduate and undergraduate statistics courses, polynomial effects are introduced as a distinct topic from interaction effects. Nonetheless, it is critical to note that on a computational and conceptual level, polynomial effects are ultimately variables interacting with themselves. For instance, Figure 5.6 shows a hypothetical relation between the quadratic of X and Y. At low levels of X, a unit increase corresponds with substantial change in Y, yet this effect diminishes as X gets larger. In other words, in typical interaction language, we can say that the effect of X on Y depends on the level of X.

Because of the similarity between polynomials and interactions, polynomial effects are often

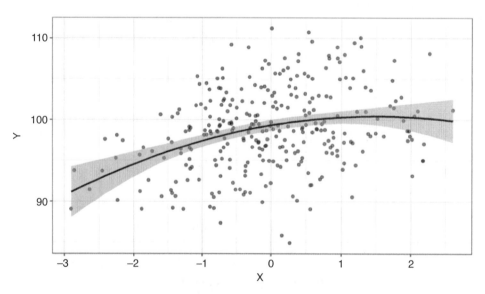

FIGURE 5.6. An outcome (Y) regressed on a quadratic of a predictor (X^2).

confounded with interactions, raising concerns of model misspecification when left unaddressed in tests of interaction (Aiken et al., 2012; Edwards, 2008; MacCallum & Mar, 1995). This is particularly an issue when variables involved in the interaction are highly correlated. For instance, for two variables X and Z, we can observe that the distinction between the product $X * Z$ and the quadratic X^2 (i.e., $X * X$) becomes lesser as the correlation between X and Z increases (and are indeed indistinguishable if they are correlated at 1.0). Resolving this issue is an area of ongoing work. Pragmatically, researchers are advised to explore the data visually for polynomial effects, and/or explicitly control for polynomials (e.g., X^2 and Z^2) when pursuing interactions (MacCallum & Mar, 1995). More recent advances in data exploratory methodologies (e.g., penalized regression models; Helwig, 2017) have shown promise in improving the distinction between interactions and polynomials via coefficient shrinkage and variable selection, which ultimately improve model specification (Signorino & Kirchner, 2018). We note, however, that more quantitative psychology research in this area is needed to increase the widespread adaptation of these methods in psychological science.

Interactions Beyond the MMR Context

The approaches we describe in this chapter lay a foundation for testing interaction effects across a range of linear regression contexts. Although many of the approaches we describe translate to more advanced methods of analysis, it is important to note that testing the concept of interaction between variables extends beyond the approaches reviewed in this chapter. Recall that the goal of interaction analysis is to determine whether and how the effect of one variable on some quantity depends on the level of another variable. Throughout, we have introduced and described product terms (e.g., $X * Z$) as a means of quantifying this question because they sufficiently capture the magnitude of interaction (i.e., "it depends") in linear MMR. Nonetheless, it is unique to the linear MMR context that product terms (e.g., $X * Z$) provide optimal estimates of the interaction effects (e.g., $X \times Z$), and we caution against using the terms *product* and *interaction* interchangeably. For instance, we allude to this concept in the multicategorical section of this chapter, in which we note that a Treatment × Sex interaction required multiple product terms, $T_1 *$ female and $T_2 *$ female, to be fully represented within the MMR. In several other modeling contexts, product terms and interactions are not identical and require considerations not articulated in this chapter to appropriately quantify an interaction effect. Although a complete treatment of this topic is beyond the scope of this chapter, we highlight several examples of this in models commonly utilized in psychology to illustrate this concept and provide resources for further reading.

As an illustration, consider the Poisson generalized linear model example provided in Figure 5.7, adapted from McCabe et al. (2021). In generalized linear models, analysts often estimate a model on a transformed linear scale (e.g., log-odds or log-counts) and then interpret effects on a more natural nonlinear scale (e.g., probabilities and counts), as shown in Figure 5.7. Specifically, this figure describes the nonlinear (i.e., exponential) relation between the count of some outcome Y and two predictors X and Z. Importantly, this figure is derived from a model in which no product terms were specified among the predictors. Despite the omission of product terms, we can see that any unit increase in X corresponds with greater increases in the count of Y when Z is relatively higher (e.g., dashed line) versus relatively lower (e.g., solid line). This is because the nonlinear nature of the model itself introduces interaction between variables automatically, irrespective of the magnitude of product terms within these models (McCabe et al., 2021). In other words, the effect of X on our outcome of interest depended on Z (as in an $X \times Z$ interaction), without estimating an $X * Z$ product term at all.

Complexities in testing the concept of interaction pervade other analytic traditions that involve nonlinear design (Kim & McCabe, 2022). For instance, time-varying effects models (Lanza & Linden-Carmichael, 2021; Tan et al., 2012),

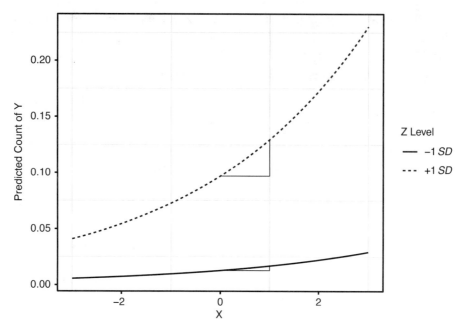

FIGURE 5.7. The relation between the predicted count of Y and X at 1 *SD* above and 1 *SD* below the mean of moderator Z. This figure shows an interaction effect represented within a Poisson model despite omission of a product term. For instance, the effect of one-unit increases in X from 0 to 1 on the count of Y was greater at 1 *SD* above the mean of Z (dashed line) compared with 1 *SD* below the mean (solid line). Adapted from "Interpreting Interaction Effects in Generalized Linear Models of Probabilities and Counts," by C. J. McCabe, M. A. Halvorson, K. M. King, X. Cao, and D. S. Kim, 2021, *Multivariate Behavioral Research*, 57(2–3), p. 255 (https://doi.org/10.1080/00273171.2020.1868966). Copyright 2021 by the Taylor and Francis Group. Adapted with permission.

which use splines to define the functional form of time, are parameterized under the assumption that a given effect varies as a complex function with time. In other words, the design of the model itself implies that each variable involved in the model interacts with time, even in the absence of specified product terms. Still other methodologies such as classification and regression trees were originally developed as a method of automatic interaction detection (Morgan & Sonquist, 1963; see also Chapter 20, this volume). The application of recursive partitioning allows these models to detect complex and high-order interaction effects, with the benefit of imposing no modeling assumptions on how the data are generated (Dwyer et al., 2018; Strobl et al., 2009; Yarkoni & Westfall, 2017).

These examples demonstrate the various ways that analysts can pursue the concept of interaction in psychological research across a variety of modeling approaches. Defined broadly, interaction effects imply that a given effect is nonlinearly associated with an outcome, specifically with respect to another variable. In the MMR context, such nonlinearities can be sufficiently addressed using product terms ($X * Z$) or polynomials (X^2) that allow their quantification when linearity is otherwise assumed in the model. Nonetheless, this may not be the case across all modeling contexts. Thus, we urge researchers to consider the question of "it depends" on a conceptual rather than purely statistical level; the statistical methods for pursuing interactions may themselves depend crucially on the specific modeling strategy employed.

References

Aiken, L. S., & West, S. G. (1991). *Multiple regression analysis: Testing and interpreting interactions*. SAGE.

Aiken, L. S., West, S. G., Luhmann, M., Baraldi, A., & Coxe, S. J. (2012). Estimating and graphing interactions. In H. Cooper, P. M. Camic, D. L. Long, A. T. Panter, D. Rindskopf, & K. J. Sher (Eds.), *APA handbook of research methods in psychology: Vol. 3. Data analysis and research publication* (pp. 101–129). American Psychological Association. https://doi.org/10.1037/13621-005

Bauer, D. J., & Curran, P. J. (2005). Probing interactions in fixed and multilevel regression: Inferential and graphical techniques. *Multivariate Behavioral Research*, *40*(3), 373–400. https://doi.org/10.1207/s15327906mbr4003_5

Brambor, T., Clark, W. R., & Golder, M. (2006). Understanding interaction models: Improving empirical analyses. *Political Analysis*, *14*(1), 63–82. https://doi.org/10.1093/pan/mpi014

Cleveland, W. S., & McGill, R. (1987). Graphical perception: The visual decoding of quantitative information on graphical displays of data. *Journal of the Royal Statistical Society. Series A (General)*, *150*(3), 192–229. https://doi.org/10.2307/2981473

Cohen, J. (1968). Multiple regression as a general data-analytic system. *Psychological Bulletin*, *70*(6, Pt. 1), 426–443. https://doi.org/10.1037/h0026714

Cohen, J., Cohen, P., West, S. G., & Aiken, L. S. (2014). *Applied multiple regression/correlation analysis for the behavioral sciences*. Psychology Press. https://doi.org/10.4324/9781410606266

Cumming, G. (2014). The new statistics: Why and how. *Psychological Science*, *25*(1), 7–29. https://doi.org/10.1177/0956797613504966

Dalal, D. K., & Zickar, M. J. (2012). Some common myths about centering predictor variables in moderated multiple regression and polynomial regression. *Organizational Research Methods*, *15*(3), 339–362. https://doi.org/10.1177/1094428111430540

Dawson, J. F. (2014). Moderation in management research: What, why, when, and how. *Journal of Business and Psychology*, *29*(1), 1–19.

Dwyer, D. B., Falkai, P., & Koutsouleris, N. (2018). Machine learning approaches for clinical psychology and psychiatry. *Annual Review of Clinical Psychology*, *14*(1), 91–118. https://doi.org/10.1146/annurev-clinpsy-032816-045037

Edwards, J. R. (2008). Seven deadly myths of testing moderation in organizational research. In C. E. Lance & R. J. Vandenberg (Eds.), *Statistical and methodological myths and urban legends: Doctrine, verity and fable in organizational and social sciences* (pp. 143–164). Routledge. https://doi.org/10.4324/9780203867266

Finsaas, M. C., & Goldstein, B. L. (2021). Do simple slopes follow-up tests lead us astray? Advancements in the visualization and reporting of interactions. *Psychological Methods*, *26*(1), 38–60. https://doi.org/10.1037/met0000266

Hallgren, K. A., McCabe, C. J., King, K. M., & Atkins, D. C. (2019). Beyond path diagrams: Enhancing applied structural equation modeling research through data visualization. *Addictive Behaviors*, *94*, 74–82. https://doi.org/10.1016/j.addbeh.2018.08.030

Hayes, A. F. (2013). *Introduction to mediation, moderation, and conditional process analysis: A regression-based approach*. Guilford Press.

Hayes, A. F., & Matthes, J. (2009). Computational procedures for probing interactions in OLS and logistic regression: SPSS and SAS implementations. *Behavior Research Methods*, *41*(3), 924–936. https://doi.org/10.3758/BRM.41.3.924

Hayes, A. F., & Montoya, A. K. (2017). A tutorial on testing, visualizing, and probing an interaction involving a multicategorical variable in linear regression analysis. *Communication Methods and Measures*, *11*(1), 1–30. https://doi.org/10.1080/19312458.2016.1271116

Helwig, N. E. (2017). Adding bias to reduce variance in psychological results: A tutorial on penalized regression. *The Quantitative Methods for Psychology*, *13*(1), 1–19. https://doi.org/10.20982/tqmp.13.1.p001

Johnson, P. O., & Fay, L. C. (1950). The Johnson-Neyman technique, its theory and application. *Psychometrika*, *15*(4), 349–367. https://doi.org/10.1007/BF02288864

Kendler, K. S., Myers, J., & Prescott, C. A. (2005). Sex differences in the relationship between social support and risk for major depression: A longitudinal study of opposite-sex twin pairs. *American Journal of Psychiatry*, *162*(2), 250–256. https://doi.org/10.1176/appi.ajp.162.2.250

Kessler, R. C., Price, R. H., & Wortman, C. B. (1985). Social factors in psychopathology: Stress, social support, and coping processes. *Annual Review of Psychology*, *36*(1), 531–572. https://doi.org/10.1146/annurev.ps.36.020185.002531

Kim, D. S., & McCabe, C. J. (2022). The partial derivative framework for substantive regression effects. *Psychological Methods*, *27*(1), 121–141. https://doi.org/10.1037/met0000440

King, G., Tomz, M., & Wittenberg, J. (2000). Making the most of statistical analyses: Improving interpretation and presentation. *American Journal of Political Science*, *44*(2), 347–361. https://doi.org/10.2307/2669316

Lanza, S. T., & Linden-Carmichael, A. N. (2021). Generalized time-varying effect models for binary and count outcomes. In S. T. Lanza & A. N. Linden-Carmichael (Eds.), *Time-varying effect modeling for the behavioral, social, and health sciences.* https://doi.org/10.1007/978-3-030-70944-0_3

Lee, S., Lei, M. K., & Brody, G. H. (2015). Confidence intervals for distinguishing ordinal and disordinal interactions in multiple regression. *Psychological Methods, 20*(2), 245–258. https://doi.org/10.1037/met0000033

Long, J. (2019). *Interactions: Comprehensive, user-friendly toolkit for probing interactions* (1.1.0). https://cran.r-project.org/package=interactions

MacCallum, R. C., & Mar, C. M. (1995). Distinguishing between moderator and quadratic effects in multiple regression. *Psychological Bulletin, 118*(3), 405–421. https://doi.org/10.1037/0033-2909.118.3.405

McCabe, C. J., Halvorson, M. A., King, K. M., Cao, X., & Kim, D. S. (2021). Interpreting interaction effects in generalized linear models of probabilities and counts. *Multivariate Behavioral Research, 57*(2-3), 243–263. https://doi.org/10.1080/00273171.2020.1868966

McCabe, C. J., Kim, D. S., & King, K. M. (2018). Improving present practices in the visual display of interactions. *Advances in Methods and Practices in Psychological Science, 1*(2), 147–165. https://doi.org/10.1177/2515245917746792

McCabe, C. J., Louie, K. A., & King, K. M. (2015). Premeditation moderates the relation between sensation seeking and risky substance use among young adults. *Psychology of Addictive Behaviors, 29*(3), 753–765. https://doi.org/10.1037/adb0000075

Meisel, S. N., Fosco, W. D., Hawk, L. W., & Colder, C. R. (2019). Mind the gap: A review and recommendations for statistically evaluating dual systems models of adolescent risk behavior. *Developmental Cognitive Neuroscience, 39*(July), 100681. https://doi.org/10.1016/j.dcn.2019.100681

Monroe, S. M., & Simons, A. D. (1991). Diathesis-stress theories in the context of life stress research: Implications for the depressive disorders. *Psychological Bulletin, 110*(3), 406.

Morgan, J. N., & Sonquist, J. A. (1963). Problems in the analysis of survey data, and a proposal. *Journal of the American Statistical Association, 58*(302), 415–434. https://doi.org/10.1080/01621459.1963.10500855

Potthoff, R. F. (1964). On the Johnson-Neyman technique and some extensions thereof. *Psychometrika, 29*(3), 241–256. https://doi.org/10.1007/BF02289721

Preacher, K. J., Curran, P. J., & Bauer, D. J. (2006). Computational tools for probing interactions in multiple linear regression, multilevel modeling, and latent curve analysis. *Journal of Educational and Behavioral Statistics, 31*(4), 437–448. https://doi.org/10.3102/10769986031004437

Schneider, R. L., Arch, J. J., & Wolitzky-Taylor, K. B. (2015). The state of personalized treatment for anxiety disorders: A systematic review of treatment moderators. *Clinical Psychology Review, 38*, 39–54. https://doi.org/10.1016/j.cpr.2015.02.004

Signorino, C. S., & Kirchner, A. (2018). Using LASSO to model interactions and nonlinearities in survey data. *Survey Practice, 11*(1), 1–10. https://doi.org/10.29115/SP-2018-0005

Strobl, C., Malley, J., & Tutz, G. (2009). An introduction to recursive partitioning: Rationale, application, and characteristics of classification and regression trees, bagging, and random forests. *Psychological Methods, 14*(4), 323–348. https://doi.org/10.1037/a0016973

Tan, X., Shiyko, M. P., Li, R., Li, Y., & Dierker, L. (2012). A time-varying effect model for intensive longitudinal data. *Psychological Methods, 17*(1), 61–77. https://doi.org/10.1037/a0025814

Tay, L., Parrigon, S., Huang, Q., & LeBreton, J. M. (2016). Graphical descriptives: A way to improve data transparency and methodological rigor in psychology. *Perspectives on Psychological Science, 11*(5), 692–701. https://doi.org/10.1177/1745691616663875

Tufte, E. R. (2001). *The visual display of quantitative information* (2nd ed.). Graphics Press.

Voyer, D., & Voyer, S. D. (2014). Gender differences in scholastic achievement: A meta-analysis. *Psychological Bulletin, 140*(4), 1174–1204. https://doi.org/10.1037/a0036620

Widaman, K. F., Helm, J. L., Castro-Schilo, L., Pluess, M., Stallings, M. C., & Belsky, J. (2012). Distinguishing ordinal and disordinal interactions. *Psychological Methods, 17*(4), 615–622. https://doi.org/10.1037/a0030003

Yarkoni, T., & Westfall, J. (2017). Choosing prediction over explanation in psychology: Lessons from machine learning. *Perspectives on Psychological Science, 12*(6), 1100–1122. https://doi.org/10.1177/1745691617693393

CHAPTER 6

EFFECT-SIZE ESTIMATION

Michael Borenstein

An *effect size* is a value that reflects the magnitude of the relationship between two variables. It captures the substantive finding that the research is intended to address, and it does so using a metric that is meaningful and intuitive.

For example, the impact of a coaching program on Scholastic Aptitude Test (SAT) (a college-admissions test) scores might be reported as a *raw difference* of 50 points. Or the impact of a program to keep recovering alcoholics from drinking might be reported as a *risk ratio* of 0.50, meaning that the program reduced the risk of drinking by 50%. Similarly, the relationship between an aptitude test score and students' actual performance in a class might be reported as a *correlation* of .80. In each case, the metric is meaningful—people working in education will understand the substantive impact of a 50-point increase in SAT scores and how this compares with the impact of other interventions. The same holds true for the risk ratio of 0.50 and the correlation of .80.

The effect size reported in a *study* serves as an estimate of the effect size in the *population*, and for that reason, the study effect size is reported with a confidence interval that reflects its precision.

For example, a mean difference might be reported as 50 points with a 95% confidence interval of 40 to 60. This indicates that the mean difference in the study is 50 points and the true (population) mean difference probably falls in the range of 40 to 60.[1] Taken together, the effect size and its confidence interval summarize the core findings of the research—"How large is the effect?" and "How precise is our estimate?"

In this chapter, I introduce the idea of an effect size and show why the effect size is generally a more appropriate index than the *p* value for summarizing the results of a study. Then, I introduce some common effect-size indexes. Other effect-size indexes are discussed briefly toward the end of the chapter.

EFFECT SIZE VERSUS TREATMENT EFFECT

The term *effect size* refers to the relationship between any two variables. When one of the variables is a deliberate intervention, then the effect size may also be called a *treatment effect*. For example, the difference in test scores for coached versus control groups may be called

---

[1] Formally, it means that if we perform an infinite number of studies and compute a confidence interval for each one, 95% of these intervals will include the true effect size.

This work was funded in part by the following grants from the National Institutes of Health: "Combining Data Types in Meta-Analysis" (AG021360) from the National Institute on Aging under the direction of Sidney Stahl, and "Power Analysis for Meta-Analysis" (DA022799) under the direction of Augusto Diana. My thanks to Larry Hedges, Julian Higgins, and Hannah Rothstein for their assistance in clarifying some of the issues discussed in this chapter.

https://doi.org/10.1037/0000320-006
APA Handbook of Research Methods in Psychology, Second Edition: Vol. 3. Data Analysis and Research Publication, H. Cooper (Editor-in-Chief)
Copyright © 2023 by the American Psychological Association. All rights reserved.

either an *effect size* or a *treatment effect*. By contrast, the difference in test scores for males versus females is an effect size but is not a treatment effect because we are not dealing with a treatment.

Thus, the difference between an effect size and a treatment effect depends on the nature of the variables and not on the index itself. Any index, such as the standardized mean difference, the risk ratio, or any other, could be called an *effect size* in one study and a *treatment effect* in another, depending on the context. In this chapter I use the more general term, *effect size*, but the distinction between an effect size and a treatment effect is one of nomenclature only. The same computational formulas apply to both.

PARAMETERS, STATISTICS, AND PRECISION

Studies work with samples, and the effect size in the sample (the *statistic*) is intended to estimate the effect size in the larger population (the *parameter*). Because the sample effect size serves as an estimate of the population effect size, any time we report a sample effect size, we also need to report how precise that estimate is (American Psychological Association [APA], 2020, p. 89). The formula for precision varies from one effect-size index to the next, but an important factor in all of these formulas is the size of the sample, with larger samples yielding more precise estimates.

Consider Figure 6.1, which uses the raw mean difference to display the impact of four different interventions on SAT scores. The standard deviation of scores is 100 points. In this context, assume that a mean difference of less than 20 points between the treated (i.e., coached) and control groups is considered trivial and a difference of more than 40 points is considered large. In Studies A and B, the *observed* effect size is large (50 points). In Study A, however, the true effect size is known precisely, whereas in Study B the true effect size could fall anywhere in the range of −12 points (the intervention is actually harmful) to +112 points. In Studies C and D, the observed effect size is trivial (10 points). In Study C, however, the true effect size is known precisely, whereas in Study D the true effect size could fall anywhere in the range of −52 points to +72 points.

The effect size and precision, taken together, summarize the key findings—that the treatment effect is large (Study A), that the effect is trivial (Study C), or that we cannot estimate the effect size precisely enough to say whether it is large or trivial (Studies B and D). As such, these are generally the values that should be highlighted in the analysis and drive the discussion section—"How large (or small) is the effect?" "How precise is our estimate?" and "What are the implications for theory and practice?"

EFFECT SIZES AND *p* VALUES

Some readers will be more familiar with the idea of *p* values than with the idea of effect sizes. One must understand how the two are related and where they differ. The purpose of the *p* value is to test the null hypothesis. The *p* value combines information about the size

Study	Diff	Lower	Upper	N*	*p* value
A	50	41	59	1,000	< .01
B	50	−12	112	20	.11
C	10	1	19	1,000	.03
D	10	−52	72	20	.75

*N per group

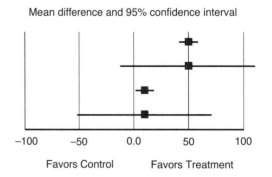

FIGURE 6.1. Effect size (Diff) and confidence intervals (Lower, Upper) for four fictional studies.

of the effect and its precision (or sample size) because it is the combination of these that speaks to the viability of the null hypothesis. By contrast, the purpose of the effect size is to reflect the magnitude of the effect, whereas the precision addresses its accuracy. For this purpose, we report the effect size and its precision (or confidence interval) as two distinct values.

The two approaches (the p value on the one hand, and the effect size with confidence interval on the other) are complementary in the sense that the p value generally falls under 0.05 if, and only if, the 95% confidence interval does not include the null value. Therefore, the researcher may elect to report both. It is important to understand that the p value and the effect size address different questions. The p value addresses the question, "Can we conclude that the true effect size is not zero?" By contrast, the effect size addresses the questions, "What is the magnitude of the relationship?" or "What is the substantive impact of the intervention?"

There are some situations in which we really do care about the first question. For example, if we anticipate that homeopathic remedies will have no impact at all on a disease, we would expect the impact of these remedies in a properly designed randomized study to be precisely zero. Therefore, it would be appropriate for the analysis to focus on the test of significance. These kinds of situations are relatively rare in social science, however.

Rather, in the vast majority of cases, it is the second question that we really care about. For example, if we perform a study to assess the impact of coaching on test scores, we probably assume that the impact of the coaching program is not precisely zero, and, therefore, we have little (if any) interest in testing the null hypothesis. What we really care about is the size of the effect—whether the coaching increases the mean score by 20 points, 50 points, or 100 points—because this is the information that tells us whether the program is practically useful and whether it is better than other alternatives (see Chapter 7, this volume).

Because researchers care about the magnitude of the effect, when a study reports a p value and fails to report an effect size, the p value is often pressed into service as a surrogate for effect size. The researcher may report that the p value is 0.75 and then proceed to discuss the "fact" that the treatment is not effective. Or, the researcher may report that the p value is < .01 and then proceed to discuss the "large" impact of the intervention. In fact, however, these conclusions are not justified. A nonsignificant p value tells us only that we cannot reject the null hypothesis. This could be because the effect size is small, but it also could be because the sample size is small (even if the effect size is large)—see Studies D and B, respectively, in Figure 6.1. Conversely, a significant p value tells us *only* that we can reject the null hypothesis. This could be because the effect size is large, but it also could be because the sample size is large (whereas the effect size is small)—see Studies A and C, respectively, in Figure 6.1.

Still, the practice of using the p value as a surrogate for effect size is difficult to extinguish. For example, suppose you are told that one study had a p value of .03 whereas another had a p value of 0.11. Most people would assume that the effect size was larger in the first study, even if they had recently read the previous paragraph (Tversky & Kahneman, 1971). It is entirely possible, however, that the effect size was substantially smaller (albeit more precise) in the first study—see Studies C and B, respectively, in Figure 6.1.

In sum, the p value combines information about the size of the effect *and* the size of the sample because both are relevant to its function, which is to assess the viability of the null hypothesis. By contrast, when we report the effect size and its confidence interval, we are reporting two distinct items of information. First, the effect size is small or large. Second, the estimate is precise or imprecise. For the studies in Figure 6.1, the key distinction should be between Studies A and B (where the effect is large) versus Studies C and D (where the effect is small). This is the distinction that is captured by the effect size. At the same time, we need to distinguish between Study A (where the effect is known precisely) and Study B (where it is not). Similarly, we need to distinguish between

Study C (where the effect is known precisely) and Study D (where it is not). These are the distinctions that are captured by confidence interval. (For a more extensive discussion of this issue, see Borenstein, 1994, 2000; Borenstein et al., 2021.)

META-ANALYSIS

Meta-analysis refers to the process of synthesizing data from a series of studies (Cooper, 2017; Borenstein et al., 2021). The meta-analysis tells us if the effect size is consistent or if it varies from study to study. If the effect size is consistent, the meta-analysis allows us to report that the effect size is robust across the studies included in the analysis and to estimate the true common effect size more precisely than is possible with any single study. If the effect sizes vary across studies, then the meta-analysis will yield a picture of how the effect size varies, and in some cases, it will allow us to identify the factors associated with the variation.

The same effect sizes that we have been discussing for the individual study also serve as the unit of currency in the meta-analysis—it is these effect sizes that we compare, combine, and contrast to perform the synthesis. Thus, in addition to providing the key summary points for the individual study, the effect size allows the study results to be used in a meta-analysis as part of the larger research endeavor. In this process, the precision that we have been reporting for the individual study helps determine how much weight to assign to each study in the meta-analysis, with more weight being assigned to the more precise studies.

CHOOSING AN EFFECT-SIZE INDEX

The process of choosing an effect-size index for a given study consists of two steps. First, we narrow the selection of effect sizes on the basis of the kinds of data reported in the study. For example, there is one set of effect-size indexes for studies that report means, another for studies that report proportions, and so on. Then, within each set, we select the effect-size index that matches the study goals. For example, one effect-size index might be based on a *difference* in proportions, whereas another is based on the *ratio* of the proportions. In the next section, I introduce some of the more common effect-size indexes for studies that report means, proportions, or the relationship between continuous variables.

EFFECT-SIZE INDEXES BASED ON MEANS

Consider a study in which students are randomly assigned to either of two groups, *treated* or *control* (200 per group). Those in the former are provided with coaching intended to improve their scores on the SAT, and those in the latter are be provided with a standard curriculum. The mean SAT scores for the two groups are 450 versus 400, with a standard deviation of 100 in each group.

In a variant of this example, consider a study in which 200 students are tested on the SAT (the pretest), spend 2 weeks being coached, and then take the actual SAT (the posttest). The mean pretest score is 400, the mean posttest score is 450, the standard deviation within either time-point is 100, and the correlation between the pretest scores and the posttest scores is 0.70. (For the present purposes, I ignore potential problems of internal validity with this design.)

The most common effect-size indexes for these kinds of studies are the *raw* mean difference and the *standardized* mean difference. The *raw* mean difference is simply the difference in means. The *standardized* mean difference is also based on the difference in means, but rather than being reported on the raw scale, it is reported on a scale that has been standardized to have a standard deviation of 1.0 within-groups.

The raw mean difference can serve as the effect-size index when the outcome is based on a scale that is widely used (such as SAT scores in the United States) or that is inherently meaningful (such as blood pressure or weight). When this condition is met, the raw mean difference has the advantage of being transparent and intuitive (we understand the practical implications of a 50-point difference on the SAT or a 20-pound difference in weight).

By contrast, when the outcome is reported on a relatively obscure scale, the raw mean difference has less to recommend it. If the reader is not familiar with the *XYZ* scale, then a report that the intervention increased the mean score by 10 points will have no real meaning (if scores on this scale range from 0 to 1,000, then 10 points may be a small difference, but if scores range from 0 to 100, then 10 points may be a very large difference). In this case, the standardized mean difference is a better option. A standardized mean difference (sometimes called *d* or Hedges' *g*) simply transforms the raw difference to a scale with a standard deviation of 1.0 within groups. On this scale, a difference of 0.50 indicates that the mean for one group was one half a standard deviation higher than the mean for the other group. As such, this effect-size index is meaningful even if the reader is not familiar with the original scale.

Another reason for using the standardized mean difference rather than the raw mean difference is to facilitate the synthesis of effect sizes across studies. If all the studies used the same scale, then the synthesis can be based on either the raw mean difference or the standardized mean difference. If the scale varies from study to study, however, then the synthesis cannot be based on the raw mean difference—for example, it makes no sense to compute an average of SAT scores (on a scale of 200–800) and American College Testing (ACT) scores (on a scale of 2–36). Therefore, if we intend to compare the effect across studies, we would use the standardized mean difference, which puts all effects onto the same scale. Here, I show how to compute the raw mean difference and the standardized mean difference—first, working with data from two independent groups, and then, working with pre- and postscores in one group.

The Raw Mean Difference
If the true (population) means in the two groups are denoted by μ_1 and μ_2, then the true (population) mean difference, *delta* (I) is defined as

$$\Delta = \mu_1 - \mu_2. \quad (6.1)$$

Computing *D* From Studies That Use Independent Groups
To estimate the raw mean difference from two independent groups, we apply the formula for I but replace the true (population) means with the estimated (sample) means.[2] If the sample means in the two groups are denoted by $\bar{Y}_1$ and $\bar{Y}_2$ then the sample estimate, *D*, is given by

$$D = \bar{Y}_1 - \bar{Y}_2. \quad (6.2)$$

Let S_1^2 and S_2^2 be the sample variances of the two groups, and n_1 and n_2 be the sample sizes in the two groups. If we assume that the two population variances are the same (as we do in most parametric data analysis techniques), so that $\sigma_1^2 = \sigma_2^2 = \sigma^2$, we pool the sample values S_1^2 and S_2^2 to obtain a more accurate estimate of the common value

$$S_{Pooled}^2 = \frac{(n_1 - 1)S_1^2 + (n_2 - 1)S_2^2}{n_1 + n_2 - 2}. \quad (6.3)$$

Then, the variance, standard error, and 95% confidence limits for *D* are given by

$$v_D = \frac{n_1 + n_2}{n_1 n_2} S_{Pooled}^2, \quad (6.4)$$

$$SE_D = \sqrt{v_D}, \quad (6.5)$$

$$LL_D = D - t_{df, 1-\alpha/2} \times SE_D, \quad (6.6)$$

and

$$UL_D = D + t_{df, 1-\alpha/2} \times SE_D. \quad (6.7)$$

The *t* value in these formulas ($t_{df, 1-\alpha/2}$) is the *t* value for the relevant degrees of freedom ($n_1 + n_2 - 2$) and the desired confidence level ($1 - \alpha/2$). For a large sample and 95% confidence interval, this *t* value will approach 1.96. We use *t* (rather than *Z*) to compute the confidence interval for the raw mean difference because this interval depends on S_{Pooled}, and this value is estimated from the sample.

---

[2]Following common practice, I use Greek letters to represent population values and Roman letters to represent sample values.

These formulas can be applied to the SAT example for two independent groups. The raw mean difference, D, is given by

$$D = 450 - 400 = 50. \tag{6.8}$$

If we assume that $\sigma_1^2 = \sigma_2^2$, then the pooled within-groups standard deviation is

$$S_{Pooled} = \sqrt{\frac{(200-1)\times 100^2 + (200-1)\times 100^2}{200+200-2}} = 100. \tag{6.9}$$

The variance, standard error, and 95% confidence limits for D are given by

$$v_D = \frac{200+200}{200\times 200}\times 100^2 = 100, \tag{6.10}$$

$$SE_D = \sqrt{100} = 10, \tag{6.11}$$

$$LL_D = 50 - 1.966 \times 10 = 30.341, \tag{6.12}$$

and

$$UL_D = 50 + 1.966 \times 10 = 69.659, \tag{6.13}$$

where 1.966 corresponds to the t value for 95% confidence and 398 degrees of freedom.

In words, D in the study is 50 points, and the true raw mean difference (I) probably falls in the range of 30.341 points to 69.659 points.

Computing D From Studies That Use Pre- and Postscores or Matched Groups

To estimate the raw mean difference from a study that reported pretest scores and posttest scores, we again apply the formula for I and replace the true (population) means with the estimated (sample) means. If the pretest and posttest means are denoted by $\bar{Y}_{Pre}$ and $\bar{Y}_{Post}$, then the sample estimate D is

$$D = \bar{Y}_{Post} - \bar{Y}_{Pre}. \tag{6.14}$$

The effect size, D, is now based on the difference from pretest scores to posttest scores (rather than the difference between independent groups), but it has the same substantive meaning. (The direction of the difference is arbitrary, and we use postscore minus prescore to yield the same direction of effect as when we used treated minus control.) The difference between using independent groups or the pre–post design is not in the estimate of the effect size but rather in the precision of the estimate. The pre–post design tends to yield a more precise estimate of the effect because the correlation between the two sets of scores typically reduces the standard error of the effect size.

To compute the standard error of D for the pre–post design, we first compute standard deviation of the difference,

$$S_{Difference} = \sqrt{S_{Pre}^2 + S_{Post}^2 - 2\times r \times S_{Pre} \times S_{Post}}, \tag{6.15}$$

where S_{Pre}^2 and S_{Post}^2 are the variance of the pretest scores and posttest scores, r is the correlation between the pretest scores and posttest scores, and S_{Pre} and S_{Post} are the standard deviation of the pretest scores and posttest scores. Then, the variance of D is given by

$$v_D = \frac{S_{Difference}^2}{n}, \tag{6.16}$$

where n is the number of pairs. Finally, the standard error of D and 95% confidence limits are given by

$$SE_D = \sqrt{v_D}, \tag{6.17}$$

$$LL_D = D - t_{df, 1-\alpha/2} \times SE_D, \tag{6.18}$$

and

$$UL_D = D + t_{df, 1-\alpha/2} \times SE_D, \tag{6.19}$$

where the t value is for $n-1$ degrees of freedom.

These formulas can be applied to the SAT example for a study with pretest scores and posttest scores. The raw mean difference, D, is given by

$$D = 450 - 400 = 50. \tag{6.20}$$

The standard error of the difference (assuming a pretest–posttest correlation of $r = .70$) is given by

$$S_{Difference} = \sqrt{100^2 + 100^2 - 2 \times 0.70 \times 100 \times 100}$$
$$= 77.460. \qquad (6.21)$$

The variance, standard error, and 95% confidence limits for D are given by

$$v_D = \frac{77.460^2}{200} = 30.000, \qquad (6.22)$$

$$SE_D = \sqrt{30.00} = 5.477, \qquad (6.23)$$

$$LL_D = 50 - 1.972 \times 5.477 = 39.199, \qquad (6.24)$$

and

$$UL_D = 50 + 1.972 \times 5.477 = 60.801, \qquad (6.25)$$

where 1.972 corresponds to the t value for 95% confidence with 199 degrees of freedom. In words, D in the study is 50, and the true raw mean difference (I) probably falls in the range of 39.199 to 60.801.

The formulas to compute D for a pre–post design can also be used for a matched design. In the SAT study, for example, this would mean that each subject was *paired* with a classmate who had a similar ranking in the class. In the formulas, the pretest scores and posttest scores become the two students' SAT scores, and the pre–post correlation is replaced with the correlation of scores for the two sets of students. As is true for the pre–post design, the use of matching tends to yield a more precise estimate of D compared with the same number of independent observations.

THE STANDARDIZED MEAN DIFFERENCE

We now turn from the raw mean difference (in the metric of the outcome scale) to the standardized mean difference (for which the difference is reported on a scale with a standard deviation of 1.0 within-groups). This effect-size index can be used for any study that reports mean differences, but it is especially useful when the outcome scale is obscure (in which case the raw mean difference is a poor choice) or when we want to compare effects based on different scales (in which case the raw mean difference is not an option).

We need to distinguish among three terms— δ, d, and Hedges' g—which are used to represent the standardized mean difference (Borenstein et al., 2021; Cohen, 1977; Hedges, 1981). *Delta* (δ) is the population parameter, the true mean difference divided by the true standard deviation, and is the value we intend to estimate. By contrast, d and Hedges' g are both sample estimates of δ. The statistic d, which is often used as the estimate of δ, is simply the sample mean difference divided by the sample standard deviation. However, d has a slight bias and tends to overestimate δ, especially in small samples. To remove this bias, we multiply d by a factor (called J) to yield an estimate called Hedges' g (Hedges, 1981).

In sum, d and Hedges' g are both intended to estimate the same parameter (δ), but the former is biased and the latter is not. It follows that we should always report Hedges' g rather than d. Nevertheless, we include d in this discussion because it is widely used. Fortunately, the difference between d and g is usually too small to have any practical implications (Hedges, 1981).

The standardized mean difference in the population, delta (δ) is defined as the raw mean difference divided by the within-group standard deviation,

$$\delta = \frac{\mu_1 - \mu_2}{\sigma}. \qquad (6.26)$$

Computing d and g From Studies That Use Independent Groups

To estimate the standardized mean difference from the data, we apply the formula for δ, but replace the true (population) means with the estimated (sample) means. If the sample means in the two groups are $\bar{Y}_1$ and $\bar{Y}_2$, then the standardized mean difference d is computed as

$$d = \frac{\bar{Y}_1 - \bar{Y}_2}{S_{Pooled}}. \qquad (6.27)$$

In the denominator, S_{Pooled} is the within-groups standard deviation, pooled across groups,

$$S_{Pooled} = \sqrt{\frac{(n_1-1)S_1^2 + (n_2-1)S_2^2}{n_1+n_2-2}}, \quad (6.28)$$

where n_1, n_2 are the sample size in the two groups, and S_1, S_2 are the standard deviations in the two groups.

The variance, standard error, and 95% confidence limits for d are given (to a very good approximation) by

$$v_d = \frac{n_1+n_2}{n_1 n_2} + \frac{d^2}{2(n_1+n_2)}, \quad (6.29)$$

$$SE_d = \sqrt{v_d}, \quad (6.30)$$

$$LL_d = d - Z_{1-\alpha/2} \times SE_d, \quad (6.31)$$

and

$$UL_d = d + Z_{1-\alpha/2} \times SE_d, \quad (6.32)$$

where $Z_{1-\alpha/2}$ is the standardized normal critical value at level $\alpha/2$ (e.g., for 95% confidence intervals, $\alpha = 0.05$ and $Z_{1-\alpha/2} = 1.96$).

As explained, d has a slight bias, tending to overestimate the absolute value of δ in small samples. To remove this bias, we compute a correction factor, J, where

$$J(df) = 1 - \frac{3}{4df-1}. \quad (6.33)$$

In this expression, df is the degrees of freedom used to estimate S_{Pooled}, which for two independent groups is $n_1 + n_2 - 2$. Then, Hedges' g, its variance, standard error, and confidence limits are given by

$$g = J(df)d, \quad (6.34)$$

$$v_g = [J(df)]^2 v_d, \quad (6.35)$$

$$SE_g = \sqrt{v_g}, \quad (6.36)$$

$$LL_g = g - Z_{1-\alpha/2} \times SE_g, \quad (6.37)$$

and

$$UL_g = g + Z_{1-\alpha/2} \times SE_g. \quad (6.38)$$

The SAT example for independent groups, presented earlier for the raw mean difference, serves here as well. Recall that the sample means are $\bar{Y}_1 = 450$, $\bar{Y}_2 = 400$; sample standard deviations $S_1 = 100$, $S_2 = 100$; and sample sizes $n_1 = n_2 = 200$. The pooled within-groups standard deviation is

$$S_{Pooled} = \sqrt{\frac{(200-1)\times 100^2 + (200-1)\times 100^2}{200+200-2}} = 100. \quad (6.39)$$

Then,

$$d = \frac{450-400}{100} = 0.500, \quad (6.40)$$

$$v_d = \frac{200+200}{200\times 200} + \frac{0.500^2}{2(200+200)} = 0.010, \quad (6.41)$$

$$SE_d = \sqrt{0.010} = 0.102, \quad (6.42)$$

$$LL_d = 0.50 - 1.96 \times 0.102 = 0.301, \quad (6.43)$$

and

$$UL_d = 0.50 + 1.96 \times 0.102 = 0.699. \quad (6.44)$$

In words, d in the study is 0.500, and the true standardized mean difference (δ) probably falls in the range of 0.301 to 0.699.

The correction factor J is

$$J(200+200-2) = 1 - \frac{3}{4\times 398 - 1} = 0.998. \quad (6.45)$$

We multiply J by d to yield Hedges' g, and we multiply J^2 by the variance of d to yield the variance of g. Thus,

$$g = 0.998 \times 0.500 = 0.499, \quad (6.46)$$

$$v_g = 0.998^2 \times 0.010 = 0.010. \quad (6.47)$$

Then, the standard error and confidence limits for g are computed as

$$SE_g = \sqrt{0.010} = 0.102, \quad (6.48)$$

$$LL_g = 0.499 - 1.96 \times 0.102 = 0.300, \quad (6.49)$$

and

$$UL_g = 0.499 + 1.96 \times 0.102 = 0.698. \quad (6.50)$$

In words, Hedges' g in the study was 0.499, and the true standardized mean difference (δ) probably falls in the range of 0.300 to 0.698.

Computing d and g From Studies That Use Pre- and Postscores or Matched Groups

We can estimate the standardized mean difference (δ) from studies that used pre- and postscores in one group or matched groups. The formula for the sample estimate of d is

$$d = \frac{\overline{Y}_{Post} - \overline{Y}_{Pre}}{S_{Pooled}}. \quad (6.51)$$

This is analogous to the formula for the standardized mean differences based on independent groups. There is, however, an important difference in the mechanism used to compute S_{Pooled}. When we are working with independent groups, the natural unit of deviation is the standard deviation within groups. Therefore, this value is typically reported or easily computed from the data that *are* reported. By contrast, when we are working with pretest scores and posttest scores, the situation is more complicated. Now, there are three standard deviations involved. One is the standard deviation of the pretest scores, and one is the standard deviation of the posttest scores (which are analogous to the standard deviations within Groups 1 and 2 when the groups are independent). The third is the standard deviation of the difference scores.

To compute S_{Pooled}, we need the standard deviation within groups. Therefore, if we have the standard deviation of the pretest scores and the standard deviation of the posttest scores, we can compute the standard deviation pooled within-groups using

$$S_{Pooled} = \sqrt{\frac{S_{Pre}^2 + S_{Post}^2}{2}}, \quad (6.52)$$

where S_{Pre} and S_{Post} are the standard deviations of the pretest scores and posttest scores. Some studies do not report these values, however, and report instead the standard deviation of the difference scores. In this case, we can compute the standard deviation pooled within-groups using

$$S_{Pooled} = \frac{S_{Difference}}{\sqrt{2(1-r)}}, \quad (6.53)$$

where r is the correlation between pairs of observations (e.g., the correlation between pretest and posttest scores). Then we can apply this estimate to compute d. (Because the correlation between pretest scores and posttest scores is required for this computation, we must assume that this correlation is known or can be estimated with high precision.)

The variance of d is given by

$$v_d = \left(\frac{1}{n} + \frac{d^2}{2n}\right) 2(1-r), \quad (6.54)$$

where n is the number of pairs. The standard error of d and the 95% confidence limits are given by

$$SE_d = \sqrt{v_d}, \quad (6.55)$$

$$LL_d = d - Z_{1-\alpha/2} \times SE_d, \quad (6.56)$$

and

$$UL_d = d + Z_{1-\alpha/2} \times SE_d. \quad (6.57)$$

As explained above, d has a slight bias, tending to overestimate the absolute value of δ in small samples. To remove this bias, we compute a correction factor, J, where

$$J(df) = 1 - \frac{3}{4df - 1}. \quad (6.58)$$

The df for computing J is $n - 1$, where n is the number of pairs. Then, Hedges' g, its variance, standard error, and 95% confidence limits are computed using

$$g = J(df) \times d, \quad (6.59)$$

$$v_g = [J(df)]^2 \times v_d, \quad (6.60)$$

$$SE_g = \sqrt{v_g}, \quad (6.61)$$

$$LL_g = g - Z_{1-\alpha/2} \times SE_g, \quad (6.62)$$

and

$$UL_g = g + Z_{1-\alpha/2} \times SE_g. \quad (6.63)$$

The SAT example for a pre–post design, presented earlier for raw mean differences, serves here as well. Recall that the sample size is 200, the pretest mean is 400, the posttest mean is 450, the standard deviation within either time-point is 100, and the correlation between pretest scores and posttest scores is 0.70.

If we start with the standard deviation of the pretest scores and the standard deviation of the posttest scores, S_{Pooled} is given by

$$S_{Pooled} = \sqrt{\frac{100^2 + 100^2}{2}} = 100. \quad (6.64)$$

Alternatively, if we start with the standard deviation of the difference, then S_{Pooled} can be estimated by

$$S_{Pooled} = \frac{77.460}{\sqrt{2(1-0.7)}} = 100. \quad (6.65)$$

The two formulas yield the same value when the sample pretest and posttest standard deviations are identical.

In either case, d, its variance, standard error, and 95% confidence limits are computed as

$$d = \frac{450 - 400}{100} = 0.500, \quad (6.66)$$

$$v_d = \left(\frac{1}{200} + \frac{0.500^2}{2 \times 200}\right)(2(1-0.7)) = 0.003, \quad (6.67)$$

$$SE_d = \sqrt{0.003} = 0.058, \quad (6.68)$$

$$LL_d = 0.50 - 1.96 \times 0.058 = 0.386, \quad (6.69)$$

and

$$UL_d = 0.50 + 1.96 \times 0.058 = 0.614. \quad (6.70)$$

In words, d in the study is 0.500, and the true standardized mean difference (δ) probably falls in the range of 0.386 to 0.614.

Finally, the correction factor J is computed as

$$J(200 - 1) = 1 - \frac{3}{4 \times 199 - 1} = 0.996, \quad (6.71)$$

and Hedges' g, its variance, standard error and confidence limits are given by

$$g = 0.996 \times 0.500 = 0.498, \quad (6.72)$$

$$v_g = 0.996^2 \times 0.003 = 0.003, \quad (6.73)$$

$$SE_g = \sqrt{0.003} = 0.058, \quad (6.74)$$

$$LL_g = 0.498 - 1.96 \times 0.058 = 0.385, \quad (6.75)$$

and

$$UL_g = 0.498 + 1.96 \times 0.058 = 0.612. \quad (6.76)$$

In words, Hedges' g in the study is 0.498, and the true standardized mean difference (δ) probably falls in the range of 0.385 to 0.612. As discussed earlier (for D), the formulas for a pre–post design can be applied also for a matched design.

EFFECT-SIZE INDEXES FOR BINARY DATA

In the previous section, I discussed effect-size indexes based on the difference in means, which are employed when outcomes are reported on a continuous scale. Now, I turn to effect-size indexes based on binary data—for which the outcome for each subject is the presence or absence of a characteristic or event. For example, a study might assign students to two groups and report the proportion in each group that passes a test, or a study might assign patients to two groups and report the proportion in each group that relapses. Although the event being recorded may be either a success (pass a test) or failure (relapse), in keeping with common practice, I use the term *risk* to refer to the proportion of subjects with the event. These data are usually presented as a 2 × 2 table such as in Table 6.1. The rows represent the groups, the columns represent the outcomes, and each subject falls into one of the four cells.

Table 6.2 shows how to convert the cell counts in Table 6.1 into proportions. For Group 1, the proportion with the event (or characteristic) is denoted p_1 and defined as A/n_1. The proportion without the event is denoted $1 - p_1$ and defined as B/n_1. Similarly, for Group 2, the proportion with the event is denoted p_2 and defined as C/n_2. The proportion without the event is denoted $1 - p_2$ and defined as D/n_2.

TABLE 6.1

A 2 × 2 Table of Cell Counts for a Prospective Study With a Binary Outcome

Group	Events	Nonevents	Total
1	A	B	n_1
2	C	D	n_2

Note. We classify a specific outcome as the "Event," and all study participants are classified as either "Event" or "Nonevent." In a study of college admissions these might be "Accepted" or "Rejected," and in a study of a medical intervention these might be "Dead" or "Alive." The outcome classified as the "Event" may be the preferred outcome (Accepted) or the alternate outcome (Rejected).

TABLE 6.2

A 2 × 2 Table of Proportions Derived From Table 6.1

Group	Events	Nonevents	Total
1	$P_1 = A/n_1$	$1 - P_1 = B/n_1$	1.0
2	$P_2 = C/n_2$	$1 - P_2 = D/n_2$	1.0

Note. This table shows how to use the data in Table 6.1 to compute the proportion of events (P) and nonevents ($1 - P$) in each group.

Three effect-size indexes commonly are used to report this kind of data (binary outcomes in two groups). One is the *risk difference*, which is simply the difference in risks, analogous to the raw difference in means for continuous data. The second is the *risk ratio*, which is the ratio of the risks, rather than the difference in risks. The third is the *odds ratio*, which is discussed in a later section.

The risk difference reflects the absolute difference in risk between the two groups. As such, it is analogous to the raw difference in means for continuous data. The risk difference is an intuitive index, but the substantive implications may depend on the absolute risks—a 10-point drop from 20% to 10% has a different substantive meaning than a 10-point drop from 80% to 70%.

The main distinction between the risk difference and the risk ratio is that the former is an absolute measure whereas the latter is a relative measure. For example, consider one study in which the treatment reduces the risk of relapse from 2% to 1%, and another study in which the treatment reduces the risk of relapse from 80% to 40%. In both studies, the risk ratio is the same (50%). But the risk difference is 1 percentage point in the first case and 40 percentage points in the second. If we are dealing with a case in which the treatment is expected to always cut the risk in half, then the risk ratio is the index that captures this expectation. By contrast, if we want to know the likely impact of the treatment for a given patient, then the risk difference is the index that addresses this question. In one case, the patient's risk drops by 1 percentage point, and in the other, risk drops by 40 percentage points.

If we elect to work with a ratio, then in addition to the risk ratio we also have the option of reporting the odds ratio. Where the *risk ratio* is the ratio of the two risks, the *odds ratio* is the ratio of the two odds (the odds in each group is the ratio of the risk of events to the risk of nonevents in that group). The risk ratio is more intuitive than the odds ratio, but the odds ratio has some useful mathematical properties that lead to its being preferred in some fields (Deeks, 2002).

Often, people in a specific field tend to favor one index over the others, which can help a researcher decide among the options. Also, it is possible to present more than one index, because the indexes provide complementary views of the effect. The relative merits of these three indexes are discussed in Deeks (2002), Fleiss and Berlin (2009), and Higgins and Thomas (2019).

Consider a study in which recovering alcoholics are assigned to either of two groups, treated (intensive support) or control (standard support). Outcome is defined by the presence or absence of relapse within the study period. The results are shown in Table 6.3. The risk of relapse is 20/100 (20%) in the treated group and 40/100 (40%) in the control group. This study serves as an example in the sections that follow.

Risk Difference

The risk difference delta (I) is defined as the difference in probabilities (or risks) in the two groups. If the risk for Groups 1 and 2 in the population are denoted by π_1 and π_2, then the risk difference (I) is defined as the difference in risks,

$$\Delta = \pi_1 - \pi_2. \quad (6.77)$$

TABLE 6.3

Events × Treatment in a Fictional Study

Group	Relapse	Stable	Total
Treated	20	80	100
Control	40	60	100

A risk difference of 0 indicates that the two risks are equal. In the relapse example (where Group 1 is treated and Group 2 is control), risk differences above 0 indicate that the risk of relapse is higher for treated group, whereas risk differences below 0 indicate that the risk of relapse is higher for the control group.

To estimate the risk difference from the study data, we apply the formula for I, but replace the true (population) risks (π_1 and π_2) with the estimates (sample) risks (p_1 and p_2). Using the notation in Tables 6.1 and 6.2, the risk difference is computed as

$$RD = p_1 - p_2 = A/n_1 - C/n_2. \quad (6.78)$$

The approximate variance, standard error, and 95% confidence limits are given by

$$V_{RD} = \frac{AB}{n_1^3} + \frac{CD}{n_2^3}, \quad (6.79)$$

$$SE_{RD} = \sqrt{V_{RD}}, \quad (6.80)$$

$$LL_{RD} = RD - Z_{1-\alpha/2} \times SE_{RD}, \quad (6.81)$$

and

$$UL_{RD} = RD + Z_{1-\alpha/2} \times SE_{RD}. \quad (6.82)$$

Applying these formulas to the example of relapse prevention in alcoholics, we compute the risk difference, variance, standard error, and confidence limits as

$$RD = 0.200 - 0.400 = -0.200, \quad (6.83)$$

$$V_{RD} = \frac{20 \times 80}{100^3} + \frac{40 \times 60}{100^3} = 0.004, \quad (6.84)$$

$$SE_{RD} = \sqrt{0.004} = 0.063, \quad (6.85)$$

$$LL_{RD} = -0.20 - 1.96 \times 0.063 = -0.324, \quad (6.86)$$

and

$$UL_{RD} = -0.20 + 1.96 \times 0.063 = -0.076. \quad (6.87)$$

In words, the risk difference in the study is −0.200, and the true risk difference (I) probably falls in the range of −0.324 to −0.076.

Risk Ratio

The risk ratio, theta (θ), is the ratio of the risks in the two groups. If the risk for Groups 1 and 2 in the population are denoted by π_1 and π_2, then the risk ratio (θ), often called the *relative risk*, is defined as the *ratio* of the risks,

$$\theta = \frac{\pi_1}{\pi_2}. \tag{6.88}$$

A risk ratio of 1.0 would indicate that the risks are equal in the two groups. In the relapse example (where Group 1 is treated and Group 2 is control), a risk ratio of less than 1.0 would indicate that the risk of relapse was lower in the treated group, whereas a risk ratio of more than 1.0 would indicate that the risk of relapse was higher in the treated group.

To estimate the risk ratio from the study data, we apply the formula for θ, but replace the true (population) risks (π_1 and π_2) with the estimates (sample) risks (p_1 and p_2). Using the notation in Tables 6.1 and 6.2, the risk ratio is computed as

$$RR = \frac{p_1}{p_2} = \frac{A/n_1}{C/n_2}. \tag{6.89}$$

It might seem that we could compute the standard error of the *RR* and then build a confidence interval using *RR* plus or minus this standard error times 1.96. However, the distribution of the risk ratio is skewed, and a more accurate confidence interval can be obtained from the log of the risk ratio. Therefore, rather than work directly with the *RR*, we work with the natural log of the *RR* (*lnRR*), compute the confidence limits in log units, and then convert these values back to the *RR* scale.

The log of the risk ratio, *ln(RR)*, is denoted *lnRR*. Then, in log units, the approximate variance, standard error, and confidence limits are

$$V_{lnRR} = \frac{1}{A} - \frac{1}{n_1} + \frac{1}{C} - \frac{1}{n_2}, \tag{6.90}$$

$$SE_{lnRR} = \sqrt{V_{lnRR}}, \tag{6.91}$$

$$LL_{lnRR} = lnRR - Z_{1-\alpha/2} \times SE_{lnRR}, \tag{6.92}$$

and

$$UL_{lnRR} = lnRR + Z_{1-\alpha/2} \times SE_{lnRR}. \tag{6.93}$$

We then convert the confidence limits back to the original scale using

$$LL_{RR} = \exp(LL_{lnRR}) \tag{6.94}$$

and

$$UL_{RR} = \exp(UL_{lnRR}). \tag{6.95}$$

Working with the data in Table 6.3 and applying the formulas above,

$$RR = \frac{20/100}{40/100} = \frac{.200}{.400} = 0.500. \tag{6.96}$$

In log units,

$$lnRR = \ln(0.500) = -0.693, \tag{6.97}$$

$$V_{lnRR} = \frac{1}{20} - \frac{1}{100} + \frac{1}{40} - \frac{1}{100} = 0.055, \tag{6.98}$$

$$SE_{lnRR} = \sqrt{0.055} = 0.235, \tag{6.99}$$

$$LL_{lnRR} = -0.693 - 1.96 \times 0.235 = -1.153, \tag{6.100}$$

and

$$UL_{lnRR} = -0.693 + 1.96 \times 0.235 = -0.233. \tag{6.101}$$

We then convert the confidence limits back to the original scale using

$$LL_{RR} = \exp(-1.153) = 0.316 \tag{6.102}$$

and

$$UL_{RR} = \exp(-0.233) = 0.792. \tag{6.103}$$

In words, the risk ratio in the study is 0.500, and the true risk ratio (θ) probably falls in the range of 0.316 to 0.792.

Odds Ratio

The odds ratio, omega (ω), is the ratio of the odds in the two groups. If the risk of the event for Group 1 in the population is denoted by π_1, then the odds of the event in Group 1 are given by $\pi_1/(1-\pi_1)$. Similarly, if the risk of the event for Group 2 in the population is denoted by π_2, then the odds of the event in Group 2 are given by $\pi_2/(1-\pi_2)$. The odds ratio is the ratio of these two odds,

$$\omega = \frac{\pi_1/(1-\pi_1)}{\pi_2/(1-\pi_2)} = \frac{\pi_1(1-\pi_2)}{\pi_2(1-\pi_1)}. \quad (6.104)$$

An odds ratio of 1.0 would indicate that the risks are equal in the two groups. In the relapse example (where Group 1 is treated and Group 2 is control), an odds ratio of less than 1.0 would indicate that the risk of relapse was lower in the treated group, whereas an odds ratio of more than 1.0 would indicate that the risk of relapse was higher in the treated group.

To estimate the odds ratio from the study data, we apply the formula for ω but replace the true (population) risks (π_1 and π_2) with the estimates (sample) risks (P_1 and P_2). Using the notation in Tables 6.1 and 6.2, the odds ratio (OR) is

$$OR = \frac{P_1(1-P_2)}{P_2(1-P_1)} = \frac{AD}{BC}. \quad (6.105)$$

As was true for the risk ratio, we compute the confidence limits in log units because of the asymmetry of confidence intervals and then convert these values to the original scale. The log of the odds ratio, $ln(OR)$, is denoted $lnOR$. Then, in log units, the approximate variance, standard error, and confidence limits are

$$V_{lnOR} = \frac{1}{A} + \frac{1}{B} + \frac{1}{C} + \frac{1}{D}, \quad (6.106)$$

$$SE_{lnOR} = \sqrt{V_{lnOR}}, \quad (6.107)$$

$$LL_{lnOR} = lnOR - Z_{1-\alpha/2} \times SE_{lnOR}, \quad (6.108)$$

and

$$UL_{lnOR} = lnOR - Z_{1-\alpha/2} \times SE_{lnOR}. \quad (6.109)$$

We convert the confidence limits back to the original scale using

$$LL_{OR} = \exp(LL_{lnOR}) \quad (6.110)$$

and

$$UL_{OR} = \exp(UL_{lnOR}). \quad (6.111)$$

Applying these formulas to the relapse example, the odds ratio is

$$OR = \frac{20 \times 60}{80 \times 40} = 0.375. \quad (6.112)$$

In log units, the odds ratio, variance, standard error and confidence limits are

$$lnOR = \ln(0.375) = -0.981, \quad (6.113)$$

$$V_{lnOR} = \frac{1}{20} + \frac{1}{80} + \frac{1}{40} + \frac{1}{60} = 0.104, \quad (6.114)$$

$$SE_{lnOR} = \sqrt{0.104} = 0.323, \quad (6.115)$$

$$LL_{lnOR} = -0.981 - 1.96 \times 0.323 = -1.613, \quad (6.116)$$

and

$$UL_{lnOR} = -0.981 + 1.96 \times 0.323 = -0.348. \quad (6.117)$$

Finally, we convert the confidence limits back to the original metric,

$$LL_{OR} = \exp(-1.613) = 0.199 \quad (6.118)$$

and

$$UL_{OR} = \exp(-0.348) = 0.706. \quad (6.119)$$

In words, the odds ratio in the study is 0.375, and the true odds ratio (ω) probably falls in the range of 0.199 to 0.706.

Notes for Binary Data

Dealing with studies in which no people possess the characteristic in question or in which there are zero events. For the risk difference, if either or both groups have zero events, we add 0.5 to each cell (A, B, C, D in Table 6.1) to compute the variance. For the risk ratio and the odds ratio, if one group has zero events, some people add 0.5 to each cell to compute the effect size and its variance. If both groups have zero events, then the risk ratio and the odds ratio are undefined.

Events versus nonevents. For the risk difference we can select either outcome (for example, "Dead" or "Alive") to serve as the "Event" (cells A and C in Table 6.1). If the risk difference for "Dead" is −0.20, then the risk difference for "Alive" is +0.20, which has the same meaning. The same holds true for the odds ratio—if the odds ratio for "Dead" is 0.50 then the odds ratio for "Alive" is 2.0 (i.e., the inverse of 0.50). Again, the substantive meaning is the same (we halve the odds by using the treatment, or double the odds by withholding it). However, the situation is different for the risk ratio. Suppose that 98/100 people are alive in one group versus 99/100 in the other. If we choose "Alive" as the event, then the impact of the treatment appears to be relatively small (risks of 0.98 vs. 0.99 translate to a risk ratio near 1.0). By contrast, if we choose "Dead" as the event, then the impact of the treatment appears to be relatively large (risks of 0.01 vs. 0.02 translate to a risk ratio of 0.50). Therefore, the decision to select one outcome or the other as the "Event" should reflect the logic of the study and not exaggerate small risks.

EFFECT-SIZE INDEXES BASED ON THE RELATION BETWEEN TWO CONTINUOUS VARIABLES

To this point I have presented effect-size indexes for analyses that compare two means and for analyses that compare two proportions. Now, I turn to analyses that assess the relationship between two sets of continuous data, that is, the kind of analysis typically reported as a correlation.

When working with means or proportions, we needed to create an effect-size index that started with two values (e.g., means or proportions) and compare them in some way (e.g., by computing a difference or ratio). By contrast, when we are working with the relation between two continuous variables, the correlation coefficient can serve as the effect-size index. The correlation is a pure measure of effect size (not affected by the sample size). Additionally, the correlation is an intuitive measure (people who work with correlations have a sense of what a given correlation means), and it is reported on a standardized scale.

Consider a study in which students who enroll in a computer-programming course are given an aptitude test on the first day of class and a final exam on the last day. The study goal is to determine the correlation between the two scores. The correlation is reported as 0.80 on the basis of a sample size of 100 students.

The true (population) value of the correlation is called rho (ρ). The sample statistic (the observed effect) is denoted by r. The sample estimate of ρ is simply the sample correlation coefficient, r. The variance of r is approximately

$$v_r = \frac{(1-r^2)^2}{n-1}, \qquad (6.120)$$

where n is the sample size.

It might seem that we could compute the standard error of r and then build a confidence interval using r plus or minus this standard error times 1.96. However, the distribution of r is skewed. Therefore, rather than work directly with r, we convert r to another metric, Fisher's z score, compute the confidence limits in the Fisher's z metric, and then convert these values back to the r scale. We use the notation Fisher's z to avoid confusion with the (unrelated) normal curve Z.

The transformation from r to Fisher's z score is given by

$$\text{Fisher's } z = 0.500 \times \ln\left(\frac{1+r}{1-r}\right). \quad (6.121)$$

The variance, standard error, and 95% confidence limits in the Fisher's z metric are (to an excellent approximation)

$$V_{\text{Fisher's } z} = \frac{1}{n-3}, \quad (6.122)$$

$$SE_{\text{Fisher's } z} = \sqrt{V_{\text{Fisher's } z}}, \quad (6.123)$$

$$LL_{\text{Fisher's } z} = \text{Fisher's } z - Z \times SE_{\text{Fisher's } z}, \quad (6.124)$$

and

$$UL_{\text{Fisher's } z} = \text{Fisher's } z + Z \times SE_{\text{Fisher's } z}. \quad (6.125)$$

Finally, the lower and upper limits are converted back to the original metric using

$$LL_r = \frac{e^{2LL_{\text{Fisher's } z}} - 1}{e^{2LL_{\text{Fisher's } z}} + 1} \quad (6.126)$$

and

$$UL_r = \frac{e^{2UL_{\text{Fisher's } z}} - 1}{e^{2UL_{\text{Fisher's } z}} + 1}. \quad (6.127)$$

We can apply these formulas to the study that reported the correlation between an aptitude test and performance in a computer programming class. The effect size r is simply 0.80. The transformation from r to Fisher's z score is given by

$$\text{Fisher's } z = 0.500 \times \ln\left(\frac{1+0.800}{1-0.800}\right) = 1.099. \quad (6.128)$$

In Fisher's z score units, the variance, standard error, and confidence limits are computed as

$$v_{\text{Fisher's } z} = \frac{1}{100-3} = 0.010, \quad (6.129)$$

$$SE_{\text{Fisher's } z} = \sqrt{0.010} = 0.102, \quad (6.130)$$

$$LL_{\text{Fisher's } z} = 1.099 - 1.96 \times 0.102 = 0.900, \quad (6.131)$$

and

$$UL_{\text{Fisher's } z} = 1.099 + 1.96 \times 0.1012 = 1.298. \quad (6.132)$$

To convert the Fisher's z score values back to a correlation, we use

$$LL_r = \frac{e^{2(0.900)} - 1}{e^{2(0.900)} + 1} = 0.716 \quad (6.133)$$

and

$$UL_r = \frac{e^{2(1.298)} - 1}{e^{2(1.298)} + 1} = 0.861. \quad (6.134)$$

In words, the correlation in the study is 0.80, and the true correlation (ρ) probably falls in the range of 0.716 to 0.861.

CONVERTING EFFECT SIZES FROM ONE INDEX TO ANOTHER

In general, we choose from among one set of effect-size indexes for data presented as means, from another set for data presented as proportions, and from another set for correlational data. However, there are formulas that can be used to convert among effect-size indices. For example, after we use means to compute a standardized mean difference, it is possible to convert that effect size to an odds ratio or a correlation. This approach is useful if we know the treatment effect for one intervention as (say) a standardized mean difference and want to see how this compares with the treatment effect for another intervention that was reported as an odds ratio or a correlation. It is also useful if we want to include different studies in a meta-analysis, and the studies reported the effects using different indices of effect size. The formulas, worked examples, and the limitations of this approach, are discussed in Borenstein et al. (2021) and Borenstein et al. (in press).

The examples in this chapter show how to compute effect sizes and confidence intervals for some of the more common study designs, such as a design that employs two independent groups or a pre–post design. Borenstein et al. (in press) extended the discussion to include additional designs (e.g., cluster-randomized trials). They also showed how to compute effect sizes when a study fails to report a full set of summary statistics (e.g., the means, standard deviations, and sample sizes) and reports, for example, only the *p* value and sample size.

The effect-size indexes introduced in this chapter are among the most widely used, but many others are used as well. Effect-size indexes for means include not only the raw mean difference and standardized mean difference but also the response ratio (the ratio of means). Effect-size indexes for proportions include not only the risk difference, risk ratio, and odds ratio but also such indexes as the *number needed to treat*, which is the number of people we need to treat to prevent one event. Similarly, this chapter was limited to effect-size indexes based on means, proportions, or correlations, but analogous effect-size indexes have been developed for other kinds of data. For example, the comparison of survival times in two groups may be captured by the difference in hazard rates of the ratio of hazard rates, analogous to the risk difference or risk ratio.

Borenstein et al.'s (in press) book is dedicated entirely to the computation of effect sizes. Other references are Borenstein (2019), Borenstein and Hedges (2019), Borenstein et al. (2021), Fleiss and Berlin (2009), Hedges and Olkin (1985), Lipsey and Wilson (2001), and Rosenthal et al. (2000).

CONCLUSION

According to the *Publication Manual of the American Psychological Association* (APA, 2020), reporting an effect size with confidence intervals can be an effective way of communicating results. In this chapter, I have tried to explain why this is so.

Almost invariably, the goal of a research study is to assess the strength of a relationship or the impact of an intervention. These are the issues that are addressed by an effect size and its confidence interval, and for this reason, it is these values that should be highlighted in the analysis and serve as the basis for the discussion. Effect sizes also enhance the larger research endeavor because they can be used to compare and synthesize estimates of effects across studies.

References

American Psychological Association. (2020). *Publication manual of the American Psychological Association* (7th ed.).

Borenstein, M. (1994). The case for confidence intervals in controlled clinical trials. *Controlled Clinical Trials, 15*(5), 411–428. https://doi.org/10.1016/0197-2456(94)90036-1

Borenstein, M. (2000). The shift from significance testing to effect size estimation. In A. S. Bellack & M. Herson (Eds.), *Comprehensive clinical psychology* (pp. 313–349). Pergamon.

Borenstein, M. (2019). *Common mistakes in meta-analysis and how to avoid them*. Biostat.

Borenstein, M., & Hedges, L. V. (2019). Effect sizes for meta-analysis. In H. Cooper, L. V. Hedges, & J. C. Valentine (Eds.), *The handbook of research synthesis and meta-analysis* (3rd ed., pp. 207–244). Russell Sage Foundation. https://doi.org/10.7758/9781610448864.14

Borenstein, M., Hedges, L. V., Higgins, J. P. T., & Rothstein, H. R. (2021). *Introduction to meta-analysis* (2nd ed.). Wiley.

Borenstein, M., Hedges, L. V., Higgins, J. P. T., & Rothstein, H. R. (in press). *Computing effect sizes for meta-analysis*. Wiley.

Cohen, J. (1977). *Statistical power analysis for the behavioral sciences* (2nd ed.). Academic Press.

Cooper, H. (2017). *Research synthesis and meta-analysis—A step-by-step approach* (5th ed.). SAGE. https://doi.org/10.4135/9781071878644

Deeks, J. J. (2002). Issues in the selection of a summary statistic for meta-analysis of clinical trials with binary outcomes. *Statistics in Medicine, 21*(11), 1575–1600. https://doi.org/10.1002/sim.1188

Fleiss, J. L., & Berlin, J. A. (2009). Effect sizes for dichotomous data. In H. Cooper, L. V. Hedges, & J. C. Valentine (Eds.), *The handbook of research synthesis and meta-analysis* (2nd ed., pp. 237–253). Russell Sage Foundation.

Hedges, L. (1981). Distribution theory for Glass's estimator of effect size and related estimators. *Journal of Educational Statistics, 6*(2), 107–128. https://doi.org/10.3102/10769986006002107

Hedges, L. V., & Olkin, I. (1985). *Statistical models for meta-analysis.* Academic Press.

Higgins, J. P. T., & Thomas, J. (Eds.). (2019). *Cochrane handbook for systematic reviews of interventions.* Wiley. https://doi.org/10.1002/9781119536604

Lipsey, M. W., & Wilson, D. B. (2001). *Practical meta-analysis.* SAGE.

Rosenthal, R., Rosnow, R. L., & Rubin, D. B. (2000). *Contrasts and effect sizes in behavioral research: A correlational approach.* Cambridge University Press.

Tversky, A., & Kahneman, D. (1971). Belief in the law of small numbers. *Psychological Bulletin, 76*(2), 105–110. https://doi.org/10.1037/h0031322

CHAPTER 7

MEASURES OF CLINICALLY SIGNIFICANT CHANGE

Russell J. Bailey, Benjamin M. Ogles, and Michael J. Lambert

Clinical research employs several statistics to estimate whether mental health treatment works. Side-by-side comparisons of treatments in clinical trials use estimates of statistical significance, effect size, and clinical significance. Each type of statistic can be used to determine whether a given difference in scores is meaningful and consequently whether the given mental health treatment has resulted in meaningful change. Although each statistic offers information to address the question of meaningful change resulting from treatment, each operates from a different rationale and communicates unique information to address the question. We review approaches for describing clinically significant change, with special focus on the most common metric. We describe how to use clinical significance in research applications, with an eye toward clinical applications. We highlight extensions of these methods, with recent and ongoing methodological innovations. Based on our review, we recommend future directions for methodological and clinical research with clinical significance.

TRADITIONAL WAYS TO ASSESS CHANGE DUE TO TREATMENT

When *statistical significance* is reported in measurements of change, the mean difference between groups exceeds what would be expected by chance alone. A staple for psychological research, finding group differences (or changes in the functioning of a group of patients in response to an intervention) to be statistically significant reduces the likelihood of *chance* findings being reported as reliable change. Differences between groups found by this method may not sufficiently address the question of whether such differences reflect practical or clinically meaningful change. For example, consider a weight loss treatment that is compared with a control group. One hundred individuals who are at extreme risk for detrimental health consequences related to their obesity are selected to participate in the study. After 2 months, those receiving treatment have lost an average of 8 pounds. The comparison group has lost, on average, no weight during the time that elapsed. The statistical test reveals a statistically significant finding in favor of the treatment group as compared with the control group. These statistical effects suggest that the differences between the groups are important as opposed to differences that are unreliable. With an average of 8 pounds weight loss, some individuals who received treatment may have lost 16 pounds, whereas others who received treatment lost no weight or even gained weight. As a group, the participants in the study remain classified as extremely obese. Even though the 50 treated individuals lost an average of 8 pounds, many, if not all of them, continue to be at risk of serious health consequences of obesity despite treatment. In a pragmatic or clinical sense, the treatment and control groups may be considered identical (with regards to meaningful change) after 2 months of treatment. The magnitude, or amount of change, must be taken into account if one wishes to understand the meaning of change.

The *effect size* statistic addresses this issue—the relative importance of the amount of change (for a more complete discussion, see Chapter 6, this volume) By standardizing group means, one can use an effect size to communicate the group's mean change score in standard deviation units. Interpreting these statistics is straightforward, as the effect size reflects the degree of change relative to overall group variability. Small effect sizes indicate smaller effects resulting from treatment, and larger effect sizes indicate larger effects. Meta-analyses (quantitative research summaries; see Chapter 24, this volume) employ effect sizes from groups of studies because effect sizes allow one to combine change scores under a standard metric and, thus, estimate an average amount of change in treatment groups from a body of primary studies simultaneously (see Nordahl-Hansen et al., 2018). However, effect sizes still do not communicate variation within the group and they do not address the clinical relevance of change. By way of illustration, an effect size of 0.8 for a treatment group indicates that the average change from baseline for all clients in the treatment group was 0.8 standard deviation units (based on baseline standard deviation; generally considered a large effect because the effect size demonstrates that the proportion of controls have a success rate of 31%, whereas the experimental group's success rate is 69%). Although meaningful in its own right, the 0.8 effect size does not communicate whether the treatment group patients met a clinically relevant criterion, such as remission of depressive symptoms. Although effect sizes may be applied to the individual, in general, effect sizes are used for between-group estimates of change or within-group estimates of change.

Another way in which group mean comparison and treatment effect sizes miss important information is when considering within-group variation. For example, a 0.8 effect size masks variation within the group by arithmetically combining the individual client with 2.0 standard deviation units of change, as well as the client with −0.5 standard deviation units of change, with the rest of the group. In early reviews of psychotherapy research Bergin (1966, 1971) noticed that treatment often increased outcome variability—more people improved while in treatment and a larger percentage deteriorated compared with untreated individuals. Bergin suggested that this increase in variability tempered the "reported effectiveness of psychological treatments" (Bergin & Lambert, 1978, p. 152) and advocated for additional research to examine the reasons for this increased variability. Investigation of clinical significance provides one way for assessing individual improvement, recovery, and deterioration.

THE CONCEPT OF CLINICAL SIGNIFICANCE

The concept of *clinical significance* arose to address the issue of clinical relevance of change scores (Jacobson et al., 1984). To speak to *clinical* relevance, researchers and clinicians are interested in whether an intervention results in a change in clinical status of the individual patient. Criteria for clinically relevant change might include a patient recovering or moving from major depression to subthreshold symptoms, from dysfunctional to functional, or from resembling the patient group to resembling the community nonpatient group. One central question in the methods of determining clinically significant change includes whether to use estimates that consider change at the level of the individual rather than the level of the group.

To address clinical relevance, the concept of clinical significance typically speaks to *individual* change more than it does group change. Statistics of clinical significance give the additional benefit of individual level information, which effect sizes, statistical significance tests, and other group-level statistics do not (Jensen & Corralejo, 2017).

In this way, researchers and clinicians can make inferences about individual patients (e.g., decisions regarding alterations to treatment such as termination, stepping up treatment intensity, determining recovery or deterioration) as well as about the impact of treatments on groups of individuals (e.g., what percentage of individual patients in a treatment group recovered, reliably improved, or deteriorated).

Clinical significance as an outcome construct can differ from remission of symptoms, although both concepts are qualitative descriptions of clinically meaningful improvement. As presented by McGlinchey et al. (2008), remission focuses on the "absence of features that originally warranted the diagnosis of a condition" (p. 26), in keeping with a more biomedical understanding of psychiatric disorders. Of note, remission criteria typically involve diagnostic considerations, but they do not necessarily entail complete absence of symptoms. Some studies use presence of a diagnosis at pretreatment and absence of symptoms necessary to meet diagnostic criteria as a method of evaluating clinically meaningful change. For example, Nyman-Carlsson et al. (2020) found that 76% of the clients treated for anorexia in both of their treatment groups no longer met the diagnostic criteria for an eating disorder following treatment. Although this chapter focuses on other methods of evaluating clinical significance, the consideration of remission in the medical literature and methods for determining remission may further inform methods of determining clinical significance.

Beutler and Moleiro (2001) illustrated the difference between statistical and clinical significance and emphasized two aspects of clinical significance: reliable change and clinically meaningful change. *Reliable change*, based on the work of Jacobson et al. (1984), refers to whether a change score drawn from a specific measure exceeds the level of change that may be present simply due to measurement error and unreliability in the outcome measure. *Clinically meaningful change* implies change that reflects clinically meaningful changes in clinical status. Beutler and Moleiro (2001) cited equivalence testing (Sheldrick et al., 2001) as one method to support the presence of clinically meaningful change. By comparing treatment groups to a normative nonpatient sample, one can test the hypothesis whether the treatment group is equivalent to nonpatients.

Equivalence testing has a different focus as compared with most methods of clinical significance, in that group change is measured and tested rather than individual change. Several researchers have considered this method of examining clinical significance in more recent studies that assess pre- and posttreatment group equivalence with normative comparison groups (e.g., Mangardich & Cribbie, 2015; van Wieringen & Cribbie, 2014).

When examining individual clinical significance, it appears that considerations of clinical significance may temper the optimism of researchers in claiming high effectiveness for interventions. Not all patients respond positively to treatment, with many patients' outcomes remaining unchanged and a small percentage of patients (about 5%–10%) deteriorating rather than improving in therapy (Lambert, 2013). Hansen et al. (2002) found an average of 58% of patients in clinical trials (from a sample of 28 trials with 2,109 patients) experienced clinically significant change. In routine care, however, the percentage of patients experiencing clinically significant change was about 14% and the deterioration rate about 8%.

One potential explanation for these rates of clinically meaningful change is that the methods are overly conservative. Almost all publications that discuss methods for assessing clinically meaningful change emphasize a focus on identifying change that is reliable or unlikely to be the result of random fluctuations in measurement. This places the focus on ensuring that changes are sufficiently large as to rule out faux change. At the same time, it may increase the possibility that individuals who made real and meaningful change are not included because of factors associated with the instrument or the method of calculation. For example, is it really more reliable for a person to change 14 points on the OQ-45 than 13 points (Outcome Questionnaire-45.2, a commonly used psychotherapy outcome measure; Lambert et al., 2004)? Ferrer and

Pardo (2019) took on this issue more directly by considering the issue of false negatives. In a data simulation study, they found that even when treatment effects are large the rate of false negatives is high. They suggested that the focus on discarding "changes produced by random variations" results in using methods that "do not perform well regarding false-negative rates" (p. 101). They provided some additional information that softens their conclusions yet still recommend further research to explore the concern of false negatives.

In terms of more modest estimates of change, further research may also be needed to examine clients who demonstrate no reliable difference after treatment. One example of moderating claims of effectiveness is provided by examination of clinically significant change in data from the National Institute of Health Collaborative Depression Project (Ogles et al., 1995). This multisite study of two psychotherapies, antidepressant medication, and a medication placebo showed all the treatments were effective with a surprisingly good showing for the medication placebo (with a manualized method of clinical management). Ultimately, the active treatments (cognitive behavior therapy [CBT], interpersonal psychotherapy [IPT], and imipramine) distinguished themselves from placebo only with the most severely disturbed cases. The outcomes of treatment as measured by the Beck Depression Inventory showed clinically significant improvement going from the depressed range to the nondepressed range after 12 weeks of treatment—50% for CBT, 64% for IPT, 66% for imipramine, and 46% for placebo with clinical management. All the treatments were a long way from being perfectly effective, and clinical significance ratings calculated for each patient made this quite clear.

EMPHASIS ON INDIVIDUAL CHANGE

Historically, the study of individual change has been the province of behaviorist research and methodology. The stimulus–response paradigm led to logically parsimonious methods of measuring baseline responses and determining changes in responses at the level of an individual organism after pairing stimuli or reinforcing behavior. Behavior therapy has, therefore, been consistently interested in measuring individual change, as the methods are conducive to such measurement (Ulrich et al., 1966).

Social validity in the 1970s was a term used by behaviorists (specifically, applied behavior analysts) to attempt external confirmation of subject change, such as confirming change with other sources in contact with the subject or comparing the subject's new behavior with that of the subject's peers. Wolf (1978) argued for establishing whether behavioral interventions and their effects are of significance to society, to ensure that the outcomes serve society generally. Behavior change that meets socially acceptable levels as determined by a functional population would be considered clinically important (Kazdin, 1977). In addition to questions of social validity, the discussion of external validity has resulted in consideration of ways to advance the generality and relevance of findings (Kazdin, 2003). Contrived laboratory conditions may not be relevant to daily experience and real-world functioning. External validity speaks to the question of how research studies reflect the real world.

In the 1980s, Jacobson worked to address clinical significance statistically and introduced a formula that is the most common for calculating clinical significance. Jacobson et al. (1984) based the method not only on the rational concept of clinical significance (as has been discussed here) but also on the empirical concept of statistical reliability. Because change scores require the calculation of the difference between two measurements, the potential exists for compounding measurement error (Cohen & Swerdlink, 1999). Such potential for error underscores the necessity of selecting highly reliable measures when designing a study's methodology. Jacobson's method attempted, however, to account statistically for possible measurement error by using parameters that are specific to the measure used to assess client functioning, thus taking into account the measure's reliability. Importantly, the Jacobson method for examining reliable change is a "distribution-based method" where the assessment of change relies exclusively on test relevant differences (e.g., psychometric properties of the measures and normative samples using the specific measure) and is not connected to some external criterion, as in "anchor-based methods" (Ferrer & Pardo, 2019, p. 97). As a result, collecting validity data to further support Jacobson's method has been repeatedly recommended (e.g., Lambert & Ogles, 2009).

Jacobson and Truax (1991) created a method to identify change scores that are both statistically reliable and clinically significant. As discussed in the section Jacobson–Truax Method, the statistical method that he initially proposed has been debated, and several alternative methods of calculating clinical significance have been proposed. Several other methods follow a similar rationale of the original measure, requiring two essential criteria for determining clinically significant change over the course of treatment: (a) the change score for the patient reflects change that is statistically reliable, and (b) the patient more closely represents the functional population than the nonfunctional population, usually determined by data collected from normal and patient samples (Jacobson & Truax, 1991).

Although not universally accepted and used, the Jacobson–Truax (JT; Jacobson & Truax, 1991) method offers criteria that can be thought of as necessary conditions for establishing clinically significant change. Neither is a sufficient condition, but it is notable that most methods of estimating clinical significance include one or both of these criteria in principle. It may well be that other conditions may be developed in the future that are necessary to establish clinical significance, but these two conditions give a logical framework for most methods of determining the clinical relevance of change.

Before discussing the JT method (Jacobson & Truax, 1991) and related methods in detail, however, it is important to note certain aspects of other methods, which attempt to establish clinical significance. These methods are briefly described in Table 7.1. In the study by Eisen et al. (2007), the authors used the *standard error of measurement* (SEM) to evaluate meaningful change according to the recommendations of McHorney and Tarlov (1995). Because the SEM is, in theory, the standard deviation of an individual score, the strategy for using it as a statistical threshold suggests that a change at the level of one SEM reflects a "minimal clinically important intra-individual change" (Eisen et al., 2007, p. 274). Ferrer and Pardo (2019) suggested that the minimally important difference term and methods are most commonly used in medicine, while the clinically meaningful change terminology and methods (which are conceptually similar) are used in psychology.

Equivalence testing does not test individual-level change but rather attempts to test the clinical meaningfulness of group-level change. Other methods use fairly standard statistics applied to individual change scores to estimate clinical significance.

Normative comparison (Kendall et al., 1999) is a useful tool in determining whether "end-state functioning . . . falls within a normative range on important measures" (p. 285). Conceptually similar to equivalence testing (or even remission of symptoms), normative comparisons combine statistical significance tests with equivalence tests to compare treated individuals to nondisturbed populations (Kendall & Grove, 1988). Blanchard and colleagues (Blanchard et al., 1990; Blanchard & Schwarz, 1988) devised a straightforward scheme to determine clinically significant change with headache. Change scores were converted to a *percentage change from baseline*, with a 50% improvement indicating a noticeable change. Some researchers argue that there are advantages to the percent improvement method when compared with the JT method for assessing reliable change. For example, Hiller et al. (2012) found that the percent improvement method produced similar or slightly higher estimates of outcome but had the advantages of being "independent of arbitrarily chosen reliabilities and reference populations" while also taking into account pretreatment severity (p. 1). Similarly, Karin et al. (2018) found that proportional models of change were a better fit to their data and linear models. In essence, clients starting with higher scores,

TABLE 7.1

Strategies for Determining Clinically Significant Change

Strategy	Relevant citation	Within-group change[a]	Clinical cutoff	Reliable change	Brief description
Effect size	Cohen, 1988	Yes, no	No	No	Change score rendered into standard deviation units, typically calculated as group effect size, but individual effect sizes can also be used.
Standard error of measurement	McHorney & Tarlov, 1995	Yes	No	Yes	The standard deviation of an individual score; it is estimated using the sample reliability coefficient and can be used as a threshold for reliable change.
Equivalence testing	Kendall, Marrs-Garcia, Nath, & Sheldrick, 1999	No	Yes	No	Typically a *t* test or other statistical significance test of group means; testing whether the posttreatment group is equivalent to functional, nontreated sample.
Normative comparison	Kendall & Grove, 1988	No	Yes	No	Combines clinical equivalence test with statistical significance test to determine whether group mean reflects clinically meaningful change.
Blanchard's method	Blanchard & Schwarz, 1988	Yes	No	No	Prescore minus postscore divided by prescore, calculated as a percentage, with 50% change as a cutoff. More common in health-related outcome literature.
Jacobson–Truax	Jacobson & Truax, 1991	Yes	Yes	Yes	Two criteria required, including passing a reliable change index (change exceeds expectation due to measurement error) and moving past a clinical cutoff demarking the boundary between functional and dysfunctional populations.

[a]This column identifies which strategies account for within-group variability of change scores.

in the severe range, and more points of symptom change, but were equivalent in terms of percentage change to clients starting in the moderate or mild range. Finally, in some populations the idea of percentage reduction in symptoms makes better conceptual sense, such as addictions (see Carroll et al., 2014, for a comparison of 15 potential indicators) or health psychology behavioral targets (e.g., headaches; Blanchard & Schwarz, 1988).

The percent improvement method can be applied to clinical practice, as shown by Lenz (2020). He noted that percentage improvement provides an index that can be used even when the client's pretreatment score falls outside the dysfunctional distribution, "can be used by clinicians with a single client" as the "calculation of the standalone value is straightforward, and can support treatment review, intervention guidance, and termination planning" (Lenz, 2020, pp. 291–292). As a result, this method has some utility and is often seen in medical research. At the same time, it fails to index entry into a range of normal functioning. Nevertheless, it allows researchers to classify specific patients as having met a criterion or not.

JACOBSON–TRUAX METHOD

The JT (Jacobson & Truax, 1991; see also Jacobson et al., 1999) method is in many ways a definitive method of establishing clinical significance, also serving as the logical basis for the other methods that followed. The JT method comprises two essential steps: (a) determine whether the pre- and postscore reflects a *statistically reliable* change, that is, the score exceeds the difference due to measurement error or other sources of error and thus represents actual change; and (b) estimate a cutoff score to separate functional and dysfunctional populations, such that a client must move from the dysfunctional to the functional population to be considered *recovered*.

The first step necessitates determining the reliability (r_{xx}) of the outcome measure used—often, the internal consistency reliability, Cronbach's alpha (Cronbach, 1951) is used instead of test–retest reliability—to calculate the SEM (S_E):

$$S_E = SD\sqrt{1 - r_{xx}} \qquad (7.1)$$

The standard deviation (SD) of the pretreatment scores is used here, although alternative methods advocate using a normative population standard deviation. The SEM can then be used to calculate the standard error of the difference, thus describing the distribution of change scores that would exist had no real change occurred:

$$S_{\text{diff}} = \sqrt{2 S_E^2} \qquad (7.2)$$

Dividing the difference in scores from pretest to posttest by the standard error of the differences result in the reliable change index (RCI):

$$\text{RCI} = \frac{(x_{\text{post}} - x_{\text{pre}})}{S_{\text{diff}}} \qquad (7.3)$$

If the RCI is greater than 1.96, then it is unlikely ($p < .05$) that the change score can be accounted for by chance alone and, therefore, represents real change. In this manner, the change score can be considered statistically reliable and not due to measurement error or other source of unreliability. The greater the reliability (r) of the outcome measure, the smaller the standard error, the smaller the standard error of the differences, and, therefore, smaller change scores are more likely to be statistically reliable, thus meeting the first of the JT (Jacobson & Truax, 1991) criteria.

The second step involves using an established cutoff point between functional and dysfunctional populations, with recovered patients not only achieving statistically reliable change but also moving into the functional population (although Jacobson & Truax, 1991, proposed two other possible cutoff points, A and B, when two contrasting groups were not available). When normative data are available for patients and nonpatients and there is overlap between these populations, then cutoff C is the weighted midpoint between the means of these populations; the calculation must also consider the size of the distribution of scores around the mean of each population:

$$\text{Cutoff C} = \frac{(SD_{\text{patient}} M_{\text{nonpatient}}) + (SD_{\text{nonpatient}} M_{\text{patient}})}{(SD_{\text{patient}} + SD_{\text{nonpatient}})} \qquad (7.4)$$

These two steps establish criteria for categorizing patients into groups according to their level of clinically significant change, as shown in Table 7.2. If both criteria are passed, the patient is classified as *recovered*. If the first criterion (RCI) is passed in the positive direction, but the second criterion is failed, the patient is classified as *improved*. If RCI is passed in the negative direction, the patient is classified as *deteriorated*, being reliably worse than at pretreatment (in addition, such patients do not pass the criterion of moving from the dysfunctional to the functional population). If the first criterion is failed, the patient is classified as *unchanged*.

The JT method has been used in hundreds of studies (see Ogles et al., 2001, for a review of studies using the JT method to that time). One recent example was published in the *Journal of*

TABLE 7.2

Criteria for Categorization of Patients' Change by Jacobson–Truax Method

Patient status	First criterion (RCI)	Second criterion (cutoff)
Recovered	Pass	Pass
Improved	Pass	Fail
Deteriorated	Pass (negative direction)	Fail
Unchanged	Fail	Fail

Note. RCI = reliable change index.

Consulting and Clinical Psychology, which requires that all treatment outcome submissions include consideration of clinical significance though not necessarily using the JT method (La Greca, 2005). Janse et al. (2020) compared high-intensive feedback with low-intensive monitoring of progress in clients participating in individual CBT. They found no statistical differences between feedback groups in terms of change in symptoms though rates of dropout were lower in the high-intensive feedback group (10.6% vs. 16.6%) and treatment duration was reduced by high intensive feedback (14 sessions vs. 16 sessions). To examine clinical significance, they calculated the RCI on the Global Symptom Index from the Symptom Checklist-90 (Derogatis & Unger, 2010) (.28 points of change on the GSI needed to be reliable change) along with establishing a cutoff for movement into the functional distribution (GSI = .65). They found no differences between the two feedback groups probably as a result of the high rates of change in both groups (clinical significance, 93 subjects in the low intensity condition vs. 96 subjects in the high intensity condition; reliable change, 11 vs. 13; no change, 23 vs. 32; and deterioration, 3 vs. 3; data obtained by request from Janse et al., 2020). This study is typical of the strategies contemporary researchers use to explore clinically significant change using the JT method after examining statistical differences between treatment groups.

ALTERNATIVE METHODS AND COMPARATIVE STUDIES

Less criticism has been applied to the logical premises of the JT (Jacobson & Truax, 1991) method than to the method of determining statistical reliability of change scores, such that a number of alternative formulas have been proposed. Several researchers suggested refinements to the formulas used to calculate either the RCI or compare with the functional group (Hageman & Arrindell, 1999; Hsu, 1999; Speer, 1992; Speer & Greenbaum, 1995; Vaganian et al., 2020).

These researchers indicated that issues, such as regression to the mean, should be accounted for in the calculations and added specifications to address those issues. Later studies (Atkins et al., 2005; Bauer et al., 2004; de Beurs et al., 2016; Eisen et al., 2007; Ronk et al., 2012, 2016; Speer & Greenbaum, 1995) examined the various methods empirically (with simulated data as well as with clinical data) to determine how these alterations classified patients. Each of these focused on the JT (Jacobson & Truax, 1991) method compared with adaptations to this method. We provide one study as an example of these types of comparative studies.

Eisen et al. (2007) examined a large number of patients ($N = 2,248$ inpatients and outpatients) and compared three methods for addressing the statistical reliability of change but did not compare the clinical cutoff of the JT method. When the Hageman and Arrindell (HA, 1999) method for calculating the RCI was compared with individual effect sizes and the SEM, the HA method was the most conservative. Interestingly, however, Eisen et al. found that the SEM was highly concordant with estimates of positive change (including changes in clinician-rated Global Assessment of Functioning Scale scores). Their support of the SEM as a method of establishing change may merit examination by other researchers because of this concordance.

A detailed exploration of other comparative studies is not necessary in this chapter,[1] especially because the main conclusion is typically the same across studies—although there may be some subtle differences in classification of clinical significance for some clients, in general, the JT method is almost always preferred for the calculation of individual change because of ease of computation and/or because the different methods are virtually indistinguishable (Atkins et al., 2005; Beadnell et al., 2016; Maassen, 2000; Speer & Greenbaum, 2002; Vaganian et al., 2020; Wolpert et al., 2015). Tangentially, although the methods of calculation tend to produce roughly similar results, different outcome measures may

---

[1] In the first edition of this chapter, these studies were examined in more detail (Lambert & Bailey, 2012).

produce large differences (e.g., Ronk et al., 2012). In particular, Nugter et al. (2019) found differences in rates of clinical significance when comparing general symptom measures versus disorder specific measures and noted that disorder specific measures provided a more complete picture of change. In addition, Ogles et al. (2001) found the JT method to be most common in the outcome literature, although the JT method is not applied uniformly across studies. For these reasons, the JT method has been the most commonly used method for most populations of therapy research over the past 30 years.[2]

Some publications have also focused on the application of clinical significance in practice (e.g., Nugter et al., 2019; Speer, 1992). For example, Westbrook and Kirk (2005) and later Kelly (2010) both provide examples of using the JT method in routine clinical practice. One appealing option in clinical settings, if appropriate data exist for the outcome measure, is to compare the clinical practice outcomes to benchmarks in research trials or to other comparative data sets (e.g., Billingham et al., 2012).

CLINICAL SIGNIFICANCE EXTENSIONS

In the 10 years since the first edition of this chapter was written, a number of researchers have published studies that attempt to extend the JT method or develop alternative methods of conceptualizing and identifying clinically meaningful change. These studies apply more modern measurement theories or statistical methods to the assessment of clinically significant change, modify assumptions, or consider clinical significance with new populations. We provide several examples here.

A continuing issue in the literature on clinical significance is the lack of validity studies to verify the meaning of distribution-based strategies for categorizing change. One recent study jumps into this important work. De Smet et al. (2020) found in a mixed-methods study of clients participating in treatment that the classifications derived by the JT method miss much of the multidimensional nature of change the clients report in post-treatment interviews. For example, while clients who met JT criteria for recovering also reported that they felt better or had a certain degree of improvement, many also reported that their gains were part of an ongoing process and that "not all difficulties had been altered" or that "some changes required more time" (p. 31). This study illustrates the need for additional work to take a more nuanced view of clinical significance assessment and therapy outcome more generally. A few earlier studies examined concurrent validity of posttreatment clinical significance categories (Ankuta & Abeles, 1993; Lunnen & Ogles, 1998; Newnham et al., 2007), but more studies are needed to address the validity of the categorization of clinically significant categories (Lambert & Ogles, 2009).

Ronk et al. (2013) followed the recommendations of Tingey et al. (1996), who argued that the traditional separation of clients into dichotomous categories—functional and dysfunctional—ignores meaningful variation within those groups. Ronk et al. (2013) suggested that an obvious example of this is represented by inpatient clients compared with outpatient clients. Using this logic, they conducted a study using the Depression Anxiety Stress Scales (DASS-21; Lovibond & Lovibond, 1995) to ascertain whether a three-distribution model might be a better representative of client change. Importantly, they found a third category that they called "recovering" fit their clinical data, which included inpatients, outpatients, and the normative sample for the DASS-21. As a result,

> clinically significant change is defined when reliable, positive movement occurs between ranges. For example, a patient who reliably moves from the outpatient to the normal range has made a clinically significant change (with a classification of

---

[2]For some populations the research standard differs from the JT method. For example, in some areas of health psychology research the Blanchard and Schwarz method (e.g., percent reduction in the headache index) is the contemporary research standard.

recovered). Likewise, a patient who reliably moves from the inpatient to the outpatient range has made clinically significant change (classification of recovering). (Ronk et al., 2013, p. 1108)

They suggested that adding this distinction can be quite meaningful for clients. Because the dichotomous categorization implies that the goal for all clients is to return to normal functioning when, in fact, classification as "recovering" by moving from the inpatient to outpatient distribution may be quite acceptable and meaningful to clients in inpatient treatment.

Saavedra et al. (2020) used contemporary statistical methods to extend calculations of clinical significance. By using moderated nonlinear factor analysis (MNLFA) to assess clinical significance, they weighted item/symptoms compared with the JT method that assumes equal item weighting of items on the outcome measure. Because client presentation is well known to be quite variable, even with the same diagnosis, the idea of weighting change on those items/symptoms that are most relevant to the individual client adds an extra idiographic element to the assessment of individual change. They found in a sample of clients receiving treatment for posttraumatic stress disorder that a higher percentage of individuals made clinically significant change using the MNLFA method, which suggests that equal weighting of items that are less relevant to the client's presentation may attenuate change assessment in the JT method.

A variation on the MNLFA extension is the use of item response theory (IRT; see Volume 1, Chapter 36, this handbook) for calculating clinical significance. Jabrayilov et al. (2016) compared calculations of clinical significance using IRT with classical test theory (CTT) in a simulation design. IRT has been proposed as a potentially useful alternative in part because IRT may "reveal subtle changes in individuals' mental health that could go unnoticed if one uses the sum scores from CTT, which ignore the pattern of the item scores"

(p. 560). They find that IRT is in fact superior to the classical method if the outcome measure has at least 20 items. In a study using the Beck Depression Inventory (BDI-II), Brouwer et al. (2013) also used IRT to assess individual change. Among other interesting findings regarding the use of IRT for assessing change, they compared IRT with the JT method (RCI) for classifying reliable change. For many individuals, the two methods lead to the same classification, but for a small number there were different classifications. They suggested that these discrepancies may be related to scores at the extremes or differences that were near the cutoff value. Based on their findings, they recommended that IRT holds promise as an alternative method for use in research and clinical practice though they also recognize that there is a need for IRT software development to facilitate the accessibility of the approach.

Another example of newer statistical methods being applied to the assessment of clinical significance involves growth mixture modeling (see Chapter 16, this volume). Flood et al. (2019) compared growth mixture modeling and the JT method as a strategy for predicting negative treatment by looking at early change in clients participating in a CBT-oriented day treatment. This study extends the typical assessment of clinical significance in that they are using the methods during treatment to predict eventual outcome rather than as a posttreatment assessment of individual change. Like other studies comparing the JT method to various alternatives, they recommend the JT method as opposed to growth mixture modeling because it was superior at predicting negative outcomes.

Though perhaps it may be considered a challenge to, rather than an extension of, the JT method, de Vries et al. (2016) used Bayesian statistics to model clinically significant change. They highlighted how use of the RCI shows an overreliance on p values as evidence rather than, as a Bayes factor does, quantifying the evidence as found in the data themselves. They showed how a Bayes factor could be estimated with a numerator capturing the likelihood of one hypothesis related to clinical significance (zero mean difference in scores before and after intervention) and the denominator capturing the likelihood of the alternative hypothesis (nonzero mean difference in scores before and after intervention). The data visually modeled with Bayes factors then showed the relative confidence one could have for each intervention subject's change representing true change. However, they pointed out that unless effect sizes are very large, the amount of evidence in the Bayesian data for true change tended to be low. Given that many effect sizes in clinical research can be moderate to small, this may be a significant limitation. Ruiz et al. (2018) provided an illustrative example of this Bayesian strategy in an interesting study evaluating a specific intervention's effectiveness. Continued exploration of the application of Bayesian methods to clinical significance may yield significant methodological improvements.

Another way in which research on clinical significance has expanded is through its application to differing populations. For example, Andresen et al. (2010) examined the degree to which measures of recovery coincide with symptom measures within clients participating in treatment for enduring mental illnesses such as schizophrenia or bipolar disorder. They found that measures that are more consistent with consumer-oriented definitions of recovery, that focus on constructs such as hope, confidence, striving, and self-identity do not correlate well with traditional symptom measures. They also found that the recovery-oriented measures did have good construct and convergent validity in that they were both correlated with one another and matched with the progressive improvement one would expect as a client moves through the theoretical stages of recovery. There is a large body of literature regarding the concept of recovery for individuals with enduring or chronic mental illness (e.g., Davidson et al., 2005; Hawthorne & Williams-Wengerd, 2019). This literature seems qualitatively different from the statistical methods used to assess clinically meaningful change in outpatient psychotherapy and could potentially be examined in a separate review.

Applying clinical significance to a broader range of clinical populations can show how treatment response rates differ according to population. Temple et al. (2020) in an individual patient data meta-analysis found a 30% recovery rate for patients being treated for emotional distress concurrent with a breast cancer diagnosis. They found that this rate is lower than other studies of mental health interventions that typically find recovery rates from 40% to 70%. Interestingly, Temple et al. also had estimates for recovery rates of patients enrolled in control groups who did not receive treatment. The control patients recovered at a rate of 15% to 25%.

A final example of clinical significance applied to expanded populations involves the investigation of the clinical significance in international contexts. Keith et al. (2011) discussed how conceptions of clinical significance in the West might be adapted, using cross cultural research, to better reflect culture-specific understandings of both treatment and outcome. Using the specific example of depression and depression treatment, they considered various contemporary methods for assessing the clinical meaningfulness of treatment outcomes with specific emphasis on normative comparisons that are informed by the culture and subjective evaluation that includes the viewpoint of multiple culturally relevant informants. Given that depression can be understood in ways that are specific to a culture, the outcome of a depression treatment can also be specific to the same culture, including what the culture determines is clinically significant change. Rolling out treatments developed in one culture (often Western-based or from the developed world) to another culture (often the developing world) may not work as anticipated, and stakeholders in those treatments need to account for these differences to determine whether the treatments are effective.

ADVANTAGES OF CLINICAL SIGNIFICANCE

Outcome research studies need to include estimates of clinical significance (preferably following the JT method explicitly; Jacobson & Truax, 1991) to establish the clinical relevance of psychotherapy change. The advantages to using clinical significance—and particularly the JT method—are numerous and extend beyond the establishment of clinical relevance. Inclusion of clinical significance requires different language about psychotherapy change. Rather than using the language of statistical significance, effect sizes, and likelihood of change on the basis of group membership, individual patients can be classified as improved, recovered, deteriorated, or unchanged. Not only is the language specific to individuals within the group but also the categorization gives face-valid terms that are clinically relevant.

Limiting statistics to traditional tests of statistical significance and effect sizes fails to examine (and, therefore, ignores) the importance of within-group variability (which is typically not unremarkable). With regard to this limitation, the JT method (Jacobson & Truax, 1991) and related methods are far superior, classifying each patient individually. However, several methods of determining clinical significance described in this chapter operate on the basis of between-group comparisons rather than within-group variations. Effect sizes, equivalence testing, and normative comparisons undoubtedly have value as clinically relevant information reported in outcome literature. Normative comparisons are especially relevant to determine the clinical cutoff criterion, in a manner not unlike the JT method. However, capturing within-group variation enables the researcher to determine the clinical significance of individual change. Individual treatment response can be measured over time, and much has been learned about the effectiveness of therapist feedback of treatment response data throughout the course of treatment (Harmon et al., 2007; Lambert et al., 2003; Lutz et al., 2006; Slade et al., 2008).

Clinical significance methods that classify individual patient treatment response have been helpful not only in making decisions about when a patient may be ready to terminate treatment (that they have reliably changed and are no more disturbed than other members of their community) but also in contributing information relevant to policy decisions, such as how many treatment sessions are needed to return individuals to a state of normal functioning. In recent years psychotherapy outcome research has addressed this question using survival analysis or related techniques to identify at what point in therapy a clinically significant change occurs for most patients (Anderson & Lambert, 2001; Hansen et al., 2002; Kopta et al., 1994). The results from these studies suggest a range of 11 to 18 sessions as the number of sessions needed to achieve clinically significant change for half of the sample starting therapy. Such information is dependent on the classification of each patient's treatment response. Perhaps most important, reporting clinical significance estimates reduces the likelihood of outcome research overestimating the benefit of mental health treatments. Taking the corpus of psychotherapy literature into account, psychotherapy appears to be generally effective in spite of specific treatments showing variability in degree of effectiveness (Lambert, 2013). Although group mean change scores may demonstrate statistically significant differences over control groups, the degree of change may be clinically nonsignificant.

Furthermore, large numbers of patients in a clinical trial may in fact deteriorate in a treatment group, whereas simultaneously the group mean shows change in the therapeutic direction. Clinical significance adds a level of precision to estimating the benefits of treatment, especially when the dual criteria of the JT method are required to define *recovered*. Greater precision in determining outcomes can lead to greater confidence in practitioners and outcome researchers with regards to the validity of a treatment effect.

Finally, clinical significance (by definition) gives information that is clinically relevant. A treatment that results in clinically significant improvement for a majority of patients undergoing the treatment provides a higher standard being met by that treatment. Clinical significance can also be used to narrow the gap between research and practice by indicating benchmarks for treatment response. As cited, progress feedback to clinicians is one application of clinical significance to practice that has been shown to be effective (i.e., resulting in clinically significant change for a large number of patients).

LIMITATIONS OF CLINICAL SIGNIFICANCE

Methods of determining clinical significance are not without limitations. Several limitations are discussed here as they have been discussed in the outcome literature. Important limitations include the plurality of methods, the lack of uniformity in applying these methods, categorization and validity problems, and the limits of the functional distribution for cutoffs. Hsu (1999) and others have spelled out the weakness of the JT method (Jacobson & Truax, 1991) in not taking into account regression toward the mean as an alternative explanation for the difference between pre- and postscores. This limitation represents less of a threat than previously thought, with the JT method showing high agreement with other methods and to be moderate in its classification of patients. The most obvious of the limitations, as demonstrated by the content of this chapter, is the diversity of methods and the failure by the field to adopt a single common metric. Multiple sources have pointed to this need for a common method.

McGlinchey et al. (2008) argued for standardized, empirically derived cutoffs to simplify comparison across outcome studies. Lambert and Ogles have argued persuasively for the use of the JT method—if not used by itself, then at least reported in addition to the results of other methods—on the basis of an explicitly pragmatic rationale (Lambert & Ogles, 2009). Reasons for this recommendation include allaying confusion about classification of recovered and deteriorated patients, the absence of evidence that the alternative methods are superior, the fact that newer methods require often-unavailable population data, the relative ease of computation of the JT method, and the simple fact, as found in Ogles et al. (2001), that it is the most commonly used method in outcome research.

The discussion of different methods takes for granted the fact that the methods are uniformly applied. Ogles et al. (2001) noted high variability in the application of methods, particularly the question of which norms are most appropriate for calculating the RCI. Although about 35% of studies they found examining clinically significant change used the JT method, many of these included some variation of the method. Hsu (1999) commented that researchers choosing between sample-specific norms or general population norms or other parameters, such as standard deviations and reliability coefficients, base their choices on a judgment about which norms are most realistic. However, no consensus exists on which norms to use. Recommended norms include the use of internal consistency reliability estimates when calculating the standard error of the difference and the use of normative data to establish the clinical cutoff (Lambert & Ogles, 2009).

An additional limitation of clinical significance methods is the problem common to all methods of categorization. Cutoff scores run the risk of misclassifying those persons scoring closest to the cutoff, which creates discrete boundaries from a continuous variable. Strategies for determining the cutoff have been discussed, but the very nature of a cutoff score runs the risk of misclassification (see also Volume 1, Chapter 38, this handbook). Following the statistical strategies of clinical significance and reliable change indices greatly reduces this risk, but this limitation concerns the *validity* of the classifications of recovered versus no change versus deteriorated. Newnham et al. (2007) found evidence to support the validity of the JT method (Jacboson & Truax, 1991), indicating that patients who were classified by the method on the basis of a self-reported symptom measure (SF-36 Health Survey, classified as *improved, recovered, no change, deteriorated*) also showed differing levels of self-reported quality of life and clinician-rated symptom distress. Such studies show promise in demonstrating convergent validity, but more validity studies are certainly needed (see Lambert & Ogles, 2009).

Using a functional distribution cutoff presents yet another limitation based on the opposing ends of the distribution of initial symptom severity scores. Inpatient populations, for example, are likely to meet the reliable change criterion by discharge, but they may not meet the clinical cutoff criterion, as they typically continue to improve after discharge. Newnham et al. (2007), for example, argued that for the inpatient population, entering a normal range of functioning may be too high a benchmark for relatively brief inpatient stays. Tingey et al. (1996) made a similar point but suggested this problem could be overcome by using gradations of normal–abnormal functioning as the goal of treatment. They argued that a return to normal functioning may be an unrealistic goal for highly disturbed individuals. For example, the patient who is severely disturbed and who receives brief inpatient treatment may only return to a level of functioning that is still within the clinical range. The use of multiple functioning cutoff points would allow their change to be classified as clinically significant. One may legitimately question whether recovery necessitates a return to the nonclinical range of functioning.

At the opposite end of the spectrum, a large minority of patients enter treatment already in the normal range, and their scores and their functioning remain in this range throughout treatment. Defining clinically significant change for this population may demand different criteria, as the clinical cutoff is a less meaningful criterion for such cases. Floor effect responses for patients presenting for treatment are neither typical nor unheard of, but both recovery and reliable change criteria would be difficult to meet under these circumstances. Yet, denial of psychiatric symptoms by a patient who presents for treatment while depressed has diagnostic implications and clinical utility, and the one-size-fits-all approach for defining meaningful change may not be suitable.

Another emerging difficulty in the assessment of clinical significance is "mission creep" with clinical significance being used as another element of group comparisons rather than for individual change. For example, Saavedra et al. (2020) pointed out that psychotherapy studies broadly (and studies of treatments for posttraumatic stress disorder more specifically) have conflated the purposes of clinical significance with group level measurement of the magnitude of group differences in contrast to the original focus on individual client change. They also noted that even when studies focus on individual change, the studies often report only on reduction in symptoms via the RCI without considering return to the nonclinical distribution.

CONCLUSION AND FUTURE DIRECTIONS

Establishing the relevance of changes made in psychological treatments necessitates a multidimensional approach including group tests of statistical significance, effect sizes, and estimates of clinical significance for individuals. Conditions for determining clinical significance include two criteria: (a) the change score exceeding a difference score that would be expected with measurement error, and (b) the movement from a dysfunctional to a functional population. The importance of clinical significance in addressing within-group variation has been demonstrated.

The advantages to using clinical significance estimates include not only establishing clinical relevance beyond statistical significance but also limiting the probability that treatment effects are overestimated. We close with some conclusions and future directions that might be gleaned from this overview of recent research regarding clinical significance.

- Many methods have been proposed and described in this chapter, with the JT method (Jacobson & Truax, 1991) being the most commonly used, the most parsimonious for calculation, and the one showing high agreement with methods attempting to revise it. Because a common limitation for clinical significance methods is the lack of a common index to report, we recommend the use of the JT method (alone or in combination with other methods) in all outcome studies to enable researchers to compare the results of studies using a common metric.

- The parameters for calculating the JT method should be commonly applied, including the use of internal consistency reliability estimates to calculate the standard error of the difference and the use of measure-specific normative data (i.e., for patient and nonpatient populations; see Beckstead et al., 2003) for establishing clinical cutoff scores. Following these recommendations would enable the comparison of

- research studies, with the goal of illuminating the effects of psychotherapy for patients.
- Although we recommend the JT method, we are eager to see continued research on other conceptualizations and statistical methods for exploring clinical significance such as percent change indices and proportional models of change.
- Similarly, newer statistical procedures such as those observed in this chapter (e.g., growth mixture modeling, IRT, MNLFA, and Bayesian approaches) deserve continued study in comparison to other methods of assessing clinical significance. Importantly, as more nuanced approaches to clinical significance are identified, concurrent development of software packages must be developed if the approaches are to be adopted. Unless newer approaches are as parsimonious to use or show a very clear advantage for conceiving and calculating meaningful change, the JT method will continue to be the standard.
- Researchers and clinicians applying clinical significance in outpatient therapies would do well to learn from colleagues studying interventions for serious and chronic mental illnesses to expand the conceptualization of recovery and to understand the broader definitions of change. In addition, taking a more nuanced view of the classic dichotomous view of outcome may be a better fit with client's conceptualizations of change and recovery (e.g., considering multiple positive outcome distributions such as recovered and recovering).
- Expanding the populations and applications of clinical significance could also be fruitful.
- The validity of distribution-based methods for assessing clinical significance needs additional research. Both concurrent and predictive validity of these categories have not been thoroughly studied. The question of different raters of clinically significant change also needs additional study.
- The finding that the outcome measure used to assess change may be more important than the method of calculation also deserves further consideration. In particular, continued work to compare more general measures with disorder-specific measures may bear fruit. The treatment outcome literature may benefit from the continued study of the concordance of clinical significance as given by different outcome measures.

As the research and application of these definitions and calculation methods continue, we hope the outcome research literature continues to address the vital question of the clinical relevance of change.

References

Anderson, E. M., & Lambert, M. J. (2001). A survival analysis of clinically significant change in outpatient psychotherapy. *Journal of Clinical Psychology, 57*(7), 875–888. https://doi.org/10.1002/jclp.1056

Andresen, R., Caputi, P., & Oades, L. G. (2010). Do clinical outcome measures assess consumer-defined recovery? *Psychiatry Research, 177*(3), 309–317. https://doi.org/10.1016/j.psychres.2010.02.013

Ankuta, G. Y., & Abeles, N. (1993). Client satisfaction, clinical significance, and meaningful change in psychotherapy. *Professional Psychology, Research and Practice, 24*(1), 70–74. https://doi.org/10.1037/0735-7028.24.1.70

Atkins, D. C., Bedics, J. D., McGlinchey, J. B., & Beauchaine, T. P. (2005). Assessing clinical significance: Does it matter which method we use? *Journal of Consulting and Clinical Psychology, 73*(5), 982–989. https://doi.org/10.1037/0022-006X.73.5.982

Bauer, S., Lambert, M. J., & Nielsen, S. L. (2004). Clinical significance methods: A comparison of statistical techniques. *Journal of Personality Assessment, 82*(1), 60–70. https://doi.org/10.1207/s15327752jpa8201_11

Beadnell, B., Stafford, P. A., Crisafulli, M. A., Casey, E. A., & Rosengren, D. B. (2016). Methods for quantifying the clinical significance of change during intervention program participation. *Evaluation & the Health Professions, 39*(4), 435–459. https://doi.org/10.1177/0163278715622663

Beckstead, D. J., Hatch, A. L., Lambert, M. J., Eggett, D. L., Vermeersch, D. A., & Goates, M. K. (2003). Clinical significance of the Outcome Questionnaire (OQ-45.2). *The Behavior Analyst Today, 4*(1), 86–97. https://doi.org/10.1037/h0100015

Bergin, A. E. (1966). Some implications of psychotherapy research for therapeutic practice. *Journal of Abnormal Psychology, 71*(4), 235–246. https://psycnet.apa.org/doi/10.1037/h0023577

Bergin, A. E. (1971). The evaluation of therapeutic outcomes. In A. E. Bergin & S. L. Garfield (Eds.), *Handbook of psychotherapy and behavior change* (pp. 217–270). Wiley.

Bergin, A. E., & Lambert, M. J. (1978). The evaluation of therapeutic outcomes. In S. L. Garfield & A. E. Bergin (Eds.), *Handbook of psychotherapy and behavior change: An empirical analysis* (2nd ed., pp. 139–189). Wiley.

Beutler, L. E., & Moleiro, C. (2001). Clinical versus reliable and significant change. *Clinical Psychology: Science and Practice, 8*(4), 441–445. https://doi.org/10.1093/clipsy.8.4.441

Billingham, D. D., Kelly, P. J., Deane, F. P., Crowe, T. P., Buckingham, M. S., & Craig, F. L. (2012). Clinically significant change to establish benchmarks in residential drug and alcohol treatment services. *International Journal of Mental Health and Addiction, 10*(6), 890–901. https://doi.org/10.1007/s11469-012-9384-3

Blanchard, E. B., Appelbaum, K. A., Radnitz, C. L., Michultka, D., Morrill, B., Kirsch, C., Hillhouse, J., Evans, D. D., Guarnieri, P., Attanasio, V., Andrasik, F., Jaccard, J., & Dentinger, M. P. (1990). Placebo-controlled evaluation of abbreviated progressive muscle relaxation and of relaxation combined with cognitive therapy in the treatment of tension headache. *Journal of Consulting and Clinical Psychology, 58*(2), 210–215. https://doi.org/10.1037/0022-006X.58.2.210

Blanchard, E. B., & Schwarz, S. P. (1988). Clinically significant changes in behavioral medicine. *Behavioral Assessment, 10*(2), 171–188.

Brouwer, D., Meijer, R. R., & Zevalkink, J. (2013). Measuring individual significant change on the Beck Depression Inventory-II through IRT-based statistics. *Psychotherapy Research, 23*(5), 489–501. https://doi.org/10.1080/10503307.2013.794400

Carroll, K. M., Kiluk, B. D., Nich, C., DeVito, E. E., Decker, S., LaPaglia, D., Duffey, D., Babuscio, T. A., & Ball, S. A. (2014). Toward empirical identification of a clinically meaningful indicator of treatment outcome: Features of candidate indicators and evaluation of sensitivity to treatment effects and relationship to one year follow up cocaine use outcomes. *Drug and Alcohol Dependence, 137*, 3–19. https://doi.org/10.1016/j.drugalcdep.2014.01.012

Cohen, J. (1988). *Statistical power analysis for the behavioral sciences* (2nd ed.). Erlbaum.

Cohen, R. J., & Swerdlink, M. E. (1999). *Psychological testing and assessment*. Mayfield.

Cronbach, L. J. (1951). Coefficient alpha and the internal structure of tests. *Psychometrika, 16*(3), 297–334. https://doi.org/10.1007/BF02310555

Davidson, L., O'Connell, M. J., Tondora, J., Lawless, M., & Evans, A. C. (2005). Recovery in serious mental illness: A new wine or just a new bottle? *Professional Psychology, Research and Practice, 36*(5), 480–487. https://doi.org/10.1037/0735-7028.36.5.480

de Beurs, E., Barendregt, M., de Heer, A., van Duijn, E., Goeree, B., Kloos, M., Kooiman, K., Lionarons, H., & Merks, A. (2016). Comparing methods to denote treatment outcome in clinical research and benchmarking mental health care. *Clinical Psychology & Psychotherapy, 23*(4), 308–318. https://doi.org/10.1002/cpp.1954

Derogatis, L. R., & Unger, R. (2010). Symptom Checklist-90-Revised. *The Corsini encyclopedia of psychology*. https://doi.org/10.1002/9780470479216.corpsy0970

De Smet, M. M., Meganck, R., De Geest, R., Norman, U. A., Truijens, F., & Desmet, M. (2020). What "good outcome" means to patients: Understanding recovery and improvement in psychotherapy for major depression from a mixed-methods perspective. *Journal of Counseling Psychology, 67*(1), 25–39. https://doi.org/10.1037/cou0000362

de Vries, R. M., Meijer, R. R., van Bruggen, V., & Morey, R. D. (2016). Improving the analysis of routine outcome measurement data: What a Bayesian approach can do for you. *International Journal of Methods in Psychiatric Research, 25*(3), 155–167. https://doi.org/10.1002/mpr.1496

Eisen, S. V., Ranganathan, G., Seal, P., & Spiro, A., III. (2007). Measuring clinically meaningful change following mental health treatment. *The Journal of Behavioral Health Services & Research, 34*(3), 272–289. https://doi.org/10.1007/s11414-007-9066-2

Ferrer, R., & Pardo, A. (2019). Clinically meaningful change: False negatives in the estimation of individual change. *Methodology: European Journal of Research Methods for the Behavioral and Social Sciences, 15*(3), 97–105. https://doi.org/10.1027/1614-2241/a000168

Flood, N., Page, A., & Hooke, G. (2019). A comparison between the clinical significance and growth mixture modelling early change methods at predicting negative outcomes. *Psychotherapy Research, 29*(7), 947–958. https://doi.org/10.1080/10503307.2018.1469803

Hageman, W. J., & Arrindell, W. A. (1999). Establishing clinically significant change: Increment of precision and the distinction between individual and group level of analysis. *Behaviour Research and Therapy, 37*(12), 1169–1193. https://doi.org/10.1016/s0005-7967(99)00032-7

Hansen, N. B., Lambert, M. J., & Forman, E. M. (2002). The psychotherapy dose-response effect and its implications for treatment delivery services. *Clinical Psychology: Science and Practice*, *9*(3), 329–343. https://doi.org/10.1093/clipsy.9.3.329

Harmon, S. C., Lambert, M. J., Smart, D. M., Hawkins, E., Nielsen, S. L., Slade, K., & Lutz, W. (2007). Enhancing outcome for potential treatment failures: Therapist-client feedback and clinical support tools. *Psychotherapy Research*, *17*(4), 379–392. https://doi.org/10.1080/10503300600702331

Hawthorne, S. C. C., & Williams-Wengerd, A. (2019). 'Effective' at what? On effective intervention in serious mental illness. *Health Care Analysis*, *27*(4), 289–308. https://doi.org/10.1007/s10728-019-00367-9

Hiller, W., Schindler, A. C., & Lambert, M. J. (2012). Defining response and remission in psychotherapy research: A comparison of the RCI and the method of percent improvement. *Psychotherapy Research*, *22*(1), 1–11. https://doi.org/10.1080/10503307.2011.616237

Hsu, L. M. (1999). Caveats concerning comparisons of change rates obtained with five methods of identifying significant client changes: Comment on Speer and Greenbaum (1995). *Journal of Consulting and Clinical Psychology*, *67*(4), 594–598. https://doi.org/10.1037/0022-006X.67.4.594

Jabrayilov, R., Emons, W. H. M., & Sijtsma, K. (2016). Comparison of classical test theory and item response theory in individual change assessment. *Applied Psychological Measurement*, *40*(8), 559–572. https://doi.org/10.1177/0146621616664046

Jacobson, N. S., Follette, W. C., & Revenstorf, D. (1984). Psychotherapy outcome research: Methods for reporting variability and evaluating clinical significance. *Behavior Therapy*, *15*(4), 336–352. https://doi.org/10.1016/S0005-7894(84)80002-7

Jacobson, N. S., Roberts, L. J., Berns, S. B., & McGlinchey, J. B. (1999). Methods for defining and determining the clinical significance of treatment effects: Description, application, and alternatives. *Journal of Consulting and Clinical Psychology*, *67*(3), 300–307. https://doi.org/10.1037/0022-006X.67.3.300

Jacobson, N. S., & Truax, P. (1991). Clinical significance: A statistical approach to defining meaningful change in psychotherapy research. *Journal of Consulting and Clinical Psychology*, *59*(1), 12–19. https://doi.org/10.1037/0022-006X.59.1.12

Janse, P. D., de Jong, K., Veerkamp, C., van Dijk, M. K., Hutschemaekers, G. J. M., & Verbraak, M. J. P. M. (2020). The effect of feedback-informed cognitive behavioral therapy on treatment outcome: A randomized controlled trial. [Supplemental]. *Journal of Consulting and Clinical Psychology*, *88*(9), 818–828. https://doi.org/10.1037/ccp0000549

Jensen, S. A., & Corralejo, S. M. (2017). Measurement Issues: Large effect sizes do not mean most people get better—Clinical significance and the importance of individual results. *Child and Adolescent Mental Health*, *22*(3), 163–166. https://doi.org/10.1111/camh.12203

Karin, E., Dear, B. F., Heller, G. Z., Gandy, M., & Titov, N. (2018). Measurement of symptom change following web-based psychotherapy: Statistical characteristics and analytical methods for measuring and interpreting change. *JMIR Mental Health*, *5*(3), e10200. https://doi.org/10.2196/10200

Kazdin, A. E. (1977). Assessing the clinical or applied importance of behavior change through social validation. *Behavior Modification*, *1*(4), 427–452. https://doi.org/10.1177/014544557714001

Kazdin, A. E. (2003). *Research design in clinical psychology* (4th ed.). Allyn & Bacon.

Keith, J. A., Verdeli, H., & Vousoura, E. (2011). Evaluating the clinical significance of depression treatment: Implications for global mental health research. *International Journal of Mental Health*, *40*(3), 3–28. https://doi.org/10.2753/IMH0020-7411400301

Kelly, P. J. (2010). Calculating clinically significant change: Applications of the Clinical Global Impressions (CGI) Scale to evaluate client outcomes in private practice. *Clinical Psychologist*, *14*(3), 107–111. https://doi.org/10.1080/13284207.2010.512015

Kendall, P. C., & Grove, W. M. (1988). Normative comparisons in therapy outcome. *Behavioral Assessment*, *10*(2), 147–158.

Kendall, P. C., Marrs-Garcia, A., Nath, S. R., & Sheldrick, R. C. (1999). Normative comparisons for the evaluation of clinical significance. *Journal of Consulting and Clinical Psychology*, *67*(3), 285–299. https://doi.org/10.1037/0022-006X.67.3.285

Kopta, S. M., Howard, K. I., Lowry, J. L., & Beutler, L. E. (1994). Patterns of symptomatic recovery in psychotherapy. *Journal of Consulting and Clinical Psychology*, *62*(5), 1009–1016. https://doi.org/10.1037/0022-006X.62.5.1009

La Greca, A. M. (2005). Editorial. *Journal of Consulting and Clinical Psychology*, *73*(1), 3–5. https://doi.org/10.1037/0022-006X.73.1.3

Lambert, M. J. (2013). Outcome in psychotherapy: The past and important advances. *Psychotherapy*, *50*, 42–51. https://doi.org/10.1037/a0030682

Lambert, M. J., & Bailey, R. J. (2012). Measures of clinically significant change. In H. Cooper, P. M. Camic, D. L. Long, A. T. Panter, D. Rindskopf, & K. J. Sher (Eds.), *APA handbook of research methods in psychology: Vol. 3. Data analysis and research*

Lambert, M. J., & Ogles, B. M. (2009). Using clinical significance in psychotherapy outcome research: The need for a common procedure and validity data. *Psychotherapy Research*, 19(4–5), 493–501. https://doi.org/10.1080/10503300902849483

Lambert, M. J., Morton, J. J., Hatfield, D., Harmon, C., Hamilton, S., & Shimokawa, K. (2004). *OQ-45 administration and scoring manual*. OQ Measures.

Lambert, M. J., Whipple, J. L., Hawkins, E. J., Vermeersch, D. A., Nielsen, S. L., & Smart, D. W. (2003). Is it time for clinicians to routinely track patient outcome? A meta-analysis. *Clinical Psychology: Science and Practice*, 10(3), 288–301. https://doi.org/10.1093/clipsy.bpg025

Lenz, A. S. (2020). Estimating and reporting clinical significance in counseling research: Inferences based on percent improvement. *Measurement & Evaluation in Counseling & Development*, 53(4), 289–296. https://doi.org/10.1080/07481756.2020.1784758

Lovibond, P. F., & Lovibond, S. H. (1995). The structure of negative emotional states: Comparison of the Depression Anxiety Stress Scales (DASS) with the Beck Depression and Anxiety Inventories. *Behaviour Research and Therapy*, 33(3), 335–343. https://doi.org/10.1016/0005-7967(94)00075-U

Lunnen, K. M., & Ogles, B. M. (1998). A multiperspective, multivariable evaluation of reliable change. *Journal of Consulting and Clinical Psychology*, 66(2), 400–410. https://doi.org/10.1037/0022-006X.66.2.400

Lutz, W., Lambert, M. J., Harmon, S. C., Tschitsaz, A., Schurch, E., & Stulz, N. (2006). The probability of treatment success, failure and duration what can be learned from empirical data to support decision making in clinical practice? *Clinical Psychology & Psychotherapy*, 13(4), 223–232. https://doi.org/10.1002/cpp.496

Maassen, G. H. (2000). Principles of defining reliable change indices. *Journal of Clinical and Experimental Neuropsychology*, 22(5), 622–632. https://doi.org/10.1076/1380-3395(200010)22:5;1-9;FT622

Mangardich, H., & Cribbie, R. A. (2015). Assessing clinical significance using robust normative comparisons. *Psychotherapy Research*, 25(2), 239–248. https://doi.org/10.1080/10503307.2014.889329

McGlinchey, J. B., Zimmerman, M., & Atkins, D. C. (2008). Clinical significance and remission in treating major depressive disorder: Parallels between related outcome constructs. *Harvard Review of Psychiatry*, 16(1), 25–34. https://doi.org/10.1080/10673220701885815

McHorney, C. A., & Tarlov, A. R. (1995). Individual-patient monitoring in clinical practice: Are available health status surveys adequate? *Quality of Life Research*, 4(4), 293–307. https://doi.org/10.1007/BF01593882

Newnham, E. A., Harwood, K. E., & Page, A. C. (2007). Evaluating the clinical significance of responses by psychiatric inpatients to the mental health subscales of the SF-36. *Journal of Affective Disorders*, 98(1–2), 91–97. https://doi.org/10.1016/j.jad.2006.07.001

Nordahl-Hansen, A., Øien, R. A., Volkmar, F., Shic, F., & Cicchetti, D. V. (2018). Enhancing the understanding of clinically meaningful results: A clinical research perspective. *Psychiatry Research*, 270, 801–806. https://doi.org/10.1016/j.psychres.2018.10.069

Nugter, M. A., Hermens, M. L. M., Robbers, S., Van Son, G., Theunissen, J., & Engelsbel, F. (2019). Use of outcome measurements in clinical practice: How specific should one be? *Psychotherapy Research*, 29(4), 432–444. https://doi.org/10.1080/10503307.2017.1408975

Nyman-Carlsson, E., Norring, C., Engström, I., Gustafsson, S. A., Lindberg, K., Paulson-Karlsson, G., & Nevonen, L. (2020). Individual cognitive behavioral therapy and combined family/individual therapy for young adults with anorexia nervosa: A randomized controlled trial. *Psychotherapy Research*, 30(8), 1011–1025. https://doi.org/10.1080/10503307.2019.1686190

Ogles, B. M., Lambert, M. J., & Sawyer, J. D. (1995). Clinical significance of the National Institute of Mental Health Treatment of Depression Collaborative Research Program data. *Journal of Consulting and Clinical Psychology*, 63(2), 321–326. https://doi.org/10.1037/0022-006X.63.2.321

Ogles, B. M., Lunnen, K. M., & Bonesteel, K. (2001). Clinical significance: History, application, and current practice. *Clinical Psychology Review*, 21(3), 421–446. https://doi.org/10.1016/S0272-7358(99)00058-6

Ronk, F. R., Hooke, G. R., & Page, A. C. (2012). How consistent are clinical significance classifications when calculation methods and outcome measures differ? *Clinical Psychology: Science and Practice*, 19(2), 167–179. https://doi.org/10.1111/j.1468-2850.2012.01281.x

Ronk, F. R., Hooke, G. R., & Page, A. C. (2016). Validity of clinically significant change classifications yielded by Jacobson–Truax and Hageman–Arrindell methods. *BMC Psychiatry*, 16(1), 187. https://doi.org/10.1186/s12888-016-0895-5

Ronk, F. R., Korman, J. R., Hooke, G. R., & Page, A. C. (2013). Assessing clinical significance of treatment outcomes using the DASS-21. *Psychological Assessment, 25*(4), 1103–1110. https://doi.org/10.1037/a0033100

Ruiz, F. J., Flórez, C. L., García-Martín, M. B., Monroy-Cifuentes, A., Barreto-Montero, K., García-Beltrán, D. M., Riaño-Hernández, D., Sierra, M. A., Suárez-Falcón, J. C., Cardona-Betancourt, V., & Gil-Luciano, B. (2018). A multiple-baseline evaluation of a brief acceptance and commitment therapy protocol focused on repetitive negative thinking for moderate emotional disorders. *Journal of Contextual Behavioral Science, 9*, 1–14. https://doi.org/10.1016/j.jcbs.2018.04.004

Saavedra, L. M., Morgan-López, A. A., Hien, D. A., Killeen, T. K., Back, S. E., Ruglass, L. M., Fitzpatrick, S., & Lopez-Castro, T. (2020). Putting the patient back in clinical significance: Moderated nonlinear factor analysis for estimating clinically significant change in treatment for posttraumatic stress disorder. *Journal of Traumatic Stress, 34*(2), 454–466. https://doi.org/10.1002/jts.22624

Sheldrick, R. C., Kendall, P. C., & Heimberg, R. G. (2001). The clinical significance of treatments: A comparison of three treatments for conduct disordered children. *Clinical Psychology: Science and Practice, 8*(4), 418–430. https://doi.org/10.1093/clipsy.8.4.418

Slade, K., Lambert, M. J., Harmon, S. C., Smart, D. W., & Bailey, R. (2008). Improving psychotherapy outcome: The use of immediate electronic feedback and revised clinical support tools. *Clinical Psychology & Psychotherapy, 15*(5), 287–303. https://doi.org/10.1002/cpp.594

Speer, D. C. (1992). Clinically significant change: Jacobson and Truax (1991) revisited. *Journal of Consulting and Clinical Psychology, 60*(3), 402–408. https://doi.org/10.1037/0022-006X.60.3.402

Speer, D. C., & Greenbaum, P. E. (1995). Five methods for computing significant individual client change and improvement rates: Support for an individual growth curve approach. *Journal of Consulting and Clinical Psychology, 63*(6), 1044–1048. https://doi.org/10.1037/0022-006X.63.6.1044

Speer, D. C., & Greenbaum, P. E. (2002). Correction to Speer & Greenbaum (1995). *Journal of Consulting and Clinical Psychology, 70*(6), 1239. https://doi.org/10.1037/0022-006X.70.6.1239

Temple, J., Salmon, P., Tudur Smith, C., Huntley, C. D., Byrne, A., & Fisher, P. L. (2020). The questionable efficacy of manualized psychological treatments for distressed breast cancer patients: An individual patient data meta-analysis. *Clinical Psychology Review, 80*, 101883. https://doi.org/10.1016/j.cpr.2020.101883

Tingey, R., Lambert, M., Burlingame, G., & Hansen, N. (1996). Assessing clinical significance: Proposed extensions to method. *Psychotherapy Research, 6*(2), 109–123. https://doi.org/10.1080/10503309612331331638

Ulrich, R., Stachnik, T., & Mabry, J. (1966). *Control of human behavior* (Vol. 1). Scott, Foresman & Company.

Vaganian, L., Bussmann, S., Gerlach, A. L., Kusch, M., Labouvie, H., & Cwik, J. C. (2020). Critical consideration of assessment methods for clinically significant changes of mental distress after psycho-oncological interventions. *International Journal of Methods in Psychiatric Research, 29*(2), e1821. https://doi.org/10.1002/mpr.1821

van Wieringen, K., & Cribbie, R. A. (2014). Evaluating clinical significance: Incorporating robust statistics with normative comparison tests. *British Journal of Mathematical and Statistical Psychology, 67*(2), 213–230. https://doi.org/10.1111/bmsp.12015

Westbrook, D., & Kirk, J. (2005). The clinical effectiveness of cognitive behaviour therapy: Outcome for a large sample of adults treated in routine practice. *Behaviour Research and Therapy, 43*(10), 1243–1261. https://doi.org/10.1016/j.brat.2004.09.006

Wolf, M. M. (1978). Social validity: The case for subjective measurement or how applied behavior analysis is finding its heart. *Journal of Applied Behavior Analysis, 11*(2), 203–214. https://doi.org/10.1901/jaba.1978.11-203

Wolpert, M., Görzig, A., Deighton, J., Fugard, A. J. B., Newman, R., & Ford, T. (2015). Comparison of indices of clinically meaningful change in child and adolescent mental health services: Difference scores, reliable change, crossing clinical thresholds and 'added value'—An exploration using parent rated scores on the SDQ. *Child and Adolescent Mental Health, 20*(2), 94–101. https://doi.org/10.1111/camh.12080

Section 3

Methods with Single Outcomes

CHAPTER 8

ANALYSIS OF VARIANCE AND THE GENERAL LINEAR MODEL

James Jaccard and Ai Bo

Analysis of variance (ANOVA) and the general linear model (multiple regression) are probably the most widely used methods of analysis in the social sciences. Traditional ANOVA is a special case of multiple regression in the sense that any statistical contrast performed in ANOVA can be replicated using multiple regression. Despite this, the two approaches have evolved from different research traditions, and hence, we treat them separately.

We begin by discussing general concepts in statistical modeling and the analysis of mean differences. For both ANOVA and multiple regression, we describe the statistical model that motivates common applications of the approaches. We then discuss topics that are frequently misunderstood or that need to be reinforced in scientific practice. We refrain from developing the technical foundations of the methods because these, as well as relevant computational formulas, are available elsewhere (e.g., Judd et al., 2009; Kirk, 2012; Maxwell et al., 2021). Instead, we opt for a more informal approach to the relevant statistics to underscore intuitive and conceptual underpinnings.

In practice, researchers typically think about multiple regression using a statistical modeling mindset. The outcome variable is expressed as a linear function of a set of explanatory variables. Researchers seek to determine the accuracy with which one can predict the outcome from the predictors (using the squared multiple correlation) and interpret the coefficients associated with each predictor in the equation. Analysts often are concerned with the percent of variation that each predictor accounts for in the outcome, both alone and independent of the other predictors. ANOVA, by contrast, is often associated with a mindset of analyzing mean differences. Researchers evaluate how means differ as a function of different variables, or *factors*, and pass judgment on the implications of those mean differences.

In point of fact, multiple regression and ANOVA each accommodate the two mindsets. That is, one can readily think of multiple regression as analyzing mean differences and how means vary as a function of variables, and one can readily think of ANOVA in terms of expressing the outcome variable as a function of a set of predictors and how well one is able to account for that outcome on the basis of the predictors. We characterize ANOVA and multiple regression from both perspectives, but we emphasize the particular mindsets that dominate applications of the respective frameworks.

We thank Kim Daniloski for contributions to this chapter reflected in the prior edition of the handbook (Jaccard & Daniloski, 2012).
https://doi.org/10.1037/0000320-008
APA Handbook of Research Methods in Psychology, Second Edition: Vol. 3. Data Analysis and Research Publication, H. Cooper (Editor-in-Chief)
Copyright © 2023 by the American Psychological Association. All rights reserved.

KEY CONCEPTS IN MODEL-BASED ANALYSIS

In this section, we highlight selected concepts relevant to model-based analysis in both ANOVA and multiple regression frameworks.

Model Predictions and Errors in Prediction

Suppose one seeks to characterize the annual income of assistant professors at universities in the United States. If we obtain data on annual income for the entire population of such individuals, we might construct a model that explains the different scores on this variable. A simple—but obviously incorrect—model is one that predicts that every individual has a score equal to the mean of all the scores. This model can be written as

$$\hat{Y}_i = \mu, \qquad (8.1)$$

where μ is the grand mean calculated across all individuals and $\hat{Y}$ is the predicted annual income for individual i.[1] For example, if the (grand) mean is $48,348, the model states that everyone has an annual income of $48,348. We define the errors in prediction as the difference between the observed and predicted scores,

$$\varepsilon_i = Y_i - \hat{Y}_i, \qquad (8.2)$$

where ε is the error score for individual i. On the basis of Equations 8.1 and 8.2, we can specify a model that completely accounts for the population scores as follows:

$$Y_i = \hat{Y}_i + \varepsilon_i, \qquad (8.3)$$

where the annual income, Y, equals the predicted annual income on the basis of our model ($\hat{Y}$) plus errors in prediction (ε). Equation 8.3 is a general expression for representing statistical models, namely, observed scores are a function of model-based predicted scores plus error. For the present case, because $\hat{Y}_i = \mu$, Equation 8.3 can be rewritten substituting μ for $\hat{Y}_i$, yielding

$$Y_i = \mu + \varepsilon_i. \qquad (8.4)$$

Indexes of the Magnitude of Errors

When working with models, we want to index how far off model predictions are, that is, the magnitude of the errors. The average of the error scores across individuals is not a useful index because the positive errors cancel the negative errors during summation and produce an average error of zero. A better index is a positive square root average of the error scores. We first calculate the average squared error,

$$\sum_{i=1}^{N} \varepsilon_i^2 / N, \qquad (8.5)$$

and then calculate the square root of this result to return the index to its original Y metric,

$$\sqrt{\sum_{i=1}^{N} \varepsilon_i^2 / N}. \qquad (8.6)$$

This index of average error is called the *standard error of estimate* and is often symbolized by σ_ε or $\sigma_{Y-\hat{Y}}$. In our example, if the standard error of estimate is $3,012, this means that the predicted scores for the model were off, on average, by $3,012. The smaller the standard error of estimate, the better the model's predictions. Note that one must take into account the metric of Y when interpreting the standard error of estimate. If Y is the number of children married couples have in their family, then a standard error of estimate that equals 3.0 for a model is considerable, indicating that predictions are off, on average, by three children. If Y is annual income in units of dollars, then a standard error of estimate that equals 3.0 is small because predicted scores are off, on average, by only $3.00. The standard error of estimate is an informative statistic, but it is rarely reported in social science research.

---

[1] We use Greek symbols for parameters based on scores for the entire population.

Be careful not to confuse it with the estimated standard error of the parameter of interest, which is an indicator of sampling error, described later. Other indexes of the magnitude of error that are similar to the standard error of estimate but that rely on indices less affected by extreme errors are described in Wilcox (2021).

The most popular index of prediction errors is the squared correlation between the observed (Y) and predicted ($\hat{Y}$) scores. In the ANOVA literature, this index is often called *eta squared* (η^2), and in multiple regression it is called the squared multiple correlation. It is based on the concept of explaining variability in the outcome measure. Specifically, variability on Y can be decomposed into two parts: (a) that which can be accounted for by the model and (b) that which represents errors in prediction. The squared multiple correlation is the proportion of variability of Y that can be explained by the model; one minus it is the proportion that is due to errors in prediction.

Modeling and Conditional Predictions

The model we used to predict the annual income of new assistant professors on the basis of the grand mean was simplistic. More complex explanatory models make predictions using additional information about each individual in the population. For example, we might hypothesize that males, on average, are paid more than females and that the biological sex of an individual therefore should be taken into account when making predictions. For this model, the predicted scores are based on the grand mean and then are further conditioned on a person being male or female. Models differ in the amount of conditional information they use and how that information is combined to make predictions.

Model Comparisons

Model comparison is a popular practice in the social sciences (Judd et al., 2009; Maxwell et al., 2021; Rodgers, 2010). In this approach, one formally documents the improvement in prediction errors as a result of adding information to a simpler model. For example, the predicted annual income of assistant professors was initially based on a model that asserted the annual income of each individual is the mean income of all individuals in the population. A more complex model that builds on this model also predicts that the annual income is equal to this mean but that income is further conditioned on other pieces of information about individuals in the population, such as sex. The extent to which errors in prediction are reduced by considering the additional information is indexed quantitatively by documenting change in the standard error of estimate or the change in the squared multiple correlation. If the more complex model does not meaningfully reduce errors in prediction, the simpler model is preferred.

Model Population Parameters and Sample Estimates of Those Parameters

Although models are posited to represent the state of affairs in a population, we seldom have access to population data. Instead, we obtain what are conceptualized as random samples from a population and then make inferences about the values of the population model using indices from the sample data. In so doing, we recognize that sampling error operates and this must be taken into account. We elaborate on sampling error in the next section.

KEY CONCEPTS FOR ANALYZING MEAN DIFFERENCES

Model-based frameworks approach data by estimating model parameters used to generate predicted scores, documenting the magnitude of prediction errors, and determining the reduction in prediction errors that result by adding information to the model. A different mindset that some researchers use when analyzing data is not to think in terms of models but instead to think of group means and ask whether those means, or some combination of them, are different from one another. For example, a researcher might ask whether the population mean annual income of assistant professors for males, μ_M, is different from the population mean for females, μ_F, and then seek to test the hypothesis that the two means are not equal. The parameter of interest is the difference between the two means,

$$\delta = \mu_M - \mu_F, \quad (8.7)$$

and researchers seek to (a) determine whether the hypothesis that δ is not zero is viable relative to the null hypothesis that δ is zero and (b) estimate the magnitude of δ. In this mindset, the dominant concepts are population–sample means and sampling error.

Sampling Error

Estimates of a population mean on the basis of sample data are invariably accompanied by sampling error. Suppose the true annual income for assistant professors in a population is $\mu = \$48,348$. A researcher, constrained by the inability to obtain data on the entire population, obtains a random sample of 100 assistant professors from the population and calculates the sample mean, M. The calculated sample mean likely will not exactly equal the population mean, and the discrepancy between the sample mean and the population mean, $M - \mu$, represents *sampling error*. Suppose the sample mean is $47,144. The amount of sampling error is $47,144 - $48,348 = -$1,204. In practice, we cannot know how much sampling error is operating in a given study because, to do so, we would need to know the value of the population mean.

Although we can never know how much sampling error is operating in a given study, statisticians have derived indexes that estimate the typical amount of sampling error that occurs if the same study were to be replicated many times using the same sample size but with a new random sample from the population each time. This estimate is called the *estimated standard error* of the parameter of interest (not to be confused with the standard error of estimate, described earlier). We use the notation SE to refer to an estimated standard error in conjunction with a Greek subscript to reflect the population parameter to which it refers. For example, SE_μ is the estimated standard error of a mean, and $SE_{\mu_1-\mu_2}$ is the estimated standard error of the difference between two means. If a researcher reports that the sample mean for $N = 100$ is $47,144 and that the estimated standard error for the mean is $1,502, this suggests that sample means based on random samples of $N = 100$ deviate, on average, about $1,502 from the true population mean. The estimated standard error of a parameter tells us, in essence, how much confidence we can have in the accuracy of a sample mean, with smaller values leading to increased confidence. If, for example, the estimated standard error of the mean annual income of assistant professors is $12, then we would have a great deal of confidence in the accuracy of the sample mean we observe because, on average, sample means deviate only $12 from the true population mean. But if the estimated standard error of the mean income is $12,000, we would not have as much confidence in the accuracy of the sample mean. Estimated standard errors must be interpreted with caution because they are only *estimates* of the typical amount of sampling error and are, themselves, subject to sampling error. Despite this caution, they can be viewed as indicators of sampling error and are useful in statistical theory and applications of that theory.

Margins of Error

In political polls in the popular media, it is customary to report an estimate of a population parameter in conjunction with a margin of error (MOE). We might be told that the percentage of people who prefer Candidate A to Candidate B is 30%, with a MOE equal to ± 5%. The MOE is a recognition of the presence of sampling error, and, like the estimated standard error, provides us with a sense of the amount of operative sampling error. We have more confidence in a poll, for example, with a small MOE (e.g., ± 5%) than one with a large MOE (e.g., ± 25%). It is surprising that most research in the social sciences fails to report MOEs when reporting means, percentages, or correlations. Reporting MOEs should be standard practice.

One way to define MOEs is to use the upper and lower limit of the 95% confidence interval

(CI) of the statistic.[2] For example, a researcher might state that the mean annual income for assistant professors is $47,144, with a MOE of ± $300. This MOE is derived from the 95% CI, which was $46,844 to $47,444. It is the width of the CI divided by two, in this case ($47,444 − $46,844)/2 = $300. In some cases, the CI will not be symmetrical about the statistic, in which case one reports the lower and upper levels of the MOE separately. When planning a study, most researchers make sample size decisions to maximize statistical power. We suggest researchers also make sample size decisions to minimize MOEs. Methods for determining sample sizes that yield a priori desired levels of MOE are in Maxwell et al. (2008). Not surprisingly, MOEs are systematically related to estimated standard errors, as both reflect sampling error.

Critical Ratios for Mean Differences

In null hypothesis testing frameworks, we seek to determine whether we can reject the null hypothesis of equal population means in favor of an alternative hypothesis of unequal population means. For the case of two means, the null and alternative hypotheses are

$$H_0: \mu_M - \mu_F = \delta = 0 \quad \text{and}$$
$$H_1: \mu_M - \mu_F = \delta \neq 0. \quad (8.8)$$

An informal way of thinking about a standard error of mean differences is that it reflects the average absolute amount of sampling error that operates in studies like the one being analyzed. Assume an estimated standard error of a mean difference is $2,000 for samples of 100 per group when comparing male and female annual income. This suggests the average discrepancy (more technically, the root-mean-square average) of the sample difference from the true population mean difference across repeated replications of the study is about $2,000. Some errors will be larger than this, some will be smaller, and some will be close to zero.

We can form a ratio that compares the sample mean difference we obtain in a study relative to this index of sampling error

$$\text{Critical ratio} = \frac{\text{Observed mean difference}}{\text{Estimated standard error of mean difference}}. \quad (8.9)$$

If we obtain a critical ratio of 2.0, this means that the observed mean difference is twice as large as what we would expect on the basis of sampling error. If we obtain a critical ratio of 3.0, this means the mean difference is three times what we would expect on the basis of sampling error. Although there is more to the underlying logic, t ratios and F ratios can be interpreted as such critical ratios. A value of 1.0 means the observed sample difference is the same as what one would expect on the basis of sampling error, given the null hypothesis of no mean difference is true. Values larger than 1.0 indicate the observed mean difference is larger than what is expected based on the sampling error. If the critical ratio is larger than an a priori stated standard (e.g., a critical value based on an α level of 0.05), we conclude the null hypothesis is unlikely.

With this background, we can now discuss model-based and mean-based conceptualizations of ANOVA and multiple regression.

THE ANOVA FRAMEWORK

A Model-Based Perspective on ANOVA

As noted, models make predictions about scores on outcome variables conditioned on information about individuals in the target population. A popular representation of ANOVA is called an *effects model* in which the conditioned information is represented as deviations from the grand mean. Returning to the example on the annual income of new assistant professors, we might hypothesize that males, on average, are paid more than females and that the biological sex of the individual should therefore be taken into account when making

---

[2]Alternatively, one can define MOE using credible intervals in Bayesian statistics (Carlin & Louis, 2000). Technically, a CI should not be interpreted as an MOE in the way a layperson might think of it but rather in terms of the formal statistical theory underlying CIs.

predictions. We define the effect of being *male* as the difference between the mean annual income for males relative to the grand mean (i.e., the typical score for all individuals including males and females, μ),

$$\tau_M = \mu_M - \mu, \qquad (8.10)$$

where τ_M is the *treatment effect*, or the effect of being "treated" as a male, and μ_M is the mean annual income for males. If the mean male annual income is $50,350 and the grand mean is $48,348, then the effect of being male is to increase annual income, on average, by $50,350 − $48,348 = $2,002 over the typical income as indexed by the grand mean. We can define a similar effect for females as the female mean minus the grand mean,

$$\tau_F = \mu_F - \mu, \qquad (8.11)$$

where τ_F is the treatment effect of being female, and μ_F is the mean annual income for females. If the mean female annual income is $46,346, then the effect of being female is to decrease annual income, on average, by $46,346 − $48,348 = −$2,002.

We can incorporate the effect of gender into the initial model as follows:

$$\hat{Y}_i = \mu + \tau_j, \qquad (8.12)$$

where τ is the treatment effect for the group j that the person i is a member of, in this case, either male or female. The complete model of observed scores is then

$$Y_i = \hat{Y}_i + \varepsilon_i = \mu + \tau_j + \varepsilon_i. \qquad (8.13)$$

The effects-based ANOVA model uses the logic that a predicted score is an additive function of the grand mean plus treatment effects associated with one or more factors (independent variables) or the interaction between those factors. For multifactor studies, rather than making predictions conditional on one piece of information (e.g., gender), we make predictions conditional on multiple pieces of information. For example, the effect-based model of observed scores for a two-factor design is

$$Y_i = \hat{Y}_i + \varepsilon_i = \mu + \tau_{A_j} + \tau_{B_k} + \tau_{AB_{jk}} + \varepsilon_i, \qquad (8.14)$$

where τ_{A_j} is the treatment effect for the group j that the individual is in on factor A, τ_{B_k} is the treatment effect for the group k that the individual is in on factor B, and $\tau_{AB_{jk}}$ is the (residualized) interaction for factors A and B.

The Cell Means Approach

If researchers use the model in Equation 8.14, they estimate and directly interpret the different parameters in the model (i.e., μ, τ_{A_j}, τ_{B_k}, and $\tau_{AB_{jk}}$) while also seeking to gain a sense of how large the errors in prediction for the model are by estimating the population standard error of estimate or the squared multiple correlation between predicted and observed scores. However, even a casual inspection of research literature reveals that few investigators focus on these parameters. It is far more common for researchers to focus on group means per se, or combinations of them, and frame questions in terms of those means. To be sure, researchers do focus on t ratios and F ratios in the effects model of ANOVA. But technically, the focus is on parameters that directly reflect mean differences between groups, not grand means and treatment effects, μ and τ. Kirk (2012) referred to this focus as a *cell means approach* and provided statistical details of the method. Given its prominence, it garners most of our attention.

The central role of contrasts in the cell mean approach. When comparing means, it is common practice for researchers to first conduct an omnibus F test for each factor in the design and then pursue follow-up contrasts that test mean differences dependent on the results of the omnibus tests. The questions addressed by omnibus tests themselves usually are not focused sufficiently, so, invariably, the analyst pursues specific contrasts of specific mean differences given a statistically significant omnibus test. These contrasts are the heart of making substantive conclusions in ANOVA. Interestingly, most of the more popular follow-up contrast strategies (e.g., the Tukey HSD test, Bonferroni tests, the Games-Howell test) were developed without an omnibus F test serving as a screen to decide whether more specific contrasts should be pursued. Studies suggest that using an omnibus F test as a screen unnecessarily lessens the statistical power of these methods (Bernhardson, 1975), so there is good reason not to use the omnibus tests unless one's substantive questions dictate otherwise. Some researchers believe that a two-step strategy that uses an omnibus F test in conjunction with follow-up t tests controls for inflated Type I error rates that result from conducting multiple follow-up tests. It turns out that this is only true if a factor has three levels (Levin et al., 1994). Given the above, we recommend analysts generally forgo omnibus tests and move directly to the specific contrasts of interest. If it is desired to control for inflated error rates due to multiple contrasts, then one should use an appropriate method, such as a modified Bonferroni method (see Appendix 8.1; Jaccard, 1998).

Given the central role that contrasts have in the cell means approach, an important question is whether there are certain kinds of contrasts that are of particular interest. Rosenthal and Rosnow (1985) suggested there are three types of contrasts that are conceptually "wired in" to factorial designs. To illustrate them, consider a numerical example using a between-subjects factorial design. The study is a hypothetical experiment in which 120 participants read a transcript of a trial and then make a judgment on whether the accused is guilty on a 0-to-10 scale, with higher scores implying a higher likelihood of guilt. A 0 was labeled as *definitely not guilty*, a 10 as *definitely guilty*, and a five as *50–50*. The investigator went to great lengths to ensure the scale points were interpreted like probabilities and divided the responses by 10 to yield an outcome metric ranging from zero to one, which reflected *subjective probability* units. All participants read identical transcripts, except that half were told the accused was African American (Level 1 of Factor A) and the other half were told the accused was European American (Level 2 of Factor A). One third of the participants in the study were European American (Level 1 of Factor B), one third were African American (Level 2 of Factor B), and one third were Latinx (Level 3 of Factor B). Thus, the design was a 2×3 factorial in which the two factors were the race/ethnicity of the accused and the three factors were the race/ethnicity of the juror, both of which were between-subjects and fixed in nature. Table 8.1 presents sample means for the design with a sample size of 20 participants per cell.

The first type of contrast that captures the interest of many researchers is the difference between marginal means representing the main effect of each factor. In our example, these are contrasts comparing mean probability judgments of guilt for the race/ethnicity of the accused person collapsing across the race/ethnicity of the juror as well as contrasts comparing mean probability judgments of guilt for the race/ethnicity of the juror collapsing across the race/ethnicity of the accused.

A second type of contrast that often is of interest is associated with interaction effects, so we digress briefly into how interaction effects are conceptualized in the cell means approach. Interaction effects can be parameterized in many ways (see Jaccard, 1998; Judd et al., 2009; Maxwell et al., 2021), but the most common way in the literature invokes the concept of moderation. An interaction is said to exist when the effect of an independent variable on a dependent variable differs depending on the value of a third variable, called a *moderator variable*. Researchers first identify the factor they want to treat as the moderator variable and the factor that is to be the focal independent variable. In some studies, the choice is theoretically obvious, such as when one wants to evaluate the effect of a cognitive behavior therapy (CBT) versus a control group (the focal independent variable) on anxiety and seeks to test whether the effectiveness of CBT varies as a function of the biological sex of the respondent (the moderator variable). In other cases, such as the juror study in Table 8.1, the choice is not so obvious. One could reasonably ask whether the effect of race/ethnicity of the

TABLE 8.1

Factorial Analysis of Variance Example

	Cell means			
	Race/ethnicity of juror (factor *B*)			
Race/ethnicity of accused (factor *A*)	EA	AA	L	Marginal mean
AA	.77	.60	.60	.66
EA	.50	.45	.50	.49
Marginal mean	.64	.52	.55	

	Simple main effects (SME)		
	Race/ethnicity of juror (factor *B*)		
Race/ethnicity of accused (factor *A*)	EA	AA	L
AA	.77	.60	.60
EA	.50	.45	.50
SME mean difference	$(.77 - .50) = .27$	$(.60 - .45) = .15$	$(.60 - .50) = .10$

Interaction contrasts

Race/ethnicity of accused (factor *A*)	Race/ethnicity of juror (factor *B*)	
	EA	AA
AA	.77	.60
EA	.50	.45
Interaction contrast	$(.77 - .50) - (.60 - .45) = .12$	
	EA	L
AA	.77	.60
EA	.50	.50
Interaction contrast	$(.77 - .50) - (.60 - .50) = .17$	
	AA	L
AA	.60	.60
EA	.45	.50
Interaction contrast	$(.60 - .45) - (.60 - .50) = .05$	

Note. EA = European American; AA = African American; L = Latinx.

accused on guilt judgments varies as a function of the race/ethnicity of the juror, or one could ask whether the effect of the race/ethnicity of the juror on guilt judgments varies as a function of the race/ethnicity of the accused. In such cases, the designation of the moderator variable should follow from how the researcher wants to frame the interaction conceptually. Statistically, it is of little consequence as to which variable is chosen to be the moderator variable. In the juror example, we will use race/ethnicity of the juror as the moderator variable. The second type of contrast that often captures the interest of researchers is whether the independent variable affects the outcome variable at each level of the moderator variable. For example, is there an effect of race/ethnicity of the accused on guilt judgments for just European American jurors? Is there an effect of race/ethnicity of the accused on guilt judgments for just African American jurors? Is there an effect for just Latinx jurors? These contrasts are called *simple main effects* (see Table 8.1).

The third type of contrast that often is of interest is an interaction contrast. These contrasts test whether one simple main effect is different in magnitude from another simple main effect. Table 8.1 presents three interaction contrasts for the juror study. The estimated effect of the ethnicity of the accused for just European Americans is $M_{A1B1} - M_{A2B1} = .77 - .50 = .27$. The estimated effect for just African Americans is $M_{A1B2} - M_{A2B2} = .60 - .45 = .15$. The difference between these effects is $[M_{A1B1} - M_{A2B1}] - [M_{A1B2} - M_{A2B2}] = .12$. If the value of this interaction contrast is zero, then the effect of the independent variable on the outcome variable is the same for the two groups in question defined on the moderator variable. An interaction contrast essentially focuses on a 2 × 2 subtable and is the difference between mean differences. We discuss strategies for testing the statistical significance of interaction contrasts shortly.

In sum, researchers using factorial designs who adopt a cell means perspective are typically interested in three types of contrasts: (a) contrasts for differences between the marginal means associated with a main effect, (b) simple main effect contrasts to determine whether an independent variable affects an outcome variable at a given level of the moderator variable, and (c) interaction contrasts that determine whether the strength of the effect of the independent variable on the outcome variable shifts from one level of the moderator variable to another level. These contrasts, of course, do not exhaust the possibilities. Ultimately, the contrasts that a researcher pursues are determined by the theory and questions one wants to address.[3]

The cell means approach to contrasts. We can now specify a general formulation for the conduct of contrasts in the cell means approach in one-way and factorial designs. Specifically, we show how to pursue contrasts of the three types noted above. We begin by defining a parameter, called a contrast value, ψ, as being a linear function of the cell means of the different groups in the experiment. For the juror example, the design has six cell means and any given contrast value can be represented as

$$\psi_m = c_1\mu_{A1B1} + c_2\mu_{A2B1} + c_3\mu_{A1B2} + c_4\mu_{A2B2} + c_5\mu_{A1B3} + c_6\mu_{A2B3}, \quad (8.15)$$

where ψ_m is the mth contrast value (an investigator can pursue more than one contrast), μ_{AjBk} is the cell mean for factor A at level j crossed with factor B at level k, and the cs are contrast coefficients that are assigned numerical values by the researcher to isolate a theoretically interesting contrast. For example, suppose a researcher desires to examine a contrast that focuses just on European Americans (level 1 of factor B) and that compares the mean when the accused is African American with the mean when the accused is European American (a simple main effect contrast). This contrast is accomplished using the following contrast values:

$$\psi_1 = (1)\mu_{A1B1} + (-1)\mu_{A2B1} + (0)\mu_{A1B2} + (0)\mu_{A2B2} + (0)\mu_{A1B3} + (0)\mu_{A2B3}. \quad (8.16)$$

The terms with contrast coefficient values of 0 drop out of the equation because a mean times 0 is 0, leaving us with

$$\psi_1 = (1)\mu_{A1B1} + (-1)\mu_{A2B1} = \mu_{A1B1} - \mu_{A2B1}, \quad (8.17)$$

which is the contrast of interest to the researcher; a researcher interested in this contrast would

---

[3] Rosnow and Rosenthal (1989) insisted that interaction effects can only be validly parameterized using residualized means per Equation 8.14. Cell mean advocates (including us) disagree. For discussion of the controversy, see Meyer (1991) and Petty and colleagues (1996).

use the contrast coefficients 1, −1, 0, 0, 0, 0 in Equation 8.15.

Suppose instead, we want to examine a contrast for the main effect of factor A where we compare the marginal mean for all cases in which the accused is African American with the corresponding marginal mean where the accused is European American. The contrast coefficients that accomplish this are

$$\psi_2 = (1/3)\mu_{A1B1} + (-1/3)\mu_{A2B1} + (1/3)\mu_{A1B2} \\ + (-1/3)\mu_{A2B2} + (1/3)\mu_{A1B3} + (-1/3)\mu_{A2B3}. \tag{8.18}$$

Note that the three means for the accused African American are each weighted by 1/3 and summed (which yields the average for the accused African American across levels of factor B), and the three means for the accused European American are each weighted by −1/3 and summed (which yields the average for the accused European American across levels of factor B, signed negatively). With rearrangement of terms, this yields

$$\psi_2 = [(1/3)\mu_{A1B1} + (1/3)\mu_{A1B2} + (1/3)\mu_{A1B3}] \\ - [(1/3)\mu_{A2B1} + (1/3)\mu_{A2B2} + (1/3)\mu_{A2B3}], \tag{8.19}$$

which yields

$$\psi_2 = [(\mu_{A1B1} + \mu_{A1B2} + \mu_{A1B3})/3] \\ - [(\mu_{A2B1} + \mu_{A2B2} + \mu_{A2B3})/3], \tag{8.20}$$

which is the contrast of interest; a researcher interested in comparing these two main effect means would use the contrast coefficients 1/3, −1/3, 1/3, −1/3, 1/3, −1/3 in Equation 8.15.

Finally, suppose we were interested in the first interaction contrast in Table 8.1. This contrast focuses on the difference between mean differences (i.e., $[\mu_{A1B1} - \mu_{A2B1}] - [\mu_{A1B2} - \mu_{A2B2}]$). The coefficients that accomplish this contrast are 1, −1, −1, 1, 0, 0. The contrast coefficients for the second interaction contrast in Table 8.1 are 1, −1, 0, 0, −1, 1 and for the third interaction contrast they are 0, 0, 1, −1, −1, 1. The common feature of these contrasts is that each is a function of the individual cell means in the design, hence the term *cell means approach*.

Sampling error and critical ratios for contrasts. In practice, the contrasts of interest are performed on sample data. When applied to samples, the sample contrast value, CV_m, serves as an estimate of its population counterpart, ψ_m. An index of sampling error can be obtained for any sample-based contrast in the form of an estimated standard error for that contrast, SE_{ψ_m}, and a critical ratio is defined, per Equation 8.3, as

$$\text{Critical Ratio} = CV_m / SE_{\psi_m}. \tag{8.21}$$

In traditional ANOVA, this critical ratio is distributed as a t distribution with degrees of freedom equal to the degrees of freedom associated with SE_{ψ_m}. The p value for the contrasts is based on the critical ratio (a t ratio). Statistical software generates these p values, SE_{ψ_m}, and a 95% CI for the contrast, allowing one to also report an MOE for the contrast. It is statistically convenient if a restriction is placed on the various contrast coefficients within a given contrast so that they sum to zero. This restriction rarely limits the ability of the researcher to pursue contrasts that are of theoretical interest. Because the critical ratio is evaluated relative to a t distribution, the contrasts are often called *single degree of freedom contrasts*.

The formulas for calculating SE_ψ and the degrees of freedom associated with it can be complex and vary depending on design features (e.g., within-subject vs. between-subject factors, fixed vs. random effects, nesting, the presence of covariates, equal or unequal n per cell), how the investigator chooses to act on design features (e.g., whether one desires the CV for marginal means to reflect weighted or unweighted composites of the cell means in the face of unequal sample sizes), and the nature of the population data itself (e.g., whether one assumes variance homogeneity in each group). Computer software simplifies the calculations for us. Indeed, the software does not even require that researchers explicitly generate contrast coefficients, instead generating them implicitly on the basis of either contrasts that are common or based on purely statistical criteria (e.g., orthogonal contrasts).

Most of us are familiar with contrasts in ANOVA paradigms under the guise of follow-up tests, post hoc tests (e.g., Tukey's HSD test), a priori contrasts, or multiple comparisons. Researchers often do not appreciate that the data of a factorial design can be expressed as a set of one-way ANOVA like cell means and then combined via Equation 8.15 to yield perspectives on main effects, simple main effects, or interaction effects. The vast majority of research that uses ANOVA eventually zeros in on one or more single degrees of freedom contrasts that are of theoretical interest and that represent the combination of cell means per Equation 8.15.

In principle, an infinite number of contrasts can be performed. However, some contrasts have redundant or overlapping information value. For three means (μ_1, μ_2, and μ_3), if we conduct the three pairwise contrasts $\psi_1 = \mu_1 - \mu_2$, $\psi_2 = \mu_1 - \mu_3$, and $\psi_3 = \mu_2 - \mu_3$, one can easily show algebraically that $\psi_3 = \psi_2 - \psi_1$. In other words, there is a dependency between the contrasts because one of them can be expressed as a function of the others. Such redundancy motivates some researchers to pursue only sets of contrasts that are nonredundant, such as the well-known case in which contrasts are orthogonal. The problem with this logic is that sometimes orthogonal contrasts make no theoretical sense or fail to address the questions that are of primary interest to the investigator. In such cases, theory should prevail as the guide to contrasts.

In sum, two models of ANOVA are common. In the statistical literature, it is common to find ANOVA framed using an effects model that emphasizes the grand mean (μ) and treatment effects (τ_{Aj}, τ_{Bk}, τ_{ABjk}) relative to that mean. In the actual research literature, however, one is much more likely to find ANOVA framed in terms of the cell means approach with its emphasis on mean contrasts. This is not to say that applications that use the effects model and its parameters are nonexistent or inappropriate. They just occur with much less frequency.

ISSUES IN THE APPLICATION OF ANOVA

In this section, we consider selected issues and controversies in the application of ANOVA. We discuss five topics: (a) outliers and the violation of model assumptions, (b) family-wise error rates, (c) the analysis of interactions, (d) indices of effect size, and (e) asserting mean equivalence. To set the stage for this section, we describe the typical approach one would encounter in the literature for analyzing the data in Table 8.1: An investigator likely would conduct a 3 × 2 factorial ANOVA on the outcome variable. F ratios are examined for the main effects and the interaction effect. If the F ratio for a main effect is statistically nonsignificant, then no further analyses for that effect are pursued and the researcher fails to reject the null hypothesis of no mean differences for that factor. If the F test for a main effect with more than two levels is statistically significant, then follow-up analyses are pursued to determine which of the group means are statistically significantly different from one another. This analysis often takes the form of statistical comparisons between all possible pairs of means for the factor. Because multiple follow-up tests are performed when executing these contrasts, a procedure is invoked to control the family-wise error rate across the pairwise contrasts. The choice of method to accomplish this varies, but the most popular methods are the Tukey HSD method and modified Bonferroni procedures. If a statistically significant F ratio for the interaction is observed, then follow-up analyses are performed to elucidate the nature of the interaction effect. The most common strategy is to apply simple main effects analysis.

This analytic strategy is fraught with controversy. We have alluded to one such controversy, namely, the use of omnibus F tests as a screen before conducting tests of contrasts. The remainder of this section considers additional controversies and issues.

Violations of Model Assumptions and Outliers

An important issue that analysts must address is whether outliers are present and whether the distributional assumptions of the relevant inferential tests are met to a satisfactory degree. When comparing means using traditional F and t tests, two key population assumptions are (a) the within-cell scores (or the error scores) on the outcome variable are normally distributed (called the *normality* assumption), and (b) the within-cell variances of the outcome variable are equal (called the *homogeneity of variance* assumption). There are other assumptions made in ANOVA, but we focus on these two assumptions because of the attention they have garnered in the statistical literature. For a discussion of additional assumptions, see Maxwell et al. (2021).

We make reference to the robustness of a test to violations of these assumptions. A statistical test is said to be robust to violations of assumptions if (a) the nominal Type I error rate (α level) set by the investigator a priori (usually 0.05) is maintained in the face of assumption violations and (b) the statistical power of the test is relatively unaffected by assumption violations. (For a more technical and nuanced discussion of robustness, see Wilcox, 2021, and Chapter 1, this volume).

The assumptions of homogeneity of variance and normality. A common perception of many researchers is that the F tests of ANOVA are quite robust to violations of normality and homogeneity of variance. This is not necessarily the case. Keselman et al. (1998) noted that ratios of largest to smallest variances of 8:1 are not uncommon in the social sciences and that such ratios can have deleterious effects on traditional t tests and F tests. Variance heterogeneity can be particularly problematic when paired with unequal sample sizes (for detailed discussions, see Maxwell et al., 2021; Wilcox, 2021). In repeated measure designs, the variance homogeneity assumption takes a special form. As an example, if there are three repeated measures for a factor (Y_1, Y_2, and Y_3), there are three possible pairs of difference scores ($Y_1 - Y_2$, $Y_1 - Y_3$, and $Y_2 - Y_3$).

The homogeneity of variance assumption is that the population variances of these difference scores are equal. This is called *sphericity*. In general, omnibus F tests are not robust to violations of sphericity, and pooled variance estimates for contrasts that are based on this assumption also are problematic (Maxwell et al., 2021).

For the normality assumption, Cressie and Whitford (1986) and Westfall and Young (1993) have raised concerns about the adverse effects of skewness on Type I errors. Wilcox (1998, 2001, 2003) described the harmful effects that skewness has on Type II errors when comparing means. Wilcox (2021) noted that although the F tests and t tests that compare means often are robust to violations of nonnormality, this is not the case when the distributions within the various experimental groups differ. For example, if the population data are normal in one condition but skewed in another condition, then the robustness of the F test can be compromised. Prudent data analysis should not simply assume F tests in ANOVA are robust to violations of variance homogeneity and normality.

Strategies for dealing with violations of homogeneity of variance and normality. A common strategy for dealing with assumption violations is to perform a preliminary test of the viability of the assumption in question and, if the test suggests a problem, perform a metric transformation or revert to a robust analytic alternative. The use of this two-step strategy has been found to be problematic for several reasons. First, many preliminary tests lack power without large sample sizes and yield nonsignificant results for testing an assumption violation even when the violation is problematic (Wilcox, 2003; Wilcox et al., 1986). Second, the crucial issue is not whether the null hypothesis of normality or variance homogeneity can be rejected, but instead estimating the *degree* to which the assumption is violated and making a decision as to whether the degree of violation is consequential. This requires documenting the *magnitude* of the assumption violation in the sample data and then using MOEs to take sampling error into account when making decisions. For example, we might find that a variance ratio comparing the variances of two groups is 4.0 with an MOE of plus or minus 3.0. The MOE suggests that the variance could be as large as 7.0 and hence could be problematic. Unfortunately, it is rare for researchers to take MOEs into account when evaluating preliminary tests. Indeed, many preliminary tests of assumptions are not amenable to analyses of the magnitude of assumption violation, permitting only the evaluation of the viability of a null hypothesis of normality or homoscedasticity. Third, many tests of nonnormality are based on asymptotic theory and perform only adequately with large sample sizes (Shapiro & Wilk, 1965). With large N, however, such tests tend to detect minor departures from normality that may be of little consequence. In addition, normality tests can be differentially sensitive to different types of nonnormality. Some tests are sensitive mostly to skew whereas others are sensitive mostly to kurtosis. Fourth, the preliminary tests often make assumptions in their own right and may perform poorly when their assumptions are violated. For example, many tests of variance homogeneity assume the population data are normally distributed (Carroll & Schneider, 1985; Keyes & Levy, 1997; Parra-Frutos, 2009). If the population data are nonnormal, then the preliminary test of variance homogeneity may be invalid. Fifth, using preliminary tests as a screen can change the sampling distribution of F tests and t tests in unpredictable ways. Although it seems reasonable, the strategy of conducting preliminary tests of model assumptions has numerous challenges and is not straightforward.

Transformation strategies for dealing with assumption violations also have been criticized. Budescu and Appelbaum (1981) found that transformations to address variance heterogeneity can create more problems than they solve in inferential tests because they can adversely affect normality (see also Blaylock et al., 1980; Doksum & Wong, 1983; Milligan, 1987; Wilcox, 1996, 1998). Transformed variables often are difficult to interpret (e.g., the mean log of annual income is not easily interpreted). In complex ANOVAs with covariates, transformations of the dependent variable can create specification error that undermines covariate control because it alters the relationships between the outcome variable and covariates. Years ago, before high-speed computers were widespread, analysts had little choice but to use transformations to make measures conform to the assumptions of the limited number of parametric statistical models available. Researchers sometimes imposed transformations to make measures follow a normal distribution even though they knew the constructs were not normally distributed in the general population (e.g., depression). Such practices are rarely needed now with modern methods.

A growing number of statisticians recommend that analysts simply abandon the more traditional F tests and t tests of ANOVA unless they are confident in assumption viability on the basis of theory or extant research. Instead, analysts should routinely use modern robust methods of analysis or, at the very least, routinely supplement traditional methods with them (Keselman et al., 2008; Wilcox, 2021). These scientists recognize that cases may occur in which defaulting to robust analytic strategies will result in some loss of statistical power and/or suboptimal probability coverage of CIs. In the long run, however, they argue that the use of robust methods will result in better Type I error protection, increased power to detect effects, and CIs that more accurately reflect the desired probability coverage (Wilcox, 1998). A general recommendation is to view traditional tests of model assumptions and remedial strategies based on transformations with caution, deferring instead to more modern robust analytic methods.

Outliers. *Outliers* are unusually small or large outcome scores that distort basic trends in the data. For example, for the scores 2, 3, 4, 5, 6, 7, 8, 9, 10, and 50, the last score is an outlier that distorts the mean and makes the use of the mean suspect as a way to characterize the central tendency of the data. Simple methods for outlier detection compare the results of an analysis when the case is included versus the results when the case is deleted. Such approaches, however, can be nondiagnostic when multiple outliers are present. For example, if there are two individuals in an analysis who distort a mean upward, deleting only one of them may not reveal an outlier effect as long as the second outlier is still included in the data. Only when both outliers are removed is their distorting character revealed. Outlier identification in ANOVA is a complex enterprise, with some of the most sophisticated work in the literature on robust statistics (for elaboration, see Wilcox, 2003, 2012, 2021; Wilcox & Keselman, 2012).

Sometimes a theory-driven decision rule emerges from outlier analysis that permits outliers to be validly eliminated from an analysis on the basis of substantive criteria. For example, in studies of sexual behavior in college students, outliers might correspond to older, married students who have returned to college after many years. Their patterns of sexual activity may be so distinct as to distort the more fundamental trends that are evident in young, unmarried students. The decision might be made to eliminate all married students (which may result in eliminating both outliers and some nonoutliers) and then to restrict inferences to nonmarried student. Such outlier elimination strategies are appropriate.

Wilcox (1998, 2006, 2012) has questioned applying traditional inferential methods to data that have eliminated outliers on the basis of simple outlier detection methods. He argued that doing so invalidates the statistical theory on which the F tests and t tests are based because of dependencies that outlier elimination can create, resulting in incorrect estimates of standard errors that yield inaccurate inferential tests. Others recommend conducting sensitivity analyses with and without outliers to determine whether conclusions change. If conclusions do change, then one moves forward with any conclusions with tentativeness.

Probably the most effective strategy for dealing with outliers is to focus on measures of central tendency that are outlier-resistant. The best-known outlier-resistant measure of central tendency is the median, but it has been found to have several undesirable statistical properties (Wilcox, 2021). An alternative to the median is a 20% trimmed mean. To calculate a trimmed mean, one places observations in ascending order and then trims away scores from the upper and lower ends of the distribution, calculating the arithmetic mean on the remaining scores. A 10% trimmed mean strips away the 10% most extreme scores from each tail of the distribution, a 20% trimmed mean strips away the 20% most extreme scores, and so on. Trimming is conducted separately for each cell of the experimental design.

An objection to trimmed means is that one throws away data, but this is not the case. *All* of the data are used to order the scores initially. Hence, all of the data are used in the calculations. In fact, a median is based on stripping away 50% of the data above and below the midpoint of the distribution and working with the single data value that occurs in the middle of the distribution. A large amount of research has shown that a 20% trimmed mean has many desirable statistical properties and, as such, it is widely used in robust statistics (Wilcox, 2021). Specialized methods based on bootstrapping are typically required for estimating the standard errors of trimmed mean differences (Wilcox, 2021).

Another approach to dealing with outliers is to empirically downweight outliers when estimating the mean and its standard error. This approach is taken for a robust measure of central tendency based on M estimation (Wilcox, 2021). Keselman et al. (2007) suggested a method of customized trimming based on the nature of skewness in the data. Their approach can lead to trimming different amounts from the upper and lower ends of the distribution.

In sum, an effective way of dealing with outliers in ANOVA is to shift attention to outlier-resistant robust estimators of central tendency, such as trimmed means or M estimators. Depending on one's substantive questions, one index might be more satisfactory than the other.

Robust alternatives to ANOVA. There is an extensive statistical literature on analyzing trimmed means and other robust indexes of central tendency (Wilcox, 2021). These methods not only use outlier-resistant indexes of central tendency but also use approaches that tend to be robust to violations of normality and variance homogeneity. The tests often have more statistical power than traditional F tests and t tests (Wilcox, 1998). Technically, when one focuses on a robust measure of central tendency in sample data, the population parameter being estimated is the counterpart of the sample statistic. For example, when calculating a trimmed mean in sample data, the parameter that is being estimated is the trimmed mean in the population. The majority of statistical analyses pursued in ANOVA have a robust counterpart tied to trimmed means or some other robust measure of central tendency. This includes the contrast strategies that are based on the cell means approach as well as omnibus tests for one-way and complex factorial designs. Wilcox (2021) has written a suite of programs available as freeware in R that can be used to execute the analyses. Researchers should be using these approaches more often.

An interesting robust approach to comparing groups is based on the analysis of quantiles (Wilcox, 2021). This strategy allows researchers to address group differences at various points in the distribution of the outcome variable. For example, to compare groups on the median of the outcome variable (which will equal the mean for symmetric distributions), one would focus on the 0.50 quantile. To compare groups on the upper portion of the distribution, one might focus on the 0.75 or 0.90 quantile, and to compare groups on the lower portion of the distribution, one might focus on the 0.25 or 0.10 quantile. Wilcox (2021) presents a single degree of freedom contrast algorithm that permits application of the quantile approach to a wide range of contexts. This approach is useful because social scientists have tended to focus only on group differences in central tendency rather than more fine-grained features of the outcome distribution.

Controlling Family-Wise Error Rates

It is typical for researchers to pursue multiple contrasts in a single study. Statisticians distinguish between two types of error rates. The first type is a *per comparison error rate*, which refers to the probability of falsely rejecting the null hypothesis for a single significance test. The probability of a Type I error for a given comparison is the α level, traditionally 0.05. The second error rate is called the *family-wise error rate* (although it goes by other names as well) and refers to the error rate across multiple contrasts. For example, if we conduct five contrasts, then the rate at which at least one chance effect occurs across the five comparisons is the family-wise error rate. Even if the per comparison error rate is 0.05, the family-wise error rate across the multiple comparisons will be larger than 0.05.

Consider a simple coin flipping analogy. If we flip a coin, two possible outcomes can occur, one of which is a "head." Suppose for the sake of argument that we treat a "head" as an error. The likelihood of observing a head on a given coin toss is $1/2 = 0.50$. This is analogous to the per comparison error rate. If we flip a coin twice, four possible outcomes can occur: head-head, head-tail, tail-head, and tail-tail. Note that a head occurs on three of the four flips, so the probability of a head occurring on at least one of the flips is $3/4 = 0.75$. This is analogous to the familywise error rate. Even though the probability of a head is 0.50 on a given flip, the probability of observing at least one head across two flips is 0.75. The same type of dynamic operates for making errors across multiple contrasts. Social scientists traditionally desire to invoke analytic methods that maintain a 0.05 error rate across multiple contrasts.

The choice of a method for controlling family-wise error rates across a set of contrasts in factorial designs is complex, and we dare not address the issue here. Interested readers are referred to Kirk (2012), Maxwell et al. (2021), Toothaker (1993), Westfall et al. (1999), and Wilcox (1996). More than 30 such procedures have been proposed in the statistical literature. Appendix 8.1 presents a modified Bonferroni method that has widespread applicability and has much to offer as a general approach to controlling family-wise error rates. It is preferable to the traditional Bonferroni method in that it has more statistical power yet maintains the family-wise error rate at the desired level. Tests with somewhat more statistical power are available, however, depending on the analytic situation.

Many investigators feel that controls for inflated error rates should be invoked whenever multiple contrasts are performed. However, using such controls reduces statistical power for a given comparison, which results in the possibility of an unacceptably high rate of Type II errors. In research areas in which sample sizes tend to be small because of practical constraints, the issue is germane because statistical power is low to begin with. In such situations, one might decide not to invoke family-wise controls because the effect on statistical power is too severe. It gives too much weight to avoiding Type I errors at the cost of making Type II errors. Bayesians also question the appropriateness of correcting for multiplicity (Dienes, 2011).

Given a large number of contrasts, researchers seek to balance the need for statistical power with the need to control the error rate for multiple contrasts. A common strategy is to define different "families" of contrasts in which the error rate for multiple contrasts is controlled within a family but not across families. How to define a family is controversial. Tradition for factorial ANOVA is to let each factor define a family of contrasts. In the juror example, the main effect for the race/ethnicity of the juror represents one family and controls for multiple contrasts for the main effect means would be invoked within that family. The main effect for the race/ethnicity of the accused is a second family, but it consists of a single contrast, and hence no controls for family-wise error rates are used. The interaction effect is a third family, but it is typically broken into two separate families: (a) those involving simple main effects and (b) those involving interaction contrasts. However, a compelling rationale for these traditions has not been made.

A common misperception among researchers is that the error rates for multiple contrasts do not inflate as long as the contrasts are orthogonal. This is not the case. The rate at which the error rate inflates is different for orthogonal versus nonorthogonal contrasts, but inflation occurs in both cases. Another common belief is that if contrasts are specified a priori, one need not control for multiple contrasts. Stating a priori that one wants to examine, say, four contrasts does not change the fact that the error rate will inflate across these contrasts. The crucial issue is not so much whether contrasts are stated a priori as whether one wants to control the error rate.

Post hoc contrasts are contrasts that are conducted on the basis of the examination of the data. For example, an investigator who conducts an experiment using a one-way design with four groups may examine the means and decide that only two of the groups exhibit a large discrepancy from each other and then proceed to conduct this contrast, ignoring all other contrasts. In some respects, the researcher has conducted analyses of all possible contrasts using a subjective criterion ("This difference looks large to me, but this difference does not") rather than a formal statistical criterion. Corrections for family-wise errors in such post hoc cases can be invoked by the well-known Scheffé method (Maxwell et al., 2021). However, the Scheffé method usually lacks power relative to its alternatives in settings other than this post hoc scenario and should not be used. We believe that researchers usually have a good sense of the contrasts they want to explore, and it is rarely the case that they engage in purely post hoc analyses on the basis of examination of means after the fact. As such, the Scheffé method should rarely be used because there are more powerful alternatives to it.

In sum, analysts must address how to deal with inflated error rates across multiple contrasts. Contrasts are partitioned into separate families and procedures to maintain the family-wise error rate at a prespecified α level are invoked. In the case of small sample sizes and low statistical power, some statisticians recommend performing contrasts both with and without family-wise controls. If a given conclusion holds across both scenarios, one moves forward with that conclusion with more confidence. If conclusions differ, one moves forward tentatively.

Interaction Analysis

The most common strategy used to explore interaction effects in the cell mean approach are contrasts focused on simple main effects. Ironically, such contrasts do not capture the essence of interactions. Simple main effects address whether an independent variable affects a dependent variable at a given level of a moderator variable. For example, we might ask whether the race/ethnicity of the accused affects judgments of the probability of guilt for European American jurors. We might also ask whether this is the case for African American jurors and whether it is the case for Latinx jurors. These are meaningful questions. However, they do not constitute an interaction effect. As noted, an interaction asks whether the effect of an independent variable on a dependent variable in one group is different from that effect for another group. A simple main effect focuses on only one group, so it cannot address this question. Only a formal interaction contrast does. To illustrate, suppose that the mean difference in salary for a sample of Latino male and Latina female assistant professors is $1,243, and the sex difference is $1,096 for a sample of African American assistant professors. Suppose that the mean difference is statistically significant for assistant professors who are Latinx ($p < .05$) but not for assistant professors who are African Americans ($p > .05$). These significance tests are simple main effect tests. Can we conclude from these data that the mean gender difference for Latinx assistant professors is larger than that for African Americans? Certainly not. Even though the mean difference was statistically significant in one group but not in the other, we can only say that there are racial/ethnic differences in sex disparities if we directly test the sex difference between the two race/ethnicities. This is an interaction contrast. Thus, to probe interactions, researchers should use interaction contrasts. Such contrasts can be pursued using appropriately defined contrast coefficients either in traditional ANOVA or with robust measures of central tendency (Wilcox, 2021).

Indices of Effect Size

Traditional null hypothesis testing in ANOVA allows one to address the question of whether a mean difference exists in the population. However, the approach says little about the magnitude of the effect. The American Psychological Association's Task Force on Statistical Inference has encouraged the reporting of effect sizes that capture the magnitude of an effect (Wilkinson, 1999). More than 60 different indexes of effect size have been suggested, and there is no consensus about which one is preferable (for reviews, see Kelley & Preacher, 2012; Kirk, 2012; Olejnik & Algina, 2000). Most (but not all) of the measures can be classified into two classes: (a) standardized indexes of effect size and (b) unstandardized indexes of effect size. Unstandardized indexes are expressed in the raw metric of the outcome measure, such as the actual mean difference between two groups. Standardized indexes are expressed in a transformed metric that is thought to have intuitive and interpretational appeal. The most commonly reported standardized effect size for ANOVA designs are Cohen's d (or variants of it) and indexes that reflect the percent of variance accounted for (e.g., omega squared, eta squared, epsilon squared). Because effect sizes are discussed in depth in other chapters of this handbook, we do not discuss them further here. However, we encourage researchers to routinely report effect size indexes. Our own preference is for the use of unstandardized rather than standardized effect size indexes in a given study because standardized indexes can be easily misinterpreted and misleading (Prentice & Miller, 1992; Rosenthal, 1995; Wilcox, 2021; Yeaton & Sechrest, 1981).

Asserting Equivalence Between Groups

A common mistake that researchers make when applying ANOVA is to accept the null hypothesis after a nonsignificant test of a contrast. The null hypothesis when comparing means traditionally states that the difference between population means is exactly zero. We can never know the exact value of the true population difference on the basis of sample data because of sampling error. Even if the mean difference between an experimental and control group in sample data is zero, this does not mean that the population mean difference is zero. If a statistically nonsignificant difference is observed in a sample, we cannot conclude that the mean difference in the population is zero. All we can conclude is that the data do not allow us to confidently say that the means are different, that is, we fail to reject the null hypothesis.

The literature is replete with cases in which, on the basis of a statistically nonsignificant interaction effect, researchers conclude that an effect of an independent variable on an outcome variable holds at each level of a potential moderator variable and that the effect is reflected in the main effect mean difference. This is tantamount to accepting the null hypothesis for the interaction effect. Researchers need to exercise caution in their conclusions, being careful not to phrase their conclusions in a way that accepts the null hypothesis (e.g., "there was no difference between the groups"). In the case of a statistically nonsignificant interaction effect, researchers should state, "We cannot confidently conclude that the effect varies across levels of the moderator variable," rather than stating that the effect is the same at all levels of the moderator variable.

Asserting group equivalence has received considerable attention in epidemiology under the rubric of equivalence testing. Most of this work evolved from pharmaceutical research that was designed to establish treatment equivalence of new medications to existing medications. Space constraints limit our ability to explain these methods, but they represent a viable approach to asserting group equivalence. Interested readers are referred to Wellek (2010).

Concluding Comments on ANOVA

There are many topics in ANOVA that we have not touched upon, including the analysis of covariance, fixed versus random effects, multilevel analysis, strategies for analyzing data with unequal sample sizes, trend analysis, complex nesting, higher order interactions, and repeated measures. For excellent discussions of these matters, see Kirk (2012) and Maxwell et al. (2021). For a detailed discussion of single degree of freedom contrast strategies in ANOVA, see Jaccard (1998) and Rosenthal and Rosnow (1985). For an excellent introduction to robust methods of analysis, see Wilcox (2021). For a discussion of model comparison approaches, see Judd et al. (2009) and Maxwell et al. (2021).

THE MULTIPLE REGRESSION FRAMEWORK AND THE GENERAL LINEAR MODEL

Multiple regression examines the relationship between a continuous outcome and two or more predictor variables. Whereas ANOVA is typically associated with studies that use factorial designs with explanatory variables that are categorical or discrete quantitative with few values, multiple regression embraces explanatory variables that usually are continuous in nature, but they also can be categorical. Traditional multiple regression focuses on the case in which the mean Y in a population is thought to be a linear function of a set predictors, in accord with the following equation:

$$\mu_j = \alpha + \beta_1 X_1 + \beta_2 X_2 \ldots + \beta_k X_k, \quad (8.22)$$

where μ_j is the population mean for a given profile of predictor scores, k is the number of predictor variables, α is a numerical constant that represents an intercept, and the various βs are numerical constants or linear coefficients that reflect how much change in μ_j will result from a one-unit change in the X variable associated with a given β, holding all other X variables constant. The various βs are often called unstandardized regression coefficients or regression coefficients for short. μ_j is assumed to be a linear function of the Xs. The intercept α is the predicted mean of Y when all predictors equal zero. For individuals, the predicted value of the outcome variable, $\hat{Y}_i$ is the mean response associated with the predictor profile that characterizes that individual (i.e., $\hat{Y}_i = \mu_j$). As in the model-based framework for ANOVA, there is variability around each mean associated with a specific predictor profile, and this represents errors in prediction, so that $Y_i = \hat{Y}_i + \varepsilon_i$. The traditional multiple regression model for individuals is, thus,

$$Y_i = \alpha + \beta_1 X_{1i} + \beta_2 X_{2i} \ldots + \beta_k X_{ki} + \varepsilon_i, \quad (8.23)$$

where i signifies an individual's standing on a given variable, and

$$\hat{Y}_i = \alpha + \beta_1 X_{1i} + \beta_2 X_{2i} \ldots + \beta_k X_{ki}. \quad (8.24)$$

In practice, we do not have access to population data and must estimate the population coefficients in Equation 8.23 from sample data. The dominant strategy for doing so is to use ordinary least squares (OLS) methods that derive sample values of the different β so as to minimize the sum of the squared error scores in the sample data. We use the letter B to represent a sample estimate of a β. As with any sample estimate, there is sampling error associated with B. Statisticians have developed indexes of the extent to which sampling error impacts our sample estimates, and these are reflected in estimated standard errors for each β, which we symbolize as SE_β. Of interest to researchers is whether the value of a β is zero because, if it is, the X variable associated with it contributes nothing to the prediction of Y. As such, researchers test the viability of the alternative hypothesis that a given β is not zero by forming a critical ratio, defined as B/SE_β. This critical ratio is essentially a single degree of freedom contrast whose sampling distribution follows a t distribution given that model assumptions are satisfied. The sampling distribution is used to derive p values, confidence intervals, and MOEs. The critical ratio and SE_β have analogous interpretations to those described for the ANOVA model, but the focus is on a β.

An excellent introduction to multiple regression analysis is provided in Cohen et al. (2003). The multiple regression model is often referred to as the *general linear model* (not to be confused with the *generalized linear model*) because it is linear in form and because it can be adapted to test a variety of research questions, including those described earlier for ANOVA. For example, it is possible to include categorical variables or factors in the regression model by using dummy variables as predictors. A dummy variable is a variable that the researcher creates to represent the different groups of the categorical variable in which individuals are assigned scores on the basis of an a priori coding scheme. The form of dummy coding used is dictated by the types of contrasts that one wants to pursue, per the cell means model described in a previous section. For a discussion of the different coding schemes and what they accomplish, see Cohen et al. (2003). For continuous variables, interaction effects can be introduced through the use of product terms discussed below. Also see Chapter 5, this volume, on interactions and Chapter 19, this volume, for extensions of interaction analysis using decision trees.

As with ANOVA, we do not focus on the statistical mechanics or intricacies of conducting multiple regression in this chapter, as these are covered in depth elsewhere (Cohen et al., 2003; Judd et al., 2009). Rather, we focus on more general issues that benefit from commentary given research practice. We address seven topics, many of which parallel those in the ANOVA section: (a) outliers and violation of model assumptions, (b) family-wise error rates, (c) the analysis of interactions, (d) indices of predictor importance, (e) the use of covariates, (f) nonlinear regression, and (g) model-based perspectives.

Violations of Model Assumptions and Outliers

The major assumptions for ANOVA, homogeneity of variance of errors and normality of errors, apply to multiple regression as well. A common misperception about assumptions in multiple regression is that they are made about the distributions of variables in the analysis. As typically applied in the research literature (vis-à-vis fixed predictor regression), the assumptions do not pertain to the criterion and predictor variables per se. Rather, the assumptions are about the population errors, namely the e.

An additional working assumption of multiple regression is the *assumption of a correctly specified model*. Model misspecification deals with two matters: (a) the accuracy of the assumed functional form relating the predictor variables to the outcome variable as well as each other; and (b) when making causal inferences, the issue of *left out variable error* (also called LOVE). For the former, when predictors are continuous, researchers assume there is a linear relationship between the scores on the predictors and the mean of the outcome as a function of those scores. If the relationship is nonlinear, the model is said to be misspecified. As well, researchers assume the predictor variables combine additively to impact the outcome. If the predictor variables do not combine additively per Equation 8.22, the model also is said to be misspecified.

LOVE applies to the use of multiple regression to make causal inferences based on the regression coefficients and refers to the assumption that all variables that directly affect the outcome relative to the other predictors have been included in the equation. If a key determinant of Y has been omitted, then one commits LOVE and the fitted model is misspecified. LOVE can create bias in coefficients and invalidate significance tests and confidence intervals. In most social science research, LOVE is inevitable. The question is not so much whether LOVE exists (because it almost always does) but whether it is of a sufficient size and nature that we will be misled in our conclusions. LOVE problems are minimized if the omitted variable has only a modest correlation with the other predictors in the equation. If the omitted variable's impact on Y is completely mediated by the predictors already in the equation, LOVE also is minimized. LOVE is most likely to introduce problems if the omitted variable is moderately correlated with other predictors and has a nontrivial, independent impact on Y. For an in-depth discussion of LOVE, see Mauro (1990) and Greene (2017).

The same issues we discussed for robustness for ANOVA apply with equal vigor to multiple regression. Many researchers believe that multiple regression analysis is robust to assumption violations, but this is not necessarily the case. Wilcox (1998, 2021) has discussed the issue in depth. Applications of preliminary tests for assumption violations have the same problems in multiple regression as they do in ANOVA. Transformations are potentially more problematic because a transformation of a given predictor can affect its correlation with all other predictors as well as the outcome. Outliers also are problematic for regression analysis, and outlier detection is even more complex than it is in simple ANOVA designs. Many traditional methods of outlier detection have limitations, but promising outlier detection methods are being pursued and available in the field of robust statistics (see Wilcox, 2021).

As with ANOVA, methods of analysis have evolved that permit the use of robust regression methods in a wide range of situations that can greatly improve on OLS regression in the face of outliers or possible assumption violations. Wilcox (2021) provided an introduction to these methods as well as freeware to implement them. As with ANOVA, some analysts argue for the adoption of these methods over OLS strategies. Many robust regression methods focus on the modeling of trimmed means or on another index of central tendency, called M estimators. A useful variant of these methods is called *quantile regression*, which models different quantiles of a distribution rather than a mean. Quantile regression methods are widely applied; recent developments of these methods are reviewed in Koenker (2017); see also Wilcox (2021).

Controlling family-wise error rates. The significance test for each coefficient in a regression equation represents a single degree of freedom test/contrast. In ANOVA, we noted the misconception that using an omnibus test as a screen generally controls the family-wise error rate for the various single degree of freedom contrasts pursued in the analysis. This also is the case for the omnibus test for the overall squared multiple correlation in multiple regression analysis. If one wants to control for family-wise error rates in multiple regression, it is better to use methods such as those in Appendix 8.1 rather than relying on omnibus tests of the squared multiple correlation.

One rarely in practice observes investigators invoking controls for family-wise error rates in multiple regression. This is because, like ANOVA, it is traditional to treat each variable or predictor as a separate family of contrasts. If multiple contrasts are pursued within a variable (such as when dummy variables are used for a categorical predictor), then family-wise error rate controls can be invoked using the method in Appendix 8.1. This also is true for interaction analysis and simple effects analysis in which multiple single-degree-of-freedom contrasts are the focus of the interaction or simple main effects. Again, as with ANOVA, the strategy is to find an optimal balance between Type I and Type II error rates.

Interaction Analysis

Moderated relationships can be tested in multiple regression in a more flexible way than in traditional ANOVA because of the ability to analyze continuous moderators and continuous focal independent variables as well as categorical ones. We consider here the case in which all variables involved in the interaction are continuous. Like ANOVA, interaction effects are usually parameterized using the framework of moderator variables. In the three variable case, there is an outcome variable (Y), a focal independent variable (X_1), and a moderator variable (X_2). The focal independent variable is thought to affect the outcome variable and that impact is indexed by the regression coefficient associated with it (i.e., β_{X1}). The value of β_{X1} is said to vary depending on the value of the moderator variable. For example, when X_2 is small, the value of β_{X1} (reflecting the effect of X_1 on Y) might be smaller or larger than when X_2 is large. The choice of which variable X_1 or X_2 takes the role of the moderator is dictated by theory and how the investigator wants to frame the interaction. The choice from a statistical standpoint is arbitrary (see Jaccard & Turrisi, 2003).

It is customary but not necessary in interaction analysis to mean-center continuous predictors. Mean-centering converts the raw scores to deviation scores by subtracting the mean of the variable from each individual's score on the variable. So, $X_{1C} = X_1 - M_{X1}$ and $X_{2C} = X_2 - M_{X2}$. The mean of the transformed scores X_{1C} and X_{2C} are both zero. Mean-centering makes the intercept and the regression coefficients more interpretable, a point that will become more apparent shortly. In regression based interaction analysis, the mean-centered focal independent variable and the mean-centered moderator variable are multiplied by each other and then the component parts and their product term are used as predictors,

$$Y_i = a + b_1 X_{1Ci} + b_2 X_{2Ci} + b_3 X_{1Ci} X_{2Ci} + \varepsilon_i. \quad (8.25)$$

The presence of the product term changes the traditional interpretation of b_1. Specifically, b_1 no longer represents a main effect but now represents a simple main effect. It is the effect of X_{1C} on Y when the other variable in the product term, in this case X_{2C}, equals zero. Because a score of zero on X_{2C} corresponds to the mean of the original X_2 variable, b_1 estimates the effect of X_1 on Y when X_2 is at its mean value. Variable b_3 is a single degree of freedom interaction contrast and is of primary interest in interaction analysis. It reflects the number of units that b_1 is predicted to change every time the moderator variable increases by one unit. For example, if X_2 increases by one unit relative to its mean, then the estimated effect of X_1 on Y is $b_1 + b_3$. If X_2 increases by two units relative to its mean, then the estimated effect of X_1 on Y is $b_1 + 2 b_3$. The mechanics of interaction analysis in multiple regression are straightforward but too involved to consider here. Interested readers are referred to Jaccard and Turrisi (2003) and McCabe and King (this volume). We focus here on points important to keep in mind as one pursues interaction analysis in multiple regression.

Median splits. It is not uncommon for researchers who have a small number of continuous predictors to pursue interaction analysis by using ANOVA instead of multiple regression, presumably because they are more familiar with the ANOVA approach to interaction analysis. Such researchers categorize the predictors into a small number of groups, usually by performing a median split on each one. The continuous predictor variable, in essence, is reduced to a 2-point scale of *low* (at or below the median) and *high* scorers, and then the data are analyzed as if they come from a factorial design. Statisticians have argued against such median split strategies for more than 20 years, and the limitations of the approach are well documented (e.g., MacCallum et al., 2002; Maxwell & Delaney, 1993). Despite this, the practice continues.

Without delving into technical matters, consider how a median split ignores valuable information. Suppose a researcher performs a median split on the Wechsler Intelligence Scale for Children (WISC) by dividing individuals into low and high groups on the basis of whether they score above or below the median score of 100. In doing so, the researcher has usurped a scale that distinguishes many gradations of intelligence and reduced it to a crude, 2-point scale. The researcher treats someone who has an IQ score of 55 as being exactly the same as someone who has an IQ score of 99 because both are in the low group. At the same time that the researcher is willing to overlook this 44-point difference in IQ, the researcher treats someone who has an IQ score of 99 as being lower in intelligence than a person who has an IQ score of 101 because the former is in the low group and the latter is in the high group. Just as damaging, the researcher acts as if the difference in IQ between someone who has a score of 99 versus someone who has a score of 101 is exactly the same as someone who has an IQ score of 60 versus someone who has an IQ score of 140. Surely, we can do better than this when pursuing interaction analysis. Multiple regression analysis allows us to do so.

The form of the interaction. When a continuous variable is part of an interaction analysis in multiple regression, it is important to keep in mind that the classic product term approach to interaction analysis tests only for an interaction that has a specific form known as a *bilinear interaction*. Other forms of interaction may be operating, but the product term can be insensitive to them. If X_1 is the focal independent variable and X_2 is the moderator variable, the product term models the coefficient for X_1 as a linear function of X_2. It is possible, however, that the coefficient for X_1 changes as a nonlinear function of X_2 and, if this is the case, the product term approach represents a misspecified model. It is important for researchers to explore various forms of interactions when pursuing interaction analysis in multiple regression in case the form of the interaction is not bilinear. For details on how to do this, see Jaccard and Turrisi (2003).

Confounds with curvilinearity. Ganzach (1997) noted that interaction effects can be observed in models in which no interaction is present but in which the relationship between a predictor and outcome variable is nonlinear in form. The application of an interaction model in such cases represents a misspecified model and can lead the theorist astray. See Ganzach (1997), Jaccard and Turrisi (2003), and Belzak and Bauer (2019) for analytic solutions to this problem.

Exclusion of component terms. It is sometimes stated that the product term ($b_3 X_{1C} X_{2C}$ in Equation 8.25) in a regression equation represents an interaction effect. Technically, the product term reflects an amalgamation of main effects and interactions. In general, it is only when the component parts of the product term ($b_1 X_{1C}$ and $b_2 X_{2C}$ in Equation 8.25) are included in the equation with the product term that interactions of the form social scientists typically study are isolated. Excluding the component parts of the product term places strong measurement demands on the analysis, as the measures must then be ratio in nature. In a multiplicative model that excludes the component parts, the squared multiple correlation and the significance test of the regression coefficient that derives from regressing Y onto the product term changes with simple rescaling of the measures of the component parts. Although there are exceptions, it is generally good practice to include the component parts of the product term in the regression equation with the product term (see Blanton & Jaccard, 2006b; Jaccard & Turrisi, 2003).

Regions of significance for simple main effects. In ANOVA, we often conduct simple main effects analysis to identify at which levels of the moderator variable we can confidently conclude that the focal independent variable affects the outcome variable. With a continuous moderator variable, this task is challenging because there are as many levels of the moderator. Potthoff (1964) developed a method, on the basis of the classic work of P. O. Johnson and Neyman (1936), that establishes *regions of significance* for the case of a continuous moderator and a dichotomous focal independent variable. The technique defines a range of scores on the moderator variable at which the population means of the two groups defined by the dichotomous focal independent variable are not expected to differ. Jaccard et al. (2012) extended the method to the case of all continuous variables as well as categorical independent variables with more than two levels.

In sum, interaction analysis with continuous predictors can be pursued in multiple regression analysis, but there are complications that need to be taken into account. These include the restrictive form of the interaction being tested and confounds with curvilinearity, among others (for additional issues, see Jaccard & Turrisi, 2003). Forming median splits is a bad strategy for interaction analysis, as is omitting the component parts of the product term from the equation.

Indices of Predictor Importance

An issue often addressed when using multiple regression is identifying the relative importance of different predictors. The intent often is to identify the most and least important predictors in an equation. Numerous strategies have been used for this purpose. One global strategy focuses on significance tests of the coefficients and declares variables that fail to yield statistically significant regression coefficients as *unimportant* and those that yield statistically significant coefficients as *important*. As straightforward as this appears, the approach is problematic. The most obvious problem is if the study has low statistical power, leading to Type II errors. This problem is more insidious than most scientists realize. Maxwell (2000) reported that the typical correlation between variables in psychological research is about 0.30. If five predictors in a population are each correlated 0.30 with the criterion, as well as 0.30 with each other, then the percent of unique explained variance in Y for each predictor is 1.5%,

and the population regression coefficient for each predictor is nonzero. The sample size necessary to obtain statistical power of 0.80 for a significance test of a regression coefficient in this scenario is about 420. Maxwell reported a simulation study in which a multiple regression analysis was conducted in this scenario using a sample size of 100. Maxwell found that the most frequently occurring pattern of results, occurring 45% of the time, was the case in which one predictor had a statistically significant regression coefficient, but the other four did not. The next most common pattern, occurring 32% of the time, was that two of the predictors had statistically significant regression coefficients, but three did not. Thus, in such situations, there is a high probability that one or two of the predictors will show statistical significance and three or four of the predictors will not. Which predictors show a significant coefficient among the five predictors is random. Results such as these should give theorists using small sample sizes (e.g., less than 100) some pause about declaring a variable *unimportant* if it receives a statistically nonsignificant regression coefficient.

A second strategy that researchers sometimes use to identify important variables is based on stepwise regression. The predictor variables act as a pool of potential variables to include in the final regression equation. Stepwise algorithms are invoked to enter variables into the equation sequentially on the basis of how much they augment the squared multiple correlation relative to predictors already in the equation (for a description of the algorithms, see Cohen et al., 2003). Adding variables to the equation ceases when the increase in model fit is no longer statistically significant. The variables that enter the equation are deemed the most important predictors and the order in which they enter the equation further discriminates their importance.

Numerous criticisms to this approach have been raised, including the misleading nature of the *p* values and significance tests (Altman & Andersen, 1989), bias in the regression coefficients (Tibshirani, 1996), and a general failure to accurately identify the variables in the true generating equation (Derksen & Keselman, 1992;

Mantel, 1970). To elaborate on one example, the first predictor that enters the equation in a stepwise analysis is the predictor that has the highest zero order correlation with the criterion. At the second step, all remaining variables are considered for inclusion relative to that first variable. Only variables that add significant unique explained variance relative to it are candidates for inclusion at the second step. Suppose X_1 has a sample correlation of 0.30 with the criterion and X_2 has a sample correlation of 0.29 and the two variables are correlated 0.80. X_1 will enter the equation first, even though its correlation with the criterion is only larger by a miniscule amount relative to X_2. X_2 will not enter the equation at later steps because its explained variance in Y is redundant with X_1. It might be the case that the correlation between X_2 and Y is larger in the population than the correlation between X_1 and Y, and the reversal of rank order in the sample data reflects nothing but sampling error. Despite this, X_1 will be given theoretical priority and enter the equation first. In this case, a relatively small amount of sampling error alters the variables that enter the equation and that ultimately are deemed as important. Judd and McClelland (1989) captured current thinking when they stated that "it seems unwise to let an automatic algorithm determine the questions we do and do not ask about our data. It is our experience and strong belief that better models and a better understanding of one's data result from focused data analysis, guided by substantive theory" (Judd & McClelland, 1989, p. 204).

Another popular approach for determining predictor importance is to compare predictors in terms of their standardized regression coefficients. Standardized coefficients are based on a multiple regression analysis in which the metric of each variable has been converted to a standard score, thereby allegedly placing all measures on a common metric. Those predictors with larger standardized coefficients are deemed as being more important than those with smaller standardized coefficients. This strategy is problematic because standardized coefficients primarily reflect unique, explained variance ignoring common variance in the predictor set. Measures of importance should take both into account. As well, differences in the coefficients could reflect sampling error. One needs to conduct formal significance tests of their difference (for such methods, see Cohen et al., 2003). In addition, the common view that standardization places the variables on a common metric is questionable (see Blanton & Jaccard, 2006a; Judd et al., 2009). Reliance on standardized coefficients requires the assumption that the variance of a predictor is constant at each combination of the other predictors. This assumption is often unrealistic (Bring, 1994). In addition, removing the variable with the smallest standardized coefficient does not necessarily result in the smallest reduction in the squared multiple correlation (Bring, 1994). Darlington (1968) noted other pitfalls with this strategy as well as an analogous strategy that is based on the squared semipart correlation associated with a predictor.

One of the more sophisticated approaches to evaluating variable importance is dominance analysis (Azen & Budescu, 2003, 2006). Budescu (1993) and J. Johnson and LeBreton (2004) argued that importance metrics for a predictor, X, in multipredictor regression contexts should simultaneously take into account (a) the contribution of X to Y when X is the only predictor, (b) the contribution of X to Y over and above all other predictors (unique explained variance), and (c) the contributions of X to Y considering different subsets of the other predictors. Dominance analysis uses all three criteria. Dominance analysis uses an index of importance called general dominance. As an example, with $k = 3$ predictors (A, B, and C), one can calculate the increase in R square that A yields relative to a model with no other predictors in it, that A yields over and above B, that A yields over and above C, and that A yields over and above B and C together. The increments are averaged within common subsets of the number of predictors (e.g., for the case where $k = 1$, then where $k = 2$, and then where $k = 3$) and then these averaged values are, in turn, averaged for the predictor in question to yield its general dominance index. The higher the index for a predictor, the more it "dominates" the other predictors in the equation.

A popular competing approach to dominance analysis that often (but not always) yields comparable results to it is an orthogonal transformation method based on relative weights by J. Johnson and LeBreton (2004). However, the method has been found to have non-trivial shortcomings, so we do not consider it here (see Thomas et al., 2014). Other intriguing approaches to predictor approaches use decision trees (Chapter 19, this volume) and generalized additive models (Wood, 2017).

The Use of Covariates

A frequent use of multiple regression is to gain perspectives on the effects of a variable on an outcome while controlling for covariates included in the regression equation. Covariates usually are not of theoretical interest but researchers include them in the prediction equation to protect against LOVE. Meehl (1971) objected to what he called atheoretical partialing of covariates. In atheoretical partialing, covariates are added to the equation simply because they might be relevant. The most common example of this is the inclusion of demographic variables, such as gender, age, and social class, in an equation without careful justification. One simply includes these variables because they are commonly used as covariates. Problems associated with atheoretical partialing were noted more than 30 years ago in a thoughtful discussion by Meehl (1971). Atheoretical partialing can increase Type II errors and can bias parameter estimates for the causal conclusions researchers seek to make (for the statistical basis, see Jaccard et al., 2006). An egregious form of atheoretical partialing occurs when a researcher classifies potential predictor variables into broad categories, such as demographic predictors, family predictors, social predictors, and personality predictors, and then includes variables from all of the categories in one large regression equation. If the coefficient associated with a given predictor is statistically nonsignificant, the variable is deemed noncausally relevant to the outcome variable. In such cases, the predictor in question may indeed be causally relevant, but the regression coefficient may not reflect this depending on the causal dynamics operating among the predictors. For example, if one of the predictors partially or completely mediates the effect of another predictor, then the regression coefficient for the target predictor will understate its causal impact on the outcome as any mediated effect of the predictor is partialed out.

Another example of atheoretical partialing occurs when a researcher unwittingly uses a covariate that is a defining part of the phenomenon being studied. For example, one might examine the impact of self-esteem on social anxiety holding constant a measure of social desirability response tendencies. However, a part of having low self-esteem is being defensive about admitting one's weaknesses and controlling one's self-presentation. By including social desirability as a covariate, the researcher partials out a defining feature of self-esteem.

Decisions about controlling covariates require careful thought. Researchers must consider the possible causal relations between predictor variables and covariates and then judiciously control for covariates in accord with the presumed causal dynamics. In general, a variable should be statistically controlled for if (a) doing so increases statistical power in a low power situation (such as including a baseline measure of the outcome as a covariate in a randomized clinical trial), (b) it removes misspecification caused by LOVE, (c) it is not a second indicator of another construct already included in the prediction equation, (d) it is not a defining feature of another predictor or the outcome, and (e) it is theoretically meaningful to include the covariate. For an excellent discussion of theoretically guided covariate inclusion, see Cinelli et al. (2019).

Nonlinear regression. Relationships between predictors and outcomes can be nonlinear, in which case applying traditional multiple regression represents application of a misspecified model. Most researchers who seek to deal with nonlinearity in the applied literature prefer to stay within the familiar confines of the general linear model when doing so. One such approach is to use polynomial regression in which additional predictors are added to the linear equation that reflect power polynomials of the target predictor. The addition of a squared predictor models a quadratic function between the predictor and the outcome and the further addition of a cubed term models a cubic function. Cohen et al. (2003) described polynomial regression in depth. A problem with polynomial regression is that it uses a relatively small class of nonlinear functions that may not adequately capture the nature of the nonlinearity in question. For example, if the relationship between X and Y is logarithmic, then the polynomial approach may not adequately model the nonlinear dynamics.

Another approach to dealing with nonlinear relationships while retaining the linear model is the use of variable transformations. For example, if Y is a logarithmic function of X, then the relationship between the log of X and Y should be linear. Y can be predicted from the log of X in the general linear model. Transformations to linearize relationships are discussed by Box and Cox (1964) and Mosteller and Tukey (1977)—see also the useful summary in Cohen et al. (2003). A problem with the transformation approach is that the metrics of the transformed variables often are nonintuitive (e.g., log income). Also, it is usually not appropriate to back-transform the coefficient associated with a transformed variable to its original metric because the back-transformed coefficient does not minimize the relevant squared error (although there are some exceptions). Finally, transforming the metric of a predictor not only changes the relationship between the predictor and the criterion but also changes the relationship between the transformed predictor and the other predictors in the equation, producing specification error.

Yet another approach to dealing with nonlinearity while staying within the comfort of the linear model is spline regression (Marsh & Cormier, 2001). Spline regression divides a curve into segments so that the relationship between X and Y is approximately linear within a segment but not necessarily across segments. Estimates of the slope within each segment are derived using OLS regression in conjunction with predictors that represent spline knots. Spline knots are points on the X continuum that define the segments. Formal tests of slope differences between segments are possible, and slope differences are expected given nonlinearity.

Finally, recent work on nonlinear regression has used methods based on smoothers and the generalized additive model (Andersen, 2009; Wilcox, 2021; Wood, 2017). In this approach, a measure of location of Y is assumed to be some function of the predictors, $f(X_1, X_2, \ldots, X_k)$, but the exact function is unknown. The location measure can be a mean, a median, a trimmed mean, or an M estimator and the function, f, is estimated nonparametrically. Estimation for a point of interest typically is based on the X continua using a small number of neighboring data points, or more technically, a weighted average of Y values, with the weights being a function of how close the vector of predictor values is to the point of interest. These methods offer a great deal of promise for nonlinear modeling in the social sciences. See Wilcox (2005, 2010, 2021) for excellent introductions.

Model Testing Perspectives on Multiple Regression

As noted, researchers tend to adopt a mindset of model fitting when using multiple regression. Thus, it is common to find explicit recognition of the use of the linear model, reports of statistics related to the coefficients in the linear model, and reports of the magnitude of error scores (in the form of squared multiple correlations). More informative fit indexes could routinely be reported, such as the standard error of estimate. Model comparisons are also common in the form of hierarchical regression, in which case one formally compares simpler models with more complex models that add predictors. Researchers often fail to appreciate that multiple regression is a method for analyzing mean outcome values and how these values vary as a function of predictor variable profiles. In this sense, its concern with means is similar to ANOVA.

Concluding Comments on Multiple Regression and the General Linear Model

As with ANOVA, there are many issues we have not addressed, including commonality analysis, cross-validation, dichotomous, count, and categorical outcomes, fixed versus random variables, hierarchical regression, latent variable regression, longitudinal regression models, measurement error, issues of metrics (use of ordinal vs. interval measures), missing data, regression-based mixture models, multicollinearity, multilevel regression, power analysis, development of prediction models, reciprocal causation models, and regression-based time-series analysis, to name a few. These topics are discussed in Cohen et al. (2003), Draper and Smith (1998), and Fox (1997). A model comparison approach to multiple regression analysis is presented by Judd et al. (2009). For robust regression, see Wilcox (2021).

CONCLUDING COMMENTS

ANOVA is a special case of multiple regression in that all of the analyses of ANOVA can ultimately be conducted using the general linear model. The general linear model, in turn, is a special case of a broader modeling perspective on the basis of generalized linear models (see Chapter 9, this volume). Generalized linear models are a special case of an even broader approach to analysis that is based on systems of linear equations, called structural equation modeling (SEM; see Volume 2, Chapter 21, this handbook; see also Muthén, 2004). Each of these frameworks has in common its focus on linear equations and, as such, the material in this chapter is fundamental to all of them. Some of the most exciting developments in linear modeling are occurring in the field of robust statistics, which is freeing analysts from the constraints of the assumptions of normally distributed data and other parametric assumptions. Robust methods are also being developed and applied to factor analysis, which ultimately should allow us to use them for latent variable regression and more advanced latent variable SEM models. Indeed, the methods discussed in Wilcox (2021) can currently be applied to many forms of SEM using limited information methods that partition a causal model into a set of linear equations and then estimate the coefficients of the equations separately rather than in a simultaneous, full information sense. The usual advantage of more efficient estimation on the basis of full information strategies may be offset by the use of efficient robust estimation methods as well as the compartmentalization of specification error that typifies limited information approaches. The linear model and the emerging robust methods surrounding it have a bright future in data analysis.

APPENDIX 8.1: MODIFIED BONFERRONI METHODS

Holm (1979; see also Holland & Copenhaver, 1988; Seaman et al., 1991) suggested a modified Bonferroni method that is more powerful than the traditional Bonferroni-based approach but adequately maintains family-wise error rates at the desired α level.

First, a p value is obtained for each contrast in the family of contrasts. The p values are then ordered from smallest to largest. If two p values are identical, they are ordered arbitrarily or using theoretical criteria. The contrast with the smallest p value is evaluated against an alpha of $0.05/k$, where k is the total number of contrasts in the family. If this leads to rejection of the corresponding null hypothesis (because the observed p value is less than the adjusted α), the next smallest p value is tested against an α level of $0.05/(k-1)$, where $k-1$ is the remaining number of contrasts. If this test leads to null hypothesis rejection, the next smallest p value is tested against an α level of $0.05/(k-2)$. The process continues until a nonsignificant difference is observed. Once a nonsignificant difference is observed, all remaining contrasts are declared nonsignificant.

The Holm method is a *step-down* method in that one adjusts the critical value for the smallest p value, then the second smallest, and so on until the largest one is reached and evaluated against an α level of 0.05. An alternative approach is to use a *step-up* procedure, such as that suggested by Hochberg (1988). The Hochberg approach is identical to the Holm (1979) procedure, but it works in the reverse direction, from the largest p value to the smallest. If the largest p value in the family of contrasts is less than 0.05, all contrasts are declared statistically significant. If the largest p value is greater than 0.05, but the next largest one is less than 0.05/4, then the contrast in question and all those with smaller p values are declared statistically significant. The Hochberg method has slightly more statistical power than the Holm method and, hence, may be preferable. However, it does not control family-wise error rates as well as the Holm method under some error structures (see Westfall et al., 1999). An alternative approach to the above methods is to use what is known as the false discovery rate method (Benjamini & Yekutieli, 2001). It is based on different statistical logic and has much to recommend it.

References

Altman, D. G., & Andersen, P. K. (1989). Bootstrap investigation of the stability of a Cox regression model. *Statistics in Medicine*, 8(7), 771–783. https://doi.org/10.1002/sim.4780080702

Andersen, R. (2009). Nonparametric methods for modeling nonlinearity in regression analysis. *Annual Review of Sociology*, 35(1), 67–85. https://doi.org/10.1146/annurev.soc.34.040507.134631

Azen, R., & Budescu, D. V. (2003). The dominance analysis approach for comparing predictors in multiple regression. *Psychological Methods*, 8(2), 129–148. https://doi.org/10.1037/1082-989X.8.2.129

Azen, R., & Budescu, D. V. (2006). Comparing predictors in multivariate regression models: An extension of dominance analysis. *Journal of Educational and Behavioral Statistics*, 31(2), 157–180. https://doi.org/10.3102/10769986031002157

Belzak, W. C. M., & Bauer, D. J. (2019). Interaction effects may actually be nonlinear effects in disguise: A review of the problem and potential solutions. *Addictive Behaviors*, 94, 99–108. https://doi.org/10.1016/j.addbeh.2018.09.018

Benjamini, Y., & Yekutieli, D. (2001). The control of the false discovery rate in multiple testing under dependency. *Annals of Statistics*, 29(4), 1165–1188. https://doi.org/10.1214/aos/1013699998

Bernhardson, C. S. (1975). Type I error rates when multiple comparison procedures follow a significant F test of ANOVA. *Biometrics*, 31(1), 229–232. https://doi.org/10.2307/2529724

Blanton, H., & Jaccard, J. (2006a). Arbitrary metrics in psychology. *American Psychologist*, 61(1), 27–41. https://doi.org/10.1037/0003-066X.61.1.27

Blanton, H., & Jaccard, J. (2006b). Tests of multiplicative models in psychology: A case study using the unified theory of implicit attitudes, stereotypes, self-esteem, and self-concept. *Psychological Review*, 113(1), 155–166. https://doi.org/10.1037/0033-295X.113.1.155

Blaylock, J., Salathe, L., & Green, R. (1980). A note on the Box–Cox transformation under heteroskedasticity. *Western Journal of Agricultural Economics*, 5(2), 129–135. https://doi.org/10.22004/ag.econ.32394

Box, G. E. P., & Cox, D. R. (1964). An analysis of transformations (with discussion). *Journal of the Royal Statistical Society: Series B. Methodological*, 26(2), 211–243. https://doi.org/10.1111/j.2517-6161.1964.tb00553.x

Bring, J. (1994). How to standardize regression coefficients. *The American Statistician*, 48(3), 209–213. https://doi.org/10.2307/2684719

Budescu, D., & Appelbaum, M. (1981). Variance stabilizing transformations and the power of the F test. *Journal of Educational Statistics*, 6(1), 55–74. https://doi.org/10.3102/10769986006001055

Budescu, D. V. (1993). Dominance analysis: A new approach to the problem of relative importance in multiple regression. *Psychological Bulletin*, 114(3), 542–551. https://doi.org/10.1037/0033-2909.114.3.542

Carlin, B. P., & Louis, T. A. (2000). *Bayes and empirical Bayes methods for data analysis* (2nd ed.). Chapman & Hall.

Carroll, R. J., & Schneider, H. (1985). A note on Levene's test for equality of variances. *Statistics & Probability Letters*, 3(4), 191–194. https://doi.org/10.1016/0167-7152(85)90016-1

Cinelli, C., Forney, A., & Pearl, J. (2019). A crash course in good and bad control. Downloaded from http://causality.cs.ucla.edu/blog/index.php/2019/08/14/a-crash-course-in-good-and-bad-control/

Cohen, J., Cohen, P., West, S. G., & Aiken, L. S. (2003). *Applied multiple regression/correlation analysis for the behavioral sciences* (3rd ed.). Erlbaum.

Cressie, N. A. C., & Whitford, H. J. (1986). How to use the two sample t-test. *Biometrical Journal. Biometrische Zeitschrift*, 28(2), 131–148. https://doi.org/10.1002/bimj.4710280202

Darlington, R. B. (1968). Multiple regression in psychological research and practice. *Psychological Bulletin*, 69(3), 161–182. https://doi.org/10.1037/h0025471

Derksen, S., & Keselman, H. (1992). Backward, forward and stepwise automated subset selection algorithms: Frequency of obtaining authentic and noise variables. *British Journal of Mathematical*

& *Statistical Psychology*, *45*(2), 265–282. https://doi.org/10.1111/j.2044-8317.1992.tb00992.x

Dienes, Z. (2011). Bayesian versus orthodox statistics: Which side are you on? *Perspectives on Psychological Science*, *6*(3), 274–290. https://doi.org/10.1177/1745691611406920

Doksum, K. A., & Wong, C. (1983). Statistical tests based on transformed data. *Journal of the American Statistical Association*, *78*(382), 411–417. https://doi.org/10.1080/01621459.1983.10477986

Draper, N., & Smith, H. (1998). *Applied regression analysis*. Wiley. https://doi.org/10.1002/9781118625590

Fox, J. (1997). *Applied regression analysis, linear models, and related methods*. SAGE.

Ganzach, Y. (1997). Misleading interaction and curvilinear terms. *Psychological Methods*, *2*(3), 235–247. https://doi.org/10.1037/1082-989X.2.3.235

Greene, W. H. (2017). *Econometric analysis*. Pearson.

Hochberg, Y. (1988). A sharper Bonferroni procedure for multiple tests of significance. *Biometrika*, *75*(4), 800–802. https://doi.org/10.1093/biomet/75.4.800

Holland, B. S., & Copenhaver, M. (1988). Improved Bonferroni-type multiple testing procedures. *Psychological Bulletin*, *104*(1), 145–149. https://doi.org/10.1037/0033-2909.104.1.145

Holm, S. (1979). A simple sequentially rejective multiple test procedure. *Scandinavian Journal of Statistics*, *6*(2), 65–70.

Jaccard, J. (1998). *Interaction effects in factorial analysis of variance*. SAGE. https://doi.org/10.4135/9781412984508

Jaccard, J., & Daniloski, K. (2012). Analysis of variance and the general linear model. In H. Cooper, P. M. Camic, D. L. Long, A. T. Panter, D. Rindskopf, & K. J. Sher (Eds.), *APA handbook of research methods in psychology: Vol. 3. Data analysis and research publication* (pp. 163–190). American Psychological Association. https://doi.org/10.1037/13621-008

Jaccard, J., Daniloski, K., & Brinberg, D. (2012). *Extending the Newman-Johnson method for interaction analysis to complex interactions* [Technical report]. Department of Psychology, Florida International University.

Jaccard, J., Guilamo-Ramos, V., Johansson, M., & Bouris, A. (2006). Multiple regression analyses in clinical child and adolescent psychology. *Journal of Clinical Child and Adolescent Psychology*, *35*(3), 456–479. https://doi.org/10.1207/s15374424jccp3503_11

Jaccard, J., & Turrisi, R. (2003). *Interaction effects in multiple regression*. SAGE. https://doi.org/10.4135/9781412984522

Johnson, J., & LeBreton, J. (2004). History and use of relative importance indices in organizational research. *Organizational Research Methods*, *7*(3), 238–257. https://doi.org/10.1177/1094428104266510

Johnson, P. O., & Neyman, J. (1936). Tests of certain linear hypotheses and their application to some educational problems. *Statistical Research Memoirs*, *1*, 57–93.

Judd, C. M., & McClelland, G. (1989). *Data analysis: A model comparison approach*. Harcourt Brace Jovanovich.

Judd, C. M., McClelland, G. H., & Ryan, C. S. (2009). *Data analysis: A model comparison approach*. Routledge.

Kelley, K., & Preacher, K. J. (2012). On effect size. *Psychological Methods*, *17*(2), 137–152. https://doi.org/10.1037/a0028086

Keselman, H. J., Algina, J., Lix, L. M., Wilcox, R. R., & Deering, K. N. (2008). A generally robust approach for testing hypotheses and setting confidence intervals for effect sizes. *Psychological Methods*, *13*(2), 110–129. https://doi.org/10.1037/1082-989X.13.2.110

Keselman, H. J., Huberty, C. J., Lix, L. M., Olejnik, S., Cribbie, R., Donahue, B., Kowalchuk, R. K., Lowman, L. L., Petoskey, M. D., Keselman, J. C., & Levin, J. R. (1998). Statistical practices of educational researchers: An analysis of their ANOVA, MANOVA, and ANCOVA analyses. *Review of Educational Research*, *68*(3), 350–386. https://doi.org/10.3102/00346543068003350

Keselman, H. J., Wilcox, R. R., Lix, L. M., Algina, J., & Fradette, K. (2007). Adaptive robust estimation and testing. *British Journal of Mathematical and Statistical Psychology*, *60*(Pt. 2), 267–293. https://doi.org/10.1348/000711005X63755

Keyes, T., & Levy, M. S. (1997). Analysis of Levene's test under design imbalance. *Journal of Educational and Behavioral Statistics*, *22*(2), 227–236. https://doi.org/10.2307/1165379

Kirk, R. (2012). *Experimental design: Procedures for the behavioral sciences*. Brooks-Cole.

Koenker, R. (2017). Quantile regression: 40 years on. *Annual Review of Economics*, *9*(1), 155–176. https://doi.org/10.1146/annurev-economics-063016-103651

Levin, J., Serlin, R., & Seaman, M. (1994). A controlled, powerful multiple comparison strategy for several situations. *Psychological Bulletin*, *115*(1), 153–159. https://doi.org/10.1037/0033-2909.115.1.153

MacCallum, R. C., Zhang, S., Preacher, K. J., & Rucker, D. D. (2002). On the practice of dichotomization of quantitative variables. *Psychological Methods*, 7(1), 19–40. https://doi.org/10.1037/1082-989X.7.1.19

Mantel, N. (1970). Why stepdown procedures in variable selection. *Technometrics*, 12(3), 621–625. https://doi.org/10.1080/00401706.1970.10488701

Marsh, L., & Cormier, D. (2001). *Spline regression models*. SAGE.

Mauro, R. (1990). Understanding LOVE (left out variables error): A method for estimating the effects of omitted variables. *Psychological Bulletin*, 108(2), 314–329. https://doi.org/10.1037/0033-2909.108.2.314

Maxwell, S., & Delaney, H. (1993). Bivariate median splits and spurious statistical significance. *Psychological Bulletin*, 113(1), 181–190. https://doi.org/10.1037/0033-2909.113.1.181

Maxwell, S. E. (2000). Sample size and multiple regression analysis. *Psychological Methods*, 5(4), 434–458. https://doi.org/10.1037/1082-989X.5.4.434

Maxwell, S. E., Delaney, H. D., & Kelley, K. (2021). *Designing experiments and analyzing data: A model comparison perspective*. Erlbaum.

Maxwell, S. E., Kelley, K., & Rausch, J. (2008). Sample size planning for statistical power and accuracy in parameter estimation. *Annual Review of Psychology*, 59, 537–563. https://doi.org/10.1146/annurev.psych.59.103006.093735

Meehl, P. E. (1971). High school yearbooks: A reply to Schwarz. *Journal of Abnormal Psychology*, 77(2), 143–148. https://doi.org/10.1037/h0030750

Meyer, D. L. (1991). Misinterpretation of interaction effects: A reply to Rosnow and Rosenthal. *Psychological Bulletin*, 110(3), 571–573. https://doi.org/10.1037/0033-2909.110.3.571

Milligan, G. (1987). The use of the arc-sine transformation in the analysis of variance. *Educational and Psychological Measurement*, 47(3), 563–573. https://doi.org/10.1177/001316448704700303

Mosteller, F., & Tukey, J. (1977). *Data analysis and regression*. Addison-Wesley.

Muthén, B. O. (2004). *Mplus technical appendices*. Muthén & Muthén.

Olejnik, S., & Algina, J. (2000). Measures of effect size for comparative studies: Applications, interpretations, and limitations. *Contemporary Educational Psychology*, 25(3), 241–286. https://doi.org/10.1006/ceps.2000.1040

Parra-Frutos, I. (2009). The behaviour of the modified Levene's test when data are not normally distributed. *Computational Statistics*, 24(4), 671–693. https://doi.org/10.1007/s00180-009-0154-z

Petty, R., Fabrigar, L., Wegener, D., & Priester, J. (1996). Understanding data when interactions are present or hypothesized. *Psychological Science*, 7(4), 247–252. https://doi.org/10.1111/j.1467-9280.1996.tb00368.x

Potthoff, R. F. (1964). On the Johnson–Neyman technique and some extensions thereof. *Psychometrika*, 29(3), 241–256. https://doi.org/10.1007/BF02289721

Prentice, D. A., & Miller, D. T. (1992). When small effects are impressive. *Psychological Bulletin*, 112(1), 160–164. https://doi.org/10.1037/0033-2909.112.1.160

Rodgers, J. L. (2010). The epistemology of mathematical and statistical modeling: A quiet methodological revolution. *American Psychologist*, 65(1), 1–12. https://doi.org/10.1037/a0018326

Rosenthal, R. (1995). Methodology. In A. Tesser (Ed.), *Advanced social psychology* (pp. 17–50). McGraw-Hill.

Rosenthal, R., & Rosnow, R. L. (1985). *Contrast analysis: Focused comparisons in the analysis of variance*. Cambridge University Press.

Rosnow, R., & Rosenthal, R. (1989). Definition and interpretation of interaction effects. *Psychological Bulletin*, 105(1), 143–146. https://doi.org/10.1037/0033-2909.105.1.143

Seaman, M. A., Levin, K. R., & Serlin, R. C. (1991). New developments in pairwise multiple comparisons: Some powerful and practicable procedures. *Psychological Bulletin*, 110(3), 577–586. https://doi.org/10.1037/0033-2909.110.3.577

Shapiro, S. S., & Wilk, M. B. (1965). An analysis of variance test for normality (complete samples). *Biometrika*, 52(3–4), 591–611. https://doi.org/10.1093/biomet/52.3-4.591

Thomas, R., Zumbo, B., Kwan, E., & Schweitzer, L. (2014). On Johnson's (2000) relative weights method for assessing variable importance: A reanalysis. *Multivariate Behavioral Research*, 49, 329–338.

Tibshirani, R. (1996). Regression shrinkage and selection via the lasso. *Journal of the Royal Statistical Society: Series B. Methodological*, 58(1), 267–288. https://doi.org/10.1111/j.2517-6161.1996.tb02080.x

Toothaker, L. E. (1993). *Multiple comparison procedures*. SAGE. https://doi.org/10.4135/9781412985178

Wellek, S. (2010). *Testing statistical hypotheses of equivalence*. Chapman.

Westfall, P., Tobias, R., Rom, D., Wolfinger, R., & Hochberg, Y. (1999). *Multiple comparisons and multiple tests: Using the SAS system*. SAS Institute.

Westfall, P. H., & Young, S. S. (1993). *Resampling based multiple testing*. Wiley.

Wilcox, R. R. (1996). *Statistics for the social sciences*. Academic Press.

Wilcox, R. R. (1998). How many discoveries have been lost by ignoring modern statistical methods. *American Psychologist, 53*(3), 300–314. https://doi.org/10.1037/0003-066X.53.3.300

Wilcox, R. R. (2001). *Fundamentals of modern statistical methods: Substantially improving power and accuracy*. Springer. https://doi.org/10.1007/978-1-4757-3522-2

Wilcox, R. R. (2003). *Applying contemporary statistical techniques*. Academic Press.

Wilcox, R. R. (2005). New methods for comparing group: Strategies for increasing the probability of detecting true differences. *Current Directions in Psychological Science, 14*, 272–275. https://doi.org/10.1111/j.0963-7214.2005.00379.x

Wilcox, R. R. (2006). Graphical methods for assessing effect size: Some alternatives to Cohen's d. *Journal of Experimental Education, 74*(4), 351–367. https://doi.org/10.3200/JEXE.74.4.351-367

Wilcox, R. R. (2010). Measuring and detecting associations: Methods based on robust regression estimators or smoothers that allow curvature. *British Journal of Mathematical and Statistical Psychology, 63*(2), 379–393. https://doi.org/10.1348/000711009X467618

Wilcox, R. R. (2012). *Modern statistics for the social and behavioral sciences: A practical introduction*. Chapman & Hall/CRC Press.

Wilcox, R. R. (2021). *Introduction to robust estimation and hypothesis testing* (5th ed.). Academic Press.

Wilcox, R. R., Charlin, V. L., & Thompson, K. (1986). New Monte Carlo results on the robustness of the ANOVA F, W, and F* statistics. *Communications in Statistics. Simulation and Computation, 15*, 933–943. https://doi.org/10.1080/03610918608812553

Wilcox, R. R., & Keselman, H. J. (2012). Modern regression methods that can substantially increase power and provide a more accurate understanding of associations. *European Journal of Personality, 26*(3), 165–174. https://doi.org/10.1002/per.860

Wilkinson, L. (1999). Statistical methods in psychology journals: Guidelines and explanations. *American Psychologist, 54*(8), 594–604. https://doi.org/10.1037/0003-066X.54.8.594

Wood, S. N. (2017). *Generalized additive models: An introduction with R* (2nd ed.). Chapman & Hall/CRC. https://doi.org/10.1201/9781315370279

Yeaton, W. H., & Sechrest, L. (1981). Meaningful measures of effect. *Journal of Consulting and Clinical Psychology, 49*(5), 766–767. https://doi.org/10.1037/0022-006X.49.5.766

CHAPTER 9

GENERALIZED LINEAR MODELS

David Rindskopf

Most social scientists are now acquainted with the general linear model, which allows one statistical method (regression) to be used to analyze data from a number of different research designs. Multiple regression can be used for the standard case with one or more continuous predictors as well as for the equivalent of a two-group *t* test, multiple-group analysis of variance (ANOVA), analysis of covariance (ANCOVA), and many more designs. The usual multiple regression, however, still has some major limitations for the data many social scientists analyze: (a) dependent (predicted, or outcome) variables in the social sciences are not always continuous, (b) the residuals (observed minus predicted values) do not always have a normal distribution, and (c) the relationships between independent and dependent variables are not always linear.

In some cases, a simple transformation (e.g., a logarithm, square root, or inverse) of the dependent variable helps solve one or more of the problems. Eventually, however, statisticians developed techniques that were correct for some of these situations—for example, log-linear models when all variables were categorical, logit models when one or more of the categorical variables were dependent and others are independent (predictor) variables, and logistic regression for binary (two-category) dependent variables (and extensions to ordered outcomes and multiple category outcomes).

Statisticians eventually realized that a large number of these models could be put into one general framework, which they named the *generalized linear model* (GLM; note the difference between *generalized* and *general*). The key initial works in this area are Nelder and Wedderburn (1972) and McCullagh and Nelder (1989). In all of the models, there is a linear function connecting the predictors (independent variables) to an outcome that is not always directly observed. This (unobserved) outcome is connected to the expected observed outcome using a transformation called a *link function*. Finally, various probability distributions are available to describe the random component of the model, which connects the observed dependent variable to the expected value in the model.

In this chapter, I show some of the most common GLMs and give examples of how they are conceptualized, fit, tested, and interpreted. I primarily use small, artificial data sets to make it possible for readers to reproduce these results on any computer package that fits GLMs. I demonstrate using the glm function in the R software package and discuss some of the other software available for fitting GLMs. Finally, I discuss various extensions of GLM to handle additional complexities that are common in social science data. I assume the reader has some familiarity with the usual analyses outside the

https://doi.org/10.1037/0000320-009
APA Handbook of Research Methods in Psychology, Second Edition: Vol. 3. Data Analysis and Research Publication, H. Cooper (Editor-in-Chief)
Copyright © 2023 by the American Psychological Association. All rights reserved.

context of GLM (e.g., logistic regression, log-linear models), although some explanatory context is provided.

Many of the steps of analysis using GLM are the same as for other methods of data analysis. As usual, begin with calculations of descriptive statistics and plots of relevant quantities. Next, decide on a strategy for building the linear part of the model. For example, how will the categorical predictors be coded? Should any predictors be centered or otherwise transformed? Will polynomial terms for continuous variables likely be needed? Interactions? Consider the possible choices for a link function and distribution; as will be seen, for some types of dependent variables there are several reasonable choices. Estimate the initial model, check the fit, and revise as necessary. Finally, interpret the results, do any needed auxiliary calculations and plots, and write about findings.

LOG-LINEAR AND LOGIT MODELS

In some cases, all variables are categorical. Consider a study of middle-school students that assesses the student's gender (male/female), race–ethnicity (Black, Hispanic, White), and whether the student is classified as having a learning disability. The data from such a study are usually displayed in a cross-tabulation such as that shown (for fictional data) in Table 9.1.

TABLE 9.1

The Relationship Among Learning Disability, Gender, and Race–Ethnicity: Observed Frequencies and Proportion Learning Disabled

Gender	Race	Learning disabled?		
		Yes	No	Proportion (yes)
Male	Black	13	27	.325
	Hispanic	14	66	.175
	White	49	151	.245
Female	Black	8	32	.200
	Hispanic	13	67	.163
	White	32	168	.160

There is quite a bit of variability among the six groups in the proportion who are classified as having a learning disability. The proportion for Hispanic males appears to be about the same as for Hispanic females, whereas in the other two race–ethnicity groups the rate is higher among males. Some of this variability might be just sampling variability, and the statistical analysis will attempt to disentangle real differences from those caused by sampling.

This data set can be approached in at least two related ways. From one perspective, the three variables are treated equally, and we look for which relationships are and are not present among them; this is the log-linear model perspective. Another perspective treats one variable (learning disability) as dependent, with the other two as explanatory (independent); this is the logit model. Both fit into the GLM framework. We begin with the logit model because it can be represented and interpreted most simply.

Logit Models

Most researchers would find it natural to express the outcome in terms of the proportion who are learning disabled in each group in the 2 (sex) × 3 (race–ethnicity) design. One would want to determine whether this proportion is related to the main effect of sex, the main effect of race–ethnicity, and whether there is an interaction between sex and race–ethnicity such that differences between males and females in the proportion of those who are classified as having a learning disability differ across race–ethnic groups. But a proportion has many flaws as a dependent variable, not the least of which is that with a linear model one can predict proportions less than zero or greater than one. Statisticians, therefore, look at transformations that do not have this flaw. The most common one first transforms a *proportion* π into an *odds*, $\pi/(1-\pi)$. Although a proportion is bounded between 0 and 1, an odds can range from 0 to infinity. Then, taking the natural (base e) logarithm of the odds, that is, $\ln[\pi/(1-\pi)]$, gives what is called a *logit transformation*. The logit can vary over the whole real number range, so that as a dependent variable, it has no values outside an allowable range as the proportion does. Another advantage of the logit transformation is symmetry: A proportion of .2 (for example) has the same logit (except for sign) as the proportion $.8 = 1 - .2$.

In GLM, the logit is called the *link function* and connects (links) the logit that we are modeling to the proportion that we observe. The usual logit model formulation for the systematic part of the model can therefore be expressed as

$$\ln\left(\frac{\pi}{1-\pi}\right) = \beta_0 + \beta_1 Sex + \beta_2 Black + \beta_3 Hisp$$
$$+ \beta_4 Sex * Black + \beta_5 Sex * Hisp \quad (9.1)$$

where π is the expected probability of being classified as having a learning disability, the two predictor variables (sex, race–ethnicity) are coded using either dummy or effect coding, as in any linear model, and, as before, ln() is the natural logarithm function. In the more general notation for GLM, we would write the model in two parts. The first part is for the linear predictor, η (eta):

$$\eta = \beta_0 + \beta_1 Sex + \beta_2 Black + \beta_3 Hisp$$
$$+ \beta_4 Sex * Black + \beta_5 Sex * Hisp \quad (9.2)$$

The second part of the specification is the link function, which in this case is the logit: $\eta = \ln\left(\frac{\pi}{1-\pi}\right)$. By writing the model this way, we allow for a simple change in the specification of the model by changing the link function, and, at the same time, we emphasize that the linear part of the model is in the form familiar to most researchers.

The probability model connecting the expected values to the observed is the *binomial distribution*. The probability model is the nonsystematic, or random, part of the GLM. The estimated values of π for each group predict the proportion who are learning disabled, and the actual number who are and are not learning disabled arise from a binomial distribution with parameters π and n, where n is the number of people in the group. In this form, the model is saturated, that is, with six groups, there are five degrees of freedom available, and Equation 9.2 uses all five degrees of freedom estimating five parameters (slopes only; the intercept, β_0, is not counted). One approach under these circumstances is to estimate the parameters of this model, test each parameter for significance, and drop nonsignificant parameters from the model in order, starting with highest level interactions. Another approach is to start with a simpler model, such as a main effects only model, and see whether the model fits sufficiently well that interactions are not needed. Here I take the latter approach; the relevant output for this model is in Exhibit 9.1. In the analysis, sex is coded 0 for males, 1 for females; Black and Hispanic are also dummy coded (and are, thus, implicitly compared with the remaining category, White).

EXHIBIT 9.1

Output for Logit Model Predicting Probability of Learning Disability

```
Coefficients:
              Estimate  Std.Error  z-value   Pr(>|z|)
(Intercept)   -1.1597   0.1520     -7.629    2.37e-14***
sex           -0.4526   0.2001     -2.261    0.0237*
black          0.3408   0.2843      1.199    0.2306
hisp          -0.2255   0.2459     -0.917    0.3592

Signif. codes:  0 '***' 0.001 '**' 0.01 '*' 0.05 '.' 0.1 ' ' 1

    Null deviance: 9.01827 on 5 degrees of freedom
Residual deviance: 0.98965 on 2 degrees of freedom
```

Note. Model includes main effects for sex and ethnicity. This model was fit using the glm function in R.

The output indicates that sex is significant; the negative coefficient indicates that those with a value of 1 (females) are lower than those with a value of 0 (males), meaning that females are less likely to be classified as having a learning disability in this population. Neither coefficient for race–ethnicity is significant, meaning that there are no significant relationships between race–ethnic group and learning disability. Is there an interaction between sex and race–ethnic group? The *residual deviance*, which in this case has a chi-square distribution, is so small (.99 with 2 degrees of freedom) that it would be impossible for an interaction term to reduce it by anywhere near a significant amount (3.84, the critical value of chi-square with 1 degree of freedom and $p = .05$). Therefore, we conclude that the only clear effect in the data is the main effect of sex, with males having a higher learning disability rate than females. (This is actually in accord with the way the data were generated; with a simulation, you can know what the right answer is.)

In discussing the fit of the model, it was noted that the residual deviance has a chi-square distribution if the model is correct. This is true for grouped data such as those we analyzed in this example but not for individual-level data. That is, here we are predicting proportions for whole groups of people; in other cases (such as the logistic regression model described in the section Logistic Regression and Its Extensions), we would be predicting the behavior of each individual, and the residuals would pertain to the individuals, not the groups. Even in that case, the deviance can help assess model fit: If the deviance is about equal to the residual degrees of freedom, the model fits reasonably well. If the deviance is much greater than the degrees of freedom (with *much greater* not being precisely defined), then the model does not fit well. For some models, this relatively large deviance may be due to obvious random sources of heterogeneity, such as large variation among subjects within groups, and the model can be extended by including a parameter for over-dispersion. Examples later in this chapter illustrate this procedure.

In some cases, residuals can be used to assess the fit of the model. The meaning of these residuals and their utility depend on the nature of the data. In this example the data are grouped, so the residuals essentially test whether the set of omitted terms (all of which are interactions) are zero. In other cases, in which the observations are made at the individual level (such as in the logistic regression example to be discussed later), the residuals refer to a prediction of the behavior of the individual, not a group; this use of residuals is more analogous to the use of residuals in ordinary regression situations. But many times the residuals for GLM are not expected to behave in quite the same way as in the linear regression case. For example, if each individual is observed only to be in one of two states, a large residual means that we predict a high probability of being in one state, but the person actually is in the other. For example, a person with a high school grade point average (GPA) of 1.3 might be predicted to have a low probability of graduating from college but nonetheless might do so. This result does not necessarily indicate that the model (or that observation) is problematic.

In many cases, the logit transform of the proportion discussed in this section will be satisfactory, but other transforms are also part of the GLM framework. One alternative viewpoint is that the unobserved dependent variable η has a normal distribution, and the observed dichotomous variable is 0 (or failure) unless η exceeds a threshold value, in which case the outcome is 1 (or success). The probability of success is therefore related to the area under the normal curve, and the transform is called a *probit*. In practice, the probit and logit models are so close that if one model fits the data well, the other usually also will do so; when scaled comparably, the predicted probabilities will differ by no more than .01. For other transformations, this is not true. For example, the complementary log–log function, $\ln[-\ln(\pi)]$, is qualitatively different from both the logit and probit. The ability to discern differences among these models generally occurs only in data with one or more continuous predictors.

Log-Linear Models

The logit model is appropriate when there is a dependent variable, such as learning disability in the previous example. When there is no obvious dependent variable, or when one wishes to treat all variables symmetrically and model all relationships among them, log-linear models are used. In this section, I use the same data set to illustrate, even though logit models seem most appropriate for these data.

Using log-linear models, the dependent variable is the cell frequency in the full contingency table, for our example, of $2 \times 3 \times 2 = 12$ cells. The terms in the model represent relationships among the variables. The most common example is the usual test for independence in a two-way cross-tabulation; in that case, the model is that the two variables (call them A and B) are independent. In the log-linear model framework, a model of independence means that only main effects for A and B are included, but not their interaction (relationship).

Frequencies are nonnegative, and the logarithm of a frequency can be any real number, so the logarithm is commonly used as the link function in the GLM framework. For a log-linear model that is equivalent to the main-effects logit model we fit, the GLM can be written as

$$\ln(F) = \beta_0 + \beta_1 Sex + \beta_2 Blk + \beta_3 Hisp + \beta_4 LD$$
$$+ \beta_5 Sex * Blk + \beta_6 Sex * Hisp$$
$$+ \beta_7 Sex * LD + \beta_8 Blk * LD$$
$$+ \beta_9 Hisp * LD \qquad (9.3)$$

where LD represents the variable *learning disabled*, Blk represents a dummy variable for Black, and $Hisp$ is a dummy variable for Hispanic. The interactions between LD and the variables Sex, Blk, and $Hisp$ are comparable to the main effects in the logit model. That is, in the logit model these terms are the effects of independent on dependent variables, but in the log-linear model they merely specify relationships (in a symmetric sense, like a correlation, rather than asymmetric as in regression). For example, the $Sex * LD$ term in the log-linear model allows a relationship between Sex and LD; in a logit model this would be a main effect of Sex (on LD).

I have specified the linear part of the model and that the link is the logarithm; the final aspect of the model is specifying the probability distribution. The usual distribution for the log-linear model is the Poisson; thus, the cell frequencies each have a Poisson distribution with means equal to the expected values given by the systematic part of the model. The Poisson is the simplest distribution for variables that represent counts (or, in general, variables that are nonnegative integers). I also discuss the Poisson distribution as it applies in other contexts later in this chapter.

The results of fitting the data in Table 9.1 using the log-linear version of the model are contained in Exhibit 9.2. The residual deviance for the log-linear model is the same as the residual deviance for the comparable logit model, indicating that the fit of the two models is identical. Next, notice that the significance levels of $LD \times Sex$, $LD \times Blk$, and $LD \times Hisp$ in the log-linear model are the same as for the effects of Sex, Blk, and $Hisp$ in the logit model. (In the R output, interactions are represented with a colon instead of the more typical asterisk.) In this case, the parameter estimates and standard errors are the same because of the coding methods used, but they will not always be. The ratio of the parameter to the standard error, called the z value in the output, will be the same, however, as will the significance level.

When would the log-linear model be used instead of the logit model? If there is no clear dependent variable, then the logit model would not be appropriate. In other cases, in which the data or the model are nonstandard (e.g., the data set is not a rectangular table), then the generality of log-linear models is useful; for details, see Rindskopf (1990).

LOGISTIC REGRESSION AND ITS EXTENSIONS

In some cases, each individual in a sample is measured on a binary (dichotomous) outcome. This outcome variable might be success or failure on some task, or that one decision rather than

EXHIBIT 9.2

Output From the glm Package in R for a Log-Linear Model Fit to the Learning Disability Data

```
Coefficients:
              Estimate   Std. Error   z value    Pr(>|z|)
(Intercept)    5.02555      0.07948    63.231    < 2e-16***
blk           -1.70196      0.19246    -8.843    < 2e-16***
ld            -1.15967      0.15201    -7.629    2.37e-14***
his           -0.86690      0.14213    -6.099    1.06e-09***
fe             0.09091      0.10792     0.842    0.3995
blk:ld         0.34078      0.28429     1.199    0.2306
ld:his        -0.22548      0.24593    -0.917    0.3592
ld:fe         -0.45260      0.20014    -2.261    0.0237*
blk:fe         0.02719      0.24642     0.110    0.9122
his:fe        -0.01525      0.18789    -0.081    0.9353

Signif. codes: 0 '***' 0.001 '**' 0.01 '*' 0.05 '.' 0.1 ' ' 1

    Null deviance: 506.86470 on 11 degrees of freedom
Residual deviance:   0.98965 on  2 degrees of freedom
```

Note. The colon (:) is used by this program to represent an interaction; the more usual notation is * or ×. The terms in bold are equivalent to terms in the logit model discussed in the text. blk = Black; ld = learning disabled; his = Hispanic; fe = female.

another is made (e.g., acquiring some post-secondary education vs. not), or that one opinion is favored over another. No matter what the context, when two choices are available, one is arbitrarily called a *success* (even if it represents an event with an undesirable outcome, such as cheating on a test) and the other outcome is called a *failure* (e.g., not cheating on a test). The goal is to model the probability of success as a function of one or more independent variables, which may be continuous, categorical, or a mixture of these types of variables. Outside the context of GLM, this is called *logistic regression*, and the link function is usually the log(odds), or logit, as discussed. The primary difference from the logit model is that in logistic regression, typically at least one predictor variable is (quasi)continuous, so that a linear relationship (on some scaling of the outcome) is expected, and modeling group frequencies is not practical because of the fineness of the scaling of the continuous variable.

As an example, we consider a (fictional) study by an industrial–organizational psychologist who is trying to determine the relationship between cognitive load and the probability of a major safety error by air traffic controllers. She simulates various amounts of traffic (on a scale from 1 to 20), measuring one air traffic controller in each condition, and assesses whether they make a potentially dangerous error (e.g., allowing planes to get too close). Suppose that the results, using 0 for no error and 1 for a major error, for amounts of traffic (in order from one to 20, with spacing to help count the corresponding amount of traffic) are as follows:

00000 00001 00111 11111

For lower amounts of traffic, controllers do not seem to make errors; for high amounts of traffic, controllers seem very likely to make an error; the transition seems to be somewhere between 10 and 12 on the complexity scale. The transition also seems to be fairly abrupt, evidenced by the long beginning string of 0s and the long ending string of 1s. This abrupt transition from 0s to 1s will cause some puzzling results.

EXHIBIT 9.3

Output for Logistic Regression Predicting, From Amount of Air Traffic, Whether a Major Error Was Made on an Air Traffic Control Task

```
glm(formula = y ~ traffic, family = binomial(link = logit))
Coefficients:
             Estimate   Std. Error   z value   Pr(>|z|)
(Intercept)  -10.5309      5.6594     -1.861     0.0628
traffic        0.9157      0.4851      1.888     0.0591

    Null deviance: 27.5256 on 19 degrees of freedom
Residual deviance:  7.1786 on 18 degrees of freedom
```

Note. The variable "y" is the dependent variable, coded 1 if a serious error was made and 0 if not; the variable "traffic" is the amount of air traffic in the simulation.

The model looks similar to that for a logit model.

$$\ln\left(\frac{\pi}{1-\pi}\right) = \beta_0 + \beta_1 Traffic \qquad (9.4)$$

where π is the probability of making a dangerous error, and *Traffic* is the amount of traffic (here it varies from 1 to 20). In terms of the GLM formulation, the link function is the logit (logarithm of the odds), and the distribution is *Bernoulli* (which can be thought of as a *binomial with one trial*). Selected parts of the output from fitting this model to the data are included in Exhibit 9.3, and a plot of the data along with the fitted response curve is in Figure 9.1. The results demonstrate a possible inconsistency between the results of two tests that often are equivalent but, in some cases, will diverge. The usual test for significance of the effect of amount of traffic is the parameter estimate divided by the standard error, distributed as a z-statistic; here this ratio is 1.888, which is not significant at $p < .05$. Another test of whether the slope for amount of traffic is significant is to compare the null model (i.e., the model that does not have a predictor) with the model that includes the predictor. The difference in the deviance values for that comparison is $27.53 - 7.18 = 20.35$, with $19 - 18 = 1$ degree of freedom, which is clearly significant, because 20.35 is much greater than 3.84, the critical value of the chi-square distribution with 1 degree of freedom. The difference between these two tests is due to prediction being too good; this makes both the slope and its standard error large, and when this happens, their ratio is no longer a valid test of significance (nor are confidence intervals accurate). Normally, one would not think of .92 as being a large slope, but it represents the change caused by a difference of only one more unit of traffic on a scale going from 1 to 20; this means that the odds of a dangerous error change by exp(.92), or about 2.5, for each increase of one unit on the traffic scale,

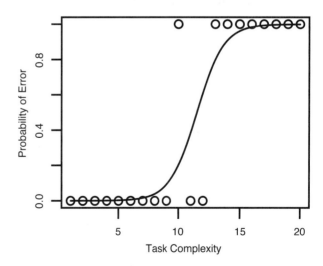

FIGURE 9.1. Plot of data on serious judgment errors by air traffic controllers as a function of task complexity. Open circles are raw data; solid line is the fit of a logistic regression model.

which is quite a large amount. (To understand this, remember that the slope is the change in the logarithm of the odds; to go back to the scale of the odds, we need the inverse of the logarithm, which is exponentiation.)

As is evident from this example, it is not always easy to detect such a problem by examining the estimate of the slope or its standard error; a more reliable method is to examine the deviance statistics. For these data, three interrelated pieces of information suggest there is a problem. First, the deviance for the null model is much greater than the degrees of freedom. The deviance does not have a chi-square distribution, so we cannot test the hypothesis of lack of fit when the predictor is omitted. Second, the deviance for the model with the predictor has a deviance well below the degrees of freedom, indicating an excellent fit. Finally, as noted, the direct test of significance for the slope using the difference in deviance values (which does have a chi-square distribution under the null hypothesis) is significant.

Extensions of the basic logistic regression model are available when the outcome variable is categorical but not dichotomous. I will describe the most typical models for unordered (nominal) and ordered outcome variables.

Nominal Response Scales

Not all categorical outcomes are dichotomous; nominal responses (unordered categorical responses) may have three, four, or more categories. Although sophisticated methods exist to model such variables (e.g., Agresti, 2013; Fox, 2016; Long, 1997), a simple approach often suffices: With k categories, the researcher forms $k - 1$ dichotomies and uses logistic regression on each outcome. For example, suppose the possible outcomes on a measure of music preference are jazz, country, rock, and classical. One might first create a dichotomy for classical versus all others. Then, for those who do not favor classical, one might create another dichotomy of jazz versus country or rock. Finally, for those who chose either country or rock, create a dichotomy contrasting these two categories. Then, three analyses are done, using the appropriate subset of people for each analysis. Naturally, this choice of dichotomies is not unique; other choices might be made depending on the hypotheses of the study. For example, a different researcher might first compare those who like jazz or classical (more serious music) with those who like country or rock. Then among those who chose either jazz or classical, she would predict which one they liked; similarly, among those who liked either country or rock, an analysis would try to differentiate their preference. Thus, dichotomies need not merely take one category at a time compared with the remaining categories. (Those familiar with orthogonal contrasts in ANOVA contexts will notice the connection to these two examples.)

Ordinal Data

When the outcome variable is ordered, an extension of the logistic regression model provides a natural framework for the analysis. Consider the case of a college that wants to validate the use of a mathematics placement test for determining whether students should be allowed to register for a particular course. It has data for 20 students who took the placement test before taking the course and the grade those students earned in the course. The test scores range from 1 to 20, with one student having achieved each score; the corresponding grades (in order of increasing test score) for those students are as follows:

0 0 0 0 2   1 1 0 1 2   2 2 3 2 3   4 4 2 4 3

where 0 represents a grade of F and 4 represents a grade of A. The course grades rise as the test scores increase, but the relationship is not perfect: One of the students with the lowest test score earned a C in the course, as did one of the highest-scoring students.

To understand the most common model for such data, consider that one could dichotomize the course grades in four ways, by considering grades of D or higher versus not (F), C or higher versus not (D or F), B or higher versus not (C, D, or F), and A versus not (B, C, D, or F). Then one could use the usual logistic regression model to predict high or low grade (using each of the four possible dichotomizations that preserve ordering) from the placement test score. The usual ordinal data model does this but with a restriction that the slope (effect of test score on the logit) is equal across the four dichotomizations. This model, called the *proportional odds model*, guarantees that the results are logically consistent: If the lines were not parallel, but were allowed to cross, then for some test score the probability of (for example) earning a B or better would be greater than the probability of earning a C or better. If the slopes differed only a little, this might occur outside the usual range of test scores, but it nonetheless represents a potential logical problem.

To fit these data, I used an extension of the glm function called *polr* (proportional odds logistic regression) in the MASS library for R. The results are contained in Exhibit 9.4. The predictor *test*, which is the score on the placement test, is clearly useful because its *t* value (coefficient divided by standard error) is 3.60.

To interpret the output, some reconceptualization is needed. In this context, it seems natural to want to model the (logit of the) probability of receiving a certain grade or higher; the statistical model, on the other hand, is set up to model the probability of receiving a certain grade or lower. (One can trick the program into doing it the other way by reversing the coding, using 0 for an A,

and so on down to 4 for an F. It is mostly a matter of personal preference for coding and interpretation.) The general form of the model, using zeta (ζ_i) to represent the intercept for category *i* and η to represent the systematic (linear) part of the model except for the intercept, is written as follows:

$$\text{logit}[\text{Probability}(\text{category } i \text{ or lower})] = \zeta_i - \eta \quad (9.5)$$

The change of sign is due to the conceptualization as the probability of category *i* or lower, rather than higher.

To take an example, the logit of the probability of getting a grade of C or lower is 8.5164 − .5825 ∗ *test*, where *test* is the score on the placement test. (The reversal of sign on the slope to become negative is correct; it indicates that the higher the test score, the lower the probability of receiving a grade of C or lower.) Thus, for a person with a test score of 10, the logit would be 8.5164 − 5.825 = 2.6914, the odds would be exp(2.6914) = 14.75, and the probability of a C or lower would then be 14.75/15.75 = .94. So we predict a student with a score of 10 would likely not do well in the course. On the other hand, with a score of 15 a student's logit would be 8.5164 − .5825(15) = 8.5164 − 8.7375 = −.22, the odds would be exp(−.22) = .80, and the probability of a C or below would be .80/1.80 = .45, which is much better.

Often the most useful way to present the results of an ordinal analysis is in the form of a plot, such as that contained in Figure 9.2. The four lines indicate the conditional probability of receiving a particular grade or higher, given the person's placement test score. The curve on the left, which rises first, is the probability of receiving at least a D (that is, passing the course); the curve on the far right, which rises last, is the probability of receiving an A. Using these curves, decision makers can easily determine the effect of making different choices for the cutpoint to allow a student into this course. For example, if it is desired to admit only students who have at least an 80% chance of getting a C or better, a cutscore

EXHIBIT 9.4

Output From glm for the Analysis of Ordinal Data

```
Call:
polr(formula = y.f ~ test, Hess = T)

Coefficients:
          Value      Std. Error   t value
Test      0.5824898  0.1616885    3.602543

Intercepts:
      Value    Std. Error   t value
0|1   3.2053   1.3040       2.4580
1|2   4.9459   1.5494       3.1921
2|3   8.5164   2.4080       3.5367
3|4   10.2955  2.7010       3.8118

Residual deviance: 36.75119
             AIC: 46.75119
```

Note. y.f = the course grade, coded starting with 0 for an F, up to 4 for an A; test = the score on the placement test, ranging from 1 to 20.

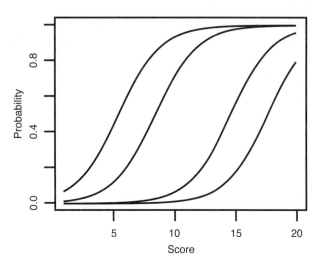

FIGURE 9.2. Probability plot for ordinal logistic model. The left-most curve is the probability of attaining a grade of at least D; the right-most curve the probability of attaining an A.

of about 11 will work. (This can be read reasonably accurately from the plot but can also be calculated exactly from the parameter estimates if such precision is desired.)

PREDICTING A COUNT VARIABLE

Suppose that we want to determine whether a particular psychological treatment can reduce the incidence of acting out in the classroom among third graders. (Assume that the behavior of each child does not affect the behavior of other children in the study, perhaps because they are in different classrooms.) We randomly assign five children to the treatment condition and another five to the control condition. After the treatment has been implemented, we count the number of times (during a 30-minute observation) that each child acts out. The counts are displayed in Exhibit 9.5.

Because the outcome is a (relatively small) count, there is good reason to doubt whether the distribution (within each group) has approximately a normal distribution. Even more serious, it seems that the variance of acting out may be greater in the control group than in the experimental group. If there were a covariate (e.g., baseline measures of acting out), we would probably also have to deal with some nonlinearity in the relationship between pretest and posttest. For all of these reasons, the usual linear model would be inappropriate, and we turn to a GLM. In this case, the Poisson distribution is the simplest to use, and in many cases, it will be sufficient. (This model is similar to that for log-linear models, where the Poisson distribution is also used.) The link function is the logarithm—that is, we will model as the dependent variable the logarithm of the expected counts,

$$\ln(Y_i) = \beta_0 + \beta_1 X_i \qquad (9.6)$$

where X is a dummy variable taking the value 1 for the treatment group and 0 for the control group.

Partial output from the R function glm is contained in Exhibit 9.6. The coefficient estimates produce a prediction equation: $\ln(y) = 1.5686 - 1.2321$ Group. The logarithm of the expected number of disruptive acts for the control group (Group = 0) is 1.5686, and the comparable value for a person in the treatment group (Group = 1) is $1.5686 - 1.2321 = .3365$. To find the predicted number of disruptive acts, we exponentiate to get $\exp(1.5686) = 4.80$ for the control group and $\exp(.3365) = 1.40$ for the experimental group. This difference between groups is large, but is it significant? We test the significance of the

EXHIBIT 9.5

Number of Times Each Child Acted Out During a 30-Min Observation Session

```
Treatment    1  1  1  1  1    0  0  0  0  0
Acting out   1  2  3  0  1    7  7  3  4  3
```

Note. Artificial data generated from a Poisson model. 0 = control condition, 1 = experimental condition.

EXHIBIT 9.6

Output From Fitting Poisson Regression to Data on Children Acting Out, Using R Function glm

```
Coefficients:
              Estimate   Std. Error   z value   Pr(>|z|)
(Intercept)    1.5686       0.2041     7.685    1.53e-14***
group         -1.2321       0.4296    -2.868    0.00413**

Signif. codes:  0 '***' 0.001 '**' 0.01 '*' 0.05 '.' 0.1 ' ' 1

    Null deviance: 17.9765 on 9 degrees of freedom
Residual deviance:  8.1193 on 8 degrees of freedom
```

Note. The variable "group" is coded 0 for control, 1 for experimental.

difference by examining the ratio of the parameter for Group to its standard error, which is evaluated against a z-distribution: $-1.2321/.4296 = -2.868$ ($p = .004$), which is strong evidence for an effect.

Another test of the same effect would compare the residual deviance statistics for the null model (i.e., the model without predictors) and the model we fit; the difference ($17.9765 - 8.1193 = 9.8572$) has a chi-square distribution with degrees of freedom equal to the difference between the degrees of freedom for the two models ($9 - 8 = 1$ degree of freedom). This value is clearly significant, as the critical value of chi-square at the .01 level is 6.64, well below the observed value of nearly 10. In this case, the methods of testing the effect give similar results, but (as seen in the logistic regression example) this convergence of results may not always occur; when they differ, the chi-square difference test will typically be more accurate.

Offsets

In some cases, we might not observe each person for the same length of time. In this case, we would model the *rate* of problem behaviors, which is the expected count (Y) divided by observation time (T). The model then becomes

$$\ln(Y_i/T_i) = \beta_0 + \beta_1 X_i \qquad (9.7)$$

Expanding the left-hand side gives

$$\ln(Y_i) - \ln(T_i) = \beta_0 + \beta_1 X_i \qquad (9.8)$$

Rearranging this produces

$$\ln(Y_i) = \ln(T_i) + \beta_0 + \beta_1 X_i \qquad (9.9)$$

On the right-hand side, it appears that the logarithm of observation time is a predictor (similar to X), but with a coefficient of 1 (i.e., the regression coefficient is fixed, not estimated). In the GLM literature, this is known as an *offset*, and most software for GLM can easily incorporate these offsets into models. The same procedure is also used in discrete–time survival models, in which the counts are the number of observed events (deaths, failures, or other events being counted), and the offset is the logarithm of the total period of observation of an individual or group.

OVERDISPERSION AND THE NEGATIVE BINOMIAL MODEL

Another extension might be required if the Poisson model is too simple. If the ratio of the model deviance to degrees of freedom is larger than 1, overdispersion is indicated. This can occur for two general types of reasons: A fixed effect is missing, or a random effect is missing. An example of the former would be a useful covariate that is omitted. Of course, one cannot always know which variables might be useful predictors, and even then it is sometimes impossible to measure the desired variables.

The other possibility is that variability among units either cannot be explained or is too complicated to explain—for example, people within groups often differ for many more reasons than we could possibly know or measure. In this case, a negative binomial distribution might provide a better fit to the data. Although the negative binomial has a sensible interpretation in its own right in certain contexts, it is equivalent to another distribution that has a more useful interpretation in the context of over-dispersion, the gamma-mixed Poisson distribution. In this interpretation, individuals with the same values on the predictor variables (here, group) would not have a constant probability of misbehaving, but their rates would vary (in the shape of a gamma distribution, to be technical). In general, this is more likely when the units of observation are individuals, such as the case here, rather than groups. In our context, it is very likely that children within each group vary in their rate of acting out, even though all are considered to do so at a high enough rate to be considered in need of treatment. (Another common context is the rate of accidents, in which people may vary in their rate of accident-proneness.)

Many software packages for GLM will allow overdispersion; for count data, the most usual distribution is the negative binomial (gamma-mixed Poisson). (In the R package I have used for all examples in this chapter, the glm.nb function in the MASS library extends the glm function to include the negative binomial distribution.)

To demonstrate fitting the negative binomial model, consider the data in Exhibit 9.7, which are similar to those in Exhibit 9.5 but with extra variation within each of the two groups. (Technical note for readers who are curious: For this example, the extra variation was created by generating data from a gamma distribution with means of 1 for the treatment group and 4 for the control group, and then sampling from a Poisson distribution to generate each number of disruptive acts.) Comparing the two tables, it is easy to see the increased variation in Exhibit 9.7 compared with Exhibit 9.5.

First, we fit the usual Poisson model to see whether the lack of fit is detected. The results are contained in Exhibit 9.8. If this model fits well, the residual deviance should be close to the degrees of freedom; the ratio of deviance to degrees of freedom is often used as a measure of overdispersion. The large residual deviance we observe in this case (compared with the degrees of freedom) indicates that the model does not fit well; we will see what effect this has on the results when we compare these results to those obtained using the negative binomial model.

The output from the negative binomial model is contained in Exhibit 9.9. The residual deviance is much lower for this model than for the Poisson model ($19.180 - 12.427 = 6.753$), which, with 1 degree of freedom difference between the models, is clearly significant. The direct comparison of the fit of these models is possible because the usual Poisson model is a restricted version (special case) of the negative binomial model in which overdispersion does not occur, so the parameter value is fixed instead of estimated. We conclude that there is overdispersion and that the negative binomial model provides a better fit than the simpler Poisson model.

Now we turn to the comparison of the two results and the interpretation. The Poisson model

EXHIBIT 9.7

Negative Binomial (Gamma-Mixed Poisson) Model: Number of Times Each Child Acted Out During a 30-Min Observation Session

Treatment	1	1	1	1	1	0	0	0	0	0
Acting out	0	4	0	0	1	4	2	0	5	4

Note. 0 = control condition, 1 = experimental condition.

EXHIBIT 9.8

Output for Poisson Model Fit to Data That Are Generated Using a Gamma-Mixed Poisson Distribution

```
Coefficients:
              Estimate   Std. Error   z value   Pr(>|z|)
(Intercept)    1.0986       0.2582     4.255    2.09e-05***
group         -1.0986       0.5164    -2.127    0.0334*

Signif. codes: 0 '***' 0.001 '**' 0.01 '*' 0.05 '.' 0.1 ' ' 1

    Null deviance: 24.412 on 9 degrees of freedom
Residual deviance: 19.180 on 8 degrees of freedom
```

Note. The variable "group" is coded 0 for control, 1 for experimental.

gives the same parameter estimates as the negative binomial model, but the Poisson results have smaller standard errors, larger z values (ratio of parameter divided by standard error), and smaller p values (significance level). In fact, if we believed the Poisson results, the group effect would be significant, but the negative binomial results would not be. Using the correct model for the research situation results in a loss of power, much to the disappointment of researchers (and analogous to what usually happens in multilevel models). Why? The extra variability within groups is extra noise, which makes detecting the signal (group differences) more difficult. Fitting the Poisson model pretends this variability does not exist and produces results that are too liberal (too significant) when the assumption of no overdispersion is false.

BINOMIAL DATA WITH OVERDISPERSION

As with the count data illustrated in the previous section, binomial data can be generated for each person in a study. For example, one might count

EXHIBIT 9.9

Output for Negative Binomial Model Fit to Data Generated From a Negative Binomial (Gamma-Mixed Poisson) Model

```
Coefficients:
              Estimate   Std. Error   z value   Pr(>|z|)
(Intercept)    1.0986       0.3978     2.762    0.00575**
group         -1.0986       0.6707    -1.638    0.10143

Signif. codes: 0 '***' 0.001 '**' 0.01 '*' 0.05 '.' 0.1 ' ' 1

(Dispersion parameter for Negative Binomial (2.1835)
family taken to be 1)

    Null deviance: 15.245 on 9 degrees of freedom
Residual deviance: 12.427 on 8 degrees of freedom

    Theta:  2.18
Std. Err.:  3.00
```

Note. The variable "group" is coded 0 for the control group, 1 for the experimental group.

EXHIBIT 9.10

Data for an Overdispersed Binomial Example

```
Person         1   2   3   4   5   6   7   8   9   10
Group          0   0   0   0   0   1   1   1   1   1
Number right   0   7   5   4   0   8   9   7   7   8
```

Note. Data for each person are the group into which they were placed (0 = control; 1 = treatment) and the number of trials (out of 10) on which they responded correctly.

how many items testing a concept are answered correctly. Under conditions in which such data are well behaved, one can merely get a total score and ignore the binomial nature of the constituent items; this is what is done when total test scores are used as if they represent a continuous normally distributed quantity in a regression or ANOVA. If many scores are at or near 0 (e.g., a very difficult test) or are at or near the maximum (e.g., a very easy test), then the distribution will be decidedly nonnormal, and other analytic methods must be used.

Several possible methods of analysis are available. One, which uses simple methodology, is to transform the proportion right and then use the usual ANOVA or regression methods. For example, the arcsine of the square root of proportions is well-known in certain fields and the logit in others. In each case, one must either have the same number of trials for each individual or use weighting to properly account for variation in number of trials. Another possibility is to use methods for nested (multilevel) data and have trials nested within individuals. In this section, I will illustrate a method that falls between these in terms of complexity.

To put the model in context, consider a study in which 10 people are randomly assigned to one of two groups. Each person is given a 10-item test at the end of the study, with one group having received a treatment (or new treatment) and the other group receiving nothing (or an old treatment). As with the example for count data, we expect that people might vary within groups for reasons additional to sampling variability in the binomial distribution of outcomes of each trial. To account for this heterogeneity in a GLM, we can allow for overdispersion in a similar manner to the situation with count data.

Simulated data are contained in Exhibit 9.10 for one such study as described. Note that the number right varies quite widely for those in control group (Group = 0), which is due to the overdispersion. For the treatment group (Group = 1), this is not evident because these people are all performing at a high level; the ceiling effect disguises the heterogeneity.

Results for fitting two models are presented in Table 9.2. The first model does not account for the variation among people, except for sampling variability in the binomial distribution. That is, the underlying probability of a correct response is the same for all people in the control group as well as for the experimental group (although

TABLE 9.2

GLM Results for a Model Without (Binomial) and With (Quasi-Binomial) Overdispersion

Parameter	Binomial	Quasi-binomial
Treatment	−2.0194	−2.0194
SE	0.4566	0.7121
t = param/SE	−4.423	−2.836
Significance	0.000001	0.0220

Note. The deviance for the binomial model was 24.885 with 8 degrees of freedom; the ratio of these is 24.885/8 = 3.111. The estimate of the dispersion parameter (param) for the quasi-binomial model was 2.43.

this probability differs for the two groups). Any difference in the number of items answered correctly is assumed to be due to differences in the treatment or sampling variability. For the second model this is not true; people within the same group are allowed to differ in their probability of answering correctly.

The first model, without overdispersion, evidently does not fit the data well; the deviance is much larger than the degrees of freedom; in fact their ratio is greater than 3. The results for the model with overdispersion differ in a predictable way from those for the model without overdispersion. The parameter estimate is unchanged, but the standard error is larger, correctly reflecting the additional source of variability among people. Because the standard error is larger, the z ratio is smaller, and, therefore, the significance level is much larger. Here, the effect of group is still significant, but in many cases, the (incorrect) model without overdispersion would indicate a significant effect but the (correct) model with overdispersion would not. (As noted, this effect also occurs in multilevel models.)

TIME TO AN EVENT (SURVIVAL MODELS)

Researchers often are interested in the amount of time people spend on various activities and in the ways that that amount of time might be increased or decreased. An educational psychologist, for example, would like to increase the amount of time students spend studying. One problem with laboratory studies in this case is that there is a limit to the amount of time one can spend observing people, so the data are often censored; that is, the person may be willing to spend more time doing some activity, but the researcher is not and, thus, ends the research session. Another problem is that such time lengths usually will not be normally distributed, and the variance will typically depend on the mean, violating the assumptions for the typical regression model. All of these issues are addressed by *survival analysis* (as it is called in the medical literature; other terms are *event history* and *failure time*, from sociology and reliability.)

For concreteness, we suppose that 10 students have been randomly assigned to one of two methods of increasing motivation to read, and, after the treatment, each is given a period of up to 60 minutes to read. If the student is still reading after 60 minutes, the experimental session is ended. Simulated data from Group 1 might be: 2, 5, 8, 19, 60* minutes, where the data are ordered from smallest to largest, and an asterisk (*) indicates censoring; comparable data from Group 2 might be: 10, 20, 60*, 60*, 60*. It appears that the second group is reading more than the first; this is evident both in the larger times and in the fact that only one student reads the maximal amount in Group 1, but three students read the maximal amount in Group 2.

Several possible distributions are commonly used for continuous–time survival data. The simplest is the exponential distribution, which was used to generate the data for this example. More complex distributions (which include the exponential as a special case) are the gamma and the Weibull. Although some survival models can be fit using GLM programs that employ certain tricks, in practice it is more straightforward to use special functions that are written for survival models. This is one case in which the generality of the model does not currently seem worth the price paid in lack of interpretability.

In some cases, time is not continuous but a small count (e.g., the number of semesters to graduate from college). In this case, a model similar to that used in Poisson regression for counts is often used.

EXTENSIONS TO THE ORIGINAL GLM FORMULATION

One extension of GLM is to explicitly model nesting of data. One situation that can be represented as a nested model involves repeated measures data, in which observations are considered to be nested within individuals. Another common situation occurs when individuals are nested within groups; examples include students within classes (and classes within schools, etc.), voters nested in election districts, people nested within neighborhoods, and employees nested within work groups. Models for nested (hierarchical) data are treated in more detail in Chapter 10 of this volume as well as in many textbooks and reference works.

A large number of latent variable models, including exploratory and confirmatory factor analysis and structural equation models, were originally conceptualized for continuous observed and latent variables. As with models for observed variables, special cases were treated individually; these include models in which the latent variable is categorical, but the observed variables are continuous (finite mixture models and cluster models); the observed variables are categorical, but the latent variables are continuous (item response theory); and both observed and latent variables are categorical (latent class analysis). Most of these models have been put into a general framework as an extension of GLMs by Skrondal and Rabe-Hesketh (2004).

One extension of the GLM involving latent variables is especially useful for some missing data problems: the use of composite link functions, as developed by Thompson and Baker (1981). In this extension, the GLM is written to apply to unobserved variables, which are then combined (summed through the composite link) to produce the observed variables. One variation of this approach can be used to fit all examples of missing categorical data discussed in Little and Rubin (2019) as well as many additional models, such as latent class models and even latent class models with missing data (for details, see Rindskopf, 1992).

Bayesian Generalized Linear Models

The most notable change in GLMs recently has been the development of Bayesian versions of GLMs. Bayesian statistics differs from classical or frequentist statistics in terms of both the basic philosophy and the use of prior (or external) information to make more accurate estimates and predictions. The Bayesian viewpoint considers parameters as random variables that have distributions, and, therefore, those distributions can be summarized and described in different ways than frequentists would do. A Bayesian, for example, can say that the probability that a parameter is in an interval is 95%, whereas that (very natural) interpretation is not available to a frequentist.

The other new idea is incorporating prior (or external) information about parameters. For example, if a test score ranges from 0 to 100, there is no possibility that the mean could be less than 0 or greater than 100, and probably the values could be narrowed based on past use of the test. In psychology, we might know that correlations among certain traits are probably positive and unlikely to be greater than .8. Bayesians can put such prior information into numerical form.

The newest methods for Bayesian model fitting are based on simulations, which has additional benefits. With these methods, it is simple to find the marginal posterior distribution of parameters, whereas older methods required integration over the remaining parameters. These new methods also allow the user to easily see the shape of the posterior distribution, so that if it is not normal, a better summary can be made than the traditional interval estimation methods.

SOFTWARE TO FIT GLMs

Most large statistical packages commonly used by psychologists have at least some facility to fit GLMs; these packages include SAS, SPSS/PASW, Statistica, and Stata. Even packages that do not explicitly include the full range of GLMs often include some separate components, such as logistic regression and log-linear models. The free software package R (https://www.rproject.org) and its commercial equivalent Splus (https://spotfire.tibco.com/Products/S-Plus-Overview.aspx) have extensive capabilities for fitting GLMs; R has been used to illustrate examples in this chapter. Several GLMs for nested data can be fit using the HLM (https://ssicentral.com) and MLwiN (https://www.cmm.bristol.ac.uk/MLwiN) packages and with add-on functions in R and Splus. For Bayesian versions of generalized linear models, the easiest transition is found in the R package arm, with its functions bayesglm and bayespolr that mimic the usual R functions glm and polr. These require little background in Bayesian theory. MCMCpack in R also has special functions for

GLMs that are simple to use. Somewhat more involved are purely Bayesian programs such as WinBUGS/OpenBUGS, jags (and rjags, the R version), and Stan. More Bayesian programs are available and in constant development; it is best to check the CRAN Task View on Bayesian statistics for the latest information on Bayesian R programs.

FURTHER READING

For those wishing an introduction to GLM, several books are available, including Dobson and Barnett (2018), which includes the Bayesian approach to GLM; Gill (2019); and Hoffmann (2004). More advanced books include Fahrmeir and Tutz (2001) and Hardin and Hilbe (2018). Books covering GLM in whole or in part, but oriented toward a particular software package, include Aitkin et al. (2009) for R; Chambers and Hastie (1992) for S; and Venables and Ripley (2002) for R and Splus. For details on the GLM as originally conceptualized, the original article introducing the topic is Nelder and Wedderburn (1972), and the current authoritative source is McCullagh and Nelder (1989). Germán Rodríguez maintains an excellent website (https://data.princeton.edu/wws509) on GLMs, which includes detailed lecture notes and data sets. Extensions and related models include generalized additive models (Hastie & Tibshirani, 1990), models for nested or longitudinal data (Lee & Nelder, 2001; Liang & Zeger, 1986; McCulloch et al., 2008; Pinheiro & Bates, 2000; Zeger & Liang, 1986), and models that include latent variables (Skrondal & Rabe-Hesketh, 2004).

Many regression texts now include material on GLM, and some are devoted mostly to the topic. An example of the former is the text by Fox (2016) and of the latter is one by Faraway (2017). Some specialized books emphasize specific aspects of generalized linear models: Hilbe (2011) concentrated on negative binomial models, Cameron and Trivedi (2013) concentrated on count data; Agresti (2013), Long (1997), and Long and Freese (2014) dealt with categorical data; Hosmer et al. (2013) dealt with logistic regression; Cox and Oakes (1984) and Singer and Willett (2003) dealt with survival data.

A few specialized technical references include Lawless (1987), who discussed negative binomial and mixed Poisson regression; McCullagh (1983), who provided the theory for quasi-likelihood functions; and Pierce and Schafer (1986), Pregibon (1981), and Williams (1987), who all dealt with residuals and outlier detection.

CONCLUSION

Most psychologists are familiar with linear models in the form of regression and ANOVA. Such models are useful as long as the dependent variable is continuous, the relationship is linear, and the residuals are normally distributed and of constant variance. Many situations require a broader class of models, however. For example, the dependent variable may be dichotomous (e.g., success–failure), unordered categorical (Republican, Democrat, Independent), ordered categorical (dislike, neutral, like), or counts (number of times a student is disruptive during class). A continuous dependent variable may not be normally distributed (e.g., waiting times might be exponentially distributed, among other possibilities). Survival analysis, both discrete and continuous versions, also require methods outside the usual regression model. GLMs include a generalization of the usual linear model to take into account many of these issues; they do this primarily by allowing different error distributions and various transformations of the dependent variable. This chapter has described and illustrated applications of the GLM, including special cases such as logistic regression, logit models, log-linear models, and Poisson regression.

References

Agresti, A. (2013). *Categorical data analysis* (3rd ed.). Wiley.

Aitkin, M., Francis, B., Hinde, J., & Darnell, R. (2009). *Statistical modelling in R*. Oxford University Press.

Cameron, A. C., & Trivedi, P. K. (2013). *Regression analysis of count data*. Econometric Society Monograph. https://doi.org/10.1017/CBO9781139013567

Chambers, J. M., & Hastie, T. J. (1992). *Statistical models in S*. Wadsworth & Brooks/Cole.

Cox, D. R., & Oakes, D. (1984). *Analysis of survival data*. Chapman and Hall.

Dobson, A. J., & Barnett, A. (2018). *An introduction to generalized linear models* (4th ed.). Taylor & Francis.

Fahrmeir, L., & Tutz, G. (2001). *Multivariate statistical modeling based on generalized linear models* (2nd ed.). Springer-Verlag. https://doi.org/10.1007/978-1-4757-3454-6

Faraway, J. J. (2017). *Extending the linear model with R: Generalized linear, mixed effects and nonparametric regression* (2nd ed.). CRC Press.

Fox, J. (2016). *Applied regression analysis and generalized linear models* (3rd ed.). Sage.

Gill, J. (2019). *Generalized linear models: A unified approach* (2nd ed.). Sage.

Hardin, J. W., & Hilbe, J. W. (2018). *Generalized linear models and extensions* (4th ed.). Stata Press.

Hastie, T. J., & Tibshirani, R. J. (1990). *Generalized additive models*. Chapman & Hall.

Hilbe, J. M. (2011). *Negative binomial regression* (2nd ed.). Cambridge University Press. https://doi.org/10.1017/CBO9780511973420

Hoffmann, J. P. (2004). *Generalized linear models: An applied approach*. Pearson, Allyn, & Bacon.

Hosmer, D. W., Lemeshow, S., & Sturdivant, R. X. (2013). *Applied logistic regression* (3rd ed.). Wiley. https://doi.org/10.1002/9781118548387

Lawless, J. E. (1987). Negative binomial and mixed Poisson regression. *The Canadian Journal of Statistics*, *15*(3), 209–225. https://doi.org/10.2307/3314912

Lee, Y., & Nelder, J. A. (2001). Hierarchical generalized linear models: A synthesis of generalized linear models, random effect models and structured dispersions. *Biometrika*, *88*(4), 987–1006. https://doi.org/10.1093/biomet/88.4.987

Liang, K. Y., & Zeger, S. L. (1986). Longitudinal data analysis using generalized linear models. *Biometrika*, *73*(1), 13–22. https://doi.org/10.1093/biomet/73.1.13

Little, R. J. A., & Rubin, D. B. (2019). *Statistical analysis with missing data* (3rd ed.). Wiley.

Long, J. S. (1997). *Regression models for categorical and limited dependent variables*. Sage.

Long, J. S., & Freese, J. (2014). *Regression models for categorical dependent variables using Stata* (3rd ed.). Stata Press.

McCullagh, P. (1983). Quasi-likelihood functions. *Annals of Statistics*, *11*(1), 59–67. https://doi.org/10.1214/aos/1176346056

McCullagh, P., & Nelder, J. A. (1989). *Generalized linear models* (2nd ed.). Chapman & Hall. https://doi.org/10.1007/978-1-4899-3242-6

McCulloch, C. E., Searle, S. R., & Neuhaus, J. M. (2008). *Generalized, linear, and mixed models* (2nd ed.). Wiley.

Nelder, J. A., & Wedderburn, R. W. M. (1972). Generalized linear models. *Journal of the Royal Statistical Society. Series A (General)*, *135*(3), 370–384. https://doi.org/10.2307/2344614

Pierce, D. A., & Schafer, D. W. (1986). Residuals in generalized linear models. *Journal of the American Statistical Association*, *81*(396), 977–986. https://doi.org/10.1080/01621459.1986.10478361

Pinheiro, J. C., & Bates, D. M. (2000). *Mixed-effects models in S and S-PLUS*. Springer-Verlag. https://doi.org/10.1007/978-1-4419-0318-1

Pregibon, D. (1981). Logistic regression diagnostics. *Annals of Statistics*, *9*(4), 705–724. https://doi.org/10.1214/aos/1176345513

Rindskopf, D. (1990). Nonstandard log-linear models. *Psychological Bulletin*, *108*(1), 150–162. https://doi.org/10.1037/0033-2909.108.1.150

Rindskopf, D. (1992). A general approach to categorical data analysis with missing data, using generalized linear models with composite links. *Psychometrika*, *57*(1), 29–42. https://doi.org/10.1007/BF02294657

Singer, J. D., & Willett, J. B. (2003). *Applied longitudinal data analysis: Modeling change and event occurrence*. Oxford University Press. https://doi.org/10.1093/acprof:oso/9780195152968.001.0001

Skrondal, A., & Rabe-Hesketh, S. (2004). *Generalized latent variable modeling: Multilevel, longitudinal and structural equation models*. Chapman & Hall/CRC. https://doi.org/10.1201/9780203489437

Thompson, R., & Baker, R. J. (1981). Composite link functions in generalized linear models. *Journal of the Royal Statistical Society Series C (Applied Statistics)*, *30*(2), 125–131. https://doi.org/10.2307/2346381

Venables, W. N., & Ripley, B. D. (2002). *Modern applied statistics with S* (4th ed.). Springer. https://doi.org/10.1007/978-0-387-21706-2

Williams, D. A. (1987). Generalized linear models diagnostics using the deviance and single case deletions. *Applied Statistics*, *36*(2), 181–191. https://doi.org/10.2307/2347550

Zeger, S. L., & Liang, K. Y. (1986). Longitudinal data analysis for discrete and continuous outcomes. *Biometrics*, *42*(1), 121–130. https://doi.org/10.2307/2531248

CHAPTER 10

MULTILEVEL MODELING FOR PSYCHOLOGISTS

John B. Nezlek

In the 10 years since the first version of this chapter was published, there has been a marked increase in the use of multilevel modeling (MLM). Although MLM was used regularly 10 years ago, it was still somewhat esoteric, at least in some quarters. Regardless, what may have once been esoteric is now commonplace. This growth means that researchers need to be familiar with MLM to understand what is being published and to conduct research and analyses that meet current standards for best practices.

Despite the growth in its use, it appears that MLM is not taught that frequently in graduate programs (Davidson et al., 2019), and this chapter is intended to provide an introduction to MLM that can serve as a basis or starting point for reading and writing articles. Individuals who have had a course may find the chapter to be a good refresher.

When writing this chapter, I assumed an understanding of basic ordinary least squares (OLS) regression would be the only statistical training readers would have. In writing this chapter, I had two goals in mind. First, I wanted readers to learn the basics of multilevel analysis. Second, I wanted to increase readers' awareness of the multilevel perspective so that they might recognize the multilevel features of the data they have collected and formulate research questions that might involve multilevel data. As Kreft and de Leeuw (1998) noted, "Once you know that hierarchies exist, you see them everywhere" (p. 1). Conversely, if you do not know how to conceptualize a multilevel data structure and the accompanying analyses, you may not see or recognize hierarchies anywhere.

In this chapter, I provide a rationale for MLM, why it is necessary, its advantages over other techniques, and so forth. I describe the basic structure of univariate multilevel analyses: the nature of the models and the types of parameters they can estimate, and how to conduct multilevel analyses, including different aspects of analyses such as centering, modeling error, weighted analyses, and categorical independent and dependent measures. I also offer suggestions about how to interpret the results of analyses and how to report results in papers.

Given that the rationale and basic structure of MLM analyses have not changed, my treatment of these topics is similar to the treatment provided in the previous version of the chapter. The sections on estimating reliability, mediation, power, and software have been updated, although by necessity, the coverage of these topics is brief. Although there have been numerous developments in MLM, including extensions of the MLM framework to address new research questions (formal modeling), this chapter does not cover these.

https://doi.org/10.1037/0000320-010
APA Handbook of Research Methods in Psychology, Second Edition: Vol. 3. Data Analysis and Research Publication, H. Cooper (Editor-in-Chief)
Copyright © 2023 by the American Psychological Association. All rights reserved.

DEFINING MULTILEVEL ANALYSIS

What Is Meant by Multilevel?

A *multilevel* data structure is one in which observations at one level of analysis are nested (or clustered or grouped) within observations at another level of analysis. Sometimes, multilevel data structures are described as "nested" or as "hierarchically nested." The critical, defining feature of such multilevel data is that observations at one level of analysis are not independent of each other. There is an interdependence among the data that needs to be taken into account. In this chapter, I focus on two-level data structures, but the framework and logic I use to describe two-level structures are applicable to data structures with more than two levels. How to conceptualize the levels of a model is considered in a separate section.

The lack of independence among observations is exemplified in studies of groups (e.g., students in classes, workers in work groups). Individuals in the same group all share the characteristics associated with their group, whereas they differ from each other in terms of individual-level characteristics. In addition, group-level characteristics, such as teacher experience or the style of group leaders, are likely to vary across groups. Therefore, individual differences such as performance can be examined in terms of explanatory variables at two levels of analysis—the individual (e.g., motivation) and the group (e.g., teacher characteristics), and members of different groups may vary in terms of measures at both levels of analysis.

The question is how to disentangle relationships between an outcome of interest and measures at different levels of analysis. For example, why are Mary's test scores higher than Jane's? Is this because Mary is smarter or works harder than Jane (individual-level relationships), or is it because Mary's teacher is better than Jane's, so the students in Mary's class tend to have higher grades on average (a group-level relationship)—or is it both? Moreover, it is possible that the individual-level relationship between how intelligent students are and their grades varies across classes. The relationship may be stronger in some classes than in others, and it may be of interest to understand (to model) the differences in such relationships among classes.

When addressing such questions, it is critical to recognize that relationships at different levels of analysis are mathematically independent. In a study in which persons are nested within groups, relationships at the between-group level tell us nothing about relationships at the within-group level and vice versa. This independence is illustrated by the data in Table 10.1 and Table 10.2. In the Table 10.1 data, the within-group relationships are positive, whereas the between-group relationships are negative, while in the Table 10.2 data, the within-group relationships are negative, and the between-group relationships are positive.

TABLE 10.1

Relationships: Positive at Within-Group Level and Negative at Between-Group Level

	Group 1		Group 2		Group 3	
	X	Y	X	Y	X	Y
	26	31	29	29	31	26
	27	32	30	30	32	27
	28	33	31	31	33	28
	29	34	32	32	34	29
	30	35	33	33	35	30
Mean	28	33	31	31	33	28

TABLE 10.2

Relationships: Negative at Within-Group Level and Positive at Between-Group Level

	Group 1		Group 2		Group 3	
	X	Y	X	Y	X	Y
	11	18	19	23	19	28
	12	17	20	22	20	27
	13	16	21	21	21	26
	14	15	22	20	22	25
	15	14	23	19	23	24
Mean	13	16	21	21	21	26

Moreover, these two examples do not exhaust the possible combinations. Relationships at the within-group level might vary across groups, some could be positive, some could be negative. Seeing such data, one might ask, "Well, which one is correct?" The answer is that neither is correct. If an analyst is interested in constructs defined at the between-group level, then the between-group relationships are correct. Conversely, if the interest is in constructs defined at the within-group level, then the within-group relationships are correct, with the caveat that these relationships may not be consistent across groups.

In MLM the term *group* refers to an organizing unit or cluster. For studies of actual groups (e.g., work groups) this creates no confusion; however, for other types of nesting (e.g., observations within persons such as in a diary study), the term *group* can be confusing. So when observations are nested within people, a person constitutes a group. In a cross-cultural study, cultures might be the groups, in a community psychology study, communities might be the groups, and so forth. Using the term *group* in this way is a tradition in MLM, and, as confusing as it may be for those unfamiliar with MLM, I follow this tradition.

Analytic Strategies for Analyzing Multilevel Data

Before describing multilevel random coefficient modeling, which is the currently accepted gold standard for analyzing multilevel data sets for psychologists, I briefly review other methods. One way to distinguish such methods is to distinguish "aggregation" versus "disaggregation" methods. In aggregation methods, within-group summary statistics are calculated (e.g., means) and then analyzed. For example, for each state in the United States, a researcher might calculate means for two variables (literacy and percent of immigrants) and then calculate a correlation at the state level. Such relationships are perfectly acceptable providing one does not commit what is called the *ecological fallacy* (Robinson, 1950), which is an assumption that the between-group relationships exist at the within-group level.

In a classic paper using the 1930 U.S. Census data, Robinson (1950) found a positive correlation between literacy and percent of residents that were foreign-born at the between-state level, which could lead one to conclude that foreign-born residents were more literate than native-born residents. In contrast, the within-state relationship was negative. The panels of data presented in Tables 10.1 and 10.2 illustrate the potential for such ecological fallacies.

In disaggregation analyses, analyses are done at only Level-1 (e.g., the individual level when persons are nested within groups), and relationships between outcomes and Level-2 measures are examined by assigning Level-2 measures to the corresponding Level-1 observations. Some analysts have used a least squared dummy variable (LSDV) approach to control for Level-2 differences in Level-1 measures. In LSDV analyses, assuming k groups, a set of dummy variables ($k - 1$) are added to the Level-1 model. Although well-intended, such analyses are fundamentally flawed in at least two ways. First, they assume that Level-1 relationships between the outcome and the predictors are identical in all groups—an untenable assumption—and second, they do not model error properly. Even if interaction terms between the dummy variables and the predictors are included (which can be unwieldy with many groups and multiple predictors), the two sources of error are not modeled properly.

In a two-level multilevel data structure, there are two sources of error: one associated with sampling Level-1 observations, and the other associated with sampling Level-2 observations. For example, in a diary study in which observations are nested within persons, there is error associated with sampling persons and with sampling days. The error associated with sampling persons is well understood, but a coefficient representing the within-person relationship between daily stress and daily anxiety for an individual also has a sampling error. A coefficient based on the two weeks a study was conducted will probably be similar to, but not the same as, a coefficient based on another two-week period. Moreover, the unreliability of such a coefficient (how much it might vary across a series of two periods) needs to be incorporated into significance tests of between-person effects.

Studies in which people are nested within groups can be understood in the same way. Most analysts would recognize that students in classes constitute a sample that is meant to represent the population of students. In parallel, the classes in which those students are nested also need to be considered as samples representing the population of classes. It is including these two sources of error simultaneously (the Level-1 error and the Level-2 error) that renders OLS analyses inappropriate. Due to the mathematics involved, OLS analyses can estimate only one error term at a time. Estimating multiple unknowns (simultaneous errors) requires maximum-likelihood estimators, which are the basis for the algorithms used by all MLM programs.

For multilevel data, maximum-likelihood procedures provide more accurate parameter estimates than comparable OLS analyses such as using OLS regression to estimate coefficients for individual Level-2 units of analysis and using those coefficients in a single-level analysis between Level-2 units. The greater accuracy of MLM using maximum-likelihood estimators is not hypothetical. It is a demonstrated fact based upon the results of Monte Carlo studies in which samples have been drawn from populations with known parameters. The sample statistics based on maximum-likelihood procedures are more accurate estimates of such population parameters than the sample statistic based on comparable OLS analyses. Full stop.

This chapter discusses using what is sometimes known as "multilevel regression." Although this technique is more or less the standard technique used by psychologists, other techniques that incorporate the hierarchical structure of a data set are used in other disciplines. See Hamaker and Muthén (2020) for a discussion of these different approaches. A detailed discussion of the statistical background of MLM is beyond the scope of this chapter. Curious readers can consult two classic references, Raudenbush and Bryk (2002) and Goldstein (2011) for more details.

The Basic Models

Consistent with the explanatory framework originally proposed by Bryk and Raudenbush (1992), I present the equations for each level of a model separately. Nevertheless, keep in mind that all coefficients at all levels of analysis are estimated simultaneously, so models consist of equations in which the outcome (y) is predicted by the intercepts at each level of analysis, the predictors that are included at each level, cross-level interactions, and the error terms. Such equations can be quite cumbersome, which is why I present models using the Bryk and Raudenbush format. I also present models in this format in my published work.

In the standard nomenclature, Level-1 coefficients are represented with βs (subscripted 0 for the intercept, 1 for the first coefficient, 2 for the second, etc.), and the basic Level-1 model is

$$y_{ij} = \beta_{0j} + r_{ij} \qquad (10.1)$$

In this model, there are i Level-1 observations for j Level-2 groups of a continuous variable y. The Level-1 observations are modeled as a function of the intercept for each group (β_{0j}, the mean of y) and error (r_{ij}), and the variance of r_{ij} is the Level-1 error.

Each Level-1 coefficient is then modeled at Level-2, and Level-2 coefficients are represented by γs. There is a separate Level-2 equation for each Level-1 coefficient. The basic Level-2 model is

$$\beta_{0j} = \gamma_{00} + \mu_{0j} \qquad (10.2)$$

In this equation, the mean of y for each of j Level-2 units of analysis (β_{0j}) is modeled as a function of the grand mean (γ_{00}—the mean of means) and error (μ_{0j}), and the variance of μ_{0j} is the Level-2 variance. When these two basic models are combined, this is referred to as a totally unconditional or null model because there are no predictors at any level of analysis. The value of unconditional models is discussed below.

Predictors can be added to this basic model at either level of analysis. Assume a study in which students are nested within classes and the outcome measure is a test score. At the within-class (individual) level, the relationship between test scores and hours of study could be examined with the following model:

$$y_{ij} = \beta_{0j} + \beta_{1j}(\text{study}) + r_{ij}$$

$$\beta_{0j} = \gamma_{00} + \mu_{0j}$$

$$\beta_{1j} = \gamma_{10} + \mu_{1j} \qquad (10.3)$$

In this model, the intercept of y (β_{0j}) for each of j Level-2 classes is modeled as a function of the mean intercept (γ_{00}) and error (μ_{0j}), and the slope (β_{1j}) representing the within-class relationship between scores and studying for each of j classes is modeled as a function of the mean slope (γ_{10}—the average relationship across all classes) and error (μ_{1j}).

In MLM, coefficients are tested for significance against 0, and in this model, the significance test of the mean slope (is the mean slope significantly different from 0) is made at Level-2, via the γ_{10} coefficient. If the γ_{10} coefficient is significantly different from 0, then the null hypothesis is rejected. The intercept is also tested for significance via the γ_{00} coefficient—is the mean intercept significantly different from 0? The meaning of these tests, that is, what the coefficients represent, will vary as a function of the measures themselves, and most importantly, the meaning will vary as a function of how the Level-1 predictors are centered, a topic discussed in the section Centering.

In MLM, the random error terms for Level-1 coefficients (the μ_{0j} and μ_{1j} terms) can also be tested for significance, and such significance tests can be used to make decisions about including or excluding random error terms from models. When an error term for a coefficient is included in a model the coefficient is referred to as a random coefficient, and when an error term is not included, the coefficient is referred to as a fixed coefficient. This topic is discussed in the section Modeling Random Error.

Predictors can also be added at Level-2. Continuing the above example, at the between-class level, the relationship between test scores and teacher experience could be examined with the following model:

$$y_{ij} = \beta_{0j} + r_{ij}$$

$$\beta_{0j} = \gamma_{00} + \gamma_{01}(\text{experience}) + \mu_{0j} \qquad (10.4)$$

In this model, the mean score for a class (the β_{0j} brought up from Level-1) is being modeled as a function of the grand mean and the experience of a teacher. If the γ_{01} coefficient is significantly different from 0, then there is a relationship between a teacher's experience and the average score for students in their class. Once again, what these Level-2 coefficients represent will vary as a function of how the Level-2 predictors are centered.

Predictors can be added at both levels of analysis simultaneously. Relationships between test scores and hours of study can be examined at the individual level, and in turn, classroom level differences in these relationships can be modeled at the between-class level as a function of teacher experience. Analyses examining such relationships are sometimes called "slopes as outcomes" analyses because a slope (a coefficient representing a relationship) from a lower level (e.g., Level-1) becomes an outcome at an upper level (e.g., Level-2).

$$y_{ij} = \beta_{0j} + \beta_{1j}(\text{study}) + r_{ij}$$

$$\beta_{0j} = \gamma_{00} + \gamma_{01}(\text{experience}) + \mu_{0j}$$

$$\beta_{1j} = \gamma_{10} + \gamma_{11}(\text{experience}) + \mu_{1j} \qquad (10.5)$$

In this model, the slope for each class (β_{1j}) is brought up from Level-1 and is modeled as a function of the mean and the experience of a teacher. If the γ_{11} coefficient is significantly different from 0, then the relationship between test scores and studying varies as a function of teacher experience. Note that *experience* is included in both Level-2 equations, a topic discussed in the section Building a Model.

Similar to OLS regression, these multilevel models are simply templates that can be applied to various types of data structures. In a study of therapeutic outcomes, clients could be nested within therapists or clinics. In diary-style studies, observations (days or certain types of events, such as social interactions) could be nested within persons. In studies relying upon reaction times, responses can be treated as nested within persons and experimental conditions can be modeled at the person level. Such applications are limited only by the insight of researchers and their ability to collect the necessary data.

DETERMINING THE MULTILEVEL STRUCTURE OF A DATA SET

How Many Levels?

In most instances, deciding about the multilevel structure of a data set should be fairly straightforward. Studies of students nested within classrooms, or days nested within persons, or clients nested within clinics are all straightforward two-level models. But what if classrooms are also nested within schools, persons are also nested within groups of some kind (e.g., culture), and clinics are also nested within counties? Should each of these be conceptualized as a three-level model? Unfortunately, in terms of simplicity's sake, the answer is "perhaps."

Two important factors need to be considered when deciding about whether to treat observations as nested. First, is there a reason to believe that there is some dependency among observations? For example, does the county in which a clinic is located really matter in terms of how measures might vary or covary? If it does, then county-level effects should be considered. Second, how many units of analysis are there at each level of analysis? When considering this question, it is important to keep in mind that within a multilevel model, each level of analysis represents a sample from a population. If we have clinics nested within counties, before deciding whether to include county as a level of analysis, we need to consider if the number of counties we have constitutes a sample that can be used to make an inference to the population of counties. Two counties would not provide such a sample, whereas 10 counties might. Such decisions need to be made on a case-by-case basis.

There are ways of examining differences across units of analysis even if there aren't enough units to constitute a level of analysis. In some cases, this may mean conducting analyses that are not formal MLM but take into account the possibility that relationships between measures vary across units of analysis. For example, if a cross-culturalist has data from 100 people in two cultures, there are not enough cultures to conduct MLM with people nested within cultures, but other types of analyses can be done—see the section Analyzing Multilevel Data Structures When MLM May Not Be Appropriate or Possible.

In other cases, levels of analysis that one might want to distinguish but for which there are not enough observations can be represented in another level of analysis. For example, in Nezlek et al. (2008), we collected daily diary data from people in four cultural groups. The planned analyses were three-level models, days nested within people who were nested within cultures. Unfortunately, four cultures did not provide a sufficient basis to estimate random effects for culture for the coefficients of interest. In other words, we did not have enough cultures to generalize to the population of cultures. In light of this, culture was represented as an individual-level variable with a series of dummy-codes, and we then compared coefficients across cultures using tests of fixed effects.

When deciding about the structure of an analysis, it is important to keep in mind that at least two lower level observations are needed for each upper level unit. For example, in two-level group study, a group needs at least two people, in a diary study, people need to provide at least two days of data, and so forth. If an upper level unit of analysis has only one lower level observation nested within it, there is no nesting, and there is no way to separate relationships at the different levels of analysis because the sampling is confounded.

Decisions about how many levels of analysis to use often reflect the tension between the law of parsimony (less is more) and the need to account for dependencies among observations. In the previous example of clinics within counties, if I had 15 or 20 counties, I would probably nest clinics within counties to take into account any dependency that might exist. Nevertheless, it is not possible to provide rules that cover all cases. In most cases, the number of levels that should be used will be obvious. When it is not, researchers will need to make decisions based upon previous practice, their knowledge of the subject matter, and perhaps preliminary analyses describing how important it is to take into account different sources (levels) of variance.

At What Level Should a Construct Be Represented?

In most cases, deciding the level of analysis at which a measure should be placed is straightforward. For example, if workers are nested within groups, then worker-level variables such as time on the job would be Level-1 variables, and group-level measures such as group size would be Level-2 variables. In a daily-diary study, day-level data such as daily stressors would be Level-1 data, and person-level data such as personality traits would be Level-2 data.

There may be times when assigning a measure to a level of analysis is not so straightforward. For example, in a study in which students are nested within classes, at what level should student sex be included? If classes have both boys and girls, then student sex is a Level-1 variable. In contrast, if classes are sexually segregated, then student sex would be a Level-2 (or classroom-level) variable.

When making such decisions, the critical issue is whether a measure varies within Level-2 units of analysis. If it does not vary, it is de facto a Level-2 variable. Although sex is an individual characteristic, if classes are sexually segregated, then for statistical purposes, sex is a classroom-level characteristic, similar to variables measuring the teacher of a class. Just as all the students in a particular classroom have the same teacher (part of the dependency captured by MLM), if all the students in a class are of the same sex, then sex becomes a classroom-level variable.

Similarly, measures that represent some type of aggregation of Level-1 measures can be treated as Level-2 measures. For example, if a measure of group cohesion based upon the similarity of scores of the individuals within a group is calculated for each group, then such a cohesion measure is a Level-2 measure because it is the same for all members of a group. The measure that served as the basis for the measure of cohesion is still treated as a Level-1 variable because there is within-group variability.

Cross-Classified and Multiple Membership Analyses

So far, this chapter has concerned nested data structures in which the nesting is straightforward and consistent. Students have been treated as nested within classrooms or schools, clients as nested within a therapist or clinic, and so forth. Nevertheless, students can change schools, and clients can change therapists. Within MLM, when the Level-2 unit within which a Level-1 observation is nested changes, this is called multiple membership. In contrast, cross-classification occurs when a Level-1 unit cannot be uniquely classified into two different classification schemes. The classic example of this is when students are treated as nested within schools and schools are treated as nested within neighborhoods, but some schools have children from different neighborhoods. There are modeling techniques that are appropriate for cross-classified and multiple membership data, and the details of how to conduct and interpret such analyses are beyond the scope of an introduction such as this. Interested readers are encouraged to consult Raudenbush and Bryk (2002) and Rabash et al. (2009) for details.

Nevertheless, when the number of cross-classified or multiple membership cases is very small, it may be appropriate to drop such cases to simplify the analyses. Such a procedure should be followed cautiously and should be included in descriptions of the analyses of the data in question. For example, multiple membership may be a meaningful datum in and of itself. Dissatisfied clients may be more likely to switch therapists than satisfied clients. If such is the case, analyses that did not include multiple membership clients could provide biased parameter estimates. The extent of such a bias would depend upon the number of cases that were dropped.

When to Use and Not to Use MLM: Relying on ICCs

Some scholars have suggested that decisions about using MLM versus comparable OLS regression should be based upon the intraclass correlations (ICC) for a set of measures. The ICC is a ratio of the between-unit variance (Level-2 variance) to the total variance (levels 1 and 2 combined). The argument (more or less) is that if there is not enough between-group variance (i.e., the ICC is low) for a measure or set of measures, then the grouped structure of the data can be ignored.

My advice regarding when to use multilevel analyses is quite simple and contrasts sharply with this position. Multilevel analyses should be used when a researcher has a multilevel (or nested) data structure of some kind. Full stop. Although apparently sensible, I do not believe that recommendations about when to use MLM based on ICCs have a sound basis.

First, and foremost, ICCs provide no indication about how relationships between variables might vary across groups. Such a possibility is represented by the data presented in Table 10.3. Assume six groups of individuals, each measured on two variables, x and y. In the data presented in the table, the ICC for both measures is 0. There is no between-group variability in either measure, and the mean for both variables is 15 in all groups. If you ignore the nested structure of the data and treat the observations as individual observations, the correlation between x and y is 0. Moreover, if you add a dummy-coded variable representing group membership, the LSDV approach described previously, the estimated relationship is also 0.

Nonetheless, inspection of these data reveals that the relationship between x and y is not 0. It is perfectly negative in groups 1, 2 and 3, and perfectly positive in groups 4, 5, and 6. Admittedly,

TABLE 10.3

Intraclass Correlations and Within-Group Relationships

Group 1		Group 2		Group 3	
x	y	x	y	x	y
13	17	13	17	13	17
14	16	14	16	14	16
15	15	15	15	15	15
16	14	16	14	16	14
17	13	17	13	17	13

Group 4		Group 5		Group 6	
x	y	x	y	x	y
13	13	13	13	13	13
14	14	14	14	14	14
15	15	15	15	15	15
16	16	16	16	16	16
17	17	17	17	17	17

such variability in relationships could be captured by including interaction terms between each of the predictors (we can assume the variable x in this case) and each of the dummy variables. Aside from the awkwardness of such procedures (imagine the model generated with a study of 12 groups with three predictors), such analyses are flawed because they do not take into account the sampling error inherent in a study in which units of analysis are sampled from two populations simultaneously—for example, the group and individual levels.

In addition, it is important to keep in mind that ICCs represent ratios of variances. Even when an ICC is low, there may still be meaningful (absolute) variance at the group level for a data set. Finally, what should the cutoff be for deciding when to use MLM, .20, .15, .30? Any cutoff is arbitrary and is difficult to justify statistically. No doubt, recommendations to ignore the grouped structure of a data set when ICCs are low are well-intended. Why use a more sophisticated technique such as MLM when a more familiar and more accessible technique such as OLS regression will suffice? Although such advice may have been appropriate at one time, given the growing familiarity with MLM and the increased accessibility of programs that can conduct MLM, researchers should use MLM to analyze their data whenever they have a multilevel data structure. Next, I discuss other ways of analyzing nested data structures when it is not appropriate to use MLM.

Analyzing Multilevel Data Structures When MLM May Not Be Appropriate or Possible

Although I am a strong advocate of using MLM to analyze nested data structures, there are times when data are nested and it is not possible to conduct the types of multilevel analyses this chapter concerns. For example, assume a researcher collects data at the individual level in three cultural groups. Technically, such a data structure would call for a two-level model in which individuals were nested within cultures. Although an MLM might be able to be fitted to the data (i.e., an MLM program might be able to analyze the data), MLM would not be appropriate for such a data set because there are not enough Level-2 observations (cultures).

Recall that earlier we considered the fact that in a multilevel data structure observations are simultaneously sampled from two populations, the population represented by the Level-1 sampling (people in this example), and the population represented by the Level-2 sampling (cultures in this example). Three cultures are simply not enough to provide a reasonable basis for making inferences about differences among cultures. How many observations are enough? It is not possible to set hard-and-fast rules for such matters, but researchers can rely on their general knowledge of statistics and inference. Aside from studies that rely on intensive repeated measures from very restricted samples (e.g., single-case studies), most researchers would probably assume that 10 or so observations would be the minimum.

Aside from commonsense notions about what constitutes a reasonable basis for drawing inferences about a population, another way to tell if MLM is not appropriate for a particular data set is to consider how well the data can estimate random effects. Assuming that coefficients are theoretically random, if there is not enough information in a data set to estimate any random error terms, then there might not be enough observations to provide the information needed to estimate random effects. For psychologists, such problems will often consist of an insufficient number of Level-2 observations (e.g., cultures, classrooms, clinics).

When considering alternatives to MLM when analyzing a multilevel data structure, researchers should note the following. The inability to estimate random error terms can/should be used as a justification only when the number of cases is small—for example, when the number of Level-2 units is small (certainly less than 10). This is because it can be difficult to estimate random error terms (particularly for slopes) even when there are many observations at both levels of analysis. The ability to estimate random error terms is only one consideration. The data structure itself is the most important thing to consider.

If a researcher decides that MLM is not appropriate for a multilevel data structure, there are reasonable alternatives. The important feature of the alternatives I recommend is that they allow for the possibility that relationships among Level-1 measures vary across Level-2 units of analysis. Returning to our three-culture example, one way of analyzing these data in a single level would be to conduct what is called a "regression by groups" analysis. A regression equation is estimated for each group (each culture in our example), and the similarity of these equations is compared with a F-ratio. Alternatively, dummy- or contrast-codes representing the interaction of culture and various predictors could be entered into an OLS regression, that is, a moderated regression. Also, correlations can be calculated for each culture and compared with a Fisher's r-z transform, and means can be compared with a one-way analysis of variance.

Although such procedures can provide significance tests of differences between groups, and significance tests of within-group relationships, it is essential to recognize their limitations. Most important, the inference of such analyses is limited to the specific groups being studied. Assume we have collected data from Spain, Greece, and the United States. A regression-by-groups analysis would allow us to conclude if coefficients from the Spanish sample were different from coefficients from the Greek or U.S. samples and so forth. Nevertheless, we could not make any inferences beyond these samples, and we could not model the differences across the samples, that is, examine how country-level differences "map onto" the differences we found between the three groups. The differences between the cultures could not be explained statistically because three cultures would not constitute a sufficient basis for making inferences about cultures in general.

CONDUCTING MULTILEVEL ANALYSES

Building a Model

The first analysis should be a model that has no predictors at any level of analysis. Such models are called "unconditional" or "null" models. Such unconditional models provide the basic descriptive statistics for a multilevel analysis. Although unconditional models typically do not test hypotheses, they provide valuable information about how the total variance of a measure is distributed across the levels of a model. Understanding the distribution of variance can also provide some ideas about how productive analyses at different levels of a model might be. For example, if most of the variance of a measure is at Level-1, it may be difficult to analyze differences in Level-1 means (intercepts) at Level-2. Note that "it may be difficult" does not imply that it will not be possible. Small amounts of variance at any level of analysis may still provide a sufficient basis for further analyses at that level. Most multilevel modelers agree that Level-1 models should be finalized before Level-2 differences in Level-1 coefficients are examined. In this instance, finalized refers to the selection of predictors and the specification of the error structure. Specifying error structures is discussed in the section Modeling Random Error.

Another important recommendation for model building is to "forward-step" rather than "backward-step" models, particularly at Level-1. Forward-stepping refers to a process that begins with the simplest model to which predictors are added one by one (or in small numbers), with tests of significance at each step. Predictors that are not statistically significant are removed from the model and then new predictors are added. Backward-stepping refers to a process in which all possible predictors are added at the outset and predictors that are not statistically significant are removed sequentially.

Although backward-stepping procedures may be common in OLS regression, because MLM analyses estimate more parameters than seemingly comparable OLS regressions, backward-stepping procedures may tax what some statisticians refer to as the "carrying capacity" of the data. In MLM, the number of parameters that are estimated increases nonlinearly as a function of the number of predictors. For example, in the basic Level-1 model, $y_{ij} = \beta_{0j} + r_{ij}$, three parameters are estimated, a fixed and random effect for the intercept ($\gamma_{00} + \mu_0$), and the Level-1 variance (r). If a predictor is added, $y_{ij} = \beta_{0j} + \beta_{1j}(x) + r_{ij}$, six parameters are estimated, a fixed and random effect for both the intercept and the slope (four), the covariance between the two random effects (one), and the Level-1 variance. If a second predictor is added, $y_{ij} = \beta_{0j} + \beta_{1j}(x_1) + \beta_{2j}(x_2) + r_{ij}$, 10 parameters are estimated, a fixed and random effect for the intercept and the two slopes (six), the covariances between the three random effects (three), and the Level-1 variance.

When adding predictors at Level-2, the norm is to have (initially) the same Level-2 predictors for each Level-1 coefficient. For example, if a Level-1 model had two predictors, $y_{ij} = \beta_{0j} + \beta_{1j}(x_1) + \beta_{2j}(x_2) + r_{ij}$, then three coefficients, the intercept and two slopes would be brought up to Level-2. If a Level-2 variable, Z, is used to model the intercept, $\beta_{0j} = \gamma_{00} + \gamma_{01}(Z) + \mu_{0j}$, then the other coefficients (the two slopes) should also be modeled as a function of Z—for example,

$\beta_{1j} = \gamma_{10} + \gamma_{11}(Z) + \mu_{1j}$ and $\beta_{2j} = \gamma_{20} + \gamma_{21}(Z) + \mu_{2j}$. The reason for doing this is that if Z is not included as a predictor for a coefficient, it is assumed that there is no relationship between that coefficient and Z. Because all coefficients in a model are being estimated simultaneously (including the covariances between coefficients), the failure to include a relationship between Z and a Level-1 coefficient may lead to a misspecified model.

This discussion of model building has focused on the technical aspects of MLM. How an analyst chooses to build a model needs to reflect the substantive questions at hand and what is considered to be best practice in a specific discipline.

Centering

Centering refers to the reference value used to estimate a slope for a predictor. For analysts whose primary experience is with OLS regression, centering can be a bit difficult to understand. In most OLS analyses, variables are centered around the sample mean, and the unstandardized intercept represents the expected value for an observation that has a value of 0 on all the predictors in a model. In contrast, within the multilevel framework, different types of centering options are available, and choosing among these options is far from automatic. A more detailed discussion of this topic and recommendations for choosing among different options can be found in Enders and Tofighi (2007).

At the upper level of analysis in a model (e.g., Level-2 in a two-level model and Level-3 in a three-level model), predictors can be centered in one of two ways, grand-mean-centered and zero-centered (sometimes referred to as uncentered). When a Level-2 predictor is grand-mean-centered, coefficients for predictors represent relationships based on deviations from the total sample mean of each predictor, and the intercept represents the expected value for an observation at the total sample mean of a predictor or set of predictors. Returning to the students within classes example used previously, if student performance is modeled as a function of teacher experience (years of teaching) as a continuous variable ($\beta_{0j} = \gamma_{00} + \gamma_{01}(experience) + \mu_{0j}$), and Experience was entered grand-mean-centered, then the Level-2 intercept of intercepts (γ_{00}) would represent the expected score for a student who had a teacher with the mean experience for the teachers in the sample.

When a Level-2 predictor is entered uncentered, coefficients for predictors represent relationships based on deviations from scores of 0 on the predictors, and the intercept represents the expected value for an observation that has a score of 0 on a predictor or set of predictors. Continuing the previous example, if sex of teacher was included at Level-2 by using a dummy-coded variable *male* (coded 1 for men, 0 for women, $\beta_{0j} = \gamma_{00} + \gamma_{01}(male) + \mu_{0j}$), and *male* was entered uncentered, then the Level-2 intercept of intercepts (γ_{00}) would represent the expected score for a female teacher (i.e., a teacher for whom *male* = 0).

At lower levels of analysis (e.g., Level-1 in a two-level model and levels-1 and 2 in a three-level model) there is a third option: Predictors can be *group-mean-centered* (sometimes referred to as centered within clusters, or CWC). When a predictor is group-mean-centered coefficients for predictors represent relationships based on deviations from the group mean of a predictor, and the intercept represents the expected value for an observation at the group mean of a predictor or set of predictors. Note that in this instance, the term *group* refers to a Level-2 unit of analysis (in a two-level model) or to units of analysis at levels 2 or 3 in a three-level model.

An important difference between group-mean centering and zero- and grand-mean centering is that when a predictor is group-mean-centered, parameter estimates are controlled for group-level differences in predictors, that is, group-level differences in means of predictors do not contribute to parameter estimates. For example, assume a diary study in which daily well-being is regressed onto daily stress. If daily stress is entered group-mean-centered, individual differences in daily stress do not influence estimates of coefficients. When predictors are group-mean-centered, the resulting coefficients are conceptually similar to the coefficients that would be estimated if a regression analysis was conducted for each Level-2 unit because predictors are estimated using deviations from the mean of each predictor in each Level-2 unit.

Centering is a critical aspect of a multilevel model because the meaning of intercepts and slopes can change dramatically as a function of changes in centering. In some senses, centering is more critical for Level-1 predictors than for Level-2 predictors (in a two-level model) because when considering centering at Level-1, the fact that Level-1 coefficients are "passed up" to Level-2 must be kept in mind. For example, assume a study of student achievement (y) in which boys and girls are nested within classrooms with the following Level-1 model. In this model, *Male* is a dummy-coded variable coded 1 for boys and 0 for girls.

$$y_{ij} = \beta_{0j} + \beta_{1j}(male) + r_{ij} \qquad (10.6)$$

If *male* is entered as an uncentered predictor, the intercept represents the expected score for girls in a classroom (i.e., when *male* = 0). If *male* is entered grand-mean-centered, the intercept now represents the classroom mean for achievement adjusted for between class differences in the distribution of boys and girls. If *male* is entered group mean-centered, then the intercept simply represents the mean for each class unadjusted for differences in sex distributions of classes. Enders and Tofighi (2007, p. 138) provided an algebraic explanation of this. Note that if a Level-1 predictor is standardized across all the observations in a data set and is entered as an uncentered predictor, it is in fact being entered as a grand-mean-centered predictor because standardizing is a form of centering based on the mean.

Regarding recommendations for when to use what type of centering, Raudenbush and Bryk (2002) noted that "no single rule covers all cases" (p. 34), so analysts will need to decide how to center predictors based on the data they have and the hypotheses of interest. Nevertheless, a few broad recommendations are possible. Generally, at Level-2, continuous predictors should be entered grand-mean-centered. If a continuous measure is entered uncentered, then the intercept represents the expected outcome for a Level-2 unit that has a score of 0 on a predictor, something that may not make much sense if a scale does not have a 0 point. If on the other hand, a Level-2 predictor has a valid 0 point (or can be transformed so that it does), entering it uncentered makes more sense. Categorical predictors (dummy or contrast/effect codes) should usually be entered uncentered to maintain the interpretability of the intercept. In general, how predictors "behave" at Level-2 can be thought of in the same way that one would think of predictors within the context of OLS regression.

Deciding how to center at Level 1 (and at Level-1 and Level-2 in a three-level model) is somewhat more complex because the coefficients from Level-1 will be brought up to Level-2. If an analyst is interested in what would be the multilevel equivalent of conducting a regression analysis for each Level-2 unit and using the resulting coefficients as dependent measures in another analysis, then Level-1 predictors should be group-mean-centered. Such analyses take out of the model Level-2 differences in Level-1 predictors. Similar to the diary study example provided previously, in a study of work groups in which individual-level productivity was modeled as a function of individual differences in job satisfaction, group-level differences in job satisfaction would not contribute to parameter estimates.

There is some disagreement regarding whether group means of Level-1 predictors should be included at Level-2 when predictors are group-mean-centered. At present, it is difficult to provide a clear recommendation regarding this, although it is worth noting that most analysts in personality and social psychology (the types of analyses with which I am more familiar) do not enter the means of group-mean-centered predictors at Level-2. Whether this norm is observed in all disciplines is another matter. Regardless, analysts who are concerned about this should run models with and without these means included to determine what impact their inclusion or exclusion has on their models, with particular attention to the impact on the substantive questions at hand.

Grand-mean-centering predictors at Level-1 adjusts the intercept for each group for group level differences in predictors. At times such adjustments are appropriate. For example, assume a school administrator wants to reward teacher performance as defined by students' success on a math test. Further assume that, on average, boys are better than girls in math, and that the number of boys and girls is not equal across classes. Such a combination would mean that teachers who had more boys in their classes would have higher average math scores than teachers who had fewer boys, assuming that all teachers were equally competent (i.e., that teacher characteristics were not related to math achievement). If some type of coded variable representing student sex was entered grand-mean-centered at Level-1, the average score in each class (the intercept) would then be adjusted for differences between classes in the number of boys and girls, allowing our administrator to have an estimate of student performance that was not confounded by differences in the gender composition of classes.

It is important to note that when Level-1 predictors are grand-mean-centered, it is incorrect to use reductions in error variances to estimate the effect sizes of Level-1 relationships. When Level-1 predictors are grand-mean-centered, between-group (Level-2) variance is introduced into the Level-1 model, meaning that relationships at Level-1 reflect a mix of variances at both levels of analysis. Finally, Level-1 predictors can be entered uncentered causing the intercept to represent the expected value in each group for an observation with a value of 0 on the predictor. This is analogous to how centering affects the intercept in Level-2 models, as explained previously.

Modeling Random Error

For each coefficient in a model, MLM can estimate a fixed effect and a random error term. The fixed effect is the focus of most hypotheses. It is an estimate of the relationship between a predictor and an outcome. Is the coefficient significantly different from 0? The random error term represents the separation of true and random error, and a coefficient for which a reliable random error term can be estimated is described as *randomly varying*. Although random errors are usually not the focus of hypotheses per se, it is important to estimate random errors properly because in MLM all coefficients are estimated simultaneously. An improperly specified random error structure can lead to inaccurate estimates of the fixed effects, or in more formal terms, a misspecified model.

Specifying error terms in MLM can be challenging. In OLS analyses, there is one error term in a model, whereas in MLM, each Level-1 coefficient can have its own error term, and the covariances between these error terms are also estimated. In a two-level model with a single predictor at Level-1, there is an error term for both the intercept and the slope. The simultaneous estimation of such errors is part of the reason MLM provides more accurate parameter estimates than comparable OLS techniques.

Although the guidelines I discuss here may not be the norm in all disciplines, this description should provide a good starting point. At the basic level, I recommend deleting from a model error terms that are not significant. "Not significant" in this instance means that they cannot be estimated with a reasonable degree of certainty. For most statistical tests, a reasonable degree of certainty is $p < .05$, but for decisions about the inclusion or exclusion of error terms, a more relaxed standard such as $p < .10$ is probably better. This more relaxed standard reflects the fact that, in most cases, the coefficients are theoretically random, and they should be modeled as such if possible. If a random error term cannot be estimated at all reliably ($p > .20$), then it should be deleted from the model so that the information contained in the data can be used to estimate other parameters. When a random error term is not modeled for a coefficient, the coefficient is described as having been *fixed*.

In most cases, the addition of Level-2 variables will not change the statistical significance of random error terms of the coefficients being brought up from Level-1. When adding a Level-2 predictor changes the statistical significance of the random error term for a Level-1 slope, analysts need to determine why this occurred. For example, including a Level-2 predictor for a Level-1 slope may account for sufficient variance in that slope to render nonsignificant a random error term that was statistically significant without the Level-2 predictor. More important, analysts need to determine if the inclusion or exclusion of such random error terms make a difference in the coefficients that are the focus of the model—which are usually the fixed effects.

There is considerable confusion about what a nonsignificant random error term means. In the truest sense, it means that there is not sufficient information in the data to separate true (fixed) variability from random variability. It does not mean that a coefficient does not vary at all. It means that the random variability cannot be modeled. This confusion is increased by the fact that when a coefficient is fixed, the estimated (fitted) values for that coefficient will all be the same because no residual Bayes estimate has been estimated for that coefficient. Bayes estimates require random effects.

Regardless, it is possible (and completely acceptable statistically) to model differences in fixed coefficients. The inability to model random variability does not mean that fixed variability cannot be modeled. If the random error term associated with a Level-1 coefficient is not significant, the error term can be dropped from the model, but this does not preclude adding a Level-2 predictor to that part of the model. When the variability in a fixed coefficient is modeled in this way, the coefficient is described as *nonrandomly varying*.

Curious readers can conduct two analyses and examine the residual files to understand this further. As discussed above, for fixed coefficients that are not modeled at Level-2, the fitted values will not vary, whereas if a Level-2 predictor is included the fitted values will vary. The ability to model variability in fixed coefficients reflects the fact that the information provided by the Level-2 predictor provides a basis to allow this. Admittedly, there are differences between nonrandomly varying coefficients and randomly varying coefficients whose variability is modeled at Level-2, but nonrandomly varying coefficients can be informative.

Although deciding if a random effect should be included in a model may be straightforward conceptually, testing random error terms for significance is not so straightforward because a random effect cannot be less than 0. As discussed by McCoach et al. (2018), different programs provide different tests of the significance of random effects. The program HLM (Raudenbush et al., 2019) provides the most straightforward test, a χ^2 based test, and readers are encouraged to familiarize themselves with how the software they use implements such tests. Moreover, readers are encouraged to be aware of how the software they use models covariances among error terms, that is, the error structure.

Interactions/Moderation

Within the multilevel framework, interactions can occur either between or within levels. Between-level interactions (sometimes referred to as cross-level interactions or cross-level moderation) occur when a relationship at a lower-level of analysis varies as a function of a measure at a level of analysis above it. In a diary study, a Level-1 (within-person) relationship might vary as a function of a Level-2 (person-level) variable such as a personality characteristic. Different programs have different procedures to conduct such "slopes as outcomes analyses," but assuming the same model is being tested, different programs will produce the same results. Such cross-level interactions were discussed previously in the section on basic models.

Testing interactions among predictors at the top level of a model is pretty much the same as testing interactions within OLS regression, and analysts are advised to consult Aiken and West (1991) and McCabe and King (Chapter 5, this volume). In such cases, the dependent measure is simply a coefficient that has been "brought up" from a lower level of analysis.

Testing interactions among predictors that are all at the same lower level of analysis (e.g., all at Level-1 in a two-level model) is conceptually similar to testing interactions at the top level of analysis, but there are important procedural differences. Consistent with the recommendations of Aiken and West (1991), for categorical predictors, I recommend simply multiplying them and entering the product uncentered into the model. This can help clarify the results because the intercept remains the expected value for an observation with a value of 0 on the predictors.

Aiken and West (1991) recommended centering continuous measures before multiplying them to create interaction terms. Consistent with this, my recommendation is to center continuous Level-1 measures within their corresponding Level-2 unit, that is, group-mean-centered. If they are not centered, problems can arise (e.g., in the multilevel setting collinearity among error terms), and if they are grand-mean-centered, then Level-2 variability in the Level-1 predictors is introduced into the Level-1 interaction term.

The procedure for creating such interaction terms varies from program to program. For example, in HLM, within-level interaction terms (within any level of analysis) need to be created outside of the HLM program and read into the save file the program uses for analysis. Regardless, when interaction terms involving centered continuous measures are entered into an analysis, I recommend entering them *uncentered* because the centering has already taken place. Moreover, entering variables representing interactions uncentered, when combined with group mean-centered predictors, simplifies the calculation of predicted values, a topic discussed in the section Preparing Papers for Publication. A detailed discussion of this topic can be found in Nezlek (2011, pp. 36–41).

Testing within-level interactions within the multilevel framework has not received that much attention in the literature, but the recommendations I provide here are consistent with what many consider to be good practice. Norms about best practice may vary across disciplines, but the issues I address here should provide, at the least, a good starting point.

Model Diagnostics and Model Fits

Occasionally, models will not converge. Similar to structural equation modeling (SEM) and other techniques that estimate solutions, the maximum likelihood estimation algorithms that are at the heart of MLM programs fit a model (a set of estimated coefficients and parameters) then change these estimates to improve the fit of the model—to get the model to fit the data more closely. When improvements of a certain size are reached, the algorithm stops. The size of the improvement that stops the algorithm is known as the convergence criterion. Sometimes, this convergence criterion cannot be reached, and an analysis will keep running until a certain number of iterations are reached. Virtually all programs allow the user to specify the convergence criterion and the number of iterations. Although there is no hard and fast rule, "solid" models will often converge in a few hundred iterations or less.

My experience is that problems with model convergence invariably reflect some type of problem with estimating error terms. Most of the time this is due to a "bad" error term (or terms), that is, error terms that cannot be estimated reliably. What occurs is that the program is trying to make improvements when improvement is not possible, and it gets caught in a loop. Occasionally (but not commonly), convergence problems are due to very high correlations between error terms. Although each of a pair of error terms might be able to be estimated reliably, if the correlation between them is too high, the algorithm will "get stuck." In my experience, such problems can occur only when correlations are very high, .98 and above.

When convergence problems are due to a bad error term, error terms that cannot be estimated reliably can be dropped from the model. The remedy is not so straightforward when convergence problems are due to an inestimable error covariance and both the error terms involved in the problematic covariance are significant. Some programs allow analysts to fix specific error covariances, and fixing a covariance would solve such a problem. If an analyst does not want to fix a covariance, then one of the error terms creating the problem can be dropped. Deciding which term to drop can be done on the basis of the impact dropping the term has on the model—less impact being more desirable than more impact.

Although the advent of high-speed computing means that even models that require thousands of iterations to converge can run fairly quickly (a matter of minutes for many analyses), analysts may want to terminate an analysis before convergence and examine the output to diagnose what is responsible when a model does not converge. My experience has been that premature termination has virtually no effect on the fixed effects in a model when convergence problems are due to problems with the error structure. For example, the fixed effects may be virtually identical for models that have run through 500 and 2,500 iterations, and so "early" models can be examined for problems with error structures.

Models may also not work because of problems with the fixed effects. Such problems are not estimation problems per se; rather they are more structural. Similar to OLS regression, if predictors are linearly dependent, a model will not converge. For example, a model will not run if a dependent measure, y, is predicted by x, z, and $x + z$. Most analysts will be experienced enough to avoid problems due to the collinearity resulting from using linear combinations of variables in an analysis, but analysts may encounter such problems when they retain the intercept in what is meant to be a "zero-intercept" model. When conducting zero-intercept models, analysts need to be certain to delete the intercept, hence the other term for such models, "no-intercept." Some applications of zero-intercept models can be found in Nezlek (2003, 2007a).

Although MLM analyses provide measures of overall model fit (a deviance statistic), unlike the tradition for SEM, fit indices do not figure prominently in the evaluation of MLM results. In MLM, the emphasis is less on the overall fit of the model (i.e., how well a model captures all of the hypothesized relationships among a set of measures) than it is on specific coefficients—for example, is the relationship between two Level-1 variables significant, does it vary as a function of a Level-2 variable, and so forth? There are situations when the fits of different models need to be compared, and deviance statistics can be used when this is necessary, but a discussion of such possibilities is well beyond the scope of this chapter. See Raudenbush and Bryk (2002) for a discussion of the questions that can be addressed by comparing the fits of different models.

SELECTED TOPICS

Missing Data

Understanding missing data within the multilevel framework requires consideration of what type of data are missing at what level of analysis. At Level-1, it is important to recognize that missing units of analysis are not missing data even though they might be considered as missing within other frameworks. For example, in a diary study in which participants are asked to provide data for 14 days, within the MLM framework, a participant who provided only 10 days of data would not be considered to have 4 days of missing data. Just as classes might have different numbers of students, individuals can have different numbers of diary entries (days, interactions, etc.). The available Level-1 observations are simply nested within the corresponding Level-2 observations.

In contrast, if participants were expected to answer a set of questions about self-esteem each day, and some participants did not answer these questions on some days (although they answered other questions), the absence of responses to the self-esteem items would be classified as missing data. Most programs easily accommodate missing data at Level-1. Sometimes, analysts might want to use listwise deletion to ensure that all analyses are based on the same set of observations. Alternatively, pairwise deletion can be used so that units of analysis are included in an analysis if they have valid observations for all the variables included in a specific analysis.

Missing data at Level-2 in a two-level model (and Level-2 and Level-3 in a three-level model) are another matter. If a Level-2 unit has a missing value on a variable that is included in a model, all the Level-1 cases associated with that Level-2 unit are eliminated from the analysis. For example, in a diary study in which days are nested within persons, if an individual has a missing value on a person-level measure (e.g., a trait), and that trait is included as a predictor at Level-2, that person and all the day-level entries associated with that person are excluded from the analysis.

Given this, analysts may want to estimate missing data to maximize the number of observations that are included in an analysis (see Chapter 2, this volume, for a discussion of estimating missing data). Regardless, analysts need to understand exactly how the software they are using treats missing data.

Standardization

By design, MLM analyses produce *unstandardized* estimates of coefficients, and most programs do not produce standardized estimates. Recently, Hamaker and Muthén (2020) discussed ways to estimate standardized slopes in MLM, and interested readers can consult this for guidance. Although other procedures to standardize coefficients have been proposed (e.g., dividing a coefficient by some type of variance estimate), such procedures are probably, at best, at the edge of being justified statistically. Nevertheless, there are ways to reduce the influence on parameter estimates of differences in the variances of measures, which makes coefficients more readily comparable.

Standardizing Level-2 variables is straightforward and puts all continuous Level-2 measures on the same metric. In studies when observations are nested within persons (e.g., diary studies), this could entail standardizing trait measures such as the five factor model, and the same type of standardization could be used when Level-2 units are not persons (e.g., clinics, schools, or work groups). Analysts will need to make such decisions about such matters based upon what makes sense within their home disciplines. For example, standardizing measures of personality at Level-2 is probably easily understood by personality psychologists who may be accustomed to interpreting regression analyses by estimating predicted values ± 1 SD from the mean. One of the advantages of standardization at Level-2 is that coefficients for Level-2 predictors represent the change in a Level-1 coefficient associated with a 1 SD increase in the Level-2 predictor. Another advantage is that differences in the variances of Level-2 predictors do not contribute to significance tests of differences between Level-2 coefficients. Testing differences between coefficients is the section Comparing Coefficients.

Standardizing Level-1 variables is not quite so straightforward. Simply standardizing in terms of the total population equates the total variances of different predictors; however, it does not equate the distribution of these variances. Moreover, analysts need to be mindful of the fact that when measures are standardized in terms of the total sample, entering a predictor uncentered is equivalent to entering it grand-mean-centered. Analysts are advised to avoid standardizing Level-1 variables within Level-2 units. For example, if students were nested within schools, it would not be appropriate to standardize scores within each school. The reason for this is that standardizing in this fashion eliminates from the model differences between Level-2 units in Level-1 measures, and such differences can be important sources of information. In general, covariance modelers prefer to work with raw data rather than standardized data because raw data have more information.

Weighted Analyses

Assigning weights to observations is not common practice for many researchers in psychology, but it is a necessity for some. Regardless, weights can be used to adjust parameter estimates for nonrepresentative samples, whether by design (intentional oversampling) or by accident. Within the multilevel framework, different weights can be used at different levels of analysis. For example, most cross-national surveys such as the European Social and World Values Surveys provide both within- and between-country weights, and analysts are strongly encouraged to use them. If weights are not provided, analysts will need to create their own, a topic that is beyond the scope of this chapter. Regardless, analysts who want to weight observations will need to determine how to do this using the software they use to conduct MLM.

Power Analysis

Estimating the power of MLM designs is considerably more complex than estimating power for most single-level designs. The power of a MLM design is influenced by the size of the fixed effects, the number of Level-1 and Level-2 observations, the distributions of variance of Level-1 measures, the random error terms associated with the fixed effects and their covariances, and of course, the Type I and Type II error rates (I think I have included most of the factors that need to be considered). At least at present, one cannot find the power of MLM designs in tables.

At present, it seems that the best way to estimate power in MLM is to conduct simulations. Such a procedure, using a combination of SAS and Mplus within the context of diary studies, is described by Bolger and Laurenceau (2013). A similar description using R is described by Nezlek and Mroziński (2020). Interestingly, for diary studies, both sets of authors conclude that about 2 weeks of data for just over 100 participants provides good power for detecting cross-level interactions.

For design purposes, simulations suggest that increasing Level-2 units increases power more than increasing Level-1 units. Of course, there is the law of diminishing returns, and the increased power resulting from increasing the number of Level-2 units from 50 to 100 is greater than the increased power resulting from increasing the number of Level-2 units from 100 to 150, and so forth. More is always better, but a lot more is not necessarily a lot better.

When thinking of the power of MLM design, I offer the following general guidelines. Also see Nezlek (2012, pp. 22–24). Intercepts are generally more reliable than slopes, which means that a study will have more power to detect relationships between Level-2 predictors and Level-1 intercepts than to detect relationships between Level-2 predictors and Level-1 slopes. In terms of examining cross-level interactions, power is determined by how large a slope is (fixed effect) and how reliable it is (random effect). See Kelley et al. (Volume 1, Chapter 10, this handbook) for a discussion of power analysis.

Effect Size Estimation

Often, researchers want to describe their results in terms of what are commonly called *effect sizes*, which, in the OLS framework, are based upon variance estimates. For example, a correlation of .5 can also be explained in terms of the fact that two measures share 25% of their variance. Within the OLS framework, estimating effect sizes using such shared variances or reductions in variance from one model to another is well-understood and is not controversial.

In contrast, within the multilevel context, estimating effect sizes using shared variances or reductions in variance is not straightforward. For example, at Level-1, it is possible to add a significant predictor without changing the residual variance. Within the OLS framework, such a situation is not possible. For OLS analyses, significance tests are based upon reductions in residual variances, and if a predictor is statistically significant, some reduction in residual variance needs to be associated with the inclusion of this predictor in a model.

Nevertheless, effect sizes can be estimated using residual variances in MLM. For example, if the Level-1 residual variance from an unconditional model is .80, and the residual variance from a model with a Level-1 predictor is .40, this represents a 50% reduction in variance. Similar calculations can be for Level-2 coefficients, keeping in mind that coefficients have their own error terms and will have their own effect size estimates.

Rights and Sterba (2019) provided a detailed description of different ways that effect sizes can be estimated in MLM. Although they provided numerous ways to estimate effect sizes, I suspect that many analysts probably will be interested in what Rights and Sterba labeled $r_w^{(f1v)}$ for Level-1 relationships and $r_b^{(f2)}$ for Level-2 relationships. These estimates are more or less equivalent to calculating the differences in residual variances from models at the same levels of analysis that have different predictors, the technique I just described. Regardless, as discussed by Rights and Sterba, analysts need to keep in mind how much of the total variability of an outcome is explained by models at each level of analysis.

Moreover, when estimating effect sizes for Level-1 models, predictors should be entered *group-mean-centered* (e.g., Kreft & de Leeuw, 1998). If predictors are entered grand-mean-centered or uncentered, Level-2 differences in the predictors will contribute to the Level-1 variance estimates. If multiple coefficients are brought up from a lower level of analysis, such estimates need to be made for each coefficient. Note also that if a Level-1 coefficient is modeled as fixed (i.e., no random error terms is estimated for it), effect sizes at Level-2 cannot be estimated using variance reductions because there is no variance to reduce.

Nonlinear Analyses

So far, MLM has been discussed in terms of continuous, linear dependent measures, which are probably the most common type of outcome with which psychologists are concerned. Nevertheless, outcomes of interest may be nonlinear. They could be categorical—for example, recidivism (yes or no)—or they could be continuous, but not normally distributed, such as peer nominations of students in classrooms.

Analyses of nonlinear outcomes require special techniques that take into account the fact that such outcomes violate a critical assumption of MLM, the independence of means and variances. For example, the variance of a binomial outcome is Npq, where N is the number of observations, p is the probability of the event, and q is $1 - p$. Other types of nonlinear outcomes (e.g., multinomial outcomes) also violate this assumption. In terms of MLM, this means that the variance of a Level-1 outcome for a Level-2 unit will vary as a function of the mean outcome within each Level-2 unit.

Similar to the need to conduct logistical regression for nonlinear outcomes in single-level data structures (see Chapter 9, this volume, for a discussion of logistical regression), MLM analyses of nonlinear outcomes require techniques that eliminate relationships between means and variances. The underlying logic of modeling nonlinear outcomes is the same as that for linear outcomes, but the algorithms differ, and the specific algorithms vary as a function of the type of outcome. For example, analyzing a dichotomous outcome requires the following (Bernoulli) model at Level-1:

$$\text{Prob}(y = 1 | \beta_{0j}) = \phi \quad (10.7)$$

In this model, a coefficient, ϕ, representing the expected log-odds is estimated for each Level-2 unit. These log-odds are then analyzed at Level-2 just as coefficients are for continuous measures, and similar to the analyses of continuous measures, predictors can be added at all levels of analysis. The form of the Level-1 model for noncontinuous outcomes will vary as a function of the nature of the outcome.

Reliability

Reliability estimates are based on covariances, and estimating reliability within the multilevel framework needs to take into account the nested structure of the data. For example, in a diary-style study (or EMA study), when measurement occasions are nested within persons, it is not appropriate to estimate reliabilities based upon means aggregated across occasions because this confounds within- and between-person variances. It is also not appropriate to calculate the reliability for each day of a study and then average the reliability coefficients because this assumes that days can be matched across people, and a basic underlying assumption of the model is that days are randomly sampled.

As discussed by Nezlek (2017), one way to estimate reliability in such a study is to conduct a multivariate MLM in which the items for a scale are nested within occasions which are nested within people. The reliability of the Level-1 intercept is the item level reliability. This technique is based on a simple decomposition of variances and is relatively easy to implement.

One disadvantage of this technique is that it assumes "tau-equivalence," that is, all items are weighted equally. Given that most analysts represent scale scores with item means, such an assumption seems to be consistent with common practice. Nevertheless, this is a strong assumption.

Other, considerably more complicated methods have been proposed that rely on multilevel factor analysis (e.g., Lai, 2021). To my knowledge, no one has determined the circumstances under which such more complicated techniques lead to meaningfully different conclusions than the simpler procedure I just described.

Mediation

Compared to examining mediation in single level data structures, examining mediation within the multilevel context requires specifying the levels of analysis of the X, M, and Y variables. For example, a 1-1-1 model exists when mediation involves only Level-1 observations, whereas a 1-2-1 model exists when X and Y are at Level-1 and the mediator is at Level-2, and so forth. Preacher et al. (2010) proposed a comprehensive framework that relies on SEM to examine mediation in multilevel designs. Although the techniques they propose have been used extensively, McNeish (2017) made a case that the models proposed by Preacher et al. may not be appropriate for smaller samples, such as when the number of Level-2 observations is less than 100.

Warning: examining mediation within the multilevel framework is complicated, even for experienced analysts. I discuss this topic only to provide the barest of introductions.

Comparing Coefficients

In MLM, it is possible to compare coefficients (or sets of coefficients) using what are called tests of fixed effects, which are tests of constraints on a model. For example, assume a Level-1 model with two predictors, $y_{ij} = \beta_{0j} + \beta_{1j}(x_1) + \beta_{2j}(x_2) + r_{ij}$. The strength of the relationship between y and x_1 can be compared to the strength of the relationship between y and x_2 by examining the impact on the fit of a model of constraining these coefficients (γ_{10} and γ_{20}) to be equal. If the constraint significantly reduces the fit, then the coefficients are not equal. Such tests can also be used in conjunction with dummy- and contrast-codes combined with different types of centering options to examine differences across the different categories of a categorical predictor. A discussion of such possibilities is provided in Nezlek (2011, pp. 25–29).

Note that the results of such comparisons are not invariant under transformation. They compare the coefficients estimated given the variances and covariances of the data being analyzed, and changing the variance of a measure will change the results of the test. In contrast, tests of individual coefficients are invariant under linear transformation. I should add that I think that the value of comparing coefficients in MLM is underappreciated.

Using Coefficients Estimated by MLM in Other Analyses

Most MLM programs allow analysts to save the estimated coefficients from analyses, providing the opportunity to use these coefficients in other analyses. Although technically possible, such analyses may not be optimal because when estimated coefficients are used outside of the multilevel framework this does not take advantage of, or take into account, the sampling error at all levels of analysis. There may be instances in which such uses are unavoidable, that is, there may not be a way to examine the hypotheses of interest within the multilevel framework. Nevertheless, analysts are encouraged to find ways to examine their questions of interest within the multilevel framework.

SOME PRACTICAL MATTERS

Preparing Papers for Publication

Norms vary widely among disciplines and journals about what should be reported, and the following guidelines need to be considered in this light.

1. *Structure of the data.* The nesting of the data (what was nested in what) should be described explicitly. This description should include the numbers of observations at each level of analysis, and for lower levels of analysis (e.g., Level-1 in a two-level model) some indication of the distribution of the number of Level-1 observations for Level-2 units (e.g., the *SD*).
2. *Centering.* The type of centering used for each predictor should be described explicitly. Coefficients (and the relationships they represent)

cannot be understood without knowing how predictors were centered.
3. *Error terms.* The basis used to include or exclude error terms should be described explicitly. A clear justification should be provided if coefficients are fixed on other than statistical grounds. Nonetheless, extended discussions of error structures are often unnecessary. Unless hypotheses explicitly concern or involve some aspects of the error structure, extended discussions may distract more than they clarify.
4. *Summary statistics.* The mean and variance estimates provided by unconditional analyses are the basic descriptive statistics for MLM analyses. These should be provided for both dependent and independent measures to provide a context for readers to understand the results.
5. *Model equations.* At present, I think the equations representing the models that were run should be presented. Perhaps after more people become more familiar with MLM, this will not be necessary. Moreover, á la Bryk and Raudenbush, I recommend presenting the equations for each level of an analysis separately. This clarifies what was done, which can be particularly helpful for readers who are not familiar with MLM.
6. *Statistics.* I encourage authors to be follow the maxim that "less is more" when presenting summary statistics. For example, the significance of gamma coefficients (Level-2) that are typically the focus of hypotheses in two-level models, is tested with an approximate t ratio. This t ratio is calculated by dividing an estimate of a fixed effect (gamma) by a standard error. This means that there is no reason to present the gamma, the t ratio, and the standard error. Any two will do. I recommend the γ (the coefficient) and the t ratio, with an accompanying p value.
7. *Predicted values.* It can be very helpful to readers if authors use predicted values to describe their results. For categorical predictors, estimated values can be calculated for different groups. For continuous predictors, coefficients can be estimated for units ± 1 *SD*. Keep in mind that the *SD* for a Level-1 measure is *not* the *SD* of that measure from a single level analysis. The Level-1 *SD* of a measure is the square root of the variance as estimated by an unconditional model. Finally, using predicted values can make real the implications of centering.
8. *Indices of model fits and sequential models.* Rarely do I see a justification for presenting indices of model fits. The fixed effects are the focus of most multilevel hypotheses, and fit indices include both the fixed and random components. Moreover, comparing models that have different fixed effects requires using full (vs. restricted) maximum likelihood estimators, and FML estimators are not as accurate as RML estimators under many conditions. Sequential comparisons of models frequently provide little information above what is available from final models. When they provide additional insights, they are certainly valuable. When they do not, they distract more than they inform.

Authors should carefully consider just how relevant certain aspects of an analysis are to the substantive questions at hand. Different disciplines may have different norms (for good reasons) regarding what details should be reported, and authors will need to recognize the importance of presenting the types of details readers expect or require.

Reading Papers That Use MLM

When reading papers that use MLM, it can be difficult to understand exactly what models were tested and precisely what the results were and what they mean, and this is true for experienced and inexperienced analysts alike. Too many authors provide lots of unnecessary information while not providing essential details. I mention this to provide some comfort to readers who are not very familiar with MLM or who find it difficult to understand an article that uses MLM. The difficulties you experience may not be due to your lack of understanding.

Admittedly, as researchers are becoming more familiar with MLM, this situation is improving over time, but there remains room for improvement.

For those who have limited experience with MLM, it might be useful to read the methods and results keeping in mind the recommendations I made for writing a paper that uses MLM. At a minimum, the data structure should be clear (usually this is the case), and centering and modeling error should be described (these are not described as often as they should be, which is 100% of the time). Once you know what to look for, reading a paper can be less arduous, perhaps even enjoyable.

Software Options

Although MLM can be conducted using various programs, it is important to note that different programs provide the same results assuming *the same models* are specified. The computational algorithms underlying MLM analyses are well understood, and there is broad agreement about their application. Nevertheless, as discussed by McCoach et al. (2018), differences in the defaults and limitations of different packages can lead to different results when what is apparently the same model is tested. Somewhat reassuringly, McCoach et al. found that estimates of fixed effects, which are the primary focus of most hypotheses, are generally consistent across different packages.

Given the large number of software options, I cannot discuss the advantages and disadvantages of each. My primary concerns are that analysts know how to specify the models they want to test and understand the output of their programs. I will note that I have worked with reasonably experienced analysts who have misspecified models (i.e., conducted models that did not test what the analyst wanted them to test) and/or have misinterpreted or misunderstood sometimes critical parts of results.

For those who are unfamiliar with MLM, I recommend starting with a program that is designed to conduct MLM such as HLM. Setting up models and interpreting the output is more straightforward in programs designed to conduct MLM than it is in general purpose programs, and in HLM specifying models is straightforward, and outputs are easy to read. For example, HLM presents error terms and their significance tests very clearly. Once an analyst is familiar with how to conduct and evaluate models, any software can be used, although I caution analysts to take into account differences in how different programs organize outputs and label parameters.

Due to its widespread and increasing use, I briefly discuss using R-modules (R Core Team, 2020) to conduct MLM. R is a powerful platform that provides the tools needed to do analyses that are unavailable in "standard" statistical packages. Nevertheless, with great power comes great responsibility, and I strongly encourage analysts who use R to familiarize themselves with MLM before they use R to analyze their data. It might be useful to conduct an analysis using a program designed to conduct MLM (such as HLM), and see how similar these results are to those produced by what is believed to be the same analysis using R.

For example, some R modules allow analysts to specify parameters that (arguably) should never be specified. In multilevel modules for R, it is possible to enter a Level-1 predictor as group-mean-centered while simultaneously modeling the accompanying random error term based on an uncentered predictor. Also, in most modules, error covariances matrices are not modeled by default. Finally, there is the proliferation of modules that can perform specialized MLM analyses. Although expert analysts may appreciate and understand the differences among them, my guess is that inexperienced analysts do not.

Suggested Readings

Scattered throughout this chapter are references to books, articles, and chapters that should be helpful to those learning MLM. To these, I should add Hox et al. (2018), a thorough and accessible introduction to MLM. In terms of using MLM, I have written two books (Nezlek, 2011, 2012), a series of articles and chapters that were intended for social and personality psychologists (Nezlek, 2001, 2003, 2007a, 2007b, 2008), and a chapter intended for cross-cultural psychologists (Nezlek, 2010). All of these were written for nonexpert readers. I mention these because I am familiar with them; other authors have written excellent texts on these subjects, for example Bolger and

Laurenceau (2013). Although these references are not recent, their coverage is not dated. Similar to the present chapter, they concern basic principles.

There is also an expanding universe of books that discuss how to use specific software to conduct MLM. The following list is meant to be representative, not exhaustive. I am certain there are others and there will be more. Mplus (Finch & Bolin, 2017; Heck & Thomas, 2015), R (Finch et al., 2019), SPSS, Stata, SAS, R, and HLM (Garson, 2020), SPSS (Heck et al., 2014). Bon voyage.

References

Aiken, L. S., & West, S. G. (1991). *Multiple regression: Testing and interpreting interactions.* SAGE Publications.

Bolger, N., & Laurenceau, J.-P. (2013). *Intensive longitudinal methods: An introduction to diary and experience sampling research.* Guilford Press.

Bryk, A. S., & Raudenbush, S. W. (1992). *Hierarchical linear models: Applications and data analysis methods* (2nd ed.). SAGE Publications.

Davidson, H., Jabbari, Y., Patton, H., O'Hagan, F., Peters, K., Cribbie, R., O'Hagan, F., Peters, K., & Cribbie, R. (2019). Statistical software use in Canadian university courses: Current trends and future directions. *Teaching of Psychology, 46*(3), 246–250. https://doi.org/10.1177/0098628319853940

Enders, C. K., & Tofighi, D. (2007). Centering predictor variables in cross-sectional multilevel models: A new look at an old issue. *Psychological Methods, 12*(2), 121–138. https://doi.org/10.1037/1082-989X.12.2.121

Finch, W. H., & Bolin, J. E. (2017). *Multilevel modeling using Mplus.* Chapman and Hall/CRC. https://doi.org/10.1201/9781315165882

Finch, W. H., Bolin, J. E., & Kelley, K. (2019). *Multilevel modeling using R.* Chapman and Hall/CRC. https://doi.org/10.1201/9781351062268

Garson, G. D. (2020). *Multilevel modeling applications in STATA®, IBM® SPSS®, SAS®, R, & HLM.* SAGE Publications.

Goldstein, H. I. (2011). *Multilevel statistical models.* John Wiley & Sons.

Hamaker, E. L., & Muthén, B. (2020). The fixed versus random effects debate and how it relates to centering in multilevel modeling. *Psychological Methods, 25*(3), 365–379. https://doi.org/10.1037/met0000239

Heck, R. H., & Thomas, S. L. (2015). *An introduction to multilevel modeling techniques: MLM and SEM approaches using Mplus* (3rd ed.). Routledge/Taylor & Francis Group. https://doi.org/10.4324/9781315746494

Heck, R. H., Thomas, S. L., & Tabata, L. N. (2014). *Multilevel and longitudinal modeling with IBM SPSS* (2nd ed.). Routledge/Taylor & Francis Group.

Hox, J. J., Moerbeek, M., & van de Schoot, R. (2018). *Multilevel analysis: Techniques and applications* (3rd ed.). Routledge/Taylor & Francis Group.

Kreft, I., & de Leeuw, J. (1998). *Introducing multilevel modeling.* SAGE Publications. https://doi.org/10.4135/9781849209366

Lai, M. H. C. (2021). Composite reliability of multilevel data: It's about observed scores and construct meanings. *Psychological Methods, 26*(1), 90–102. https://doi.org/10.1037/met0000287

McCoach, D. B., Rifenbark, G. G., Newton, S. D., Li, X., Kooken, J., Yomtov, D., Gambino, A. J., & Bellara, A. (2018). Does the package matter? A Comparison of five common multilevel modeling software packages. *Journal of Educational and Behavioral Statistics, 43*(5), 594–627. https://doi.org/10.3102/1076998618776348

McNeish, D. (2017). Multilevel mediation with small samples: A Cautionary note on the multilevel structural equation modeling framework. *Structural Equation Modeling, 24*(4), 609–625. https://doi.org/10.1080/10705511.2017.1280797

Nezlek, J. B. (2001). Multilevel random coefficient analyses of event- and interval-contingent data in social and personality psychology research. *Personality and Social Psychology Bulletin, 27*(7), 771–785. https://doi.org/10.1177/0146167201277001

Nezlek, J. B. (2003). Using multilevel random coefficient modeling to analyze social interaction diary data. *Journal of Social and Personal Relationships, 20*(4), 437–469. https://doi.org/10.1177/02654075030204002

Nezlek, J. B. (2007a). A multilevel framework for understanding relationships among traits, states, situations and behaviours. *European Journal of Personality, 21*(6), 789–810. https://doi.org/10.1002/per.640

Nezlek, J. B. (2007b). Multilevel modeling in research on personality. In R. W. Robins, R. C. Fraley, & R. F. Krueger (Eds.), *Handbook of research methods in personality psychology* (pp. 502–523). Guilford Press.

Nezlek, J. B. (2008). An Introduction to multilevel modeling for social and personality psychology. *Social and Personality Psychology Compass, 2*(2),

842–860. https://doi.org/10.1111/j.1751-9004.2007.00059.x

Nezlek, J. B. (2010). Multilevel modeling and cross-cultural research. In D. Matsumoto & F. J. R. van de Vijver (Eds.), *Cross-Cultural research methods in psychology* (pp. 299–345). Oxford University Press. https://doi.org/10.1017/CBO9780511779381.015

Nezlek, J. B. (2011). *Multilevel modeling for social and personality psychology*. SAGE Publications. https://doi.org/10.4135/9781446287996

Nezlek, J. B. (2012). *Diary methods for personality and social psychology*. SAGE Publications. https://doi.org/10.4135/9781446287903

Nezlek, J. B. (2017). A practical guide to understanding reliability in studies of within-person variability. *Journal of Research in Personality, 69*, 149–155. https://doi.org/10.1016/j.jrp.2016.06.020

Nezlek, J. B., & Mroziński, B. (2020). Applications of multilevel modeling in psychological science: Intensive repeated measures designs. *L'Année Psychologique, 120*(1), 39–72. https://doi.org/10.3917/anpsy1.201.0039

Nezlek, J. B., Sorrentino, R. M., Yasunaga, S., Otsubo, Y., Allen, M., Kouhara, S., & Shuper, P. A. (2008). Cross-cultural differences in reactions to daily events as indicators of cross-cultural differences in self-construction and affect. *Journal of Cross-Cultural Psychology, 39*(6), 685–702. https://doi.org/10.1177/0022022108323785

Preacher, K. J., Zyphur, M. J., & Zhang, Z. (2010). A general multilevel SEM framework for assessing multilevel mediation. *Psychological Methods, 15*(3), 209–233. https://doi.org/10.1037/a0020141

R Core Team. (2020). *R: A language and environment for statistical computing*. https://www.r-project.org/

Rabash, J., Steele, F., Bowne, W. J., & Goldstein, H. (2009). *A user's guide to MLwiN, v2.10*. University of Bristol. https://www.bristol.ac.uk/cmm/media/software/mlwin/downloads/manuals/2-32/manual-web.pdf

Raudenbush, S. W., & Bryk, A. S. (2002). *Hierarchical linear models: Applications and data analysis methods* (2nd ed.). SAGE Publications.

Raudenbush, S. W., Bryk, A. S., Cheong, Y. F., & Congdon, R. (2019). *HLM 8 for Windows* (8.02). Scientific Software International.

Rights, J. D., & Sterba, S. K. (2019). Quantifying explained variance in multilevel models: An integrative framework for defining R-squared measures. *Psychological Methods, 24*(3), 309–338. https://doi.org/10.1037/met0000184

Robinson, W. S. (1950). Ecological correlations and the behavior of individuals. *American Sociological Review, 15*(3), 351–357. https://doi.org/10.2307/2087176

Section 4

METHODS WITH OUTCOMES MEASURED OVER TIME

CHAPTER 11

LONGITUDINAL DATA ANALYSIS

Andrew K. Littlefield

Longitudinal data have been used in various disciplines relating to behavioral and health sciences to address a myriad of research questions. Gold-standard approaches to understanding causality, such as randomized controlled trials that involve experimental manipulation(s), are inherently based on longitudinal data. Within many areas of psychological science, longitudinal data have been collected in the absence of any explicit experimental manipulation(s). These observational research designs involve the repeated assessments of constructs relevant to psychological science, such as measures of cognitive functioning, psychopathology, and personality. Although repeated assessments are often based on self-report measures, longitudinal data are increasing in other areas such as neuroscience (e.g., King et al., 2018).

Advances in the quantitative literature, combined with modern developments in software (e.g., Mplus; Muthén & Muthén, 1998–2017) and various types of research designs (e.g., ecological momentary assessment; Trull & Ebner-Priemer, 2013), have resulted in a plethora of options regarding analytic approaches for various types of longitudinal data. Indeed, across the three volumes of this handbook, there are dedicated chapters on the topics of repeated measures of daily processes (Volume 1, Chapter 16), collecting longitudinal data (Volume 2, Chapter 18), time-series designs (Volume 2, Chapter 34), multilevel modeling (Chapter 10, this volume), event history analysis (Chapter 12, this volume), latent state–trait models (Chapter 13, this volume), latent variable modeling of continuous growth (Chapter 14, this volume), differential equation models of change (Chapter 15, this volume), and estimating change in multiple constructs in three-levels of nested data (Chapter 16, this volume). Table 11.1 provides a representation of some of the more commonly used models and a brief description of their typical use, and Figure 11.1 shows a graphical representation of the models highlighted in Table 11.1.

Given that other chapters in this handbook focus more intensively and extensively on many of these models, the primary goal of this chapter on longitudinal data analyses is to provide an overview of critical issues related to research design and statistical analyses to facilitate an appreciation of repeated measures data. To accomplish this objective, a range of conceptual and methodological issues common to different longitudinal models is presented with the intent of orienting readers toward significant issues in planning, implementing, and interpreting longitudinal research. These issues are foundational and enhance or constrain the ability of a specific longitudinal design and associated statistical model to address specific research questions. When appropriate, any unique features associated with

This is an update to the original chapter by Michael Windle (2012).
https://doi.org/10.1037/0000320-011
APA Handbook of Research Methods in Psychology, Second Edition: Vol. 3. Data Analysis and Research Publication, H. Cooper (Editor-in-Chief)
Copyright © 2023 by the American Psychological Association. All rights reserved.

TABLE 11.1

Longitudinal Data Analytic Techniques and Models

Model	Use
Autoregressive models (Markov simplex models)	Useful to measure rank-order stability of repeatedly measured manifest or latent variables by regressing $t+1$ score on score at t, and allows for the modeling of measurement error and correlated residuals (Curran & Bollen, 2001). Increasingly recognized as providing unclear estimates of between- versus within-person sources of variance when expanded to cross-lagged panel models (e.g., Littlefield et al., 2022).
Latent growth models	Useful to measure intraindividual change trajectories for repeatedly measured data in which individuals may vary in terms of initial levels, rate of change, and final level (Chapter 14, this volume; T. E. Duncan et al., 2006; Meredith & Tisak, 1990)
Multilevel models	Useful to analyze hierarchically structured data with lower level observations nested, or clustered, within higher levels (e.g., repeatedly measured observations nested within individuals; Chapter 10, this volume; Hox, 2010; Raudenbush, 2001)
Mixture models of longitudinal data	Useful to identify subgroups within a population that manifest distinctive change trajectories (Nagin, 2005)
Latent state–trait models	Useful to decompose covariance relations of repeatedly measured manifest or latent variables into components representing across-time common trait variance, time-specific state variance, and error variance (Chapter 13, this volume)
Latent transition analysis	Useful for analyzing categorical manifest variables and discrete latent variables to test stage-sequential models of individual growth (L. M. Collins, 2002)
Event history models	Useful for analyzing longitudinal data regarding the occurrence and timing of discrete, repeatable, and nonrepeatable events (Chapter 12, this volume; Singer & Willett, 2003)
Time-series models	Useful for analyzing longitudinal data typically with many occasions of measurement (e.g., 80 consecutive days of daily reports) to model time trends in a sequence of observations via both autoregressive and moving average processes (Volume 2, Chapter 34, this handbook; Box & Jenkins, 1970; Hershberger et al., 1996)

a particular model of change (e.g., latent change score models) are provided. A structural equation modeling (SEM) framework is most often used in this chapter to illustrate longitudinal methodological issues. Also, this chapter focuses principally on longitudinal models for which n (i.e., number of subjects) is substantially larger than t (i.e., number of waves of measurement). Therefore, this chapter does not specifically focus on single-subject designs or longitudinal quantitative models (e.g., time series) where $t > n$ (or where t is very large), although time-series models are covered in Volume 2, Chapter 34, this handbook.

RESEARCH DESIGN ISSUES RELEVANT TO LONGITUDINAL MODELS

In conducting longitudinal research, there are general issues to consider that are relevant to basically any research design, including cross-sectional data. For example, those who design longitudinal studies need to consider both internal and external validity (Campbell & Stanley, 1966). *Internal validity* refers to various design characteristics of a study (e.g., use of control group, matching subjects on baseline characteristics) that facilitate excluding alternative methodological explanations for study findings. For example, nonrandom assignment of subjects to treatment and control groups could threaten the internal validity of study findings that may be affected by initial (nonrandom) systematic differences between the groups. *External validity* refers to the generalizability of study findings to samples and populations beyond those used in a given study. Findings from an intervention study designed to reduce sexual behavior among White adolescents many not generalize to non-White adolescents, for example, since there may be differences between racial–ethnic groups with regard to the onset, prevalence, and causes of sexual behavior.

Autoregressive Models (Markov Simplex Models)

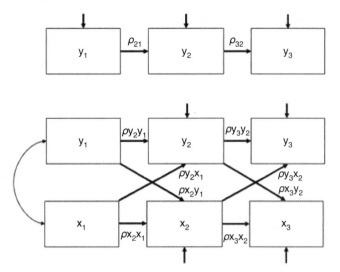

ρ represents the autoregressive relation among repeated assessments (e.g., ρ_{21} for the top figure between y_1 and y_2) when pointed directly forward and the cross-lagged relation when pointed from one construct (y) to the other (x) (e.g., $\rho x_2 y_1$ for x_2 regressed on y_1).

Latent Growth Model

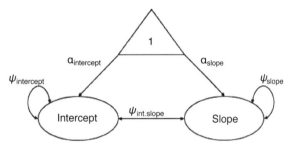

$\alpha_{intercept}$ = mean of the random intercept; α_{slope} = mean of the random slope; $\psi_{intercept}$ = variance of the random intercept; ψ_{slope} = variance of random slope; $\psi_{int.slope}$ = covariance of intercept and slope.

FIGURE 11.1. Figures of models described in Table 11.1.

In addition to these more common concerns (for an extensive discussion of threats to internal and external validity, see Baltes et al., 1977; Campbell & Stanley, 1966), there are threats to internal and external validity that are particularly prominent in longitudinal research (e.g., subject attrition, cohort effects, and maturation effects) that bear elaboration. Five issues of particular relevance to longitudinal research designs are covered here: (a) sample selection and generalizability of findings, (b) attrition and selectivity bias, (c) repeated application of measures (e.g., response familiarity and learning and habituation), (d) selection of an appropriate longitudinal statistical model to address substantive research questions, and (e) longitudinal coverage validity.

Sample Selection and Generalizability of Findings

Across multiple study designs, the judicious choice of a sample is inextricably associated with research questions of interest and is consequential with regard to the ability to draw statistical and

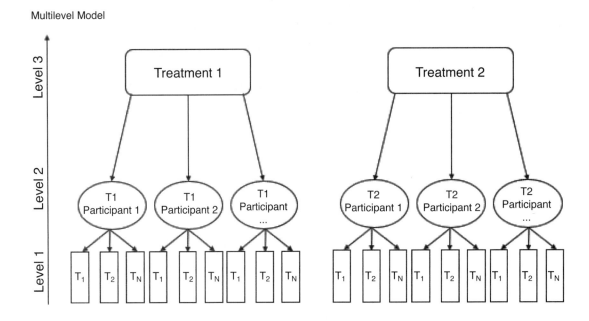

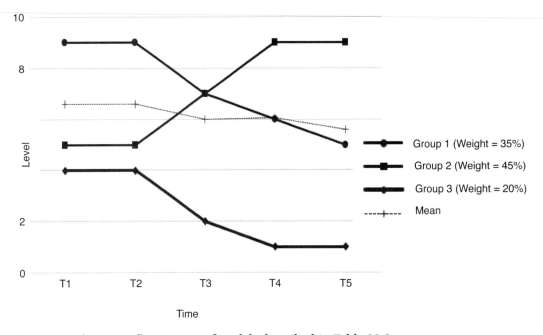

Figure 11.1 (*Continued*). Figures of models described in Table 11.1.

substantive inferences for other populations. Population-based, representative samples are desirable to address some research questions (e.g., to derive national, population-based estimates of the prevalence of psychiatric disorders and how these prevalences change across time). As is true with any longitudinal data, it is imperative that such designs use the same methods of assessment across time to ensure any changes reflect "true" changes in prevalence rather than method effects. For example, Vergés et al. (2011) provided evidence that marked changes in lifetime estimates for alcohol use disorders across a 10-year period in two nationally representative epidemiological samples were likely due to methodological differences across the two surveys. There are also many situations in which it is not necessary to use a population-based sampling

Latent State-Trait Model

Latent Transition Analysis

FIGURE 11.1 (*Continued*). Figures of models described in Table 11.1.

strategy either because the research question does not necessitate such sampling (e.g., a focus on a given subpopulation, such as individuals who are positive for family history of alcoholism) or it may not be feasible (e.g., because of limited financial resources). Discussions of these alternative sampling designs and associated benefits and costs are beyond the scope of this chapter (see Volume 2, Chapter 16, this handbook). One must recognize that sample selection serves as a critical feature in planning a study and in interpreting the data because of the limits that it places on generalizing the findings to other populations.

In longitudinal research, it is imperative that sampling considerations are viewed within the context of changes that may vary according to the sample selected and thereby may affect the generalizability of findings across time. For example, some data suggest that age of onset for substance use typically occurs earlier for White than Black students (Johnston et al., 2009).

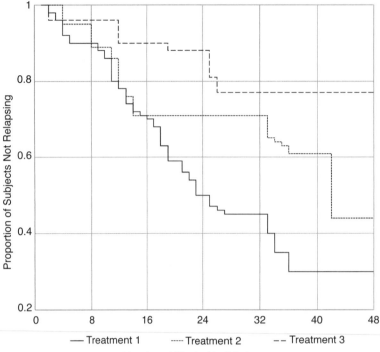

FIGURE 11.1 (*Continued*). Figures of models described in Table 11.1.

Thus, if a longitudinal study sought to understand factors that contribute to the age of onset for substance use, it would be key to begin the assessments at an age early enough to capture the critical period for onset for White students and continue the assessments for enough time to capture the critical period for Black students. Similarly, for research questions about developmental processes, it is important to consider age-related issues that may influence the sampling of different age groups. There should be a strong correspondence between the age groups selected for study, temporal design features (e.g., number and spacing of intervals of measurement), and the age-appropriate psychometric adequacy of selected measures to investigate the developmental processes of interest.

Attrition and Selectivity Bias

A major concern in longitudinal research is the role of attrition and selective dropout on resulting parameter estimates and quantitative models of change (e.g., estimated mean levels and changes in mean levels across time and range restrictions on variables across time that could affect standard errors of measurement). With regard to attrition, if participants drop out (i.e., do not continue to participate in a longitudinal study) completely at random across the sample (Little & Rubin, 1987), then a primary loss with regard to statistical inference is one of statistical power (i.e., a smaller sample size to conduct statistical tests of hypotheses). Attrition of this sort is of concern and substantial investment should be made to retain the larger sample size; however, assuming that the number of missing values is not large, the impact may be minimal and missing values may be estimated to retain the larger sample size for hypothesis testing (see the upcoming section Missing Data Estimation With Longitudinal Data). Additionally, one could plan to sample an initial larger sample with anticipated attrition so that attrition does not adversely affect statistical power. Completely at random dropout is the exception rather than the rule in most longitudinal studies, and a more common concern is the possibility of selective attrition (or dropout) that may bias estimated parameters and model fit statistics.

For example, in long-term (multiyear), longitudinal studies of childhood and adolescent problem behaviors (e.g., alcohol and substance use, delinquent activity), those participants with higher levels of problem behaviors often drop out at higher rates than those participants lower on problem behaviors (Wolke et al., 2009). Similarly, in longitudinal studies of older adults, differential mortality may occur across time such that those who are unhealthier die earlier, resulting in a more restricted, healthier sample for the prospective study. Differential attrition may introduce selectivity bias into statistical models that affect critical parameter estimates (e.g., mean scores, variance estimates) that are used in statistical models (e.g., parameters associated with intercepts and slopes in the latent-growth model) and, thereby, influence statistical and substantive inferences. For instance, if none of the adolescents at the higher end of delinquency participated at follow-up waves of measurement after Wave 1 in a longitudinal study of delinquency (e.g., because of dropping out of school), then mean-level estimates of delinquency are likely to be substantially lower and variance estimates are likely to be restricted (i.e., a smaller range of scores). Likewise, in a prospective study of changes in cognitive functioning among older adults, differential mortality may disproportionately eliminate those with lower cognitive functioning (e.g., because of vascular difficulties or dementia), thereby affecting critical parameters of change associated with cognitive abilities because of right censoring of the age distribution. Fortunately, investigators can implement a number of procedures to maximize the retention of subjects in longitudinal studies (see Volume 2, Chapter 18, this handbook).

Despite one's best efforts, however, some level of attrition is probable in most longitudinal studies. There are a number of data analytic methods used to identify the extent of attrition effects and potential selectivity bias. Briefly, researchers typically perform a series of statistical tests between those who continued (C) to participate in the study and those who dropped out (D) on variables measured at a common wave of assessment (e.g., baseline or Wave 1 assessment). For instance, in a simple two-wave design, group comparisons between C and D would be made on variables assessed at Wave 1. The kinds of analyses could include univariate tests (e.g., chi-square tests for sex differences in the proportion of those who dropped out; one-way analysis of variance models for continuous dependent variables with group as the independent variable) or multivariate tests (e.g., multiple dependent variables by groups C and D). Another more rigorous test would be to specify a simultaneous, two-group (groups C and D) SEM to evaluate the omnibus hypothesis of the equality of variance–covariance matrixes across groups (Vandenberg & Lance, 2000), though this approach would require a relatively large number of observations in group D to be feasible.

One must also recognize that making statistical comparisons between groups C and D on Wave 1 variables does not provide a comprehensive method of analysis with regard to drawing inferences about the relative equality of the two samples. First, it is possible that not all of the important variables that could have distinguished groups C and D were included in the Wave 1 comparisons. Therefore, selection bias could occur because of heterogeneity across groups C and D on non-measured (omitted) Wave 1 variables. Second, and perhaps more important, without data beyond Wave 1 for group D, one does not know the developmental trajectories and predictors of those trajectories for these individuals that may distinguish them from group C across time. There could be small differences between groups C and D at Wave 1 or omitted variables that exacerbate group differences across time to influence differentially developmental trajectories.

Consider a longitudinal study on adolescent delinquency where group differences were not indicated between C and D on Wave 1 variables. Let us assume, however, that we did not assess intelligence at Wave 1, though lower scores would have predicted not only dropping out of the study but also dropping out of school and contributing to cross-time trajectories marked by fewer higher wage opportunities and social drift downward. In this case, an unmeasured Wave 1 variable (intelligence) that distinguished groups C and D had long-term impacts developmentally on upstream factors (e.g., education attainment, higher wage job opportunities) that would have contributed to diverging developmental trajectories of growth for groups C and D. Although often difficult to implement, when possible, a long-term follow-up of at least a subset of the D group on critical variables is one method of attempting to examine the level of selective bias introduced by the D group. In many instances, however, this is not possible, and it is important to bear in mind how selective dropout may temper statistical inferences and substantive conclusions about study findings (see the upcoming Missing Data Estimation With Longitudinal Data section).

Confounds Associated With the Repeated Application of Measures

The selection of measures in longitudinal designs is especially important because there must be greater sensitivity to a range of possible inadvertent (confounding) effects associated with repeated measurement that may undermine the validity and interpretation of longitudinal research findings. For example, there may be reactivity effects associated with measures that affect not only measurement at time t but also time $t + n$ (Baltes et al., 1977). King et al. (2018) found that some data suggest various delay discounting measures (that presumably assess a type of "impulsivity") demonstrate marked test–retest stability across various time intervals (e.g., Odum, 2011). In Kirby (2009), test–retest stability was high ($rs > .63$), though mean discount rates increased across assessments, suggesting (by the interpretation of the test) that the participants were becoming more impulsive. An alternate interpretation is that participants were becoming increasingly reactive to the test. Research has also found that merely completing health behavior assessments and self-monitoring of behavior is associated with behavior change (e.g., Butryn et al., 2007; Sanchez-Craig et al., 1996).

Response learning and habituation in repeated measures designs are also concerns (Baltes et al., 1977). For example, based on the observation that age relations with cognitive functioning differed across cross-sectional and longitudinal data, Salthouse (2014) demonstrated that subjects who had prior experience with a cognitive task exhibited higher scores relative to subjects from the same cohort who were task-naïve. These findings indicated that experiences with the cognitive tasks on the first occasion inflates scores on the second occasion in longitudinal data. That is, despite the common perspective that longitudinal data are superior to cross-sectional data for addressing a multitude of research questions, these findings suggest estimates from cross-sectional data may be more accurate for determining age relations with cognitive functioning compared to longitudinal data. Repeated measurement of survey and questionnaire items could contribute to habituation in the willingness of participants to expend energy in reading and responding to items rather than just responding in the manner that they recall (correctly or incorrectly) they did on a prior measurement occasion. Such responses would introduce systematic bias in repeatedly measured response variables that may limit or undermine inferences in prospective data.

Selection of an Appropriate Longitudinal Statistical Model

Given that longitudinal data are much more expensive and time-intensive to collect compared with cross-sectional data, it is often the case that researchers who seek to apply a longitudinal model (or models) to a given data set were not closely involved in many key aspects of the initial study design (e.g., sampling strategy, selection of instruments, timing of assessments, age span under consideration). Thus, a major task among researchers who use existing longitudinal data sets is determining an appropriate analytic approach to address a given set of research questions informed by an accessible set of longitudinal data. On one hand, a positive aspect of the relatively recent development of longitudinal models is their range and flexibility in addressing a seemingly infinite number of research questions (provided a requisite number of repeated assessments for a given analytic approach). On the other hand, given the sheer number of potential approaches for longitudinal data analysis, selecting an appropriate longitudinal statistical model, or even a set of models to compare and contrast, can be a daunting task.

In longitudinal research, the issue of model specification (and misspecification) becomes increasingly complex because there is often uncertainty with regard to specifying models of change for several reasons. First, it is often unknown what the time course is for various developmental phenomena and the extent of individual variation in intraindividual change across which time periods (e.g., infancy, adolescence). For example, the full range of biological processes associated with pubertal development span a wide age range (e.g., 8–15 years), and there is considerable individual variation in onset and rate of growth features across sex groups, racial and ethnic groups, and so on (e.g., Abreu & Kaiser, 2016). Modeling how these individual differences in intraindividual change interrelate with other behaviors (e.g., symptoms of depression, cognitive growth) is challenging. Second, it is typically not known a priori which predictors, assessed when and how (e.g., self-report, behavioral observations), are optimal in moving toward the explanation of developmental processes and outcomes. Third, at present, for many fields of study we do not know enough about the developmental processes under investigation to know how frequently we should be assessing individuals, or how often and for how long we should conduct follow-ups for intervention research. Further, much of these decisions are yoked to other considerations (e.g., the amount and the timespan of funding to collect prospective data), which, as noted above, is often out of the control of researchers who actually apply longitudinal data analysis to existing longitudinal data.

With these issues in mind, model specification involves the clear delineation of the statistical model in terms of variables and their interrelationships (e.g., independent and dependent variables, mediators, measurement error structures, residual covariance relations) that correspond to a testable, hypothesized model (Rogosa, 1979). Basically, the model specification demonstrates one's conceptual or theoretical expectation of the interrelationships among a set of variables with regard both to the internal structure of measures and to the hypothesized structural relationships among variables.

As with other writers, the perspective here is that there is not one "right model" for a given set of longitudinal data. For example, Berry and Willoughby (2017) (emphasis theirs) noted, "At the end of the day, it is difficult to know whether one has specified the 'right' model. However, with some theory-driven comparisons, one hopes to feel increasingly confident about specifying the *least wrong* model" (p. 1203). In "Right-Sizing Statistical Models for Longitudinal Data," by Wood et al. (2015), model selection is discussed under the heading of "There is No 'Right' Model, but We May Determine Which Models are 'Better'" (p. 472).

One important consideration on the road towards specifying a "least wrong" (or perhaps, "less wrong") model of longitudinal data is to define clearly what type of change is of interest. Although *change* is a common focus in most applications of longitudinal data analysis, one must understand there are various types of change that can be examined with repeated assessments. King et al. (2018) noted indices of change include mean-level change (variability in the average scores for a given sample on some repeated assessment across time), rank-order consistency (relative ordering of individuals on some measure across time), and individual differences in within-person change (variability in trajectories of repeated assessments across individuals; Roberts & Mroczek, 2008). Notably, different combinations of types of change can occur within the same set of repeated assessments. For example, there may be pronounced mean-level decreases for some repeated assessment in a given sample (e.g., reductions in alcohol use between the ages of 20 and 30 in a sample of young adults), which would indicate change, but the same data may demonstrate high rank-order consistency (e.g., the same individuals who drank more relative to others in the sample at age 20 also drank more at age 30), which would indicate stability. There may be invariance of mean levels across time, suggesting stability, but this apparent stability may be driven by extensive within-person changes that vary across individuals (with as many participants increasing to a given degree as there are participants decreasing at the same degree, resulting in an overall consistent mean level across time).

Ram and Grimm (2015) provided a taxonomy of three different change processes (i.e., incremental change processes, transformational change processes, and stability-maintenance processes). These authors posited that most developmental studies test incremental change processes, such that changes in repeated assessments are thought to occur relatively smoothly across time. This is not surprising, given that the vast majority of analytic approaches in psychological sciences assume linear effects (e.g., the general linear model), including many analytic approaches for longitudinal data analysis (e.g., the standard latent growth model comprises a random intercept and a linear slope; see Chapter 14, this volume). Conversely, these authors noted that stability-maintenance processes (e.g., homeostatic systems) and transformational change (where new characteristics or abilities develop in relatively rapid, nonlinear transitions) are less studied and may require modeling multiple forms of change processes (e.g., exponential, sigmoidal, or splines; see Ram & Grimm, 2015, for more details). Again, this is not entirely surprising, given the number of necessary repeated assessments grows as one moves away from linear modeling.

Closely related to determining the type of change one wishes to consider is determining the appropriate level of analysis. As opposed to cross-sectional data, longitudinal data allow for the examination of within-person change processes—that is, how a given individual's level on some measure (or measures) differ(s) from their own average(s) across time, and how within-person variance in one construct relates to within-person variance on another construct.

It is increasingly recognized that some very common approaches to longitudinal data analysis, such as the cross-lagged panel model (CLPM), fail to appropriately tease apart within- versus between-sources of variance. CLPMs are an extension of autoregressive models (Table 11.1 and Figure 11.1) that include repeated assessments of two constructs across time. For example, say alcohol use (AU) and a personality characteristic such as extraversion (EX) are assessed yearly across a five-year period in a cohort of young adults. In addition to AU at time $T + 1$ being (auto)regressed onto AU at time T, AU at time $T + 1$ is also regressed onto EX at time T; the so-called *cross-lag*. In a parallel fashion, EX at time $T + 1$ is both autoregressed onto EX and cross-lagged on AU at time T. Across multiple disciplines within the psychological sciences, this analytic approach is thought to inform temporal precedence or transactional relations (e.g., A causes B, which in turn causes A at a later time point) among constructs assessed across time. Littlefield et al.

(2022) showed that CLPM is commonly used within the addiction field, with papers such as "Which Came First: The Readiness or the Change? Longitudinal Relationships Between Readiness to Change and Drinking Among College Drinkers" (S. E. Collins et al., 2010) highlighting the idea these models can inform temporal precedence among constructs.

Despite the broad use of these models, recent research on the CLPM demonstrated this approach cannot distinguish within- and between-person sources of variance (e.g., Berry & Willoughby, 2017; Curran et al., 2014; Hamaker et al., 2015). The primary limitation of the CLPM is that it suffers from a major variable omission issue: It assumes that there are no stable between-person differences among the constructs assessed across time, beyond the implied relations among the autoregressive paths. Hamaker et al. (2015) stated,

> if stability of the constructs is to some extent of a trait-like, time-invariant nature, the inclusion of autoregressive parameters will fail to adequately control for this. As a result, the estimates of the cross-lagged regression coefficients will be biased, which may lead to erroneous conclusions regarding the underlying causal pattern. (p. 102)

They demonstrate the standard CLPM is nested within a random-intercept model (i.e., a model that accounts for traitlike variance across assessments), such that the CLPM assumes none of the variances and covariances among measurements across time are due to traitlike stability. Berry and Willoughby (2017) simulated data to show that the cross-lagged estimates from a standard CLPM (i.e., a model that omits traitlike, time-invariant sources of variance) amalgamates between- and within-person relations, resulting in estimates "that are difficult (or impossible) to interpret meaningfully" (p. 1187). Fortunately, there are alternative models that implement structured residuals (i.e., variables that capture within-person variation at a given wave via latent variables) that allow for within-variation to be teased apart from between-person variance as well as the modeling of concurrent and prospective within-person relations (see Littlefield et al., 2022, for more details).

Another issue that complicates longitudinal modeling is that different approaches can yield different conclusions regarding "change" as a function of another variable (or set of variables). The heart of the issue involves adjusting (or not) for baseline differences in longitudinal models when variables correlate at baseline (which is almost always the case in nonexperimental, observational studies). Lord's paradox (Lord, 1967) illustrated this issue in a hypothetical data situation that involved a baseline binary variable (i.e., biological sex) and two repeated assessments of weight. Lord was able to demonstrate that one would yield different conclusions depending on if the measures of weight were analyzed within a repeated-measures ANOVA framework (which suggested there is no effect of sex on change between the two assessments) compared with an ANCOVA framework that adjusted for baseline levels of weight and then examined the relation between biological sex and weight at the second assessment (which yielded a relation between biological sex and weight at the second assessment; see Lord, 1967). For clarity in this chapter, the two approaches are referred to as the gain score approach (the ANOVA framework in Lord's paper) versus the residualized change approach (the ANCOVA framework from Lord's paper).

This paradox is well documented as driven by overlap at baseline between the variable thought to predict change (e.g., biological sex in Lord's, 1967, example) with the baseline assessment of another variable measured repeatedly across time (e.g., weight in Lord's example). Indeed, Kim (2018) and Farmus et al. (2019) formulated equations that index the discrepancy between the two approaches for binary and continuous covariates, respectively (see these studies for more details).

What has varied across time is recommendations for which approach should be applied to longitudinal data analysis. Much has been written regarding this issue (e.g., Campbell & Kenny, 2002; Pearl, 2016; Van Breukelen, 2006; van Breukelen, 2013; Wainer & Brown, 2004; Werts & Linn, 1969;

Werts & Linn, 1971; Wright, 2020), with disagreements about the validity and utility of one approach compared with another. Although historically the gain score approach has been criticized on the grounds that measurement error can have negative consequences for assessing change using difference scores (Cronbach & Furby, 1970; Lord, 1956), there have been various criticisms of the residualized change approach, include recent suggestions that the residualized approach is problematic. Castro-Schilo and Grimm (2018) compared the two approaches in simulated data (that involved a binary baseline variable and two repeated assessments of a continuous outcome) and concluded,

> We hope our discussion thus far has clarified that, if we have different populations with different levels of the outcome at baseline, the residualized change model is not appropriate because it will necessarily be biased. We believe the difference score model is a better choice in nonrandomized studies (p. 47)

and, "In sum, with current advances in methodology, especially with LCS [latent change score] models with multiple indicators, there is little room (if any) for residualized change approaches in nonrandomized studies" (p. 51).

Similarly, Farmus et al. (2019) noted in contexts involving all continuous variables that

> the problematic regression based model that covaries out pretest scores is currently being applied in psychology literature more often than models that do not covary pretest scores, and that the conditions leading to the artifact (i.e., spurious effects) were met in a significant amount of studies reviewed (p. 1)

and

> When baseline scores are correlated with scores on the predictors of change, regardless of whether the predictor is continuous or categorical, it is important that researchers adopt a gain score model to eliminate the chance that the relationship between the predictor and the amount of change is affected by the correlation between pretest scores and the continuous predictor. (p. 8)

Although some have argued that the residualized change approach has greater statistical power compared with the gain score approach, using centering approaches (i.e., centering values around the baseline values) can provide estimates that are consistent with the gain score approach yet have the statistical power of the residualized change approach (Lin & Larzelere, 2020).

In many ways, this contention reflects more general issues involving the scientific utility of adjusting versus not adjusting for variables within statistical models (e.g., Lynam et al., 2006). More specifically, Meehl (1971) in "High School Yearbooks: A Reply to Schwarz," questioned the wisdom of thoughtlessly controlling for variables (i.e., including covariates without consideration of the implied underlying model) in statistical models. The focus was on prior critique by Schwarz (1970), which suggested one should adjust for social class when examining the relation between social participation in high school and the later development of schizophrenia. Among other things, Meehl (1971) posed the question that ostensibly would be asked when adjusting for social class in this scenario:

> Do high school students who later develop schizophrenia but who differ from the average preschizophrenic by coming from higher social class backgrounds, show less social participation than a non-random sample of nonpreschizophrenic controls selected for having somewhat lower class backgrounds than students generally? Maybe the answer to this funny question is scientifically interesting, but it is unclear to me why it would be. (p. 146)

Essentially, similar questions are asked when taking the residualized change approach to assessing change. For example, using Lord's (1967) hypothetical example comparing weight change across two assessments as a function of biological sex (where males weighed more than females at baseline), the residualized change approach ostensibly asks the question "Do males who differ from other males by being below average in weight show increased weight gain across time compared to females who differ from other females by being above average in weight?" Meehl's (1971) recommendation to the field was for researchers to report both adjusted and unadjusted estimates, and similar suggestions have been made in regard to robustness testing results from longitudinal models (e.g., Angrist & Pischke, 2009). However, many studies only use one approach, with the majority focused on using residualized change scores (e.g., Farmus et al., 2019; Lin & Larzelere, 2020). Studies that do examine the robustness of findings across methods are often left with contradictory results that can be difficult to explain and are heavily scrutinized.

For example, Cooper et al. (2008) examined changes in drinking motives and alcohol involvement across a 15-year period spanning adolescence into young adulthood. Two primary analytic approaches were used to examine the relations between motives and alcohol involvement: multilevel modeling (that is consistent with the gain score approach) and a multiple regression (that is consistent with the residualized change approach). Using the multilevel modeling approach, drinking motives at baseline (either enhancement or coping motives) were positively related to the intercept (baseline levels) of alcohol involvement variables (e.g., usual alcohol consumption, drinking problems) but negatively related to the linear slope of alcohol involvement across time (i.e., those with higher baseline levels of drinking motives made sharper decreases in alcohol involvement across time). Conversely, the multiple regression approach showed that, when adjusting for baseline alcohol involvement, drinking motives positively predicted subsequent alcohol involvement. Despite the authors providing cogent explanations for the divergent findings (i.e., essentially highlighting the differences in assumptions made by the two approaches and referring to Lord's paradox), the published paper included two footnotes and a paragraph in the limitation section further addressing these discrepancies (with both footnotes and the in-text paragraph totaling over 900 words). The authors also made statements that were unlikely to be required if only one approach was used (e.g., "We cannot unequivocally rule out the possibility of statistical artifact as the cause of the differing results" p. 498).

Given these issues, how should researchers proceed in determining approaches for longitudinal modeling? It is helpful to realize the equivalency across various types of models. Several authors (see Coman et al., 2013; Curran, 2003; Newsom, 2017; Skrondal & Rabe-Hesketh, 2004; Voelkle, 2007) have demonstrated that more common statistical tests for repeated measures analysis (e.g., the paired t test) can be replicated using SEM with latent variables (e.g., modified latent growth curve models, LCS models). This is perhaps confusing to some, given many readers have a certain connotation when considering latent variables. For example, latent variables estimated using confirmatory factor analysis are thought to model error-free constructs (e.g., Castro-Schilo & Grimm, 2018). However, in their most basic (and most used) specifications, approaches such as latent growth modeling (see Voelkle, 2007) and latent change score analysis (see McArdle, 2009) merely use latent variables as convenient approaches to mathematically capture change.

For example, LCS models (see McArdle, 2009; Figure 11.2) utilize SEM to create latent variables that capture different types of change. As opposed to autoregressive models that estimate the relation between Time 1 and Time 2 of a given construct (e.g., alcohol use at Time 1 and alcohol use at Time 2, equivalent to regressing alcohol use at Time 2 onto alcohol use at Time 1), latent change score models force this path to unity (1). The residual variance of the Time 2 measurement is then set to 0, as is its observed

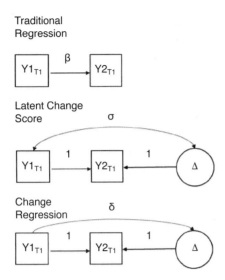

FIGURE 11.2. Traditional regression, latent change score, and change regression models. Adapted and simplified (exogenous and endogenous variances, disturbances, and mean structure are not shown) from "Latent Variable Modeling of Differences and Changes With Longitudinal Data," by J. J. McArdle, 2009, *Annual Review of Psychology*, *60*(1), pp. 577–605 (https://doi.org/10.1146/annurev.psych.60.110707.163612). Copyright 2009 by Annual Reviews.

mean. A latent variable (referred to here as *delta*) with a single indicator, the Time 2 measurement, is then created. The factor loading from this latent variable is also set to unity. The variance and mean of this latent variable are freely estimated. The LCS is then either regressed on the Time 1 assessment (resulting in a change regression model per McArdle's wording, consistent with the residualized change approach discussed here) or is correlated with the Time 1 assessment (resulting in a LCS model per McArdle, consistent with the gain score approach discussed above; see Figure 11.2).

When modeling LCS models onto manifest variables (which are more commonly used in LCS compared to using latent variables as indicators of latent change factors), it can be shown that (a) the estimate of a baseline covariate on a variable created by subtracting the baseline assessment from the follow-up assessment is identical to the estimate that would be obtained from a LCS model, and (b) the estimate of a baseline covariate on the Wave 2 assessment when adjusting for the Wave 1 assessment (i.e., a two-predictor regression model) is the same as the estimate that would be obtained from a change regression model, and (c) the estimates across the latent change score model and the change regression model can differ.

It can also be shown that the LCS approach results in a change variable that is consistent with a latent slope estimated in a latent growth modeling framework when the assumption of linear change is valid. That is, assuming change in linear (the assumption of most latent growth models [LGMs]) and no missing data, one can obtain the same estimate of the influence of a baseline covariate on (a) a latent slope from a LGM with multiple assessments, (b) a latent variable capturing change from a latent change model that only involves the first and last assessment, and (c) a variable created by subtracting scores at the first assessment from scores at the last assessment. In addition to the types of equivalency noted previously, one must note that different longitudinal SEM (as well as other types of models) can yield similar or identical fit to the data (briefly, how well the assumptions in a given model match observed data; see Tomarken & Waller, 2003). For example, given that both the ANOVA and ANCOVA approaches are just-identified models (i.e., models with zero degrees of freedom and, thus, fit the data perfectly), these two contrasting approaches would yield identical fit to the data despite providing drastically different results. Thus, model fit will not always allow researchers to adjudicate between potential longitudinal models.

Longitudinal Coverage Validity

Longitudinal coverage validity (alternatively temporal design validity) refers to the relative adequacy of a proposed longitudinal design in terms of the number and spacing of time points, and the duration of the study, to capture the change phenomena related to the research question under investigation. As with other factors that contribute to the limitations regarding the interpretation of longitudinal findings previously discussed (e.g., selective dropout, response habituation; Baltes et al., 1977), the structure of the repeated measures design (i.e., the frequency, density, and duration of assessments across time) also contributes to the interpretation and validity of longitudinal findings.

For instance, a four-wave longitudinal research design focused on changes in intellectual development that assessed children every 5 years may have relatively weak longitudinal coverage validity, given changes in intellectual development occur much more rapidly than what would be obtained in such a design (Sternberg & Berg, 1992). Likewise, daily recordings of alcohol use for the past 30 days may provide useful information to address some research questions (e.g., indexing daily variation in alcohol use), but it would be limited in addressing research questions about the long-term health consequences of alcohol use (e.g., alcohol use and liver cirrhosis).

Notably, recent advances in longitudinal models that enable investigators to better tease apart between- and within-person sources of variance, such as approaches that utilize structured residuals (see Littlefield et al., 2022, for more details), may require investigators to rethink the utility of time lags that are common in many longitudinal designs (e.g., lags that span months or even years). Differences in the timing of assessments have been demonstrated to influence statistical significance as well as the directionality of influences among variables in designs that do a poor job in disentangling between- and within-person sources of variance, such as the standard CLPM (e.g., Sher & Wood, 1997). Issues related to the timing of assessments also have implications for models that allow for a purer focus on within-person variance. This type of variance is typically assessed by indexing individual fluctuations around a person-centered mean. For example, for an individual that consumes three standard drinks of alcohol per day on average, a daily drinking occasion that involved consuming one standard drink would be below average for this person. Consistently, a drinking occasion involving five standard drinks would be above average for this individual. SEM approaches allow for this type of within-person variance to be captured by including factors that reflect between-person sources of variance (e.g., a random intercept) as well as within-person sources of variance (e.g., structured residuals that index time-specific variations around an individual's latent mean assessed across time).

Littlefield et al. (2022) discussed that longer time lags may not be ideal when measuring within-person relations across time, given within-person relations may occur more proximally, rather than distally, across time. For example, Littlefield et al. examined the prospective relation between temptation to drink and depression symptoms in a well-known treatment sample from the addiction literature (Project MATCH; see Littlefield et al., 2022, for more details). The assessments used in this study spanned six-month intervals. Using alternative models to the oft-criticized CLPM (e.g., latent growth modeling with structured residuals; Curran et al., 2014), there was little evidence that within-person variance in temptation to drink predicted subsequent within-person variance in depression symptoms (and vice versa), despite strong evidence of between-person covariation among these constructs across time (i.e., those that tended to be higher in temptation to drink across the assessment intervals also tended to be higher in depression symptoms; see Jackson & Sher, 2003, for similar findings involving alcohol use disorder and psychological distress within a sample of college students assessed across emerging and young adulthood at intervals spanning at least one year). The lack of prospective relations is not necessarily surprising within the MATCH data set, given the 6-month intervals and considering the focus on within-person variance. To put another way, why would it necessarily be true that individuals that were above average (for themselves) in, say, temptation to drink at a given assessment be more likely to be above average (for themselves) in depression symptoms six months later? To some extent, such nuanced considerations have been masked with the frequent use of designs such as the standard CLPM, which combines between- and within-person sources of variance. In summary, larger time lags may be insufficient to capture prospective within-person relations that are likely to occur across shorter time intervals, and this possibility may become clearer as approaches that tease apart between- and within-person sources of variance (e.g., Chapter 13, this volume; Littlefield et al., 2022) are more commonly used.

The number and spacing of assessments also have implications for longitudinal approaches that index within-person changes across the entire sampling period, such as a linear slope from a standard latent growth model. For example, L. M. Collins and Graham (2002) demonstrated the length between intervals could potentially mask nonlinear trajectories. Others have demonstrated that transactional processes among variables (e.g., A→B and B→A) may have different time-bound functional relations. That is, demonstrating a lagged relationship in one direction at one interval does not preclude the other directional relation at a different (potentially longer or shorter) interval (see Sher & Wood, 1997; Sher et al., 1996). Singer and Willett (2003) demonstrated that more waves of measurement $(t + n)$ relative to (t), where t = number of times of measurement, and n = additional measurement points, results in increased reliability of measurement for growth parameters related to the shape and rate of change (similar to findings by Raudenbush & Chan, 1993). For many longitudinal models, at least four waves of data collection are desirable to facilitate the testing of a range of hypotheses about parameters related to initial status, shape, rate of growth, and alternative covariance error structures without needing to impose constraints to appropriately identify the model (T. E. Duncan et al., 2006; Windle, 2000).

As described here, longitudinal coverage validity requires researchers to be quite thoughtful regarding the type of change that is of interest and the presumed temporal relations among time. This may be particularly relevant for designs that base assessments on specific timespans rather than event-based assessments (i.e., when an assessment occurs based on the presence of a given event such as first use of alcohol; see Chapter 12, this volume). Unfortunately, given the multiple types of expense associated with longitudinal data (e.g., monetary, time), it remains likely that many researchers that seek to use longitudinal data to address research questions will not be involved in many of the crucial decisions involving study design that can clearly have an impact on model parameters and, thus, substantive conclusions. Given this reality, researchers engaging in longitudinal data analysis need to be mindful of the influence any study design has on findings garnered from applying analytic approaches to existing data sets.

Accelerated or cohort-sequential longitudinal designs. As just noted, there are various expenses that are unique to longitudinal research compared to cross-sectional research (e.g., a long time to collect data). Bell (1953) proposed the notion of *convergence* to resolve the limitations of standard (single cohort) longitudinal designs and cross-sectional designs. The approach proposed by Bell involved limited repeated measurement occasions for independent age cohorts, such that across time there was overlap among some of the age groups. This conceptual and methodological approach has been widely adopted in the developmental sciences literature under the designation *cohort-sequential design* and by others as *accelerated research design* (T. E. Duncan et al., 2006; Glenn, 2005).

For example, Jackson et al. (2014) used a cohort-sequential design to study drinking related phenomenon during adolescence. Specifically, over 1,000 adolescents were assessed across a 3-year period. Participants were divided across sixth, seventh, and eighth grades at baseline. Given yearly assessments were used, the final data set involved assessments spanning the sixth grade from the 10th grade. Notably, a standard single-cohort design would have taken 5 years to cover the same time span. This approach also allows for the examination of time-informed research questions (e.g., how do rates of alcohol use change from sixth to eighth grade?) after 1 year of data collection. Further, it is possible to address questions related to cohort effects (Glenn, 2005; Rogosa, 1979). Given the overlap in assessment periods (e.g., all cohorts provide data during the eighth grade) and the different ages that are assessed within and across cohorts, this type of design also permits longitudinal examinations that would only be possible over a longer period of assessment for the standard single-cohort design. For example, Littlefield et al. (2016) used these data to examine the development and codevelopment of specific types of impulsivity from ages spanning 11 to 16 using latent growth modeling (see Littlefield et al., 2016, for more details) by creating a person–period data set (see Singer & Willett, 2003). That is, the assessments are arranged by age (rather than by cohort), with a separate row for each person for each observed period. Despite the many strengths of the accelerated longitudinal design, these types of data require special considerations that are not typical in the single-cohort design (e.g., the threat of age by cohort interactions; see S. C. Duncan et al., 1996; Galbraith et al., 2017).

OTHER METHODOLOGICAL CONSIDERATIONS

Ensuring longitudinal structural invariance of a given latent variable and approaches to missing data estimation are also central to longitudinal data analysis. These topics are reviewed in the following section.

Tests of Invariance Across Time

Longitudinal data analysis permits various types of invariance to be examined. A psychometric prerequisite to examine change in a construct across time (e.g., changes in sensation seeking across adolescence) is structural (or factorial) invariance (Widaman et al., 2010). Structural invariance is a type of measurement invariance (see Cheung & Rensvold, 2002) that tests to what extent a given latent variable (e.g., sensation seeking) shows the same relation to manifest indicators (e.g., items from a scale assessing sensation seeking) across time. Without structural invariance, it is difficult to draw conclusions about mean-level comparisons that may be scaled differently or even assess different phenomena across time. The three primary types of invariance include *configural invariance* (briefly, similar factor loadings in terms of signs and maintaining the same number of factors across time), *metric invariance* (briefly, factor loadings are equivalent across time), and *scalar invariance* (briefly, intercepts, or the estimate of indicators when the latent variable is equal to zero, are equal across time). When indicators are categorical (e.g., binary items, ordinal items such as Likert-like items), invariance testing is essentially attempting to rule out the presence of differential item functioning as a function of time through the lens of item response theory (see Meade et al., 2005; Millsap, 2010). Evidence for structural invariance reduces concerns that the latent variable itself is changing across time (in terms of how latent variables relate to manifest indicators) and allows for greater confidence when comparing (for example) changes in latent means for a given construct.

There are other longitudinal applications that include tests of invariant relations. For example, one could test if a time-varying covariate (i.e., a covariate that is thought to change across time, such as drinking motives throughout emerging adulthood) shows similar relations to a repeated construct of interest (e.g., alcohol use) at each assessment. Autoregressive relations among the same repeated construct (e.g., structured residuals of within-person variance in a given construct) could also be tested for equivalency (i.e., invariance) across time (e.g., determining if the autoregressive relation between within-person variance in a given construct is the same across each assessment period). It is important to ensure equal spacing between assessments for some types of invariance testing (e.g., autoregressive processes across time), given equivalency in path estimates across different spans of time (e.g., 6 months vs. a year) would actually imply differential relations between constructs as a function of time. For example, say a construct is assessed at baseline (W1), 6 months (W2) later, and then two years later (W3). Demonstrating equivalency between the W1 and W2 assessment to the W2 and W3 assessment would indicate the rank-order stability is much higher between the second and third assessment (given the longer time lag) compared with the first and second assessments.

Missing Data Estimation With Longitudinal Data

Given the attrition problem in longitudinal research, investigators are confronted with the issue of missing data. Historically, the easiest ways to address this issue involved a range of ad hoc procedures such as eliminating the data of participants with missing data (e.g., listwise or pairwise deletion) or using mean imputation (i.e., replacing the missing value with the mean score of the sample that did participate). The limitations of these methods are not recommended because they can contribute to biased and inefficient parameter estimates and incorrect standard errors and confidence intervals (Graham, 2009).

Fortunately, there have been major advances in missing data estimation (Enders, 2010; Graham, 2009). Little and Rubin (1987) described three different models of missingness. Data that are missing completely at random (MCAR) means missing data are a random sample of all the types of participants (e.g., males) in a given data set. Missing at random (MAR) practically means conditionally missing at random (see Graham, 2009). That is, MAR implies that once missingness has been adjusted by all available variables in a given data set (e.g., biological sex), the remaining missingness is completely random (i.e., it does not depend on some unmeasured variables). If the data are missing as a function of unobserved variables, the data are said to be missing not at random (MNAR). Graham provided an excellent and easy to digest overview of further details involving missing data considerations.

One important point made by Graham (2009) regards "myths" of missing data, such that the data must be minimally MAR to permit estimating procedures (e.g., maximum likelihood or multiple imputation) compared with other, more traditional approaches (e.g., using only complete case data). Graham noted that when assumptions of MAR have been violated, this impacts the more traditional methods as well as more modern data estimation procedures but tends to have a greater effect on the older procedures. Thus, Graham concluded that in the vast majority of circumstances, estimating missing data is a better approach compared with the older procedures, regardless of the model of missingness (i.e., MCAR, MAR, MNAR).

CONCLUSION

There have been major advances in quantitative longitudinal models across the years that provide unparalleled opportunities to pursue research questions about the stability and change of behaviors as well as about the predictors of such change. There are a multitude of analytic approaches to longitudinal data analysis, and more detailed accounts of some of these models are provided in other chapters in this handbook. This chapter has attempted to provide some of the more general issues to consider for those designing longitudinal research studies, analyzing extant data (e.g., via secondary data analysis), or critically reading and evaluating the literature. Threats to internal and external validity abound in research applications in the behavioral and health sciences, and they are compounded in longitudinal studies because of across-time change issues that are central to interpreting prospective findings. A focus on change requires more rigorous conceptual, measurement, and structural models to account for the dynamic, time-ordered relationships among variables that unfold across time.

As detailed in this chapter, perspectives regarding the utility of some approaches to provide meaningful estimates of longitudinal relations have shifted in recent years. Despite the extensive use of cross-lagged panel models and other approaches that are based on residualized change, many researchers have recently highlighted the shortcomings of these methods. As demonstrated by our exploration of Lord's paradox, different substantive conclusions clearly can be reached as a basis of modeling choice when individuals differ in variables measured at the baseline assessment (which is almost always the case in nonexperimental, observational studies). Indeed, given the marked differences in findings as a function of approach, some may question the ultimate utility of conducting longitudinal data analysis in nonexperimental data. Lord (1967) himself had the following gloomy conclusion to his paradox:

> In the writer's opinion, the explanation is that with the data usually available for such studies, there simply is no logical or statistical procedure that can be counted on to make proper allowances for uncontrolled preexisting differences between groups. The researcher wants to know how the groups would have compared if there had been no preexisting uncontrolled differences. The usual research study of this type is attempting to answer a question that simply cannot be answered in any rigorous way on the basis of available data. (p. 305)

Consistent with other perspectives regarding psychological science (Lilienfeld, 2017), I would stress instead that humility and transparency should be emphasized in the use of longitudinal data analysis within the psychological (and other) sciences (Ioannidis, 2016; McFall, 1996). There are many important insights that can be gleamed from longitudinal data that are simply not viable in cross-sectional research, including obtaining clues regarding causal relations among variables (Sher et al., 2004). Despite these strengths, researchers should often temper their conclusions regarding strong evidence for causality gleamed from prospective observational data in the absence of clear instrumental variables. Although directional, prospective relations are often lionized in the literature, perhaps there should be a greater emphasis on identifying correlated changes among constructs across time (see Littlefield et al., 2012) and linking time-specific covariation in within-person variance across shorter time intervals (see Littlefield et al., 2022). At the very least, researchers that employ longitudinal data analysis need to be aware of the assumptions and limitations of the specific approach that is used in a given data analytic context and how conclusions from a given approach will be consistent or inconsistent with other reasonable analytic choices.

References

Abreu, A. P., & Kaiser, U. B. (2016). Pubertal development and regulation. *The Lancet. Diabetes & Endocrinology*, *4*(3), 254–264. https://doi.org/10.1016/S2213-8587(15)00418-0

Angrist, J., & Pischke, S. (2009). *Mostly harmless econometrics: An empiricists' companion*. Princeton University Press. https://doi.org/10.1515/9781400829828

Baltes, P. B., Reese, H. W., & Nesselroade, J. R. (1977). *Life-span developmental psychology: Introduction to research methods*. Wadsworth.

Bell, R. Q. (1953). Convergence: An accelerated longitudinal approach. *Child Development*, *24*(2), 145–152. https://doi.org/10.2307/1126345

Berry, D., & Willoughby, M. T. (2017). On the practical interpretability of cross-lagged panel models: Rethinking a developmental workhorse. *Child Development*, *88*(4), 1186–1206. https://doi.org/10.1111/cdev.12660

Box, G. E. P., & Jenkins, G. M. (1970). *Time-series analysis: Forecasting and control*. Holden-Day.

Butryn, M. L., Phelan, S., Hill, J. O., & Wing, R. R. (2007). Consistent self-monitoring of weight: A key component of successful weight loss maintenance. *Obesity*, *15*(12), 3091–3096. https://doi.org/10.1038/oby.2007.368

Campbell, D. T., & Kenny, D. A. (2002). *A primer on regression artifacts*. Guilford Press.

Campbell, D. T., & Stanley, J. C. (1966). *Experimental and quasi-experimental designs for research*. Rand McNally.

Castro-Schilo, L., & Grimm, K. J. (2018). Using residualized change versus difference scores for longitudinal research. *Journal of Social and Personal Relationships*, *35*(1), 32–58. https://doi.org/10.1177/0265407517718387

Cheung, G. W., & Rensvold, R. B. (2002). Evaluating goodness-of-fit indexes for testing measurement invariance. *Structural Equation Modeling*, *9*(2), 233–255. https://doi.org/10.1207/S15328007SEM0902_5

Collins, L. M. (2002). Using latent transition analysis to examine the gateway hypothesis. In D. Kandel & M. Chase (Eds.), *Examining the gateway hypothesis: Stages and pathways of drug involvement* (pp. 254–269). Cambridge University Press. https://doi.org/10.1017/CBO9780511499777.013

Collins, L. M., & Graham, J. W. (2002). The effect of the timing and spacing of observations in longitudinal studies of tobacco and other drug use: Temporal design considerations. *Drug and Alcohol Dependence*, *68*(Suppl. 1), 85–96. https://doi.org/10.1016/S0376-8716(02)00217-X

Collins, S. E., Logan, D. E., & Neighbors, C. (2010). Which came first: The readiness or the change? Longitudinal relationships between readiness to change and drinking among college drinkers. *Addiction, 105*(11), 1899–1909. https://doi.org/10.1111/j.1360-0443.2010.03064.x

Coman, E. N., Picho, K., McArdle, J. J., Villagra, V., Dierker, L., & Iordache, E. (2013). The paired *t*-test as a simple latent change score model. *Frontiers in Psychology, 4*, 738. https://doi.org/10.3389/fpsyg.2013.00738

Cooper, M. L., Krull, J. L., Agocha, V. B., Flanagan, M. E., Orcutt, H. K., Grabe, S., Dermen, K. H., & Jackson, M. (2008). Motivational pathways to alcohol use and abuse among Black and White adolescents. *Journal of Abnormal Psychology, 117*(3), 485–501. https://doi.org/10.1037/a0012592

Cronbach, L. J., & Furby, L. (1970). How should we measure "change"—Or should we? *Psychological Bulletin, 74*(1), 68–80. https://doi.org/10.1037/h0029382

Curran, P. J. (2003). Have multilevel models been structural equation models all along? *Multivariate Behavioral Research, 38*(4), 529–569. https://doi.org/10.1207/s15327906mbr3804_5

Curran, P. J., Howard, A. L., Bainter, S. A., Lane, S. T., & McGinley, J. S. (2014). The separation of between-person and within-person components of individual change over time: A latent curve model with structured residuals. *Journal of Consulting and Clinical Psychology, 82*(5), 879–894. https://doi.org/10.1037/a0035297

Curran, P. T., & Bollen, K. A. (2001). The best of both worlds: Combining autoregressive and latent curve models. In L. M. Collins & A. G. Sayer (Eds.), *New methods for the analysis of change* (pp. 107–135). American Psychological Association. https://doi.org/10.1037/10409-004

Duncan, S. C., Duncan, T. E., & Hops, H. (1996). Analysis of longitudinal data within accelerated longitudinal designs. *Psychological Methods, 1*(3), 236–248. https://doi.org/10.1037/1082-989X.1.3.236

Duncan, T. E., Duncan, S. C., & Stryker, L. A. (Eds.). (2006). *Latent variable growth curve modeling: Concepts, issues, and applications* (2nd ed.). Erlbaum.

Enders, C. K. (2010). *Applied missing data analysis*. Guilford Press.

Farmus, L., Arpin-Cribbie, C. A., & Cribbie, R. A. (2019). Continuous predictors of pretest-posttest change: Highlighting the impact of the regression artifact. *Frontiers in Applied Mathematics and Statistics, 4*, 64. https://doi.org/10.3389/fams.2018.00064

Galbraith, S., Bowden, J., & Mander, A. (2017). Accelerated longitudinal designs: An overview of modelling, power, costs and handling missing data. *Statistical Methods in Medical Research, 26*(1), 374–398. https://doi.org/10.1177/0962280214547150

Glenn, N. D. (2005). *Cohort analysis* (2nd ed.). SAGE. https://doi.org/10.4135/9781412983662

Graham, J. W. (2009). Missing data analysis: Making it work in the real world. *Annual Review of Psychology, 60*(1), 549–576. https://doi.org/10.1146/annurev.psych.58.110405.085530

Hamaker, E. L., Kuiper, R. M., & Grasman, R. P. (2015). A critique of the cross-lagged panel model. *Psychological Methods, 20*(1), 102–116. https://doi.org/10.1037/a0038889

Hershberger, S. L., Molenaar, P. C. M., & Corneal, S. E. (1996). A hierarchy of univariate and multivariate structural time series models. In G. A. Marcoulides & R. E. Schumacker (Eds.), *Advanced structural equation modeling: Issues and techniques* (pp. 159–194). Erlbaum.

Hox, J. J. (2010). *Multilevel analysis: Techniques and applications* (2nd ed.). Routledge. https://doi.org/10.4324/9780203852279

Ioannidis, J. P. A. (2016). Evidence-based medicine has been hijacked: A report to David Sackett. *Journal of Clinical Epidemiology, 73*, 82–86. https://doi.org/10.1016/j.jclinepi.2016.02.012

Jackson, K. M., Roberts, M. E., Colby, S. M., Barnett, N. P., Abar, C. C., & Merrill, J. E. (2014). Willingness to drink as a function of peer offers and peer norms in early adolescence. *Journal of Studies on Alcohol and Drugs, 75*(3), 404–414. https://doi.org/10.15288/jsad.2014.75.404

Jackson, K. M., & Sher, K. J. (2003). Alcohol use disorders and psychological distress: A prospective state-trait analysis. *Journal of Abnormal Psychology, 112*(4), 599–613. https://doi.org/10.1037/0021-843X.112.4.599

Johnston, L. D., O'Malley, P. M., Bachman, J. G., & Schulenberg, J. E. (2009). *Monitoring the Future national survey results on drug use, 1975–2008: Vol. I. Secondary school students* (NIH Publication No. 09-7402). National Institute on Drug Abuse.

Kim, S. B. (2018). Explaining Lord's paradox in introductory statistical theory courses. *International Journal of Statistics and Probability, 7*(4), 1–10. https://doi.org/10.5539/ijsp.v7n4p1

King, K. M., Littlefield, A. K., McCabe, C. J., Mills, K. L., Flournoy, J., & Chassin, L. (2018). Longitudinal modeling in developmental neuroimaging research: Common challenges, and solutions from developmental psychology. *Developmental Cognitive Neuroscience, 33*, 54–72. https://doi.org/10.1016/j.dcn.2017.11.009

Kirby, K. N. (2009). One-year temporal stability of delay-discount rates. *Psychonomic Bulletin & Review, 16*(3), 457–462. https://doi.org/10.3758/PBR.16.3.457

Lilienfeld, S. O. (2017). Microaggressions: Strong claims, inadequate evidence. *Perspectives on Psychological Science, 12*(1), 138–169. https://doi.org/10.1177/1745691616659391

Lin, H., & Larzelere, R. E. (2020). Dual-centered ANCOVA: Resolving contradictory results from Lord's paradox with implications for reducing bias in longitudinal analyses. *Journal of Adolescence, 85*(1), 135–147. https://doi.org/10.1016/j.adolescence.2020.11.001

Little, R. J. A., & Rubin, D. B. (1987). *Statistical analysis with missing data.* Wiley.

Littlefield, A. K., King, K. M., Acuff, S. F., Foster, K. T., Murphy, J. G., & Witkiewitz, K. (2022). Limitations of cross-lagged panel models in addiction research and alternative models: An empirical example using project MATCH. *Psychology of Addictive Behaviors. 36*(3), 271–283. https://doi.org/10.1037/adb0000750

Littlefield, A. K., Stevens, A. K., Ellingson, J. M., King, K. M., & Jackson, K. M. (2016). Changes in negative urgency, positive urgency, and sensation seeking across adolescence. *Personality and Individual Differences, 90*, 332–337. https://doi.org/10.1016/j.paid.2015.11.024

Littlefield, A. K., Vergés, A., Wood, P. K., & Sher, K. J. (2012). Transactional models between personality and alcohol involvement: A further examination. *Journal of Abnormal Psychology, 121*(3), 778–783. https://doi.org/10.1037/a0026912

Lord, F. M. (1956). The measurement of growth. *Educational and Psychological Measurement, 16*(4), 421–437. https://doi.org/10.1177/001316445601600401

Lord, F. M. (1967). A paradox in the interpretation of group comparisons. *Psychological Bulletin, 68*(5), 304–305. https://doi.org/10.1037/h0025105

Lynam, D. R., Hoyle, R. H., & Newman, J. P. (2006). The perils of partialling: Cautionary tales from aggression and psychopathy. *Assessment, 13*(3), 328–341. https://doi.org/10.1177/1073191106290562

McArdle, J. J. (2009). Latent variable modeling of differences and changes with longitudinal data. *Annual Review of Psychology, 60*(1), 577–605. https://doi.org/10.1146/annurev.psych.60.110707.163612

McFall, R. M. (1996). Making psychology incorruptible. *Applied & Preventive Psychology, 5*(1), 9–15. https://doi.org/10.1016/S0962-1849(96)80021-7

Meade, A. W., Lautenschlager, G. J., & Hecht, J. E. (2005). Establishing measurement equivalence and invariance in longitudinal data with item response theory. *International Journal of Testing, 5*(3), 279–300. https://doi.org/10.1207/s15327574ijt0503_6

Meehl, P. E. (1971). High school yearbooks: A reply to Schwarz. *Journal of Abnormal Psychology, 77*(2), 143–148. https://doi.org/10.1037/h0030750

Meredith, W., & Tisak, J. (1990). Latent curve analysis. *Psychometrika, 55*(1), 107–122. https://doi.org/10.1007/BF02294746

Millsap, R. E. (2010). Testing measurement invariance using item response theory in longitudinal data: An introduction. *Child Development Perspectives, 4*(1), 5–9. https://doi.org/10.1111/j.1750-8606.2009.00109.x

Muthén, L. K., & Muthén, B. O. (1998–2017). *Mplus user's guide* (8th ed.). Muthén & Muthén.

Nagin, D. S. (2005). *Group-based modeling of development.* Harvard University Press. https://doi.org/10.4159/9780674041318

Newsom, J. T. (2017). Structural models for binary repeated measures: Linking modern longitudinal structural equation models to conventional categorical data analysis for matched pairs. *Structural Equation Modeling, 24*(4), 626–635. https://doi.org/10.1080/10705511.2016.1276837

Odum, A. L. (2011). Delay discounting: Trait variable? *Behavioural Processes, 87*(1), 1–9. https://doi.org/10.1016/j.beproc.2011.02.007

Pearl, J. (2016). Lord's paradox revisited (Oh Lord! Kumbaya!). *Journal of Causal Inference, 4*(2), 20160021. https://doi.org/10.1515/jci-2016-0021

Ram, N., & Grimm, K. (2015). Growth curve modeling and longitudinal factor analysis. In W. Overton & P. C. M. Molenaar (Eds.), *Handbook of child psychology: Vol. 1. Theoretical models of human development* (7th ed., pp. 1–31). Wiley. https://doi.org/10.1002/9781118963418.childpsy120

Raudenbush, S. W. (2001). Comparing personal trajectories and drawing causal inferences from longitudinal data. *Annual Review of Psychology, 52*(1), 501–525. https://doi.org/10.1146/annurev.psych.52.1.501

Raudenbush, S. W., & Chan, W. S. (1993). Application of a hierarchical linear model to the study of adolescent deviance in an overlapping cohort design. *Journal of Consulting and Clinical Psychology, 61*(6), 941–951. https://doi.org/10.1037/0022-006X.61.6.941

Roberts, B. W., & Mroczek, D. (2008). Personality trait change in adulthood. *Current Directions in*

Psychological Science, 17(1), 31–35. https://doi.org/10.1111/j.1467-8721.2008.00543.x

Rogosa, D. (1979). Causal models in longitudinal research: Rationale, formulation, and interpretation. In J. R. Nesselroade & P. B. Baltes (Eds.), *Longitudinal research in the study of behavior and development* (pp. 263–302). Academic Press.

Rogosa, D., Brandt, D., & Zimowski, M. (1982). A growth curve approach to the measurement of change. *Psychological Bulletin*, 92(3), 726–748. https://doi.org/10.1037/0033-2909.92.3.726

Salthouse, T. A. (2014). Why are there different age relations in cross-sectional and longitudinal comparisons of cognitive functioning? *Current Directions in Psychological Science*, 23(4), 252–256. https://doi.org/10.1177/0963721414535212

Sanchez-Craig, M., Davila, R., & Cooper, G. (1996). A self-help approach for high-risk drinking: Effect of an initial assessment. *Journal of Consulting and Clinical Psychology*, 64(4), 694–700. https://doi.org/10.1037/0022-006X.64.4.694

Schwarz, J. C. (1970). Comment on "High school yearbooks: A nonreactive measure of social isolation in graduates who later became schizophrenic." *Journal of Abnormal Psychology*, 75(3), 317–318. https://doi.org/10.1037/h0029360

Sher, K. J., Gotham, H. J., & Watson, A. L. (2004). Trajectories of dynamic predictors of disorder: Their meanings and implications. *Development and Psychopathology*, 16(4), 825–856. https://doi.org/10.1017/S0954579404040039

Sher, K. J., Wood, M. D., Wood, P. K., & Raskin, G. (1996). Alcohol outcome expectancies and alcohol use: A latent variable cross-lagged panel study. *Journal of Abnormal Psychology*, 105(4), 561–574. https://doi.org/10.1037/0021-843X.105.4.561

Sher, K. J., & Wood, P. K. (1997). Methodological issues in conducting prospective research on alcohol-related behavior: A report from the field. In K. J. Bryant, M. Windle, & S. G. West (Eds.), *The science of prevention: Methodological advances from alcohol and substance abuse research* (pp. 3–41). American Psychological Association. https://doi.org/10.1037/10222-001

Singer, J. D., & Willett, J. (2003). *Applied longitudinal data analysis*. Oxford University Press. https://doi.org/10.1093/acprof:oso/9780195152968.001.0001

Skrondal, A., & Rabe-Hesketh, S. (2004). *Generalized latent variable modeling: Multilevel, longitudinal, and structural equation models*. Chapman & Hall. https://doi.org/10.1201/9780203489437

Sternberg, R. J., & Berg, C. A. (Eds.). (1992). *Intellectual development*. Cambridge University Press.

Tomarken, A. J., & Waller, N. G. (2003). Potential problems with "well fitting" models. *Journal of Abnormal Psychology*, 112(4), 578–598. https://doi.org/10.1037/0021-843X.112.4.578

Trull, T. J., & Ebner-Priemer, U. (2013). Ambulatory assessment. *Annual Review of Clinical Psychology*, 9(1), 151–176. https://doi.org/10.1146/annurev-clinpsy-050212-185510

Van Breukelen, G. J. (2006). ANCOVA versus change from baseline had more power in randomized studies and more bias in nonrandomized studies. *Journal of Clinical Epidemiology*, 59(9), 920–925. https://doi.org/10.1016/j.jclinepi.2006.02.007

van Breukelen, G. J. (2013). ANCOVA versus CHANGE from baseline in nonrandomized studies: The difference. *Multivariate Behavioral Research*, 48(6), 895–922. https://doi.org/10.1080/00273171.2013.831743

Vandenberg, R. J., & Lance, C. E. (2000). A review and synthesis of the measurement invariance literature: Suggestions, practices, and recommendations for organizational research. *Organizational Research Methods*, 3(1), 4–70. https://doi.org/10.1177/109442810031002

Vergés, A., Littlefield, A. K., & Sher, K. J. (2011). Did lifetime rates of alcohol use disorders increase by 67% in 10 years? A comparison of NLAES and NESARC. *Journal of Abnormal Psychology*, 120(4), 868–877. https://doi.org/10.1037/a0022126

Voelkle, M. C. (2007). Latent growth curve modeling as an integrative approach to the analysis of change. *Psychology Science*, 49(4), 375–414.

Wainer, H., & Brown, L. M. (2004). Two statistical paradoxes in the interpretation of group differences: Illustrated with medical school admission and licensing data. *The American Statistician*, 58(2), 117–123. https://doi.org/10.1198/0003130043268

Werts, C. E., & Linn, R. L. (1969). Lord's paradox: A generic problem. *Psychological Bulletin*, 72(6), 423–425. https://doi.org/10.1037/h0028331

Werts, C. E., & Linn, R. L. (1971). Problems with inferring treatment effects from repeated measures. *Educational and Psychological Measurement*, 31(4), 857–866. https://doi.org/10.1177/001316447103100407

Widaman, K. F., Ferrer, E., & Conger, R. D. (2010). Factorial invariance within longitudinal structural equation models: Measuring the same construct across time. *Child Development Perspectives*, 4(1), 10–18. https://doi.org/10.1111/j.1750-8606.2009.00110.x

Windle, M. (2000). A latent growth curve model of delinquent activity among adolescents. *Applied Developmental Science*, 4(4), 193–207. https://doi.org/10.1207/S1532480XADS0404_2

Windle, M. (2012). Longitudinal data analysis. In H. Cooper, P. M. Camic, D. L. Long, A. T. Panter, D. Rindskopf, & K. J. Sher (Eds.), *APA handbook of research methods in psychology, Vol. 3. Data analysis and research publication* (pp. 245–266). American Psychological Association. https://doi.org/10.1037/13621-012

Wolke, D., Waylen, A., Samara, M., Steer, C., Goodman, R., Ford, T., & Lamberts, K. (2009). Selective drop-out in longitudinal studies and non-biased prediction of behaviour disorders. *The British Journal of Psychiatry, 195*(3), 249–256. https://doi.org/10.1192/bjp.bp.108.053751

Wood, P. K., Steinley, D., & Jackson, K. M. (2015). Right-sizing statistical models for longitudinal data. *Psychological Methods, 20*(4), 470–488. https://doi.org/10.1037/met0000037

Wright, D. B. (2020). Allocation to groups: Examples of Lord's paradox. *The British Journal of Educational Psychology, 90*(S1), 35–49. https://doi.org/10.1111/bjep.12300

CHAPTER 12

EVENT HISTORY ANALYSIS

Fetene B. Tekle and Jeroen K. Vermunt

In social and behavioral sciences in general, and in psychology in particular, researchers are often interested in the occurrence of events such as the formation or ending of formal and informal relationships (e.g., marital unions, friendships, love relationships), the onset of and recovery from mental disorders, the entry into and exit from a job, the experience of stressful and pleasant life events (e.g., accidents, dying of a parent, being in love for the first time), and the transition across developmental stages. Mortality may also be the event of interest, though that is the more typical event in biomedical studies. Data on the occurrence of the event(s) of interest can be collected using either retrospective or prospective study designs and will contain information on whether the event(s) of interest occurred to the individuals in the sample and, if so, on the time of occurrence. In addition to information on the timing of the event(s) of interest, there will usually also be information on sociodemographic covariates, risk factors, and/or the treatment or intervention received if there is any.

Event history data make it possible to determine at what time periods the event of interest is most likely to occur, as well as to determine why some individuals experience the event earlier than others and why some do not experience the event of interest at all during the study period. Although event history data give opportunities to answer such questions, they also pose certain challenges that cannot be dealt with using standard data analysis methods such as linear and logistic regression analysis (Allison, 1982; Tuma & Hannan, 1979; Willett & Singer, 1993). More specifically, simple linear and logistic regression methods are not suited for dealing with two distinctive features of event history data; that is, with censoring and time-varying covariates. Censoring is a specific kind of missing data problem, namely, that for some individuals it is not known when the event occurs because they did not experience the event during the observation period. Linear regression analysis of such censored data yields biased results and logistic regression analysis yields loss of information. Moreover, standard regression models lack a way to incorporate time-varying covariates, covariates that may change their value over time. In order to deal with censoring and time-varying covariates, we need special regression techniques that are known as *event history models*, *hazard models*, *survival models*, *failure time models*, and *duration models*.

The main distinction made in the field of event history analysis is between continuous-time methods (when the event time can take on any nonnegative value) and discrete-time methods (when the event time can take on a finite set of values). In this chapter, we focus on discrete-time techniques as a part of a course for graduate-level

https://doi.org/10.1037/0000320-012
APA Handbook of Research Methods in Psychology, Second Edition: Vol. 3. Data Analysis and Research Publication, H. Cooper (Editor-in-Chief)
Copyright © 2023 by the American Psychological Association. All rights reserved.

students or as a reference for applied researchers. Although continuous-time methods are predominant in the statistical literature (Blossfeld & Rohwer, 2002; Broström, 2022; Collett, 2015; Vermunt, 1997), discrete-time methods are the more commonly used ones in psychological research as well as in other social and behavioral sciences, not only because they are conceptually simpler but also because one will seldom have real continuous-time data. Sometimes events can only occur at regular discrete-time points (e.g., weekly, monthly, yearly), whereas in other situations events can occur in continuous time. The measurement, however, yields discrete-time data, for example, when a survey asks the age or year of the formation of a relationship, marriage, or divorce instead of the exact date. In both situations, using discrete-time methods instead of methods that are developed for continuous event time is more appropriate. Even if the measurement scale of the event time is continuous, discrete-time techniques can be used to approximate the results that would be obtained with continuous-time methods (Vermunt, 1997; Yamaguchi, 1991). Additionally, discrete-time techniques are computationally and conceptually simpler and, thus, easier to understand by social and behavioral scientists, and they can serve as a good starting point for understanding the more advanced continuous-time methods.

In the next section, an empirical example that will be used throughout this chapter is introduced. Some basic terminologies of event history analysis are presented in the section State, Event, Duration, Risk Period, Risk Set, and Censoring. The section When to Use Event History Analysis explains why special regression techniques are needed for event history analysis. Describing Event Time Distribution presents the statistical concepts used for describing event time distributions—the hazard and survival functions—and shows how a grouped data method similar to the actuarial method can be used to estimate these functions. The section Discrete-Time Event History Models covers regression models for discrete-time event history data in which the hazard rate—or the probability of event occurrence at a particular point in time—is related to covariates.

AN EMPIRICAL EXAMPLE

Throughout this chapter, we use a real-life example to illustrate the concepts and modeling approaches for event-history data.

Example: Adolescents' Relationship

The example is about an adolescent's first romantic relationship experience. The data is taken from a small-scale survey of 145 adolescents in the Netherlands (Vinken, 1998). Vermunt (2002) used latent class analysis to construct a typology based on four events in the adolescent's first experience with a romantic relationship: "sleeping with someone," "going out," "having a steady friend," and "being very much in love." Here, we use the event of sleeping with someone for the first time to illustrate the methods of event history analysis discussed in this chapter. Besides information on the occurrence of the four events, binary time-constant (i.e., fixed) covariates, youth centrism (YC), gender (G), and education (E) are available. Youth centrism is a measure of the extent to which young people perceive their peers as a positively valued ingroup and perceive adults as a negatively valued outgroup. The dichotomous YC scale that is used here was constructed by Vinken (1998).

State, Event, Duration, Risk Period, Risk Set, and Censoring

In order to understand the nature of event history data and the purpose of event history analysis, one must understand the following concepts: state, event, risk period, and censoring (Yamaguchi, 1991). These concepts are illustrated below using the example introduced in the previous section.

The first step in an event history analysis is to define the discrete states that one wishes to distinguish. *States* are the categories of the variable, the dynamics of which one wishes to explain. At every particular point in time, each person occupies exactly one state. In our first experience with romantic relationships example, each adolescent is either in the state "never slept with someone" or "has slept with someone." An *event* is a transition from one state to another, that is, from an origin state to a destination state. In our example, the event sleeping with someone for the first time is the transition from the state of never having slept with someone to the state of having slept with someone. Clearly, in our application, the event of interest can occur only once because it is not possible to exit the destination state (called an *absorbing state*). In other applications, the event(s) of interest may occur several times (*recurrent events*), such as recovery from depression, which is the transition between the states depressed and nondepressed.

Another important concept is the risk period. Clearly, not all persons can experience each of the events under study at every point in time. To be able to experience a particular event, one must first occupy the original state, that is, one must be at risk of the event concerned. The period that someone is at risk of a particular event— or exposed to a particular risk—is called the *risk period*. Usually it is straightforward to identify the persons at risk of the event, such as in our romantic relationships example in which adolescents that have never slept with someone at a particular age are at risk of experiencing the event of sleeping with someone for the first time at that age. The risk period(s) for a recovery from depression are the period(s) that a subject stayed in the origin state depressed. A strongly related concept is the *risk set*. The risk set at a particular point in time is formed by all subjects who are at risk of experiencing the event concerned at that point in time.

Using these concepts, *event history analysis* can be defined as the analysis of the duration of the nonoccurrence of an event during the risk period. When the event of interest is "sleeping with someone for the first time," the analysis concerns the duration of nonoccurrence of the experience of sleeping with someone, in other words, the time that adolescents remained in the state "never slept with someone." In practice, as we demonstrate below, the dependent variable in an event history model is not duration or time itself but a transition probability or hazard rate. *Event history modeling*, therefore, can also be defined as the analysis of the probability (or rate) of occurrence of the event of interest during the risk period. In the romantic relationships example this concerns an adolescent's probability of sleeping with someone given that this did not happen before.

As we indicated previously, an issue that always receives a great amount of attention in discussions on event history analysis is censoring, where a distinction should be made between *left* and *right censoring*. These two forms of censoring refer to missing information on the time of nonoccurrence of the event of interest *before* and *after* the observation (or follow-up) period, respectively. Here, we consider only the more common right-censoring problem, and we refer interested readers to Broström (2022), Kalbfleisch and Prentice (2002), Tuma and Hannan (1979), Vermunt (2009), and Yamaguchi (1991) for discussions of alternative censoring mechanisms and their implications.

An observation is called (*right*) *censored* if it is known that an individual did not experience the event of interest during a certain amount of time (during follow-up period), but the exact time at which the event was experienced is unknown. In the recovery from depression example, a censored observation would be an individual who was in the depressed state at the end of the study or who dropped out from the study. For such a person, we know the duration of the depression till that moment but not whether or when they will recover from depression, which means that the duration of nonoccurrence of recovery is only partially observed for such a person. In the romantic relationships example, a censored observation would be an adolescent who has not experienced sleeping with someone before the age at which the survey took place. This partial information is called the *censoring time*.

More formally, let T be the event time and U the censoring time. The duration of nonoccurrence of an event that can actually be observed is $Y = \min(T, U)$; that is, we observe the true event time when it is smaller than the censoring time and vice versa. Methods for event history analysis define a model for the dependent variable Y (and, thus, not for T). However, because it is also relevant to make a distinction between event and censoring times, an event indicator variable has to be defined. For right-censored event data, the event indicator for ith person is defined as

$$Event_i = \begin{cases} 1 \text{ if } T_i \leq U_i \\ 0 \text{ if } T_i > U_i \end{cases}$$

In other words, $Event_i$ equals 1 if we observe the event time and 0 if the observation is censored.

While traditional regression methodology such as linear or logistic regression analysis does not provide a way of simultaneously analyzing observed and censored event times, as we show later, event-history-analysis methodology provides a way of considering both simultaneously. Next we explain when these event-history-analysis methods are more appealing in relation to research problems in practice.

WHEN TO USE EVENT HISTORY ANALYSIS?

To determine whether the method of event history analysis is applicable in a specific situation, one has to examine the research problem or question and a study's methodological features. A research's method of analysis calls for event history analysis if the research's question is centered on whether and, if so, when events occur. Data can be collected prospectively or retrospectively, over a short or a long period of time, in an experiment or an observational study. The beginning time that is an initial starting point when no one under study has yet experienced the target event, but everybody is in the risk set, has to be identified. The time of a target event whose occurrence is being studied can be measured in years, months, days, or minutes; however, a meaningful scale needs to be chosen. In the romantic relationships example, the research question is when young adolescents have their first experience of sleeping with someone and whether predictors affect the timing of this event. Clearly, the target event is the transition to sleeping with someone for the first time. The beginning time is the time at which none of the subjects under study has experienced the event but all are in the risk set of the event sleeping with someone. Because data are collected retrospectively, measuring the time precisely of the first experience of sleeping with someone in months, days, or smaller grids of time is not practical. During the data collection, subjects may recall the period of the event in terms of the age at which the event happened. Thus, it is logical to consider age in years as the unit of scale for event period in our example.

DESCRIBING EVENT TIME DISTRIBUTION

Discrete Versus Continuous Time

The manner in which the basic statistical concepts of event history analysis are defined depends on whether the time variable T, indicating the duration of nonoccurrence of an event, is assumed to be continuous or discrete. Of course, it seems logical to assume T to be a continuous variable in the sense that the event of interest may occur literally at any time defined on $(0, \infty)$. In many situations, however, this assumption is not realistic for two reasons. Firstly, in many cases, T is not measured accurately enough to be treated as strictly continuous. Respondents can usually give dates and times only in ranges or round numbers, even if encouraged by interviewers to be more precise. Secondly, the events of interest can sometimes only occur at finite particular points in time, which are discrete (taking a finite set of values, for example, $t_1, t_2, \ldots, t_L$).

Regardless of the assumption whether T is a discrete or continuous variable, the main aim of event history analysis is characterizing the probability distribution of the random variable T. An additional objective is typically to gain an understanding on how risk factors and covariates affect the event times. This second objective can be addressed by modeling the probability distribution of T in terms of potentially explanatory variables. Even though these objectives are common to any event history analysis, the way the statistical methods are formulated depends on whether the measurement of the time variable is assumed to be discrete or continuous. We describe in the next subsection possible ways of characterizing the probability distribution of T and give modeling strategies of the probability distribution of T in terms of possible explanatory variables in the section Discrete-Time Event History Models.

Discrete-Event Time Distributions

Let T be a discrete random variable indicating the event time, and t_l the lth discrete-time point, with $l = 1, 2, \ldots$ and $0 < t_1 < t_2 < \ldots$ There are three equivalent ways to characterize the probability distribution of the event time T. The simplest is as $f(t_l) = \Pr(T = t_l)$ or as the probability of experiencing an event at $T = t_l$. Another possibility is via the survival function $S(t_l)$, which is the probability of not having the event before and in time interval t_l or, equivalently, the probability of having the event after t_l. It is defined as follows:

$$S(t_l) = \Pr(T > t_l) = 1 - \Pr(T \leq t_l), \quad l = 1, 2, \ldots$$

A third option is to use the discrete-time hazard probability $h(t_l)$, which is the conditional probability that the event occurs at $T = t_l$ given that it did not occur prior to $T = t_l$ (given $S(t_{l-1})$). Mathematically, the hazard is given as

$$h(t_l) = \Pr(T = t_l | T \geq t_l) = \Pr(T = t_l | T > t_{l-1})$$
$$= \frac{\Pr(T = t_l)}{\Pr(T > t_{l-1})} = \frac{f(t_l)}{S(t_{l-1})} \quad (12.1)$$

What is important is that both $f(t_l)$ and $S(t_l)$ can be expressed in terms of $h(t_l)$. Using the fact that $f(t_l) = S(t_{l-1}) - S(t_l)$, Equation 12.1 can be rewritten as

$$h(t_l) = \frac{S(t_{l-1}) - S(t_l)}{S(t_{l-1})} = 1 - \frac{S(t_l)}{S(t_{l-1})}$$

By rearranging this last equation, we obtain

$$S(t_l) = S(t_{l-1})[1 - h(t_l)] \quad (12.2)$$

Using $S(t_0) = 1$, no individual experienced an event before and in $T = t_0$, this last equation leads to the required expression that

$$S(t_l) = \prod_{k=1}^{l}[1 - h(t_k)]$$

where $\prod$ is a product sign and the term in brackets is a complementary of the hazard function, which is the conditional probability that the event occurs at time t_k given that it did not occur prior to t_k. The equation implies that the survival probability to the end of lth time is the product of survival probabilities at each of earlier time points. By using Equations 12.2 and 12.1, the following expression is also obtained for the probability of experiencing an event at time t_l, $f(t_l)$:

$$f(t_l) = h(t_l)\prod_{k=1}^{l-1}[1 - h(t_k)] \quad (12.3)$$

Estimating Event Time Distribution

The grouped-data or life-table method (Cox, 1972; Merrell, 1947) and the Kaplan-Meier estimator (Kaplan & Meier, 1958) are two descriptive methods for estimating the event time distribution from a sample. Next, we discuss the grouped-data method for discrete-event times.

Grouped-data or life-table method for discrete-event times. The most straightforward way to describe the event history in a sample is to construct grouped data by merging event times in groups or intervals. This method is well known as the life-table method. The life-table method enables the computation of nonparametric estimates of the survival and hazard functions in separate intervals over time. The distribution of event times is divided into a certain number of intervals. For each interval we can then identify the number of subjects entering the respective interval without having experienced the event, the number of cases that experienced the event in the respective interval, and the number of cases that were lost or censored in the respective interval.

Based on those numbers, several additional statistics can be computed.

- **Number of cases at risk (risk set r_l).** This is the number of subjects who are at risk of experiencing the event of interest within the specific interval. This number is the number of cases that entered the respective interval.
- **Proportion of cases that experience the event (hazard h_l).** This proportion is computed as the ratio of the number of cases experiencing the event within the interval divided by the number of cases at risk in the interval.
- **Cumulative proportion surviving (survival function S_l).** This is the cumulative proportion of cases surviving up to the end of respective interval.
- **Median survival time.** This is the survival time at which the cumulative survival function is equal to 0.5.

Life-Table Method for Adolescents' Romantic Relationships Example

Table 12.1 shows a life table for the data on adolescents' experience on sleeping with someone. We have information from 142 individuals on whether the event of sleeping with someone had happened of not and, if it did, when. It turns out that 90.1% of these adolescents experienced the event before the time of data collection.

A natural definition of the beginning time (t_0) for an analysis of this data set is an age at which none of the adolescents experienced the event of interest, or equivalently, an age at which all subjects are at risk of experiencing the event. It does, however, not make sense to start at age 0 because the youngest age at which the event happened is 12, which means that the hazard rate is 0 and the survival probability is 1 for all ages prior to 12. Without loss of information we can, therefore, use age 11 as the beginning time for the event history analysis. By dividing into a series of rows indexing the age intervals (Column 1), a life table for the romantic relationships example in Table 12.1 contains information on the number of adolescents who entered the age interval (Column 2), censored during the age interval (Column 3), and experienced the event sleeping with someone during the age interval (Column 4).

TABLE 12.1

Life Table Describing the Ages of the Event Sleeping With Someone for the First Time for a Sample of 142 Adolescents

	Number			Proportion	
Age interval	Entering interval	Withdrawing during interval (censored)	Slept with someone for the first time during interval	Slept with someone for the first time during interval (hazard)	Has not slept with someone at the end of the interval (survival function)
[11, 12)	142	0			1.0000
[12, 13)	142	0	1	0.0070	0.9930
[13, 14)	141	0	0	0.0000	0.9930
[14, 15)	141	0	2	0.0142	0.9789
[15, 16)	139	0	11	0.0791	0.9014
[16, 17)	128	0	19	0.1484	0.7676
[17, 18)	109	0	23	0.2110	0.6056
[18, 19)	86	0	21	0.2442	0.4577
[19, 20)	65	0	11	0.1692	0.3803
[20, 21)	54	0	20	0.3704	0.2394
[21, 22)	34	0	11	0.3235	0.1620
[22, 23)	23	0	3	0.1304	0.1408
[23, 24)	20	6	3	0.1500	0.1190
[24, 25)	11	8	3	0.2727	0.0865

The age intervals in Table 12.1 partition the times of the event occurrence in such way that each interval contains a range of ages that include the initial time and excludes the concluding time. The width of the intervals is set to 1 year for ease of presentation. Conventional mathematical notation [brackets] denotes inclusions and (parenthesis) denote exclusions. Thus, bracket is used for each interval's initial time while parenthesis is used for the concluding time. In total there are 14 age intervals with each having 1 year length, $[11, 12), [12, 13), \ldots, [24, 25)$. In general, the definition of the time intervals of a life table should be based on a relevant time unit and respect the way events occur. Data whose time unit is days, weeks, or months may require wider intervals compared with data whose time unit is years, but the grouping should always be such that it yields a series of time intervals $[t_0, t_1), [t_1, t_2), \ldots, [t_{l-1}, t_l), [t_l, t_l+1), \ldots$, and so on. No events occur during the 0th interval, which begins at time t_0 and ends just before t_1. This interval represents what is called the *beginning of time*. Any event occurring at t_1 or later but before t_2, is classified as an event happening during the first time interval $[t_1, t_2)$. The lth time interval, $[t_l, t_l+1)$, begins immediately at time t_l and ends just before time t_l+1.

The next column in the life table contains the number of adolescents who enter each successive age interval without experiencing the event or censoring in the previous intervals. This number is the risk set for the discrete-time life-table description. As shown in Column 3 of Table 12.1, censoring happens for some cases in the last two age groups. For these cases, the event sleeping with someone has not happened at the time of data collection. The only known information is that those adolescents have not experienced the event until ages 24 (in the age interval $[23, 24)$) and 25 (in the age interval $[24, 25)$), respectively. Column 4 contains the number of events that occurred in each age interval. As can be seen, the risk set or the number in Column 2 for each interval is the risk set of previous interval minus the sum of the numbers in Columns 3 and 4 of the previous interval.

Column 5 in Table 12.1 shows the proportion of each interval's risk set that experiences the event during the interval. Thus, these are conditional probabilities (or hazards) that the event occurs to an individual in lth interval given that the event did not occur to that person before the lth interval. In fact, the proportions in Column 6 are maximum likelihood estimates of the discrete-time hazard given in Equation 12.1 (Singer & Willett, 1993, 2003). That means, we estimate the discrete-time hazard for each interval in the life table by the proportion of the risk set that experiences the event within the interval. These proportions are mathematically obtained by dividing the numbers in Column 4 by the numbers in Column 2, that is,

$$\hat{h}(t_l) = \frac{\text{number of events in interval } l}{\text{number at risk in interval } l} \quad (12.4)$$

where $\hat{h}(t_l)$ is an estimate of the discrete hazard probability at time t in interval l.

Hence, the estimate of hazard is $\hat{h}(t_1) = 0.0070$ for a time in the first interval, and the estimate is 0 for the second interval as none of the adolescents experienced the event in the second interval, $\hat{h}(t_3) = 0.0142$, and so on. The discrete-time hazard is a probability, which implies that its value always lies between 0 and 1. A helpful way of examining the time dependence of the hazard probabilities is to graph their values over time. The top panel of Figure 12.1 plots the estimated hazard function based on the proportions in Column 5 of Table 12.1. The risk of event occurrence (sleeping with someone for the first time) among the adolescents at ages below 16 is small. The risk in general increases with time starting from age 16 until age 19 where it drops suddenly. It again increases in the interval $[20, 21)$ and starts to decrease thereafter. Finally, there is an increase from starting from age 23. In general, the "risky" time periods for experiencing the event are from age 16 with a high peak at age 20. The estimated hazard probabilities at each time interval describe the distribution of event occurrence for a random sample of individuals from a homogenous population. In next section, Discrete-Time Event History Models, we show

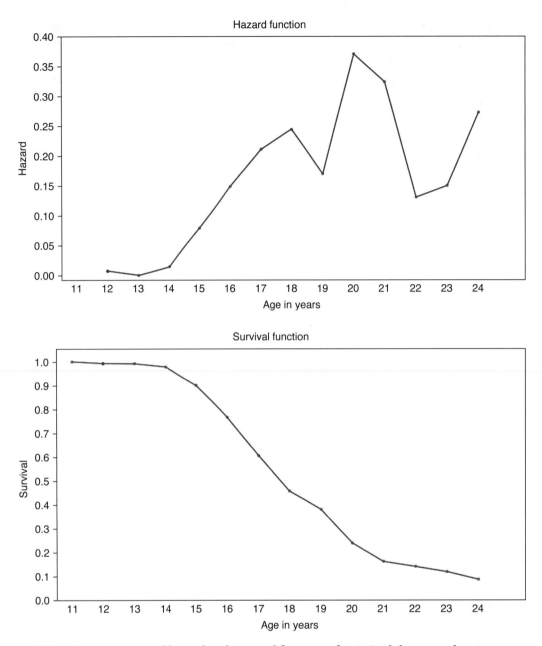

FIGURE 12.1. Estimated hazard and survival functions for 142 adolescents sleeping with someone for the first time.

how individual difference in the hazard probabilities can be investigated using regression models including predictor variables (e.g., gender and education level).

The proportion of adolescents who have not slept with someone until the end of each time interval (who survived) is shown in Column 6 of Table 12.1. This proportion is an estimate of the survival function given in Equation 12.2. Because no one has experienced the event before age 12, the estimate of survival function for the 0th interval, $\hat{S}(t_0)$, is 1. The estimate for the 1st interval is then the product of the survival function of the 0th interval and the probability of surviving (not having the event) during the 1st interval. This latter probability is just the complement of the hazard probability in the 1st interval, $1 - \hat{h}(t_1) = 1 - 0.0070$. Thus, the estimate of the survival function for the 1st interval is $\hat{S}(t_1) = \hat{S}(t_0)[1 - \hat{h}(t_1)] = 1 \times [1 - 0.0070] = 0.9930$, implying that 99.3% of the adolescents did not experience the event until the end of the 1st interval. In general, the estimate of the hazard function for *l*th interval is

$$\hat{S}(t_l) = \hat{S}(t_{l-1})\left[1 - \hat{h}(t_l)\right] \quad (12.5)$$

The survival function over time declines to 0, which is the lower bound for the survival probability. A useful way to examine the survival function is again to graph the estimates of survival function over time. The bottom panel of Figure 12.1 graphs the survival function based on the estimates in Column 6 of Table 12.1. Unlike the hazard function that can increase, decrease, or remain constant over time, the survival function never increases. For intervals with no events occurring (for example interval [13, 14)), the survival function remains steady at the value of previous interval. The survival function drops rapidly in those periods where the hazard is high, and the survival function declines slowly at the time periods with low hazard.

The life-table estimates of the discrete-time hazard and survival functions yield two alternative descriptions of the event time's distribution. The interest is usually also on the summary statistics or center of the distribution. If there were no censoring, the center of the event time distribution could be estimated using sample mean. Due to censoring, however, the event time is not known for all individuals, and the sample mean cannot be used as an estimate of the center of the distribution. Instead, another measure of central tendency is often used in event history analysis: the median survival time. As a measure of center of the distribution, the estimated median survival time is the value of time (here age) for which the value of the estimated survival function is 0.5. The median survival time, or the 50th percentile for the survival function, is not necessarily the same as the point in time up to which 50% of the sample survived without the event. The median survival time corresponds to the point in time up to which 50% of the sample survived without the event only if there were no censored observations prior to this time (which is the case in the adolescents' romantic relationships example).

A closer look at the estimate of the survival function in Column 7 of Table 12.1 shows that 0.6056 of the adolescents survived to the end of the interval [17, 18) and the proportion drops below 0.5 to 0.4577 in the interval [18, 19). The median survival time, therefore, could be reported as age between 17 and 18. If needed, the estimate of median survival time can be more accurately obtained by interpolation between the two intervals that have survival estimates close to 0.5 on both sides at the top and bottom. In the current example, the two intervals are [17, 18) and [18, 19). Let t_m be the initial time for the interval when the sample survival function is just above 0.5 (age 17), let $\hat{S}(t_m)$ represent the value of the sample survival function of that interval, let t_{m+1} and $\hat{S}(t_{m+1})$ be the initial time and sample survival function, respectively, for the following interval (when the survival function is just below 0.5). Then, following linear interpolation, the estimated median survival time is

$$\hat{Mdn} = t_m + \left[\frac{\hat{S}(t_m) - 0.5}{\hat{S}(t_m) - \hat{S}(t_{m+1})}\right](t_{m+1} - t_m) \quad (12.6)$$

For the current example the interpolation is illustrated using the following simple sketch.

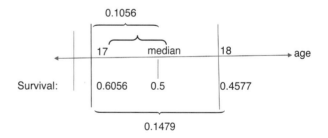

$$\text{Median} = 17 + [(0.6056 - 0.5)/(0.6056 - 0.4577)]$$
$$(18 - 17)$$
$$= 17 + (0.1056)/(0.1479) = 17.7$$

In our application there are no censored cases for the intervals prior to [18, 19), which contains the median survival time. As a result, the median survival time 17.7 is also the age at which 50% of the sample units experienced the event.

Hazard functions are the most useful tools in describing patterns of event occurrence as they are sensitive to the unique risk associated with each time period while the survival functions accumulate information across time periods. Thus, by examining the variation over time in the magnitude of the hazard function, we identify when events are likely, or unlikely, to occur. The median survival time identifies the center of the distribution, and it tells little about the distribution of event times. It is an "average" event time but relatively less sensitive to the extreme values.

The life-table method for estimating hazard and survival functions using discrete-time event data is similar to the actuarial method for estimating these functions using continuous-time event data. These methods differ only in the assumption about the occurrence of events and censorings within intervals. The discrete-time method assumes events and censorings occur at the endpoint of the time interval, which means that all those who entered the interval are in the risk set throughout the interval. The actuarial method, however, assumes that both events and censorings are distributed equally throughout the interval, which means that the risk set changes during an interval. In the actuarial method, the risk set is estimated as the average number of person at risk during the interval, which leads to slight modifications of Equations 12.4 and 12.5 for this method. More details about the actuarial method are given elsewhere (Cutler & Ederer, 1958; Kaas et al., 2008; Mould, 1976; Singer & Willett, 2003).

The description and estimation of the event time distributions discussed so far assumes a single homogeneous group of subjects. However, in practice researchers are also interested in identifying factors that affect the occurrence and timing of the event of interest. For example, in intervention or experimental studies, the interest is to estimate the effects of the intervention on the probability of occurrence of the event over time. Therefore, we move from the discussion of method for describing event time distribution to regression models that allow including predictors such as sociodemographic covariates and experimental conditions. The objective is to determine the relationship between those predictors and the likelihood of event occurrence. The specific modeling approach again depends on whether the event time is treated as discrete or continuous. We, therefore, in the following section, discuss assumption of discrete-event times, and we refer readers to Blossfeld and Rohwer (2002), Broström (2022), Collett (2015), and Vermunt (1997) for well-developed methodologies on continuous event time models. Regression models for discrete-event time data are better known in literature as discrete-time survival models (DTSMs). Even though originally discrete and continuous time models were formulated separately by Cox (1972), asymptotically the two models are equivalent. That is, as the discrete-time interval get smaller and smaller, a DTSM becomes more and more similar to a continuous time model (Allison, 1982; D'Agostino et al., 1990; Petersen, 1991; Thompson, 1977; Yamaguchi, 1991).

DISCRETE-TIME EVENT HISTORY MODELS

Cox (1972) was the first to propose models for censored data. He proposed discrete-time models for tied event data alongside his formulation of proportional hazard modeling for continuous time data. A *tie* refers to the situation in which several subjects experience the event at the same specific time, which is something that in a strict continuous-time framework should not occur. When there are many ties in the data, a discrete-time model is more appropriate. The discrete-time modeling approach involves using a logistic regression model for a person–period data set. For all time points until a person either experiences the event or is censored, the dependent variable is an indicator of whether or not an individual experienced the event at that same point in time (Allison, 1982; Singer & Willett, 1993).

As discussed in the previous section, in contrast to the other distributions for event history data, the hazard function is the most important element in event history analysis for at least three reasons.

First, it shows the risk of event occurrence at each time period; it tells us whether and when an event is likely to occur. Second, the event history analysis is able to deal with censored cases because the hazard always includes both censored and noncensored cases. Third, the sample survival function cannot be computed directly for a given time point when there is censoring, but the survival function can be estimated indirectly from the hazard function. In general, the mathematical relationships described earlier between the distributions of event history data can be used to obtain estimates of other distributions ($S(t_l)$ and $f(t_l)$) if the estimate of hazard is known. By using the hazard $h(t_l)$ as the left-hand side variable in a regression model, one can relate hazard distribution to the covariates of interest. Because hazards are (conditional) probabilities bounded by 0 and 1, they can be transformed using logit link function so that the transformed hazard is unbounded and can easily be regressed on covariates and time variables. That means, instead of modeling the hazard probability directly, the logit of the hazard probability is used as the left-hand side variable in a (generalized) linear model. The logit hazard at time $T = t_l$ for a person with covariate value X is given by

$$\text{logit}[h_X(t_l)] = Log_e\left[\frac{h_X(t_l)}{1-h_X(t_l)}\right] = \alpha_l D_l + \beta X \quad (12.7)$$

where $Log_e[c]$ is the natural logarithm of c, $h_X(t_l)$ is the hazard or conditional event probability at time t_l for a person with covariate value X, D_l is a dummy variable indicating the time period ($D_l = 1$, if $T = t_l$ and 0 otherwise), α_l is the intercept parameter at time point $T = t_l$ representing the logit hazard when $X = 0$ (baseline logit hazard at time t_l), and β is the slope parameter that shows the effect of the covariate X on the logit hazard. When there are more covariates, Equation 12.7 can be extended by including the covariates and corresponding β parameters at the right-hand side of the equation. That means, for a person with covariate values $X_1, X_2, \ldots, X_p$ the logit hazard is

$$\text{logit}[h_X(t_l)] = Log_e\left[\frac{h_{X_p}(t_l)}{1-h_{X_p}(t_l)}\right]$$
$$= \alpha_l D_l + \beta_1 X_1 + \beta_2 X_2 + \cdots + \beta_p X_p$$
$$= \alpha_l + \sum_{k=1}^{p} \beta_k X_k \quad (12.8)$$

where $h_{X_p}(t_l)$ is the hazard or conditional probability at time t_l for a person with p covariate values $X_1, X_2, \ldots, X_p$, and β_k is the parameter that shows the effect of the covariate X_k on the logit hazard controlling for other covariates in the model, $k = 1, \ldots, p$.

Equation 12.8 is a discrete-time event history model. When the value of all covariates are equal to zero, the logit hazard in Equation 12.8 reduces to the baseline logit hazard

$$\text{logit}(h_0(t_l)) = Log_e\left[\frac{h_0(t_l)}{1-h_0(t_l)}\right] = \alpha_l D_l \quad (12.9)$$

where $h_0(t_l)$ is the baseline hazard or conditional probability with covariate values equal to 0 at time t_l.

The expression $\frac{h_{X_p}(t_l)}{1-h_{X_p}(t_l)}$ is the odds of event occurrence at time t_l, and the model in Equation 12.8 represents the log-odds of event occurrence as a function of time period and covariates. By using an inverse function of the natural logarithm, exponential function, in Equation 12.8, the odds of an event can be expressed as

$$\frac{h_{X_p}(t_l)}{1-h_{X_p}(t_l)} = \exp(\alpha_l D_l)\exp\left(\sum_{k=1}^{p}\beta_k X_k\right) \quad (12.10)$$

By using Equation 12.9, this last equation can be rewritten as

$$\frac{h_{X_p}(t_l)}{1-h_{X_p}(t_l)} = \frac{h_0(t_l)}{1-h_0(t_l)}\exp\left(\sum_{k=1}^{p}\beta_k X_k\right) \quad (12.11)$$

The discrete-time event history model, therefore, implies that the odds of having the event at each discrete-time point are $\exp(\sum_{k=1}^{p}\beta_k X_k)$ times for subjects characterized by covariate values $X_1, X_2, \ldots, X_p$ compared with subjects in the baseline group (subjects characterized by covariate values $X_1 = 0, X_2 = 0, \ldots, X_p = 0$). The model also implies that, controlling for other covariates, an increase in one unit of X_k increases (or decreases depending on the sign of β_k) the odds of having the event $\exp(\beta_k)$ times. When the covariate effects are time-independent (that is, when there are no time-covariate interactions), the model is a proportional odds model. That means, the ratio of odds of having an event among a group characterized by particular covariate values and the baseline group, $\dfrac{h_{X_p}(t_l)}{1-h_{X_p}(t_l)} \Big/ \dfrac{h_0(t_l)}{1-h_0(t_l)}$, is constant over time. The proportional odds model is similar to the Cox proportional hazards model for continuous event times with respect to this property. While the ratio of odds is time-constant for the proportional odds model, the ratio of hazard rates is time-constant for the Cox's proportional hazards model. As discussed in more detail in the next section, the proportional odds assumption can be tested and relaxed by including interaction effects of time and covariates in the model.

An advantage of the discrete-time event history model compared with the continuous-time event history model is that we can use the usual logistic regression options of most available computer programs for the estimation of the parameters. The structure of the input data, however, differs between the usual logistic regression analysis and the use of logistic regression for discrete-time event history analysis. While the former uses one observation for each sample subject, the latter uses multiple observations for each subject. Accordingly, the event history data for the logistic regression must be arranged in a specific way as described in the next subsection.

Construction of Input Data

The discrete-event time model described above uses a logistic regression approach. However, unlike standard logistic regression analysis, such an analysis is not based on a person-oriented data set, but instead it requires a person–period data set in which each person may have a different number of records depending on the duration or stay in the risk set. In a typical person-oriented data set, each person has one record (case) of data. Because researchers often keep event history data in a person-oriented data set format, conversion to a person–period data set that contains for each person as many records as the time (period) they stay in the risk set without experiencing the event or censoring is needed. Table 12.2 illustrates such a conversion using three subjects from the adolescents' romantic relationships data. The smallest event time is 12, and the maximum is 24. Among the three adolescents whose data on some of the variables are shown in Table 12.2, the event times are known for the first and third (ID 2 and 12 reported event time at age 15). An adolescent with ID 9 is censored, that is, the event has not occurred during data collection and his age is 24. In the converted person–period data set, subjects have different number of records depending on how long they stay before they experience the event or censoring. The period variable is included in the data set to indicate the time to which the corresponding record refers for each adolescent from age 12 and above. Since the first event occurs in the data set at age 12, interest in event history is restricted to ages 12 and above. The period variable takes on the values 12, 13, 14, and 15 for each of adolescent with ID 2 and 12 to indicate that these four records describe their corresponding status in the periods from age 12 until the occurrence of the event at age 15. For the adolescent with ID 9, the variable period takes on the values 12 through 24 to indicate that those are the ages represented in the 13 records. The set of dummy variables D_{12} through D_{24} are also created to represent each time period in the logistic regression model for the discrete-time event history model. The dummy variable $D_l = 1$, if period $= t_l$ and 0 otherwise. A dichotomous event indicator is created for the occurrence of sleeping with someone for the first time to indicate whether a person experiences the event during the time period concerned (0 = no event, 1 = event). For each individual, the event indicator is 0 in every record except the last. Noncensored adolescents experience the event in their last

TABLE 12.2

Conversion of a Person-Oriented Data Set Into a Person–Period Data Set for Adolescents' Relationships Data

Original data set (person-oriented data set)

ID	Time	Censor	Gender
2	15	No	Female
9	24	Yes	Male
12	15	No	Male

Converted person–period data set

ID	Period	D_{12}	D_{13}	D_{14}	D_{15}	D_{16}	D_{17}	D_{18}	D_{19}	D_{20}	D_{21}	D_{22}	D_{23}	D_{24}	Sleeping with someone (event)	Gender
2	12	1	0	0	0	0	0	0	0	0	0	0	0	0	0	Female
2	13	0	1	0	0	0	0	0	0	0	0	0	0	0	0	Female
2	14	0	0	1	0	0	0	0	0	0	0	0	0	0	0	Female
2	15	0	0	0	1	0	0	0	0	0	0	0	0	0	1	Female
9	12	1	0	0	0	0	0	0	0	0	0	0	0	0	0	Male
9	13	0	1	0	0	0	0	0	0	0	0	0	0	0	0	Male
9	14	0	0	1	0	0	0	0	0	0	0	0	0	0	0	Male
9	15	0	0	0	1	0	0	0	0	0	0	0	0	0	0	Male
9	16	0	0	0	0	1	0	0	0	0	0	0	0	0	0	Male
9	17	0	0	0	0	0	1	0	0	0	0	0	0	0	0	Male
9	18	0	0	0	0	0	0	1	0	0	0	0	0	0	0	Male
9	19	0	0	0	0	0	0	0	1	0	0	0	0	0	0	Male
9	20	0	0	0	0	0	0	0	0	1	0	0	0	0	0	Male
9	21	0	0	0	0	0	0	0	0	0	1	0	0	0	0	Male
9	22	0	0	0	0	0	0	0	0	0	0	1	0	0	0	Male
9	23	0	0	0	0	0	0	0	0	0	0	0	1	0	0	Male
9	24	0	0	0	0	0	0	0	0	0	0	0	0	1	0	Male
12	12	1	0	0	0	0	0	0	0	0	0	0	0	0	0	Male
12	13	0	1	0	0	0	0	0	0	0	0	0	0	0	0	Male
12	14	0	0	1	0	0	0	0	0	0	0	0	0	0	0	Male
12	15	0	0	0	1	0	0	0	0	0	0	0	0	0	1	Male

period, so the variable event takes on the value 1 in that last period as shown for ID 2 and 12. Censored adolescents never experience at the periods shown in the data, so the variable event remains 0 throughout the records as shown for ID 9. Values of the time-constant covariates are repeated in each time period. Only values for the covariate gender are shown in Table 12.2 due to space limitation. SPSS (IBM Corp., 2020), SAS (SAS Institute., 2013), and R software (R Core Team, 2021) syntaxes to convert the person-oriented data set to person–period data set are given in Appendix 12.1.

The person–period data set contains all information on survival time, including the information for censored observations. Once a person–period data set is created, existing procedures in general statistical packages can be directly used for event history analysis without any modifications for censoring. As a descriptive analysis, a cross-tabulation of the variables period and event that can be obtained using CROSSTABS procedure of SPSS or SAS procedure FREQ (SAS Institute) gives estimates of hazard or conditional probability at each time period as shown in Column 5 of Table 12.1.

Maximum Likelihood Estimates

The likelihood function (Myung, 2003) for the discrete-event time model expresses the probability that we would observe the specific pattern of event occurrence actually observed over time. The likelihood function is composed of as many terms as there are records in the person–period data set. The probability that the ith individual experiences the event at time period t_l, given that the event has not occurred before, is $h_i(t_l)$. During the time period when individual i experiences the event (the variable event = 1 in the person–period data set), they contribute $h_i(t_l)$ to the likelihood function. The probability that ith individual does not experience the event in time period t_l, given that the event has not occurred before, is $[1 - h_i(t_l)]$. During the time periods when individual i does not experience the event (when the variable event = 0), they contribute $[1 - h_i(t_l)]$ to the likelihood function. The contributions are mathematically expressed using the likelihood function as

$$\text{Likelihood} = \prod_{i=1}^{n} \prod_{l=1}^{L_i} h_i(t_l)^{event_{il}} [1 - h_i(t_l)]^{(1 - event_{il})}$$

(12.12)

where $\prod$ is a product sign, n is the total number of subjects (sample size), L_i is the number of records for ith person in the person–period data set and $event_{il}$ is the value on the variable event (either 0 or 1) for ith person at lth period. The two product signs ensure that the likelihood function multiplies the contributions of each record in the person–period data set across all individuals via the first product sign and across all time periods for each individual via the second product sign. Since event is coded with either 0 or 1, only one of the two terms ($h_i(t_l)$ or $[1 - h_i(t_l)]$) contributes to the likelihood function at each record in the person–period data set. In time period when the event does occur, only the first term remains while the second term becomes 1. In time periods when the event does not occur, only the second term remains while the first term becomes 1.

By using the notation $h_{Xp}(t_l)$ for the conditional probability of an ith individual with p covariates from Equation 12.8 in Equation 12.12 instead of $h_i(t_l)$, the likelihood function can be written as a function of unknown parameters αs for the baseline hazards and βs for the effects of the covariates. The objective of maximum likelihood estimation is to find estimates of the parameters that maximize the likelihood function. In practice the logarithm of the likelihood (log-likelihood) function is used as it is mathematically more tractable. Thus, the values of αs and βs that maximize the log-likelihood function should be obtained. In fact, the routines for logistic regression model available in most standard statistical packages (e.g., SPSS, SAS, Stata, R) provide estimates of the parameters of the discrete-event time model that maximize the log-likelihood function when a proper person–period data set is used. Thus, statistical routines of logistic regression to regress the event indicator variable on the dummy variables for time indicators and the selected p covariates in the person–period data set can be used to obtain the maximum likelihood estimates of the parameters in the discrete-event time model.

Example: Discrete-Event Time Model for Adolescents' Romantic Relationships Data

To illustrate the procedures of fitting, interpreting, and testing statistical statements (hypothesis) for the discrete-event time model, we use the adolescents' relationships data. The person–period data set with records of 1093 for the event of sleeping with someone for the first time and the covariates youth-centrism (YC), gender (G), education (E), and dummy variable D_l as indicator of time period t_l (see the section Construction of Input Data) is used to fit the following models:

Model 1: $\text{logit}(h_0(t_l)) = \alpha_l D_l$
Model 2: $\text{logit}(h_X(t_l)) = \alpha_l D_l + \beta_1 YC$
Model 3: $\text{logit}(h_X(t_l)) = \alpha_l D_l + \beta_2 G + \beta_3 E$
Model 4: $\text{logit}(h_X(t_l)) = \alpha_l D_l + \beta_1 YC + \beta_2 G + \beta_3 E$

Model 1 contains only the time periods, and it describes the hazard profile over time. The model is estimated using the dummy variables for time with a no intercept option of logistic model in standard software. Model 1 helps to find the risk of event occurrence at each time period and identify the important periods (ages) where the event is common among the adolescents. The parameters αs for each time period are the logit of the hazard (log odds). From these parameters the odds of event occurrence can be obtained by exponentiation of the parameters. The conditional probabilities or hazards of event occurrence can be obtained from the parameter estimates using

$$h(t_l) = \frac{1}{1+\exp[-(\alpha_l)]} \quad (12.13)$$

The estimates of the parameters of discrete-event time model and the corresponding hazards for the baseline or reference group (when covariate values YC, G, and E are equal to 0) under each of the four models fitted for the adolescents' relationships data are shown in Table 12.3. An increase in hazard shows higher risk of event occurrence. A closer look at hazards (based on estimates of parameters) in Model 1 shows that this baseline model (a model without a covariate) gives exactly the result on hazard probability of a life-table analysis we have in Table 12.1. Thus, using the baseline model the hazard at each time period computed in the life table can be obtained.

The baseline model estimates the overall population profile of the risk across time and indicates when events are more likely to occur. In order to know whether the hazard profile is different for adolescents with different values on the covariate youth centric, the dummy variable youth centric (YC = 1 if youth centric and 0 if not youth centric) is considered in addition to the time period variables as given in Model 2. The parameter estimates are given under Model 2 in Table 12.3. The estimates of the parameters $\alpha_{12}, \alpha_{13}, \ldots, \alpha_{23}, \alpha_{24}$ under Model 2 represent the baseline log odds of hazard profile at each of the time periods for the nonyouth-centric group of adolescents (a reference group with YC = 0). The parameter β_1 is a shift parameter that displaces the baseline log odds of hazard profile for the youth-centric group (YC = 1). The estimated log odds for YC is 0.310 with corresponding odds ratio of 1.363 (exp(0.310)). This indicates that youth-centric adolescents are about 1.4 times more likely than nonyouth-centric adolescents to experience the event sleeping with someone for the first time (if at risk).

Model 3 contains the covariates G and E in addition to the time-period dummy variables. The baseline (or reference group) contains subjects with value 0 for G and E, that is, low-educated female adolescents. The estimates of the parameters αs for the reference group is shown as log odds under Model 3 in Table 12.3. The corresponding hazard (probability) of event occurrence at each time for the reference group is also shown in Table 12.3 under the column Model 3. The parameter β_2 in Model 3 is a shift parameter that displaces the baseline log odds of hazard profile for male adolescents (G = 1) keeping the values of E constant. The estimated log odds for G in Model 3 is –0.542 with the corresponding odds ratio of 0.581 (exp(–0.542)), controlling for education. Similarly, the parameter β_3 in Model 3 is a shift parameter that displaces the baseline log odds of hazard profile for highly educated adolescents (E = 1) keeping G constant. The estimated log odds for E is –0.112 with the corresponding odds ratio of 0.894 (exp(–0.112)), controlling for G.

Model 4 includes the covariates YC, G, and E in addition to the time-period dummy variables. The baseline (or reference group) consists of subjects with value 0 for YC, G, and E, that is nonyouth-centric, low-educated, female adolescent. The estimates of the parameters αs for the reference group is shown as log odds under Model 4 in Table 12.3. The corresponding hazard (probability) of event occurrence at each time for the reference group are shown in the last columns of Table 12.3. The parameter β_1 in Model 4 is a shift parameter that displaces the baseline log odds of hazard profile for the youth-centric group (YC = 1) keeping gender and education constant. The estimated log odds for YC is 0.483 with the corresponding odds ratio of 1.620 (exp(0.483)), controlling G and E. Similarly, the parameter β_2 in Model 4 is a shift parameter that displaces the baseline log odds of hazard profile for male

TABLE 12.3
Parameter Estimates and Goodness of Fit Statistic for the Discrete-Event Time Models Fitted to Adolescents' Relationships Data

Covariate	Parameter	Model 1		Model 2		Model 3		Model 4	
		Log odds (estimates)	Baseline hazard	Log odds (estimates)	Baseline hazard	Log odds (estimates)	Baseline hazard	Log odds (estimates)	Baseline hazard
D_{12}	α_{12}	−4.949	0.0070	−5.062	0.0063	−4.780	0.0083	−4.872	0.0076
D_{13}	α_{13}	−21.203	0.0000	−21.312	0.0000	−21.053	0.0000	−21.135	0.0000
D_{14}	α_{14}	−4.241	0.0142	−4.353	0.0127	−4.071	0.0168	−4.158	0.0157
D_{15}	α_{15}	−2.454	0.0791	−2.566	0.0714	−2.274	0.0933	−2.360	0.0863
D_{16}	α_{16}	−1.747	0.1484	−1.851	0.1358	−1.552	0.1748	−1.625	0.1645
D_{17}	α_{17}	−1.319	0.2110	−1.421	0.1945	−1.165	0.2378	−1.236	0.2251
D_{18}	α_{18}	−1.130	0.2442	−1.232	0.2258	−0.978	0.2733	−1.043	0.2606
D_{19}	α_{19}	−1.591	0.1692	−1.683	0.1567	−1.363	0.2038	−1.418	0.1950
D_{20}	α_{20}	−0.531	0.3703	−0.625	0.3486	−0.318	0.4212	−0.364	0.4100
D_{21}	α_{21}	−0.738	0.3234	−0.823	0.3051	−0.417	0.3972	−0.447	0.3901
D_{22}	α_{22}	−1.897	0.1304	−1.956	0.1239	−1.564	0.1731	−1.543	0.1761
D_{23}	α_{23}	−1.735	0.1500	−1.785	0.1437	−1.389	0.1996	−1.360	0.2042
D_{24}	α_{24}	−0.981	0.2727	−1.011	0.2668	−0.670	0.3385	−0.656	0.3416
Youth-centrism (YC, yes = 1)	β_1			0.310				0.483	
Gender (G) (male = 1)	β_2					−0.542		−0.592	
Education (E) (high = 1)	β_3					−0.112		−0.059	
−2LL		645.979		643.933		623.299		619.356	

adolescents (G = 1) keeping the values of YC and E constant. The estimated log odds for G is –0.592 with the corresponding odds ratio of 0.553 (exp(–0.592)), controlling YC and E. Thus, the odds of sleeping with someone for the first time for boys is 0.553 times that for girls. The estimate of β_3 is interpreted in a similar fashion for E by keeping YC and G constant.

The likelihood ratio test (e.g., Rao, 1973) is used to test the significance of the effects of the covariates in each of the models. The –2 log likelihood statistic (–2LL), which is often displayed in outputs from commonly used statistical software (e.g., SPSS) for logistic regression routine, is the deviance statistic for the discrete-event history models. A deviance statistic is always greater than 0, and the smaller the deviance the better the fit of the model to the observed data. The last row of Table 12.3 shows the deviance statistics for the four models we fit for the adolescents' romantic relationships data.

A likelihood ratio test compares deviance statistics for the comparison of two nested models. Two models are called *nested* when both contain the same parameters and one of the models has at least one additional parameter. That is, one is obtained by having a constraint on the additional parameters in the other model. In the current example, Model 1 can be obtained from all other models by imposing constraints that the parameters corresponding to the covariates YC, G, and E are set to 0. Thus, Model 1 is nested within all other models. Model 4 contains all parameters involved in other models. Thus, Model 4 is the biggest model with all parameters of interest. For the likelihood ratio test, the difference in deviance statistics for two nested models will asymptotically have a chi-square distribution on k degrees of freedom (df), where k is the number of additional parameters in a bigger model in terms of parameters. When the difference in deviance statistic is larger than the critical value for chi-square distribution, we reject the null hypothesis that the model with fewer number of parameters (reduced model) and conclude that some of the additional covariates in the model with more number of parameters (full model) have significant effect on the log odds of event occurrence. When the difference in the deviance statistic is small, we fail to reject the reduced parsimonious model and we conclude that the reduced model is as good as the full model. In the current example, the difference between deviance statistics for Model 1 and Model 2 is 2.046 (= 645.979 – 643.933), which is smaller than the critical value of chi-square distribution with df =1 at a 5% level of significance ($\chi^2_{1(0.05)}$ = 3.84). Thus, Model 2 is not statistically better than Model 1 and the covariate YC alone has no effect on the log odds of event occurrence. However, it turns out that the covariate YC indeed has an effect after the variables G and E are controlled as discussed in the next section. The difference in deviance statistics between Model 1 and Model 3 is 22.680 (= 645.979 – 623.299). Because there are two more parameters in Model 3 compared with Model 1 (βs for G and E), the df for the chi-square is now 2. Because the difference in deviance, 22.680 is greater than the chi-square value ($\chi^2_{2(0.05)}$ = 5.99), we reject the reduced model (Model 1) and conclude that Model 3 gives a better fit of the data in such a way that at least one of the covariates involved in the model (G and E) have significant effect on the log odds of event occurrence. Having Model 3, which contains G and E, we may be interested to know the effect of YC given that G and E are controlled. We can compare Models 3 and 4 for that purpose. The comparison between Models 1 and 2 gives the effect of YC without controlling the variables G and E. However, the comparison between Models 3 and 4 helps to test whether YC has an effect on hazard probabilities after controlling the covariates G and E.

The difference in deviance statistics between Model 3 and Model 4 is 3.943 (= 623.299 – 619.356). Because there is only one more parameter in Model 4 compared with Model 3 (β_1 for YC), the df for the chi-square is 1. Because the difference in deviance, 3.943, is slightly greater than the chi-square value ($\chi^2_{1(0.05)}$ = 3.84), we conclude that YC has significant effect after controlling the covariates G and E.

Polynomial Specification of Time Period

The dummy variables for time period that included in the discrete-event time model helps to maintain the shape of the baseline logit hazard function. The use of $T_1, T_2, \ldots, T_L$ as a representation of the L discrete-time points in the model puts no specification on the shape of the hazard functions and further makes the interpretation of the parameters in the discrete-event history model easier. Each of the coefficients of the dummy variables for time periods, α_l, is interpreted as the population value of logit hazard in time period l for the baseline group, for $l = 1, 2, \ldots, L$. The use of dummy variables representation for time periods in the model is encouraged as it does not put any constraint on the shape of the baseline model and facilitates interpretation of the coefficients. However, when there are many discrete-time periods, L is large; the model needs the inclusion of many dummy variables representation for the time periods. This leads the model to be overparameterized and lacking parsimony (Efron, 1988; Fahrmeir & Wagenpfeil, 1996; Singer & Willett, 2003). Thus, using an alternative approach for the representation of time periods in the discrete-event time model is required when there are many time points. The option of considering the time periods as if they are continuous covariates and a specification of polynomial model for the baseline logit hazard function gives a more parsimonious model provided that the fit of the model to the data is not compromised (Mantel & Hankey, 1978; Singer & Willett, 2003). The variable period in person–period data set whose values represent the time period that the record describes, as shown in Table 12.2, can easily be used as a continuous covariate in polynomial representation of time in the discrete-event time models. The polynomial representation could be linear, quadratic, cubic, or a higher degree polynomial. The choice could also be a logarithmic transformation of time or any other kind of function of time depending on the theoretical or practical motivation for such functions. In situations where the polynomial model is not prespecified, search for the appropriate polynomial model can begin from the most simple one to the more complex models guided by statistical test for model comparison. As outlined by Singer and Willett (2003), a formal goodness of test should confirm that the selected polynomial fits the data as good as the model with dummy variable representation of time period ("general" model). That means, a likelihood ratio test should confirm that there is no statistically significance difference between a polynomial model representation of time period for baseline logit hazard and Model 1, in the adolescents' relationships data example. Table 12.4 displays the deviance statistics and the differences in deviance statistics for the likelihood ratio test to identify an appropriate polynomial representation of time periods for the adolescents' relationships data. The df for the

TABLE 12.4

Polynomial Representations for Time Period in a Baseline Discrete-Event Time Model for Adolescents' Relationships Data

	Polynomial model for the baseline logit hazard	Number of parameters	−2LL	Difference in −2LL in comparison to Previous model	Difference in −2LL in comparison to General model
Linear	$\text{logit}(h_0(t_i)) = a_0 + b_1(\text{period}_i - 12)$	2	704.967		58.988
Quadratic	$\text{logit}(h_0(t_i)) = a_0 + b_1(\text{period}_i - 12) + b_2(\text{period}_i - 12)^2$	3	663.291	41.676	17.312
Cubic	$\text{logit}(h_0(t_i)) = a_0 + b_1(\text{period}_i - 12) + b_2(\text{period}_i - 12)^2 + b_3(\text{period}_i - 12)^3$	4	660.710	2.581	14.731
General	$\text{logit}(h_0(t_i)) = \alpha_{12} T_{12} + \cdots + \alpha_{24} T_{24}$	13	645.979		

test is the difference in the number of parameters in the models to be compared. The difference in deviance statistics between the linear and the general model, 58.988, is greater than the chi-square value ($\chi^2_{11(0.05)} = 19.68$). Thus, the fit of the linear model is not as good as the general model. The next candidate model is the quadratic model. The difference in deviance statistics between quadratic and general models, 17.312, is less than the chi-square value ($\chi^2_{10(0.05)} = 18.31$). Thus, the fit of the quadratic model is as good as the general model. We found the same result for the cubic model. A comparison between the quadratic and cubic models, however, shows that the cubic model is not significantly better than the quadratic model (the difference in deviances, 2.581, is less than chi-square value ($\chi^2_{1(0.05)} = 3.84$)). Thus, quadratic polynomial representation of the time periods is parsimonious in its number of parameters while it fits the data as well as the general model for the discrete-event time models for the adolescents' romantic relationships data.

The parameters in the polynomial models are estimated using the same procedure as earlier using maximum likelihood method. The logistic regression model routines in the commonly used software can be used with a little modification of the data set. First, a new variable needs to be formed from the variable period within the person–period data set. Then, depending on the degree of the polynomial that we want to fit, a series of additional variables should be recomputed from the new variable to represent each polynomial term in the model. For example, in the current data example, a new variable ($period - 12$) is first computed from the variable period and then, for the representation of quadratic term ($period - 12$)^2, is recomputed. In general, the new variable can be obtained by subtracting a constant c from period ($period - c$) and then other series of variables can be obtained by taking the power of this variable to represent each polynomial term in the model. The choice of the constant c is arbitrary, however; c should be within the range of the observed event time periods. The constant c is in fact the time period at which the estimated logit hazard (probability) of event occurrence for the baseline group is the estimate of the intercept in the polynomial model. For example, the estimate of the parameter a_0 for the current example is the sample estimate of the logit hazard of event occurrence for the baseline group at time period (age) 12.

In general, for the linear model, the intercept parameter a_0 represents the value of the logit hazard when the covariate is 0. The covariate in the current linear models is ($period - c$). Thus, a_0 represents the value of the logit hazard when the period is equal to c. The slope parameter, b_1, is unaffected by the subtraction of constant c from the time period, and it represents the increase (or decrease) in logit hazard per unit increase in time. For the quadratic model, the intercept still represents the value of the logit hazard in time period c. The slope parameter, too, still measures the increase (or decrease) in logit hazard per unit increase in time but now only at one particular instant, time period c. The curvature parameter, b_2, in quadratic model specifies whether the logit hazard function is convex with a trough (U shape) or concave with a peak ($\cap$ shape). If b_2 is positive, the hazard function is convex, and if it is negative, the shape is concave. The time period at which the hazard function reaches its peak or trough is given by $[c - \frac{1}{2}(b_1/b_2)]$.

For example, the estimates of the parameters a_0, b_1, and b_2 for the quadratic model of the adolescents' relationships data are -5.551, 1.191, and -0.075, respectively, that is, the quadratic model for the baseline group is logit($h_0(t_l)$) $= -5.551 + 1.19(period - 12) - 0.075(period - 12)^2$. This implies that the estimate of the logit hazard at age 12 for the baseline is -5.551 (compare with the result in Table 12.3) and that the instantaneous rate of change in logit hazard at age 12 is 1.191. Because the estimate for b_2, -0.075, is negative, the hazard function is concave reaching its peak at time period (age) $[12 - \frac{1}{2}(1.191/-0.075)] = 19.94$. The peak of the hazard function is after age 19 and close to age 20 implying that the risk of the event, sleeping with someone for the first time, is highest at age 20.

Time-Varying Covariates

In previous sections, we considered covariates that have constant values with time. However, the values of some covariates for each person may change over time in practice. With a little modification, it is possible to relate the occurrence of the event of interest to covariates that change their values with time using the discrete-event history model. One of the advantages of using person–period data set is that it naturally allows a time-varying covariate simply to take on its appropriate value for each person in each record or period. In the adolescents' romantic relationships example, we focused in this chapter on the event of sleeping with someone for the first time and discussed the effect of time constant covariates youth-centrism (YC), gender (G), and education (E). As mentioned in the section When to Use Event History Analysis, the survey had also collected the time at which the adolescents experienced the events "going out," "having a steady friend," and "being very much in love" for the first time. It may be hypothesized that the occurrence of these events could have an effect on the timing of our event of interest, sleeping with someone for the first time. For simplicity and ease of presentation we consider only the effect of going out on the timing of sleeping with someone for the first time. The value on covariate going out (OUT) for each person at period l will be 0 if the person did not go out for the first time until period l. The value changes to 1 when a person goes out for the first time at period l. Thus, the covariate OUT is a time-varying binary covariate in this example as its value changes with time. More technically, the covariate is defined as

$$OUT_l = \begin{cases} 0, & \text{if a person did not go out at time } l \\ 1, & \text{if a person goes out at time } l \\ & \text{or before} \end{cases}$$

The data values can easily be appended in the person–period data set, for example, next to the last column of Table 12.2.

Considering the quadratic model specification for the baseline group, the model with both time constant and time-varying covariate is given by

$$\text{logit}(h_X(t_l)) = a_0 + b_1(period_l - 12) \\ + b_2(period_l - 12)^2 + \beta_1 YC \\ + \beta_2 G + \beta_3 E + \beta_4 OUT_l \quad (12.14)$$

Note that the time constant covariates YC, G, and E do not have subscript l while the time-varying covariate OUT has a subscript l to indicate that the data values for the variable OUT can be different values at different time periods for the same person. The parameter β_4 represents the difference in risk of the event sleeping with someone for the first time among adolescents who recently or previously experienced going out and those who have still not experienced going out controlling for other covariates. Because the covariate OUT is time-varying, its effect does not contrast static group but adolescents who differ by unit value on the covariate OUT at each point in time, that is, individuals can switch group membership, and the adolescents who constitute the comparison group differ in each time period even if we are comparing two groups—those who have experienced going out and who have not. Thus, the interpretation of the time-varying covariate's effect must be attached to each point in time period. In contrast, for the time constant covariates, we need not to attach a time point in the interpretation of the covariate's effect as the group members to be compared and data values of the covariate at each time period are constant. As the last model in Equation 12.14 assumes time invariant effects of both the time constant and time-varying covariates, that is, the effects on logit hazard in each time period is constant. Although the values of the time-varying covariate and the members of the groups to be compared may vary over time period, the difference between the logit hazard functions for the two groups to be compared in this example is constant and identical in every time period.

By fitting the model in Equation 12.14 for the adolescents' relationships data, we get

$$\text{logit}(h_X(t_l)) = -6.544 + 0.734(period_l - 12)$$
$$- 0.043(period_l - 12)^2 + 0.508YC$$
$$- 0.549G + 0.054E + 2.629OUT_l$$

Comparing the model that excludes the time-varying covariate OUT and this last equation using deviance statistic shows that the time-varying covariate is statistically significant controlling for the effect of the other covariates. The estimates of the parameters for the time constant covariates are interpreted in a similar way as we did in the section Example: Discrete-Event Time Model for Adolescents' Romantic Relationships Data. For example, the estimate of the parameter β_2, -0.549, for gender could be interpreted as odds ratio by taking the exponent of the estimate, that is, controlling for the effect of other covariates in the model, the odds of sleeping with someone for the first time for boys is 0.578 (exp(–0.549)) times that of female adolescents. In another words, the odds of sleeping with someone for the first time are 1.73 (= 1/0.578) times for girls. In a similar way, by taking the exponent of the estimate of the parameter β_4, (exp (2.629) = 13.866), at every age from 12 to 24 years the odds of sleeping with someone for the first time are about 14 times higher for adolescents who experienced the event of going out earlier and subsequent times compared with those who remain without the experience of going out controlling for the effect of the other covariates in the model. The risk of sleeping with someone increases only in those time periods concurrent with or subsequent to, the event of going out. Before the event going out occurs, those adolescents who are later at greater risk of sleeping with someone are not different from other adolescents who stay without the event going out.

Proportionality Assumption of the Discrete-Event Time Models

The models we have considered so far assume that the covariates have an identical effect in every time period under the study, which is known as the *proportionality assumption*. The assumption is crucial for the estimation procedure of most parametric hazard models for continuous time data. However, in the discrete-time event history models presented previously, apart from simplification of the models, there is no such requirement in the estimation procedure. In some practical situations this assumption is restrictive and can be relaxed by including an interaction term between the covariates and the time period. An inclusion of an interaction term between a covariate and time period allows the effects of the covariate to depend on time instead of being constant at all time periods. The interaction term with the covariate of interest can be made using the dummy variable representation of time period or the alternative polynomial representation. For the current example, the interaction terms are constructed by multiplying each of the covariate YC, G, E, and OUT by the variable (*period* – 12) linear term of the polynomial representation. The nonproportional discrete-event time model is estimated in each case by including the interaction term in Equation 12.14. One can test whether an effect of a covariate depends on time by comparing the model with proportionality assumption and the model that includes an interaction term between the covariate and time period. As explained earlier, comparison of the deviance statistics helps to make the comparison of the models. Because none of the differences in deviance statistics between Equation 12.14 and the models that include the interaction terms showed a statistical significance for the current example, the detailed results are not shown here. Thus, the data from adolescents' romantic relationships example offer little evidence that the effects of the covariates change over time.

Competing-Risk Models

In the models we have considered so far, there is a single destination state from the origin state. In some applications there may be more than one way of (or reason for) exiting an origin state. Such reasons or destination states are referred as *competing risks* (Chiang, 1991; David & Moeschberger, 1978). For example, in the analysis of mortality or death rates, one may want to distinguish different causes of death; in the analysis of partnership formation, one may transit from single state to either marriage or cohabitation (without formal marriage). The hazard in such cases is defined for single types of event, but now we have one for each competing risk. Suppose there are D mutually exclusive destination states, then the hazard of event type d at time t_l is

$$h^{(d)}(t_l) = \Pr(\text{event of type } d \text{ at time } t_l | T \geq t_l)$$

The hazard that no event of any type occurs at t_l given survival to time period t_{l-1} is

$$h^{(0)}(t_l) = 1 - \sum_{d=1}^{D} h^{(d)}(t_l)$$

The survival function that the events occur after time t_l is the same as the probability that no event of any type occurs until and including time t_l is

$$S(t_l) = h^{(0)}(t_1) \times h^{(0)}(t_2) \times \cdots \times h^{(0)}(t_{l-1})$$

The model that relates the hazards to the covariates when individuals may leave the origin state to different destination states is the competing-risk model. There are two approaches to model the hazards. One approach is to model the hazards of each competing risk separately using the discrete-event time model discussed so far, treating all other events as censored. This approach models the underlying risk of a particular event in the absence of all other risks. The other approach is modeling the hazards of the competing risks simultaneously using a multinomial logistic model.

For the multinomial logistic model, the person–period data set discussed earlier needs a minor change. A multinomial event indicating categorical variable (response variable) E_{ild} needs to be defined indicating occurrence and type of event d at time period t_l for ith person. The response categories of E_{il} are 0 (no event), 1, 2, ..., D. The multiple records in the person–period data set for each person should be defined until one of the events or censoring occurs. The multinomial logistic model that contrasts event type d with no event for a person with covariates $X_1, X_2, \ldots, X_p$ is given by

$$Log_e\left(\frac{h^d_{X_p}(t_l)}{h^0_{X_p}(t_l)}\right) = \alpha^d_l + \sum_{k=1}^{p}\beta^d_k X_k \quad (12.15)$$

Comparison of this last model with the model in Equation 12.8 shows that a separate set of time and covariate effects (α^d_l and β^d_k) are included for each type of event via the index d. Some of the covariates can be time-varying and may need subscript l for such covariates in Equation 12.15. For the multinomial logistic model in Equation 12.15 we estimate D equations contrasting each of the competing risks with no event. Further contrasts to compare the competing risks among each other can then be obtained from those D equations. For example, for partnership formation, two contrasts (marriage with single ["no event"], cohabitation with single) can be obtained using model in Equation 12.15. The remaining contrast, marriage with cohabitation, may be estimated from the other two contrasts. Using the modified person–period data set, a multinomial logistic model for discrete-event time data in Equation 12.15 can be estimated using routines developed for standard multinomial logistic model in the commonly available software (e.g., SPSS, SAS, Stata, R).

Unobserved Heterogeneity

In the models discussed so far, variability in the hazard of event occurrence is explained using observed covariates and risk factors. However, even after controlling for these observed characteristics, some subjects are be more likely to experience the event than others as a result of unobserved subject-specific risk factors. This unobserved heterogeneity in the hazard is sometimes referred to as *frailty* (Hougaard, 1984, 1995). If there are subject-specific unobserved factors that affect the hazard, the estimated form of the hazard function at the population or group level tends to be different from those at the subject level. For example, if the hazards of all subjects in a population are constant over time, the aggregate population hazard decreases. This can be explained by what is called a *selection effect*; that is, high-risk subjects tend to have the event first, leaving lower-risk subjects in the population. Therefore, as time goes on the risk population is increasingly depleted of those subjects most likely to experience the event, leading to a decrease in the population hazard. Because of this selection, we may see a decrease in the population hazard even if individual hazards are constant (or even increasing). This selection effect not only affects the time dependence but may, for example, also yield spurious time-covariate effects (Vermunt, 2002, 2009).

The common way to deal with unobserved heterogeneity is to include random effects (or subject-specific effects) in the models discussed so far. This involves the inclusion of a time-constant latent covariate in the model, and it requires an assumption about the distributional form of the latent variable. Mare (1994) and Vermunt (1997, 2002) presented discrete-time variants of such models. The amount of unobserved heterogeneity is determined by the variance of the latent variable, where the larger the variance the more unobserved heterogeneity. The interpretation of the regression parameters β also changes when random effects are included. In the models discussed so far without random effects, $\exp(\beta)$ is an odds ratio, and it compares the odds of an event for two randomly selected individuals with values one unit apart on covariate X keeping the same values for other covariates in the model. In a model with random effects, $\exp(\beta)$ is an odds ratio only when the random effects are held constant, that is, if we are comparing two hypothetical individuals with the same random effect values. Using models with random effects makes sense when it can be expected that important time-constant risk factors are not included in the model. Failure to control for such unobserved factors may bias the estimates of the factors included in the model. Discrete-time models with random effects can be defined using software for multilevel logistic regression analysis. Routines for continuous-time modeling sometimes often contain provisions for specifying models with unobserved heterogeneity (e.g., the Stata routines stcox and streg).

FINAL REMARKS

This chapter is a gentle introduction to event history analysis for discrete-event times. These methods were introduced to social and behavioral scientists by Allison (1982), Vermunt (1997, 2009), Singer and Willett (1993, 2003), and Yamaguchi (1991). These methods are still relatively unknown and not widely used in psychology, despite their appropriateness for many research questions. We have shown that with an appropriate restructuring of the data set, the software routines that are familiar to the applied researchers can be used for discrete-event history analysis. That is, no specialized software is needed to perform a discrete-event time analysis. The methods presented here are technically manageable and could also be used as an introduction to understanding of more advanced methods in continuous event time analysis, as, for example, described by Vermunt (1997, 2009) and Willett and Singer (1993).

Logistic regression analysis is adopted to relate the hazard of event occurrence to covariates. With an appropriate data restructuring, both the censoring problem and the inclusion of time-varying covariates are managed. The discussion was confined to only right censoring. Left censoring is less common in practice and, in general, difficult to deal with than right censoring. The method was extended for competing risks using multinomial logistic model. More advanced techniques to account for unobserved heterogeneity were briefly discussed. Other more advanced topics that were not discussed in this chapter are models for multivariate events, covariates containing measurement error, missing data on covariates, and recurrent events.

Models for multivariate events consider distributions of two or more distinct event time variables and jointly model the time variables (Vermunt & Moors, 2005; Wei et al., 1989). The objective of simultaneous modeling is to take into account the fact that the occurrence of one life event might directly affect the hazard for another type of event. When the covariates or predictor variables are subject to measurement error the estimates of regression coefficients and their corresponding confidence intervals may be biased and corrections are needed (Nakamura, 1992; Rosner et al., 1990; Vermunt, 1996). When a covariate is partially missing, excluding the subjects with partially missing covariate values from the analysis leads to biased parameter estimates unless the missing mechanism is missing completely at random (Little & Rubin, 1987). *Recurrent events* refers to the situation in which subjects may experience the event of interest more than once, for example, repeated divorce or marriage, asthma attacks, child birth, employment, injury, and prison. Different techniques are suggested in the literature for the analysis of recurrent event data. Lim et al. (2007) compared those methods using empirical data of the pediatric firearm victim's visit to the Children's Wisconsin Trauma Center and all other hospitals in the Milwaukee metropolitan area between 1990 and 1995.

APPENDIX 12.1: SYNTAXES FOR THE CONVERSION OF PERSON-ORIENTED DATA SET TO PERSON–PERIOD DATA SET, ADOLESCENTS' ROMANTIC RELATIONSHIPS DATA

<u>SPSS Syntax</u>

```
*first open the data file 'relationships.sav', which can be obtained from one of the authors.
do repeat D=D12 to D24 /ptime=12,13,14,15,16,17,18,19,20,21,22,23,24.
    if (time_sleeping > ptime) D=0.
    if (time_sleeping=ptime) D=1-censind1.
end repeat.
execute.
VARSTOCASES
   /ID=id
   /MAKE event FROM D12 D13 D14 D15 D16 D17 D18 D19 D20 D21 D22 D23 D24
   /INDEX=period(13)
   /KEEP=boy loweduc youthcen
   /NULL=DROP.
COMPUTE period=period+11.
EXECUTE.
*Making dummy variables for modeling
do repeat D=D12 to D24 /ptime=12,13,14,15,16,17,18,19,20,21,22,23,24.
    if (period >ptime) D=0.
    if (period=ptime) D=1.
    if (period<ptime) D=0.
end repeat.
execute.
```

<u>SAS Syntax</u>

```
*Creating a person-period dataset from a person-level dataset;
*Assuming the person-level dataset exists in drive C;
data relationships_pp1;
```

```
set 'c:\relationships';
do period= 12 to 24 ;
    if (time_sleeping > period) then event= 0;
    else if (time_sleeping = period) then event=1-censind1;
    else if (time_sleeping< period) then delete;
     output;
end;
keep id boy loweduc youthcen period event;
run;
proc print
data=relationships_pp1;
 run;
data relationships_pp;
 set relationships_pp1;
 array AD[12:24] D12-D24;
 do dummy =12 to 24;
  if (period eq dummy) then AD[dummy]=1;
  else
   AD[dummy]=0;
  end;
   drop dummy;
  run;
proc print
 data=relationships_pp;
 run;
```

R Syntax (R core team (2021))

```
# Assuming the person-level csv dataset exists in drive C
relationships.data<-read.csv("c:/relationships.csv")
relationships.data<-as.data.frame(relationships.data)
DD<-
c("D12","D13","D14","D15","D16","D17","D18","D19","D20","D21","D22","D23","D24")
relationships.data[DD]<-0
relationships.data<-relationships.data[!is.na(relationships.data$time_sleeping),]
uniqueid<-unique(relationships.data$id)
size<-length(uniqueid)
tempdata<-tempdata.all<-data.frame()
for (i in 1:size){
   tempdata<-relationships.data[relationships.data$id==uniqueid[i],]
   tempdata$period<-12
   tempdata[,8]<-1
   maxtime<-tempdata$time_sleeping
      for (j in 13:maxtime){
          tempdata2<-relationships.data[relationships.data$id==uniqueid[i],]
          tempdata1<-tempdata2
```

```
                tempdata1$period<-j
                tempdata1[,j-4]<-1
                tempdata <-rbind(tempdata,tempdata1)
        }
    tempdata.all<-rbind(tempdata.all,tempdata)
    tempdata<-data.frame()
}
tempdata.all$event <- ifelse(tempdata.all$time_sleeping>tempdata.all$period, 0, 1-
tempdata.all$censind1)
# exporting the person-period data to excel file
ExportExcelData<-tempdata.all[,c(1,21,8:20,22,3:5)]
write.csv(ExportExcelData,"c:/relationships_Person_period_data.csv",row.names = FALSE)
```

References

Allison, P. (1982). Discrete-time methods for the analysis of event histories. In S. Leinhardt (Ed.), *Sociological methodology* (pp. 61–98). Jossey-Bass. https://doi.org/10.2307/270718

Blossfeld, H.-P., & Rohwer, G. (2002). *Techniques of event history modeling: New approaches to causal analysis* (2nd ed.). Lawrence Erlbaum Associates.

Broström, G. (2022). *Event history analysis with R* (2nd ed.). Chapman & Hall/CRC.

Chiang, C. L. (1991). Competing risks in mortality analysis. *Annual Review of Public Health, 12*(1), 281–307. https://doi.org/10.1146/annurev.pu.12.050191.001433

Collett, D. (2015). *Modelling survival data in medical studies* (3rd ed.). Chapman & Hall/CRC. https://doi.org/10.1201/b18041

Cox, D. R. (1972). Regression models and life tables. *Journal of the Royal Statistical Society: Series B. Methodological, 34*(2), 187–202. https://doi.org/10.1111/j.2517-6161.1972.tb00899.x

Cutler, S. J., & Ederer, F. (1958). Maximum utilization of the life table method in analyzing survival. *Journal of Chronic Diseases, 8*(6), 699–712. https://doi.org/10.1016/0021-9681(58)90126-7

D'Agostino, R. B., Lee, M. L., Belanger, A. J., Cupples, L. A., Anderson, K., & Kannel, W. B. (1990). Relation of pooled logistic regression to time dependent Cox regression analysis: The Framingham Heart Study. *Statistics in Medicine, 9*(12), 1501–1515. https://doi.org/10.1002/sim.4780091214

David, H. A., & Moeschberger, M. L. (1978). *The theory of competing risks.* Griffin.

Efron, B. (1988). Logistic regression, survival analysis, and the Kaplan-Meier curve. *Journal of the American Statistical Association, 83*(402), 414–425. https://doi.org/10.1080/01621459.1977.10480613

Fahrmeir, L., & Wagenpfeil, S. (1996). Smoothing hazard functions and time-varying effects in discrete duration and competing risks models. *Journal of the American Statistical Association, 91*(436), 1584–1594. https://doi.org/10.1080/01621459.1996.10476726

Hougaard, P. (1984). Life table methods for heterogeneous populations: Distributions describing the heterogeneity. *Biometrika, 71*(1), 75–83. https://doi.org/10.1093/biomet/71.1.75

Hougaard, P. (1995). Frailty models for survival data. *Lifetime Data Analysis, 1*(3), 255–273. https://doi.org/10.1007/BF00985760

IBM Corp. (2020). *IBM SPSS statistics for Windows* (Version 27.0) [Computer software]. IBM Corp.

Kaas, R., Goovaerts, M., Dhaene, J., & Denuit, M. (2008). *Modern actuarial risk theory: Using R* (2nd ed.). Springer. https://doi.org/10.1007/978-3-540-70998-5

Kalbfleisch, J., & Prentice, R. (2002). *The statistical analysis of failure time data* (2nd ed.). Wiley. https://doi.org/10.1002/9781118032985

Kaplan, E. L., & Meier, P. (1958). Nonparametric estimation from incomplete observations. *Journal of the American Statistical Association, 53*(282), 457–481. https://doi.org/10.1080/01621459.1958.10501452

Lim, H. J., Liu, J., & Melzer-Lange, M. (2007). Comparison of methods for analyzing recurrent events data: Application to the emergency department visits of pediatric firearm victims.

Accident Analysis and Prevention, 39(2), 290–299. https://doi.org/10.1016/j.aap.2006.07.009

Little, R. J. A., & Rubin, D. B. (1987). *Statistical analysis with missing data*. Wiley.

Mantel, M. H., & Hankey, B. F. (1978). A logistic regression analysis of response time data where the hazard function is time dependent. *Communications in Statistics. Theory and Methods, 7*(4), 333–347. https://doi.org/10.1080/03610927808827627

Mare, R. D. (1994). Discrete-time bivariate hazards with unobserved heterogeneity: A partially observed contingency table approach. In P. V. Marsden (Ed.), *Sociological methodology* (pp. 341–383). Basil Blackwell. https://doi.org/10.2307/270987

Merrell, M. (1947). Time-specific life table contrasted with observed survivorship. *Biometrics, 3*(3), 129–136. https://doi.org/10.2307/3001948

Mould, R. F. (1976). Calculation of survival rates by the life table and other methods. *Clinical Radiology, 27*(1), 33–38. https://doi.org/10.1016/S0009-9260(76)80011-6

Myung, I. J. (2003). Tutorial on maximum likelihood estimation. *Journal of Mathematical Psychology, 47*(1), 90–100. https://doi.org/10.1016/S0022-2496(02)00028-7

Nakamura, T. (1992). Proportional hazards model with covariates subject to measurement error. *Biometrics, 48*(3), 829–838. https://doi.org/10.2307/2532348

Petersen, T. (1991). The statistical analysis of event histories. *Sociological Methods & Research, 19*(3), 270–323. https://doi.org/10.1177/0049124191019003002

Rao, C. R. (1973). *Linear statistical inference and its application* (2nd ed.). Wiley. https://doi.org/10.1002/9780470316436

R Core Team. (2021). *R: A language and environment for statistical computing* (Version 3.4.1) [Computer software]. R Foundation for Statistical Computing. https://www.R-project.org/

Rosner, B., Spiegelman, D., & Willett, W. C. (1990). Correction of logistic regression relative risk estimates and confidence intervals for measurement error: The case of multiple covariates measured with error. *American Journal of Epidemiology, 132*(4), 734–745. https://doi.org/10.1093/oxfordjournals.aje.a115715

SAS Institute. (2013). *Base SAS 9.4 procedures guide: Statistical procedures* (5th ed.). SAS Institute.

Singer, J. D., & Willett, J. B. (1993). It's about time: Using discrete-time survival analysis to study duration and the timing of events. *Journal of Educational Statistics, 18*(2), 155–195.

Singer, J. D., & Willett, J. B. (2003). *Applied longitudinal data analysis: Methods for studying change and event occurrence*. Oxford University Press. https://doi.org/10.1093/acprof:oso/9780195152968.001.0001

Thompson, W. A., Jr. (1977). On the treatment of grouped observations in life studies. *Biometrics, 33*(3), 463–470. https://doi.org/10.2307/2529360

Tuma, N. B., & Hannan, M. T. (1979). Approaches to the censoring problem in analysis of event histories. In K. F. Schuessler (Ed.), *Sociological methodology* (pp. 209–240). Jossey-Bass. https://doi.org/10.2307/270772

Vermunt, J. K. (1996). *Log-linear event history analysis: A general approach with missing data, unobserved heterogeneity, and latent variables*. Tilburg University Press.

Vermunt, J. K. (1997). *Advanced quantitative techniques in the social sciences series: Vol. 8. Log-linear models for event histories*. Sage Publications.

Vermunt, J. K. (2002). A general latent class approach to unobserved heterogeneity in the analysis of event history data. In J. Hagenaars & A. McCutcheon (Eds.), *Applied latent class analysis* (pp. 383–407). Cambridge University Press. https://doi.org/10.1017/CBO9780511499531.015

Vermunt, J. K. (2009). Event history analysis. In R. Millsap & A. Maydeu-Olivares (Eds.), *Handbook of quantitative methods in psychology* (pp. 658–674). Sage. https://doi.org/10.4135/9780857020994.n27

Vermunt, J. K., & Moors, G. B. D. (2005). Event history analysis. In B. Everitt & D. Howell (Eds.), *Encyclopedia of statistics in behavioral science* (pp. 568–575). Wiley.

Vinken, H. (1998). *Political values and youth centrism. Theoretical and empirical perspectives on the political value distinctiveness of Dutch youth centrists*. Tilburg University Press.

Wei, L. J., Lin, D. Y., & Weissfeld, L. (1989). Regression analysis of multivariate incomplete failure time data by modeling marginal distributions. *Journal of the American Statistical Association, 84*(408), 1065–1073. https://doi.org/10.1080/01621459.1989.10478873

Willett, J. B., & Singer, J. D. (1993). Investigating onset, cessation, relapse, and recovery: Why you should, and how you can, use discrete-time survival analysis to examine event occurrence. *Journal of Consulting and Clinical Psychology, 61*(6), 952–965. https://doi.org/10.1037/0022-006X.61.6.952

Yamaguchi, K. (1991). *Event history analysis*. Sage Publications.

CHAPTER 13

LATENT STATE–TRAIT MODELS

Rolf Steyer, Christian Geiser, and Christiane Loßnitzer

Latent state–trait models were developed in reaction to the person-situation debate in differential psychology (e.g., Anastasi, 1983; Bowers, 1973; Endler & Magnusson, 1976; Epstein, 1979, 1980; Mischel, 1998). At about the same time, the distinction between states and traits became an issue (e.g., Cattell, 1966, 1979; Cattell & Scheier, 1961; Nesselroade and Bartsch, 1977; Spielberger, 1972). Some researchers sought to assess states using items that ask for mood states (How do you feel/think right now?) and traits using items asking for traits (How do you feel/think, in general?) (e.g., Spielberger, 1972). Others sought to define and measure traits by aggregation of behavioral observations over representative samples of situations (e.g., Epstein, 1979, 1980), and still others tried to assess states and traits by different latent variables in structural equation models (e.g., Ormel & Schaufeli, 1991) and/or different behavior of latent states and traits in such models. For example, Hertzog and Nesselroade (1987) suggested distinguishing between states and traits based on the size of autocorrelations in longitudinal data. Such autocorrelations should be high for traits and low for states. But what is high and what is low? Hertzog and Nesselroade also suggested a more fundamental idea: "Generally it is certainly the case that most psychological attributes will neither be, strictly speaking, traits or states. That is, attributes can have both trait and state components" (p. 95). Conceptualizations in contemporary areas of research such as Fleeson's (2001) theory of traits as density distributions of states map well onto the idea of distinguishing between trait and state components in the measurement of social science attributes.

Moreover, Steyer and Schmitt (1994) and, more recently, Hamaker et al. (2015) highlighted the importance of accounting for trait-like individual differences in longitudinal statistical analyses. Failure to account for stable between-person differences can lead to biased estimates of causal effects, for example, in autoregressive/cross-lagged panel models.

In the late 1980s and early 1990s, Steyer and his associates defined trait and state latent variables explicitly within a new measurement theoretical framework (e.g., Majcen et al., 1988; Steyer & Schmitt, 1990a, 1990b; Steyer et al., 1990, 1992). Steyer (1987, 1989) introduced the basic concepts of *latent state–trait* (LST) *theory* and developed *latent state–trait* models—specific structural equation models in which the latent variables can be interpreted as latent state or latent trait components. In the late 1990s, *state change* (Steyer et al., 1997) and *trait change models* (Eid & Hoffmann, 1998; Steyer et al., 2004) were introduced. State change models allow examining changes in latent states (which, according to LST theory, contain both trait and situational components) by using latent difference score variables. Trait change models also use a latent difference score approach and can be used to separate more enduring trait changes from more short-term, situation-specific influences.

Furthermore, research on multitrait–multimethod (MTMM) analysis has led to new ways of defining and modeling method effects (e.g., Eid, 2000; Pohl & Steyer, 2010; Pohl et al., 2008). These new approaches have been applied to model measure-specific (or indicator-specific) effects in LST models (Eid et al., 1999), as well as models with latent state and trait change variables (Geiser, 2009; Geiser et al., 2010a, 2010b; Vautier et al., 2008). Furthermore, LST models have been extended to *multiconstruct models* that serve to simultaneously study the associations between the state and trait components pertaining to different psychological variables (e.g., Dumenci & Windle, 1998; Eid et al., 1994; Steyer et al., 1990, 2000). For example, Eid et al. (1994) used multiconstruct LST models to examine the validity of mood questionnaires by correlating the trait and state residual components across different measures of mood. In their study, latent factors representing trait mood were highly (.78) correlated across different mood scales, whereas state residual components showed more modest associations between .32 and .45. Finally, there has been an important revision of the basic concepts of states and traits (Steyer et al., 2015). This revised theory is called *LST-R theory*.

In this chapter, we first define the basic concepts of LST-R theory, present the assumptions defining various LST-R models, and show how to introduce latent state and latent trait variables. We then discuss why the inclusion of method factors is often required in models of LST-R theory and present different ways of constructively defining method factors in LST-R models. Finally, we discuss multiconstruct models as well as other extensions of LST-R models.

BASIC CONCEPTS OF LST-R THEORY

LST-R theory is motivated by two truisms. The first one is that *a person is never in a situational vacuum*. According to Anastasi (1983), we never observe a person, but always a person-in-a-situation. This was the motivation for developing LST theory in the late 80s and early 90s of the last century. The second truism that necessitated the revision of the original LST theory (Steyer et al., 2015) is that *there is no person without a past*. This implies that a person observed at time t_1 should be distinguished from the same person observed at another time t_2. In other words, we always observe a person-at-time-t-in-a-situation-s_t. And, a person at-time-t_1-in-a-situation-s_{t1} is always a part of this person at time t_2 if t_2 is later than t_1 (Steyer et al., 2015, for a mathematical formulation of this idea and its implications).

In LST-R theory, we do not simply assume that there is, for example, a latent variable that we label "trait factor" or "state factor." Instead, the latent variables are defined constructively, using well-defined concepts of probability theory referring to the underlying *random experiment*. Formally speaking, random variables always refer to a random experiment, which is the kind of empirical phenomenon with which the theory deals. In the following list, we describe the random experiment considered in LST-R theory at a conceptual level (the mathematical details are described in Steyer et al., 2015):

1. A person (or, more generally, an observational unit u) is sampled from a set of persons at Time t_0 before their behavior is observed.
2. The person is making experiences before their behavior is recorded.
3. The person is in a specific (typically unknown) situation when their behavior is observed at Time t_1.
4. Measurements are taken at Time t_1, for example, through questionnaires, tests, or observations.
5. Steps 2 through 4 are repeated for subsequent time points.

Referring to this kind of random experiment, we can introduce the following random variables on which the fundamental concepts of LST-R theory are based:

1. Y_{it}: the observables, the values of which represent the observations of an attribute at time t.

Because we consider making several observations of the same attribute at time t (e.g., several items or scales), the subscript i indicates the ith observation of the attribute.

2. U_t: the person variable pertaining to time t. A value u_t of U_t is the person-at-time t.
3. S_t: the situation variable pertaining to time t. A value s_t of S_t represents the situation in which the person-at-time t is when he or she is assessed at this time.

It is not necessary that we observe the situations (i.e., the values of the situation variable S_t) in which the measurements are made. It is sufficient to assume that we always assess "a person-at-time-t-in-a-situation-s_t." Using these random variables, we can define the *latent state variable*

$$\tau_{it} := E(Y_{it}|U_t, S_t). \tag{13.1}$$

Its values $E(Y_{it}|U_t = u_t, S_t = s_t)$ are the conditional expectations of Y_{it} given the person u_t and the situation s_t in which the person is when Y_{it} is observed. In contrast, the *latent trait variable* is defined by

$$\xi_{it} := E(Y_{it}|U_t). \tag{13.2}$$

Its values $E(Y_{it}|U_t = u_t)$ are the conditional expectations of Y_{it} given the person-at-time t. Furthermore, the *measurement error variable* is defined to be the residual

$$\varepsilon_{it} := Y_{it} - \tau_{it}. \tag{13.3}$$

Its values are the differences between the observed score of Y_{it} and the latent state $E(Y_{it}|U_t = u_t, S_t = s_t)$ score. Finally, the *latent state residual* is the difference

$$\zeta_{it} := \tau_{it} - \xi_{it}. \tag{13.4}$$

Its values are the deviations of the latent state values from the latent trait values.

These are the four fundamental theoretical concepts of LST-R theory. Note that these concepts are defined on the sole assumption that a person is sampled and repeatedly observed at several time points t, and that the observables Y_{it} have finite expectations. This guarantees that the conditional expectations and their residuals—and, therefore, also the latent state and latent trait variables—are well-defined. Based on Equations 13.3 and 13.4, each observed variable Y_{it} can be additively decomposed into three theoretical (latent) components: a *measurement error* component ε_{it}, a *trait* component ξ_{it}, and a *state residual* component ζ_{it}. The sum of the trait and the state residual components is the *latent state* component τ_{it}.

Furthermore, we can also define the *reliability*

$$Rel(Y_{it}) := Var(\tau_{it})/Var(Y_{it}) \tag{13.5}$$

of Y_{it}, which gives the proportion of true score (reliable) variance in Y_{it}. In contrast, the *consistency*

$$Con(Y_{it}) := Var(\xi_{it})/Var(Y_{it}) \tag{13.6}$$

is a quantity describing the degree to which the latent trait ξ_{it} determines the observable Y_{it}. Finally, the *occasion specificity*

$$Spe(Y_{it}) := Var(\zeta_{it})/Var(Y_{it}) \tag{13.7}$$

represents the degree to which the situation and/or the interaction between person and situation determines the observable Y_{it}.

IMPLICATIONS OF THE DEFINITIONS OF LATENT STATES AND LATENT TRAITS

The definitions of latent state and latent trait variables and the associated residuals, the measurement error and the latent state residual variables, imply several properties of these concepts (Table 13.1). These properties are special cases of the general properties of conditional expectations and their residuals (e.g., Steyer & Nagel, 2017). These properties cannot and need not be tested empirically, in the same way as the fact that "a bachelor is unmarried" cannot be tested empirically. Being unmarried is a logical

TABLE 13.1

Properties of the Basic Concepts of Latent State–Trait-Revised Theory

Equation	Equation number	Description
Decomposition of variables and variances		
$\tau_{it} = \xi_{it} + \zeta_{it}$	(i)	Decomposition of latent state variables (τ_{it}) into trait (ξ_{it}) and state residual variables (ζ_{it})
$Y_{it} = \tau_{it} + \varepsilon_{it}$	(ii)	Decomposition of measured variables (Y_{it}) into latent state variables (τ_{it})
$= \xi_{it} + \zeta_{it} + \varepsilon_{it}$	(iii)	and measurement error variables (ε_{it})
$Var(\tau_{it}) = Var(\xi_{it}) + Var(\zeta_{it})$	(iv)	Variance decomposition of latent state variables
$Var(Y_{it}) = Var(\tau_{it}) + Var(\varepsilon_{it})$	(v)	Variance decomposition of measured variables
$= Var(\xi_{it}) + Var(\zeta_{it}) + Var(\varepsilon_{it})$	(vi)	
Coefficients		
$Con(Y_{it}) = Var(\xi_{it})/Var(Y_{it})$	(vii)	Consistency coefficient
$OSpe(Y_{it}) = Var(\zeta_{it})/Var(Y_{it})$	(viii)	Occasion-specificity coefficient
$Rel(Y_{it}) = Con(Y_{it}) + OSpe(Y_{it})$	(ix)	Reliability coefficient
Other properties		
$E(\zeta_{it}) = 0$	(x)	State residual variables have means of zero
$Cov(\varepsilon_{it}, \zeta_{it}) = 0$	(xi)	Measurement error variables are uncorrelated with state residual variables
$Cov(\zeta_{it}, \zeta_{js}) = 0, s \neq t$	(xii)	State residual variables pertaining to different time points are uncorrelated
$Cov(\varepsilon_{it}, \tau_{js}) = 0, s \leq t$	(xiii)	Measurement error variables are uncorrelated with latent state variables pertaining to the same or previous time points
$Cov(\varepsilon_{it}, \xi_{js}) = 0, s \leq t$	(xiv)	Measurement error variables are uncorrelated with latent trait variables pertaining to the same or previous time points
$Cov(\zeta_{it}, \xi_{js}) = 0, s \leq t$	(xv)	State residual variables are uncorrelated with latent trait variables pertaining to the same or previous time points
$E[\zeta_{it}|f(U_s)] = 0, s \leq t$, for all mappings $f(U_s)$ of U_s	(xvi)	Mean-independence of the residual ζ_{it} given a mapping of the person variable at Time $s \leq t$
$E(\varepsilon_{it}) = 0$	(xvii)	Measurement error variables have means of 0
$E[\varepsilon_{it}|f(U_s, S_t)] = 0, s \leq t$, for all mappings $f(U_s, S_t)$ of (U_s, S_t)	(xviii)	Mean-independence of the measurement error ε_{it} given a mapping of the person variable at Time $s \leq t$ and the situation variable at Time t
$Cov(\varepsilon_{it}, \varepsilon_{js}) = 0, s \neq t$	(xix)	Measurement error variables pertaining to different time points are uncorrelated

Note. All properties in this table hold for all $i, j = 1, \ldots, m$, and all $s, t = 1, \ldots, n$, assuming that the expectations $E(Y_{it})$ and the variances $Var(Y_{it})$ are finite.

implication of the concept of a "bachelor." The only thing that can be tested empirically is whether a particular man is a bachelor. Analogously, we cannot and need not empirically test whether a measurement error variable ε_{it} is correlated with a latent state residual ζ_{js} (see Equation xi in Table 13.1) or whether a latent state residual ζ_{it} is correlated with a latent state residual ζ_{js} pertaining to a different time point (see Equation xii in Table 13.1). These correlations are zero by definition of these theoretical concepts, and these properties also hold in every model of the theory (see the next section).

Knowing these properties is useful because they restrict the class of models that can be considered models of LST-R theory. If we consider a latent variable model in which a term ζ_{it} is correlated with a term ζ_{js}, then we can conclude that at least one of these terms is not a latent state residual as previously defined (see Eid et al., 2017, for a discussion of a new model based on these implications).

MODELS OF LATENT STATE–TRAIT THEORY

The theoretical concepts introduced in the previous section are well-defined and do not rest on any restrictive assumptions that could be wrong in an empirical application. This is true even though we do not know the expectations, variances, and covariances of the theoretical variables and/or the coefficients of reliability, consistency, and occasion specificity. However, assumptions that could be wrong in applications have to be introduced if we want to compute these parameters from other parameters that are empirically estimable. Introducing such assumptions defines specific models of LST-R theory. In Table 13.2, we provide a summary of the models described in the following sections.

Single-Trait Model

The *single-trait model* (Figure 13.1) is a very simple longitudinal model. It allows us to test the rather restrictive hypothesis that measures reflect a perfectly trait-like attribute with no situation or person-situation interaction influences. In this model, latent state variables τ_{it} are perfect linear functions of a single stable trait factor ξ. The model does not include latent state residual variables and, therefore, does not allow for situation or person-situation interaction effects. According to the model, individual differences in observed scores Y_{it} can only be due to trait differences between individuals or random measurement error.

The single-trait model is defined by two assumptions. The first one is

$$\tau_{it} = \lambda_{it0} + \lambda_{it1}\xi, \quad \lambda_{it0}, \lambda_{it1} \in \mathrm{IR}. \quad (13.8)$$

By fixing $\lambda_{110} = 0$ and $\lambda_{111} = 1$, the latent trait variable ξ is defined to be equal to ξ_{11}, the trait variable pertaining to the first observable at the first time point (Y_{11}). In addition, with these constraints, $\xi_{11} = \tau_{11}$, so that the trait variable ξ is also identical with the latent state variable pertaining to Y_{11}. An alternative method for fixing the scale and mean of ξ is to set $E(\xi) = 0$ and $Var(\xi) = 1$. With these alternative constraints, the latent trait ξ is defined to be a linear function of any of the measure-specific latent trait variables ξ_{it}. According to the second assumption, the measurement error variables are uncorrelated,

$$Cov(\varepsilon_{it}, \varepsilon_{js}) = 0, \quad \text{for } (i,t) \neq (j,s). \quad (13.9)$$

Figure 13.1 displays the path diagram of such a model for two observations at each of two occasions (time points). According to this model, the latent state and latent trait components of a given observable Y_{it} are linear functions of each other, for all four observables. This means that there are neither situation effects nor interactions between person and situation. The only sources of variance in the observables are interindividual differences in trait scores and measurement error. Unidimensionality means that we assume the different observations of the same attribute at each point of time to measure the same latent trait ξ, although perhaps on a different scale. These different scales are represented by the corresponding differences in the intercepts λ_{it0} and slope coefficients λ_{it1}. Finally, the model allows for a restricted pattern of trait changes in terms of time-varying intercepts λ_{it0} and slope coefficients λ_{it1}.

As noted before, this model is very crude and simplistic because it assumes that the observables only depend on a common trait and measurement error. The model ignores situation-specific influences and person-situation interactions. It is too restrictive for most applications, as shown by studies of personality traits (Deinzer et al., 1995; Schmukle & Egloff, 2005), values (Schmitt et al., 1993), EEG measures (Hagemann & Naumann, 2009; Hagemann et al., 2002, 2005), cerebral blood flow (Hermes et al., 2009), cortisol in saliva (Hellhammer et al., 2007; Kirschbaum et al., 1990), and mood states (e.g., Eid et al., 1994; Steyer et al., 1989).

Multistate Model

A much more realistic model is the *multistate model* (Figure 13.2), which allows for multiple correlated latent state factors that need not be perfect linear functions of a single-trait factor. Therefore, the

TABLE 13.2

Summary of Latent State–Trait-Revised Models Presented in This Chapter

Model name	Figure	Description/assumptions[a]	Implications	Uses	Limitations
Singletrait	13.1	States are (deterministic) linear functions of a single trait	Aside from measurement errors, the attribute is a trait; no situation or person-situation interaction effects	Test whether an attribute is a pure trait	Very restrictive for most social science attributes
Multistate	13.2	State variables pertaining to the same time point are (deterministic) linear functions of an occasion-specific latent state factor	Attributes need not be perfectly trait-like	Examine stability of states through their correlations, determine $Rel(Y_{it})$	No separation of trait and state residual components
Singletrait-multistate (STMS)	13.3	State variables are decomposed into a trait factor and occasion-specific state residual factors	Variance can be decomposed into trait, state residual, and error components	Determine $Con(Y_{it})$ and $OSpe(Y_{it})$	Does not account for variable-specific effects
Latent state change	13.4a, b, and c	Equivalent to multistate model but include latent change score variables	Attribute can change over time; inter-individual differences in change are made explicit	Examine inter-individual differences in state change	Does not separate trait change from state residual influences
Linear latent growth	13.4d	Change in latent states can be described by a linear function	State change follows a known linear function	Test whether true scores change over time as described by the linear function	Assumption of linear change for all individuals is restrictive
STMS with m method factors	13.5a	m uncorrelated method factors	Accounts for indicator heterogeneity (method effects)	Improve model fit when indicators contain measure-specific variance	Method factors lack clear psychometric definition; can lead to overfactorization
STMS with $m-1$ method factors	13.5b	$m-1$ correlated residual method factors; states and method factors are uncorrelated	Reference observable is contrasted against remaining observables latent state, trait, and state residual variables are specific to the reference measure	Determine measure-specific variance components relative to a reference measure	Requires choice of a reference measure
Multistate model with difference method factor and reference states	13.5c	Method effects as latent differences from a reference state; states and method factors can be correlated	Latent state, trait, and state residual variables are specific to the reference measure	Account for measure-specific effects relative to a reference measure	Requires choice of reference measure; no separation of measure-specific variance components
Multistate model with difference method factor and common states	13.5d	Method effects as latent differences from a common state; states and method factors can be correlated	State factors are common to all measures	Account for measure-specific effects	No separation of measure-specific variance components
LST model with measure-specific traits	13.6	Trait components can be measure-specific; state residual components are shared across measures	Measures can reflect different traits but share the same situation and interaction components	Model heterogeneity of observables and analyze measure-specific trait factors	No common trait factor; many trait factors required in designs with many measured variables
Multiconstruct LST model	13.7	Multiconstruct extension of STMS model	Different attributes may contain related trait and state residual components	Relate trait and state residual components across attributes	

[a]All models assume that measurement error variables are uncorrelated. The minimal design for all models is two measured variables per attribute measured on two measurement occasions.

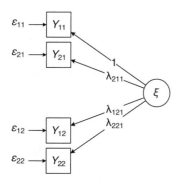

FIGURE 13.1. Single-trait model for two measured variables and two time points. ξ = latent-trait factor.

different Y_{it} variables measured at the same time point are positive linear functions of each other. In contrast to the single-trait model, the multistate model allows for situation effects and/or interactions between persons and situations because the latent state variables reflect both trait and state residual components. Sources of variance in the observables Y_{it} are now interindividual trait differences, situation and/or interaction effects, as well as measurement errors.

In this model, latent state variables are not decomposed into trait and state residual (occasion-specific) components. Nonetheless, we can estimate the extent of trait influences, we can consider the correlations between the latent state variables pertaining to different time points, the *latent state stabilities*.

multistate model allows for situation-specific influences. The multistate model is defined by

$$\tau_{it} = \lambda_{it0} + \lambda_{it1}\tau_t, \quad \lambda_{it0}, \lambda_{it1} \in \mathrm{IR}. \quad (13.10)$$

By fixing $\lambda_{1t0} = 0$ and $\lambda_{1t1} = 1$, the common latent state variables τ_t are defined to be equal to τ_{1t}, the latent state variables pertaining to the first observable (Y_{1t}) at each time point. An alternative method for fixing the scale and mean of τ_t is to set $E(\tau_t) = 0$ and $Var(\tau_t) = 1$. With these alternative constraints, the latent state-variable τ_t is defined to be a linear function of any of the measure-specific latent state variables τ_{it}. We again assume uncorrelated measurement errors (see Equation 13.9).

Figure 13.2 shows the multistate model for two observations and two time points. According to this model, the latent state components of

Single-Trait–Multistate Model

To separate state and trait components, we must introduce the trait component into the model as well. The *single-trait–multistate model* (Figure 13.3) is the simplest kind of model in which this is achieved. It is defined by

$$\tau_{it} = \lambda_{it0} + \lambda_{it1}\tau_t, \quad \lambda_{it0}, \lambda_{it1} \in \mathrm{IR} \quad (13.11)$$

and

$$\xi_{it} = \gamma_{it0} + \gamma_{it1}\xi, \quad \gamma_{it0}, \gamma_{it1} \in \mathrm{IR}. \quad (13.12)$$

The latent state variables τ_t can again be unambiguously defined by setting $\lambda_{1t0} = 0$ and

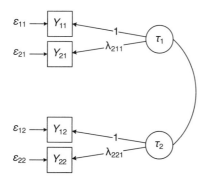

FIGURE 13.2. Multistate model for two measured variables and two time points.

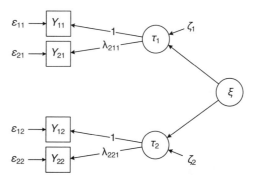

FIGURE 13.3. Single-trait–multistate model for two measured variables and two time points. ξ = latent-trait factor.

$\lambda_{1t1} = 1$, or $E(\tau_t) = 0$ and $Var(\tau_t) = 1$, for each $t = 1, \ldots, T$. The latent trait variable ξ can be unambiguously defined by setting $\gamma_{110} = 0$ and $\gamma_{111} = 1$, or $E(\xi) = 0$ and $Var(\xi) = 1$. Fixing the scales of the latent state variables τ_t by $\lambda_{1t0} = 0$ and $\lambda_{1t1} = 1$ and the scale of the latent trait variable ξ by $\gamma_{110} = 0$ and $\gamma_{111} = 1$ implies $\tau_t = \tau_{1t}$ and $\xi = \xi_{11}$. In contrast, with $E(\tau_t) = 0$, $Var(\tau_t) = 1$, $E(\xi) = 0$ and $Var(\xi) = 1$, the latent state variable τ_t is a linear function of any of the measure-specific latent state variables τ_{it}, and the latent trait variable ξ is a linear function of any measure-specific latent trait variable ξ_{it}. We again assume uncorrelated measurement error variables (see Equation 13.9).

Some algebra shows that Equation 13.12 is equivalent to

$$\tau_t = \gamma_{t0} + \gamma_{t1}\xi + \zeta_t, \quad \gamma_{t0}, \gamma_{t1} \in \mathrm{IR}. \qquad (13.13)$$

The assumptions of the single-trait–multistate model are illustrated in the path diagram displayed in Figure 13.3, again for two observations and two time points. In designs with just two time points, we have to fix both coefficients γ_{11} and γ_{21} to be equal to 1 or set $Var(\xi) = 1$ with the additional constraint $\gamma_{11} = \gamma_{21}$. Otherwise, this part of the model would not be identified. This equality restriction on the trait loadings is not required when there are three or more time points.

As in the multistate model, the latent state components of different Y_{it} variables measured at the same time point are positive linear functions of each other. Additionally, we assume that each common latent state variable τ_t can be decomposed into a linear function of a common trait component ξ and a time-specific latent state residual component ζ_t.

As the multistate model, this model allows for situation effects and/or interactions between persons and situations. However, it additionally decomposes the state components into a trait and a state residual. Sources of variance in the observables are now interindividual differences in trait scores (represented by ξ), situation and/or interaction effects (represented by ζ_t),

and measurement errors (represented by ε_{it}). Figure 13.3 shows that both ξ and ζ_t determine the latent state variables τ_t. As in the multistate model, we assume that the two different observations of the same attribute at each point of time measure the same latent state variable τ_t, again perhaps on a different scale. Hence, this model also allows for change in the attribute considered. However, this time it is assumed that this change is due to situation and/or interaction effects or systematic changes in the trait components that would be reflected in time-varying intercept or loading (slope) coefficients. By constraining intercepts and loadings to be time invariant for each variable, we can test whether trait changes occurred. Note that for a design with only two occasions of measurement, we must assume that the coefficients γ_{t1} are identical. Otherwise, the variance of ξ (or the coefficient γ_{t1}) would not be identified. This is different for designs with three or more time points for which the γ_{t1} coefficients could vary across time.

Some Methodological Remarks

Note the way in which the latent variables have been constructed in all three classes of models. In the first step, we defined the latent variables in LST-R theory based on conditional expectations of observed variables. We then introduced assumptions regarding the relationships between these latent variables, implying the existence of certain common latent variables, the *common latent state variables* τ_t and the *common latent trait variable* ξ. Hence, instead of just "assuming" the existence of a latent variable such as τ_t, we explicitly defined all latent variables as mathematical functions of other well-defined random variables such as Y_{it}, U_t, and S_t. Although we do not know the values of these latent variables, we know that they exist and that they are random variables referring to the same random experiment as the observables. More important, knowing the observables Y_{it}, we also know the substantive meaning of their conditional expectations and the latent variables, which are linear functions of these conditional expectations. This constructive way of introducing latent variables can also be followed in more complex models. Let us start with introducing *latent state change variables*.

Latent State Change Models

Modeling change has been puzzling researchers for many decades (e.g., Collins & Horn, 1991; Collins & Sayer, 2001; Cronbach & Furby, 1970; Harris, 1963). In 1997, Steyer et al. showed how to introduce the difference between two latent state variables as a single latent variable into a structural equation model by specifying the loadings in a particular way. In 2000, McArdle and Bell showed that latent difference variables can also be introduced utilizing a trivial equation such as

$$\tau_2 = \tau_1 + (\tau_2 - \tau_1). \tag{13.14}$$

Using this equation, the path diagram of the multistate model presented in Figure 13.2 turns into the diagram presented in Figure 13.4a.

For three occasions, we have the choice between the *baseline model* (see Figure 13.4b) and the *neighbor model* (Figure 13.4c). In the baseline model, the latent state change variables represent latent state change compared with the first occasion of measurement, whereas in the neighbor model we consider the latent change variables with respect to adjacent time points, that is, we consider change between Times 1 and 2 as well as change between Times 2 and 3.

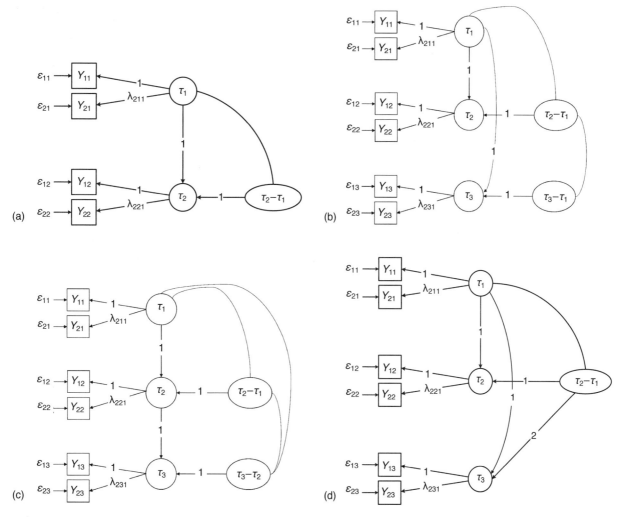

FIGURE 13.4. (a) Latent state-change model for two measured variables and two time points. (b) Baseline change model for three time points. (c) Neighbor change model for three time points. (d) Linear growth curve model for three time points.

A Linear Growth Curve Model

To formulate a model postulating linear change in the latent states between three occasions of measurement, the simplest way is to modify the multistate model as specified in Figure 13.4d. According to this model, the latent state variable at Time 2 is the sum of the latent state variable at Time 1 plus the latent change variable between Times 1 and 2,

$$\tau_2 = \tau_1 + (\tau_2 - \tau_1), \qquad (13.15)$$

whereas the latent state variable at Time 3 is the sum of τ_1 plus two times the latent change variable between Times 1 and 2,

$$\tau_3 = \tau_1 + 2(\tau_2 - \tau_1). \qquad (13.16)$$

Hence, in this model we postulate a linear growth curve for every individual. Comparing this model to one of the models depicted in Figures 13.4b or 13.4c allows testing the hypothesis of linear growth. Modeling quadratic and other forms of growth is possible as well. Mayer et al. (2012) presented a general way how to construct these kinds of models.

These models have sometimes been referred to as "curve-of-factors models" (McArdle, 1988) or "second-order growth models" (e.g., Hancock et al., 2001; Sayer & Cumsille, 2001) as they model individual latent trajectories by means of second-order factors, the growth curve components—as opposed to conventional growth curve models that employ only a single indicator per time point. The advantage of second-order growth curve models is that they allow for a proper separation of systematic variance from measurement error variance. In contrast, in conventional (first-order) growth models, measurement error variance cannot be separated from systematic occasion-specific variance, as there is only one single indicator per time point (Geiser et al., 2013). Bishop et al. (2015) showed how different types of multiple-indicator latent growth curve models can be formulated based on LST-R theory.

Latent Trait Change Models

The ideas outlined so far can also be extended to latent trait change (e.g., Eid & Hoffmann, 1998; Steyer et al., 2015). However, these models require more than just two occasions of measurement. In principle, we need at least two occasions for each latent trait variable for which we may consider trait change. If these design requirements are satisfied, we may introduce latent trait change variables using the same principles as for the construction of the latent state change models. Steyer et al. (2004) gave an example.

Method Factors

The LST-R models presented so far do not always show a good fit in empirical applications. One reason is that each observable may contain a *measure-specific component* (sometimes referred to as an *indicator-specific effect*) that is not shared with the other measures of the latent state variable. Such a measure-specific component can be due to a specific response format, item wording, or rater effects (Eid & Diener, 2006). In cross-sectional designs, this measure-specific component is not separable from random measurement error; however, in longitudinal designs where the same indicators are measured repeatedly, stable measure-specific variance and measurement error variance can be disentangled (see also Marsh & Grayson, 1994; Raffalovich & Bohrnstedt, 1987). Note that the values of these measure-specific components represent the person-specific effects of using a particular measure instead of another particular measure, or in other terms, the person-specific effects of using a particular method (of measurement) instead of another particular method. Hence, these components are also called *method factors*.

Different approaches are available to model person-specific method effects in LST-R models (for a detailed discussion, see Geiser & Lockhart, 2012). Historically, uncorrelated method factors for each of m measured variables were used to model person-specific method effects (e.g., Steyer et al., 1992; Figure 13.5a). However, modeling one method factor for each observable has the disadvantage that these method factors cannot be

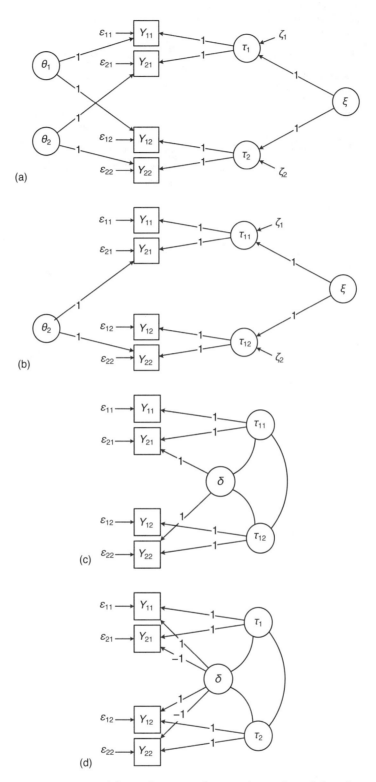

FIGURE 13.5. (a) Singletrait–multistate (STMS) model with m method factors v_i. (b) STMS model with $m - 1$ method factors v_i. The first observable Y_{1t} serves as reference indicator. (c) Multistate model with latent difference method factor δ and reference latent state variables. (d) Multistate model with latent difference method factor δ and common latent state variables.

constructively defined based on the concepts of LST theory (Eid, 1996). Furthermore, the model may overfit the data and shared method effects between similar methods are not accounted for because method effects are assumed to be uncorrelated (Eid, 2000).

Method Factors Defined as Residuals

Approaches that define a reference measure and consider only $m - 1$ correlated residual method factors (Eid, 2000; Eid et al., 1999) are now frequently applied in LST-R models (Courvoisier et al., 2008; Eid et al., 1999; Geiser & Lockhart, 2012; Geiser et al., 2010a, b).

Using the index r to denote the reference method (or reference measure), we consider the regression $E(\tau_{it}|\tau_{rt})$, where $i \neq r$ and $E(\tau_{it}|\tau_{rt})$ denotes the conditional expectation of a true score variable τ_{it} given the true score variable τ_{rt} pertaining to the reference measure r at time t. The method variables v_{it} are defined as residuals:

$$v_{it} := \tau_{it} - E(\tau_{it}|\tau_{rt}). \tag{13.17}$$

The method variables v_{it} reflect that part of a nonreference true score variable τ_{it} that is mean-independent of the (reference) true score variable τ_{rt}; therefore, $E(v_{it}|\tau_{rt}) = 0$. Note that there is a separate method variable v_{it} for each indicator i, $i \neq r$. To separate method effects from random measurement error, we introduce a homogeneity assumption according to which all method variables pertaining to the same observable i differ only by a multiplicative constant κ_{its},

$$v_{it} = \kappa_{its} v_{is}. \tag{13.18}$$

This assumption implies the existence of a *common* method factor v_i for each nonreference measure as illustrated in Figure 13.5b. Note that without loss of generality, we have selected the first measure ($i = 1 = r$) as reference in Figure 13.5b. Therefore, there is no method factor for the first measure. The general equations for this model are

$$Y_{it} = \begin{cases} \lambda_{rt0} + \lambda_{rt1}\tau_{rt} + \varepsilon_{rt}, & \text{for } i = r \\ \lambda_{it0} + \lambda_{it1}\tau_{rt} + \kappa_{it}v_i + \varepsilon_{it}, & \text{for } i \neq r, \end{cases} \tag{13.19}$$

where $\kappa_{it} \in \mathbb{R}$.

Note that the definition of method factors as regression residuals with respect to a reference measure implies that there are $m - 1$ method factors v_i. Each of these method factors has a mean of zero and is assumed to be uncorrelated with all state factors τ_{rt} pertaining to the same construct but may be correlated with other method factors v_j as well as with state factors pertaining to other constructs in multiconstruct models (discussed later in this chapter).

The correlations $Corr(v_i, v_j)$ between different method factors may be of interest if certain measures share a common method effect relative to the reference measure (e.g., two items may be more similar in wording relative to a third item). Note that with only two measures and only two time points, both loadings κ_{it} on the method factor must be fixed to a nonzero value to achieve identification (e.g., $\kappa_{i1} = \kappa_{i2} = 1$). For applications of the residual method factor approach see Eid et al. (1999) and Geiser and Lockhart (2012).

Method Factors Defined as Differences Between True Score Variables

Suppose we have two observables that, at each of two occasions of measurement, measure the same latent state variable. Then

$$\tau_{11} = \tau_{11} \text{ and } \tau_{21} = \tau_{11} \tag{13.20}$$

as well as

$$\tau_{12} = \tau_{12} \text{ and } \tau_{22} = \tau_{12} \tag{13.21}$$

will hold. However, in practice this is very difficult to achieve. So what if we fail? Then, instead of Equations 13.20 and 13.21, the equations

$$\tau_{11} = \tau_{11} \text{ and } \tau_{21} = \tau_{11} + (\tau_{21} - \tau_{11}) \tag{13.22}$$

and

$$\tau_{12} = \tau_{12} \text{ and } \tau_{22} = \tau_{12} + (\tau_{22} - \tau_{12}) \tag{13.23}$$

still hold. In fact, these equations are tautological, that is, they are always true. Note that the differences $\tau_{21} - \tau_{11}$ and $\tau_{22} - \tau_{12}$ between the two true score variables at the two occasions are the systematic differences between the two observables at each of the two occasions. If the two observables are intended to measure the same latent state, then the differences

$$\delta_1 := \tau_{21} - \tau_{11} \text{ and } \delta_2 := \tau_{22} - \tau_{12} \quad (13.24)$$

exactly represent the individual effects of using method 2 instead of method 1 at time points 1 and 2, respectively. While δ_1 represents the method factor pertaining the occasion 1, δ_2 is the method factor pertaining to occasion 2 (Pohl et al., 2008).

However, why should these two method factors be different if the same methods are applied at the two occasions of measurement? Hence, it is plausible to assume $\delta_1 = \delta_2$, which allows us to drop the subscript

$$\delta := \delta_1 = \delta_2 \quad (13.25)$$

where δ represents the *method factor* assumed to be identical for both occasions of measurement. Note that τ_{11} is a constituting component of δ. Hence, it will correlate with δ, and the same applies to τ_{12}. The resulting model is represented in Figure 13.5c.

Method Factors for Common Latent State Variables

Constructing method factors as latent residuals or latent difference variables in the way outlined above implies that the latent state variables occurring in the path diagrams in Figures 13.5b and 13.5c are *specific* to the first measure. In fact, the latent state variables presented in the path diagram are the true score variable τ_{11} of the first observable Y_{11} at occasion 1 and the true score variable τ_{12} of the first observable Y_{12} at occasion 2. If, however, we would like to have a *common latent state variable* for both measures at each of the two time points, we can define such a common latent state variable by simply taking the averages

$$\eta_1 := (\tau_{11} + \tau_{21})/2 \text{ and } \eta_2 := (\tau_{12} + \tau_{22})/2 \quad (13.26)$$

of the two true score variables involved (see Pohl & Steyer, 2010, for extensions allowing for different loadings). Now

$$\tau_{11} = \eta_1 + (\tau_{11} - \eta_1) \text{ and } \tau_{21} = \eta_1 + (\tau_{21} - \eta_1) \quad (13.27)$$

as well as

$$\tau_{12} = \eta_2 + (\tau_{12} - \eta_2) \text{ and } \tau_{22} = \eta_2 + (\tau_{22} - \eta_2) \quad (13.28)$$

trivially hold. Furthermore, some algebra shows that $\tau_{11} - \eta_1 = -(\tau_{21} - \eta_1)$ and $\tau_{12} - \eta_2 = -(\tau_{22} - \eta_2)$. The values of the difference variable $\tau_{11} - \eta_1$ are the deviations of the Measure 1–specific individual latent state variables from the common latent state variable at Time 1. Again, it is plausible to assume that the difference variables $\delta_1 := \tau_{11} - \eta_1$ and $\delta_2 := \tau_{12} - \eta_2$ are identical, because the observables Y_{11} and Y_{12} are assessed with identical measurement methods at the two occasions of measurement. Hence, if we assume

$$\delta := \tau_{11} - \eta_1 = \tau_{12} - \eta_2, \quad (13.29)$$

the resulting model is represented in Figure 13.5d.

In this model, the individual method effects are represented by an *effect parametrization* that compares the latent state scores of Measures 1 and 2 to the average of the latent state scores of the two measures. In contrast, in the model displayed in Figure 13.5c, the individual method effects are represented by a *contrast parametrization* that compares the latent state scores of Measure 2 to the latent state scores of the first measure. Both parameterizations are equivalent to each other. Note, however, that not only the contents of the method factors are different between the two models. Instead, the content of the latent state variables is different as well. In the effect parameterization, there is a *common latent state variable* defined to be the average of the two measure-specific latent state variables τ_{it}. In the contrast parametrization, there is a *specific latent state variable*, the specific latent state variables τ_{1t} pertaining to the first measure. Hence, we have the choice, but the choice has consequences for the substantive interpretation of both, the method factors and the common latent state variables.

The same is true also for Eid's (2000) residual method factor approach, as the meaning of the state and method factors depends on the choice of the reference indicator in this approach. Geiser (2021) provided guidelines for choosing a particular reference indicator in practical applications of the residual method factor approach.

THE MODEL WITH MEASURE-SPECIFIC TRAIT VARIABLES

Another way to account for method effects is to consider as many trait factors as there are measures (as opposed to assuming only one general trait factor for all indicators; Figure 13.6). The trait factors in this model are measure-specific (e.g., Eid, 1996). High correlations of measure-specific trait factors indicate that method effects are small, whereas low or moderate correlations indicate high method-specificity (i.e., each observable may reflect a different facet of the construct). The model with measure-specific trait factors has the advantage that no method factors are required to model method effects and that each trait factor is clearly interpretable as the stable component of a specific observable. On the other hand, the model does not separate method effects from trait effects. Hence, in contrast to models with residual method factors, variance components due to a reference trait cannot be separated from variance due to a specific (residual) trait. For an application with measure-specific trait variables see Irwin et al. (2018).

The basic ideas outlined here can be generalized to more than two measures and more than two occasions of measurement, as well as to models with unequal loadings of the observables on the latent variables (Pohl & Steyer, 2010). Furthermore, method factors can also be combined with latent change variables and with models including latent trait variables such as the single-trait–multistate model.

MULTICONSTRUCT MODELS

In multiconstruct models, state and trait components of two or more constructs are considered simultaneously (Figure 13.7). Multiconstruct models have been presented among others by Dumenci and Windle (1998), Eid et al. (1994), Steyer et al. (1990), and Vautier (2004). In these models, correlations between the trait components pertaining to different psychological variables can be analyzed. Correlations between state residual components pertaining to the same measurement occasion indicate the degree to which the effects of a specific measurement occasion (or situation and person-situation interaction effects) generalize across different psychological variables. For example, Eid et al. (1994) found a correlation of .78 between the latent trait variable pertaining to a mood level scale and the latent trait variable underlying repeatedly measured mood states. In addition, Eid et al. (1994) reported significant correlations between the state residual factors pertaining to different constructs on the same measurement occasion ($.32 \leq r \leq .45$) indicating a substantial amount of shared occasion-specific variance.

Schermelleh-Engel et al. (2004) extended multiconstruct models to hierarchical models. Hierarchical models allow for the estimation of interesting additional variance components. However, the third-order latent variables intro-

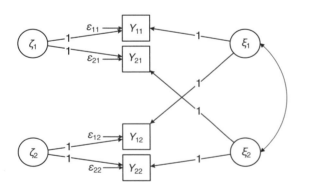

FIGURE 13.6. Latent state–trait model with measure-specific trait variables (multitrait–multistate model).

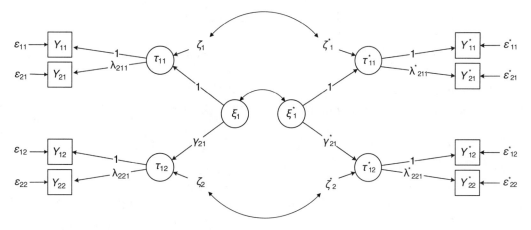

FIGURE 13.7. Multiconstruct latent state–trait model for two constructs and two time points.

duced in the models are not well-defined based on LST-R theory. Therefore, their meaning is less clear than the meaning of the variables in the models presented above.

MODELS WITH AUTOREGRESSION

In the previously described models, latent trait variables account for all the stability in observed variables over time. This assumption can be too simplistic for real-world applications in which short-term carry-over effects are common. For example, momentary deviations of mood states from mood traits due to a positive or negative event are often correlated with the same deviations on immediately following measurement occasions. Such autocorrelations of occasion residuals are especially common when measurement occasions are closely spaced in time (e.g., multiple measurements taken across the same week or even within a single day). Models with autoregression such as Kenny and Zautra's (1995) trait-state error model take such short-term, carry-over effects into account. Cole et al. (2005) presented a multiple-indicator extension of the trait-state error model that provides greater stability and flexibility. Eid et al. (2017) showed how models with autoregression can be defined based on LST-R theory. Prenoveau (2016) provided a review and tutorial of different models with autoregression.

OTHER EXTENSIONS

Eid (1996; see also Eid & Hoffman, 1998) and Thielemann et al. (2017) presented models for ordered categorical (ordinal) outcomes. Models in which traits and states are represented by latent classes are described in Eid (2007; Eid & Langeheine, 1999). Tisak and Tisak (2000) combined the idea of modeling latent trait change with the idea of modeling occasion-specificity and presented a comprehensive framework for modeling variability and change in a single model. Mixture distribution models (Courvoisier et al., 2007) allow identifying a priori unknown subgroups (latent classes) of individuals that differ, for example, in their "traitedness" or proneness to occasion-specific influences.

Another line of research has developed models for multimethod measurement designs (e.g., different raters assessing depression and anxiety of children on multiple time points). Multimethod models (Courvoisier et al., 2008; Koch et al., 2017; Scherpenzeel & Saris, 2007; Vautier, 2004) allow answering questions of stability versus occasion-specificity simultaneously for different methods.

Geiser et al. (2015) presented models for designs that include both random (unknown) and fixed (known) situations. Their models allow examining main effects of situations and person-situation interactions in designs in which individuals' scores are recorded across different known or experimentally manipulated situations. Hintz et al. (2019) extended this approach to multimethod designs in which method effects (e.g., due to the use of multiple reporters) can be studied in addition to fixed and random situation effects. Geiser et al. (2016) showed how multi-group models can be used to study changes in both mean levels and state variability following interventions or experimental manipulations. Various other LST-R models with applications in the Mplus computer software are described in Geiser (2021).

SUMMARY AND CONCLUSION

About 30 years ago, LST theory was introduced and the first LST models were applied to psychological data. As shown in this chapter, since then, LST theory has seen numerous extensions that facilitate and broaden its applicability in psychological research. One strength of LST-R theory is that its theoretical concepts are formally defined, leading to a clear interpretation of all latent variables in LST-R models. The various extensions illustrate that the rigorous mathematical foundation and constructive definition of the latent variables do not attenuate but rather enhance the flexibility of the approach, while at the same time allowing for a clear interpretation of all theoretical concepts defined within this framework. Other latent variable models can suffer in their theoretical strength and empirical applicability if the latent variables are not formally defined but just "assumed to be there"—without explicating the random experiment that underlies the phenomenon under study and without specifying how the scores of the latent variables depend on the outcomes of the random experiment.

One advantage of the constructive definition of latent variables is that we know exactly which correlations among latent variables must be zero by definition. Consequently, the theory provides clear guidelines regarding which latent variables can be correlated in empirical applications. We believe that in the future, other areas of latent variable research will also benefit from formally defining latent variables.

References

Anastasi, A. (1983). Traits, states, and situations: A comprehensive view. In H. Wainer & S. Messick (Eds.), *Principles of modern psychological measurement* (pp. 345–356). Erlbaum.

Bishop, J., Geiser, C., & Cole, D. A. (2015). Modeling latent growth with multiple indicators: A comparison of three approaches. *Psychological Methods, 20*(1), 43–62. https://doi.org/10.1037/met0000018

Bowers, K. S. (1973). Situationism in psychology: An analysis and a critique. *Psychological Review, 80*(5), 307–336. https://doi.org/10.1037/h0035592

Cattell, R. B. (1966). The data box: Its ordering of total resources in terms of possible relational systems. In R. B. Cattell (Ed.), *Handbook of multivariate experimental psychology* (pp. 67–128). Rand McNally.

Cattell, R. B. (1979). *Personality and learning theory* (Vol. 1). Springer.

Cattell, R. B., & Scheier, I. H. (1961). *The meaning and measurement of neuroticism and anxiety.* Ronald.

Cole, D. A., Martin, N. C., & Steiger, J. H. (2005). Empirical and conceptual problems with longitudinal trait-state models: Introducing a trait-state-occasion model. *Psychological Methods, 10*(1), 3–20. https://doi.org/10.1037/1082-989X.10.1.3

Collins, L. M., & Horn, J. L. (1991). *Best methods for the analysis of change: Recent advances, unanswered questions, future directions.* American Psychological Association. https://doi.org/10.1037/10099-000

Collins, L. M., & Sayer, A. G. (2001). *New methods for the analysis of change.* American Psychological Association. https://doi.org/10.1037/10409-000

Courvoisier, D. S., Eid, M., & Nussbeck, F. W. (2007). Mixture distribution latent state-trait analysis: Basic ideas and applications. *Psychological Methods, 12*(1), 80–104. https://doi.org/10.1037/1082-989X.12.1.80

Courvoisier, D. S., Nussbeck, F. W., Eid, M., Geiser, C., & Cole, D. A. (2008). Analyzing the convergent and discriminant validity of states and traits: Development and applications of multimethod latent state-trait models. *Psychological Assessment, 20*(3), 270–280. https://doi.org/10.1037/a0012812

Cronbach, L. J., & Furby, L. (1970). How should we measure "change": Or should we? *Psychological Bulletin, 74*(1), 68–80. https://doi.org/10.1037/h0029382

Deinzer, R., Steyer, R., Eid, M., Notz, P., Schwenkmezger, P., Ostendorf, F., & Neubauer, A. (1995). Situational effects in trait assessment: The FPI, NEOFFI and EPI questionnaires. *European*

Journal of Personality, 9(1), 1–23. https://doi.org/10.1002/per.2410090102

Dumenci, L., & Windle, M. (1998). A multitrait-multioccasion generalization of the latent trait-state model: Description and application. *Structural Equation Modeling, 5*(4), 391–410. https://doi.org/10.1080/10705519809540114

Eid, M. (1996). Longitudinal confirmatory factor analysis for polytomous item responses: Model definition and model selection on the basis of stochastic measurement theory. *Methods of Psychological Research Online, 1,* 65–85.

Eid, M. (2000). A multitrait-multimethod model with minimal assumptions. *Psychometrika, 65*(2), 241–261. https://doi.org/10.1007/BF02294377

Eid, M. (2007). Latent class models for analyzing variability and change. In A. Ong & M. van Dulmen (Eds.), *Handbook of methods in positive psychology* (pp. 591–607). Oxford University Press.

Eid, M., & Diener, E. (2006). *Handbook of multimethod measurement in psychology.* American Psychological Association. https://doi.org/10.1037/11383-000

Eid, M., & Hoffmann, L. (1998). Measuring variability and change with an item response model for polytomous variables. *Journal of Educational and Behavioral Statistics, 23*(3), 193–215. https://doi.org/10.3102/10769986023003193

Eid, M., Holtmann, J., Santangelo, P., & Ebner-Priemer, U. (2017). On the definition of latent state-trait models with autoregressive effects: Insights from LST-R theory. *European Journal of Psychological Assessment, 33*(4), 285–295. https://doi.org/10.1027/1015-5759/a000435

Eid, M., & Langeheine, R. (1999). The measurement of consistency and occasion specificity with latent class models: A new model and its application to the measurement of affect. *Psychological Methods, 4*(1), 100–116. https://doi.org/10.1037/1082-989X.4.1.100

Eid, M., Notz, P., Steyer, R., & Schwenkmezger, P. (1994). Validating scales for the assessment of mood level and variability by latent state-trait analyses. *Personality and Individual Differences, 16*(1), 63–76. https://doi.org/10.1016/0191-8869(94)90111-2

Eid, M., Schneider, C., & Schwenkmezger, P. (1999). Do you feel better or worse? The validity of perceived deviations of mood states from mood traits. *European Journal of Personality, 13*(4), 283–306. https://doi.org/10.1002/(SICI)1099-0984(199907/08)13:4<283::AID-PER341>3.0.CO;2-0

Endler, N. S., & Magnusson, D. (Eds.). (1976). *Interactional Psychology and Personality.* Wiley.

Epstein, S. (1979). The stability of behavior: I. On predicting most of the people much of the time. *Journal of Personality and Social Psychology, 37*(7), 1097–1126. https://doi.org/10.1037/0022-3514.37.7.1097

Epstein, S. (1980). The stability of behavior: II. Implications for psychological research. *American Psychologist, 35*(9), 790–806. https://doi.org/10.1037/0003-066X.35.9.790

Fleeson, W. (2001). Toward a structure-and process-integrated view of personality: Traits as density distributions of states. *Journal of Personality and Social Psychology, 80*(6), 1011–1027.

Geiser, C. (2009). *Multitrait-multimethod-multioccasion modeling.* Akademische Verlagsgemeinschaft München.

Geiser, C. (2021). *Longitudinal structural equation modeling with Mplus: A latent state-trait perspective.* Guilford Press.

Geiser, C., Eid, M., Nussbeck, F. W., Courvoisier, D. S., & Cole, D. A. (2010a). Analyzing true change in longitudinal multitrait-multimethod studies: Application of a multimethod change model to depression and anxiety in children. *Developmental Psychology, 46*(1), 29–45. https://doi.org/10.1037/a0017888

Geiser, C., Eid, M., Nussbeck, F. W., Courvoisier, D. S., & Cole, D. A. (2010b). Multitrait-multimethod change modeling. *AStA. Advances in Statistical Analysis, 94*(2), 185–201. https://doi.org/10.1007/s10182-010-0127-0

Geiser, C., Griffin, D., & Shiffman, S. (2016). Using multigroup-multiphase latent state-trait models to study treatment-induced changes in intra-individual state variability: An application to smokers' affect. *Frontiers in Psychology, 7,* 1043. https://doi.org/10.3389/fpsyg.2016.01043

Geiser, C., Keller, B., & Lockhart, G. (2013). First- versus second-order latent growth curve models: Some insights from latent state-trait theory. *Structural Equation Modeling, 20*(3), 479–503. https://doi.org/10.1080/10705511.2013.797832

Geiser, C., Litson, K., Bishop, J., Keller, B. T., Burns, G. L., Servera, M., & Shiffman, S. (2015). Analyzing person, situation and person × situation interaction effects: Latent state-trait models for the combination of random and fixed situations. *Psychological Methods, 20*(2), 165–192. https://doi.org/10.1037/met0000026

Geiser, C., & Lockhart, G. (2012). A comparison of four approaches to account for method effects in latent state-trait analyses. *Psychological Methods, 17*(2), 255–283. https://doi.org/10.1037/a0026977

Hagemann, D., Hewig, J., Seifert, J., Naumann, E., & Bartussek, D. (2005). The latent state-trait structure of resting EEG asymmetry: Replication and extension. *Psychophysiology, 42*(6), 740–752. https://doi.org/10.1111/j.1469-8986.2005.00367.x

Hagemann, D., & Naumann, E. (2009). States vs. traits: An integrated model for the test of Eysenck's arousal/arousability hypothesis. *Journal of Individual Differences, 30*(2), 87–99. https://doi.org/10.1027/1614-0001.30.2.87

Hagemann, D., Naumann, E., Thayer, J. F., & Bartussek, D. (2002). Does resting electroencephalograph asymmetry reflect a trait? an application of latent state-trait theory. *Journal of Personality and Social Psychology, 82*(4), 619–641. https://doi.org/10.1037/0022-3514.82.4.619

Hamaker, E. L., Kuiper, R. M., & Grasman, R. P. (2015). A critique of the cross-lagged panel model. *Psychological Methods, 20*(1), 102–116. https://doi.org/10.1037/a0038889

Hancock, G. R., Kuo, W., & Lawrence, F. R. (2001). An illustration of second-order latent growth models. *Structural Equation Modeling, 8*(3), 470–489. https://doi.org/10.1207/S15328007SEM0803_7

Harris, C. W. (Ed.). (1963). *Problems in measuring change*. The University of Wisconsin Press.

Hellhammer, J., Fries, E., Schweisthal, O. W., Schlotz, W., Stone, A. A., & Hagemann, D. (2007). Several daily measurements are necessary to reliably assess the cortisol rise after awakening: State- and trait components. *Psychoneuroendocrinology, 32*(1), 80–86. https://doi.org/10.1016/j.psyneuen.2006.10.005

Hermes, M., Hagemann, D., Britz, P., Lieser, S., Bertsch, K., Naumann, E., & Walter, C. (2009). Latent state-trait structure of cerebral blood flow in a resting state. *Biological Psychology, 80*(2), 196–202. https://doi.org/10.1016/j.biopsycho.2008.09.003

Hertzog, C., & Nesselroade, J. R. (1987). Beyond autoregressive models: Some implications of the trait-state distinction for the structural modeling of developmental change. *Child Development, 58*(1), 93–109. https://doi.org/10.2307/1130294

Hintz, F., Geiser, C., & Shiffman, S. (2019). A latent state-trait model for analyzing states, traits, situations, method effects, and their interactions. *Journal of Personality, 87*(3), 434–454. https://doi.org/10.1111/jopy.12400

Irwin, H. J., Marks, A. D. G., & Geiser, C. (2018). Belief in the paranormal: A state, or a trait? *The Journal of Parapsychology, 82*(1), 24–40. https://doi.org/10.30891/jopar.2018.01.03

Kenny, D. A., & Zautra, A. (1995). The trait-state-error model for multiwave data. *Journal of Consulting and Clinical Psychology, 63*(1), 52–59. https://doi.org/10.1037/0022-006X.63.1.52

Kirschbaum, C., Steyer, R., Eid, M., Patalla, U., Schwenkmezger, P., & Hellhammer, D. H. (1990). Cortisol and behavior: 2. Application of a latent state-trait model to salivary cortisol. *Psychoneuroendocrinology, 15*(4), 297–307. https://doi.org/10.1016/0306-4530(90)90080-S

Koch, T., Schultze, M., Holtmann, J., Geiser, C., & Eid, M. (2017). A multimethod latent state-trait model for structurally different and interchangeable methods. *Psychometrika, 82*(1), 17–47. https://doi.org/10.1007/s11336-016-9541-x

Majcen, A.-M., Steyer, R., & Schwenkmezger, P. (1988). Konsistenz und Spezifität bei Eigenschafts- und Zustandsangst [Consistency and specificity of trait anxiety and state anxiety]. *Zeitschrift für Differentielle und Diagnostische Psychologie, 9*, 105–120.

Marsh, H. W., & Grayson, D. (1994). Longitudinal confirmatory factor analysis: Common, time-specific, item-specific, and residual-error components of variance. *Structural Equation Modeling, 1*(2), 116–145. https://doi.org/10.1080/10705519409539968

Mayer, A., Steyer, R., & Mueller, H. (2012). A general approach to defining latent growth components. *Structural Equation Modeling, 19*(4), 513–533. https://doi.org/10.1080/10705511.2012.713242

McArdle, J. J. (1988). Dynamic but structural equation modeling of repeated measures data. In R. B. Cattell & J. Nesselroade (Eds.), *Handbook of multivariate experimental psychology* (2nd ed., pp. 561–614). Plenum Press. https://doi.org/10.1007/978-1-4613-0893-5_17

McArdle, J. J., & Bell, R. Q. (2000). An introduction to latent growth models for developmental data analysis. In T. D. Little, K. U. Schnabel, & J. Baumert (Eds.), *Modeling longitudinal and multilevel data: Practical issues, applied approaches, and specific examples* (pp. 69–107, 269–281). Erlbaum.

Mischel, W. (1998). *Personality and assessment*. Wiley.

Nesselroade, J. R., & Bartsch, T. W. (1977). Multivariate perspectives on the construct validity of the trait-state distinction. In R. B. Cattell & R. M. Dreger (Eds.), *Handbook of modern personality theory* (pp. 221–238). Hemisphere.

Ormel, J., & Schaufeli, W. B. (1991). Stability and change in psychological distress and their relationship with self-esteem and locus of control: A dynamic equilibrium model. *Journal of Personality and Social Psychology, 60*(2), 288–299. https://doi.org/10.1037/0022-3514.60.2.288

Pohl, S., & Steyer, R. (2010). Modeling common traits and method effects in multitrait-multimethod analysis. *Multivariate Behavioral Research, 45*(1), 45–72. https://doi.org/10.1080/00273170903504729

Pohl, S., Steyer, R., & Kraus, K. (2008). Modelling method effects as individual causal effects. *Journal of the Royal Statistical Society. Series A (General)*, *171*(Pt. 1), 41–63.

Prenoveau, J. M. (2016). Specifying and interpreting latent state-trait models with autoregression: An illustration. *Structural Equation Modeling*, *23*(5), 731–749. https://doi.org/10.1080/10705511.2016.1186550

Raffalovich, L. E., & Bohrnstedt, G. W. (1987). Common, specific, and error variance components of factor models: Estimation with longitudinal data. *Sociological Methods & Research*, *15*(4), 385–405. https://doi.org/10.1177/0049124187015004003

Sayer, A. G., & Cumsille, P. E. (2001). Second-order latent growth models. In L. M. Collins & A. G. Sayer (Eds.), *New methods for the analysis of change* (pp. 179–200). American Psychological Association. https://doi.org/10.1037/10409-006

Schermelleh-Engel, K., Keith, N., Moosbrugger, H., & Hodapp, V. (2004). Decomposing person and occasion-specific effects: An extension of latent state-trait (LSI) theory to hierarchical LST models. *Psychological Methods*, *9*(2), 198–219. https://doi.org/10.1037/1082-989X.9.2.198

Scherpenzeel, A., & Saris, W. E. (2007). Multitrait-multimethod models for longitudinal research. In K. van Montfort, A. Satorra, & H. Oud (Eds.), *Longitudinal models in the behavioral and related sciences* (pp. 381–401). Erlbaum.

Schmitt, M., Schwartz, S. H., Steyer, R., & Schmitt, T. (1993). Measurement models for the Schwartz Values Inventory. *European Journal of Psychological Assessment*, *9*(2), 107–121.

Schmukle, S. C., & Egloff, B. (2005). A latent state-trait analysis of implicit and explicit personality measures. *European Journal of Psychological Assessment*, *21*(2), 100–107. https://doi.org/10.1027/1015-5759.21.2.100

Spielberger, C. D. (1972). Anxiety as an emotional state. In C. D. Spielberger (Ed.), *Anxiety: Current trends in theory and research* (Vol. 1, pp. 23–49). Academic Press. https://doi.org/10.1016/B978-0-12-657401-2.50009-5

Steyer, R. (1987). Konsistenz und Spezifität: Definition zweier zentraler Begriffe der Differentiellen Psychologie und ein einfaches Modell zu ihrer Identifikation [Consistency and specificity: Definition of two central concepts of differential psychology and a simple model for their identification]. *Zeitschrift für Differentielle und Diagnostische Psychologie*, *8*, 245–258.

Steyer, R. (1988). *Experiment, Regression und Kausalität. Die logische Struktur kausaler Regressionsmodelle* [Experiment, regression, and causality. The logical structure of causal regression models] [Unpublished habilitation thesis]. University of Trier, Trier, Germany.

Steyer, R. (1989). Models of classical psychometric test theory as stochastic measurement models: Representation, uniqueness, meaningfulness, identifiability, and testability. *Methodika*, *3*, 25–60.

Steyer, R. (2005). Analyzing individual and average causal effects via structural equation models. *Methodology: European Journal of Research Methods for the Behavioral and Social Sciences*, *1*(1), 39–54. https://doi.org/10.1027/1614-1881.1.1.39

Steyer, R., & Eid, M. (2001). *Messen und Testen* [*Measurement and testing*]. Springer. https://doi.org/10.1007/978-3-642-56924-1

Steyer, R., Eid, M., & Schwenkmezger, P. (1997). Modeling true intraindividual change: True change as a latent variable. *Methods of Psychological Research Online*, *2*(1), 21–33.

Steyer, R., Ferring, D., & Schmitt, M. J. (1992). States and traits in psychological assessment. *European Journal of Psychological Assessment*, *8*, 79–98.

Steyer, R., Krambeer, S., & Hannöver, W. (2004). Modeling latent trait-change. In K. Van Montfort, H. Oud, & A. Satorra (Eds.), *Recent developments on structural equation modeling: Theory and applications* (pp. 337–357). Kluwer Academic Press.

Steyer, R., Majcen, A.-M., Schwenkmezger, P., & Buchner, A. (1989). A latent state-trait anxiety model and its application to determine consistency and specificity coefficients. *Anxiety Research*, *1*(4), 281–299. https://doi.org/10.1080/08917778908248726

Steyer, R., Mayer, A., Geiser, C., & Cole, D. A. (2015). A theory of states and traits—Revised. *Annual Review of Clinical Psychology*, *11*(1), 71–98. https://doi.org/10.1146/annurev-clinpsy-032813-153719

Steyer, R., & Nagel, W. (2017). *Probability and conditional expectation*. Wiley.

Steyer, R., Partchev, I., & Shanahan, M. (2000). Modeling true intra-individual change in structural equation models: The case of poverty and children's psychosocial adjustment. In T. D. Little, K. U. Schnabel, & J. Baumert (Eds.), *Modeling longitudinal and multiple-group data: Practical issues, applied approaches, and specific examples* (pp. 109–126). Erlbaum.

Steyer, R., & Schmitt, M. (1990a). The effects of aggregation across and within occasions on consistency, specificity, and reliability. *Methodika*, *4*, 58–94.

Steyer, R., Schmitt, M., & Eid, M. (1999). Latent state-trait theory and research in personality and individual differences. *European Journal of Personality, 13*(5), 389–408. https://doi.org/10.1002/(SICI)1099-0984(199909/10)13:5<389::AID-PER361>3.0.CO;2-A

Steyer, R., & Schmitt, M. J. (1990b). Latent state-trait models in attitude research. *Quality & Quantity: International Journal of Methodology, 24*(4), 427–445. https://doi.org/10.1007/BF00152014

Steyer, R., & Schmitt, T. (1994). The theory of confounding and its application in causal modeling with latent variables. In A. Von Eye & C. C. Clogg (Eds.), *Latent variables analysis: Applications for developmental research* (pp. 36–67). Sage.

Steyer, R., Schwenkmezger, P., & Auer, A. (1990). The emotional and cognitive components of trait anxiety: A latent state-trait model. *Personality and Individual Differences, 11*(2), 125–134. https://doi.org/10.1016/0191-8869(90)90004-B

Thielemann, D., Sengewald, M.-A., Kappler, G., & Steyer, R. (2017). A probit latent state IRT model with latent item-effect variables. *European Journal of Psychological Assessment, 33*(4), 271–284. https://doi.org/10.1027/1015-5759/a000417

Tisak, J., & Tisak, M. S. (2000). Permanency and ephemerality of psychological measures with application to organizational commitment. *Psychological Methods, 5*(2), 175–198. https://doi.org/10.1037/1082-989X.5.2.175

Vautier, S. (2004). A longitudinal SEM approach to STAI data:two comprehensive multitrait-multistate models. *Journal of Personality Assessment, 83*(2), 167–179. https://doi.org/10.1207/s15327752jpa8302_11

Vautier, S., Steyer, R., & Boomsma, A. (2008). The true-change model with individual method effects: Reliability issues. *British Journal of Mathematical & Statistical Psychology, 61*(2), 379–399. https://doi.org/10.1348/000711007X206826

CHAPTER 14

LATENT VARIABLE MODELING OF CONTINUOUS GROWTH

David A. Cole, Jeffrey A. Ciesla, and Qimin Liu

The goal of this chapter is to review several types of structural equation models designed to estimate continuous growth in a targeted construct over time. We begin by describing the kinds of questions that such models can address, the data characteristics that are necessary for the application of these methods, and the broad assumptions that underlie these methods. The chapter primarily focuses on two general types of continuous growth models. The first is a single-measure, latent growth approach in which latent trends are estimated from a time series of data on a particular variable. The second is a multiple-indicator latent growth model, which requires multiple of the same construct at multiple waves and involves the extraction of a latent variable at each wave and then the extraction of latent trends in this latent variable over time. Finally, we note the development of new methods for assessing continuous change, providing references for the interested reader.

SETTING THE STAGE: THE KINDS OF QUESTIONS

Latent variable models of continuous growth can be used to address a wide range of questions. One set of questions focuses on the fundamental characterization of the growth trajectory itself. We have argued that understanding the longitudinal structure of our measures is as necessary for longitudinal research as understanding the factor structure of our measures is for cross-sectional research (Cole & Maxwell, 2009). These questions include:

- Is there an observable, nonzero trajectory of change over time?
- What is the shape of such change?
- When is change more or less rapid?
- On which longitudinal parameters (e.g., intercept, slope) are there reliable individual differences that might be predicted by other variables?
- How much time must elapse before change in the targeted construct can be detected?

Without reliable answers to these often-overlooked questions, researchers run the expensive risk of launching longitudinal studies that attempt to (a) predict change in constructs over periods of time when the targeted construct does not actually change, (b) find correlates of individual differences in change in variables for which reliable individual differences in change do not occur, (c) discover correlates of linear change when actual change is nonlinear, and (d) predict change over time intervals that are too brief or too long to capture change reliably.

A second set of questions pertains to correlates of change in the targeted construct. Change in the targeted variable can be variously conceptualized as a cause, a predictor, a correlate, or a consequence of another variable. This other variable has a temporal structure that may or may not mirror that of the target variable. This means that we must graduate from the simple question "What variables predict which outcomes?" to questions like:

- Which dimensions of change in one set of variables are related to which dimensions of change or growth in the target variable?
- Over what time intervals or time frames does this relation exist?
- Is this relation equally strong for various subgroups of the targeted population?

Failure to address these more sophisticated questions can result in what Kimball (1957) referred to as Type III error—"the error committed by giving the right answer to the wrong problem" (p. 134). Consequently, we run the risk of missing important relations that do exist and finding spurious evidence of apparent relations that do not.

Data Set Requirements

Latent variable models of growth require certain types of data. Clearly, one needs to have repeated assessments of a given construct over time. Although the assessment schedule is often constant (e.g., monthly, annually), this is not a necessity; waves can be unevenly spaced. However, latent variable growth models require that the assessment schedule is the same for all participants. Other analytic procedures have been developed, such as hierarchical linear modeling, that can accommodate variable assessment schedules; however, such procedures have other limitations not inherent in latent variable models of growth (see Curran, 2003).

It is also important that the scaling of the outcome variable should be consistent over time. Frequently, this consistency is achieved by the use of the same instrument at each wave. Unfortunately, this is not always possible. Sometimes researchers must utilize different measures of a construct at different waves, perhaps because change in participant ages requires the use of developmentally appropriate assessments. In some cases, standardized scores can be an effective way of handling shifts in measurement; however, too-casual standardization can subtly generate serious problems to which the researcher must be alert.[1]

The number of waves necessary for latent variable models of growth depends on the shape of change that the researcher seeks to investigate. To investigate first-order or linear change, three waves are needed. Second-order or quadratic models require four waves. To achieve model identification of ith-order polynomials (e.g., cubic, quadratic), $i + 2$ waves of data are needed. We note that, with highly restrictive model constraints (e.g., fixing the slope loadings to constrain variance and covariance of slope factors), it is possible to achieve model identification with one fewer wave (see Duncan et al., 2006, p. 19), but this approach is not generally recommended.

As in most data-analytic methods, one ideally would not have missing data. In longitudinal studies, however, various patterns of missing data are the norm. A wide range of methods exist for handling missing data in latent growth models. Of these, multiple imputation methods and full information maximum likelihood estimation (FIML) have particular advantages (see Widaman, 2006, for a review). Savalei and Bentler (2009) recommended a two-stage approach to missing data, in which the variance–covariance matrix is first recovered and then the model is fitted on the recovered variance–covariance matrix. Two advantages accrue with this approach. First, recovery of variance–covariance matrix

---

[1] Three problems are particularly common. First, in some cases, changing the metric can change the nature or meaning of the variable. For example, the shift from raw scores to scale scores on IQ tests controls for expected age differences. Second, standardization of each time-specific variable relative to its own mean will completely detrend the data. At every time point, the mean will become zero, masking real growth that might have been evident in the unstandardized variables. Third, to avoid this (second) problem, researchers sometimes standardize a time series of variables relative to the mean and variance of a reference time point. This procedure, however, rests on the potentially untenable assumption of homoscedasticity.

allows incorporation of auxiliary variables (i.e., variables that pertain to missingness but may not relate to the specified model). Second, the two-stage approach has advantages in small samples compared with FIML. Furthermore, its performance is comparable with FIML in simulation studies and with real data. Some of these methods (e.g., FIML) are available in many of the commonly available statistical computer packages that enable latent growth curve analysis (e.g., AMOS, Arbuckle, 2019; LISREL, Jöreskog & Sörbom, 2003; Mplus, Muthén & Muthén, 2017; lavaan, Rosseel, 2012).

Assumptions

A commonly overlooked assumption of latent growth curve (LGC) models is also the most basic: The specified growth trajectory should be reasonable for the phenomenon being studied over the window of time it is measured. Typically, this involves the assumption of continuous, noncyclical change during the study. However, extensions of LGC models have been developed to allow for discrete change (Chou et al., 2004).

It is also important to be mindful of the influence of time and the spacing of measurements. First, results only pertain to the time frame covered by data collection. An adolescent boy may grow 3 inches per year over 3 years, but extrapolating this trajectory to conclude that he will exceed a height of 20 feet by retirement would clearly be absurd. Further, assessment intervals that are too short or too long can significantly influence observed trajectories. Exceedingly long intervals can obscure growth trends and hide complexities in the shape of change. Intervals that are too short can result in the failure to detect significant growth, or in the detection of small, uninteresting trends. An important related point pertains to the difference between modeling age versus wave. Often, the time that elapses between measurement occasions or waves of a study represents a relatively arbitrary duration. Nevertheless, estimates of growth will be calibrated against whatever temporal metric is used, be it arbitrary or not. Researchers interested in growth should give serious consideration to using age or time instead of wave or measurement in order to calibrate growth relative to a metric with which readers are more likely to be familiar.

Time (or age) can be encoded in a wide variety of ways in LGC modeling. The most common method sets all loadings for the latent intercept at 1.0 and sets the loadings for latent growth at $0, 1, 2, 3, \ldots t - 1$ for time points 1 to t, respectively. Importantly, the intercept represents level of the dependent variable at the time point with a latent growth factor loading of zero. When the growth factor loading for Time 1 equals zero, the intercept represents the level of the dependent variable at baseline (i.e., at Wave 1 of the study), and the latent slope variable represents change from that point. Alternative treatments of time may be useful for other research questions. For example, using a zero-growth factor loading for the last wave of measurement (i.e., $1 - t \ldots -3, -2, -1, 0$) allows the intercept to represent value of the dependent variable at the end of the study. Researchers can then use other variables to predict final rather than initial levels of the dependent variable. In still other cases, researchers can specific the intercept at a time point that minimizes the either the variance of the dependent variable and/or intercept-slope covariance (aka the "aperture" or "bowtie knot"; Hancock & Choi, 2006), a useful strategy to find the time point when individuals are estimated to be most similar in their true amount of the dependent variable (Hancock & Choi, 2006).

Additionally, other treatments of time can be used to model nonlinear growth. Most common is the use of multiple latent growth factors with higher order polynomials as their loadings, enabling the researcher to model growth as a function of an intercept and linear ($0, 1, 2, 3 \ldots t - 1$), quadratic ($0, 1, 4, 9 \ldots [t - 1]^2$), etc. Further, researchers can allow for multiple linear trajectories or "splines." For example, the first spline might have loadings of 0, 1, 2, 3, 4, 5, and a second factor might have loadings of 0, 0, 0, 1, 2. In such a model, the first linear factor estimates the general trend of linear growth in the study, whereas the second linear factor estimates change in growth after Wave 3. A potential application of this model would be to test the hypothesis that the growth rate of drinking changes from early to late adolescence (when participants reach the legal drinking age). We note, however, that estimation of nonlinear shape can involve additional parameters, which requires a greater sample size in order to obtain precise estimates.

Finally, researchers can also use freed-loading LGC, in which some the growth factor loadings are freely estimated (see Bollen & Curran, 2006, pp. 98–103). To set the metric of the latent growth variable, one loading is set at 0 and another is set at 1. One example sets growth factor loadings at Times 1 through 6 to be 0, 1, *, *, *, *, where asterisks represent freely estimated loadings (Meredith & Tisak, 1990). In such a model, the fixed factor loadings establish the (arbitrary) metric for the latent growth factor, and the free factor loadings are interpreted relative to the change from Time 1 to Time 2. For example, an estimated Time 3 factor loading of 1.5 would imply that half as much growth occurred from Time 2 to 3 than from Time 1 to 2. Another useful method sets the final factor loading at 1 (0, *, *, *, 1), in which case each estimated loading represents the proportion of overall growth that has occurred since Time 1 (McArdle, 1988). Such approaches are a bit more exploratory, as the shape of the trajectory over time is not specified a priori.

As LGC models are typically estimated using maximum likelihood estimation, multivariate normality of the outcome variable is also assumed. Relatedly, the outcome variable is assumed to be measured on an interval or ratio scale. Specific extensions of LGC have been created for non-normal, noninterval outcomes (Duncan et al., 2006, pp. 165–178) and for zero-inflated count data (Liu & Powers, 2007) using a dual-trajectory growth model for the growth processes in zero inflation growth and in the Poisson count but will not be discussed here.

Single-Measure, Latent Growth Modeling

Probably the most basic latent variable approach to continuous change is what we will refer to as a *single-measure, latent growth model*. This approach starts with a single measure of a particular construct obtained at multiple time points from a (relatively large) sample. In most forms of this approach, the elapsed time between any pair of waves is assumed to be the same for all participants; however, the elapsed time between one wave and the next need not be the same for all pairs of waves. That is, the waves can be unevenly spaced, as long as the spacing is the same for all participants. (We note, however, that the assumption of consistent timing across participants is often violated, as researchers allow for sometimes very different time lags between the same waves for different people. Such discrepancies can reduce reliability, diminish power, and introduce bias.) If complete data are available for all participants, such analyses can be conducted using only four kinds of information: an index of elapsed time (e.g., wave, age, months) as well as means, variances, and covariances (or means, standard deviations, and correlations).

In this section, we consider LGC models appropriate for testing several common types of hypotheses. We start with a relatively simple intercept-only model (with waves that are equally spaced in time). We then proceed to test increasingly complex models in which more growth parameters are added. In the second model, we add and test growth parameters representing a linear growth trajectory. In the third model, we consider the case in which growth accelerates or decelerates over time. That is, we add and test parameters that represent a quadratic trajectory over time. We demonstrate the execution of all three analyses with an example data set.

Example. For the relatively simple linear growth model, let us imagine that we have data from 300 cases on a random variable Y_i at each of five evenly space waves (where $i = 1$ to 5). Table 14.1 contains the means, standard deviations, and correlations for these variables. Table 14.1 also contains a sixth variable, TX, which we will save for analyses later in the chapter.

Although we are interested in linear growth, we test a series of nested or hierarchical models. We begin with the intercept-only model depicted

TABLE 14.1

Means, Standard Deviations, and Correlations for Five Waves of Data on Random Variable Y_i (Plus a Sixth Variable Called TX), $N = 300$

Variable	TX	Y_1	Y_2	Y_3	Y_4	Y_5
TX	1.000					
Y_1	0.019	1.000				
Y_2	0.125*	0.204***	1.000			
Y_3	−0.005	0.192***	0.202***	1.000		
Y_4	0.083	0.170**	0.225***	0.140*	1.000	
Y_5	0.092	0.233***	0.145*	0.284***	0.271***	1.000
Mean	0.473	6.933	7.607	8.452	9.133	9.737
SD	0.713	1.613	1.768	1.534	1.699	1.669

*$p < .05$; **$p < .01$; ***$p < .001$.

in Figure 14.1A. In this model, the variance of Y_i is partitioned into two parts: that due to a latent intercept random variable and that due to random error. As the factor loadings are all fixed at 1.0, the latent intercept can be conceptualized as the time invariant factor that underlies Y_1 to Y_5. This model allows for individual differences in the latent intercept but does not allow for systematic change in Y over time. The model has seven free parameters to be estimated: the mean (M) and variance (V) of the latent intercept and the five error variances $V(e_i)$. All other means are fixed at zero, and all other path coefficients are fixed at unity. This model fits the data in Table 14.1 quite poorly, as indicated by a large and significant $\chi^2_{(13)} = 512.20$ ($p < .001$) and a very large value for the root-mean-square error of approximation (RMSEA) of 0.358 (90% confidence interval [CI; 0.332, 0.385]). We concluded that an intercept-only model did not fit the data.

We followed this with the linear growth model depicted in Figure 14.1B. This model contains three additional parameters: a mean and variance for a latent slope random variable and the covariance between the latent intercept and slope, C(int, slp). This model appeared to fit the data well, as indicated by a nonsignificant $\chi^2_{(10)} = 10.28$ ($p > .40$), as well as large values for the comparative fit index (CFI = 0.997) and the incremental fit index (IFI = 0.997), and a small value for the RMSEA = 0.010 (90% CI [0.000, 0.064]). As the intercept-only model and the linear growth model are hierarchically related, they can be statistically compared. The difference between the models was significant, $\Delta\chi^2_{(3)} = 501.92$ ($p < .001$), indicating that the linear model fit the data significantly better than did the intercept-only model.[2]

Before interpreting the linear model, however, testing an even higher order model is prudent to rule out at least some possibility of nonlinear growth, which (if ignored) could bias parameter estimates in the linear model. Here we tested the model in Figure 14.1C, containing a latent intercept, a latent slope, and a latent quadratic random variable. This model contains four new parameters: the mean and variance of the latent quadratic random variable and the covariances of the quadratic term with the intercept and

---

[2]The χ^2 tests the difference between the model-implied means and covariances and the observed means and covariances. Significant values imply that the model does not represent the data to some degree. It can be argued, however, that no model is completely right. Even when the degree of model misfit is small (and potentially tolerable), the χ^2 becomes increasingly sensitive as sample sizes become larger, sometimes leading investigators to dismiss potentially acceptable models. As with any inferential statistic, one should examine the magnitude of the discrepancy before deciding to dismiss the model. Several indices are often used for this purpose. The CFI and IFI provide indices of relative fit, assessing whether the current model provides a superior fit to a null model, with values greater than 0.95 representing good fits. The RMSEA is especially useful as it has a known confidence interval. RMSEAs closer to 0 (or at least less than 0.06) suggest a good fit. Other procedures are available for the assessment of model fit and research continues to examine which are most appropriate latent growth modeling (Wu et al., 2009).

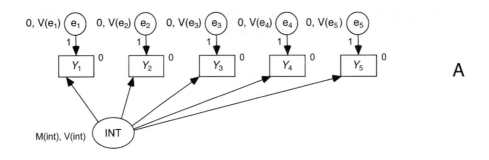

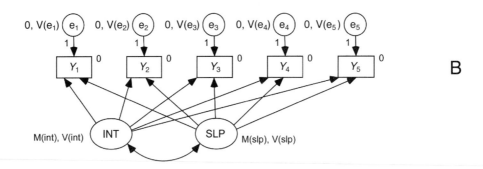

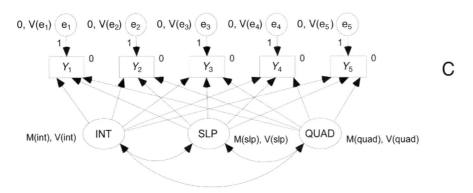

FIGURE 14.1. Three univariate latent growth curve models: A. Intercept-only model (INT loadings = 1); B. Linear model (INT loadings = 1; SLP loadings = 0, .25, .50, .75, 1.00); C. Quadratic model (INT loadings = 1; SLP loadings = 0, .25, .50, .75, 1.00; QUAD loadings = 0, .0625, .25, .5625, 1.0). INT = intercept; SLP = linear slope; QUAD = quadratic term.

slope. Note that the factor loadings for the latent quadratic variable are fixed at values equal to the squares of the loadings for the latent linear variable (i.e., $0^2 = 0$, $.25^2 = .0625$, $.5^2 = .25$, $.75^2 = .5625$, $1^2 = 1$), thus forcing this latent variable to be the quadratic term. This model also fit the data well, as shown by a nonsignificant $\chi^2_{(6)} = 7.43$ ($p > .28$), as well as large values for the CFI = 0.99 and the IFI = 0.99, and a small value for the RMSEA = 0.028 (90% CI [0.000, 0.084]). However, the model did not represent a significantly better fit than did the linear model, $\Delta\chi^2_{(4)} = 2.85$ ($p > .50$). Furthermore, the variance and mean of the latent quadratic variable were nonsignificant, suggesting that there was not a reliable quadratic trend in the data. Consequently, in the interest of parsimony, we elected to interpret the linear model.

Parameter estimates for the linear model appear in Table 14.2. The means of both the slope and the intercept were significantly different from zero. Interpretation of these parameters depends upon the scaling of time. Here, we scaled Waves 1 through 5 to be 0, .25, .50, .75 and 1.0 (as shown in the loading of Y_i onto the latent slope variable). Because Wave 1 is encoded as 0 in this analysis, the intercept represents the value of Y where time equals 0 (Wave 1). Thus, our estimate of the intercept reveals that the expected value of Y at Wave 1 (or Time 0) is 6.95. We also observe this to be statistically significant, meaning that this expected value is significantly different from zero. The significant variance of the intercept (0.53) indicates that there are reliable individual differences in the Wave 1 values of Y. With respect to the slope, the estimate indicated that the value is equal to 2.84 and is statistically significant. This represents the expected change in the dependent variable for every 1-unit change in time. Given our scaling of time, this is the expected change from Waves 1 to Wave 5. The significance of the mean slope value indicates that this is significantly different from zero. The variability of the slopes (0.337) is not significant, however. This suggests that although the scores on the dependent variable are increasing over time, there is no significant individual differences in this rate of change. Scores are significantly increasing but increasing at roughly the same rate for all participants. Finally, we see that the covariation of the intercepts and slopes is –0.04 and is not significant. In general, a positive covariance would suggest that higher intercepts are associated with more positive slopes. Conversely, a negative covariance reveals that higher intercepts are associated with smaller or even negative slopes, a finding that may signify regression to the mean (see Campbell & Kenny, 1999). Alternatively, in a developmental context, negative covariance could occur because of ceiling or floor effects (Wang et al., 2008).

Usually, researchers would like to see evidence of reliable variance in parameters (e.g., intercept or slope) before attempting to explain or predict individual differences in such parameters. Based on the current results, a researcher might legitimately seek predictors of individual differences in the intercept, but not the slope. Nevertheless, let us imagine that the researcher forged ahead despite these early results. For example, the researcher might be interested in whether the latent growth of Y differed for individuals receiving treatment as compared to those receiving placebo in a randomized treatment-control group design. For such a data set, we simply add the TX variable in Table 14.1. TX is a dichotomous variable, on which 0s represent membership in the control group and 1s signify membership in the treatment group. Figure 14.2 depicts a model in which TX is added as a potential predictor of both the intercept and the slope of the latent grow of Y. This model fits the data well, with a $\chi^2_{(13)} = 14.78$ ($p > .32$), as well as large values for the CFI = 0.98 and the IFI = 0.98, and a small value for the RMSEA = 0.021 (90% CI [0.000, 0.063]). Examination of the model parameter estimates, however, reveals that the effect of TX on the intercept was 0.084 ($SE = 0.109$), and the effect of TX on the slope was 0.109 ($SE = 0.155$). Both were nonsignificant ($p > .40$). Attempting to predict individual differences in growth in

TABLE 14.2

Parameter Estimates for Univariate Latent Growth Model

Parameter	Estimate	Standard error	t test	p value
INT → Y_1	1.00	—	—	—
INT → Y_2	1.00	—	—	—
INT → Y_3	1.00	—	—	—
INT → Y_4	1.00	—	—	—
INT → Y_5	1.00	—	—	—
SLP → Y_1	0.00	—	—	—
SLP → Y_2	0.25	—	—	—
SLP → Y_3	0.50	—	—	—
SLP → Y_4	0.75	—	—	—
SLP → Y_5	1.00	—	—	—
Mean of INT	6.95	0.08	89.38	< .001
Mean of SLP	2.84	0.11	25.82	< .001
Var of INT	0.53	0.18	2.945	0.003
Var of SLP	0.337	0.39	0.865	0.387
Cov (INT, SLP)	–0.04	0.227	–0.178	0.859

Note. INT = intercept; SLP = slope.

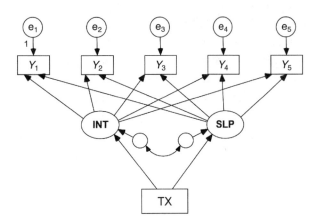

FIGURE 14.2. Univariate linear latent growth curve model with TX as a predictor. INT = intercept; SLP = slope.

the absence of reliable variance in the latent growth parameters would seem to be a fruitless endeavor.

MULTIVARIATE LATENT GROWTH MODELING

Even though the univariate growth models (like the ones above) do extract latent growth parameters, they are limited in that they represent the latent growth of the manifest variable. Manifest variable Y represents only one measure of the underlying construct. In the social sciences, most manifest variables are fallible, imperfect measures of the construct they were designed to measure. By obtaining multiple measures of the underlying construct at each wave of a longitudinal study, it may be possible (a) to extract a time series of latent variables (one variable per wave) that represents the underlying construct of interest and (b) to model the growth of these latent variables, not just the growth of their fallible indicators.

In this section, we demonstrate the use of multivariate latent growth curve modeling to test for evidence of a latent intercept, a latent slope, and a latent quadratic trend. We also demonstrate the utility of this method for revealing treatment differences in latent growth. As we will see, the multivariate approach can reveal trends and relations that may be missed by the univariate approach.

For this demonstration, we used the data in Table 14.3. As in the previous example, we have data at five waves. Unlike the previous example, however, we have three measures (not just one) of the underlying construct at each wave. We call these variables X_i, Y_i, and Z_i. In fact, Y_i is exactly the same variable that we used in the univariate example. (Note: we have put the statistics for Y_i in bold face to highlight the fact that these are *exactly* the same values from Table 14.1 that we analyzed in the univariate LGC case.)

Here, we focus on the strategy that Duncan et al. (2006, pp. 68–74) referred to as the *curve of factors* approach (McArdle, 1988). (In the same book, they contrasted this approach with a *factor of curves* model—a second-order growth curve model building on a parallel process model, which we will not review in this chapter.) We walk through a series of models that we recommend and apply each of them to the data set contained in Table 14.3. This series contains four models: (a) a measurement model, (b) an intercept-only model, (c) a linear model, and (d) a quadratic model. As will become evident, the linear model proves to be optimal. We contrast its results with those of the univariate LGC linear model from above.

Measurement Model

We begin with a measurement model. In this model, depicted in the upper panel of Figure 14.3, we extract one latent variable (ξ_i) per wave from the three manifest variables (X_i, Y_i, Z_i) obtained at that wave. In this model, we place no constraints on the means, variances, or covariances of the latent variables. This model fit the data well, with $\chi^2_{(90)} = 102.95$ ($p > .16$), CFI = 0.99, IFI = 0.99, and RMSEA = 0.022 (90% CI [0.000, 0.040]). Standardized and unstandardized parameter estimates appear in Table 14.4. Using this model as a starting place, we can address several important issues:

1. Are the factor loadings reasonably large (and significantly different from zero)? In this case, the answer is yes (see Table 14.4).

TABLE 14.3

Means, Standard Deviations, and Correlations for Five Waves of Data on Random Variables X_i, Y_i, and Z_i (Plus TX), $N = 300$

	TX	X_1	Y_1	Z_1	X_2	Y_2	Z_2	X_3	Y_3	Z_3	X_4	Y_4	Z_4	X_5	Y_5	Z_5
TX	1															
X_1	-.017	1														
Y_1	**.019**	.560	1													
Z_1	-.044	.776	.601	1												
X_2	.113	.308	.223	.365	1											
Y_2	**.125**	.306	**.204**	.379	.578	1										
Z_2	.124	.382	.278	.462	.832	.640	1									
X_3	.011	.248	.237	.253	.265	.221	.354	1								
Y_3	**-.005**	.249	**.192**	.281	.309	**.202**	.348	.508	1							
Z_3	-.052	.331	.271	.345	.369	.305	.431	.797	.586	1						
X_4	.017	.336	.222	.357	.327	.236	.374	.325	.329	.402	1					
Y_4	**.083**	.233	**.170**	.242	.318	**.225**	.367	.236	**.140**	.309	.552	1				
Z_4	.087	.378	.251	.373	.410	.318	.460	.347	.302	.451	.824	.609	1			
X_5	.188	.170	.197	.155	.365	.226	.364	.403	.258	.393	.430	.319	.461	1		
Y_5	**.092**	.205	**.233**	.233	.249	**.145**	.303	.351	**.284**	.354	.353	**.271**	.345	.564	1	
Z_5	.142	.255	.252	.269	.416	.226	.429	.436	.323	.450	.468	.402	.516	.825	.638	1
M	0.472	10.072	6.933	13.080	11.034	7.607	14.333	11.881	8.452	15.480	13.048	9.133	16.928	13.808	9.737	18.093
SD	0.713	1.639	1.613	1.870	1.775	1.768	1.981	1.623	1.534	1.848	1.694	1.699	1.955	1.858	1.669	2.121

Note. Significant correlations are bolded.

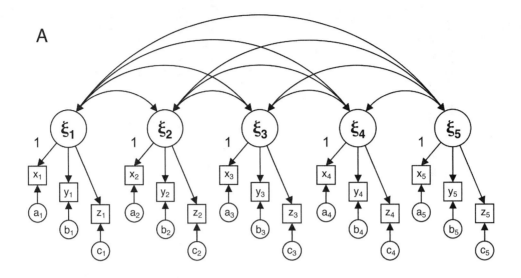

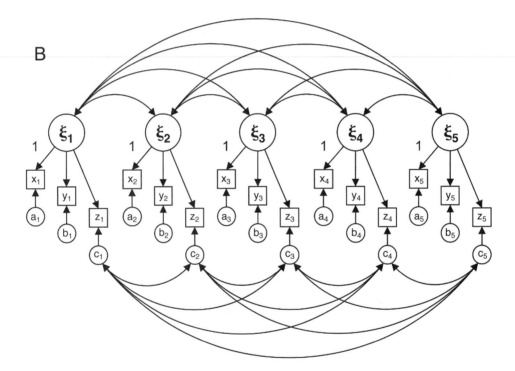

FIGURE 14.3. Measurement models (A) without correlated disturbances and (B) with correlated disturbances (correlated disturbances are also included for the X variables and for the Y variables, but are not shown so as to avoid the visual clutter).

2. Such simple measurement models sometimes will not fit longitudinal data. When measures X, Y, and Z are repeated at each wave, the residual error variances at one wave are often correlated with their counterparts at subsequent waves. When such correlations exist, they must be modeled—usually by allowing carefully selected pairs of residuals to correlate (see LaGrange & Cole, 2008). Such a model is depicted in the lower panel of Figure 14.3. Failure to allow for such correlated residuals in longitudinal designs can result in biased parameter estimates (Marsh, 1993). In the current case, however, the full and reduced

TABLE 14.4

Measurement Model Parameter Estimates

Parameter	ξ_1	ξ_2	ξ_3	ξ_4	ξ_5
Unstandardized loadings					
X	1.00	1.00	1.00	1.00	1.00
Y	0.69	0.69	0.71	0.70	0.71
Z	1.30	1.30	1.30	1.30	1.31
Standardized loadings					
X	0.83	0.85	0.83	0.86	0.85
Y	0.60	0.61	0.62	0.61	0.66
Z	0.94	0.98	0.95	0.96	0.97
Correlations					
ξ_1	1.00				
ξ_2	0.49	1.00			
ξ_3	0.39	0.46	1.00		
ξ_4	0.43	0.49	0.49	1.00	
ξ_5	0.30	0.45	0.50	0.56	1.00
Means	10.07	11.04	11.88	13.05	13.81
SDs	1.36	1.50	1.35	1.45	1.57

models in Figure 14.3 were not significantly different, $\Delta\chi^2_{(30)} = 32.50$ ($p > .40$), so we proceeded with the more parsimonious measurement model as shown in the upper panel of Figure 14.3. (One could argue, however, that these correlations are never truly zero and that modeling them, despite their nonsignificance, could reduce bias.)

3. The good fit of this model also reveals that the expected values of the manifest variables (i.e., the manifest means) are proportionate to the latent variable means and reflect no evidence of measurement bias. In other words, $E(Y_i) = \lambda E(\xi_i) + \tau$, where λ is the the factor loading for Y_i and τ is bias, which is 0.

4. In longitudinal designs, measurement invariance across waves is highly desirable. A key part of such invariance is that the factor loadings for X, Y, and Z at one wave are equivalent to their counterparts at other waves. Such equivalences provide some assurance that the latent variable does not change qualitatively over time. Examination of the factor loadings in Table 14.4 reveals a high degree of cross-wave consistency.

If a well-fitting (and theoretically justified) measurement model is found, it should be incorporated into the LGC model. If, however, a suitable measurement model cannot be constructed, proceeding with multivariate LGC will almost inevitably come to naught—as LGC models are more restrictive than the measurement model and therefore will typically provide worse fits to the data.

Growth Model

We began with a multivariate intercept-only LGC model. This model provided a very poor fit to the data, as indicated by a large and significant $\chi^2_{(103)} = 1002.80$ ($p < .001$), a low CFI = 0.67, a low IFI = 0.67, and a large RMSEA = 0.171 (90% CI [0.161, 0.181]). Clearly, having only a latent intercept was insufficient to explain the observed means, the covariances, or both.

Next, we tested a model with both a latent intercept and a latent slope. This model is depicted in the upper panel of Figure 14.4. This model fit the data well, with a $\chi^2_{(100)} = 114.99$ ($p > .14$), CFI = 0.99, IFI = 0.99, and RMSEA = 0.022 (90% CI [0.000, 0.039]). Adding the linear trend clearly improved the fit enormously.

To rule out the possibility of nonlinear growth, we tested a model with a latent intercept, slope, and quadratic term. This model appeared to fit the data well, with a $\chi^2_{(96)} = 113.56$ ($p > .14$), CFI = 0.99, IFI = 0.99, and RMSEA = 0.025 (90% CI [0.000, 0.041]). We noted two things, however. First, the fit was not significantly better than that for the linear model, $\Delta\chi^2_{(4)} = 1.43$ ($p > .50$). And second, out-of-range parameter estimates emerged. Specifically, the estimated variances of the latent slope and quadratic variables were negative. Such problems can occur when a model is over-parameterized.

For the sake of fit and parsimony, we elected to interpret the linear LGC model. Parameter estimates for the structural components of this model appear in the upper portion of Table 14.5. (The measure model parameters were essentially identical to those in Table 14.4.) Strong evidence emerged for the existence of both a latent intercept and slope, in that the means and variances for

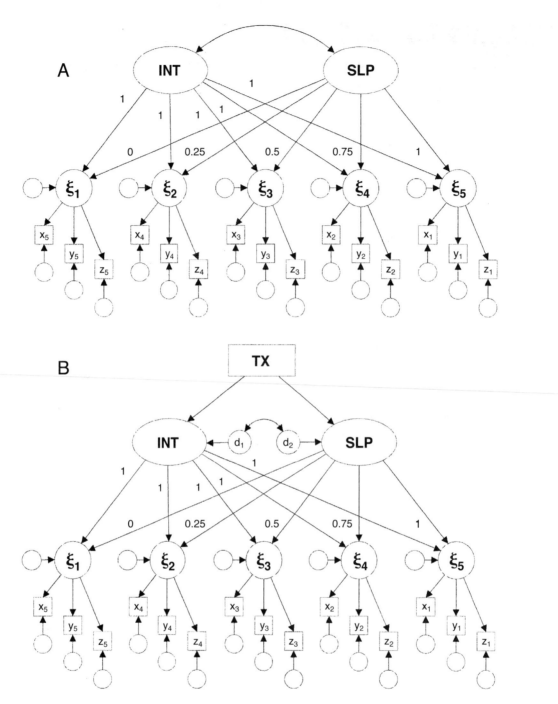

FIGURE 14.4. Linear models (A) without TX as predictor and (B) with TX as predictor. INT = intercept; SLP = slope.

both latent growth parameters were significantly greater than zero for all ($p < .001$). Furthermore, no out-of-range parameter estimates emerged.

With this justification, we tested our final model, in which we added TX as a predictor of the latent intercept and the latent slope (see lower panel of Figure 14.4). This model generated a marginally significant chi-square, $\chi^2_{(113)} = 139.02$ ($p < .049$); however, all other goodness-of-fit indices were excellent: CFI = 0.99, IFI = 0.99, and RMSEA = 0.028 (90% CI [0.002, 0.042]). There were no out-of-range parameter estimates. Consequently, we deemed this model to be a good fit and examined key parameter estimates (see lower

TABLE 14.5

Structural Model Parameter Estimates for Two LGC Models

Parameter	Estimate	SE	t test	p value
LGC model with intercept and slope				
mean (INT)	10.07	0.08	120.90	0.001
mean (SLP)	3.80	0.11	33.30	0.001
var (INT)	1.00	0.15	6.74	0.001
var (SLP)	1.02	0.27	3.79	0.001
cov (INT, SLP)	−0.28	0.16	−1.69	0.092
LGC model with TX predicting intercept and slope				
mean (TX)	0.472	0.041	11.47	0.001
var (TX)	0.507	0.041	12.23	0.001
β (TX → INT)	−0.03	0.105	−0.28	0.777
β (TX → SLP)	0.30	0.134	2.26	0.024
Intercept (INT)	10.09	0.097	104.06	.001
Intercept (SLP)	3.66	0.130	28.16	.001

Note. LGC = latent growth curve; INT = intercept; SLP = slope.

portion of Table 14.5). The TX variable was not significantly related to the latent intercept; however, TX was a significant predictor of the latent slope ($p < .02$). Given the 0,1 coding of TX, we see that the difference in slope between the Control group (TX = 0) and the Treatment group (TX = 1) was 0.30. Given that the standard deviation of the latent slope was 1.01, this represents an effect size of $d = 0.30$ (a small to medium effect, according to Cohen's (1977) criteria.

COMPARING UNIVARIATE AND MULTIVARIATE APPROACHES TO LGC ANALYSIS

Our univariate and multivariate results can be compared because variable Y that was the focus of our univariate LGC was embedded in the larger data set that was the focus of our multivariate analyses. As we will see, this comparison favors the multivariate approach in several ways. Some of the disadvantages of the univariate approach, however, are accentuated by our choice of variables. Although variable Y is not a bad variable, it was psychometrically weaker than X and Z (as seen by a close examination of their standardized factor loadings in Table 14.4). If the univariate approach were applied to a stronger variable, some of its disadvantages would diminish; however, other disadvantages would not.

The first disadvantage was one of reduced power. The univariate approach did not reveal that the latent slope had reliable variance, whereas the multivariate approach did. Faced with the univariate results, a prudent researcher might not attempt to explain individual differences in slope, figuring that it would be pointless to try to predict something that was not there. The multivariate approach, however, did uncover significant variance in the latent slope variable—a finding that might encourage further examination of the effect.

A second power-related concern also arose. TX differences in the slope were nonsignificant in the univariate approach but significant in the multivariate approach. The relatively small effect of TX on latent slope went undetected by the univariate approach; however, the enhanced power of the multivariate LGC resulted in a significant effect. Needless to say, such results are not guaranteed. This apparent power differential simply affects the likelihood of finding a significant effect when such an effect actually exists. Furthermore, if the variable selected for univariate analysis had been psychometrically stronger, the power differential would likely have been smaller.

Third, the multivariate approach to LGC analysis allowed us to test a variety of factors that the univariate LGC approach either assumed to be true or simply ignored. In particular, the multivariate approach allowed us to

1. examine the convergent validity of our measures of the underlying construct,
2. test for evidence of additive measurement bias before engaging in LGC,
3. test for measurement invariance across waves, and
4. test and (if necessary) model over-time correlated disturbances for repeated measures.

Failure to pass any of these tests would have provided warning signs for the researcher engaged in multivariate LGC analysis. The univariate method, however, provides no such opportunity. The researcher must assume that all of these potential problems do not exist. Further, the researcher cannot construct models that allow for violations of these assumptions. When these problems do exist, two outcomes are possible. At best, the univariate model will simply fail to fit the data (or will generate intractable out-of-range parameter estimates that prevent further interpretation of the results). At worst, the researcher will fail to reject the model and proceed with the interpretation of parameter estimates that are most likely biased and misleading.

MULTIGROUP LGC

Frequently, researchers are interested in examining trajectories in an outcome variable among two or more populations. One potential approach is to utilize dummy coded exogenous variables as predictors of slopes and intercepts. This method enables the investigator to test whether the observed group differences in growth parameters are statistically significant. Such methods might be used to test, for example, if the emergence of depressive symptoms during adolescence differs for girls versus boys. As parsimonious as this approach may be, a more flexible method is multigroup LGC analysis. In this approach, the growth parameters can be simultaneously, but separately, estimated for each group. This enables testing group differences not only on the mean slope and intercept but on the variances and covariances of these parameters as well. Furthermore, researchers can examine whether exogenous predictors of the growth parameters differ from group to group. For example, are there gender differences in the degree to which age of pubertal onset predicts trajectory of depressive symptoms? Multigroup LGC models can be somewhat complex in implementation and interpretation. Fortunately, some excellent chapters have been dedicated to his topic (see Bollen & Curran, 2006, pp. 162–187; Duncan et al., 2006, pp. 81–92).

NEW DIRECTIONS

Latent Difference Score Analyses

Throughout this chapter, we have reviewed the latent growth curve models in which functions of lines are used to characterize mean level changes in measured variables. Intercepts, linear slopes, and higher order functions summarize individual growth. In some cases, however, the underlying latent change may not neatly map onto such functions. An alternative LGC approach that does not impose growth functions upon the phenomenon of interest is called latent difference score analysis (LDS; McArdle & Hagamami 2001; McArdle & Nesselroade, 1994). In this approach, wave-to-wave differences in the outcome variable are explicitly modeled as separate parameters in a structural model. Following classical true score test theory, the manifest variable at each wave is first separated into a latent true score and a wave-specific error term. For every wave subsequent to the first, a latent difference score is created such that

$$\Delta y(t) = y(t) - y(t-1). \quad (14.1)$$

These latent difference scores can then be modeled in a number of different ways. One method for modeling these difference scores is what McArdle and colleagues referred to as the *dual change score* model. Here, latent differences are allowed to vary as a function of a constant change score (α), and a proportionate change score (β), as expressed: $\Delta y(t) = \alpha + \beta * y(t-1)$. When α is nonzero, this reflects the addition of some constant at every wave, producing linear growth. When β is nonzero, this reflects the addition of some value which is proportionate to the score at the prior wave, producing nonlinear growth. The model is directly analogous to compound interest models in accounting.

Importantly, these change parameters can be allowed to vary from person to person. As such, inter-individual variation in change is captured by some model parameters. Also, predictors of the change parameters can be including in the model, allowing researchers to ask such questions as, "Is gender related to wave-to-wave differences? And, how many units of change are anticipated at each wave?"

Furthermore, the LDS model can be extended to the bivariate case so that the researcher can investigate change scores in two constructs simultaneously. This allows the researcher to examine whether wave-to-wave changes in one variable are associated with changes in another variable. For example, the α for variable X may be correlated with the α for variable Y, or the βs for these variables may be correlated. Wave-specific changes in the one variable can be used as predictors of subsequent *changes* in another variable. For example, "Is change in diet between ages 10 and 11 predictive of change in height from ages 11 to 12?"

The LDS model can be examined using most structural equation modeling packages. It is important to note that equal wave spacing over time is critical to LDS modeling, though this is not a requirement of LGC. Despite this restriction and the complexities in its implementation, LDS modeling provides an important tool for researchers who are particularly interested in modeling how wave-to-wave *change* in one variable may be related to wave-to-wave changes in another.

Differential Structural Equation Modeling

Another innovation in the modeling of change is differential structural equation modeling (dSEM), developed by Boker and colleagues (Boker, 2001; Boker & Nesselroade, 2002). Boker noted that many phenomena in psychology and health are self-regulatory. That is, organisms often respond to stimuli with an effort to return the system to homeostasis. For example, when overheated, the human body will attempt to cool itself, yet when cold, the body will attempt to warm itself. Further, regulatory systems often respond to external stimuli in a manner that is proportionate to the environmental challenge. A small challenge is met with a gradual and limited reaction, but an environmental crisis may necessitate a greater response.

Consider an experiment in which individuals are subjected to specific changes in room temperature, such that the temperature is raised to 100°F, and then lowered to 30°F, only to then be raised back to 100°F degrees, and so on, for 10 full cycles before normal room temperature is restored. Further, imagine that physiological markers of thermoregulation (e.g., blood vessel constriction and dilation, skin conductance) are measured among these individuals during the experiment. The researcher collects data from a large sample of individuals and seeks to model the dynamic physiological responses to thermoregulatory challenges. In this case, the predictor variable (room temperature) follows a cyclical, sine-wave pattern. Accordingly, we may wish to examine whether physiological responses to changes in heat follow this same pattern. These patterns cannot be captured by more conventional LGC methods.

Using differential calculus, dSEM models three parameters of change for both the predictor and outcome variables: the current level, the rate of change (i.e., the first derivative of the outcome), and the acceleration of change (i.e., the second derivative of the outcome). As a result, we have repeated measures of six manifest variables in our example: current room temperature, rate of change, and acceleration of change in room temperature, and current physiology as well as its rate and acceleration of change. Via a series of model comparisons, one can address such questions as, are physiological thermoregulatory mechanisms most influenced by *current* temperature, *changes* in temperature, or *accelerations* in temperature change?

With dSEM, one can also study the effect of a system on itself over time. For example, in some systems, a cyclical pattern may slow over time and eventually reach stasis, rather like the slowing of a pendulum. Alternatively, a system may become dysregulated or demonstrate larger shifts over time. Changes such as these are modeled in dSEM by examining the direct influence of the first derivative (linear change) on the second derivative (acceleration). When this effect is negative, the cyclical changes decrease in magnitude and the system approaches homeostasis. When this effect is positive, the cyclical changes are growing in magnitude. When this path is zero, the cyclical change is unchanged. In our example, the investigator can examine whether, over the course of repeated temperature fluctuations, the body will slow in its regulatory responses. Finally, such models can be used to examine individual characteristics as predictors of these parameters. Using multiple groups, one can examine whether gender, medications, or obesity affect physiological changes due to temperature variations.

Recent development of dSEM further emphasizes the continuous nature of time. Compared with traditional discrete-time models, dSEM explicitly accounts for measurement intervals, which are often unevenly spaced. The growing popularity of ecological momentary assessments, experience sampling, and ambulatory assessments has enhanced the ecological validity of many psychological measures. Measurements often occur randomly throughout the day or after specified trigger events. As such, the timing of the measurement contains additional information that can afford greater nuance when assessing the dynamics of time-varying variables. The advantages to treating time as a continuous variable and allowing uneven measurement spacing have encouraged further methodological developments in dSEM. Methodologists have extended dSEM for use with panel data (Oud & Jansen, 2000; Voelkle et al., 2012), cross-lagged panel data (Kuiper & Ryan, 2018), hierarchical models (Driver & Voelkle, 2018), and mediation analyses (Deboeck & Preacher, 2016).

At present, dSEM is not widely used in psychological research. One possible reason is its mathematical complexity. A second reason is that most psychological theories anticipate linear (or at least noncyclical) relations. However, as psychological theories become more nuanced and as continuous-time assessment technologies become more popular, dSEM may become a more widely used methodology.

Trait-State Models

A third recent development in the modeling of continuous change concerns the application of trait-state modeling (see Steyer et al., Chapter 13, this volume). Psychology has sometimes made a discrete distinction between trait-like and state-like constructs. Traits are thought to be highly stable across time and/or situations. In contrast, states have been conceptualized as constructs that show little stability or are highly reactive to situational demands. Such a strict distinction, however, may not pertain to most psychological constructs, which may actually contain varying degrees of both trait-like and state-like characteristics. Kenny and Zautra (1995) referred to this as a "continuum of traitness" in psychological measures.

Trait-state-occasion (TSO) models (Ciesla et al., 2007; Cole et al., 2005) enable researchers to partition the variance of a given construct into that which is due to a time-invariant (or trait-like) construct and that which is due to a set of time-varying (or occasion) constructs. Using this terminology, a person's state at any point in time reflects both kinds of influences. Only by examining repeated measures of a construct over time can the effects of trait and occasion factors be distinguished.

To describe how the TSO model accomplishes this goal, consider a researcher who collects two measures of anxiety annually from participants over a four-year period. At each wave, a latent anxiety variable is extracted. The variance of these latent variables is then partitioned into two sources: a wave-specific occasion factor (O_t) and a time-invariant trait (T) factor. The occasion factors are part of an autoregressive submodel, allowing some degree of occasion factor stability from wave to wave.

This type of modeling allows the researcher to investigate potentially different correlates of both the trait and the occasion factors. For example, genetic factors may relate more strongly to the trait factor, whereas situational variables may better predict the wave-to-wave variations in the occasion factors. Cole et al. (2006) utilized TSO modeling to investigate the association between depressive symptoms and stressful life events in a sample of adolescents. Disentangling the time-varying from the time-invariant components of depressive symptoms enabled the cleaner identification of variables that predicted the time-varying components of depression.

Last, dynamic SEM methods (Asparouhov et al., 2018) offer an alternative way to model growth. Conventional growth models can face challenges given intensive longitudinal designs due to rapid increase in the numbers of parameters to estimate. This can lead to prohibitive computational costs and sample size requirements. Dynamic SEM incorporates multilevel modeling, time-series modeling, SEM, and time-varying effects. As a result, dynamic SEM is capable of decomposing the correlations between variables into person-specific, between-observation, between-variable, and time-varying effects.

Dynamic SEM can apply to multiple-subject and multiple-measure data. Unlike most growth models, dynamic SEM has the potential to generalize not only to the population outside the studied sample but also to future observations outside the studied time for the studied sample. As an extension of the cross-classified modeling framework (Asparouhov et al., 2018), dynamic SEM decomposes the observed score into person-specific effects, time-specific effects, and deviation of the person at particular times. Individual-specific, time-invariant observed covariates, and latent variables contribute to the individual-specific components. Similarly, time-specific components can be explained by individual-invariant, time-specific observed covariates, and latent variables. Furthermore, deviations can be modeled by observed covariates and latent variables for the individual at particular times. These relations can be represented as structural and measurement equations in SEM. Random slopes, loadings, and residual variances can also be specified, as well as moving-average terms. Moreover, dynamic SEM can be used to model continuous time effects. Dynamic SEM holds wide appeal given the increasing availability and popularity of intensive longitudinal data in psychology.

CONCLUSION

In this chapter, we have described multiple methods for modeling continuous growth and related forms of longitudinal change in a construct. Of these, latent growth curve models are currently the most widely used in psychological research; however, the LDS, dSEM, TSO, and dynamic SEM models also provide very useful tools in specific situations. None of the models presented in this chapter is inherently superior to the others. Each simply examines change in a particular way. Researchers who study growth should be aware of the various structural equation modeling options that are available. Deciding between these methods should be based on one's understanding of the longitudinal structure of the construct under investigation.

References

Arbuckle, J. L. (2019). *Amos 26.0 user's guide*. IBM SPSS.

Asparouhov, T., Hamaker, E. L., & Muthén, B. (2018). Dynamic structural equation models. *Structural Equation Modeling, 25*(3), 359–388. https://doi.org/10.1080/10705511.2017.1406803

Boker, S. (2001). Differential models and "differential structural equation modeling of intraindividual variability." In L. M. Collins & A. G. Sayer (Eds.), *New methods for the analysis of change* (pp. 5–27). American Psychological Association. https://doi.org/10.1037/10409-001

Boker, S., & Nesselroade, J. R. (2002). A method for modeling the intrinsic dynamics of intraindividual variability: Recovering the parameters of parameters of simulated oscillators in multiwave panel data. *Multivariate Behavioral Research, 37*, 127–160. https://doi.org/10.1207/S15327906MBR3701_06

Bollen, K. A., & Curran, P. J. (2006). *Latent curve models: A structural equation perspective*. John Wiley and Sons.

Campbell, D. T., & Kenny, D. A. (1999). *A primer on regression artifacts. Methodology in the social sciences*. Guilford Press.

Chou, C.-P., Yang, D., Pentz, M. A., & Hser, Y.-I. (2004). Piecewise growth curve modeling approach for longitudinal prevention study. *Computational Statistics & Data Analysis, 46*(2), 213–225. https://doi.org/10.1016/S0167-9473(03)00149-X

Ciesla, J. A., Cole, D. A., & Steiger, J. H. (2007). Extending the trait-state-occasion model: How important is within-wave measurement equivalence? *Structural Equation Modeling*, *14*(1), 77–97. https://doi.org/10.1207/s15328007sem1401_4

Cohen, J. (1977). *Statistical power analysis for the behavioral sciences*. Lawrence Erlbaum Associates.

Cole, D. A., Martin, N. C., & Steiger, J. H. (2005). Empirical and conceptual problems with longitudinal trait-state models: Introducing a trait-state-occasion model. *Psychological Methods*, *10*(1), 3–20. https://doi.org/10.1037/1082-989X.10.1.3

Cole, D. A., & Maxwell, S. E. (2009). Statistical methods for risk-outcome research: Being sensitive to longitudinal structure. *Annual Review of Clinical Psychology*, *5*(1), 71–96. https://doi.org/10.1146/annurev-clinpsy-060508-130357

Cole, D. A., Nolen-Hoeksema, S., Girgus, J., & Paul, G. (2006). Stress exposure and stress generation in child and adolescent depression: A latent trait-state-error approach to longitudinal analyses. *Journal of Abnormal Psychology*, *115*(1), 40–51. https://doi.org/10.1037/0021-843X.115.1.40

Curran, P. J. (2003). Have multilevel models been structural equation models all along? *Multivariate Behavioral Research*, *38*(4), 529–569. https://doi.org/10.1207/s15327906mbr3804_5

Deboeck, P. R., & Preacher, K. J. (2016). No need to be discrete: A method for continuous time mediation analysis. *Structural Equation Modeling*, *23*(1), 61–75. https://doi.org/10.1080/10705511.2014.973960

Driver, C. C., & Voelkle, M. C. (2018). Hierarchical Bayesian continuous time dynamic modeling. *Psychological Methods*, *23*(4), 774–799. https://doi.org/10.1037/met0000168

Duncan, T. E., Duncan, S. C., & Strycker, L. A. (2006). *An introduction to latent variable growth curve modeling: Concepts, issues, and applications* (2nd ed.). Lawrence Erlbaum Associates.

Hancock, G. R., & Choi, J. (2006). A vernacular for linear latent growth models. *Structural Equation Modeling*, *13*(3), 352–377. https://doi.org/10.1207/s15328007sem1303_2

Jöreskog, K. G., & Sörbom, D. (2003). *LISREL 8.7 for MAC OS 9 and X* [Computer Software]. Scientific Software International.

Kenny, D. A., & Zautra, A. (1995). The trait-state-error model for multiwave data. *Journal of Consulting and Clinical Psychology*, *63*(1), 52–59. https://doi.org/10.1037/0022-006X.63.1.52

Kimball, A. W. (1957). Errors of the third kind in statistical consulting. *Journal of the American Statistical Association*, *52*(278), 133–142. https://doi.org/10.1080/01621459.1957.10501374

Kuiper, R. M., & Ryan, O. (2018). Drawing conclusions from cross-lagged relationships: Re-considering the role of the time-interval. *Structural Equation Modeling*, *25*(5), 809–823. https://doi.org/10.1080/10705511.2018.1431046

LaGrange, B., & Cole, D. A. (2008). An expansion of the trait-state-occasion model: Accounting for shared method variance. *Structural Equation Modeling*, *15*(2), 241–271. https://doi.org/10.1080/10705510801922381

Liu, H., & Powers, D. A. (2007). Growth curve models for zero-inflated count data: An application to smoking behavior. *Structural Equation Modeling*, *14*(2), 247–279. https://doi.org/10.1080/10705510709336746

Marsh, H. W. (1993). Stability of individual differences in multiwave panel studies: Comparison of simplex models and one-factor models. *Journal of Educational Measurement*, *30*(2), 157–183. https://doi.org/10.1111/j.1745-3984.1993.tb01072.x

McArdle, J. J. (1988). Dynamic but structural modeling of repeated measures data. In J. R. Nesselroade & R. B. Cattell (Eds.), *The handbook of multivariate psychology* (2nd ed., pp. 561–614). Springer. https://doi.org/10.1007/978-1-4613-0893-5_17

McArdle, J. J., & Hagamami, F. (2001). Latent difference score structural models for linear dynamic analyses with incomplete longitudinal data. In L. M. Collins & A. G. Sayer (Eds.), *New methods for the analysis of change* (pp. 139–175). American Psychological Association. https://doi.org/10.1037/10409-005

McArdle, J. J., & Nesselroade, J. R. (1994). Using multivariate data to structure developmental change. In S. H. Cohen & H. W. Reese (Eds.), *Life-span developmental psychology: Methodological contributions. The West Virginia University Conferences on Life-Span Developmental Psychology* (pp. 223–267). Lawrence Erlbaum Associates.

Meredith, W., & Tisak, J. (1990). Latent curve analysis. *Psychometrika*, *55*(1), 107–122. https://doi.org/10.1007/BF02294746

Muthén, L. K., & Muthén, B. O. (2017). *Mplus user's guide* (8th ed.). Muthén & Muthén.

Oud, J. H. L., & Jansen, R. A. R. G. (2000). Continuous time state space modeling of panel data by means of SEM. *Psychometrika*, *65*(2), 199–215. https://doi.org/10.1007/BF02294374

Rosseel, Y. (2012). lavaan: An R package for structural equation modeling. *Journal of Statistical Software*, *48*(2), 1–36. https://doi.org/10.18637/jss.v048.i02

Savalei, V., & Bentler, M. (2009). A two-stage approach to missing data: Theory and application to auxiliary variables. *Structural Equation*

Modeling, 16(3), 477–497. https://doi.org/10.1080/10705510903008238

Voelkle, M. C., Oud, J. H. L., Davidov, E., & Schmidt, P. (2012). An SEM approach to continuous time modeling of panel data: Relating authoritarianism and anomia. *Psychological Methods, 17*(2), 176–192. https://doi.org/10.1037/a0027543

Wang, L., Zhang, Z., McArdle, J. J., & Salthouse, T. A. (2008). Investigating Ceiling Effects in Longitudinal Data Analysis. *Multivariate Behavioral Research, 43*(3), 476–496. https://doi.org/10.1080/00273170802285941

Widaman, K. F. (2006). Missing data: What to do with or without them. *Monographs of the Society for Research in Child Development, 71*(3), 42–64.

Wu, W., West, S. G., & Taylor, A. B. (2009). Evaluating model fit for growth curve models: Integration of fit indices from SEM and MLM frameworks. *Psychological Methods, 14*(3), 183–201. https://doi.org/10.1037/a0015858

CHAPTER 15

DYNAMICAL SYSTEMS AND DIFFERENTIAL EQUATION MODELS OF CHANGE

Steven M. Boker and Robert G. Moulder

Theories that account for psychological change are generally concerned with how change comes about. That is, given that a person is in a particular state and in a particular context, in what manner would we expect the persons' state to change? The change so described could be a second-to-second change in emotional or cognitive state, it could be a longer term change in attitudes or behaviors over a period of days, or it could even be developmental changes that occur over a time span of years. The field of differential equations was developed in order to estimate meaningful parameters that describe physical systems undergoing change over time. These parameters describe characteristics of systems that have intuitive meaning due to our immersion in the physical world.

For instance, both people and tennis balls are describe as being "resilient"; we say that resilient people "bounce back" from adversity. Does the resilience of a person involve a form of elasticity? Using differential equations, we can test whether the equations for the dynamics of elasticity are similar to the dynamics of resilient people. Dynamical systems theories allow the specification and testing of statistical models that parameterize the intuitive descriptions we commonly use for psychological phenomena. These models can be fit to data using standard statistical packages and give a better understanding of not just whether a variable's change follows a straight line or a line with a curve, but how that variable's change may evolve over time in a wide variety of contexts and starting states.

To test ideas from dynamical systems, one must master methods for fitting dynamical systems models to observed data from psychological processes. There are a variety of reasons for approaching data analysis in this manner. The logic was stated eloquently by Hotelling (1927) when he contrasted the use of curve-fitting methods similar to growth curve modeling with the use of differential equation models:

> While the customary method presents us with smooth, attractive curves to describe what has happened in the past and under known conditions, there must always be considerable hesitation about prolonging these curves into the future and the unknown. We have indeed, like Patrick Henry, no lamp to light our footsteps in the future save the past; but it does not follow that our future path is to be found as an analytic prolongation of some curve drawn among our old footprints.

Funding for this work was provided in part by NIH Grant 1R21DA024304–01. Any opinions, findings, and conclusions or recommendations expressed in this material are those of the authors and do not necessarily reflect the views of the National Institutes of Health.
https://doi.org/10.1037/0000320-015
APA Handbook of Research Methods in Psychology, Second Edition: Vol. 3. Data Analysis and Research Publication, H. Cooper (Editor-in-Chief)
Copyright © 2023 by the American Psychological Association. All rights reserved.

> Rather do we require an analysis of causes, a study of the tendencies manifested repeatedly in the past upon the repeated occurrence of conditions which we term essential, and in spite of the variation of other conditions which we consider non-essential. (p. 286)

Let us consider Hotelling's (1927) statement from the perspective of latent variable modeling. The level of some latent state may predict how that state is likely to change in the immediate future. If so, there is some relationship between the latent variable and its derivatives with respect to time. In a very real sense, this relationship between level and change of the latent state is a characteristic of self-regulation for the latent state. In mathematical terms, the latent variable has intrinsic dynamics. Estimating the parameters that relate a variable to its time derivatives gives us a way to characterize how a within-individual process might regulate and respond to exogenous influences. In this way, we are able to describe and understand a whole family of possible trajectories that might occur given changes in a person's context.

A second reason why these models are appealing is that they can be constructed to test our *casual* use of physical analogies to describe *causal* processes. For instance, one might read an article that discusses "mood swings." The use of such a physical analogy in scientific writing is common—such analogies are easily understood by the reader in an intuitive way. The reader can be expected to have had the physical memory of sitting on a swing and directly feeling the changes in forces as the swing ascends and descends. Simultaneously, the word "swing" conveys a sense of return, the "weightlessness" of an emotional high, and the "heavy burden" of an emotional low. By triggering such memories, physical analogies literally produce a feeling of visceral understanding.

But just because something is easily conveyed does not mean that it is a good analogy for the psychological process in question. Or it might be that a given naive analogy is actually accurate in more ways than one might initially think. A swing implies momentum. Is there a concept equivalent to momentum that is implied by changes in mood? How do we test the implications of a physical analogy?

Because differential equations allow us the ability to express physical analogies unambiguously, we can test the adequacy of the language we use in psychological descriptions. This is a powerful use of statistical modeling—there is the chance that the analysis of experimental data will change the words we use when we speak about psychological processes.

As another example, consider the word "resiliency" (Boker, Montpetit, et al., 2010). A person is said to be resilient when they bounce back from an adverse life event. A physical object that is resilient will bounce back, and the equations for this phenomenon are given by Hooke's law of elasticity. The words we use to describe psychological regulation frequently imply physical analogies, and we can translate those analogies into differential equations that describe the physical properties that are invoked by the analogies.

To test a theory that is described by differential equations, one must have access to repeated observations data from a sample of individuals. Then, there are methods for estimating regression parameters that relate the derivatives to one another. There are two main groups of methods. The first group of methods uses the integral form of the differential equation and includes estimation techniques such as Kalman filtering (e.g., Molenaar & Newell, 2003), the exact discrete method (Singer, 1993), and the approximate discrete method (Oud & Jansen, 2000).

This chapter focuses on the use of a second group of methods that fits the differential equations without taking an integral. These methods include generalized local linear approximation (GLLA; Boker, Deboeck, et al., 2010) and latent differential equations (LDEs; Boker et al., 2004). GLLA estimates derivatives in a preprocessing step, whereas LDE estimates the regression parameters of interest as a structural model from the covariances of latent derivatives. Examples of specifying LDE models are given later in the chapter, but first a few introductory examples of differential equations are presented.

LINEAR DIFFERENTIAL EQUATIONS

To better understand how to choose a differential equation model for a given theory, it is instructive to consider some of the simple linear systems that are in use. These systems have been chosen as illustrative because in their integral form they become familiar regression models.

First-Order Differential Equations

A *first-order* differential equation is one in which the first derivative is the only derivative term to appear. One can think of a first derivative as an instantaneous estimate of a slope at a given moment in time. Suppose we have repeated measurements of a variable x. We will write the first derivative of at x time t as $\dot{x}(t)$.

A simple, and perhaps oversimplified, model for change is that the first derivative is a constant; thus, change has a constant slope. This assumption is made in longitudinal analysis with linear regression when time is the predictor variable. The model can be written as the linear differential equation,

$$\dot{x}(t) = b_1, \qquad (15.1)$$

where b_1 is a constant coefficient. This says that the rate of change of x is b_1 and does not depend on time. Note that if we have an estimated value for b_1, we do not have a specific trajectory—we have a *family* of trajectories that look like the light gray lines in Figure 15.1a. A specific trajectory is defined if we choose an *initial condition*, that is, a value for x at time $t = 0$. The dark line in Figure 15.1a plots the expected trajectory for $x(0) = -10$. The specific integral of Equation 15.1 is

$$x(t) = b_0 + b_1 t. \qquad (15.2)$$

Once the equation has been integrated, it gains a constant, b_0, that represents the initial conditions for the equation. This equation is familiar to anyone who has fit a univariate regression wherein b_0 is termed the intercept and b_1 the slope.

There are only two differences between Equations 15.1 and 15.2. The first is that the specific integral form included an intercept term, which means it refers to a specific trajectory rather than a family of trajectories. The other difference is that if Equation 15.1 were fit as a regression, the residual term would refer to error in estimation of the slope, whereas in Equation 15.2, the residual term would refer to error in estimation of the score. There are specific integrals for all linear systems, so these systems can be fit statistically either in the integral or differential form depending on how the researcher wishes to formulate his or her questions.

Another popular model for change is the autoregression model where scores at some time t are regressed on scores on a previous time $t - \mathrm{I}\,t$. The autoregression model is called a discrete time model because a discrete amount of time $\mathrm{I}\,t$ elapses between observations. A fact that is generally ignored by those fitting autoregressive models is that the coefficients of the discrete time model are dependent on the choice of $\mathrm{I}\,t$. All too often, autoregression results sections state without justification that the assumption is made that $\mathrm{I}\,t = 1$. This problem is eliminated when the autoregressive model is written as a continuous time linear first-order differential equation in which the slope is proportional to the difference from equilibrium,

$$\dot{x} = \zeta x(t). \qquad (15.3)$$

Note that $\mathrm{I}\,t$ does not appear in this equation, and so there is no dependency between the elapsed time between occasions of measurement and the coefficient ζ. Here we specify the first-order coefficient as the Greek letter zeta (ζ) to distinguish the fact that it is a continuous time parameter. Again, there is no intercept term b_0, so this system defines a family of curves as shown in the light gray lines in Figure 15.1c. This family of curves converges onto a single value, a *point equilibrium*, over the long run when $\zeta < 0$. For example, after participating in a learning-to-criterion study, participants might exhibit a forgetting curve that converged to a person-specific point equilibrium.

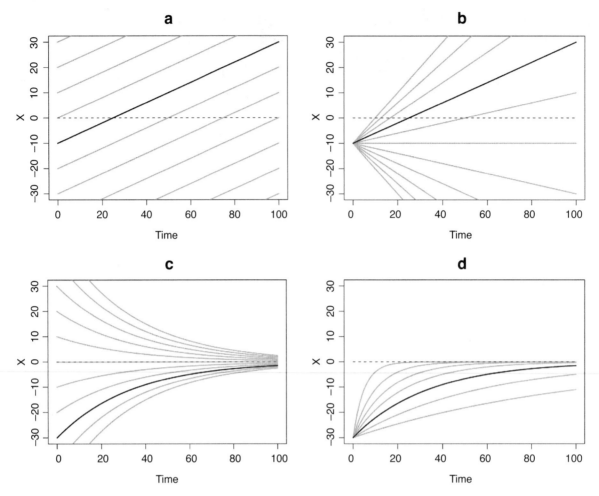

FIGURE 15.1. Trajectory plots of (a, b) Equation 15.1 and (c, d) Equation 15.3. Gray lines are examples drawn from the family of trajectories that fit each model. (a, c) Plot example trajectories with the same b_1 but with different values of b_0. (b, d) Plot example trajectories with the same b_0 but different values of b_1. For c and d, the horizontal dotted line at zero is the point equilibrium. The linear trajectories plotted in a and b do not have a point equilibrium except for the trivial example when the slope is zero.

Equilibrium values are important when considering the correspondence between one's theory and a specific model. One should ask oneself: What is the expected long-run behavior of an individual? Is the psychological process under study expected to be homeostatic? Or is the process expected to cycle, such as, for example, sleep–wake cycles, hunger cycles, or seasonal affective disorder? First-order processes never form a cyclic process. The simplest system that is cyclic is a second-order linear process.

Furthermore, one should note that the equilibrium for Equation 15.3 is equal to zero. That is, for ζ to be estimated without bias, the data must be centered around the equilibrium. Estimating the equilibrium to subtract its value from the data is a more difficult problem than is often assumed (for a discussion, see Boker & Bisconti, 2006). If the expected long-run equilibrium value of a process is known, one should subtract that value. If the equilibrium for each person in a sample can be estimated, then each individual's equilibrium values should be subtracted from their data. When equilibrium values are unknown, individuals' data are frequently centered about their respective means or about a linear trend. In the time series literature, this is known as an instance of *prewhitening* a time series. But one should not just blindly subtract the mean without giving consideration to whether there is something else one knows about the expected value of the equilibrium of the process in question.

The specific integral of Equation 15.3 is

$$x(t) = b_3 + e^{\ln(b0)+\zeta t} \quad (15.4)$$

$$= b_3 + b_0 e^{\zeta t}, \quad (15.5)$$

where the asymptotic equilibrium is $\lim_{t \to \infty} x(t) = b_3$, b_0 is the intercept (value of the function at $t = 0$), and ζ describes the overall curvature of the exponential curve. Note that $x(t)$ is an exponential function of time, which is why the value of I t must not be ignored if one chooses to fit a discrete time autoregressive model.

There are many uses of first-order linear differential equations. In particular, one may wish to test theories that include something akin to damping: how a regulatory process might return to equilibrium if it were displaced from its equilibrium by some exogenous influence. For instance, if one considers resilience to be long term adaptation, the rate of adaptation could be modeled as a damping parameter (Boker, Montpetit, et al., 2010).

Linear second-order differential equations. Many psychological processes can be expected to show fluctuations about some equilibrium value (Figure 15.2). For instance, one might consider affect as having a trait-like component,

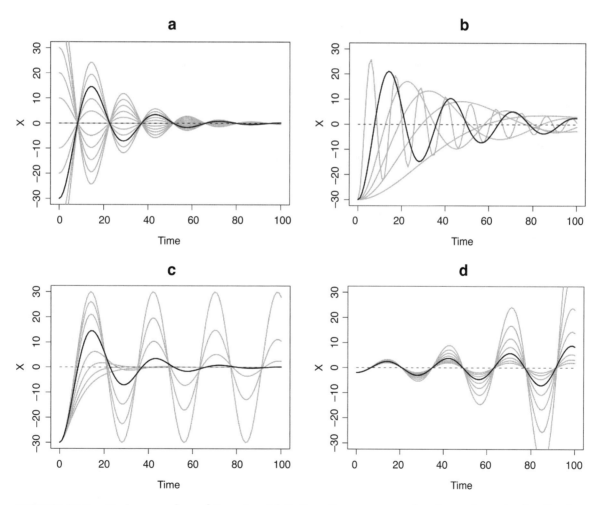

FIGURE 15.2. Trajectory plots of Equation 15.6. Gray lines are examples drawn from the family of trajectories that fit the model under different conditions. (a) Example trajectories with the same η and ζ but with different initial conditions for $x(0)$. (b) Example trajectories with the same initial conditions and ζ but different values of η. (c, d) Example trajectories with the same initial conditions and η but with (c) $\zeta < 0$ and (d) $\zeta > 0$. The horizontal dotted line at zero is the point equilibrium.

an equilibrium value around which one's affect scores might fluctuate on a day-to-day basis. These fluctuations may exhibit an intrinsic dynamic. A simple model that allows cyclic fluctuation is a second-order linear differential equation with a damping term. This can be written as

$$\ddot{x}(t) = \eta x(t) + \zeta \dot{x}(t), \quad (15.6)$$

where x is the displacement from equilibrium and $\dot{x}(t)$ and $\ddot{x}(t)$ are the first and second derivatives, respectively. If the system oscillates, the parameter η is related to the frequency of oscillation. One over the frequency is the wavelength (i.e., the elapsed time between successive peaks of the oscillation). When $\eta < 0$ and $(\eta + \zeta^2/4) < 0$, the equation is termed a damped linear oscillator and has a wavelength (interval of time between successive peaks) of $\lambda = 2\pi/\sqrt{-(\eta + \zeta^2/4)}$. Note that in physics, the coefficient η is written as $\eta = -\omega^2$ so that η is constrained to be less than zero. While this makes sense when thinking about pendulums or mass–spring systems, this constraint need not be imposed on psychological systems.

Time-Delay Embedding

To estimate dynamics from a time series, one must capture the time-dependent part of the data. One of the most effective ways of capturing time dependence is called *time-delay embedding* (Sauer et al., 1991; Takens, 1985; Whitney, 1936).

Suppose a time series X has been recorded for P repeated occasions on N individuals. If the original time series X is ordered by occasion j within individual i, then the series of all observations $x_{(i,j)}$ can be written as a vector of scores.

$$X = \left\{ \begin{array}{l} x_{(1,1)}, x_{(1,2)}, \ldots, x_{(1,P)}, x_{(2,1)}, x_{(2,2)}, \ldots, \\ x_{(2,P)} \ldots, x_{(N,1)}, x_{(N,2)}, \ldots, x_{(N,P)} \end{array} \right\} \quad (15.7)$$

If this vector is considered to be a data column and a participant ID column and occasion number column are prepended to each row, the resulting data are in what sometimes referred to as "tall format" or "long format." There are P rows in this data matrix belonging to each participant. In order to apply the latent differential equation method, the data must first be converted into a format in which the time dependency is captured row-by-row: a time-delay embedding of the data.

For N people, each of whom has been sampled P times, a five-dimensional time-delay embedded matrix $X^{(5)}$ can be constructed as

$$X^{(5)} = \begin{bmatrix} x_{(1,1)} & x_{(1,2)} & x_{(1,3)} & x_{(1,4)} & x_{(1,5)} \\ x_{(1,2)} & x_{(1,3)} & x_{(1,4)} & x_{(1,5)} & x_{(1,6)} \\ \vdots & \vdots & \vdots & \vdots & \vdots \\ x_{(1,P-4)} & x_{(1,P-3)} & x_{(1,P-2)} & x_{(1,P-1)} & x_{(1,P)} \\ x_{(2,1)} & x_{(2,2)} & x_{(2,3)} & x_{(2,4)} & x_{(2,5)} \\ x_{(2,2)} & x_{(2,3)} & x_{(2,4)} & x_{(2,5)} & x_{(2,6)} \\ \vdots & \vdots & \vdots & \vdots & \vdots \\ x_{(2,P-4)} & x_{(2,P-3)} & x_{(2,P-2)} & x_{(2,P-1)} & x_{(2,P)} \\ x_{(N,1)} & x_{(N,2)} & x_{(N,3)} & x_{(N,4)} & x_{(N,5)} \\ \vdots & \vdots & \vdots & \vdots & \vdots \\ x_{(N,P-4)} & x_{(N,P-3)} & x_{(N,P-2)} & x_{(N,P-1)} & x_{(N,P)} \end{bmatrix}.$$

$$(15.8)$$

This operation captures the time dependency in the data into the five columns of each row of the matrix so that these five columns can act as manifest variable indicators for latent variable derivatives (see Boker, Deboeck, et al., 2010, for R code). The covariance between these latent derivatives can then be used as a means to estimate the coefficients of differential equations (see von Oertzen & Boker, 2010, for effects of time-delay embedding on coefficient precision).

There is a choice to make in constructing the time-delay embedded matrix: how many columns should be in the matrix. Improper choice of this user-defined parameter may lead to significant bias in parameter estimation. A number of methods exist for estimating an appropriate number of columns for specific individual statistical modeling applications (e.g., Hu et al., 2014; Sauer et al., 1991). In practice, however, five is the minimum number of columns required to estimate a second-order differential equation while maintaining sufficient degrees of freedom for model stability. Also, when fitting a model that has a suspected oscillation, it is best to choose a number of columns such that the interval of time delay between the first column and the last column that is between one quarter and one half the interval of time that elapses during one full cycle of the suspected oscillation. One may find that the total delay can be as long as three quarters of a cycle without the model breaking down, but a total delay longer than three quarters of a cycle approaches the Nyquist limit. Models estimated with total delay near or above the Nyquist limit of one full cycle are underidentified and will produce erratic and uninterpretable results. Additionally, model stability and parameter estimates may be poor when time series lengths from individual participants are less than approximately 20 observations each (Oud, 2017).

Robustness to time sampling interval misspecification. Time sampling interval misspecification (i.e., when sampling intervals within or between individuals is not constant) is common in time series and intensive longitudinal data. Data with time sampling interval misspecification, including data with missing at random or missing completely at random observations, may introduce bias to model parameter estimates. An advantage of using a time-delayed embedded matrix approach to estimating dynamics is that model parameters estimated from time-delay embedded matrices are robust against bias due to sampling interval misspecification. Simulation work shows that ignoring time sampling interval when constructing a time-delay embedded matrix yields comparable estimates to those derived from data with no time sampling interval misspecification, or when model parameters are corrected to account for time sampling interval misspecification (Boker et al., 2018).

SPECIFYING LATENT DIFFERENTIAL EQUATION MODELS

LDE models can be fit using many popular structural equation modeling programs. Example OpenMx (Neale et al. 2016) scripts of the LDE models presented in this section can be found at https://openmx.ssri.psu.edu/.

First-Order Univariate LDE

A first-order LDE for Equation 15.3 can be specified as shown in the path diagram in Figure 15.3. The loading matrix **L** (Equation 15.9) contains fixed values such that F and $\dot{F}$ are the latent intercept and slope of the variable x. The rows of **L** are centered around the middle row of **L**, and thus the latent intercept is estimated at the time of measurement of the middle column of the time-delay embedded matrix $\mathbf{X}^{(5)}$. Note that the second column of **L** includes the value I t, which is the interval of elapsed time between observations in the time series.

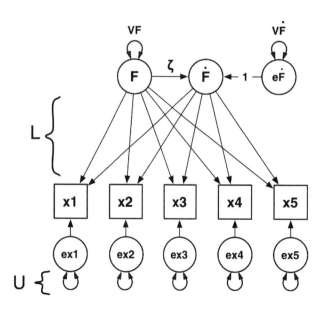

FIGURE 15.3. Univariate first-order latent differential equation path model. The loading matrix is represented by the fixed paths labeled L and the uniquenesses by U.

$$L = \begin{bmatrix} 1 & -2\Delta t \\ 1 & -1\Delta t \\ 1 & 0 \\ 1 & 1\Delta t \\ 1 & 2\Delta t \end{bmatrix} \quad (15.9)$$

Now, using the RAM (McArdle & McDonald, 1984) SEM conventions, we can write the matrices **A** and **S** to specify the regression coefficients, variance, and covariance relations among the latent derivatives as

$$A = \begin{bmatrix} 0 & 0 \\ \zeta & 0 \end{bmatrix} \quad (15.10)$$

$$S = \begin{bmatrix} V_F & 0 \\ 0 & V_{\dot{F}} \end{bmatrix}. \quad (15.11)$$

A diagonal matrix **U** is created to hold the residual variances of the time-delay embedded matrix $X^{(5)}$

$$U = \begin{bmatrix} u_x & 0 & 0 & 0 & 0 \\ 0 & u_x & 0 & 0 & 0 \\ 0 & 0 & u_x & 0 & 0 \\ 0 & 0 & 0 & u_x & 0 \\ 0 & 0 & 0 & 0 & u_x \end{bmatrix} \quad (15.12)$$

which are all constrained to be equal to one another. Finally, the expected covariance matrix, **R**, of the time-delay embedded matrix $X^{(5)}$ can be written as

$$R = L(I-A)^{-1} S(I-A)^{-1'} L' + U. \quad (15.13)$$

This SEM model can now be fit to data using any of a variety of structural equation modeling packages. In practice, it is a good idea to place a lower bound near zero on the variance term $V_{\dot{F}}$ in case the differential equation performs particularly well in explaining the variance of the first derivative. Doing so will ensure that the optimizer does not search for parameters that would result in negative residual variances.

Second-Order Univariate LDE

For processes that include oscillation, a second-order LDE may be specified as shown in Figure 15.4. This model is highly similar to the first-order LDE model in the previous section, except that there is now a latent second derivative and the latent structural model has been altered to estimate Equation 15.6.

The fixed loading matrix **L** now has three columns. The first two columns are the same as in Equation 15.9, while the third column can be constructed from the second column in the following manner (Boker et al., 2004). Let the second column of **L** be denoted as the vector v. Then the third column of **L** is $v^2/2$ minus the mean of $v^2/2$. In the current example, the matrix **L** becomes

$$L = \begin{bmatrix} 1 & -2\Delta t & 2\Delta t^2 \\ 1 & -1\Delta t & .5\Delta t^2 \\ 1 & 0 & 0 \\ 1 & 1\Delta t & .5\Delta t^2 \\ 1 & 2\Delta t & 2\Delta t^2 \end{bmatrix}. \quad (15.14)$$

Another variant of this loading matrix can be calculated from the results of Deboeck (2010).

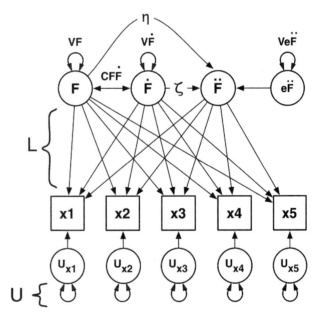

FIGURE 15.4. Univariate second-order latent differential equation path model. The loading matrix is represented by the fixed paths labeled L and the uniquenesses by U.

Again, the latent structure can be defined using the RAM convention as

$$A = \begin{bmatrix} 0 & 0 & 0 \\ 0 & 0 & 0 \\ \eta & \zeta & 0 \end{bmatrix}, \quad (15.15)$$

and

$$S = \begin{bmatrix} V_F & C_{F\dot{F}} & 0 \\ C_{F\dot{F}} & V_{\dot{F}} & 0 \\ 0 & \zeta & V_{\ddot{F}} \end{bmatrix}. \quad (15.16)$$

If a diagonal matrix U is constructed as shown in Equation 15.12, then Equation 15.13 can again be used to calculate the expected covariance for the time-delay embedded matrix $X^{(5)}$.

In practice, it is recommended to first fit a saturated covariance-only model by setting the A matrix to all zeros and the S matrix to be all free parameters. Then, the total variance, $totalV_{\ddot{F}}$, of the second derivative can be estimated. Note that if V_F is more than about 500 times larger than $totalV_{\ddot{F}}$, then SEM software may run into machine precision problems and not be able to give good estimates for the differential equation coefficients. In this case, it is recommended to standardize the indicator variable X prior to creating the time-delay embedded matrix.

When writing an SEM program script to fit this model, it is a good idea to place a lower bound on $V_{\ddot{F}}$ so that the residual variance is constrained to be greater than zero. After running the saturated covariance-only model and the target differential equation model, a pseudo-R^2 can be calculated as $1 - (V_{\ddot{F}}/totalV_{\ddot{F}})$.

OTHER DIFFERENTIAL EQUATION MODELS

The LDE method is general, in that there is no restriction on the differential equation specified between the latent derivatives. Third- and fourth-order differential equations can be created by adding more columns to the L matrix and using more columns in the time-delay embedded matrix.

Three other variants may be useful for psychological data: multivariate second-order LDEs, coupled second-order LDEs, and multilevel LDEs.

Multivariate Second-Order LDE

A multivariate generalization of the LDE model can be created by using more than one variable while time-delay embedding and modifying the L matrix to both account for the multiple variables and to estimate the within-occasion factor loadings. For instance, a latent construct such as positive affect may be indicated by multiple subtests. The covariances between the estimated latent construct and its derivatives can be used to estimate the intrinsic dynamics of the factor as shown in Figure 15.5. Just as in cross-sectional between-persons designs, multivariate measurement is likely to result in a better, more reliable, and more meaningful construct than a univariate measure.

Coupled Second-Order LDE

When there are two processes of interest, a coupled model may be estimated. Examples of this type of system include coupling of disclosure and intimacy between married partners (Boker & Laurenceau, 2005), coupling between hormones and eating behavior in young women (Boker, Deboeck, et al., 2010), and coupling between negative affect and stress in older adults (Montpetit et al., 2010). While this type of model has often been fit using variants of local linear approximation, a better method involves an LDE model such as shown in Figure 15.6 (Boker & Laurenceau, 2007).

The model in Figure 15.6 is called proportional asymmetric coupling because the same proportion between the displacement and first derivative effects accounts for both the within-process intrinsic dynamic and between-processes coupling,

$$\ddot{x}(t) = \eta_x x(t) + \zeta_x \dot{x}(t) + \gamma_y(\eta_y y(t) + \zeta_y \dot{y}(t)) + e_{\ddot{x}}(t)$$
$$\ddot{y}(t) = \eta_y y(t) + \zeta_y \dot{y}(t) + \gamma_x(\eta_x x(t) + \zeta_x \dot{x}(t)) + e_{\ddot{y}}(t),$$
(15.17)

where γ_y and γ_x are the proportional coupling coefficients. For instance, consider a husband and wife. Proportional coupling means that the same frequency and damping parameters that regulate

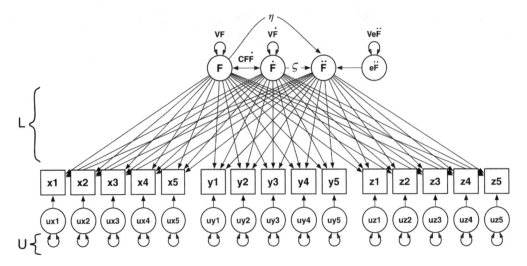

FIGURE 15.5. Multivariate linear second-order latent differential equation model with three indicator variables.

the husband's behavior also influence the wife. Asymmetric coupling means that the effect of the husband on the wife is not necessarily equal to the effect of the wife on the husband.

One note of caution when estimating coupled oscillator models: When $\eta_x = \eta_y$, the coupled oscillator model is empirically unidentified. Thus, if two processes have nearly the same intrinsic frequency, the coupling parameters γ_x and γ_y cannot be estimated. When this is the case, one may find that during the estimation procedure the coupling parameters grow very large. If x and y have the same variance, is unrealistic to expect a coupling parameter to be greater than one or less than negative one. In practice, constraining the coupling parameters $-0.8 < \gamma < 0.8$ can help a coupled model converge to realistic values.

Multilevel Second-Order LDE

It is often unrealistic to assume that the aggregate dynamic is a reasonable approximation of the within-person processes. In fact, it may be that no

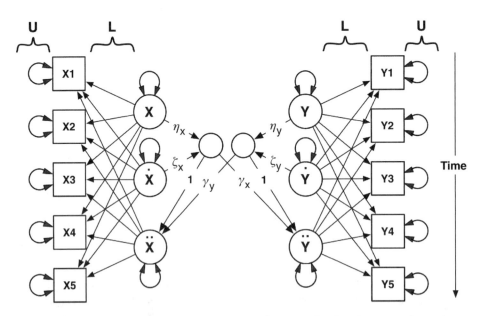

FIGURE 15.6. Coupled linear second-order latent differential equation model with one indicator variable per process and proportional asymmetric coupling.

single person's dynamic resembles the dynamic of the aggregate (Molenaar, 2004). In such cases, a multilevel model is an appropriate way to account for the within-person dynamics prior to estimating the mean and variance of the coefficients of the differential equation of interest. An empirical example of such a system is the process of grief in recent widows (Bisconti et al., 2006), where individual differences in initial conditions as well as dynamics were taken into account using a model where indicators of social support were used as second level predictors. For the widowhood data set, this multilevel model was written as

$$\ddot{x}_i(t) = \eta_{ix} x_i(t) + \zeta_i \dot{x}_i(t) + e_i(t)$$
$$\eta_i = c_1 + y_i + z_i + w_i + u_{1i}$$
$$\zeta_i = c_2 + y_i + z_i + w_i + u_{2i}, \qquad (15.18)$$

where c_1 and c_2 were the mean values of η and ζ, respectively, y_i was perceived control, z_i was emotion-focused social support, w_i was problem-focused social support for widow i, and u_{1i} and u_{2i} were the residuals from the second level model. Higher levels of emotion-focused coping were found to be related to greater values of damping (i.e., more negative values of ζ) and thus quicker damping of oscillations to equilibrium. In addition, greater values of perceived control were related to slower oscillations (i.e., values of η closer to zero).

Fourth-Order LDE

As previously discussed, researchers must choose the number of columns in a time-delay embedded matrix for use with a LDE model. Poor choice of this user-defined parameter may introduce significant bias to second-order LDE model parameter estimates. One approach to alleviate this bias is to construct a constrained fourth-order latent differential equation (FOLDE) model as opposed to a second-order LDE, as shown in Figure 15.7 (Boker et al., 2019).

The FOLDE model is an extension of the second-order LDE model that estimates additional third- and fourth-order latent derivatives, while

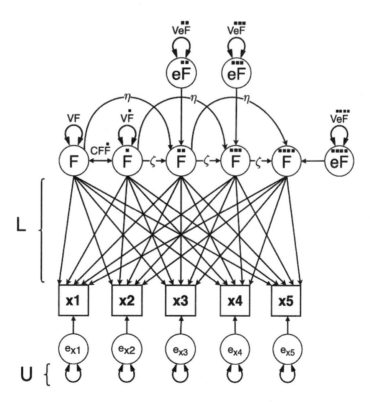

FIGURE 15.7. Univariate constrained fourth-order LDE path model. The loading matrix is represented by the fixed paths labeled L and the uniquenesses by U.

making constraints on the relationships between all derivatives. Under the FOLDE framework, the **L**, **A**, **S** and **U** matrices under RAM convention are as follows:

$$L = \begin{bmatrix} 1 & -2\Delta t & (-2\Delta t)^2/2 & (-2\Delta t)^3/6 & (-2\Delta t)^4/24 \\ 1 & -1\Delta t & (-2\Delta t)^2/2 & (-1\Delta t)^3/6 & (-1\Delta t)^4/24 \\ 1 & 0 & 0 & 0 & 0 \\ 1 & 1\Delta t & (1\Delta t)^2/2 & (1\Delta t)^3/6 & (1\Delta t)^4/24 \\ 1 & 2\Delta t & (2\Delta t)^2/2 & (2\Delta t)^3/6 & (2\Delta t)^4/24 \end{bmatrix},$$
(15.19)

$$A = \begin{bmatrix} 0 & 0 & 0 & 0 & 0 \\ 0 & 0 & 0 & 0 & 0 \\ \eta & \zeta & 0 & 0 & 0 \\ 0 & \eta & \zeta & 0 & 0 \\ 0 & 0 & \eta & \zeta & 0 \end{bmatrix},$$
(15.20)

$$S = \begin{bmatrix} V_F & C_{F,\dot{F}} & 0 & 0 & 0 \\ C_{F,\dot{F}} & V_{\dot{F}} & 0 & 0 & 0 \\ 0 & 0 & V_{\ddot{F}} & 0 & 0 \\ 0 & 0 & 0 & V_{\dddot{F}} & 0 \\ 0 & 0 & 0 & 0 & V_{\ddddot{F}} \end{bmatrix},$$
(15.21)

and

$$U = \begin{bmatrix} u_x & 0 & 0 & 0 & 0 \\ 0 & u_x & 0 & 0 & 0 \\ 0 & 0 & u_x & 0 & 0 \\ 0 & 0 & 0 & u_x & 0 \\ 0 & 0 & 0 & 0 & u_x \end{bmatrix}.$$
(15.22)

A matrix is constructed such that relationships between successive derivatives are constrained to be equal (ζ), and relationships between every other derivative are constrained to be equal (η).

The second-order LDE model is nested within the FOLDE model. As such, the FOLDE model has more degrees of freedom compared with the second-order LDE model and will always fit at least as well as a second-order LDE model. Thus, in most applications, the FOLDE model will be the preferable model to fit to a data set, as opposed to a second-order LDE (see Boker et al., 2019, for R code).

DATA CONSIDERATIONS

First- and second-order linear differential equations have been explored extensively and can be fit reasonably in the context of either integral or differential form. To fit second-order differential equations requires a sampling interval that is no less than one sixth the estimated wavelength of the hypothesized cycle. For instance, weekly cycles would require sampling at least once a day. Without at least six samples per cycle, there are insufficient degrees of freedom in the data to uniquely determine all the parameters, variances, and error terms. Higher order differential equations will require more samples per cycle; as degrees of freedom in the model increase, so too must the degrees of freedom in the data.

The absolute minimum number of samples per person required to fit a differential equation is the minimum number of samples per cycle. However, in that case, there are no degrees of freedom left to estimate individual differences in parameters, and thus the assumption must be made that all persons have the same regulatory process. When measurement instruments have high internal consistency, intensive longitudinal designs with as few as 20 samples per person can estimate individual differences in dynamic parameters, but to the extent that instruments are poor measures of a latent process, greater numbers of observations per person will be required. Recent work suggests that when estimating first- and second-order processes using time-delay embedding, adding observations within individual has more effect on power than adding persons (von Oertzen & Boker, 2010).

CONCLUSION

Differential equation models hold great promise to help estimate meaningful coefficients for psychological processes. How quickly does an emotional regulation system oscillate? How quickly do oscillations damp to equilibrium after a significant emotional shock? How do husbands and wives regulate their own and one another's need for intimacy and disclosure? Differential equation models can be constructed to test hypotheses about the language we use to describe psychological phenomena, language that is frequently drawn from physical analogy: bouncing back, emotional swings, absorbing shocks, interpersonal friction, cognitive inertia, the force of an argument. Not all such naïve physical analogies will turn out to map onto the physical world. But when scientists use these words from dynamics to describe psychological phenomena, intuitive analogies are drawn and inferences are evoked that need to be tested. The resulting models fit Hotelling's (1927) desire for "an analysis of causes, a study of the tendencies manifested repeatedly in the past upon the repeated occurrence of conditions which we term essential, and in spite of the variation of other conditions which we consider non-essential" (p. 286).

References

Bisconti, T. L., Bergeman, C. S., & Boker, S. M. (2006). Social support as a predictor of variability: An examination of the adjustment trajectories of recent widows. *Psychology and Aging*, 21(3), 590–599. https://doi.org/10.1037/0882-7974.21.3.590

Boker, S. M., & Bisconti, T. L. (2006). Dynamical systems modeling in aging research. In C. S. Bergeman & S. M. Boker (Eds.), *Methodological issues in aging research* (pp. 185–229). Lawrence Erlbaum Associates.

Boker, S. M., Deboeck, P. R., Edler, C., & Keel, P. K. (2010). Generalized local linear approximation of derivatives from time series. In S.-M. Chow, E. Ferrer, & F. Hsieh (Eds.), *Statistical methods for modeling human dynamics: An interdisciplinary dialogue* (pp. 161–178). Taylor & Francis.

Boker, S. M., & Laurenceau, J. P. (2005). Dynamical systems modeling: An application to the regulation of intimacy and disclosure in marriage. In T. A. Walls & J. L. Schafer (Eds.), *Models for intensive longitudinal data* (pp. 195–218). Oxford University Press.

Boker, S. M., & Laurenceau, J. P. (2007). Coupled dynamics and mutually adaptive context. In T. D. Little, J. A. Bovaird, & N. A. Card (Eds.), *Modeling ecological and contextual effects in longitudinal studies of human development* (pp. 299–324). Lawrence Erlbaum Associates.

Boker, S. M., Montpetit, M. A., Hunter, M. D., & Bergeman, C. S. (2010). Modeling resilience with differential equations. In P. C. M. Molenaar & K. M. Newell (Eds.), *Individual pathways of change: Statistical models for analyzing learning and development* (pp. 183–206). American Psychological Association. https://doi.org/10.1037/12140-011

Boker, S. M., Moulder, R. G., & Sjobeck, G. R. (2019). Constrained fourth order latent differential equation reduces parameter estimation bias for damped linear oscillator models. *Structural Equation Modeling*, 27(2), 202–218. https://doi.org/10.1080/10705511.2019.1641816

Boker, S. M., Neale, M. C., & Rausch, J. (2004). Latent differential equation modeling with multivariate multi-occasion indicators. In K. van Montfort, H. Oud, & A. Satorra (Eds.), *Recent developments on structural equation models: Theory and applications* (pp. 151–174). Kluwer Academic Publishers. https://doi.org/10.1007/978-1-4020-1958-6_9

Boker, S. M., Tiberio, S. S., & Moulder, R. G. (2018). Robustness of time delay embedding to sampling interval misspecification. In K. van Montfort, J. H. L. Oud, & M. C. Voelkle (Eds.), *Continuous time modeling in the behavioral and related sciences* (pp. 239–258). Springer. https://doi.org/10.1007/978-3-319-77219-6_10

Deboeck, P. R. (2010). Estimating dynamical systems: Derivative estimation hints from Sir Ronald A. Fisher. *Multivariate Behavioral Research*, 45(4), 725–745. https://doi.org/10.1080/00273171.2010.498294

Hotelling, H. (1927). Differential equations subject to error, and population estimates. *Journal of the American Statistical Association*, 22(159), 283–314. https://doi.org/10.1080/01621459.1927.10502963

Hu, Y., Boker, S., Neale, M., & Klump, K. L. (2014). Coupled latent differential equation with moderators: Simulation and application. *Psychological Methods*, 19(1), 56–71. https://doi.org/10.1037/a0032476

McArdle, J. J., & McDonald, R. P. (1984). Some algebraic properties of the Reticular Action Model for moment structures. *British Journal of Mathematical and Statistical Psychology*, 37(2), 234–251. https://doi.org/10.1111/j.2044-8317.1984.tb00802.x

Molenaar, P. C. M. (2004). A manifesto on psychology as idiographic science: Bringing the person back into scientific psychology, this time forever. *Measurement: Interdisciplinary Research and Perspectives*, 2(4), 201–218.

Molenaar, P. C. M., & Newell, K. M. (2003). Direct fit of a theoretical model of phase transition in oscillatory finger motions. *British Journal of Mathematical and Statistical Psychology*, *56*(2), 199–214. https://doi.org/10.1348/000711003770480002

Montpetit, M. A., Bergeman, C. S., Deboeck, P. R., Tiberio, S. S., & Boker, S. M. (2010). Resilience-as-process: Negative affect, stress, and coupled dynamical systems. *Psychology and Aging*, *25*(3), 631–640. https://doi.org/10.1037/a0019268

Neale, M. C., Hunter, M. D., Pritikin, J. N., Zahery, M., Brick, T. R., Kirkpatrick, R. M., Estabrook, R., Bates, T. C., Maes, H. H., & Boker, S. M. (2016). OpenMx 2.0: Extended structural equation and statistical modeling. *Psychometrika*, *81*(2), 535–549. https://doi.org/10.1007/s11336-014-9435-8

Oud, J. H. L. (2017). Comparison of four procedures to estimate the damped linear differential oscillator for panel data. In K. van Montfort, J. Oud, & A. Satorra (Eds.), *Longitudinal models in the behavioral and related sciences* (pp. 19–39). Routledge. https://doi.org/10.4324/9781315091655-2

Oud, J. H. L., & Jansen, R. A. R. G. (2000). Continuous time state space modeling of panel data by means of SEM. *Psychometrika*, *65*(2), 199–215. https://doi.org/10.1007/BF02294374

Sauer, T., Yorke, J., & Casdagli, M. (1991). Embedology. *Journal of Statistical Physics*, *65*(3,4), 95–116.

Singer, H. (1993). Continuous-time dynamical systems with sampled data, errors of measurement and unobserved components. *Journal of Time Series Analysis*, *14*(5), 527–545. https://doi.org/10.1111/j.1467-9892.1993.tb00162.x

Takens, F. (1985). Detecting strange attractors in turbulence. In A. Dold & B. Eckman (Eds.), *Lecture notes in mathematics 1125: Dynamical systems and bifurcations* (pp. 99–106). Springer–Verlag.

von Oertzen, T., & Boker, S. M. (2010). Time delay embedding increases estimation precision of models of intraindividual variability. *Psychometrika*, *75*(1), 158–175. https://doi.org/10.1007/s11336-009-9137-9

Whitney, H. (1936). Differentiable manifolds. *Annals of Mathematics*, *37*(3), 645–680. https://doi.org/10.2307/1968482

CHAPTER 16

A MULTIVARIATE GROWTH CURVE MODEL FOR THREE-LEVEL DATA

Patrick J. Curran, Chris L. Strauss, Ethan M. McCormick, and James S. McGinley

One of the most vexing challenges that has faced the behavioral sciences over the past century has been how to optimally measure, summarize, and predict individual variability in stability and change over time. It has long been known that a multitude of advantages are associated with the collection and analysis of repeated measures data; indeed, longitudinal data have become nearly requisite in many disciplines within the behavioral sciences. The challenge of how best to empirically capture individual change cuts across every aspect of the empirical research endeavor, including study design, psychometric measurement, subject sampling, data analysis, and substantive interpretation. Although many textbooks have been devoted to each of these research dimensions, here we have the much more modest goal of exploring just one specific type of longitudinal data analytic method: the multivariate growth model.

Given our love of jargon in the social sciences, our field has coined a rather large number of terms to describe patterns of intraindividual change over time. Whether the term is *growth models, growth trajectories, growth curves, latent trajectories, developmental curves, latent curves, time paths,* or *latent developmental growth curve time path trajectories of growth*,[1] all tend to refer to the same thing. Namely, repeated measures are collected on a sample of individuals followed over time, and models are designed to capture both the mean and variance components associated with patterns of stability and change over time (Hoffman, 2015; McArdle, 2009).

There are two broad types of growth models: the structural equation model (SEM) and the multilevel linear model (MLM). Whereas the SEM approaches the repeated measures as observed indicators of an underlying latent-growth process (e.g., Bollen & Curran, 2006; McArdle, 1988; Meredith & Tisak, 1990), the MLM approaches these data as the hierarchical structuring of repeated measures nested within the individual (e.g., Bryk & Raudenbush, 1987; Raudenbush, 2001; Singer & Willett, 2003). A great deal of prior research has explored the similarities and dissimilarities of these two approaches, and the lines that demarcate the SEM and MLM are becoming increasingly blurred with the passing of each year (e.g., Bauer, 2003; Curran, 2003; McNeish, 2016; Mehta & Neale, 2005; Newsom, 2002; Willett & Sayer, 1994). Suffice it to say that both methods are powerful and flexible approaches to the analysis of longitudinal data, the optimal choice of which depends strictly on the

---

[1]OK, so we made up that last one.

All computer code and output are available at https://curran.web.unc.edu/. This chapter is an update and expansion of Curran, McGinley, et al. (2012), and we are indebted to Daniel Serrano and Chelsea Burfeind for their important contributions to the earlier work.

https://doi.org/10.1037/0000320-016
APA Handbook of Research Methods in Psychology, Second Edition: Vol. 3. Data Analysis and Research Publication, H. Cooper (Editor-in-Chief)
Copyright © 2023 by the American Psychological Association. All rights reserved.

characteristics of the substantive question and the experimental design at hand (Raudenbush, 2001).

That said, here we focus exclusively on the growth model as estimated within the framework of the MLM, which stems directly from the substantive question on which we are currently working. As we will describe in greater detail, we are interested in the longitudinal development of *trust* and *integrity* in cadets attending the United States Military Academy (USMA) at West Point.[2] We quickly encounter, however, a significant challenge in applying standard multilevel growth models to our data. The three-level MLM is well developed for examining stability and change in a single outcome variable (e.g., trajectories of trust). Furthermore, the two-level model is well developed for examining stability and change in two or more outcome variables at once (e.g., trajectories of trust and trajectories of integrity). Our substantive research focus, however, is on the simultaneous codevelopment of trust and integrity, yet the nesting of time within cadets and cadets within squads results in a three-level data structure. We must then expand the standard three-level univariate growth model to allow for growth in two or more outcomes over time. This is our purpose here.

The two-level multivariate growth model has been well developed within the MLM (e.g., MacCallum et al., 1997), and this framework was extended to allow for three levels of nesting in Curran, McGinley, et al. (2012). Here we update and expand upon the methods of Curran, McGinley, et al. where we review the current models available to estimate growth in two or more outcomes within the two-level MLM, extend these models to allow for three levels of nesting, and demonstrate this model using real data.[3] Although by the end of our chapter we will find ourselves up to our eyeballs in equations, we make a concerted effort to retain a significant focus on the practical application of these techniques to real social science data in the face of the unavoidable yet necessary technical explication of the models.

We begin with a review of the univariate two-level growth model, and we consider predictors that do and do not change over time. We then draw on existing methods to extend this two-level model to include two or more outcomes at once. We take a step back and review the univariate three-level growth model, and we again consider predictors that do and do not change over time. We then generalize the multivariate methods for the two-level model for data characterized by three levels of nesting. Once defined, we demonstrate these methods using real empirical data drawn from the longitudinal study of leadership and trust in a sample of cadets enrolled at the USMA at West Point. We conclude with potential limitations of our approach, and we offer recommendations for the use of these methods in practice.

TWO-LEVEL GROWTH MODELS

We begin our exploration of the unconditional growth model using a slightly modified version of notation used by Raudenbush and Bryk (2002, Equations 6.1 and 6.2). This notational scheme will allow us to easily expand the univariate two-level model to the more complex multivariate and three-level models that we present later.

Unconditional Two-Level Univariate Growth Model

We can define the Level-1 equation for a two-level linear growth model as

$$y_{ti} = \pi_{0i} + \pi_{1i} time_{ti} + e_{ti}, \quad (16.1)$$

where y_{ti} is the measure of outcome y at time t ($t = 1, 2, \ldots, T$) for individual i ($i = 1, 2, \ldots, N$); π_{0i} and π_{1i} are the intercept and slope that define the linear trajectory unique to individual i;

---

[2] We sincerely thank Dr. Patrick Sweeney (Wake Forest University) and Dr. Kurt Dirks (Washington University) for their generous provision of these data to be used in our demonstrations presented here.
[3] There have been recent advances in SEM-based approaches to incorporating higher level nesting that we do not address here; see McNeish, Stapleton and Silverman (2017) and Preacher, Zhang, and Zyphur (2016) for more details.

$time_{ti}$ is the numerical measure of time at assessment t for individual i; finally, e_{ti} is the time- and individual-specific residual. Time is often coded as $time_{ti} = t - 1$, so the intercept of the trajectory represents the initial assessment, although many other coding schemes are possible (e.g., Biesanz et al., 2004). Here we focus on a linear trajectory, but our developments directly expand to a variety of functional forms.

An important aspect of this model is that it is assumed that the individually varying parameters that define the growth trajectory (e.g., the intercept and slope) are themselves random variables. We can thus define Level-2 equations for these terms as

$$\pi_{0i} = \beta_{00} + r_{0i}$$
$$\pi_{1i} = \beta_{10} + r_{1i}, \quad (16.2)$$

where β_{00} and β_{10} are the mean intercept and slope pooling over all individuals, and r_{0i} and r_{1i} are the deviation of each individual's trajectory parameter from their respective means.

The Level-1 and Level-2 expressions are primarily for pedagogical purposes, and the actual model of interest is the reduced form expression that results from the substitution of the Level-2 equations into the Level-1 equation. Substituting Equation 16.2 into Equation 16.1 results in

$$y_{ti} = (\beta_{00} + \beta_{10}time_{ti}) + (r_{0i} + r_{1i}time_{ti} + e_{ti}), \quad (16.3)$$

defined as in Equations 16.1 and 16.2. The first parenthetical term contains the fixed effects; these represent the mean intercept and mean linear slope pooling over all individuals. The second parenthetical term contains the individual deviations that constitute the random effects; the variance of these deviations represents the individual variability at both the Level-1 and Level-2 parts of the model. These random effects are an important component of any growth modeling application, but they are of particular interest to the models that we work to develop here. We will, thus, consider both the Level-1 and Level-2 deviations a bit more closely.

The Level-1 residuals (i.e., e_{ti}) are assumed to be multivariate normally distributed with a mean of zero and covariance matrix $\mathbf{R}$; more formally, this is expressed as $e_{ti} \sim MVN(0, \mathbf{R})$ where $\mathbf{R}$ is the $T \times T$ covariance matrix and T is the total number of repeated observations. For example, for four repeated measures (i.e., $T = 4$) the Level-1 residual matrix is given as

$$\mathbf{R} = \begin{bmatrix} \sigma_1^2 & & & \\ 0 & \sigma_2^2 & & \\ 0 & 0 & \sigma_3^2 & \\ 0 & 0 & 0 & \sigma_4^2 \end{bmatrix}, \quad (16.4)$$

where a different residual variance is allowed at each time-point. The zeros in the off-diagonal elements reflect that there are no between-time residual covariances estimated. A number of alternative error structures are possible (e.g., the commonly used structure of equal variance over all time-points, or the allowance for correlated time-adjacent residuals, and so on), but we will primarily consider the heteroscedastic error structure for the models we examine here.

The Level-2 residuals are also assumed to be multivariate normally distributed with means of zero and covariance matrix $\mathbf{T}$; more formally, this is given as $[u_{0i}, u_{1i}] \sim MVN(0, \mathbf{T})$ where $\mathbf{T}$ is a $P \times P$ covariance matrix for which P is the total number of random effects at Level 2. For example, for a linear growth model with a random intercept and slope (i.e., $P = 2$), the Level-2 covariance matrix is given as

$$\mathbf{T} = \begin{bmatrix} \tau_{00} & \\ \tau_{10} & \tau_{11} \end{bmatrix}, \quad (16.5)$$

where τ_{00} is the variance of the intercepts, τ_{11} is the variance of the slopes, and τ_{10} is the covariance between the intercepts and slopes. Larger Level-2 variance components imply greater individual variability in the starting point and rate of change over time. Recall that we are interested in the initial level and subsequent rate of change in self-reported trust of cadets at West Point. Significant variance components at Level 2 would imply that some cadets start higher versus lower in their initial reports of trust, and some cadets increase more rapidly versus less rapidly in the development of trust over time. In contrast, as these Level-2 random effects approach zero, this implies that cadets are becoming more and more similar to one another in terms of the values of the parameters that define their trajectories. At the extreme, if the variance components are equal to zero, then all cadets follow precisely the same trajectory; that is, each individual is characterized by the same initial level of trust and increase in trust at the same rate over time.

Importantly, larger random effects at Level 2 also suggest that one or more predictors could potentially be included to partially or wholly explain the individual variability in trajectory parameters (e.g., the intercepts and linear slopes). For example, say that the random effects suggested that cadets vary meaningfully in both their initial levels of trust and in their rates of change in trust over time. Then one or more time-specific or cadet-specific predictors could be included in the model to differentiate cadet-to-cadet variability in starting point and rate of change over time. This would allow us to build a more comprehensive model of possible determinants of developmental trajectories of trust, and it is to these conditional models we turn next.

Conditional Two-Level Univariate Growth Model: Time-Invariant Covariates

The prior models are sometimes called *unconditional* because there are no measured covariates used to predict the random parameters that define the growth trajectory.[4] We can easily expand the unconditional growth model to include one or more predictors at either Level 1, Level 2, or both. Predictors that are stable characteristics of the individual that do not change as a function of time are called *time-invariant covariates* (or TICs), and these are entered into the Level-2 equations.

Examples of TICs might be biological sex, country of origin, ethnicity, or certain genetic characteristics. In some applications, the TIC might in principle change over time, but for empirical or substantive reasons, only the initial assessment is considered (e.g., Curran et al., 1997). Because TICs only enter at Level 2, the Level-1 equation remains as defined in Equation 16.1. However, the Level-2 equation is expanded to include one or more person-specific measures that are constant over time.

For example, assuming a linear growth model defined at Level 1, a single person-specific TIC, denoted w_i, is included as

$$\pi_{0i} = \beta_{00} + \beta_{01} w_i + r_{0i}$$
$$\pi_{1i} = \beta_{10} + \beta_{11} w_i + r_{1i}, \quad (16.6)$$

where β_{01} and β_{11} capture the expected shift in the conditional means of the intercept and slope components associated with a one-unit shift in the TIC. For example, positive coefficients would reflect that higher values on the TIC are associated with higher initial values and steeper (or more positive) rates of change over time. Importantly, these shifts in the conditional means are independent of the passage of time, highlighted by the fact that the TICs are not subscripted by t to represent time. Thus, one might find that the developmental trajectories of trust in male cadets are defined by a different starting point and different rate of change relative to female cadets. These TICs could even be allowed to interact with one another; for example, the difference in trajectories of trust between male and female cadets could depend in part on the biological sex of the squad leader.

The inclusion of TICs is a powerful component of the MLM growth model. However, there may be important covariates we want to consider that are *not* constant over time. Instead, one or more covariates might take on a unique value at any given time-point, and treating these as invariant

---

[4]This is a bit of a misnomer given that time is a predictor at Level 1, yet the term *unconditional* commonly implies no predictors in *addition* to the measure of time.

over time would be inappropriate (Curran & Bauer, 2011). This type of predictor can be included within the MLM as a *time-varying covariate*.

Conditional Two-Level Univariate Growth Model: Time-Varying Covariates

In contrast to the TICs that are assumed to be constant over time, time-varying covariates (or TVCs) can take on a unique value at any given point in time. For example, covariates such as peer influence, anxiety, delinquency, or substance use would be expected to change from time-point to time-point, and it is critical that these temporal fluctuations be incorporated into the model (e.g., Curran & Bauer, 2011; Curran, Lee, et al., 2012). Because the value of the TVC is unique to a given individual and a given time-point, these covariates enter directly into the Level-1 equations.

For example, the Level-1 model with a single TVC, denoted z_{ti}, is given as

$$y_{ti} = \pi_{0i} + \pi_{1i} time_{ti} + \pi_{2i} z_{ti} + e_{ti}. \quad (16.7)$$

Although π_{0i} and π_{1i} continue to represent the individual-specific intercept and slope components of the growth trajectory, these are now *net* the influence of the TVC (and vice versa). In other words, these are the parameters of the trajectory of the outcome controlling for the effects of the TVC. The impact of the TVC on the outcome is captured in π_{2i} which represents the shift in the mean of the outcome y at time t per one-unit shift in the TVC at the same time t. Importantly, whereas the TICs shift the conditional means of the trajectory parameters, the TVCs shift the conditional means of the outcome above and beyond the influence of the underlying growth trajectory.[5] For example, the outcome of interest might be a cadet's trust, and the TVC is a measure of perceived integrity in that same individual; the TVC model would allow for the estimation of a developmental trajectory of trust, while simultaneously including the time-specific influence of perceived integrity. Allowing integrity to vary in value over time is a marked improvement over using just the initial measure of integrity as a TIC because much additional time-specific information is incorporated into the model.

A particularly interesting aspect of the TVC model is that the magnitude of the effect of the TVC on the outcome can vary randomly across individuals. The inclusion of this random effect is not required and would be determined on the basis of substantive theory or empirical necessity. This can most clearly be seen in the Level-2 equations that correspond to the TVC model defined in Equation 16.7

$$\pi_{0i} = \beta_{00} + r_{0i}$$
$$\pi_{1i} = \beta_{10} + r_{1i}$$
$$\pi_{2i} = \beta_{20} + r_{2i}, \quad (16.8)$$

where β_{00}, β_{10}, and β_{20} represent the mean of each random term, and the corresponding residuals represent the individually varying deviations around these means. Including the term r_{2i} allows for the magnitude of the relation between the TVC and the outcome to vary randomly over individuals; omitting this term implies that the magnitude of the TVC effects is constant for all individuals. These Level-2 equations could easily be expanded to include one or more TICs to examine predictors of each random Level-1 effect, but we do not explore this further here (for further details, see Raudenbush & Bryk, 2002; Singer & Willett, 2003).

The TVC model offers a powerful and flexible method for examining individual variability in change over time as a function of one or more predictors that also vary as a function of time. One aspect of the TVC model that must be appreciated is that whereas an explicit growth process is estimated with respect to the outcome (i.e., y_{ti}), no such growth process is estimated with respect to the TVC (i.e., z_{ti}). In other words, although the TVC can take on unique values

---

[5]Because of space constraints we do not address the important issue of disaggregating the within-person and between-person effects of the TVC on the outcome. See Curran and Bauer (2011); Curran et al. (2014); Curran, Lee, et al. (2012); and Hoffman (2015) for further details.

at any given time-point, it is not systematically related to the passage of time (e.g., Curran & Bauer, 2011). In many applications of the TVC model, this restriction is completely appropriate. One might be interested in examining trajectories of reading ability having controlled for the time-specific effects of days of instruction missed (Raudenbush & Bryk, 2002, p. 179) or in examining trajectories of heavy alcohol use having controlled for the time-specific effects of a new marriage (Curran et al., 1998) or in a large variety of applications of daily diary studies (e.g., Bolger et al., 2003). In all of these examples, the TVC would not even be theoretically expected to change systematically over time. There are a variety of other examples in which the TVC is uniquely well suited to test the important questions of substantive interest.

Yet there are other situations in which substantive theory would not only predict that the TVC might take on different values over time, but that the TVC is itself developing systematically as a function of time. That is, the TVC may be expected to be characterized by a smoothed underlying trajectory that is defined by both fixed and random effects (Curran & Bauer, 2011; Curran et al., 2014). Our earlier hypothetical example considered the development of trust as the outcome and perceived integrity as the TVC. However, this strongly assumes that integrity is not developing systematically over time. Yet theory predicts that both trust and integrity codevelop systematically over time, and arbitrarily treating one of these constructs as a criterion and the other as a TVC would not correspond to our substantive theory. Furthermore, the core theoretical question of interest may not be related to how the *time-specific* value of the TVC is related to the *time-specific* value of the outcome (as is tested in the TVC model); instead, it may be how the parameters of the *trajectory* of the TVC relate to the parameters of the *trajectory* of the outcome. This is sometimes described as examining how two or more constructs "travel together" through time (e.g., McArdle, 1989). To test questions such as these, we must move to a multivariate growth model that allows for the simultaneous estimation of growth in both the outcome and the TVC (Curran & Hancock, 2021).

Two-Level Multivariate Growth Model

Our goal is to define a model that allows for the estimation of growth processes in two or more constructs simultaneously. This is a distinct challenge given that the standard multilevel model is inherently univariate in that it is limited to a single criterion measure (e.g., Raudenbush & Bryk, 2002, Equation 14.1). These univariate models have been expanded to the multivariate setting by Goldstein (1995), Goldstein et al. (1993), and MacCallum et al. (1997), among others; we are both inspired by and draw upon this collected body of work in pursuit of our developments here.

The key to approaching this problem is to stack our multiple criterion variables into a newly created variable that is nominally univariate (i.e., the model "thinks" there is just *one* variable), but this variable actually contains repeated assessments on two or more outcomes stacked on top of each other. This is sometimes called a *synthesized* variable (e.g., MacCallum et al., 1997). We will then incorporate a series of dummy variables as exogenous predictors that will give us full control of which specific outcomes we are referencing within different parts of the model; the dummy variables serve as "toggles" that bring variables in and out as we need them. This will ultimately allow us to use our standard univariate multilevel modeling framework to fit what is in actuality a rather complex multivariate structure.

We begin by defining a simple linear growth model at Level 1, but we will add superscripts to all of the terms to identify to which outcome the term is associated. We use a linear trajectory here, but a variety of alternative functional forms could be used instead. Furthermore, a different form of growth could be used for each of the individual outcomes (e.g., linear in one outcome and quadratic in another). The general expression for $k = 1, 2, \ldots, K$ multivariate outcomes is

$$y_{ti}^{(k)} = \pi_{0i}^{(k)} + \pi_{1i}^{(k)} time_{ti}^{(k)} + e_{ti}^{(k)}. \tag{16.9}$$

So $y_{ti}^{(1)}$ would represent the outcome for the first construct (where $k = 1$; e.g., trust) and $y_{ti}^{(2)}$ would represent the outcome for the second construct (where $k = 2$; e.g., integrity), and so on. The Level-2 equations are also modified to denote whether the term is associated with the first criterion measure ($k = 1$) or the second ($k = 2$)

$$\pi_{0i}^{(k)} = \beta_{00}^{(k)} + r_{0i}^{(k)}$$
$$\pi_{1i}^{(k)} = \beta_{10}^{(k)} + r_{1i}^{(k)}. \qquad (16.10)$$

Compare this with Equation 16.2 to see the direct parallel between the Level-2 univariate and multivariate expressions. Finally, the reduced form expression is given as:

$$y_{ti}^{(k)} = \left(\beta_{00}^{(k)} + \beta_{10}^{(k)} time_{ti}^{(k)}\right) + \left(r_{0i}^{(k)} + r_{1i}^{(k)} time_{ti}^{(k)} + e_{ti}^{(k)}\right). \qquad (16.11)$$

We can combine these equations into a multivariate expression in which there is a single synthesized criterion variable that we arbitrarily denote dv_{ti} to represent the dependent variable dv at time t for individual i. In other words, we manually create a new variable in the data set that stacks the multiple outcome variables into a single-column vector. Because multiple outcomes are now contained in a single variable, we must include additional information to distinguish which specific element belongs to which specific outcome. To do this, we create two or more new variables (denoted δ_k) that are simple binary dummy variables that represent which specific outcome is under consideration. There are K dummy variables, one each for $k = 1, 2, \ldots, K$ outcomes. The dummy variable is $\delta_k = 1$ for construct k, and is equal to zero otherwise. (We show a specific example of this in a moment.)

Finally, we can fit a single model to this new data structure in which a separate growth process is simultaneously fitted to each outcome k, the specific outcome of which is toggled in or out of the equation using an overall summation weighted by the dummy variables (e.g., MacCallum et al., 1997). More specifically, the general expression for the reduced-form model is

$$dv_{ti} = \sum_{k=1}^{K} \delta_k \left[\begin{array}{c} \left(\beta_{00}^{(k)} + \beta_{10}^{(k)} time_{ti}^{(k)}\right) \\ + \left(r_{0i}^{(k)} + r_{1i}^{(k)} time_{ti}^{(k)} + e_{ti}^{(k)}\right) \end{array} \right]. \qquad (16.12)$$

In words, Equation 16.12 defines the growth trajectory for each of K outcomes of interest, and the dummy codes include or exclude the relevant values in the synthesized dependent variable through the overall summation.

To further explicate this, we can consider just the bivariate case in which $K = 2$. We define $k = 1$ to represent y_{ti} and $k = 2$ to represent z_{ti}, and we superscript with y and z to identify to which outcome each term belongs. For example, y might represent *trust* and z might represent *integrity*. In this case, Equation 16.12 simplifies to

$$dv_{ti} = \delta_y \left[\begin{array}{c} \left(\beta_{00}^{(y)} + \beta_{10}^{(y)} time_{ti}^{(y)}\right) \\ + \left(r_{0i}^{(y)} + r_{1i}^{(y)} time_{ti}^{(y)} + e_{ti}^{(y)}\right) \end{array} \right]$$
$$+ \delta_z \left[\begin{array}{c} \left(\beta_{00}^{(z)} + \beta_{10}^{(z)} time_{ti}^{(z)}\right) \\ + \left(r_{0i}^{(z)} + r_{1i}^{(z)} time_{ti}^{(z)} + e_{ti}^{(z)}\right) \end{array} \right]. \qquad (16.13)$$

This expression highlights that this requires an atypical definition of the model relative to the standard two-level TVC growth model. To see this, we will first distribute the two binary variables and gather up our terms

$$dv_{ti} = \left(\beta_{00}^{(y)} \delta_y + \beta_{10}^{(y)} \delta_y time_{ti}^{(y)}\right)$$
$$+ \left(r_{0i}^{(y)} \delta_y + r_{1i}^{(y)} \delta_y time_{ti}^{(y)} + e_{ti}^{(y)} \delta_y\right)$$
$$+ \left(\beta_{00}^{(z)} \delta_z + \beta_{10}^{(z)} \delta_z time_{ti}^{(z)}\right)$$
$$+ \left(r_{0i}^{(z)} \delta_z + r_{1i}^{(z)} \delta_z time_{ti}^{(z)} + e_{ti}^{(z)} \delta_z\right). \qquad (16.14)$$

There are two somewhat odd things about this expression relative to the usual univariate growth model.

First, *there is no overall intercept term for this reduced-form model*. Instead, the intercept for the first outcome (i.e., y_{ti}) is captured in the main effect of the first dummy variable (i.e., $\beta_{00}^{(y)} \delta_y$); similarly, the intercept for the second outcome (i.e., z_{ti}) is captured in the main effect of the second dummy variable (i.e., $\beta_{00}^{(z)}\delta_z$). Second, *the linear slope for each outcome is captured in the interaction between each dummy variable and time.* Specifically, the linear slope for the first outcome (i.e., y_{ti}) is captured in the interaction of the first dummy variable and time (i.e., $\beta_{10}^{(y)}\delta_y time_{ti}^{(y)}$); the linear slope for the second outcome (i.e., z_{ti}) is captured in the interaction of the second dummy variable and time (i.e., $\beta_{10}^{(z)}\delta_z time_{ti}^{(z)}$). Thus, the main effects of the dummy variables represent the outcome-specific intercepts, and the interactions between the dummy variables and time represent the outcome-specific slopes. See MacCallum et al. (1997) for an excellent description and demonstration of this model with three outcomes.

There are a number of advantages to this model expression, a key one of which is the inclusion of more complex error structures at both Level 1 and Level 2 than is possible within the univariate TVC growth model. The reason is that the covariance structure not only holds within each construct separately (e.g., for the repeated assessments of y_{ti} alone, and for z_{ti} alone), but it also holds *across* construct (e.g., relating y_{ti} to z_{ti}). For example, a univariate growth model of trust examines covariance structures only within trust; and a univariate growth model of integrity examines covariance structures only within integrity. But a multivariate growth model of trust and integrity allows for the examination of covariance structures *between* trust and integrity both at the time-specific (i.e., Level 1) and trajectory-specific (i.e., Level 2) parts of the model. This can be critically important information to include, not only in terms of properly modeling the joint structure of the observed data but also in terms of fully evaluating the substantive research question of interest (Curran & Hancock, 2021).

For example, consider the Level-1 covariance structure for the bivariate model of y_{ti} and z_{ti} (i.e., the model defined in Equation 16.14). The corresponding Level-1 covariance structure is

$$\left[e_{1i}^{(y)}, e_{2i}^{(y)}, e_{3i}^{(y)}, e_{4i}^{(y)}, e_{1i}^{(z)}, e_{2i}^{(z)}, e_{3i}^{(z)}, e_{4i}^{(z)}\right]$$

$\sim MVN(0, \mathbf{R})$ with matrix elements

$$\mathbf{R} = \left[\begin{array}{cccc|cccc} \sigma_1^{2(y)} & & & & & & & \\ 0 & \sigma_2^{2(y)} & & & & & & \\ 0 & 0 & \sigma_3^{2(y)} & & & & & \\ 0 & 0 & 0 & \sigma_4^{2(y)} & & & & \\ \hline \sigma_{11}^{(z,y)} & 0 & 0 & 0 & \sigma_1^{2(z)} & & & \\ 0 & \sigma_{22}^{(z,y)} & 0 & 0 & 0 & \sigma_2^{2(z)} & & \\ 0 & 0 & \sigma_{33}^{(z,y)} & 0 & 0 & 0 & \sigma_3^{2(z)} & \\ 0 & 0 & 0 & \sigma_{44}^{(z,y)} & 0 & 0 & 0 & \sigma_4^{2(z)} \end{array}\right].$$

(16.15)

The upper left quadrant represents the Level-1 residual covariance structure among the four repeated assessments of y_{ti}; this is equivalent to those of the univariate model shown in Equation 16.4. Similarly, the lower right quadrant represents the Level-1 residual covariance structure among the four repeated assessments of z_{ti}. However, critically important information is contained in the lower left quadrant in the form of the within-time but across-construct residual covariance structure.

For example, the element $\sigma_{11}^{(z,y)}$ represents the covariance between the Level-1 residuals of y_{ti} and z_{ti} at the first time-point (i.e., $t = 1$). This captures the part of *trust* at Time 1 that is unexplained by the trajectory of trust (so the difference between the observed value and the underlying trajectory) that covaries with the part of *integrity* at Time 1 that is unexplained by the trajectory of integrity. This provides a way to include potentially important covariances among the time-specific Level-1 residuals across the two or more multivariate outcomes, the omission of which could artificially inflate the variance components at Level 2.

The multivariate model also allows us to examine across-construct covariances among the Level-2 random effects. Again consider just two outcomes y_{ti} and z_{ti} where each is defined by a linear trajectory. The corresponding Level-2 covariance structure is $[r_{0i}^{(y)}, r_{1i}^{(y)}, r_{0i}^{(z)}, r_{1i}^{(z)}] \sim MVN(0, \mathbf{T})$ with matrix elements

$$T = \begin{bmatrix} \tau_{00}^{(y)} & & & \\ \tau_{10}^{(y)} & \tau_{11}^{(y)} & & \\ \hline \tau_{00}^{(z,y)} & \tau_{01}^{(z,y)} & \tau_{00}^{(z)} & \\ \tau_{10}^{(z,y)} & \tau_{11}^{(z,y)} & \tau_{10}^{(z)} & \tau_{11}^{(z)} \end{bmatrix}. \quad (16.16)$$

The upper left and lower right quadrants represent the covariance structure of the growth parameters within outcome y_{ti} and outcome z_{ti}, respectively (as corresponds to the same elements for the univariate model presented in Equation 16.5). However, the lower left quadrant represents the covariance structure of the growth parameters *across* the two outcomes. More specifically, the covariance between the two random intercepts is $\tau_{00}^{(z,y)}$, between the two random slopes is $\tau_{11}^{(z,y)}$, between the intercept of z_{ti} and the slope of y_{ti} is $\tau_{01}^{(z,y)}$, and between the slope of z_{ti} and the intercept of y_{ti} is $\tau_{10}^{(z,y)}$.

These covariances (and their standardized correlation counterparts) can be extremely interesting. For example, a positive value for $\tau_{11}^{(z,y)}$ would imply that steeper rates of change on trust are associated with steeper rates of change in integrity (and vice versa), and this would be consistent with the notion that development in the two constructs is in some way related over time. Furthermore, a negative value for $\tau_{01}^{(z,y)}$ would imply that larger initial values of integrity are associated with less steep rates of change in trust over time (and vice versa), and this would be consistent with the notion that the initial values of integrity are in some way associated with the rates of change on trust. These across-construct covariances are often of key interest when attempting to understand how growth in one construct is related to growth in another construct. Furthermore, these covariances are only available via the multivariate growth model given that the standard multilevel model is limited to the estimation of trajectory parameters for one outcome at a time (e.g., as defined in Equation 16.7).

The Inclusion of One or More Predictors

Just as with the univariate model, the multivariate model can contain one or more predictors at either Level 1, Level 2, or both (Hoffman, 2015). Furthermore, interactions can be estimated within or across levels of analysis. In expectation of our later models, we focus on the inclusion of a single TIC, denoted w_i, entered at Level 2. For example, we are interested in the relation between the extent to which cadets view their fellow squad members as *benevolent* at the initial time period and how their trajectories of trust and integrity change over time. We will, thus, include a cadet-specific measure of perceived benevolence in fellow squad members at the initial time period with the goal of examining how initial perceived benevolence impacts the simultaneous unfolding of trust and integrity over time. The Level-1 equation remains as before (i.e., Equation 16.9), but the Level-2 equation is expanded to include the TIC

$$\pi_{0i}^{(k)} = \beta_{00}^{(k)} + \beta_{01}^{(k)} w_i + r_{0i}^{(k)}$$
$$\pi_{1i}^{(k)} = \beta_{10}^{(k)} + \beta_{11}^{(k)} w_i + r_{1i}^{(k)}. \quad (16.17)$$

All of these terms are defined as before, but now the regression parameters linking the TIC to the random intercept and slope are unique to outcome k (e.g., $\beta_{01}^{(k)}$ and $\beta_{11}^{(k)}$).

The Level-2 equation is again substituted into the Level-1 equation to result in the reduced-form expression for the model. For example, for two outcomes denoted y and z, this expression is

$$dv_{ti} = \delta_y \begin{bmatrix} \left(\beta_{00}^{(y)} + \beta_{10}^{(y)} time_{ti}^{(y)} + \beta_{01}^{(y)} w_i + \beta_{11}^{(y)} w_i time_{ti}^{(y)} \right) \\ + \left(r_{0i}^{(y)} + r_{1i}^{(y)} time_{ti}^{(y)} + e_{ti}^{(y)} \right) \end{bmatrix}$$
$$+ \delta_z \begin{bmatrix} \left(\beta_{00}^{(z)} + \beta_{10}^{(z)} time_{ti}^{(z)} + \beta_{01}^{(z)} w_i + \beta_{11}^{(z)} w_i time_{ti}^{(z)} \right) \\ + \left(r_{0i}^{(z)} + r_{1i}^{(z)} time_{ti}^{(z)} + e_{ti}^{(z)} \right) \end{bmatrix}.$$
$$(16.18)$$

Each bracketed term is multiplied by the dummy variable associated with that particular outcome (i.e., δ_y and δ_z). As such, the regression of the random intercept on the TIC is captured in the interaction between the dummy variable and the TIC (i.e., $\beta_{01}^{(y)} \delta_y w_i$ and $\beta_{01}^{(z)} \delta_z w_i$). Similarly, the regression of the random slope on the TIC is captured in the interaction between the dummy variable, time, and the TIC (i.e., $\beta_{11}^{(y)}\delta_y w_i time_{ti}$ and $\beta_{11}^{(z)}\delta_z w_i time_{ti}$). As with the univariate two-level model, the TIC shifts the conditional means of the random intercepts and slopes per unit shift in the TIC. In the multivariate model, however, these mean shifts affect all outcomes simultaneously.

Now that we have laid out the model equations, we find that a key practical challenge in fitting these models to real data is the need to restructure the data in a way that is not necessarily intuitive but that is needed to allow for proper model estimation. Despite the nonintuitiveness, a bit of careful thought shows that this can be accomplished in a straightforward manner; we demonstrate this in the next section and provide a detailed appendix showing this in SAS and R.[6]

Data Structure for the Two-Level Multivariate Growth Model

An example of the data structure for the standard organization for the univariate TVC model is presented in the left panel of Table 16.1. A sample data structure is given for four individuals where column i denotes the identification number of each person, column t denotes time-point, column y_{ti} denotes the criterion (e.g., *trust*), column z_{ti} denotes the TVC (e.g., *integrity*), and column w_i denotes a Level-2 TIC (e.g., *benevolence*). This is precisely how the data would be structured in the standard univariate growth model with one TVC and one TIC.

Compare this standard structure with that presented in the right panel of Table 16.1 that has been reformatted for the bivariate model. Note that these are *precisely* the same data as are shown in the left panel except for three key differences. First, the values on y_{ti} and z_{ti} are now strung out in a single column labelled dv_{ti}; this represents the newly synthesized criterion variable that we manually created and will be the unit of analysis for the multivariate model. Second, the TIC remains constant across individuals but

TABLE 16.1

Standard Data Structure for a Four Time-Point, Two-Level, Univariate Growth Model With One Time-Varying Covariate (Left Panel) and the Modified Data Structure for a Four Time-Point, Two-Level, Bivariate Growth Model (Right Panel)

i	t	y_{ti}	z_{ti}	w_i	i	t	dv_{ti}	w_i	δ_y	δ_z
1	1	y_{11}	z_{11}	w_1	1	1	y_{11}	w_1	1	0
1	2	y_{21}	z_{21}	w_1	1	1	z_{11}	w_1	0	1
1	3	y_{31}	z_{31}	w_1	1	2	y_{21}	w_1	1	0
1	4	y_{41}	z_{41}	w_1	1	2	z_{21}	w_1	0	1
2	1	y_{12}	z_{12}	w_2	1	3	y_{31}	w_1	1	0
2	2	y_{22}	z_{22}	w_2	1	3	z_{31}	w_1	0	1
2	3	y_{32}	z_{32}	w_2	1	4	y_{41}	w_1	1	0
2	4	y_{42}	z_{42}	w_2	1	4	z_{41}	w_1	0	1
3	1	y_{13}	z_{13}	w_3	2	1	y_{12}	w_2	1	0
3	2	y_{23}	z_{23}	w_3	2	1	z_{12}	w_2	0	1
3	3	y_{33}	z_{33}	w_3	2	2	y_{22}	w_2	1	0
3	4	y_{43}	z_{43}	w_3	2	2	z_{22}	w_2	0	1
4	1	y_{14}	z_{14}	w_4	2	3	y_{32}	w_2	1	0
4	2	y_{24}	z_{24}	w_4	2	3	z_{32}	w_2	0	1
4	3	y_{34}	z_{34}	w_4	2	4	y_{42}	w_2	1	0
4	4	y_{44}	z_{44}	w_4	2	4	z_{42}	w_2	0	1
					3	1	y_{13}	w_3	1	0
					3	1	z_{13}	w_3	0	1
					3	2	y_{23}	w_3	1	0
					3	2	z_{23}	w_3	0	1
					3	3	y_{33}	w_3	1	0
					3	3	z_{33}	w_3	0	1
					3	4	y_{43}	w_3	1	0
					3	4	z_{43}	w_3	0	1
					4	1	y_{14}	w_4	1	0
					4	1	z_{14}	w_4	0	1
					4	2	y_{24}	w_4	1	0
					4	2	z_{24}	w_4	0	1
					4	3	y_{34}	w_4	1	0
					4	3	z_{34}	w_4	0	1
					4	4	y_{44}	w_4	1	0
					4	4	z_{44}	w_4	0	1

is now repeated for each outcome. Third, there are two new dummy variables, denoted δ_y and δ_z, each of which is equal to one when the corresponding element in dv_{ti} is from that construct, and zero otherwise. For example, in the first row of data $\delta_y = 1$ and $\delta_z = 0$ because the element of dv_{ti} is

---

[6]All computer code and model results are available from the first author or at https://curran.web.unc.edu/

from outcome y_{ti}; similarly, in the second row of data $\delta_y = 0$ and $\delta_z = 1$ because the element of dv_{ti} is from outcome z_{ti}. This pattern repeats throughout the entire data matrix. The two-level multivariate growth model can now be fitted directly to these newly structured data.

THREE-LEVEL GROWTH MODELS

The two-level models and associated synthesized data structures we have discussed thus far have been generally well established for a number of decades (e.g., MacCallum et al., 1997). However, there is an unresolved issue in need of addressing. Namely, the two-level model assumes that the repeated measures are nested within individual but the individual subjects in the sample are *independent*. In other words, it is strongly assumed that no two cadets are any more or less similar than any other two cadets. This assumption is commonly met in practice, especially when subjects are obtained using some form of simple random sampling procedure and subjects are not themselves nested in some higher structure (e.g., Raudenbush & Bryk, 2002).

However, there are many situations in which not only are the repeated measures nested within individuals but also individuals are, in turn, nested within groups. A common example is when repeated measures are nested within children, and children are in turn nested within classroom; or repeated measures are nested within patients, and patients are nested within hospitals. In our case here, we have repeated measures nested within cadet, and cadets are in turn nested within squads. Such a data structure would violate the assumptions of the two-level model because two cadets who are members of the same squad are likely to be more similar to one another than two cadets from different squads. A major strength of the multilevel model is the natural way that it may be expanded to many complex sampling designs, including three levels of nesting. But these models are understandably more complex, and we must closely consider how the necessary expansions are possible in the multivariate case.

Three-Level Unconditional Univariate Growth Model

We will begin by briefly returning to the two-level *univariate* model and extending this to allow for three levels of nesting, and then expand these expressions to include a third level of nesting. Recall that our motivating example is time nested within cadet, and cadet is nested within squad. The Level-1 model thus becomes

$$y_{tij} = \pi_{0ij} + \pi_{1ij} time_{tij} + e_{tij}, \quad (16.19)$$

where t and i continue to represent time and individual, respectively, but now j denotes group membership at Level 3 ($j = 1, 2, \ldots, J$). More specifically, y_{tij} is the obtained measure on outcome y at time t for individual i nested in group j; π_{0ij} and π_{1ij} are the intercept and slope for individual i in group j; $time_{tij}$ is the numerical measure of time at time t for individual i in group j, and e_{tij} is the time-, individual-, and group-specific residual where $e_{tij} \sim MVN(\mathbf{0}, \mathbf{R})$.

The Level-2 equations logically expand such that

$$\pi_{0ij} = \beta_{00j} + r_{0ij}$$
$$\pi_{1ij} = \beta_{10j} + r_{1ij}, \quad (16.20)$$

where β_{00j} and β_{10j} are the group-specific intercept and slope of the linear trajectory. These terms are sometimes a bit tricky to think about at first. The group-specific intercept and slope (i.e., β_{00j} and β_{10j}) represent the mean of the intercepts and the mean of the slopes of the growth trajectories for all of the individuals nested within group j. For example, these might represent the mean initial value and mean rate of change in trust for all of the cadets who are nested within a given squad j. As such, the residuals r_{0ij} and r_{1ij} represent the deviation of each individual's intercept and slope around their group-specific mean values. That is, the residuals capture the variability of each cadet's trajectory of trust around their own squad-specific mean trajectory of trust. More formally, this is given as $[r_{0ij}, r_{1ij}] \sim MVN(\mathbf{0}, \mathbf{T}_\pi)$; we will explore the $\mathbf{T}_\pi$ covariance matrix of random effects more closely in a moment.

Finally, given the three-level structure of the data, the group-specific intercepts and slopes (e.g., β_{00j} and β_{10j}) themselves vary randomly across groups. The Level-3 equations are thus

$$\beta_{00j} = \gamma_{000} + u_{00j}$$
$$\beta_{10j} = \gamma_{100} + u_{10j}, \quad (16.21)$$

where γ_{000} and γ_{100} represent the grand mean intercept and slope pooling over all individuals and all groups, and the residual terms u_{00j} and u_{10j} capture the deviation of each group-specific value from the grand means, and $[u_{00j}, u_{10j}] \sim$ MVN $(0, \mathbf{T}_\beta)$. The reduced form expression for the three-level univariate growth model is

$$y_{tij} = (\gamma_{000} + \gamma_{100} time_{tij})$$
$$+ (u_{00j} + r_{0ij} + u_{10j} time_{tij} + r_{1ij} time_{tij} + e_{tij}).$$
$$(16.22)$$

See Raudenbush and Bryk (2002, Chapter 8) for an excellent description of the general three-level model as well as a discussion of studying individual change within groups.

A key characteristic of this model is the estimation of random components at both Levels 2 and 3, and the covariance structures of these random effects will be of specific interest in the models described in the upcoming section cleverly called Three-Level Multivariate Growth Model. In the two-level model, the Level-2 covariance matrix was denoted $\mathbf{T}$. In the three-level model, however, there is a separate $\mathbf{T}$ matrix at Level 2 and at Level 3. This is why we must distinguish these $\mathbf{T}$ matrixes with the use of an additional subscript: $\mathbf{T}_\pi$ for Level 2 and $\mathbf{T}_\beta$ for Level 3. Let us first consider the covariance structure of the residuals at Level 2 captured in $\mathbf{T}_\pi$.

For a linear model defined at Level 1, the Level-2 covariance matrix takes the form

$$\mathbf{T}_\pi = \begin{bmatrix} \tau_{\pi_{00}} & \\ \tau_{\pi_{01}} & \tau_{\pi_{11}} \end{bmatrix}, \quad (16.23)$$

where $\tau_{\pi_{00}}$ represents the Level-2 variance of the intercepts, $\tau_{\pi_{11}}$ the variance of the slopes, and $\tau_{\pi_{01}}$ the covariance between the intercepts and slopes. These are sometimes challenging estimates to interpret given that they reside at the middle level of nesting. Specifically, these estimates represent the amount of variability among the individual-specific trajectories within group (e.g., variability among trajectories of trust for each cadet sharing the same squad). Thus, larger values reflect greater person-to-person variability in the trajectories within group; similarly, smaller values reflect greater person-to-person similarity in the trajectories within group. At the extreme, if these variance components equal zero, then each person within the group is characterized by precisely the same trajectory. For example, a larger value of $\tau_{\pi_{11}}$ would imply greater variability in rates of change in trust among cadets within the same squad. If $\tau_{\pi_{11}} = 0$ then every cadet within each squad is characterized by precisely the same developmental trajectory of trust over time. Although this implies that there is no cadet-to-cadet variability in the development of trust within squad, this does *not* imply that there is no meaningful squad-to-squad variability in the development of trust over time. To assess this, we must turn to the Level-3 covariance matrix of random effects.

The covariance matrix of random effects at the third level of analysis is denoted $\mathbf{T}_\beta$. For the linear model with full random effects (as defined in Equation 16.22), the elements of this matrix are

$$\mathbf{T}_\beta = \begin{bmatrix} \tau_{\beta_{00}} & \\ \tau_{\beta_{01}} & \tau_{\beta_{11}} \end{bmatrix}, \quad (16.24)$$

where $\tau_{\beta_{00}}$ represents the Level-3 variance of the intercepts, $\tau_{\beta_{11}}$ the variance of the slopes, and $\tau_{\beta_{01}}$ the covariance between the intercepts and slopes. In contrast to the Level-2 variance components that capture individual-level variability of the trajectory parameters *within* group (e.g., squad), $\mathbf{T}_\beta$ captures the group-to-group level variability of the trajectory parameters *between* group.

For example, larger values of $\tau_{\beta_{00}}$ and $\tau_{\beta_{11}}$ would indicate greater squad-to-squad variability in intercepts and slopes; that is, some squads are characterized by higher versus lower starting points on the outcome variables and larger versus smaller rates of change over time. Alternatively, smaller values indicate less variability in the trajectory parameters across squad. As such, larger variance components would imply that there are potentially meaningful differences in the squad-level trajectories of trust over time across the set of squads; some squads might be defined by higher starting points and steeper rates of change, whereas others are not. At the extreme, values of zero reflect that all squads are governed by the same trajectory parameters; for example, all squads are defined by the same starting point of trust and same rate of change in trust over time. Indeed, in this extreme case, the three-level model simplifies to the two-level structure defined earlier given that there is no meaningful squad-to-squad variability.

To briefly summarize, the Level-1 variance components reflect the time-specific variations in trust around each cadet's trajectory of trust; the Level-2 variance components reflect the cadet-specific variations in the trajectories of trust around the mean trajectory of trust within each squad; and the Level-3 variance components reflect the squad-specific variations in the trajectories of trust around the grand mean trajectory of trust pooling over all cadets and all squads. This breakdown of the random effects is one of the most elegant aspects of the three-level model: The total variability observed in trust can be simultaneously broken down into *time*-specific, *cadet*-specific, and *squad*-specific effects. And if meaningful random effects are identified at any level of analysis, one or more predictors can be included to attempt to explain these variations.

Three-Level Conditional Univariate Growth Model

Just as with the two-level model, covariates can be included at any level of analysis. In the three-level model, however, predictors can be time specific (i.e., Level-1 model), person specific (i.e., Level-2 model), or group specific (i.e., Level-3 model). Using our previous terminology, TVCs would thus appear at Level 1, and individual- and group-specific TICs would appear at Levels 2 and 3, respectively. Given our primary interest in change in two or more constructs over time, here we focus just on the TVCs at Level 1; inclusion of TICs is a natural extension of the two-level model described earlier (e.g., Raudenbush & Bryk, 2002, pp. 241–245).

The Level-1 equation for a simple linear growth model with one TVC is defined as

$$y_{tij} = \pi_{0ij} + \pi_{1ij}time_{tij} + \pi_{2ij}z_{tij} + e_{tij}, \quad (16.25)$$

where z_{tij} is the time-, person-, and group-specific TVC, and π_{2ij} captures the relation between the TVC and the outcome at time-point t. The magnitude of the relation between the TVC and the outcome can vary randomly over individual with corresponding Level-2 equations

$$\pi_{0ij} = \beta_{00j} + r_{0ij}$$
$$\pi_{1ij} = \beta_{10j} + r_{1ij}$$
$$\pi_{2ij} = \beta_{20j} + r_{2ij}, \quad (16.26)$$

where β_{20j} represents the relation between the TVC and the outcome pooling over all individuals within group j. Finally, the magnitude of these within-group specific effects can itself vary over group, and this is captured in the Level-3 equations

$$\beta_{00j} = \gamma_{000} + u_{00j}$$
$$\beta_{10j} = \gamma_{100} + u_{10j}$$
$$\beta_{20j} = \gamma_{200} + u_{20j}. \quad (16.27)$$

The reduced form results from the substitution of Equation 16.27 into 16.26, and Equation 16.26 subsequently into Equation 16.25. Although tedious, it is interesting to see the full set of collected terms

$$y_{tij} = (\gamma_{000} + \gamma_{100}time_{tij} + \gamma_{200}z_{tij})$$
$$+ (u_{10j} + r_{0ij})time_{tij} + (u_{2ij} + r_{tij})z_{tij}$$
$$+ (u_{00j} + r_{0ij} + e_{tij}). \quad (16.28)$$

This model is in the same form as its two-level counterpart with the key exception that an additional covariance matrix is allowed to capture between-group variability at the third level of nesting. We again assume, however, that although the TVC can take on a different numerical value at each time-point t, the TVC itself is assumed to not change systematically over time. Whether by theoretical rationale or empirical necessity, there are many situations in which we would like to expand the univariate three-level model to simultaneously capture growth in two or more constructs over time. It is to this we now turn.

Three-Level Multivariate Growth Model

The expansion of the multivariate growth model from two to three levels of nesting is both intuitive and straightforward (Curran, McGinley, et al., 2012). Just as we expanded the univariate growth model to allow for individuals to be nested within group, we will expand the multivariate model in precisely the same way. Indeed, we will use the same dummy variable approach to combine the multiple outcomes into a single three-level model. The only difference here is that the reduced form expression is more complex because of the nesting of time within individual within group.

The general expression is

$$dv_{tij} = \sum_{k=1}^{K} \delta_k \left[\begin{array}{c} \left(\gamma_{000}^{(k)} + \gamma_{100}^{(k)} time_{tij}^{(k)}\right) \\ + \left(\begin{array}{c} u_{00j}^{(k)} + r_{0ij}^{(k)} + u_{10j}^{(k)} time_{tij}^{(k)} \\ + r_{1ij}^{(k)} time_{tij}^{(k)} + e_{tij}^{(k)} \end{array} \right) \end{array} \right] \quad (16.29)$$

for $k = 1, 2, \ldots, K$ outcomes. There is no need to modify the notation for the dummy variables to include information about group membership because the dummy variables only demarcate to which outcome variable the numerical value belongs; this is not unique to time, person, or group and thus directly follows our earlier developments. For the bivariate case ($K = 2$) this simplifies to

$$dv_{tij} = \delta_y \left[\begin{array}{c} \left(\gamma_{000}^{(y)} + \gamma_{100}^{(y)} time_{tij}^{(y)}\right) \\ + \left(\begin{array}{c} u_{00j}^{(y)} + r_{0ij}^{(y)} + u_{10j}^{(y)} time_{tij}^{(y)} \\ + r_{1ij}^{(y)} time_{tij}^{(y)} + e_{tij}^{(y)} \end{array} \right) \end{array} \right]$$
$$+ \delta_z \left[\begin{array}{c} \left(\gamma_{000}^{(z)} + \gamma_{100}^{(z)} time_{tij}^{(z)}\right) \\ + \left(\begin{array}{c} u_{00j}^{(z)} + r_{0ij}^{(z)} + u_{10j}^{(z)} time_{tij}^{(z)} \\ + r_{1ij}^{(z)} time_{tij}^{(z)} + e_{tij}^{(z)} \end{array} \right) \end{array} \right], \quad (16.30)$$

where the first bracketed term captures the three-level growth process for outcome y_{tij} (e.g., *trust*) and the second bracketed term captures the three-level growth process for outcome z_{tij} (e.g., *integrity*). As before, these two growth processes need not be the same (e.g., the first could be linear and the second quadratic). As with the two-level multivariate expression, the definition of the model is atypical relative to the standard three-level growth model. The main effects of the two dummy codes are again the intercept of each construct and the interaction between each dummy code and time are again the slope of each construct.

The key benefit stemming from this rather complex (yet intuitively appealing) model is the ability to explicitly incorporate various covariance structures among the residual terms at all three levels both within and across constructs. The Level-1 covariance structure for this model is the same as that defined in Equation 16.15 for the two-level model. However, the covariance structures at Levels 2 and 3 can become quite interesting. Given the similarity in the types of inferences that can be drawn, here we will focus primarily on the Level-2 covariance structure as estimated both within and across the multivariate outcomes (i.e., $\mathbf{T}_\pi$). However, all of our descriptions would generalize naturally to the Level-3 covariance structure (i.e., $\mathbf{T}_\beta$). Furthermore, these generalizations offer unique insights into the relations among growth trajectories at the level of the group. Thus $\mathbf{T}_\pi$ captures the random components of individual-level trajectories nested within groups, and $\mathbf{T}_\beta$ captures the random components of group-level trajectories across groups. Only the three-level model provides this joint estimation of within- and between-group effects (the specific parameterization of which would depend on substantive theory and empirical necessity).

To remain concrete, we will continue to consider the three-level bivariate growth model defined in Equation 16.30. There is thus a linear trajectory estimated for both outcomes, and all trajectory parameters are allowed to vary both at Level 2 and Level 3. The joint covariance structure for the two growth processes at Level 2 is contained in the matrix $\mathbf{T}_\pi$. The specific elements of this matrix are

$$\mathbf{T}_\pi = \begin{bmatrix} \tau^{(y)}_{\pi_{00}} & & & \\ \tau^{(y)}_{\pi_{10}} & \tau^{(y)}_{\pi_{11}} & & \\ \tau^{(z,y)}_{\pi_{00}} & \tau^{(z,y)}_{\pi_{01}} & \tau^{(z)}_{\pi_{00}} & \\ \tau^{(z,y)}_{\pi_{10}} & \tau^{(z,y)}_{\pi_{11}} & \tau^{(z)}_{\pi_{10}} & \tau^{(z)}_{\pi_{11}} \end{bmatrix}. \quad (16.31)$$

Note the substantial similarity to the Level-2 covariance matrix from the two-level bivariate growth model defined in Equation 16.16. The critical difference between the Level-2 covariance matrix $\mathbf{T}$ from the two-level model and the Level-2 covariance matrix $\mathbf{T}_\pi$ from the three-level model is that the latter explicitly accounts for the clustering of individuals within groups at the highest level of nesting. If we were to fix the Level-3 covariance matrix to zero (e.g., $\mathbf{T}_\beta = 0$), then the three-level model would reduce to the two-level model and the Level-2 covariance matrices defined in Equations 16.16 and 16.31 would be equal (e.g., $\mathbf{T} = \mathbf{T}_\pi$). How cool is that?

The same pattern as was observed in the $\mathbf{T}$ matrix defined in Equation 16.16 holds here. Namely, the upper left and lower right quadrants represent the variance components of the trajectory parameters of the individuals nested within each group for outcome y and outcome z, respectively. Furthermore, the lower left quadrant represents the variance components across the two outcomes. For example, the element $\tau^{(z,y)}_{\pi_{00}}$ captures the covariance between the random intercepts on outcome z with the random intercepts on outcome y; this element assesses the extent of similarity in the starting points of the trajectories of z and y of individuals nested within group. Similarly, the element $\tau^{(z,y)}_{\pi_{11}}$ captures the covariance between the random slopes on outcome z with the random slopes on outcome y; this assesses the extent of similarity in the rates of change of the trajectories of z and y. Finally, the element $\tau^{(z,y)}_{\pi_{10}}$ captures the covariance between the random slopes on z and the random intercepts on y, and $\tau^{(z,y)}_{\pi_{01}}$ the covariance between the random intercepts on z with the random slopes on y. As with the two-level models, these covariances can be standardized into correlations for interpretation and effect size estimation.

These covariance estimates are often of key substantive interest when testing hypotheses regarding stability and change over time. As in the two-level bivariate growth model, the lower-left quadrant of the $\mathbf{T}_\pi$ matrix captures the similarity or dissimilarity in patterns of growth in the two outcomes over time. This can provide insight into a variety of interesting questions. For example, to what extent are the starting points of the trajectories of trust and integrity related? Is the rate of change in trust systematically related to the rate of change in integrity? Do individuals who report higher initial levels of trust also report steeper rates of change in integrity (and vice versa)? The key advantage of the three-level model is that these relations are estimated while properly allowing for the nesting of individuals within groups. Furthermore, similarly intriguing insights can be gained about group-level characteristics of growth through the Level-3 variance components (i.e., $\mathbf{T}_\beta$) that would not otherwise be accessible via the two-level model. For example, on average, do squads that are characterized by higher initial levels of trust tend to increase more steeply in integrity over time? These are just a few of the many advantages of the multivariate–multilevel growth models.

The Inclusion of One or More Predictors

One or more predictors can be included at any of the three levels of analyses. Furthermore, interactions can be estimated within one level, across two levels, or even across all three levels. Because the equations are direct extensions of those already defined, we do not repeat these here. For example, the inclusion of a single TIC at Level 2 follows the same structure as was defined in Equation 16.18 but with the addition of the necessary Level-3 error terms (for full details, see Raudenbush & Bryk, 2002, Chapter 8). We again do not detail the important topic of disaggregation of effects, whether this be within- and between-person, or within- or between-group, although standard methods used in univariate MLMs would directly apply here (e.g., Curran & Bauer, 2011; Hoffman, 2015).

DATA STRUCTURE FOR THE THREE-LEVEL MULTIVARIATE GROWTH MODEL

The data structure required to fit the three-level bivariate growth model is a direct extension of that used for the two-level model. For example, the left panel in Table 16.2 presents the standard data structure used to fit the three-level TVC model defined in Equation 16.22 to four individuals with the inclusion of a Level-2 TIC. There is more information here than was required for the two-level model given the need to simultaneously track group membership. Thus, column j denotes group, column i denotes individual, and column t denotes time. Subjects 1 and 2 are members of Group 1, and Subjects 3 and 4 are members of Group 2. Finally, y_{tij} is the observed outcome variable, z_{tij} is the TVC, and w_{ij} is the person-specific TIC. To combine the outcome and the TVC into a bivariate model, these must be restructured under a single column as the newly constructed (or synthesized) dependent variable.

These restructured data are shown in the right panel of Table 16.2. Columns j, i, and t all remain as before, but there is a newly created column labelled dv_{tij}; this is the newly synthesized variable that is a stacked vector of y_{tij} and z_{tij}. The TIC w_{ij} is again repeated over both the outcome variables. Finally, the binary variables denoted δ_y and δ_z again identify to which construct each element of the synthesized variable belongs. Note the significant similarities between the data structures presented

TABLE 16.2

Standard Data Structure for a Four Time-Point, Three-Level, Univariate Growth Model With One Time-Varying Covariate (Left Panel) and the Modified Data Structure for a Four Time-Point, Three-Level, Bivariate Growth Model (Right Panel)

j	i	t	y_{tij}	z_{tij}	w_{ij}	j	i	t	dv_{tij}	w_{ij}	δ_y	δ_z
1	1	1	y_{111}	z_{111}	w_{11}	1	1	1	y_{111}	w_{11}	1	0
1	1	2	y_{211}	z_{211}	w_{11}	1	1	1	z_{111}	w_{11}	0	1
1	1	3	y_{311}	z_{311}	w_{11}	1	1	2	y_{211}	w_{11}	1	0
1	1	4	y_{411}	z_{411}	w_{11}	1	1	2	z_{211}	w_{11}	0	1
1	2	1	y_{121}	z_{121}	w_{21}	1	1	3	y_{311}	w_{11}	1	0
1	2	2	y_{221}	z_{221}	w_{21}	1	1	3	z_{311}	w_{11}	0	1
1	2	3	y_{321}	z_{321}	w_{21}	1	1	4	y_{411}	w_{11}	1	0
1	2	4	y_{421}	z_{421}	w_{21}	1	1	4	z_{411}	w_{11}	0	1
2	3	1	y_{132}	z_{132}	w_{32}	1	2	1	y_{121}	w_{21}	1	0
2	3	2	y_{232}	z_{232}	w_{32}	1	2	1	z_{121}	w_{21}	0	1
2	3	3	y_{332}	z_{332}	w_{32}	1	2	2	y_{221}	w_{21}	1	0
2	3	4	y_{432}	z_{432}	w_{32}	1	2	2	z_{221}	w_{21}	0	1
2	4	1	y_{142}	z_{142}	w_{42}	1	2	3	y_{321}	w_{21}	1	0
2	4	2	y_{242}	z_{242}	w_{42}	1	2	3	z_{321}	w_{21}	0	1
2	4	3	y_{342}	z_{342}	w_{42}	1	2	4	y_{421}	w_{21}	1	0
2	4	4	y_{442}	z_{442}	w_{42}	1	2	4	z_{421}	w_{21}	0	1
						2	3	1	y_{132}	w_{32}	1	0
						2	3	1	z_{132}	w_{32}	0	1
						2	3	2	y_{232}	w_{32}	1	0
						2	3	2	z_{232}	w_{32}	0	1
						2	3	3	y_{332}	w_{32}	1	0
						2	3	3	z_{332}	w_{32}	0	1
						2	3	4	y_{432}	w_{32}	1	0
						2	3	4	z_{432}	w_{32}	0	1
						2	4	1	y_{142}	w_{42}	1	0
						2	4	1	z_{142}	w_{42}	0	1
						2	4	2	y_{242}	w_{42}	1	0
						2	4	2	z_{242}	w_{42}	0	1
						2	4	3	y_{342}	w_{42}	1	0
						2	4	3	z_{342}	w_{42}	0	1
						2	4	4	y_{442}	w_{42}	1	0
						2	4	4	z_{442}	w_{42}	0	1

in Table 16.1 and Table 16.2. The only meaningful difference is that Table 16.1 implies that the four individuals are independent, whereas Table 16.2 explicitly captures information about the group (that is, *squad* in our example) to which each individual belongs.

We have now fully explicated the multivariate growth model for three levels of nesting, and we have described the data structure needed for estimation. We now turn to the application of these models to evaluate several research hypotheses about the development of trust and integrity over time using real empirical data drawn from a longitudinal study of military cadets.

EMPIRICAL EXAMPLE: THE LONGITUDINAL DEVELOPMENT OF TRUST IN MILITARY CADETS

The core constructs of trust, influence, and leadership have long been a critically important focus of past and ongoing military research. Despite the wealth of knowledge that has been gathered, little is known about how trust and influence codevelop over time (e.g., Dirks et al., 2021; Sweeney, 2007; Sweeney et al., 2009). Gaining a better understanding of the etiological process that underlies the development of the determinants of trust and how trust subsequently affects influence is critical both from a theoretical and practical standpoint. Theoretically, a more rigorous study of these etiological processes would provide a greater and more nuanced understanding of the underlying developmental model; practically, understanding how leadership, trust, and influence develop, are maintained, and are potentially lost can directly inform how these important characteristics might be fostered and supported, particularly in a military training environment such as the USMA.

We focus on three specific dimensions that are related to trust and influence (Mayer & Davis, 1999): trustworthiness, integrity, and benevolence. All three constructs were assessed as each cadet's perception of their fellow squad members; there were 542 individual cadets, each nested within one of 131 squads. *Trustworthiness* represents the confidence or faithfulness a cadet holds in their fellow squad members; *integrity* represents the cadet's perception that fellow squad members adhere to ethical or moral principles; and *benevolence* represents the cadet's perception that fellow squad members care about the cadet's well-being. Our ultimate interest is in how these characteristics relate to influence (e.g., the ability of one individual to affect the behavior of another), but here we will specifically examine how trustworthiness and integrity codevelop over time and how initial levels of benevolence impact this developmental process.

Design

Data were obtained from 542 male and female cadets who attended the USMA at West Point. Cadets were assessed between one and four times throughout a single academic year (144 cadets were assessed once, 124 twice, 131 three times, and 136 four times), resulting in a total of 1,329 Person × Time observations. Although there was some subject attrition over time, these rates were modest and were addressed in the estimation of the multilevel models under the assumption that the data were missing at random (e.g., Allison, 2002). Although the structure of these data constitutes five levels of hierarchical nesting (repeated assessments nested within cadets; cadets nested within squads; squads nested within platoons; and platoons nested within companies) for purposes of demonstration, we focus here on the first three levels of nesting: time, cadet, and squad. More specifically, the 542 cadets were nested in 131 squads, which were nested in 39 platoons, which were nested in 10 companies. The mean number of cadets per squad was 4.08 with a range of 1 to 22. Although we are ignoring the nesting of squads in platoon, and platoons in company, preliminary analysis indicated that these fourth and fifth levels of nesting introduced only trivial dependence into the data (e.g., all intraclass correlations were less than .01).

Measures

We drew three measures from a much larger assessment battery given to each cadet at each time-point. We are interested in the cadets' report of *trust*, *integrity*, and *benevolence* of all of the other cadets that belong to their own squad[7] using items drawn from Mayer and Davis (1999). All three measures were assessed at all four time points; we considered the four repeated measures of

---

[7]That is, cadets reported on all of their fellow squad members as a unitary group and not on each squad member individually.

trust and integrity and the initial assessment of benevolence that we used as a TIC. Further analysis might consider also growth in benevolence (e.g., a multivariate growth model with three outcomes), although we do not pursue these models here.

Trust was computed as the mean of four items, and integrity and benevolence as the mean of three items. All items were rated on a 7-point ordinal scale ranging from 1 (*strongly disagree*) to 7 (*strongly agree*). Reliability coefficients ranged from .89 to .92 across the four time-points for trust, from .89 to .93 for integrity, and was .88 for the initial assessment of benevolence. Sample items for trust include "I feel secure in having my members of squad make decisions that critically affect me as a cadet" and "I would be willing to rely on my members of squad in a critical situation, such as combat." Sample items for integrity include "I like my members of squads' values" and "Sound principles seem to guide my members of squads' behavior." Finally, sample items for benevolence include "My members of squad are very concerned about my welfare" and "My members of squad will go out of their way to help me."

Summary Statistics

The mean reported levels of trust and integrity were both high at the first time-point and were generally increasing over time. On a scale ranging from one to seven, the sample means and standard deviations (*SD*) are as follows: for trust, Time 1 = 5.14 (*SD* = 1.22), Time 2 = 5.25 (*SD* = 1.13), Time 3 = 5.33 (*SD* = 1.14), and Time 4 = 5.54 (*SD* = 1.12); for integrity, Time 1 = 5.65 (*SD* = 0.87), Time 2 = 5.68 (*SD* = 0.88), Time 3 = 5.67 (*SD* = 0.98), and Time 4 = 5.85 (*SD* = 0.83); and for benevolence, at Time 1 = 5.40 (*SD* = 1.02). The within- and across-construct correlations between trust and integrity over time showed a general autoregressive pattern in which there were stronger correlations among observations taken closer in time compared with observations taken further apart in time. For example, the correlation between trust at Time 1 and trust at Time 2 was .51, at Times 1 and 3 was .46, and at Times 1 and 4 was .33. Trust and integrity also showed strong correlations both within and across time. For example, the correlation between trust at time 1 and integrity at Time 1 was .61, at Time 2 was .70, at Time 3 was .75, and at Time 4 was .76. Finally, the correlation between trust at Time 1 and integrity at Time 2 was .61, at Time 1 and Time 3 was .35, and at Time 1 and Time 4 was .31.

Results

We followed an analytic strategy that might be commonly used in practice: We estimated a total of four multilevel models: two univariate unconditional three-level growth models of trust and integrity independently, one unconditional three-level bivariate growth model of trust and integrity jointly, and one conditional three-level bivariate growth model of trust and integrity with benevolence as a TIC. We present each of these models in turn.

Univariate Three-Level Growth Model: Trust

We began by fitting a series of alternative functional forms to the repeated measures of trust (e.g., intercept only, linear, quadratic), and standard likelihood ratio tests (LRTs) indicated that a linear trajectory was optimal. Furthermore, additional LRTs indicated that the optimal structure for the random effects was defined by homoscedastic residuals at Level 1, a random intercept and random slope at Level 2, and a random intercept at Level 3. This covariance structure allowed for variability among the repeated measures within each cadet (Level 1), variability in starting point and rate of change in trust across cadets within squad (Level 2), and variability in starting point across squads (Level 3). The grand mean intercept was 5.16 and mean slope was .11, and both were significantly different from zero ($p < .001$). This result indicated that there was a rather high initial level of cadet trust in their fellow squad members (5.16 on a 1-to-7 scale) and that trust increased linearly over the four time-points. Furthermore, there were significant variance components at all three levels of analysis,

TABLE 16.3

Estimates, Standard Errors, and z Ratios for All Random Effects From the Three-Level Univariate Growth Model of Perceived Trust

Covariance parameter	Estimate	Standard error	z ratio	p value
Level-1 residual ($\hat{\sigma}^2$)	0.526	0.034	15.44	< .001
Level-2 intercept ($\hat{\tau}_{\pi_{00}}$)	0.870	0.103	8.47	< .001
Level-2 intercept-slope covariance ($\hat{\tau}_{\pi_{01}}$)/correlation	−0.151/−.54	0.038	−4.00	< .001
Level-2 slope ($\hat{\tau}_{\pi_{11}}$)	0.089	0.019	4.59	< .001
Level-3 intercept ($\hat{\tau}_{\beta_{00}}$)	0.078	0.042	1.86	= .031

indicating potentially meaningful variability in time-specific levels of trust around each cadet's trajectory, cadet-specific trajectories around squad-specific mean trajectories, and squad-specific intercepts around the grand intercept. There was also a significant negative covariance between the intercept and slope, indicating that higher initial levels of trust were associated with less steep increases over time. All point estimates and standard errors for these random effects are presented in Table 16.3.

Univariate Three-Level Growth Model: Integrity

We followed the same model building strategy for the four repeated measures of integrity as we used for trust. The final model for integrity was defined and evaluated using the same structure as we used for trust. The optimal fitting model was defined by a linear trajectory with homoscedastic errors at Level 1, a random intercept and random slope at Level 2, and just a random intercept at Level 3. The mean intercept was 5.65 ($p < .0001$), and mean slope was .04 ($p = .028$) indicating that, as we saw with the trust outcome, there was a rather high initial level of perceived integrity among fellow squad members (5.65 on a 1-to-7 scale) and that integrity increased linearly over the four time points. Furthermore, the Level-1 residual variance significantly differed from zero, as did the Level-2 random intercept and slope; however, the covariance between the intercept and slope was not significantly different from zero. Finally, the Level-3 random intercept was marginally significant ($p = .072$). The point estimates and standard errors for these random effects are presented in Table 16.4.

TABLE 16.4

Estimates, Standard Errors, and z Ratios for All Random Effects From the Three-Level Univariate Growth Model of Perceived Integrity

Covariance parameter	Estimate	Standard error	z ratio	p value
Level-1 residual ($\hat{\sigma}^2$)	0.397	0.026	15.43	< .001
Level-2 intercept ($\hat{\tau}_{\pi_{00}}$)	0.393	0.059	6.61	< .001
Level-2 intercept-slope covariance ($\hat{\tau}_{\pi_{01}}$)/correlation	−0.029/−.30	0.021	−1.42	= .16
Level-2 slope ($\hat{\tau}_{\pi_{11}}$)	0.025	0.011	2.19	= .014
Level-3 intercept ($\hat{\tau}_{\beta_{00}}$)	0.037	0.026	1.46	= .072

Bivariate Three-Level Growth Model: Trust and Integrity

There were significant fixed effects defining a linear trajectory for both trust and integrity, and there were significant (and one marginally significant) random effects at all three levels of analysis. Each of the univariate models was estimated in isolation, however, and we do not yet know how trust and integrity are related over time. One option would be to use one measure as the outcome and one as the TVC. Not only would the choice of which measure would be the outcome and which the TVC be arbitrary (because we are equally interested in both), but the standard TVC model would be inappropriate given the systematic growth in both constructs (e.g., Curran & Bauer, 2011; Curran, Lee, et al., 2012).[8] We will thus use the multivariate techniques defined earlier to estimate a single bivariate model linking trust and integrity at the level of the trajectories while accounting for the nesting of cadet within squad (i.e., Equation 16.30).

The bivariate model was estimated consistent with Equation 16.30. Linear trajectories were estimated for both trust and integrity. Homoscedastic errors were estimated for both constructs at Level-1, and these residuals were allowed to covary within time, across construct (e.g., the residuals for trust and integrity covaried within Times 1, 2, 3, and 4, but they did not covary across time). Random intercepts and slopes were estimated at Level 2, and these were allowed to covary across construct (e.g., the intercepts and slopes for both trust and integrity freely covaried with one another). Finally, random intercepts were estimated at Level 3, and these two effects were allowed to covary across construct.

As expected, fixed effects and within-construct random effects estimates were similar to those obtained through the previous univariate growth models, and we do not report these again here. However, of primary interest in this model were the cross-construct correlations among the random effects. For cadets nested within squads (i.e., Level 2), the initial level of trust was significantly and positively correlated with the initial level of integrity ($r = .74$, $p < .001$); thus cadets reporting higher initial values on one construct tended to report higher initial values on the other. The slope of trust was significantly and positively correlated with the slope of integrity ($r = .78$; $p < .001$). This suggests that steeper increases in one construct were associated with steeper increases in the other construct, indicating that trust and integrity codevelop over time. Interestingly, there were nonsignificant covariances between the initial value of trust and change in integrity and between the initial value of integrity and change in trust. This indicates that the starting point on one construct did not inform the subsequent rate of change in the other construct. Finally, the covariance between the initial status of trust and the initial status of integrity was nonsignificant at the level of the squad (i.e., Level 3), indicating that squad-specific means of the initial values of trust and integrity were not systematically related.

Bivariate Three-Level Growth Model: Benevolence as a TIC

Given that both trust and integrity show significant cadet-to-cadet variability in initial status and rate of change, we next introduced benevolence as a Level-2 TIC to help explain this variability.[9] As we described, the substantive question is whether initial levels of perceived benevolence predict later changes in both trust and integrity. Table 16.5 presents the fixed effects from this conditional three-level bivariate growth model. Benevolence was significantly and positively predictive of initial levels of both trust and integrity. This finding indicates that higher values of

---

[8]It may seem equally arbitrary for us to then include the initial assessment of benevolence as a TIC and not consider systematic growth in this construct as well. However, our initial theoretical question relates to the initial status of benevolence on trajectories of trust and integrity, and this model would be logically extended to include the estimation of growth in all three constructs simultaneously in subsequent analysis.

[9]The unconditional models were both based on a sample of $N = 542$ cadets. However, only $n = 344$ cadets reported on benevolence at the initial time period. The conditional model is thus based on the subsample of $n = 344$. To examine the potential impact of this reduction in sample size, we reestimated the conditional model using multiple imputation methods with 10 imputed data sets so that all 542 cadets were retained. The results for the pooled imputed analysis were nearly identical to that of the restricted sample.

TABLE 16.5

Fixed-Effects Estimates for Three-Level Bivariate Growth Model of Trust and Integrity With Benevolence as a Level-2 Time-Invariant Covariate

Coefficient	Estimate	Standard error	t ratio	p value
Trust intercept	5.124	0.041	126.09	< .001
Trust slope	0.096	0.026	3.69	= .0002
Integrity intercept	5.660	0.037	151.42	< .001
Integrity slope	0.026	0.021	1.28	= .199
Benevolence → trust intercept	0.894	0.039	22.88	< .001
Benevolence → trust slope	−0.195	0.025	−7.81	< .001
Benevolence → integrity intercept	0.523	0.036	14.66	< .001
Benevolence → integrity slope	−0.090	0.020	−4.56	< .001

Note. The first four rows represent the conditional means of the intercept and slope for trust and integrity, respectively; the second four rows represent the regression of the intercept and slope of trust and integrity on the level-2 measure of benevolence.

perceived benevolence at the initial time period were systematically related to higher values of both perceived trust and integrity. Interestingly, benevolence was significantly and negatively predictive of changes in both trust and integrity over time. This indicates that higher values of perceived benevolence at the initial time period were systematically related to less steep increases in both trust and integrity over time. Although this may initially seem like a paradoxical finding because of the negative relation, we must graphically probe this cross-level interaction to better understand the nature of this relation.

Following the strategies described in Curran et al. (2006) and Preacher et al. (2006), we probed the interaction between benevolence and change over time in trust and integrity and calculated the model-implied trajectories at plus and minus one standard deviation around the mean. Figure 16.1 shows that trust is significantly increasing over time, but only for those cadets who reported lower levels of initial benevolence; for those reporting higher benevolence, trust remains stably high (or slightly decreasing) across all four time-points. Figure 16.2 shows a similar pattern for integrity such that lower values of initial benevolence are associated with steeper increases in integrity over time. However, the magnitude of the relation between benevolence and change in integrity is smaller than is the relation between benevolence and change in trust. Further research is needed to better understand the nature of these rather complex relations.

Summary

Pooling over our set of results, we can draw several initial conclusions about the relations between cadet ratings of trust, integrity, and benevolence both within and across time. First, both trust and integrity were characterized by positive linear trajectories spanning the academic year at West Point. Second, there was significant variability in both the intercepts and the slopes of these trajectories among cadets nested within squad. This suggests that, within squads, some cadets are reporting higher versus lower initial levels of trust and integrity, and some are reporting steeper versus less steep changes over time. Third, the initial levels of both trust and integrity vary across squad as well. This finding indicates that the mean squad-level initial reports of each of these constructs varies from squad to squad. Thus some squads are characterized by higher overall initial levels of trust and integrity, whereas some squads are not.

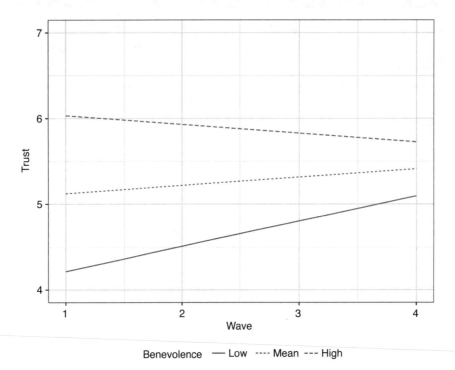

FIGURE 16.1. Model-implied trajectories of trust at high, medium, and low levels of perceived benevolence.

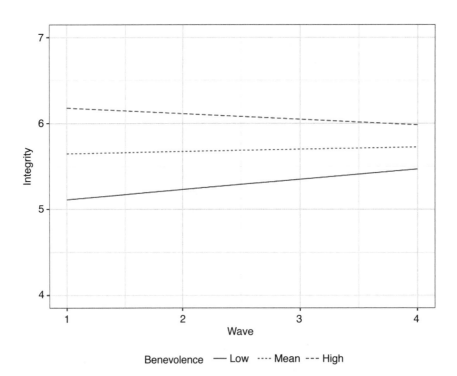

FIGURE 16.2. Model-implied trajectories of integrity at high, medium, and low levels of perceived benevolence.

Importantly, the bivariate model indicated that the trajectories of trust and integrity are systematically related to one another within and across time. In fact, the results showed strong correlations between both the initial levels and the rates of change over time between trust and integrity. This pattern of findings suggests that these two constructs "codevelop" (e.g., Curran & Hancock, 2021) across the span of the academic year. These across-construct relations could only be identified in the bivariate model in which change in each construct is estimated simultaneously. Interestingly, however, the initial level on one construct was not systematically related to the rate of change on the other. Finally, we considered benevolence as a Level-2 TIC and these results indicated significant relations between initial levels and rates of change for both trust and integrity. Probing of the cross-level interactions indicated that trust and integrity increased significantly more steeply for cadets who reported lower initial levels of perceived benevolence; for cadets reporting higher initial levels of benevolence, both trust and integrity remained high and stable, if not showing some slight decrease over time.

Again, we did not intend these analyses to be a rigorous test of our underlying theoretical model about the development of trust over time and the impact of this developmental process on later influence. Instead, we examined a specific sub-question relating to the unfolding of trust and integrity over time and the impact of initial benevolence on this process primarily to highlight the potential advantages and disadvantages of our proposed model. These models could be expanded in a variety of ways to better capture the complexities of the unfolding of these behaviors over time.

CONCLUSION

Our motivating substantive questions focused on the development of trust in cadets attending the USMA at West Point, and this analysis involved three levels of nesting: repeated measure nested within cadet, and cadet nested within squad. The multilevel growth-modeling framework was thus an ideal analytic method for testing our proposed hypotheses. Although prior work has proposed a multivariate–multilevel growth model for two levels of nesting, we are unaware of any prior attempts to extend this model to account for three levels of nesting. Explicating and demonstrating this three-level multivariate growth model has been our motivating goal here.

Although the equations necessary to define the multivariate three-level growth model are many, the underlying conceptual framework is as straightforward as it is elegant. We set out a principled approach to (a) design a model to examine individual variability in trajectories of trust and integrity within each cadet, (b) determine how these trajectories varied both within and between squads, (c) estimate the degree of correspondence between the two trajectories over time, and (d) test the extent to which benevolence influenced the parameters that defined the developmental trajectory within each cadet. Although a standard multilevel TVC model could be estimated to examine trust as the outcome and integrity as the TVC (or vice versa), whatever measure was defined as the TVC is assumed to not systematically vary with the passage of time. Yet there was clear evidence that both measures were increasing systematically over time, and thus arbitrarily treating one as the TVC would result in a misspecified model that did not evaluate the specific research hypotheses at hand.

More important, only the multivariate growth model allowed for the simultaneous estimation of growth in both trust and integrity, which in turn provides an explicit estimate of the covariance structure among the set of parameters that defines each of the trajectories. This analytic approach means that we can obtain estimates of the degree to which the initial levels of trust are related to changes in integrity, or the initial levels of integrity are related to changes in trust, or even the degree to which changes in trust are related to changes in integrity. The relation between changes in trust and changes in integrity was of primary substantive interest, and the multivariate growth model provides a means with which to directly and rigorously test our hypotheses.

The models we describe here could be extended in a number of interesting ways. We considered measures that were continuously and normally distributed, but these models can be estimated with such discrete outcomes as binary, ordinal, or count outcomes. We only considered simultaneous growth in two constructs, but this model could be extended to include three or even more outcomes (as was done by MacCallum et al., 1997, in the two-level framework). Although we used linear functions for both of our outcomes, these functional forms need not be the same; the functions can be mixes of linear, piecewise linear, or curvilinear trajectories over time. Finally, we only considered a single Level-2 time-invariant predictor; it is straightforward to include one or more predictors at any of the three levels of analysis as well as the inclusion of interactions within or across levels. Taken together, this approach offers a variety of significant strengths.

Despite these many strengths, there are of course associated limitations. First, although partially missing data can be included for each of the outcome measures, complete case data are required for the exogenous covariates (although multiple imputation methods can be used in some circumstances to address this problem; Enders, 2010). Second, as with the traditional fixed effects regression model, all measured variables are assumed to be error free; any measurement error that exists attenuates the estimated regression coefficients relative to their population values. Third, the examination of the two outcome measures at the level of the trajectories is strictly a between-person comparison. In other words, the model-implied relations between trust and integrity are evaluated at the level of the cadet-specific trajectories. Additional analytic work would be needed to simultaneously obtain both between-person (i.e., at the level of the trajectory) and within-person (i.e., at the level of specific time assessments) components of the relation between the two outcomes (for further discussion, see Curran & Bauer, 2011; Curran & Hancock, 2021; Curran et al., 2014; Curran, Lee, et al., 2012; Hamaker et al., 2015).

We have drawn on existing developments within the two-level multivariate–multilevel model and the three-level univariate–multilevel model to describe a general three-level growth model for two or more correlated outcomes. Because this model is embedded within the standard multilevel analytic framework, we can draw on all the strengths of this modeling tradition to provide a powerful and flexible method for testing a broad range of proposed hypotheses within the behavioral sciences. We have found these techniques to be highly applicable in our own work, and we hope that our discussion might be of some use to you in your own.

References

Allison, P. (2002). *Missing data* (Sage University Papers Series: Quantitative Applications in the Social Sciences, No. 07-136). SAGE.

Bauer, D. J. (2003). Estimating multilevel linear models as structural equation models. *Journal of Educational and Behavioral Statistics*, 28(2), 135–167. https://doi.org/10.3102/10769986028002135

Biesanz, J. C., Deeb-Sossa, N., Papadakis, A. A., Bollen, K. A., & Curran, P. J. (2004). The role of coding time in estimating and interpreting growth curve models. *Psychological Methods*, 9(1), 30–52. https://doi.org/10.1037/1082-989X.9.1.30

Bolger, N., Davis, A., & Rafaeli, E. (2003). Diary methods: Capturing life as it is lived. *Annual Review of Psychology*, 54(1), 579–616. https://doi.org/10.1146/annurev.psych.54.101601.145030

Bollen, K. A., & Curran, P. J. (2006). *Latent curve models: A structural equation approach*. Wiley.

Bryk, A. S., & Raudenbush, S. W. (1987). Application of hierarchical linear models to assessing change. *Psychological Bulletin*, 101(1), 147–158. https://doi.org/10.1037/0033-2909.101.1.147

Curran, P. J. (2003). Have multilevel models been structural equation models all along? *Multivariate Behavioral Research*, 38(4), 529–569. https://doi.org/10.1207/s15327906mbr3804_5

Curran, P. J., & Bauer, D. J. (2011). The disaggregation of within-person and between-person effects in longitudinal models of change. *Annual Review of Psychology*, 62(1), 583–619. https://doi.org/10.1146/annurev.psych.093008.100356

Curran, P. J., Bauer, D. J., & Willoughby, M. T. (2006). Testing and probing interactions in hierarchical linear growth models. In C. S. Bergeman & S. M. Boker (Eds.), *The Notre Dame Series on Quantitative Methodology: Vol. 1. Methodological issues in aging research* (pp. 99–129). Erlbaum.

Curran, P. J., & Hancock, G. R. (2021). The challenge of modeling co-developmental processes over time. *Child Development Perspectives*, *15*(2), 67–75. https://doi.org/10.1111/cdep.12401

Curran, P. J., Howard, A. L., Bainter, S. A., Lane, S. T., & McGinley, J. S. (2014). The separation of between-person and within-person components of individual change over time: A latent curve model with structured residuals. *Journal of Consulting and Clinical Psychology*, *82*(5), 879–894. https://doi.org/10.1037/a0035297

Curran, P. J., Lee, T. H., Howard, A. L., Lane, S. T., & MacCallum, R. C. (2012). Disaggregating within-person and between-person effects in multilevel and structural equation growth models. In J. Harring & G. Hancock (Eds.), *Advances in longitudinal methods in the social and behavioral sciences* (pp. 217–253). Information Age Publishing.

Curran, P. J., McGinley, J. S., Serrano, D., & Burfeind, C. (2012). A multivariate growth curve model for three-level data. In H. Cooper (Ed.), *APA Handbook of research methods in psychology* (Vol. 3, pp. 335–358). American Psychological Association. https://doi.org/10.1037/13621-017

Curran, P. J., Muthén, B. O., & Harford, T. C. (1998). The influence of changes in marital status on developmental trajectories of alcohol use in young adults. *Journal of Studies on Alcohol*, *59*(6), 647–658. https://doi.org/10.15288/jsa.1998.59.647

Curran, P. J., Stice, E., & Chassin, L. (1997). The relation between adolescent alcohol use and peer alcohol use: A longitudinal random coefficients model. *Journal of Consulting and Clinical Psychology*, *65*(1), 130–140. https://doi.org/10.1037/0022-006X.65.1.130

Dirks, K. T., Sweeney, P. J., Dimotakis, N., & Woodruff, T. (2021). Understanding the change and development of trust and the implications for new leaders. *Journal of Business Ethics*, 1–20. https://doi.org/10.1007/s10551-021-04902-4

Enders, C. K. (2010). *Applied missing data analysis*. Guilford Press.

Goldstein, H. (1995). *Multilevel statistical models* (2nd ed.). Halsted.

Goldstein, H., Rasbash, J., Yang, M., Woodhouse, G., Pan, H., Nuttall, D., & Thomas, S. (1993). A multilevel analysis of school examination results. *Oxford Review of Education*, *19*(4), 425–433. https://doi.org/10.1080/0305498930190401

Hamaker, E. L., Kuiper, R. M., & Grasman, R. P. (2015). A critique of the cross-lagged panel model. *Psychological Methods*, *20*(1), 102–116. https://doi.org/10.1037/a0038889

Hoffman, L. (2015). *Longitudinal analysis: Modeling within-person fluctuation and change*. Routledge. https://doi.org/10.4324/9781315744094

MacCallum, R. C., Kim, C., Malarkey, W. B., & Kiecolt-Glaser, J. K. (1997). Studying multivariate change using multilevel models and latent curve models. *Multivariate Behavioral Research*, *32*(3), 215–253. https://doi.org/10.1207/s15327906mbr3203_1

Mayer, R., & Davis, J. (1999). The effect of the performance appraisal system on trust for management: A field quasi-experiment. *Journal of Applied Psychology*, *84*(1), 123–136. https://doi.org/10.1037/0021-9010.84.1.123

McArdle, J. J. (1988). Dynamic but structural equation modeling of repeated measures data. In J. R. Nesselroade & R. B. Cattell (Eds.), *Handbook of multivariate experimental psychology* (2nd ed., pp. 561–614). Plenum Press. https://doi.org/10.1007/978-1-4613-0893-5_17

McArdle, J. J. (1989). Structural modeling experiments using multiple growth functions. In P. Ackerman, R. Kanfer, & R. Cudeck (Eds.), *Learning and individual differences: Abilities, motivation, and methodology* (pp. 71–117). Erlbaum.

McArdle, J. J. (2009). Latent variable modeling of differences and changes with longitudinal data. *Annual Review of Psychology*, *60*(1), 577–605. https://doi.org/10.1146/annurev.psych.60.110707.163612

McNeish, D., Stapleton, L. M., & Silverman, R. D. (2017). On the unnecessary ubiquity of hierarchical linear modeling. *Psychological Methods*, *22*(1), 114–140. https://doi.org/10.1037/met0000078

McNeish, D. M. (2016). Using data-dependent priors to mitigate small sample bias in latent growth models: A discussion and illustration using Mplus. *Journal of Educational and Behavioral Statistics*, *41*(1), 27–56. https://doi.org/10.3102/1076998615621299

Mehta, P. D., & Neale, M. C. (2005). People are variables too: Multilevel structural equations modeling. *Psychological Methods*, *10*(3), 259–284. https://doi.org/10.1037/1082-989X.10.3.259

Meredith, W., & Tisak, J. (1990). Latent curve analysis. *Psychometrika*, *55*(1), 107–122. https://doi.org/10.1007/BF02294746

Newsom, J. (2002). A multilevel structural equation model for dyadic data. *Structural Equation Modeling*, *9*(3), 431–447. https://doi.org/10.1207/S15328007SEM0903_7

Preacher, K. J., Curran, P. J., & Bauer, D. J. (2006). Computational tools for probing interactions in multiple linear regression, multilevel modeling, and latent curve analysis. *Journal of Educational and Behavioral Statistics*, *31*(4), 437–448. https://doi.org/10.3102/10769986031004437

Preacher, K. J., Zhang, Z., & Zyphur, M. J. (2016). Multilevel structural equation models for assessing moderation within and across levels of analysis. *Psychological Methods, 21*(2), 189–205. https://doi.org/10.1037/met0000052

Raudenbush, S. W. (2001). Comparing personal trajectories and drawing causal inferences from longitudinal data. *Annual Review of Psychology, 52*(1), 501–525. https://doi.org/10.1146/annurev.psych.52.1.501

Raudenbush, S. W., & Bryk, A. S. (2002). *Hierarchical linear models: Applications and data analysis methods* (2nd ed.). SAGE.

Singer, J., & Willett, J. (2003). *Applied longitudinal data analysis: Modeling change and event occurrence.* Oxford University Press. https://doi.org/10.1093/acprof:oso/9780195152968.001.0001

Sweeney, P. J. (2007). Trust: The key to combat leadership. In D. Crandall (Ed.), *Leadership lessons from West Point* (pp. 252–277). Jossey-Bass.

Sweeney, P. J., Thompson, V. D., & Blanton, H. (2009). Trust and influence in combat: An interdependence model. *Journal of Applied Social Psychology, 39*(1), 235–264. https://doi.org/10.1111/j.1559-1816.2008.00437.x

Willett, J., & Sayer, A. (1994). Using covariance structure analysis to detect correlates and predictors of individual change over time. *Psychological Bulletin, 116*(2), 363–381. https://doi.org/10.1037/0033-2909.116.2.363

SECTION 5

MULTIVARIATE METHODS

CHAPTER 17

EXPLORATORY FACTOR ANALYSIS AND CONFIRMATORY FACTOR ANALYSIS

Keith F. Widaman and Jonathan Lee Helm

COMMON FACTOR ANALYSIS AND ITS USES

Common factor analysis is arguably the most popular and useful method for identifying underlying dimensions that can account mathematically for behavior in a given domain. Applied first to test scores in the ability domain, Spearman (1904, 1927) proposed novel calculations that became known as factor analysis and used his results to argue for the existence of g, or general intelligence, the single dimension common to all tests of mental ability. Later, Thurstone (1931, 1935, 1938, 1947) generalized the common factor model to include multiple factors. Then, Thurstone and his colleagues (e.g., Thurstone, 1938; Thurstone & Thurstone, 1941) identified and replicated seven dimensions of mental ability known as Primary Mental Abilities. The most commonly accepted, current structure of the mental ability domain is often referred to as the Cattell-Horn-Carroll (or CHC) model, based on work by Cattell (1963, 1971), Horn (e.g., Horn & Hofer, 1992; Horn & Noll, 1997), and Carroll (1993). In the CHC model, three strata of factors are posited. At the lowest stratum, perhaps 30 or so primary abilities can be identified. At the second stratum, eight or nine dimensions have been replicated, including factors for fluid intelligence (Gf) and crystallized intelligence (Gc). At the third stratum, a single dimension has been posited—identified as general intelligence, or g—although some dispute whether this dimension can be justified theoretically (e.g., Horn & McArdle, 2007; Horn & Noll, 1997).

Factor analysis has also been applied to many other domains, notably personality. The most widely accepted taxonomy of personality factors is known as the Big Five, with the dimensions of Extraversion, Agreeableness, Conscientiousness, Neuroticism, and Openness to experience. One can trace the origins of the Big Five personality constructs to studies from the mid-1940s or even earlier (see Fiske, 1949; Thurstone, 1934), and a consistent stream of research studies from the late 1950s to the present have offered convincing evidence that the Big Five dimensions can be recovered in data from many sources (e.g., self-reports, observer reports, reports by family members or friends) across an impressive number of cultures (Goldberg, 1993).

Factor analysis has been of central importance in evaluating empirical evidence, adjudicating conflicting conjectures, and developing usable dimensional taxonomies for mental abilities, personality, and other domains. Due to its foundational importance in research, the goal of this chapter is to provide a general introduction

---

All data and analysis scripts for analyses reported in this chapter are available at https://osf.io/r2my8.
https://doi.org/10.1037/0000320-017
APA Handbook of Research Methods in Psychology, Second Edition: Vol. 3. Data Analysis and Research Publication, H. Cooper (Editor-in-Chief)
Copyright © 2023 by the American Psychological Association. All rights reserved.

to both exploratory factor analysis and confirmatory factor analysis, noting similarities and differences between the methods. Several empirical applications also will be provided to illustrate the use of these methods.

EXPLORATORY FACTOR ANALYSIS

Exploratory factor analysis (EFA) is a method for characterizing dimensions of individual difference in a domain of behavior without imposing an a priori structure. Indeed, Thurstone (1947) argued that factor analysis was of greatest use in initial explorations of a domain because a successful analysis would isolate the major dimensions of individual difference within the domain. Once the primary dimensions have been identified and replicated, later research can investigate the basis of individual differences on these dimensions.

Theoretical Orientation

Spearman (1904), Thurstone (1947), and others have long argued that scientific goals are furthered most by understanding varied phenomena in a domain in terms of a smaller number of dimensions that can account for the phenomena in an economical fashion. Economy of representation, however, was not the only or even the principal driving force. Instead, factor analysis was considered the optimal way to isolate the underlying behavioral processes that generate the myriad forms of behavior that reflect a particular domain of content.

Key Equations

The fundamental equation of EFA is a data model that specifies the relations of common factors (or latent variables) to the manifest variables (MVs) in an analysis. This model is a linear model for the MVs that represents MVs Y_j ($j = 1, \ldots, p$) as additive, linear functions of one or more underlying unobserved common factors or latent variables (LVs), or

$$Y_{ji} = \tau_j + \lambda_{j1}W_{1i} + \lambda_{j2}W_{2i} + \cdots + \lambda_{jr}W_{1i} + \theta_j U_{ji} \quad (17.1)$$

where Y_{ji} is the score of individual i ($i = 1, \ldots, N$) on MV j, τ_j is the intercept (or mean) of MV j, λ_{jk} is the loading of MV j on LV k ($k = 1, \ldots, r$), W_{ki} is the score of person i on LV k, θ_j is the loading of MV j on the jth unique factor, and U_{ji} is the score of person i on the jth unique factor.

The EFA model thus embodies the mathematical representation of p MVs as linear functions of r LVs (with $r < p$) and p unique factors. The r LVs are identified as common factors because they each have effects on two or more MVs. Variance in MV j that is explained by the set of LVs is termed the communality of variable j, which is typically represented as h_j^2.

In contrast, each of the p unique factors has an effect on a single MV, and each of the p MVs has its own unique factor. Variance of the unique factor for MV j is often represented as u_j^2. However, the unique variance for variable j can be conceived as the sum of two sources of variance: (a) specific variance, s_j^2, which is reliable variance in MV j that is linearly unrelated to the common factors; and (b) error variance, e_j^2, which is random measurement error.

Given the preceding partitioning, which presumes that unique factors are uncorrelated with common factors and assuming that variance of MV j is standardized to 1.0, communality of MV j is h_j^2, unique variance is u_j^2, and $h_j^2 + u_j^2 = 1$. But, reliable variance of MV j, or r_{jj}, can be represented as $r_{jj} = h_j^2 + s_j^2$. Thus, communality of MV j is a lower bound estimate of its reliability. Also, the EFA model can be seen as a generalization of the classical test theory decomposition of a MV into true and error components, a generalization that contains more than one true (i.e., common factor) score and a specific factor.

Equation 17.1 can be expressed in matrix form as

$$\mathbf{Y} = \boldsymbol{\tau} + \boldsymbol{\Lambda}\mathbf{W} + \boldsymbol{\Theta}\mathbf{U} \quad (17.2)$$

where $\mathbf{Y}$ is a ($p \times 1$) random vector (i.e., for a random observation or person), $\boldsymbol{\tau}$ is a ($p \times 1$) vector of intercepts, $\boldsymbol{\Lambda}$ is a ($p \times r$) matrix of loadings of the p MVs on the r common factors, $\mathbf{W}$ is an ($r \times 1$) random vector of common factor scores for the person, $\boldsymbol{\Theta}$ is a ($p \times p$) diagonal matrix of loadings of the p MVs on the p unique factors, and U is a $(p \times 1)$ random vector of unique factor scores. Assuming that common factor scores and unique factor scores have expected values of zero, that unique factors are uncorrelated with common factor scores, and unique factors are mutually uncorrelated and have variances of 1.0, one can postmultiply each side of Equation 17.2 by its transpose and take expectations, resulting in

$$E(Y) = \tau \qquad (17.3)$$

and

$$E(YY') = \Sigma_{YY} = \Lambda WW'\Lambda' + \Theta UU'\Theta'$$
$$= \Lambda\Psi\Lambda' + \Theta^2 \qquad (17.4)$$

where the means of MVs are in τ (Equation 17.3). Further, the covariance structure of the MVs is shown in Equation 17.4, where Σ_{YY} is the $(p \times p)$ population covariance matrix among MVs, Ψ is the expected value of WW', the $(r \times r)$ matrix of covariances among common LVs, Θ^2 is the $(p \times p)$ diagonal matrix of covariances among unique factors because the expected value of UU' is an identity matrix, and other symbols were defined above.

Obtaining a sample of observations and computing the sample matrix of covariances among MVs, S, enables one to express parameters in Equation 17.4 as

$$S \approx \hat{\Lambda}\hat{\Psi}\hat{\Lambda}' + \hat{\Theta}^2 = \hat{\Sigma} \qquad (17.5)$$

wherein carets above matrices indicate parameter estimates in these matrices, and all symbols were defined above. Equation 17.5 implies that the sample covariance matrix is approximated by the r-dimensional common factor solution, which in turn yields an estimate of the population covariances among MVs under the assumption that the model holds in the population.

EFA models are typically fit to matrices of correlations among MVs, rather than matrices of covariances. If D_s is a diagonal matrix of standard deviations of the MVs, then pre- and postmultiplying Equation 17.4 by the inverse of D_s yields

$$D_s^{-1}\Sigma_{YY}D_s^{-1} = D_s^{-1}(\Lambda\Psi\Lambda' + \Theta^2)D_s^{-1}$$
$$= D_s^{-1}(\Lambda\Psi\Lambda')D_s^{-1} + D_s^{-1}\Theta^2 D_s^{-1}, \text{ so}$$
$$P_{YY} = \Lambda^*\Psi\Lambda^{*\prime} + \Theta^{2*} \qquad (17.6)$$

where P_{YY} is the population correlation matrix among MVs, $\Lambda^*(= D_s^{-1}\Lambda)$ is the correlation-metric matrix of loadings of MVs on factors, $\Theta^{2*}(= D_s^{-1}\Theta^2 D_s^{-1})$ is the population correlation-metric matrix of unique variances, and other symbols were defined previously. Thus, in correlation metric, three matrices—the matrix of covariances among MVs, the factor loading matrix, and the unique factor covariance matrix—are simply rescaled versions of their counterparts in covariance metric, and the matrix of correlations (or covariances) among LVs is unchanged.

In a sample of observations, the sample matrix of correlations among MVs, R, can be represented analogously to Equation 17.5, specifically,

$$R \approx \hat{\Lambda}^*\hat{\Psi}\hat{\Lambda}^{*\prime} + \hat{\Theta}^{2*} = \hat{P} \qquad (17.7)$$

where all matrices contain parameter estimates, and all symbols were defined above. Equation 17.7 states that the sample correlation matrix R is approximated by the r-dimensional common factor solution $\hat{\Lambda}^*\hat{\Psi}\hat{\Lambda}^{*\prime} + \hat{\Theta}^{2*}$, which in turn yields an estimate of the population correlations among MVs, $\hat{P}$, under the assumption that the model holds in the population.

Steps in Exploratory Factor Analysis

Selection of observations. Selection of observations (e.g., participants) is an underemphasized aspect of EFA studies. Selection of observations involves at least two matters: (a) the selection mechanism, or how observations are selected from the population for inclusion in a study; and (b) the number of observations to be included in the analysis.

In factor analytic studies, treatments are typically not evaluated, so random assignment of persons to treatments is not an issue. Instead, selection of observations from a population is far more important. Differing recommendations have been made regarding selection of observations (i.e., persons). Some (e.g., Guilford, 1964) argued that samples of participants should be as homogeneous as possible; others (e.g., Gorsuch, 1988) opined that samples of participants should exhibit substantial variability. A middle ground position is that one should (a) define clearly the population from which observations were selected, (b) note whether observations were randomly and representatively sampled from the population or whether some form of nonrandom selection occurred (e.g., obtaining a sample of convenience), and (c) describe whether any participants either declined to participate or failed to complete the entire set of tests and were excluded from analyses, as this may lead to unrepresentativeness of the final sample.

The second aspect of selection of observations—determining the minimum number of observations for an analysis—has had a varied history. In early work (e.g., Spearman, 1904), little or no attention was paid to number of observations. Later, experts in factor analysis often recommended that researchers follow a particular rule, such as obtaining at least 5 times the number of observations as MVs. But, MacCallum and colleagues (1999, 2001) showed that simple rules of thumb for the number of observations could not be justified if the intent was to recover the population factor structure. Instead, recovery of population factors is a complex function of communality of variables, number of indicators per factor, and sample size. In truly exploratory studies, no hard and fast rules for the proper sample size given the number of MVs can generally be recommended. Instead, larger sample sizes are better, and replication of factor patterns across samples provides greater assurance that an accurate factor structure has been obtained.

Selection of manifest variables. Selection of MVs to be included in an EFA is a topic of more common discussion than selection of observations but deserves still greater attention (cf. Little et al., 1999). In a pioneering study, Thurstone (1938) attempted to assemble a battery of tests that would span the domain of mental abilities. This meant designing a set of tests with as many kinds of content and mental operation as possible. Thurstone was ambitious, but hindsight reveals that his large batteries of tests failed to include indicators for many factors that have subsequently been replicated. Still, as a general rule, careful consideration of the domain of content to be represented in the factor analysis should lead to attempts to ensure that all facets of the domain are reflected in the MVs to be analyzed.

Common factor analysis was developed for analyzing continuous MV scores as functions of continuous LV scores; test scores, which are sums of multiple item scores, often conform well to this approach. For over 75 years, however, researchers have factor-analyzed item scores, and several key issues arise in item factor analysis. One issue is domain coverage. Factor-analyzing an existing instrument can help a researcher revise a scale, perhaps discarding items that appear not to reflect the major factors in the instrument or reformulating the dimensional structure of the instrument (see Floyd & Widaman, 1995). Here, a researcher may not be able to select the MVs analyzed, as this selection is mandated by the aim of evaluating the factor structure of an existing instrument. Experience with an existing scale, however, may lead a researcher to conclude that important aspects of the behavioral domain have, inadvertently or deliberately, been excluded. In such cases, researchers can supplement an existing instrument with additional pertinent items to see whether this will result in a more adequate, theoretically compelling representation.

Other issues in item factor analysis are more mathematical or statistical because item scores are often not continuous but fall on binary ($0 = no$, $1 = yes$) or ordered-categorical (e.g., 1-to-5 *agree-disagree*) Likert scales. Artifactual "difficulty" factors can occur when analyzing binary data, a fact that has long been known (Guilford, 1941; Wherry & Gaylord, 1944). Problems arising in analyses of Likert scale data, however, have often not been recognized, where standard factor analyses of item data are conducted with impunity. Many contributions have been made regarding proper ways to analyze binary and ordered-categorical variables (e.g., Bock et al., 1988; McDonald & Ahlawat, 1974; Millsap & Yun-Tein, 2004; B. O. Muthén, 1978, 1984; Wirth & Edwards, 2007). Researchers should be forewarned that standard factor analytic methods may yield biased results when applied to item-level data, if items have fewer than five ordered categories. Items obtained on Likert scales with five or more categories appear to function much like continuous variables (for exceptions, see Rhemtulla et al., 2012). However, researchers should examine item distributions (e.g., via frequency tables or histograms) to ensure that all response options for each item are endorsed, lest, for example, a 5-category Likert-scaled item may become an item with four or fewer categories if some response options are not endorsed by anyone. Interested readers should consult the works cited above as well as the chapters by Grimm and Widaman and by Gottfredson et al. (see Volume 1, Chapters 35 and 36, this handbook) for additional discussion.

Estimation. Estimation of parameters of the EFA model involves, principally, estimation of loadings of MVs on LVs. This step in an analysis is often referred to as *extraction of factors*. Referring to Equation 17.7, the estimation step involves estimating loadings in $\hat{\Lambda}^*$, typically under the restriction that the matrix of correlations among factors, $\hat{\Psi}$, is an identity matrix. In an identity matrix, all off-diagonal values are zero, so extracted factors are orthogonal (or mutually uncorrelated). The first factor explains the maximal amount of covariation among MVs, the second factor the maximal amount of remaining covariation among MVs while being orthogonal to the first factor, the third factor the maximal amount of remaining covariation among MVs while being orthogonal to the first two factors, etc. After factors have been extracted and the number of factors has been determined (see below), factors can be rotated, and the orthogonality constraint on factors can be relaxed. Rotation, discussed below, involves the transformation or spatial reorientation of the LVs so the mathematical description of the MVs is simplified.

For many years, noniterative methods of estimation were used, including, among others, centroid estimation and principal axes (PA) extraction (Harman, 1976; Thurstone, 1947). The PA method yields a least squares fit of the factor model to the sample correlation matrix, so it is preferred over the centroid method, a hand-computational approximation to the PA. To extract the PA, one must estimate communality for each MV. Communality is the complement of unique variance (i.e., $h_j^2 = 1 - u_j^2$), so one subtracts a diagonal matrix of estimated uniquenesses from each side of Equation 17.7, giving $\mathbf{R} - \hat{\mathbf{\Theta}}^{2*} \approx \hat{\Lambda}^* \hat{\Psi} \hat{\Lambda}^{*\prime}$. The matrix on the left of this equation, $\mathbf{R} - \hat{\mathbf{\Theta}}^{2*}$, is the reduced correlation matrix, as diagonal values of unity in $\mathbf{R}$ are reduced by estimates of unique variance. $\mathbf{R} - \hat{\mathbf{\Theta}}^{2*}$, therefore, has communality estimates on its diagonal.

Several methods of communality estimation have been proposed. One of the most commonly used is the squared multiple correlation (SMC) of MV j with the remaining $(p - 1)$ MVs as predictors. Guttman (1956) proved that the SMC is a lower bound estimate of communality, and this theoretical property has been the primary basis for the use of the SMC as communality estimate. The highest correlation in the row (MAXR), however, was often used by Thurstone as a communality estimate, and the MAXR appears often to provide a more accurate estimate of communality than does the SMC, which tends to have a negative bias. Widaman (1993) illustrated the negative bias in factor loadings and positive bias in factor correlations that result from use of SMCs that are underestimates of communality. The choice here, therefore, is between an estimator of communality (SMC) that has strong theoretical rationale, but is often negatively biased, versus an estimator (MAXR) that has a more informal rationale but is often a more accurate estimator of communality; given this choice, we recommend the MAXR.

Once communalities are estimated, factor loadings can be estimated from the reduced correlation matrix $\mathbf{R} - \hat{\mathbf{\Theta}}^{2*}$. The PA solution is an eigenvector-eigenvalue decomposition of $\mathbf{R} - \hat{\mathbf{\Theta}}^{2*}$.

An eigenvector is a unit-length vector defining a direction in multidimensional space, and its associated eigenvalue represents variance on that dimension. $\mathbf{R} - \hat{\mathbf{\Theta}}^{2*}$ is approximated by the eigensolution $\mathbf{VD}_l\mathbf{V}'$, where $\mathbf{V}$ contains the first r eigenvectors of $\mathbf{R} - \hat{\mathbf{\Theta}}^{2*}$, and $\mathbf{D}_l$ is a diagonal matrix containing the r largest eigenvalues. If we define $\hat{\mathbf{\Lambda}}^* = \mathbf{VD}_l^{1/2}$, $\mathbf{R} - \hat{\mathbf{\Theta}}^{2*} \approx \hat{\mathbf{\Lambda}}^*\hat{\mathbf{\Lambda}}^{*\prime}$. This method is labeled *PA extraction of factors using prior communality estimates*. Once a set of factors has been estimated, the researcher must decide on the number of factors (see below). The PA solution obtained in this fashion yields a least squares fit to the correlation matrix conditional on the communality estimates used. Different methods of communality estimation will result in different estimated factor loadings, although these differences typically are rather small.

With the advent of efficient computer algorithms over the past 4 decades or more, iterative methods of estimation have become more popular. Iterative methods employ a loss (or discrepancy) function. For example, the unweighted least squares (ULS) discrepancy function is

$$F_{ULS} = \sum_j \sum_{k \leq j} (r_{jk} - \hat{\rho}_{jk})^2 \quad (17.8)$$

where r_{jk} is the observed correlation between MVs j and k, and $\hat{\rho}_{jk}$ is the reproduced correlation between MVs j and k. One first selects a number of factors to retain, and ULS estimation then minimizes F_{ULS}, providing a least squares fit of an r-dimensional model to the data. ULS simultaneously estimates parameters in the factor and unique variance matrices to minimize the discrepancy between observed and reproduced correlations among MVs. Indirectly, ULS iteratively estimates communality to obtain its optimal least-squares fit to the observed correlations. ULS provides fit that is either comparable to or better than the fit of PA estimation using prior communality estimates because the latter method is conditional on the communality estimates employed. If the correlation matrix is well conditioned, widely varying initial communality estimates—from unities to zero—have been found to converge to the same final solution if a stringent iterative ULS stopping criterion is used (Widaman & Herringer, 1985).

Another commonly used iterative estimation method is the method of maximum likelihood (ML). As with ULS, ML estimation requires selection of r, the number of common factors, to enable estimation to proceed. Under ML, estimates of factor loadings and unique variances are obtained that maximize the likelihood of the observed data. ML estimation is based on the ML discrepancy function, which can be written as

$$F_{ML} = \ln|\mathbf{\Sigma}| - \ln|\mathbf{S}| + tr(S\mathbf{\Sigma}^{-1}) - p \quad (17.9)$$

where ln | | represents the natural log of the determinant of a matrix, the tr operator obtains the sum of the diagonal elements of a matrix, and all other symbols have been previously defined. In an empirical application, the sample estimate of the population covariance matrix is substituted in Equation 17.9, yielding a sample ML discrepancy function of

$$\hat{F}_{ML} = \ln|\hat{\mathbf{\Sigma}}| - \ln|\mathbf{S}| + tr(S\hat{\mathbf{\Sigma}}^{-1}) - p \quad (17.10)$$

in which symbols were previously defined.

If an ML solution with r factors reproduces the sample covariances (or correlations) among MVs well, $\hat{\mathbf{\Sigma}}$ will approximate $\mathbf{S}$, and the ML discrepancy function will tend toward zero. The ML discrepancy function is bounded below by zero and will attain a value of zero only when $\hat{\mathbf{\Sigma}} = \mathbf{S}$. Thus, larger values of the ML discrepancy function indicate poorer fit of the factor model to the data. Jöreskog (1967) presented efficient algorithms for ML estimation of factor models, and ML estimation is widely available in EFA packages.

The major difference among the preceding methods of estimation is a choice between conditioning on particular communality estimates versus conditioning on the number of LVs. The (noniterative) PA solution yields a least squares fit of an EFA model to data conditional on the prior estimates of communality used in the analysis. Conversely, iterative methods of estimation such as ULS and ML provide optimal fit of an EFA model to data that are conditional on the choice of a given number of LVs. Because neither communality nor the correct number of LVs is known with certainty, particularly when first investigating a domain, the optimal choice for estimating parameters in EFA is unclear. We recommend that investigators try multiple methods of estimation to determine whether the choice makes a difference. Evidence has accumulated that ML estimation can "miss" small but replicable factors that PA and ULS successfully identify (e.g., MacCallum & Tucker, 1991), and one cannot be sure that all factors in a domain are equally and fully represented when first investigating a domain. PA and ULS estimation are, therefore, likely to be preferred to ML estimation in fully exploratory studies.

Other methods of estimation are available, including generalized least squares (GLS), alpha factor analysis, and canonical factor analysis (Harman, 1976; Mulaik, 2010). However, noniterative PA, ULS, and ML estimation are by far the most commonly used methods of estimation, and practicing scientists would have little need to move beyond these three methods.

Number of factors. Selection of the number of factors to retain is one of the most important steps in an EFA. Retaining an improper number of factors will have practical impacts, such as affecting factor loadings and correlations among rotated factors and may have important negative effects on theory, if the analysis is used to support arguments about the structure of a domain. The goal of the analyst, therefore, is to identify the optimal number of factors in a given analysis. Three general methods have been proposed for selecting the number of factors to retain: mathematical rules, statistical tests, and rules of thumb.

The first category subsumes *mathematical rules* and is aligned most prominently with three lower bounds discussed by Guttman (1954). The weakest lower bound, currently the default test for number of factors in most computer programs, corresponds to the number of factors with eigenvalues greater than 1.0 with unities on the diagonal. The middle lower bound is the number of factors with eigenvalues greater than 0.0 with the square of the MAXR on the diagonal. The strongest lower bound is the number of factors with eigenvalues greater than 0.0 with SMCs on the diagonal. In his derivations, Guttman assumed the presence of population data and the r-dimensional solution fit the data perfectly in the population. Neither of these assumptions is likely to be even approximately true in any empirical application, reducing the utility of Guttman's bounds. Cliff (1988) provided a trenchant critique of the weakest lower bound, along with demonstration of a failure to identify the correct number of factors. In Monte Carlo evaluations, none of the Guttman bounds has performed well, with the weakest lower bound at times underestimating and at times overestimating the correct number of factors and the strongest lower bound seriously overestimating the number of factors (e.g., Hakstian et al., 1982; Tucker et al., 1969; Zwick & Velicer, 1982, 1986).

A second mathematical rule for determining the number of factors is the minimum average partial (MAP) correlation procedure (Velicer, 1976). Velicer (1976) argued that, as one extracted principal components that account for common variance, the average partial correlation among MVs will decrease until the correct number of factors is reached, after which point the average partial correlation will increase. The optimal number of factors to retain is the solution with the smallest average partial correlation. The MAP test has performed well as an indicator of the number of factors in a number of Monte Carlo studies (e.g., Zwick & Velicer, 1986).

The second general approach to determining the number of factors comprises *statistical tests*. The most commonly used statistical test is the likelihood ratio (LR) test statistic under ML estimation. The LR test statistic is, essentially, a test of misfit of an r-dimensional factor solution to the matrix of covariances among MVs. A significant test statistic, therefore, implies that the r-dimensional solution should be rejected in favor of an alternative with at least $r+1$ factors. The LR test is based on misfit of the factor model and sample size (N). Specifically, $(N-1)\hat{F}_{ML}$ is approximately distributed as a chi-squared variate with degrees of freedom equal to $p(p+1)/2 - k$, where p is the number of MVs and k is the number of parameter estimates in the r-factor model. Because r^2 constraints are required to identify an r-factor EFA model, the degrees of freedom for the test statistic are calculated as $((p-r)^2 - (p+r))/2$. A significant test statistic implies rejection of the hypothesis that an r-factor solution fits the data perfectly due to significant levels of residual covariation unexplained by the model. Of course, holding the ML fit function value constant, the ML test statistic is a direct function of sample size, so trivial levels of model misfit are increasingly likely to lead to rejection of a reasonable model as sample size increases. Statistical tests for the number of factors are available under other methods of estimation (Browne, 1984), but these other methods of estimation are rarely used in EFA.

The third category of tests for the number of factors comprises *rules of thumb*. One of the most commonly used rules of thumb is the scree test (Cattell, 1966). *Scree* is a geological term referring to rock fragments, gravel, and silt that accumulate at the base of steep mountains due to erosion. Cattell adopted the name *scree* to describe a common pattern observed when plotting the eigenvalues for factors in the order in which they are extracted. Unrotated factors are in a conditionally variance maximized orientation, such that each factor explains the greatest amount of remaining variance conditional on factors that have already been extracted. Thus, if one plots eigenvalues of factors in the order in which they were extracted, the first factor will explain the most variance, and succeeding factors will explain less and less variance. Using the scree test, one looks for an elbow in the eigenvalue curve to retain the r common factors (or "mountains") and discard the $(p-r)$ remaining dimensions (or "scree"). The $(p-r)$ factors in the scree section of the plot, thus, represent fragmentary factors that explain too little variance to be useful.

A second rule of thumb, parallel analysis, is based on the premise that factors extracted from real data should explain more variance than factors extracted from random data. This idea was first proposed by Horn (1965) for use with principal component analysis (PCA), a method to be discussed below. Horn plotted PCA eigenvalues from real data on the same plot as corresponding PCA eigenvalues from a random data matrix with the same number of observations and MVs. He argued that one should not retain a dimension from real data that explained less than the corresponding dimension from random data. Humphreys and colleagues rapidly generalized this method to EFA and identified the method as parallel analysis (Humphreys & Ilgen, 1969), demonstrated its utility in classic data (Humphreys & Montanelli, 1975), and provided regression weights for predicting random data eigenvalues that had been obtained using PA extraction with SMCs as communality estimates (Montanelli & Humphreys, 1976). A researcher can, therefore, extract factors from real data using PA extraction with SMCs as communality estimates, use the Montanelli and Humphreys equations to obtain estimated random data eigenvalues, and plot the two sets of eigenvalues in a single plot to ensure that no factor from real data explains less variance than the corresponding factor from random data. Many computer programs now allow a researcher to ask for a parallel analysis with random data eigenvalues estimated anew, generating these from rapid simulation of random data. In this connection, the "devil is in the details," and computer program details are often rather opaque. Users should ensure that the same method of extraction is used in both real and random data to ensure comparability of eigenvalues. Further, many have argued that an eigenvalue from real data should exceed the 95th percentile of the distribution of random data eigenvalues for the corresponding dimension, rather than the mean of this distribution; details on such issues are beyond the scope of this chapter. We note that many publications during the past 30 years have investigated parallel analysis in the PCA context. Because PCA is not an EFA procedure (see below), however, we stress here only the use of parallel analysis in an EFA context.

A third rule of thumb for the number of factors was proposed by Tucker and Lewis (1973). To counter the tendency of the ML statistical test to suggest rejection of reasonable EFA models in the presence of trivial misfit if sample size is large, Tucker and Lewis developed a reliability coefficient for ML factor analysis. The Tucker-Lewis index (TLI) is computed as

$$\text{TLI} = \frac{\frac{\chi_0^2}{df_0} - \frac{\chi_s^2}{df_s}}{\frac{\chi_0^2}{df_0} - 1} \quad (17.11)$$

where χ_0^2 and χ_s^2 represent the ML test statistic for a null (or 0-factor) model and a substantive model s, respectively, and df_0 and df_s are the degrees of freedom for the test statistics for the two models, respectively. When analyzing a number of classic data sets, Tucker and Lewis found that the ML test statistic often supported rejecting a model with the commonly accepted number of factors in favor of a model with additional factors, whereas their reliability coefficient attained a value around .95 or higher for the presumably correct number of factors. Tucker and Lewis then argued that a TLI value of .95 or above be used to indicate that an EFA model provided close fit to data, even if the ML test statistic implied the model was rejectable statistically. Bentler and Bonett (1980) argued for a more lenient criterion of .90 or above, but more recent research (e.g., Hu & Bentler, 1999) has restored .95 as a reasonable TLI value to attain to index close fit to data.

A fourth useful rule of thumb is based on the root mean square error of approximation (RMSEA), first proposed by Steiger and Lind (1980). The RMSEA was formulated to reflect misfit of a model in the population. Any EFA model will fail to fit a correlation or covariance matrix for at least two reasons: sampling variability and misfit in the population. Sampling variability is a readily acknowledged source of model misfit. A model that fits perfectly in the population, therefore, will have some misfit in any sample due to sampling variability, so the correct EFA model will not have a $\hat{F}_{ML} = 0$. Because the expected value of the ML test statistic for the correct model for a set of data is equal to the df for the model, or $E((N-1)\hat{F}_{ML}) = df$, the expected value of the ML fit function is $(df/(N-1))$ for the correct model. All structural models, however, including EFA models, are only approximations to reality (cf. MacCallum et al., 2007) due to many replicable sources of variance (e.g., nonlinearity of relations between LVs and MVs, presence of minor factors). Because these perturbing influences represent misfit in the population, the expected value of the ML fit function for any empirical model is likely to deviate above $(df/(N-1))$. The point estimate of the RMSEA, $\hat{\varepsilon}$, is calculated as

$$\hat{\varepsilon} = \sqrt{\frac{\max\{[\hat{F}_{ML} - (df/(N-1))], 0\}}{df}} \quad (17.12)$$

(all symbols were previously defined). Browne and Cudeck (1993) stated that broad experience with the RMSEA indicated that values of .05 or less indicated close fit of a model to data, .05 to .08 indicated adequate fit, .08 to .10 indexed poor fit, and over .10 indexed unacceptable fit.

One useful adjunct in using the RMSEA is that the sampling variability of $\hat{\varepsilon}$ is available, so an interval estimate of $\hat{\varepsilon}$ can be calculated. If the lower limit of the 90% confidence interval (CI) of the RMSEA includes .05, close fit of an EFA model to the data cannot be rejected at $\alpha = .05$. Further, if the lower limit of the 90% CI includes zero, perfect model fit cannot be rejected.

Monte Carlo simulation studies and analyses of classic EFA data sets have supported the use of the scree and parallel analysis criteria as indicators of the correct number of factors (e.g., Zwick & Velicer, 1982, 1986). Less work has been performed on the TLI and RMSEA as "tests" for the number of factors, although the use of these indicators to assess close fit of an EFA model to data is appropriate. No single procedure for determining the number of factors to retain is always correct, and data examples can be constructed that will make a given test fail to function properly. As a result, the best advice is to use several methods of determining the number of factors, using the results of these tests along with interpretability of the resulting factors as the best way to arrive at an acceptable solution.

Rotation of factors. Once the number of factors is determined, factors typically must be rotated to an interpretable orientation. As noted earlier, factors are initially extracted to meet a mathematical criterion of maximal variance explanation, but this is an arbitrary, if mathematical criterion. Once extracted, factors can be rotated freely to an infinite number of alternative solutions in r-dimensional space and still provide an equally good mathematical description of the correlation matrix. Rotation involves the transformation or reorientation of the factors so the factors fall closer to clusters of vectors representing MVs, thereby simplifying the mathematical description of MVs. The mathematical criterion used to extract factors need not result in a scientifically meaningful representation of the data. For example, if the complexity of a MV is the number of LVs on which it loads at a nonzero level, most MVs have complexity r in the unrotated solution, with nonzero loadings on all factors. This solution fails to conform to the theoretical orientation of Thurstone (1947) regarding scientific use of factor analysis—that any behavioral phenomenon should, in general, be explained in terms of a small number of factors.

A second and equally important problem with an unrotated factor solution is the lack of invariance in this solution. If MVs are deleted from or added to an analysis, the loadings of MVs on unrotated factors will change, sometimes substantially. Thurstone argued, however, that any acceptable method of factor analysis should leave the factorial description of a MV unchanged if the MV were moved from one battery to another that reflected the same LVs. Thus, to be an acceptable factor solution, the factorial description of a given MV must be invariant, rather than varying haphazardly as occurs in the matrix of extracted, or unrotated, factors.

Five criteria for simple structure were provided succinctly by Thurstone (1947). Among these criteria were that (a) each row of the factor matrix should have at least one zero, so the complexity of each MV should be no more than $(r-1)$, and (b) each column of the factor matrix should have at least r zeroes. The zero loadings that Thurstone sought to achieve on a factor fall in the so-called hyperplane for the factor, where the hyperplane is an $(r-1)$ dimensional space orthogonal to the influence of the given factor. Loadings within the $\pm.10$ (or $\pm.20$) range are often described as *falling in the hyperplane*, and these are usually treated as if they were essentially zero. The criteria for simple structure outlined the appearance a factor matrix should have an appearance that was simpler to characterize than was the pattern exhibited by the unrotated factor solution.

The nature of a simple structure solution should be appropriate for the data and the behavioral domain. Many researchers seem to think that all variables must have complexity 1—exhibiting a nonzero loading on only one of the r factors—for simple structure to be attained. This is incorrect. Indeed, Thurstone (1947) presented a number of alternative simple structure patterns that had variables with complexity 2 or more, and his famous box problem (Thurstone, 1947, pp. 369–376) had at least two variables with nonzero loadings on all factors. The guiding principle underlying simple structure is that each MV should be as simple as possible in factorial description, given the behavioral phenomena under study.

Factor rotations can be either orthogonal or oblique. Orthogonal rotations involve rigid transformation of the factorial dimensions, retaining the 90-degree separation among all factors. Under orthogonal rotation, the matrix of correlations among rotated factors remains an identity matrix, with factor variances of unity and zero correlations among factors. With orthogonal rotation, the factor matrix is simplified as much as possible under the constraint that the correlations among factors remain maximally simple (i.e., uncorrelated). The alternative to orthogonal rotation is oblique rotations, discussed first by Tucker (1940). Under oblique rotation, the orthogonality constraint among factors is relaxed, so factors are allowed to correlate. The added complexity of allowing factors to correlate is, however, often justified by a much simpler matrix of factor loadings. In the ability domain, all MVs tend to be positively correlated. Orthogonal rotation often leads to loadings by the MVs that define a factor in the .5 to .8 range, but remaining loadings on a factor frequently fall outside the ±.10 hyperplane, often falling between .20 and .30. Although these loadings are too small for interpretation, they are not zero. Under oblique rotation, researchers can often obtain a rotated solution with the majority of nondefining loadings within the ±.10 or ±.15 hyperplane, loadings that are much closer to zero, although this simplicity is bought at the price of factors that correlate.

For many years, rotation of factors was done by hand, using methods of plotting points and time-consuming matrix multiplication to reorient the factors. With the availability of computers in the early 1950s, researchers developed mathematical criteria to embody Thurstone's criteria for simple structure, and algorithmic rotation via computer program is called analytic rotation. The most widely used orthogonal analytic rotation is varimax (Kaiser, 1958), a rotational criterion to maximize the variance of loadings simultaneously within rows and within columns of the factor loading matrix. Crawford and Ferguson (1970) showed that the varimax rotation was a member of the orthomax family of rotations, a family of rotations that could be generated by varying a multiplier that varied the effect of simplicity of each factor on the rotational criterion. A multiplier of zero resulted in the quartimax criterion, which considered only row simplicity; a multiplier of unity led to the varimax criterion; a multiplier of 2 resulted in the equamax criterion, which gave more weight to column simplicity than did varimax, etc.

Oblique analytic rotations were also heavily under development, and many researchers compared results of different rotations. In a set of major comparisons, Hakstian (1971) and Hakstian and Abell (1974) concluded that the Harris-Kaiser orthoblique (Harris & Kaiser, 1964) and promax (Hendrickson & White, 1964) rotations led to rotated solutions that more closely approximated the "accepted" solutions for classic factor analysis data sets than did other rotations. In recent years, additional methods of oblique analytic rotation have been developed (see Browne, 2001, for a review). These newer rotational criteria are not available in the major statistical packages but can be used in the Comprehensive Exploratory Factor Analysis (CEFA) program (Browne et al., 2010) and in some other packages (e.g., some are available in Mplus, Muthén & Muthén, 1998–2017).

Researchers use results of rotated factor solutions in a number of ways. They might use a rotated solution simply to identify the several subsets of variables that load highly on different factors. If used in this fashion, precise and clean simple structure may not be the object of the analysis, and the rather crude result of an orthogonal rotation may be sufficient. However, if a researcher wished to use EFA with the goal of revising an instrument and ultimately engaging in confirmatory factor analysis or structural equation modeling using the revised scale or battery, oblique rotation of factors is the only meaningful approach to rotation that should be used.

Interpretation. Following rotation of factors, each factor must be interpreted. In early applications of factor analysis (e.g., Thurstone, 1938), researchers often extracted and rotated more factors than were finally interpreted, leaving uninterpreted factors in a limbo state with unknown utility or importance. This was an accepted practice at a time when extraction and rotation of factors was time-consuming and laborious, sometimes taking months to complete. Today, extraction and rotation of factors are done with tremendous speed, and inclusion of extra, uninterpreted factors is rarely accepted. Rotation of the correct number of factors is the ideal, although this is a problematic goal in EFA given the exploratory nature of the analysis. A researcher, therefore, might inadvertently underextract factors (i.e., extract too few factors) or overextract factors (i.e., extract too many factors). Research on under- and overextraction of factors indicates that underextraction does more harm to rotated solutions than does overextraction (e.g., Wood et al., 1996). Thus, if one were to err, erring on the side of too many factors will likely affect the factor solution negatively less than will extracting too few factors.

Interpretation of factors usually proceeds by considering what aspect the MVs that load highly on a factor have in common. If all variables that load highly on a factor involve giving speedy, correct answers to simple numeric problems (e.g., addition, subtraction), the factor could be identified as *Numerical Facility*. This approach to interpretation involves primarily the pattern of loadings separately in each column of the factor matrix. Just as important as attention to high loadings in a column, however, interpretation can at times be facilitated by considering the factors that have approximately zero loadings for a given MV. Factor loadings are regression weights for predicting MVs from LVs, and an essentially zero, hyperplanar loading for a MV on a given LV implies that the LV has no effect on the MV if other LVs are held constant. Attention to these facets of loading matrix may afford unique opportunity to interpret factors.

Factor scores. As shown in Equation 17.1, the factor model represents MVs as weighted linear combinations of LV scores. The LV score matrix contains important information—the implied score for each individual on each LV. Because factors are true score variables, LV scores represent the true score for each person on each LV. Unfortunately, factor scores are not uniquely determined under EFA. Several methods for estimating factor scores have been proposed over the years, such as regression estimates and least squares estimates (see Harman, 1976; Tucker, 1971).

Different methods of factor score estimation, however, lead to different factor score estimates, a problem that has been identified as *factor score indeterminacy*.

The indeterminacy of factor scores was identified initially in the 1920s, but interest in the problem faded during the 1930s and 1940s as many of the key developments of multiple factor analysis were pursued. The 1970s, however, saw a rebirth of interest in factor score indeterminacy, leading to major controversy. The two sides in the controversy were aligned as follows: The pro-EFA position was that the EFA model was the preferred model, that indeterminacy of factor scores was a problem to be accommodated, and that the problem was minimized in well-researched domains in which a large number of MVs with high loadings could be relied upon to identify each LV. The contra-EFA position was that PCA (see below) was essentially the same as EFA, that PCA did not suffer from factor score indeterminacy because component scores could be computed directly, and that the conditions cited for lack of concern about factor scores—many MVs loading highly on factors—were rarely, if ever, met.

Interest in factor score indeterminacy has once again waned, but good historical accounts are available (e.g., Steiger, 1979, 1994). One reason for the decline of interest is the rise of confirmatory factor analysis and structural equation modeling, which allow a researcher to investigate relations among factors without having to estimate factor scores. A second reason may be touting of robust estimates of factor scores. Precise estimates of factor scores appear to work well in the sample on which the analysis was performed, but the matrices of factor scoring weights appear not to cross-validate well in new samples. Robust factor weighting schemes—such as summing up standard scores on MVs that load highly on a factor—work almost as well as precise factor score weights in the derivation sample but seem to cross-validate much better in new samples. Still, the last word on the matter of factor score indeterminacy has not been written, and continued interest in the problem will probably remain for some time.

An Empirical Example

To illustrate the methods of EFA discussed previously, an empirical example is helpful.

In 1961, Bechtoldt investigated whether the factor structure of a set of tests could be replicated across two random subsamples from a population. To do so, he used 17 of the 21 variables from the cross-validation sample ($N = 437$) in Thurstone and Thurstone (1941), discarding four variables that did not meet psychometric criteria for quality. Bechtoldt randomly divided the sample of participants into two subsamples, with Sample 1 consisting of 212 participants and Sample 2 of 213 participants. Correlations among a selected set of 12 tests from Bechtoldt (1961) are shown in Table 17.1, along with the means and standard deviations of variables, for each sample. Correlations among MVs in Sample 1 are shown below the diagonal of Table 17.1, and those for Sample 2 are shown above the diagonal.

Selection of observations from the population and selection of MVs were beyond control in the current application. However, a reading of Thurstone and Thurstone (1941) leads one to infer that the sample was reasonably representative of school children in Chicago. The 12 MVs consisted of revised and improved versions of tests that had been used before by Thurstone and his colleagues, so were probably an optimal selection. The 12 MVs consisted of (a) three tests for a Verbal Comprehension (V) factor—Sentences, Vocabulary, and Completion—that require participants to extract meaning from text; (b) three tests for a Word Fluency (W) factor—First Letters, Four Letter Words, and Suffixes—that reflect fast access to, or quick retrieval from, long-term memory of words with particular structural features (e.g., words beginning with "st"), regardless of the meaning of the words; (c) three tests for a Reasoning (R) factor—Letter Series, Pedigrees, and Letter Grouping—that require participants to infer the rule relating elements in a problem and then provide the required next element or relation; and (d) three tests for a Spatial (S) factor—Flags, Figures, and Cards—that index speed in two-dimensional rotation and verification of figural stimuli. More detail can be found in Thurstone and Thurstone (1941).

Several tests for the number of factors were applied to the data from Sample 1, with results shown in Table 17.2. The first data column of Table 17.2 shows eigenvalues from PA extraction with unities on the diagonal, and three dimensions had eigenvalues over 1.0. The second data column lists eigenvalues from PA extraction with SMCs on the diagonal, and five dimensions had positive eigenvalues. Guttman's weakest lower bound, therefore, implies the presence of three dimensions, whereas the strongest lower bound implies five dimensions.

Eigenvalues from PA extraction with SMCs on the diagonal and estimated random data eigenvalues computed using the Montanelli and Humphreys (1976) equations, in the second and third data columns of Table 17.2, respectively, were plotted in Figure 17.1. As shown in Figure 17.1, four factors had relatively large eigenvalues, and the eigenvalues for the fifth and succeeding factors were very small. Moreover, the first four factors from real data had eigenvalues greater than those for the corresponding factors from random data, whereas the fifth and sixth random data factors had larger eigenvalues than corresponding factors for real data. The scree and parallel analysis criteria, thus, imply the presence of four factors. Furthermore, the values from the MAP criterion, shown in the fourth data column of Table 17.2, agree with the scree and parallel analysis criteria, as the average partial correlation was lowest for the four-factor solution.

The final three indicators of the number of factors were associated with ML estimation. As shown in Table 17.2, factor solutions with 1, 2, or 3 factors had significant test statistics, implying rejection of these solutions. The solution with 4 common factors, however, was not rejectable. In addition, the TLI and RMSEA were both in unacceptable ranges for solutions with 1, 2, or 3 common factors. Both, however, had very acceptable values for the four-factor solution. In summary, most indicators for the number of factors converged on four factors as the optimal solution, and only the indicators based on Guttman's bounds failed to agree on this decision.

TABLE 17.1
Correlations Among 12 Manifest Variables (MVs), With Means and SDs, in Two Samples, From Bechtoldt (1961)

Variable	ID[a]	Sen	Voc	Com	FLet	FLW	Suff	LSer	Ped.	LGrp	Flag	Fig.	Card
Sentences	Sen		.828	.776	.439	.432	.447	.447	.541	.380	.117	.051	.151
Vocabulary	Voc	.833		.779	.493	.464	.489	.432	.537	.358	.121	.077	.146
Completion	Com	.761	.772		.460	.425	.443	.401	.534	.359	.193	.180	.174
First Letters	FLet	.402	.446	.394		.674	.590	.381	.350	.424	.178	.081	.158
Four Letter Words	FLW	.275	.358	.275	.627		.541	.402	.367	.446	.223	.192	.239
Suffixes	Suff	.374	.473	.426	.516	.480		.288	.320	.325	.118	.007	.114
Letter Series	LSer	.536	.507	.490	.404	.330	.327		.555	.598	.252	.203	.257
Pedigrees	Ped	.567	.514	.512	.365	.275	.323	.671		.452	.085	.129	.151
Letter Grouping	LGrp	.468	.404	.430	.375	.317	.285	.622	.538		.270	.203	.293
Flags	Flag	.103	.109	.342	.176	.161	.079	.289	.277	.287		.593	.651
Figures	Fig	.019	.045	.227	.104	.138	.007	.160	.165	.181	.672		.684
Cards	Card	.077	.105	.294	.095	.049	.012	.200	.208	.207	.606	.728	
Sample 1 Mean		13.42	27.03	31.97	36.65	11.08	9.07	12.40	16.10	13.32	25.08	22.70	26.45
Sample 1 SD		4.730	10.317	10.795	9.778	4.655	4.106	5.725	7.678	4.171	12.427	12.798	12.215
Sample 2 Mean		13.75	26.71	31.89	36.18	10.85	8.46	12.46	16.45	13.35	24.44	22.01	24.85
Sample 2 SD		4.651	10.797	10.581	11.152	5.312	4.513	5.718	7.651	3.879	11.256	11.451	11.523

Note. Tabled values are correlations from Sample 1 ($N = 212$) below diagonal and from Sample 2 ($N = 213$) above the diagonal, with means and SDs as noted. Adapted from "An Empirical Study of the Factor Analysis Stability Hypothesis," by H. P. Bechtoldt, 1961, *Psychometrika, 26*(4), pp. 411–412 (https://doi.org/10.1007/BF02289771).

[a]ID = short name for each MV.

TABLE 17.2

Information for Deciding on the Number of Factors to Retain for Sample 1 From Bechtoldt (1961)

	Eigenvalues				Measures from maximum likelihood estimation				
Factor	PCA	EFA	Random	MAP	χ^2	df	prob	TLI	RMSEA (CI)
1	5.01	4.61	0.48	.267	607.92	54	<.0001	.522	.221 (.205–.236)
2	2.21	1.80	0.35	.241	267.99	43	<.0001	.758	.158 (.140–.176)
3	1.24	0.77	0.28	.241	127.59	33	<.0001	.869	.117 (.096–.138)
4	0.92	0.50	0.22	.225	24.81	24	.41	.998	.014 (.000–.058)
5	0.52	0.01	0.15	.276	10.31	16	.85	1.016	.000 (.000–.036)
6	0.45	−0.03	0.08	.332					
7	0.39	−0.07		.376					
8	0.37	−0.08		.457					
9	0.31	−0.12		.546					
10	0.25	−0.14		.694					
11	0.19	−0.15							
12	0.15	−0.19							

Note. PCA = principal component analysis; EFA = exploratory common factor analysis, principal axes extraction, squared multiple correlations as communality estimates; Random = estimated random data values; MAP = minimum average partial correlation criterion; χ^2 = likelihood ratio chi square; df = degrees of freedom; prob = probability level for likelihood ratio chi square; TLI = Tucker-Lewis index; RMSEA (CI) = root mean square error of approximation (with its confidence interval in parentheses).

Two obliquely rotated four-factor solutions for the Sample 1 data are shown in Table 17.3. In the left half of Table 17.3, the solution obtained using PROC FACTOR in SAS (Version 9.4) is shown, a solution using ML estimation and Harris-Kaiser orthoblique rotation with an exponent of zero. The three tests hypothesized to load highly on each factor did indeed load highly, with defining loadings ranging between .53 and .89 across factors. Of the 36 loadings that were expected to be small (nine loadings per factor), 30 of the 36 fell within the ±.10 hyperplane, and only two of the six loadings outside the ±.10 hyperplane were .20 or larger. This solution would be considered a very clean exploratory factor solution, and the largest deviation from expected values was the .25 loading of Suffixes on V. Also note the relatively high correlations among the first three factors and the low correlations of the S factor with the first three factors.

The rotated solution shown in the right half of Table 17.3 is an EFA performed using Mplus (Muthén & Muthén, 1998–2017), with ML estimation and geomin rotation. Loadings in this solution are very similar to those reported in the left half of the table. This solution, however, has the additional information of the standard error (SE) for each parameter estimate (cf. Cudeck & O'Dell, 1994). The three large, defining loadings on each factor had t values of 7.5 or higher, as expected. This solution suggests, however, that

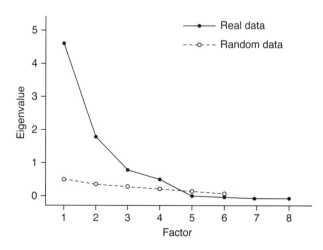

FIGURE 17.1. Plot of eigenvalues of the correlation matrix for Sample 1 from Bechtoldt (1961), compared with the plot of estimated eigenvalues from random data.

TABLE 17.3

Rotated Four-Factor EFA Solutions for 12 MVs in Sample 1 From Bechtoldt (1961), SAS and Mplus Output

| | SAS PROC FACTOR | | | | | Mplus EFA | | | | |
| | Factor | | | | | Factor | | | | |
Variable	V	W	R	S	h^2	V	W	R	S	h^2
Sentences	.84	−.05	.15	−.09	.84	**.83** (.05)	−.04 (.03)	*.16* (.06)	−.04 (.03)	.84
Vocabulary	.89	.11	−.03	−.04	.85	**.88** (.04)	*.12* (.05)	−.02 (.04)	.01 (.02)	.85
Completion	.82	.01	.01	.20	.77	**.81** (.04)	.01 (.03)	.01 (.04)	**.26** (.05)	.77
First Letters	.08	.70	.08	.01	.62	.09 (.08)	**.70** (.07)	.08 (.08)	.01 (.04)	.62
Four Letter Words	−.06	.84	.00	.03	.67	−.05 (.03)	**.83** (.06)	.00 (.05)	.03 (.04)	.67
Suffixes	.25	.53	−.02	−.07	.44	*.25* (.09)	**.53** (.07)	−.02 (.07)	−.05 (.05)	.44
Letter Series	−.00	.02	.85	.00	.74	−.00 (.04)	.02 (.04)	**.86** (.06)	−.03 (.04)	.74
Pedigrees	.15	−.03	.68	.03	.61	.15 (.08)	−.03 (.04)	**.69** (.08)	.02 (.04)	.61
Letter Grouping	−.00	.07	.67	.06	.52	−.00 (.06)	.07 (.07)	**.68** (.08)	.04 (.05)	.52
Flags	−.03	.04	.16	.72	.61	−.04 (.05)	.02 (.04)	.16 (.08)	**.72** (.04)	.61
Figures	−.02	.05	−.04	.89	.78	−.02 (.04)	.04 (.04)	−.05 (.06)	**.90** (.03)	.78
Cards	.08	−.08	.02	.81	.68	.08 (.06)	−.09 (.06)	.01 (.04)	**.82** (.03)	.68
			Factor correlations							
V	1.00					1.00				
W	.44	1.00				**.41** (.07)	1.00			
R	.62	.47	1.00			**.60** (.06)	**.46** (.08)	1.00		
S	.11	.12	.24	1.00		.07 (.08)	.13 (.08)	*.29* (.08)	1.00	

Note. V = Verbal Comprehension; W = Word Fluency; R = Reasoning; S = Spatial; h^2 = communality. Tabled values are factor loadings or factor correlations, with standard errors in parentheses where appropriate. SAS details: ML estimation, Harris-Kaiser orthoblique rotation, with power = 0; Mplus details: ML estimation, Geomin rotation. Boldfaced loadings had z-ratios greater than 5.0, italicized loadings had z-ratio between 2.0 and 5.0.

the .26 loading of Comprehension on S (z = 5.2) is a substantially larger deviation from the expected hyperplanar loading than was the .25 loading of Suffixes on V (z < 3.0). Because the loadings are of approximately the same magnitude, the additional information provided by the SE allows one to assess the importance of the deviation from zero of these loadings. Note also that SEs for the factor correlations reveal that the first three factors—V, W, and R – are rather strongly and significantly correlated, with t values of 5.5 or higher, and that the fourth factor, S, is significantly related only to the R factor.

Common Factor Analysis Versus Principal Component Analysis

One continuing issue in exploratory analyses is the choice between EFA and PCA. A single, seemingly minor difference exists between EFA and PCA: EFA accounts for off-diagonal covariation among MVs, after estimating communalities. In contrast, PCA is conducted on the correlation matrix **R** with unities on the diagonal, accounting for maximal amounts of total variance of MVs, not off-diagonal covariation. A matrix formulation for PCA is

$$\mathbf{R} = \mathbf{FF}' + \mathbf{GG}' \qquad (17.13)$$

where **F** is a ($p \times r$) truncated solution containing the first r components, and **G** is a ($p \times [p-r]$) matrix of the ($p-r$) discarded components.

Recall that an EFA solution involves a total of ($p + r$) factors, r common factors and p unique factors. In contrast, PCA involves representing the p MVs in terms of only p dimensions: r components in the **F** matrix in Equation 17.13

and $(p - r)$ components in the **G** matrix. The component space of **G** is orthogonal to the component space of **F**, so the r components in **F** can be rotated orthogonally or obliquely without concern for the discarded components in **G**. The residuals in **G**, however, have a covariance structure represented by **GG**′, and these residuals are not mutually uncorrelated as are the unique factors in **Θ** in the EFA model. Given the unknown and potentially haphazard nature of these residual covariances, PCA is not a "statistical model" in the usual sense but is a data reduction technique.

One central question is how closely PCA results (cf. Equation 17.13) approximate EFA results (cf. Equation 17.2). Some argue that EFA and PCA solutions are similar and that PCA is an efficient approximation to EFA (e.g., Goldberg & Velicer, 2006; Thompson, 2004; Velicer & Jackson, 1990). However, the PCA model is not a common factor model (in fact, it is not a data-generating model at all) and should not be used as substitute for one. Among others, Widaman (1993, 2007) demonstrated the positive bias in loadings and negative bias in correlations among obliquely rotated dimensions from use of PCA relative to values from EFA. Parameter estimates from EFA also should generalize to confirmatory factor analysis (CFA; see the upcoming section Confirmatory Factor Analysis), whereas parameter estimates from PCA may find little generalization to CFA. Widaman (2018) provided the most recent, up-to-date portrayal of differences between EFA and PCA, contrasting the two techniques on several core issues. He argued that estimates in PCA are difficult to interpret with confidence and often appear to be impossible to justify. PCA estimates do not have distributions expected of comparable EFA estimates. Proponents of PCA might not be aware of these problems, having apparently never discussed or tried to justify these matters (for details, see Widaman, 2018). The upshot of these concerns is that use of PCA as an approximation to EFA should be strongly discouraged, and EFA methods should be used if the goal of a study is the representation of MVs as functions of LVs.

CONFIRMATORY FACTOR ANALYSIS

Confirmatory factor analysis arose in the 1960s with development of efficient algorithms for ML estimation of parameters in factor analysis models and recognition that certain restrictions, such as fixing particular factor loadings to be precisely zero, were hypotheses that could be tested statistically. Early contributions to CFA by Jöreskog (e.g., 1969, 1971a, 1971b) were quickly followed by a spate of publications by researchers who understood the power of confirmatory factor analysis to provide statistical tests of hypothesized factor structures.

The CFA approach is based on the same basic linear model as described above for EFA, except that the model is usually formulated as a covariance, not correlation, structure (Cudeck, 1989). That is, MVs are modeled as linear combinations of the LVs, as shown in Equation 17.1. The major difference between EFA and CFA is the unrestricted estimation of parameters in EFA, allowing rotation to an infinite number of alternative orientations of the factors versus the restricted estimation of parameters in CFA that typically yields an unrotatable solution. Theory and prior research are used to formulate the restrictions in a CFA model, and the resulting analytic machinery of CFA offers a surprisingly wide array of models to be investigated. CFA can be seen as a restricted form of EFA, which implies a restricted set of options in CFA relative to EFA. However, exploiting options for placement of fixed and free parameter estimates results in a general CFA model that affords far greater flexibility than the standard EFA model, and the variety of models that can be investigated under CFA is far, far broader than under EFA.

Steps in Confirmatory Factor Analysis

Selection of observations. Key issues surrounding selection of observations for CFA differ little from those for EFA, so discussion here can be brief. Random and representative selection of observations from a carefully delineated population is ideal. Researchers, however, are often keen to investigate whether factor solutions obtained in prior research, usually on European American or majority culture participants, will generalize to participants from other populations. In such studies, the procedures for drawing the sample from the population must be carefully outlined to diminish the force of an alternative explanation in terms of unrepresentative sampling if an expected factor structure is not confirmed.

Selection of manifest variables. Ideally, MVs in a CFA have been used in earlier EFA studies so the psychometric properties and likely factor loadings for the MVs are known. Further, rather than ensuring that a domain of content is covered by MVs in an analysis, researchers often select a small set of the best indicators for each factor. So, rather than a widely varying selection of MVs, research is based on a careful selection of the best indicators. If these indicators load highly on LVs in a CFA, little concern regarding the results of analyses should arise.

Specification. Specification of a CFA model involves identifying the number of factors and placement of fixed, free, and constrained model parameters. Fixing any model parameter is a constraint that it must take on a specified value. Two kinds of constraints can be distinguished—minimally sufficient identification (MSI) constraints and overidentifying restrictions. MSI constraints are those that identify the scale of the LVs and identify all parameter estimates in the model. At least r^2 MSI constraints must be invoked to identify a covariance structure model (cf. Equation 17.4), where r is the number of factors. Because r^2 constraints are required to estimate parameters, these are called MSI constraints. If only r^2 constraints are made, the resulting model is equivalent to an EFA model under ML; the associated CFA model will have the same chi-square and degrees of freedom as an EFA model with the same number of factors. The CFA model will be fully a rotatable factor model that is rotated to an a priori orientation, as shown in the next two paragraphs.

LVs have no inherent scale, and certain MSI identification constraints set or fix the scale of the LVs. One common approach is to fix the variance of each LV to unity, by fixing or constraining diag $(\Psi) = I$, and fixing the mean of each LV to zero. This approach provides LVs that have some properties akin to z-scores, such as a mean of zero and a variance of 1.0. An alternative set of MSI constraints is to fix one factor loading per LV to unity, which then allows the variance of the LV to be estimated. Let us assume that the former approach—fixing LV variances to unity—is taken; this accounts for r of the MSI constraints for the covariance structure. The remaining $r(r-1)$ MSI constraints are invoked by fixing certain factor loadings to zero. Consider the following CFA model matrices Λ, Ψ, and Θ^2:

$$\Lambda = \begin{bmatrix} \lambda_{11} & 0^* \\ \lambda_{21} & \lambda_{22} \\ \lambda_{31} & \lambda_{32} \\ 0^* & \lambda_{42} \\ \lambda_{51} & \lambda_{52} \\ \lambda_{61} & \lambda_{62} \end{bmatrix} \quad \Psi \begin{bmatrix} 1^* & sym \\ \psi_{21} & 1^* \end{bmatrix} \quad \Theta^2 = \text{diag} \begin{bmatrix} \theta_{11} \\ \theta_{22} \\ \theta_{33} \\ \theta_{44} \\ \theta_{55} \\ \theta_{66} \end{bmatrix}$$

(17.14)

where the first three MVs (corresponding to the first three rows of Λ) are presumed to be indicators of the first LV and the second three MVs are indicators for the second LV. Because two LVs are shown in these matrices, a total of $r^2 = 2^2 = 4$ MSI constraints must be made. Two of these MSI constraints are indicated by the asterisked values of 1 on the diagonal of Ψ, and the remaining two MSI constraints are shown as the asterisked values of 0 in the two columns of Λ. The placement of MSI constraints was determined in the following way, which can be generalized to models with any number of factors: (a) select a "leading" indicator for each factor, selecting the very best indicator of the factor based on prior research, if such can be determined (here, MV1 is the "leading" indicator for the first LV, and MV4 is the "leading" indicator for LV2); (b) estimate the factor loading for the "leading" indicator on its factor, but fix to 0 the factor loadings for the "leading" indicator on all other factors; (c) for the "nonleading" indicators of a factor, estimate

all loadings for these variables on all other factors;
(d) fix to 1.0 the variances of all LVs in Ψ;
(e) estimate all correlations among LVs; and
(f) freely estimate diagonal values of Θ^2, which are variances of unique factors.

The model in Equation 17.14 has r^2 MSI constraints, so it is equivalent to an EFA model. The model is simply an EFA model estimated using CFA software but rotating the first LV right through the first MV and the second LV directly through the fourth MV. Because the first factor is collinear with the first MV, the first MV cannot load on any other factors, hence, its fixed 0 loadings on other factors. Similar constraints hold for the fourth MV.

Converting the CFA model in Equation 17.14 into a typical, restricted CFA model would involve constraining four of the estimated factor loadings to be zero but keeping the remaining six factor loadings freely estimated. This involves invoking the second type of constraint—overidentifying restrictions. Specifically, if the loadings of the second and third MVs on the second LV (i.e., λ_{22} and λ_{32}) and the loadings of the fifth and sixth MVs on the first LV (i.e., λ_{51} and λ_{61}) were fixed at zero, the resulting model would be a CFA model that is a restricted version of the model shown in Equation 17.14. The resulting CFA model would have four more df than the model shown in Equation 17.14 because four fewer parameter estimates were made.

Given the foregoing, one can see that a standard CFA model is a restricted factor model, or a restricted version of an EFA model. Typical CFA models are not confirmatory in a strong sense, meaning that a researcher does not test whether particular numerical values for certain model parameters can be confirmed or verified in a new sample. Instead, the typical CFA model involves obtaining best-fit estimates of all model parameters given a particular restricted pattern of fixed and free loadings. Adequate fit of a restricted CFA model thus "confirms," or supports, the researcher's conjecture that a restricted form of factor model is consistent with the data. The restricted form of a CFA model means that it is no longer a freely rotatable solution, as rotation would fail to retain the pattern of fixed zero loadings in the model. Furthermore, although not often performed, a researcher could test the fit of a CFA model against that of a freely rotatable EFA model with the same number of factors, because the CFA model is nested within the EFA model. This test could be quite informative, providing a statistical test of the worsening of fit associated with the overidentifying restrictions in the CFA model.

Estimation. In CFA, parameters can be estimated using any of a number of methods of estimation. Available methods include ULS, ML, GLS, and a host of variants of these that provide test statistics and standard errors that are robust to violations of normality assumptions (e.g., Browne, 1984; Satorra & Bentler, 1994; Savalei, 2010). Although myriad methods of estimation are available, the more esoteric methods are not frequently used. Instead, standard ML estimation is the method used in the vast majority of applications. Fortunately, ML estimation appears to be relatively robust to moderate or even fairly extensive violations of distributional assumptions, so its use in most studies is probably not a matter of major concern. If violation of assumptions is a concern, we recommend comparing results of ML estimation against those using a robust method of estimation. If important differences in results are obtained, then method of estimation is a matter of concern, and the researcher should justify the choice of method.

Evaluation. Evaluation of fit of a CFA model is typically done on at least two levels—the global fit of the overall CFA model and a more detailed consideration of each parameter estimate. Global fit of the CFA model can be evaluated using statistical indices or indices of practical fit that are a function of the statistical indices. In an earlier section on ML estimation in EFA, we discussed the use of the likelihood ratio (LR) chi-square test statistic; this test statistic is used in most CFA studies as a statistical indicator of model misfit. A significant test statistic provides a statistical basis for rejection of the model tested. Because the test statistic is a direct function of sample size, trivial model misfit can lead to a significant test statistic if sample size is large, and important model misfit may not lead to a rejectable test statistic if sample size is small. In general, sample size should be 150 or larger to ensure adequate power to reject a poorly fitting model, and the test statistic tends to become overly powerful when sample size exceeds 500 (but cf. MacCallum et al., 1999). Care must, therefore, be taken in evaluating the ML test statistic.

Adjuncts to the statistical index of fit are found in practical fit indices of global fit of a model to data. Several practical fit indices were discussed in the Number of Factors section, including the TLI and the RMSEA. Many additional practical fit indices have been developed. One class of fit indices are called *information indices*, and these include the Akaike information criterion (AIC), the consistent AIC (or CAIC), and the Bayesian information criterion (BIC). Information indices represent the LR statistic for a model given the data, with some form of penalty for model complexity (i.e., number of parameter estimates; see Vrieze, 2012) These information criteria do not fall on a standardized metric; however, various models can be compared using these criteria; therefore, among several competing models, the model with the smallest (i.e., most negative) AIC is the optimally fitting model. Similar comparisons among models can be performed using the CAIC and the BIC. Based on simulation studies, the CAIC and BIC indices appear to be better indicators of the correct model than does the AIC. Interested readers can consult Hu and Bentler (1999) for a comprehensive evaluation of different indicators of practical fit, particularly with regard to optimal cut-off points for different indices, and Widaman and Thompson (2003) for a comparison of incremental fit indices.

The second, more detailed level of model evaluation is conducted by considering each parameter estimate in a CFA model against its standard error (SE). A critical ratio (CR), distributed asymptotically as a z-ratio, can be formed by dividing a parameter estimate by its SE. The tradition in the field is to deem any parameter with a CR of 2.0 or larger to be significant at the .05 level, and the p-level for each CR is reported by most structural modeling programs. On a statistical basis, therefore, the evaluation of model parameters is highly structured.

Parameter estimates in CFA can also be evaluated with regard to their magnitude, supplementing a statistical evaluation with one based on practical importance. No hard-and-fast rules are available here, but simulation studies have often used .4, .6, and .8 standardized factor loadings to represent low, medium, and high levels of communality, respectively. Absent firmer bases, these values can be used to evaluate standardized factor loadings. Further, Cohen (1988) used .10, .30, and .50 to indicate small, medium, and large correlations, so these values can be used when interpreting the magnitude of the correlations among factors.

Readjustment. Readjustment of a CFA model consists of the respecification of fixed and/or free parameter estimates. Any respecification can be done on either of two grounds: (a) a priori and (b) empirical. A priori grounds for respecifying a model might be pursued to compare competing conjectures under different models for a given set of data. For example, in prior research, certain investigators may have found evidence that a three-factor structure underlies items on a given scale, whereas the developer of the scale sought to assess just two factors. Alternative CFA models could be formulated that were consistent with each of these competing schemes, and the relative fit of these alternate a priori models could be compared.

Researchers can also use empirical bases for model respecification to improve model fit to the data. Most structural modeling programs report modification indices, which estimate the change in chi-square if a particular fixed parameter were estimated. Experts on factor analysis differ with regard to recommendations concerning modification indices. Some experts advise never to base model respecification on modification indices due to capitalization on chance that readily occurs. Bolstering this position is Monte Carlo simulation work on specification searches, which has generally concluded that such searches rarely arrive at the model that generated the data (e.g., MacCallum, 1986). Other experts (e.g., Sörbom, 1989) see clear value in using modification indices to aid model respecification, as these indices reflect ways the data are informing the researcher of a need to account for particular patterns in data. If modification indices are used to modify the specification of a model, experts urge that these model modifications be cross-validated in an independent sample to verify their replicability.

An Empirical Example

To exemplify the use of CFA, we reanalyzed the data from Sample 1 of Bechtoldt (1961). Specifically, we fit a model with a "perfect" restricted factor pattern, with the three tests for Verbal Comprehension loading on the first factor, the three Word Fluency tests loading on the second factor, three tests for Reasoning on the third factor, and the three Spatial tests on the fourth factor. The resulting model had a significant ML test statistic, $\chi^2 (48) = 106.51, p < .001$, suggesting rejection of the highly restricted model. Practical fit indices included a TLI of .943 and RMSEA of .076, 90% CI [.056, .095], which were of borderline acceptability. Furthermore, because this CFA model was nested with the four-factor EFA model presented earlier, the worsening of fit moving from the EFA model to the restricted CFA model could be tested. The resulting difference test was significant, $\Delta\chi^2 (24) = 81.70, p < .001$.

Modification indices suggested that freeing the loading of the Completion test on the Spatial factor would maximally improve model fit. Relaxing this factor loading constraint led to Model 2, which had a statistical test statistic that was of borderline significance, $\chi^2 (47) = 71.28, p < .02$. Although this test statistic was significant at $\alpha = .05$, it was not rejectable at $\alpha = .01$. Moreover, the improvement in statistical fit associated with the one additional parameter estimate was clearly significant, $\Delta\chi^2 (1) = 35.23, p < .001$. The practical fit indices of TLI = .976 and RMSEA = .049, 90% CI [.023, .072], suggested that this model fit the data closely. To avoid any further potential capitalization on chance, we ceased model fitting at this point.

The results of the CFA analysis are shown in Table 17.4, which reports standardized factor loadings and correlations among factors. The factor pattern had a highly constrained form, with leading loadings on each factor varying between .65 and .92 and having z-ratios above 10.0. The only deviation from a perfect pattern of loadings was the .26 ($SE = .04$) loading of Completion on the Spatial factor, a relatively small loading, but one that appeared to be required for the CFA model to fit the data closely. The correlations among factors in Table 17.4 tend to be slightly higher than corresponding values shown for EFA models in Table 17.3. The primary basis for this is the fact that a number of small, positive non-hyperplanar loadings were accommodated in the EFA solution in Table 17.3, but these loadings were fixed at 0 in the CFA model in Table 17.4. To account for these small but nonzero contributions that are fixed to 0 in the CFA model required somewhat higher factor intercorrelations in the latter model.

Advanced Forms of Confirmatory Factor Analysis

To demonstrate the flexibility of the CFA approach to analyses, we will discuss several advanced forms of analysis. Due to space limitations, the presentation here necessarily will be brief, but we trust the reader will get a sense of the many interesting ideas that can be formulated and tested within the general CFA framework.

Multiple-group CFA. Multiple groups of participants can be identified by subsetting data as a function of person characteristics such as sex or ethnic status. A crucial scientific question quickly arises: Are factors identified in one group the same factors as those identified in other groups? This question has been studied under the rubric of factorial invariance.

Work on factorial invariance can be traced back over the past 60 years or more, with key contributions by Meredith (1964a, 1964b, 1993), Jöreskog (1971a), and Horn, McArdle, and Mason (1983), among others. To pursue factorial

TABLE 17.4

Confirmatory Factor Analysis for 12 MVs in Sample 1 From Bechtoldt (1961)

Variable	Factor				h²
	V	W	R	S	
Sentences	**.91** (.02)	.0*	.0*	.0*	.84
Vocabulary	**.92** (.02)	.0*	.0*	.0*	.84
Completion	**.81** (.03)	.0*	.0*	**.26** (.04)	.76
First Letters	.0*	**.83** (.04)	.0*	.0*	.69
Four Letter Words	.0*	**.73** (.04)	.0*	.0*	.54
Suffixes	.0*	**.65** (.05)	.0*	.0*	.42
Letter Series	.0*	.0*	**.85** (.03)	.0*	.71
Pedigrees	.0*	.0*	**.79** (.03)	.0*	.63
Letter Grouping	.0*	.0*	**.72** (.04)	.0*	.51
Flags	.0*	.0*	.0*	**.77** (.04)	.60
Figures	.0*	.0*	.0*	**.87** (.03)	.76
Cards	.0*	.0*	.0*	**.82** (.03)	.67

	Factor correlations			
V	1.0*			
W	**.56** (.06)	1.0*		
R	**.69** (.05)	**.57** (.06)	1.0*	
S	.09 (.08)	.15 (.08)	*.31* (.07)	1.0*

Note. V = Verbal Comprehension; W = Word Fluency; R = Reasoning; S = Spatial; h² = communality. Tabled values are standardized factor loadings and factor correlations, with standard errors in parentheses. Boldfaced parameters had z-ratios greater than 5.0, italicized parameters had z-ratio between 2.0 and 5.0. *Values fixed at reported values to identify model.

invariance, a model akin to Equations 17.3 and 17.4 can be written as

$$E(Y_g) = \tau_g + \Lambda_g \alpha_g \quad (17.15)$$

$$E(Y_g Y_g') = \Sigma_{YY_g} = \Lambda_g \Psi_g \Lambda_g' + \Theta_g \quad (17.16)$$

where the g subscript ($g = 1, \ldots, G$) is an indicator of group membership, α_g is a vector of mean differences for group g, and other symbols were defined previously. The g subscript on the matrices in Equations 17.15 and 17.16 indicates that different parameter estimates may be present for corresponding parameters across groups. The g subscript on a given matrix, however, can be deleted if parameter estimates are constrained to numerical invariance across groups.

Widaman and Reise (1997) synthesized prior work to identify four levels of factorial invariance, which are (a) configural invariance, or invariance across groups of the pattern of fixed and free factor loadings in Λ; (b) weak factorial invariance, or invariance across groups of estimated loadings in Λ; (c) strong factorial invariance, or invariance across groups of estimated loadings in Λ and measurement intercepts in τ; and (d) strict factorial invariance, or invariance across groups of estimated loadings in Λ, measurement intercepts in τ, and unique factor variances in Θ. If strong or strict factorial invariance holds across groups, a researcher has putative evidence that the same factors have been found across groups. Given this, group differences in means and variances on the factors are open for study. Further, if strict factorial invariance holds, all between-group differences in means and variances on MVs are a function of between-group differences in mean and variance on the LVs. Thus, in a mathematical sense, the latent variables explain or represent all group differences on MVs.

Factorial invariance and its implications have been matters of great interest. In addition to the preceding sources, interested readers should consult additional literature, including Browne and Arminger (1995), Cheung and Rensvold (1999), Levy and Hancock (2007), Little (1997), McArdle (1996), McArdle and Cattell (1994), Millsap and Meredith (2007), and Widaman and Olivera-Aguilar (in press).

The preceding approach to testing factorial invariance can be applied to the data from the two samples of participants contained in Table 17.1. First, we standardized the grand mean to zero and overall variance to one across groups for each MV, following procedures outlined by Jöreskog (1971a; input data sets and analysis scripts are available at https://osf.io/r2my8). We then fit a nonoverlapping simple structure solution in both groups, with the three key indicators of each factor having the only nonzero loadings on each factor. This model, Model 1, had generally adequate fit, with χ^2 (96) = 179.86, $p < .001$, and practical fit indices of TLI = .959 and RMSEA = .064, 90% CI [.049, .078]. However, the loading of the Completion test on the S factor in Sample 1 and the loading of the Pedigrees test on the V factor in Sample 2 had large modification indices. After freeing both of these loadings in both samples, the resulting configural invariance model, termed Model 1a, had very close fit to the data, with χ^2 (92) = 118.15, $p = .03$, TLI = .987, and RMSEA = .037, 90% CI [.011, .055]. Model 1a had significantly better fit than did Model 1, $\Delta\chi^2$ (4) = 61.71, $p < .001$, and practical fit indices were much improved, supporting the addition of the two extra loadings in each sample.

Model 2 was the weak factorial invariance model, which was identical to Model 1a but enforced numerical invariance of factor loadings. The fit of Model 2 was very good, with χ^2 (102) = 132.14, $p = .02$, and TLI = .986, and RMSEA = .037, 90% CI [.014, .054]. Importantly, Model 2 showed a nonsignificant worsening of fit associated with the invariance constraint on factor loadings, $\Delta\chi^2$ (10) = 13.99, ns, and practical fit indices were essentially unchanged.

The next model, Model 3, was the strong factorial invariance model, which was identical to Model 2 except that invariance of measurement intercepts was invoked. The fit of Model 3 was also very good, with χ^2 (110) = 138.60, $p = .03$, and TLI = .988, and RMSEA = .035, 90% CI [.010, .052]. Compared with Model 2, Model 3 showed a nonsignificant worsening of fit associated with the invariance constraint on intercepts, $\Delta\chi^2$ (8) = 6.46, ns, and practical fit indices improved slightly.

The final model considered here, Model 4, was the strict factorial invariance model, which was identical to Model 3 except that invariance of unique variances was enforced. The fit of Model 4 was very good, with χ^2 (122) = 145.70, $p = .07$, and TLI = .991, and RMSEA = .030, 90% CI [.000, .047]. Supporting the invariance constraints on unique variances, the fit of Model 4 was not significantly worse than that of Model 3, $\Delta\chi^2$ (12) = 7.10, ns, and practical fit indices once again improved slightly.

Parameter estimates from Model 4 are shown in Table 17.5. The three primary indicators of each factor had large loadings, ranging between .62 and .91 and having CRs of 12 or higher. The two nonhypothesized loadings of Completion on the S factor, $\lambda = .20$ ($SE = .03$) and Pedigrees on the V factor, $\lambda = .25$ ($SE = .05$), had CRs of 5.93 and 4.68, respectively, so were significant at $p < .001$. Because all parameter estimates in τ, Λ, and Θ in the top half of Table 17.5 were invariant across samples, any differences across groups are captured by the moments (i.e., means, variances, covariances) of the latent variables. As shown in the bottom half of Table 17.5, factor means were fixed at zero in Sample 1 to identify the model; mean differences in Sample 2 showed small and nonsignificant variation from Sample 1 values. Factor variances were fixed at unity in Sample 1 to identify the model; estimated variances on factors in Sample 2 differed somewhat, but generally nonsignificantly from unity. Finally, both the factor covariances and their standardized values (i.e., correlations) appeared to vary little across samples. Thus, in the present application, parameter estimates in the three measurement

TABLE 17.5

Multiple-Group Confirmatory Factor Analysis for 12 MVs in Samples 1 and 2, From Bechtoldt (1961)

Variable	τ	Factor				Θ
		V	W	R	S	
Sentences	−.01 (.07)	**.90** (.05)	.0*	.0*	.0*	**.17** (.02)
Vocabulary	−.01 (.07)	**.91** (.05)	.0*	.0*	.0*	**.16** (.02)
Completion	.00 (.07)	**.82** (.05)	.0*	.0*	**.20** (.03)	**.25** (.02)
First Letters	.04 (.06)	.0*	**.75** (.05)	.0*	.0*	**.31** (.04)
Four Letter Words	.03 (.06)	.0*	**.70** (.05)	.0*	.0*	**.40** (.04)
Suffixes	.03 (.06)	.0*	**.62** (.05)	.0*	.0*	**.54** (.04)
Letter Series	−.01 (.07)	.0*	.0*	**.87** (.06)	.0*	**.29** (.04)
Pedigrees	−.01 (.06)	*.25* (.05)	.0*	**.56** (.06)	.0*	**.46** (.04)
Letter Grouping	−.01 (.06)	.0*	.0*	**.75** (.06)	.0*	**.47** (.04)
Flags	.04 (.07)	.0*	.0*	.0*	**.81** (.06)	**.41** (.04)
Figures	.04 (.07)	.0*	.0*	.0*	**.89** (.06)	**.29** (.04)
Cards	.04 (.07)	.0*	.0*	.0*	**.88** (.06)	**.31** (.04)

Factor	Factor mean	Factor covariances			
		Sample 1			
V	.0*	1.0*	.56	.65	.11
W	.0*	**.56** (.06)	1.0*	.57	.15
R	.0*	**.65** (.05)	**.57** (.07)	1.0*	.32
S	.0*	.11 (.08)	.15 (.08)	*.32* (.07)	1.0*
		Sample 2			
V	.02 (.10)	**1.03** (.15)	.62	.57	.13
W	−.09 (.12)	**.76** (.13)	**1.44** (.24)	.59	.23
R	.02 (.11)	**.55** (.10)	**.67** (.12)	**.89** (.15)	.35
S	−.10 (.10)	.11 (.07)	*.24* (.09)	*.29* (.08)	**.77** (.12)

Note. V = Verbal Comprehension; W = Word Fluency; R = Reasoning; S = Spatial; h^2 = communality. Tabled values are parameter estimates, with standard errors in parentheses. Boldfaced parameters had z-ratios greater than 5.0, italicized parameters had z-ratio between 2.0 and 5.0. In factor covariance matrices, covariances are shown below the diagonal, correlations above the diagonal. *Values fixed at reported values to identify model.

matrices—τ, Λ, and Θ—demonstrated clear invariance across the two samples, and parameter estimates in the remaining two matrices—α and Ψ—also exhibited a high degree of similarity across samples. These results provide strong support for the claim that the same factors were identified in the two samples.

Longitudinal factor models. The issue of invariance of factors across groups can be generalized across the dimension of time. Here, the important scientific question concerns whether the LVs identified at one point in time are the same as those at other points in time. This is a crucial question because tracking growth over time requires the implicit assumption that one is assessing the same construct across time. Longitudinal CFA models can embody and test this assumption, to determine whether strong or strict factorial invariance holds across time.

The testing of levels of invariance—from configural invariance to strict factorial invariance—follows the same steps as outlined above for multiple-group modeling. The one difference in longitudinal models is the need to allow covariances among unique factors for the same indicator across the multiple times of measurement. This is a reasonable a priori specification, as unique factors are hypothesized to consist of a combination of specific (i.e., reliable) variance and random error. The longitudinal stability of the specific portion of the unique factor is, therefore, the basis for such covariances among uniquenesses. Among the many sources that could be offered, Ferrer et al. (2008), Hancock et al. (2001), McArdle (1988, 2007), Meredith and Horn (2001), Tisak and Meredith (1989), and Widaman et al. (2010) provide accessible discussions of details.

Analyses of multitrait-multimethod data. In a seminal publication, Campbell and Fiske (1959) discussed convergent and discriminant validation using the multitrait-multimethod (MTMM) matrix. Convergent validation was shown if measures of the same construct had relatively high correlations with one another, and discriminant validation was supported if measures of different constructs had lower levels of correlation. Campbell and Fiske discussed four rules for interpreting trends in MTMM matrices. The Campbell and Fiske rules are useful, but nonindependence among comparisons made statistical evaluation of evidence difficult.

With the advent of CFA, researchers quickly saw utility in CFA models for evaluating trends in MTMM matrices. As one interesting aside, modeling MTMM data aligns well with CFA—but not EFA—because a specific LV structure must be hypothesized prior to analyses. If t trait constructs are assessed using each of m methods, the p MVs in a fully crossed MTMM matrix consist of $(t \times m)$ MVs. The factor loading matrix Λ can be structured with $(t + m)$ factors. Each trait factor would have m loadings, one from each method of measurement; each method factor would have t loadings, one from each trait assessed by that method. Covariances among factors in Ψ could be structured into a $([t + m] \times [t + m])$ matrix, with freely estimated correlations among t trait factors, freely estimated correlations among m method factors, and correlations between trait and method factors fixed at zero for identification. This model is often termed the *correlated trait–correlated method* (CT-CM) model.

One of the first to demonstrate the utility of CFA models for evaluating MTMM data was Jöreskog (1971b), who presented an analysis of one matrix from Campbell and Fiske (1959). To reconcile discrepancies in prior work, Widaman (1985) offered a taxonomy of CFA models for MTMM data that cross-classified four trait structures with four method structures, yielding 16 models that afforded interesting model comparisons. Widaman noted that trait factor loadings were direct and useful indicators of convergent validation, as they reflect the alignment of each MV with its respective trait factor. Method factor loadings are indicators of the degree to which a MV was imbued with the biasing influence of variance due to method of measurement. Finally, correlations among trait factors provide a useful index of discriminant validation, with correlations nearer zero providing stronger evidence of discriminant validation of trait constructs.

A major problem with the CT-CM model was its marked tendency to fail to converge or to converge to a solution with unacceptable estimates (e.g., negative unique variances). To alleviate these problems, different options for representing method effects were proposed. Marsh (1989) reintroduced a variation of MTMM model specification, first proposed by Kenny (1976; cf. Kenny & Kashy, 1992), in which shared method effects are represented by covariances among unique factors in the Θ matrix, rather than by method factors. Later, Eid (2000) introduced a modified CT-CM model in which one method factor is selected as a reference and, thus, is deleted, leading to the CT-C(M-1) model, designed to improve empirical identification of parameters in the CT-CM model and improve the likelihood of model convergence.

Rather than discard the CT-CM model, with its close alignment with Campbell and Fiske (1959) theory, some recent work has fortified the CT-CM model. Castro-Schilo et al. (2016) showed how to augment, or systematically uncross, the MTMM matrix with carefully identified MVs, a method that substantially improved the performance of models. Then, Helm et al. (2017) touted Bayesian estimation, rather than ML, for fitting models to standard, fully crossed MTMM data, and this eliminated virtually all problems of lack of convergence and presence of out-of-bound estimates. More recent summaries of multimethod approaches to research are contained in Eid and Diener (2006) and Helm (2022), and chapters in these volumes, especially the latter, provide up-to-date summaries of different structural modeling approaches to evaluating MTMM data.

RECENT EXTENSIONS OF EXPLORATORY AND CONFIRMATORY FACTOR ANALYSIS

The past decade has seen a range of advances for both EFA and CFA approaches. These advances aim not only to improve estimation of EFA and CFA but also seek to identify new methods that combine the benefits of the well-established CFA and EFA approaches described throughout this chapter. Because this chapter focuses on EFA and CFA, we provide only brief overviews of these extensions and point readers to the relevant literature.

The advent of Bayesian structural equation modeling (BSEM; B. Muthén & Asparouhov, 2012) allowed researchers to specify prior distributions on model parameters, which could in turn be used to augment both CFA and EFA. For example, using prior distributions with small variances, cross-loadings that were typically forced to zero in CFA may be estimated, creating an EFA-like loading pattern (B. Muthén & Asparouhov, 2012). Or, using a "spike and slab prior," factor loadings may be essentially selected into the model (Lu et al., 2016), and factors with near-zero loadings for all variables would be inherently selected out of the model. Via the benefits of Bayesian estimation (i.e., specification of prior distributions), therefore, the estimation algorithm could (conceptually) test for the number of latent variables (as done across multiple EFAs) and include small cross-loadings for those latent variables.

In a different vein, recent advances in structural equation modeling have enabled simultaneous estimation of (a) rotatable factor loading matrices and (b) direct effects amongst latent factors, leading some to refer to these advances as a combination of exploratory (factor rotation) and confirmatory (estimation of direct effects) factor models. Generally referred to as *exploratory structural equation modeling* (ESEM; Asparouhov & Muthén, 2009), the approach allows users to specify blocks of manifest variables that should be used for forming a set of latent variables in a manner similar to EFA (i.e., all possible loadings estimated), a separate set of manifest variables that can be specified in a manner similar CFA (i.e., zero and estimated loadings), and direct effects amongst latent variables. The set of variables used in an "EFA-like" manner will lead to many smaller cross-loadings that would likely be forced to zero in a CFA, which can help to prevent overestimation of latent variable correlations and direct effects. Furthermore, ESEM has been extended to test for measurement invariance of the EFA-like factor loading pattern across independent groups or time (Asparouhov & Muthén, 2009), providing greater fusion of the benefits across CFA (testing of measurement invariance) and EFA.

SUMMARY COMMENTS

The first publication on factor analysis (Spearman, 1904) appeared over a century ago, yet the use of factor analysis in all of its forms seems still to be on the ascendant. For the first half of the 20th century, factor analysis was limited by the complexity of the calculations required. During the 1930s and 1940s, many factor analytic studies were published, but these tended to be authored by a methodologically sophisticated elite in the field. With the advent of computers and efficient analysis algorithms in the 1950s and 1960s, factor analysis could routinely be used by practicing scientists in a wide array of domains. In addition to exploring new domains, researchers used EFA to explore the dimensionality of existing scales.

Experts on factor analysis have long had concerns about misuses of the method. Thurstone (1937) and Guilford (1952) gave early outlines of misuses of factor analysis, and Comrey (1978), Floyd and Widaman (1995), Fabrigar et al. (1999), and Reise et al. (2000) provided further comments.

Factor analysis is a powerful method, but one that can be misused, consciously or not. Using program package defaults—PCA extraction, retaining components with eigenvalues greater than 1.0, rotating with varimax—routinely leads to much poorer factor solutions than using well-considered EFA procedures.

Many existing sources provide additional information on use of factor analysis. For EFA, the classic texts by Thurstone (1947) and Harman (1976) provide a wealth of valuable material, Gorsuch (1983) is a very good introductory guide, and Mulaik (2010) is a recent, state-of-the-art presentation of advanced techniques. McDonald (1985) placed factor analysis squarely within the psychometric tradition, and McDonald (1999) provided a unified treatment of classical and modern test theory, including the place of EFA and CFA in psychological measurement. Finally, Brown (2015) gives a state-of-the-art presentation of CFA, including many special cases. Armed with these sources, we can look forward to the next century of expanding use of factor analytic methods to explore and confirm patterns in behavioral data in increasingly precise fashion.

References

Asparouhov, T., & Muthén, B. (2009). Exploratory structural equation modeling. *Structural Equation Modeling, 16*(3), 397–438. https://doi.org/10.1080/10705510903008204

Bechtoldt, H. P. (1961). An empirical study of the factor analysis stability hypothesis. *Psychometrika, 26*(4), 405–432. https://doi.org/10.1007/BF02289771

Bentler, P. M., & Bonett, D. G. (1980). Significance tests and goodness of fit in the analysis of covariance structures. *Psychological Bulletin, 88*(3), 588–606. https://doi.org/10.1037/0033-2909.88.3.588

Bock, R. D., Gibbons, R., & Muraki, E. (1988). Full-information item factor analysis. *Applied Psychological Measurement, 12*(3), 261–280. https://doi.org/10.1177/014662168801200305

Brown, T. A. (2015). *Confirmatory factor analysis for applied research* (2nd ed.). Guilford Press.

Browne, M. W. (1984). Asymptotically distribution-free methods for the analysis of covariance structures. *British Journal of Mathematical and Statistical Psychology, 37*(1), 62–83. https://doi.org/10.1111/j.2044-8317.1984.tb00789.x

Browne, M. W. (2001). An overview of analytic rotation in exploratory factor analysis. *Multivariate Behavioral Research, 36*(1), 111–150. https://doi.org/10.1207/S15327906MBR3601_05

Browne, M. W., & Arminger, G. (1995). Specification and estimation of mean and covariance structure models. In G. Arminger, C. Clogg, & M. E. Sobel (Eds.), *Handbook of statistical modeling for the social and behavioral sciences* (pp. 185–249). Plenum. https://doi.org/10.1007/978-1-4899-1292-3_4

Browne, M. W., & Cudeck, R. (1993). Alternative ways of assessing model fit. In K. A. Bollen & J. S. Long (Eds.), *Testing structural equation models* (pp. 136–162). Sage.

Browne, M. W., Cudeck, R., Tateneni, K., & Mels, G. (2010). *CEFA: Comprehensive exploratory factor analysis* (Version 3.04) [Computer software and manual]. Retrieved from https://psychology.osu.edu/dr-browne-software

Campbell, D. T., & Fiske, D. W. (1959). Convergent and discriminant validation by the multitrait-multimethod matrix. *Psychological Bulletin, 56*(2), 81–105. https://doi.org/10.1037/h0046016

Carroll, J. B. (1993). *Human cognitive abilities: A survey of factor-analytic studies*. Cambridge University Press. https://doi.org/10.1017/CBO9780511571312

Castro-Schilo, L., Grimm, K. J., & Widaman, K. F. (2016). Augmenting the correlated trait-correlated method model for multitrait-multimethod data. *Structural Equation Modeling, 23*(6), 798–818. https://doi.org/10.1080/10705511.2016.1214919

Cattell, R. B. (1963). Theory of fluid and crystallized intelligence: A critical experiment. *Journal of Educational Psychology, 54*(1), 1–22. https://doi.org/10.1037/h0046743

Cattell, R. B. (1966). The scree test for the number of factors. *Multivariate Behavioral Research, 1*(2), 245–276. https://doi.org/10.1207/s15327906mbr0102_10

Cattell, R. B. (1971). *Abilities: Their structure, growth, and action*. Houghton Mifflin.

Cheung, G. W., & Rensvold, R. B. (1999). Testing factorial invariance across groups: A reconceptualization and proposed new method. *Journal of Management, 25*(1), 1–27. https://doi.org/10.1177/014920639902500101

Cliff, N. (1988). The eigenvalues-greater-than-one rule and the reliability of components. *Psychological Bulletin, 103*(2), 276–279. https://doi.org/10.1037/0033-2909.103.2.276

Cohen, J. (1988). *Statistical power analysis for the behavioral sciences* (2nd ed.). Erlbaum.

Comrey, A. L. (1978). Common methodological problems in factor analytic studies. *Journal of Consulting and Clinical Psychology*, *46*(4), 648–659. https://doi.org/10.1037/0022-006X.46.4.648

Crawford, C. B., & Ferguson, G. A. (1970). A general rotation criterion and its use in orthogonal rotation. *Psychometrika*, *35*(3), 321–332. https://doi.org/10.1007/BF02310792

Cudeck, R. (1989). Analysis of covariance matrices using covariance structure models. *Psychological Bulletin*, *105*(2), 317–327. https://doi.org/10.1037/0033-2909.105.2.317

Cudeck, R., & O'Dell, L. L. (1994). Applications of standard error estimates in unrestricted factor analysis: Significance tests for factor loadings and correlations. *Psychological Bulletin*, *115*(3), 475–487. https://doi.org/10.1037/0033-2909.115.3.475

Eid, M. (2000). A multitrait-multimethod model with minimal assumptions. *Psychometrika*, *65*(2), 241–261. https://doi.org/10.1007/BF02294377

Eid, M., & Diener, E. (Eds.). (2006). *Handbook of multimethod measurement in psychology*. American Psychological Association. https://doi.org/10.1037/11383-000

Fabrigar, L. R., Wegener, D. T., MacCallum, R. C., & Strahan, E. J. (1999). Evaluating the use of exploratory factor analysis in psychological research. *Psychological Methods*, *4*(3), 272–299. https://doi.org/10.1037/1082-989X.4.3.272

Ferrer, E., Balluerka, N., & Widaman, K. F. (2008). Factorial invariance and the specification of second-order latent growth models. *Methodology*, *4*(1), 22–36. https://doi.org/10.1027/1614-2241.4.1.22

Fiske, D. W. (1949). Consistency of the factorial structures of personality ratings from different sour sources. *Journal of Abnormal and Social Psychology*, *44*(3), 329–344. https://doi.org/10.1037/h0057198

Floyd, F. J., & Widaman, K. F. (1995). Factor analysis in the development and refinement of clinical assessment instruments. *Psychological Assessment*, *7*(3), 286–299. https://doi.org/10.1037/1040-3590.7.3.286

Goldberg, L. R. (1993). The structure of phenotypic personality traits. *American Psychologist*, *48*(1), 26–34. https://doi.org/10.1037/0003-066X.48.1.26

Goldberg, L. R., & Velicer, W. F. (2006). Principles of exploratory factor analysis. In S. Strack (Ed.), *Differentiating normal and abnormal personality* (2nd ed., pp. 209–237). Springer.

Gorsuch, R. L. (1983). *Factor analysis* (2nd ed.). Erlbaum.

Gorsuch, R. L. (1988). Exploratory factor analysis. In J. R. Nesselroade & R. B. Cattell (Eds.), *Handbook of multivariate experimental psychology* (2nd ed., pp. 231–258). Plenum. https://doi.org/10.1007/978-1-4613-0893-5_6

Guilford, J. P. (1941). The difficulty of a test and its factor composition. *Psychometrika*, *6*(2), 67–77. https://doi.org/10.1007/BF02292175

Guilford, J. P. (1952). When not to factor analyze. *Psychological Bulletin*, *49*(1), 26–37. https://doi.org/10.1037/h0054935

Guilford, J. P. (1964). Zero correlations among tests of intellectual abilities. *Psychological Bulletin*, *61*(6), 401–404. https://doi.org/10.1037/h0048576

Guttman, L. (1954). Some necessary conditions for common-factor analysis. *Psychometrika*, *19*(2), 149–161. https://doi.org/10.1007/BF02289162

Guttman, L. (1956). "Best possible" systematic estimates of communality. *Psychometrika*, *21*(3), 273–285. https://doi.org/10.1007/BF02289137

Hakstian, A. R. (1971). A comparative evaluation of several prominent methods of oblique factor transformation. *Psychometrika*, *36*(2), 175–193. https://doi.org/10.1007/BF02291397

Hakstian, A. R., & Abell, R. A. (1974). A further comparison of oblique factor transformation methods. *Psychometrika*, *39*(4), 429–444. https://doi.org/10.1007/BF02291667

Hakstian, A. R., Rogers, W. T., & Cattell, R. B. (1982). The behavior of number-of-factors rules with simulated data. *Multivariate Behavioral Research*, *17*(2), 193–219. https://doi.org/10.1207/s15327906mbr1702_3

Hancock, G. R., Kuo, W.-L., & Lawrence, F. R. (2001). An illustration of second-order latent growth models. *Structural Equation Modeling*, *8*(3), 470–489. https://doi.org/10.1207/S15328007SEM0803_7

Harman, H. H. (1976). *Modern factor analysis* (3rd ed.). University of Chicago Press.

Harris, C. W., & Kaiser, H. F. (1964). Oblique factor solutions by orthogonal transformations. *Psychometrika*, *29*(4), 347–362. https://doi.org/10.1007/BF02289601

Helm, J. L. (Ed.). (2022). *Advanced multitrait-multimethod analyses for the behavioral and social sciences*. Routledge.

Helm, J. L., Castro-Schilo, L., & Oravecz, Z. (2017). Bayesian versus maximum likelihood estimation of multitrait-multimethod confirmatory factor models. *Structural Equation Modeling*, *24*(1), 17–30. https://doi.org/10.1080/10705511.2016.1236261

Hendrickson, A. E., & White, P. O. (1964). Promax: A quick method for rotation to oblique simple structure. *British Journal of Statistical Psychology*, *17*(1), 65–70. https://doi.org/10.1111/j.2044-8317.1964.tb00244.x

Horn, J. L. (1965). A rationale and test for the number of factors in factor analysis. *Psychometrika*, *30*(2), 179–185. https://doi.org/10.1007/BF02289447

Horn, J. L., & Hofer, S. M. (1992). Major abilities and development in the adult period. In R. J. Sternberg & C. A. Berg (Eds.), *Intellectual development* (pp. 44–99). Cambridge University Press.

Horn, J. L., & McArdle, J. J. (2007). Understanding human intelligence since Spearman. In R. Cudeck & R. C. MacCallum (Eds.), *Factor analysis at 100: Historical developments and future directions* (pp. 205–247). Erlbaum.

Horn, J. L., McArdle, J. J., & Mason, R. (1983). When is invariance not invariant: A practical scientist's look at the ethereal concept of factor invariance. *Southern Psychologist*, *1*(4), 179–188.

Horn, J. L., & Noll, J. (1997). Human cognitive capabilities: Gf-Gc theory. In D. P. Flanagan, J. L. Genshaft, & P. L. Harrison (Eds.), *Contemporary intellectual assessment: Theories, tests, and issues* (pp. 53–91). Guilford Press.

Hu, L., & Bentler, P. M. (1999). Cutoff criteria for fit indexes in covariance structure analysis: Conventional criteria versus new alternatives. *Structural Equation Modeling*, *6*(1), 1–55. https://doi.org/10.1080/10705519909540118

Humphreys, L. G., & Ilgen, D. R. (1969). Note on a criterion for the number of common factors. *Educational and Psychological Measurement*, *29*(3), 571–578. https://doi.org/10.1177/001316446902900303

Humphreys, L. G., & Montanelli, R. G., Jr. (1975). An investigation of the parallel analysis criterion for determining the number of factors. *Multivariate Behavioral Research*, *10*(2), 193–205. https://doi.org/10.1207/s15327906mbr1002_5

Jöreskog, K. G. (1967). Some contributions to maximum likelihood factor analysis. *Psychometrika*, *32*(4), 443–482. https://doi.org/10.1007/BF02289658

Jöreskog, K. G. (1969). A general approach to confirmatory maximum likelihood factor analysis. *Psychometrika*, *34*(2), 183–202. https://doi.org/10.1007/BF02289343

Jöreskog, K. G. (1971a). Simultaneous factor analysis in several populations. *Psychometrika*, *36*(4), 409–426. https://doi.org/10.1007/BF02291366

Jöreskog, K. G. (1971b). Statistical analysis of sets of congeneric tests. *Psychometrika*, *36*(2), 109–133. https://doi.org/10.1007/BF02291393

Kaiser, H. F. (1958). The varimax criterion for analytic rotation in factor analysis. *Psychometrika*, *23*(3), 187–200. https://doi.org/10.1007/BF02289233

Kenny, D. A. (1976). An empirical application of confirmatory factor analysis to the multitrait-multimethod matrix. *Journal of Experimental Social Psychology*, *12*(3), 247–252. https://doi.org/10.1016/0022-1031(76)90055-X

Kenny, D. A., & Kashy, D. A. (1992). Analysis of the multitrait-multimethod matrix by confirmatory factor analysis. *Psychological Bulletin*, *112*(1), 165–172. https://doi.org/10.1037/0033-2909.112.1.165

Levy, R., & Hancock, G. R. (2007). A framework of statistical tests for comparing mean and covariance structure models. *Multivariate Behavioral Research*, *42*(1), 33–66. https://doi.org/10.1080/00273170701329112

Little, T. D. (1997). Mean and covariance structures (MACS) analyses of cross-cultural data: Practical and theoretical issues. *Multivariate Behavioral Research*, *32*(1), 53–76. https://doi.org/10.1207/s15327906mbr3201_3

Little, T. D., Lindenberger, U., & Nesselroade, J. R. (1999). On selecting indicators for multivariate measurement and modeling with LVs: When "good" indicators are bad and "bad" indicators are good. *Psychological Methods*, *4*(2), 192–211. https://doi.org/10.1037/1082-989X.4.2.192

Lu, Z. H., Chow, S. M., & Loken, E. (2016). Bayesian factor analysis as a variable-selection problem: Alternative priors and consequences. *Multivariate Behavioral Research*, *51*(4), 519–539. https://doi.org/10.1080/00273171.2016.1168279

MacCallum, R. (1986). Specification searches in covariance structure modeling. *Psychological Bulletin*, *100*(1), 107–120. https://doi.org/10.1037/0033-2909.100.1.107

MacCallum, R. C., Browne, M. W., & Cai, L. (2007). Factor analysis models as approximations. In R. Cudeck & R. C. MacCallum (Eds.), *Factor analysis at 100: Historical developments and future directions* (pp. 153–175). Erlbaum.

MacCallum, R. C., & Tucker, L. R. (1991). Representing sources of error in the common-factor model: Implications for theory and practices. *Psychological Bulletin*, *109*(3), 502–511. https://doi.org/10.1037/0033-2909.109.3.502

MacCallum, R. C., Widaman, K. F., Preacher, K. J., & Hong, S. (2001). Sample size in factor analysis: The role of model error. *Multivariate Behavioral Research*, *36*(4), 611–637. https://doi.org/10.1207/S15327906MBR3604_06

MacCallum, R. C., Widaman, K. F., Zhang, S., & Hong, S. (1999). Sample size in factor analysis. *Psychological Methods*, *4*(1), 84–99. https://doi.org/10.1037/1082-989X.4.1.84

Marsh, H. W. (1989). Confirmatory factor analyses of multitrait-multimethod data: Many problems and a few solutions. *Applied Psychological Measurement, 13*(4), 335–361. https://doi.org/10.1177/014662168901300402

McArdle, J. J. (1988). Dynamic but structural equation modeling of repeated measures data. In J. R. Nesselroade & R. B. Cattell (Eds.), *Handbook of multivariate experimental psychology* (2nd ed., pp. 561–614). Plenum. https://doi.org/10.1007/978-1-4613-0893-5_17

McArdle, J. J. (1996). Current directions in structural factor analysis. *Current Directions in Psychological Science, 5*(1), 11–18. https://doi.org/10.1111/1467-8721.ep10772681

McArdle, J. J. (2007). Five steps in the structural factor analysis of longitudinal data. In R. Cudeck & R. C. MacCallum (Eds.), *Factor analysis at 100: Historical developments and future directions* (pp. 99–130). Erlbaum.

McArdle, J. J., & Cattell, R. B. (1994). Structural equation models of factorial invariance in parallel proportional profiles and oblique confactor problems. *Multivariate Behavioral Research, 29*(1), 63–113. https://doi.org/10.1207/s15327906mbr2901_3

McDonald, R. P. (1985). *Factor analysis and related methods*. Erlbaum.

McDonald, R. P. (1999). *Test theory*. Erlbaum.

McDonald, R. P., & Ahlawat, K. S. (1974). Difficulty factors in binary data. *British Journal of Mathematical & Statistical Psychology, 27*(1), 82–99. https://doi.org/10.1111/j.2044-8317.1974.tb00530.x

Meredith, W. (1964a). Notes on factorial invariance. *Psychometrika, 29*(2), 177–185. https://doi.org/10.1007/BF02289699

Meredith, W. (1964b). Rotation to achieve factorial invariance. *Psychometrika, 29*(2), 187–206. https://doi.org/10.1007/BF02289700

Meredith, W. (1993). Measurement invariance, factor analysis and factorial invariance. *Psychometrika, 58*(4), 525–543. https://doi.org/10.1007/BF02294825

Meredith, W., & Horn, J. (2001). The role of factorial invariance in modeling growth and change. In L. M. Collins & A. G. Sayer (Eds.), *New methods for the analysis of change* (pp. 203–240). American Psychological Association. https://doi.org/10.1037/10409-007

Millsap, R. E., & Meredith, W. (2007). Factorial invariance: Historical perspectives and new problems. In R. Cudeck & R. C. MacCallum (Eds.), *Factor analysis at 100: Historical perspectives and future directions* (pp. 131–152). Erlbaum.

Millsap, R. E., & Yun-Tein, J. (2004). Assessing factorial invariance in ordered-categorical measures. *Multivariate Behavioral Research, 39*(3), 479–515. https://doi.org/10.1207/S15327906MBR3903_4

Montanelli, R. G., Jr., & Humphreys, L. G. (1976). Latent roots of random data correlation matrices with squared multiple correlations on the diagonal: A Monte Carlo study. *Psychometrika, 41*(3), 341–348. https://doi.org/10.1007/BF02293559

Mulaik, S. A. (2010). *Foundations of factor analysis* (2nd ed.). Chapman & Hall.

Muthén, B., & Asparouhov, T. (2012). Bayesian structural equation modeling: A more flexible representation of substantive theory. *Psychological Methods, 17*(3), 313–335. https://doi.org/10.1037/a0026802

Muthén, B. O. (1978). Contributions to factor analysis of dichotomous variables. *Psychometrika, 43*(4), 551–560. https://doi.org/10.1007/BF02293813

Muthén, B. O. (1984). A general structural equation model with dichotomous, ordered categorical, and continuous latent variable indicators. *Psychometrika, 49*(1), 115–132. https://doi.org/10.1007/BF02294210

Muthén, L. K., & Muthén, B. O. (1998–2017). *Mplus user's guide* (8th ed.) [Computer software]. Muthén & Muthén.

Reise, S. P., Waller, N. G., & Comrey, A. L. (2000). Factor analysis and scale revision. *Psychological Assessment, 12*(3), 287–297. https://doi.org/10.1037/1040-3590.12.3.287

Rhemtulla, M., Brosseau-Liard, P. E., & Savalei, V. (2012). When can categorical variables be treated as continuous? A comparison of robust continuous and categorical SEM estimation methods under suboptimal conditions. *Psychological Methods, 17*(3), 354–373. https://doi.org/10.1037/a0029315

Satorra, A., & Bentler, P. M. (1994). Corrections to test statistics and standard errors in covariance structure analysis. In A. von Eye & C. C. Clogg (Eds.), *LVs analysis: Applications for developmental research* (pp. 399–419). Sage.

Savalei, V. (2010). Small sample statistics for incomplete nonnormal data: Extensions of complete data formulae and a Monte Carlo comparison. *Structural Equation Modeling, 17*(2), 241–264. https://doi.org/10.1080/10705511003659375

Sörbom, D. (1989). Model modification. *Psychometrika, 54*(3), 371–384. https://doi.org/10.1007/BF02294623

Spearman, C. (1904). "General intelligence," objectively determined and measured. *The American Journal of Psychology, 15*(2), 201–293. https://doi.org/10.2307/1412107

Spearman, C. (1927). *The abilities of man*. Macmillan.

Steiger, J. H. (1979). Factor indeterminacy in the 1930s and 1970s: Some interesting parallels. *Psychometrika*, *44*(2), 157–167. https://doi.org/10.1007/BF02293967

Steiger, J. H. (1994). Factor analysis in the 1980's and the 1990's: Some old debates and some new developments. In I. Borg & P. P. Mohler (Eds.), *Trends and perspectives in empirical social research* (pp. 201–224). Walter de Gruyter. https://doi.org/10.1515/9783110887617.201

Steiger, J. H., & Lind, J. C. (1980, May). *Statistically based tests for the number of common factors*. Paper presented at the annual meeting of the Psychometric Society, Iowa City, IA, United States.

Thompson, B. (2004). *Exploratory and confirmatory factor analysis: Understanding concepts and applications*. American Psychological Association. https://doi.org/10.1037/10694-000

Thurstone, L. L. (1931). Multiple factor analysis. *Psychological Review*, *38*(5), 406–427. https://doi.org/10.1037/h0069792

Thurstone, L. L. (1934). The vectors of mind. *Psychological Review*, *41*(1), 1–32. https://doi.org/10.1037/h0075959

Thurstone, L. L. (1935). *The vectors of mind*. University of Chicago Press.

Thurstone, L. L. (1937). Current misuse of the factorial methods. *Psychometrika*, *2*(2), 73–76. https://doi.org/10.1007/BF02288060

Thurstone, L. L. (1938). Primary mental abilities. *Psychometric Monographs*, No. 1.

Thurstone, L. L. (1947). *Multiple factor analysis*. University of Chicago Press.

Thurstone, L. L., & Thurstone, T. G. (1941). Factorial studies of intelligence. *Psychometric Monographs*, No. 2.

Tisak, J., & Meredith, W. (1989). Exploratory longitudinal factor analysis in multiple populations. *Psychometrika*, *54*(2), 261–281. https://doi.org/10.1007/BF02294520

Tucker, L. R. (1940). The role of correlated factors in factor analysis. *Psychometrika*, *5*(2), 141–152. https://doi.org/10.1007/BF02287872

Tucker, L. R. (1971). Relations of factor score estimates to their use. *Psychometrika*, *36*(4), 427–436. https://doi.org/10.1007/BF02291367

Tucker, L. R., Koopman, R. F., & Linn, R. L. (1969). Evaluation of factor analytic research procedures by means of simulated correlation matrices. *Psychometrika*, *34*(4), 421–459. https://doi.org/10.1007/BF02290601

Tucker, L. R., & Lewis, C. (1973). A reliability coefficient for maximum likelihood factor analysis. *Psychometrika*, *38*(1), 1–10. https://doi.org/10.1007/BF02291170

Velicer, W. F. (1976). Determining the number of components from the matrix of partial correlations. *Psychometrika*, *41*(3), 321–327. https://doi.org/10.1007/BF02293557

Velicer, W. F., & Jackson, D. N. (1990). Component analysis versus common factor analysis: Some issues in selecting an appropriate procedure. *Multivariate Behavioral Research*, *25*(1), 1–28. https://doi.org/10.1207/s15327906mbr2501_1

Vrieze, S. I. (2012). Model selection and psychological theory: A discussion of the differences between the Akaike information criterion (AIC) and the Bayesian information criterion (BIC). *Psychological Methods*, *17*(2), 228–243. https://doi.org/10.1037/a0027127

Wherry, R. J., & Gaylord, R. H. (1944). Factor pattern of test items and tests as a function of the correlation coefficient: Content, difficulty, and constant error factors. *Psychometrika*, *9*(4), 237–244. https://doi.org/10.1007/BF02288734

Widaman, K. F. (1985). Hierarchically nested covariance structure models for multitrait-multimethod data. *Applied Psychological Measurement*, *9*(1), 1–26. https://doi.org/10.1177/014662168500900101

Widaman, K. F. (1993). Common factor analysis versus principal component analysis: Differential bias in representing model parameters? *Multivariate Behavioral Research*, *28*(3), 263–311. https://doi.org/10.1207/s15327906mbr2803_1

Widaman, K. F. (2007). Common factors versus components: Principals and principles, errors and misconceptions. In R. Cudeck & R. C. MacCallum (Eds.), *Factor analysis at 100: Historical developments and future directions* (pp. 177–203). Erlbaum.

Widaman, K. F. (2018). On common factor and principal component representations of data: Implications for theory and for confirmatory replications. *Structural Equation Modeling*, *25*(6), 829–847. https://doi.org/10.1080/10705511.2018.1478730

Widaman, K. F., Ferrer, E., & Conger, R. D. (2010). Factorial invariance within longitudinal structural equation models: Measuring the same construct across time. *Child Development Perspectives*, *4*(1), 10–18. https://doi.org/10.1111/j.1750-8606.2009.00110.x

Widaman, K. F., & Herringer, L. W. (1985). Iterative least squares estimates of communality: Initial estimate need not affect stabilized value. *Psychometrika*, *50*(4), 469–477. https://doi.org/10.1007/BF02296264

Widaman, K. F., & Olivera-Aguilar, M. (in press). Investigating measurement invariance using confirmatory factor analysis. In R. H. Hoyle (Ed.), *Handbook of structural equation modeling* (2nd ed.). Guilford Press.

Widaman, K. F., & Reise, S. P. (1997). Exploring the measurement invariance of psychological instruments: Applications in the substance use domain. In K. J. Bryant, M. Windle, & S. G. West (Eds.), *The science of prevention: Methodological advances from alcohol and substance abuse research* (pp. 281–324). American Psychological Association. https://doi.org/10.1037/10222-009

Widaman, K. F., & Thompson, J. S. (2003). On specifying the null model for incremental fit indices in structural equation modeling. *Psychological Methods, 8*(1), 16–37. https://doi.org/10.1037/1082-989X.8.1.16

Wirth, R. J., & Edwards, M. C. (2007). Item factor analysis: Current approaches and future directions. *Psychological Methods, 12*(1), 58–79. https://doi.org/10.1037/1082-989X.12.1.58

Wood, J. M., Tataryn, D. J., & Gorsuch, R. L. (1996). Effects of under- and overextraction on principal axis factor analysis with varimax rotation. *Psychological Methods, 1*(4), 354–365. https://doi.org/10.1037/1082-989X.1.4.354

Zwick, W. R., & Velicer, W. F. (1982). Factors influencing four rules for determining the number of components to retain. *Multivariate Behavioral Research, 17*(2), 253–269. https://doi.org/10.1207/s15327906mbr1702_5

Zwick, W. R., & Velicer, W. F. (1986). Comparison of five rules for determining the number of components to retain. *Psychological Bulletin, 99*(3), 432–442. https://doi.org/10.1037/0033-2909.99.3.432

CHAPTER 18

LATENT CLASS AND LATENT PROFILE MODELS

Brian P. Flaherty, Liying Wang, and Cara J. Kiff

Psychology's concern with unobservable constructs has necessitated the development of appropriate research design and analytic techniques. Beginning in earnest with Thurstone (1935), continuous latent variable models have a long history in psychometrics (Cudeck & MacCallum, 2007). Factor analysis models (see Chapter 17, this volume) have coevolved with psychometrics, leading to sophisticated current-day measurement approaches, such as item response (Embretson & Reise, 2000; Volume 1, Chapter 37, this handbook) and latent difference score models (McArdle, 2001). As a discipline, psychology embraces factor models, leading to their frequent and sometimes automatic use. For example, stage and typological theories, such as Piaget's theory of cognitive development (Piaget, 1960), Kohlberg's theory of moral development (Kohlberg, 1963), and Baumrind's parenting styles (Baumrind, 1967), have typically been analyzed with continuous variable approaches, even though a categorical approach arguably better represents these categorical constructs.

Outside of psychology, scaling people along a continuum has not always been a primary interest. Taxonomy research in biology seeks to hierarchically organize data, and cluster analysis approaches developed accordingly (Blashfield & Aldenderfer, 1988; Jain, 2010). *Cluster analysis* refers broadly to a class of approaches that group observations in terms of similarity. In sociology, seeking to categorize individuals led to Lazarsfeld's initial development of latent class models (Lazarsfeld & Henry, 1968). Concurrently, latent profile models were introduced in psychology (Gibson, 1959). Latent class and latent profile models both model subgroups in a population.

Unlike the development of factor analysis and psychometrics in psychology, these other analytic approaches have not also been connected to advances in measurement. Many cluster analysis techniques are algorithmic (i.e., rule-based) approaches, lacking a probability model for both measurement and statistical inference. In contrast, latent class and latent profile models are statistical models, primarily employed as descriptive, data-partitioning tools. They are not typically treated as a model for a latent construct deserving serious consideration as a measurement model. Thus, in addition to introducing latent class and latent profile analysis, this chapter considers the use of these models as measurement models.

CONCEPTUAL OVERVIEW

Researchers commonly choose latent class and latent profile models when they expect different types of people or observations in a study. Rather than assume homogeneity—that is, a single set of

https://doi.org/10.1037/0000320-018
APA Handbook of Research Methods in Psychology, Second Edition: Vol. 3. Data Analysis and Research Publication, H. Cooper (Editor-in-Chief)
Copyright © 2023 by the American Psychological Association. All rights reserved.

probability distributions and associations hold for an entire population—distributions and associations may differ based on unobservable subgroup membership. As a result, these models readily accommodate heterogeneity. If a population contains subgroups with different distributions and patterns of association, and those subgroups are ignored, then the analytic model is misspecified and unlikely to provide useful information. In this case, it is unlikely that the sample averaged estimates are meaningful or accurately capture phenomena of interest. This parallels a regression model with a missing, but important moderator. Estimated main effects are incorrect. Applications of latent class and latent profile models include temperament types in young children (Beekman et al., 2015; Scott et al., 2016), children's disruptive behavior problems (Racz et al., 2016), adolescent socialization (Cumsille et al., 2006), activity-related health behaviors (Parker et al., 2019), and patterns of substance use (Banks et al., 2020; Flaherty, 2002; O'Connor & Colder, 2005).

We review and discuss these two basic models. Then we illustrate these models with parallel analyses of a single nicotine-dependence data set. Subscales are treated as continuous for the latent profile analysis and dichotomized for latent class analysis with binary items. Binary data are not necessary for latent class analysis, but simplify the presentation. Analyzing the same data with both latent class and latent profile models highlights similarities and differences between the models. No argument is made for which model is better for this particular data or construct.

LATENT CLASS MODELS

A primary goal of latent class models is to partition a heterogeneous population into homogenous subgroups, that is, the latent classes or latent profiles. Just as relative position on a latent factor is expected to predict how someone answers a set of items, latent class or profile membership is expected to predict item responses. Viewed from the item level, we treat the items in a depression scale as indirect indicators of a latent depression factor. Similarly, the items in a latent class or profile analysis may be considered indicators of an unobservable class membership.

To aid discussion, we use LC to abbreviate latent class, LCA for latent class analysis, LP for latent profile, LPA for latent profile analysis, and LC/LP and LCA/LPA to refer to both models at the same time. Historically, LCA used categorical items and LPA used continuous items. Now however, the term LC is often used to refer to any model including an unmeasured categorical variable. For this chapter, we use LCA and LPA as originally described.

The standard LC model is for nominal, potentially polytomous items (for ordinal indicators, see Rost, 1988; for mixed indicators, Moustaki, 1996). The LC model has two types of estimates: LC proportions and conditional response probabilities. The LC proportions are the percent of the population expected to be members of the LCs. The conditional response probabilities are the estimates linking items and the latent variable. Specifically, they are the probabilities that members of a particular class endorse an item response. Table 18.1 contains fabricated LC estimates to illustrate the model.

This example contains two classes and three binary items intended to measure nicotine dependence. (This example is not identified and thus, not estimable, but it is sufficient to convey the ideas.) The columns of Table 18.1 correspond to the items and the rows are the LCs. The probability of a yes response is given in the

TABLE 18.1

Latent Class (LC) Model Illustration

LC	When you haven't had a cigarette for a while, you feel you need to have one to feel better	Compared with when you started smoking, you now need to smoke more to feel the effects	You smoke the same number of cigarettes every day
1 (30%)	0.2	0.5	0.9
2 (70%)	0.9	0.9	0.9

Note. The probability of a yes or true response is shown.

table. The probability of a no response is simply $1 - P(Y|LC)$ with binary data. This notation, $P(Y|LC)$, is shorthand meaning the probability of a yes response to an item given membership in a particular class LC. For precise notation, see the references given.

Table 18.1 contains examples of good and poor measurement items. The first column is a good item for measuring members of each class. People in the first class (LC 1) have a 0.2 probability of replying yes to this item, meaning that a no response is a likely characteristic of people in Class 1. Conversely, people in LC 2 have a 0.9 probability of replying yes. This item provides relatively clear information about a defining characteristic of members of each class. The next two items are not equally good class indicators. The second measures LC 2 well, but provides no information about people in LC 1. That is, the second item contains the same information as a fair coin flip for people in LC 1. This does not mean one would necessarily throw out Item 2. Item 2 could be a salient, theoretically important measure of LC 2, and retained for that reason. Item 3 does not help us distinguish the classes. Item responses are equally likely for members of both classes. If these were the only two classes we sought to measure, Item 3 should be replaced. But if the population included more classes, Item 3 could distinguish other classes from the two shown in Table 18.1.

Response probabilities are used to interpret the classes. The first class is unlikely to endorse craving (Item 1), is mixed on nicotine tolerance (Item 2), and likely endorses continuity of smoking (Item 3). So, LC 1 smokes similarly over days but tends not to experience cravings between cigarettes. Perhaps they are very light smokers and not (or minimally) nicotine-dependent. The LC proportions are given in parentheses in the first column. LC 1 includes 30% of the sample. Members of LC 2 are likely to endorse all the items positively and could be labeled nicotine-dependent.

Notice that good estimates are near 1.0 (e.g., $P(Y)$ for LC 2 across items and $P(N)$ for LC 1 for Item 1). The closer endorsement probabilities are to 1.0, the more highly linked that characteristic is to class membership. This is analogous to factor analysis when the loadings approach an absolute value of 1.0. In Table 18.1, members of LC 2 have a 90% probability of replying yes to Item 1, and 10% are expected to reply no. One way to interpret this 10% is as measurement error—meaning that all members of LC 2 should have replied yes. However, it can also be interpreted as within class response variability of the characteristic in question. In applied problems, it is often probably both (Flaherty & Shono, 2021).

The individual parameter estimates provide the basis for interpreting the classes and for evaluating the measurement characteristics of the items (Clogg & Manning, 1996; Flaherty, 2002). However, the actual data of an LCA are response pattern frequencies. A response pattern is a set of responses to all the measured items. In the three-item example, YYY is one example of a response pattern. With three binary items, there are a total of eight possible response patterns (2^3) and response pattern frequencies. Highlighting the pattern orientation of LCA, one can calculate class membership probabilities for each response pattern (referred to as item–set reliabilities and posterior class membership probabilities). For example, respondents providing the response pattern YYY will have a high probability of membership in LC 2 (e.g., 0.93) and a correspondingly low probability of LC 1 membership (e.g., 1 − .93, or .07). Response patterns that are less expected or less clearly linked to a LC will typically have weaker class membership probabilities. For example, the response pattern NYN would likely have class membership probabilities closer to 50/50, psychometrically unreliable. (For more detail, including the equations explaining reliability in LCA and an empirical example, see Flaherty, 2002.)

LCA is a nonparametric procedure with relatively few assumptions. First, it is assumed that the LCs are mutually exclusive and exhaustive, meaning that every entity in a population is a member of one and only one LC. Furthermore, it is assumed the members of a class are homogeneous, that is, the conditional response probabilities describe everyone in the class equally well. Third, the assumption of conditional independence means the item responses are statistically independent after we know a person's LC membership. This is a common assumption of simple measurement models and implies that class membership is responsible for item covariation. This assumption can be examined by estimating residual dependencies (Hagenaars, 1988).

From Table 18.1, we can also illustrate the number of estimates in a given LC model. Let C denote the number of classes in a model. The number of estimated LC proportions is $C - 1$. This is because any one LC proportion can be calculated by subtracting the sum of the rest from 1.0. The conditional response probabilities also sum to 1 for every item–LC combination. As described in the previous paragraph, for binary data, if the $P(Y|LC)$ is 0.9, then $P(N|LC)$ is 0.1. If there were four response categories, only three response probabilities would be estimated. Therefore, if R denotes the number of response categories for an item, the number of response probabilities estimated is $C(R - 1)$ for that item. For the total number of estimates, this is simply the sum across all the items. The number of response categories can vary across items in any given analysis.

An important step in LCA applications involves assessing the estimability (also called empirical identification) of a given model. Is a set of parameter estimates best and unique? The likelihood function for LC models is often *multimodal*, meaning that there are multiple solutions to the likelihood function (referred to as local maxima or local modes). LC models are commonly estimated via maximum likelihood which typically relies on an iterative computer algorithm and requires starting values. Running only one set of start values to completion leads to one set of estimates, but one cannot be sure if these are the best set of estimates for the current data (i.e., the maximum likelihood estimate [MLE]). A model may be identified, meaning theoretically there is sufficient information to uniquely identify and estimate the population parameters; however, an identified model may be inestimable, meaning a given data set does not contain enough information to estimate the model. Therefore, one should run many sets of random start values to assess estimability. Ideally, many or most sets of random start values converge to the same, best-fitting solution, and there are no other solutions that fit nearly as well. In this case, it is likely the model has been estimated well. However, in practice, one can obtain two or more sets of estimates that fit the data nearly as well yet have different substantive conclusions. In this case, there is no statistical basis to prefer one model over another, and either a simpler model should be fit or more data should be obtained. Model simplification includes fitting fewer classes and parameter restrictions (discussed in the section Additional Topics; see also Flaherty, 2002; Formann, 1985).

Research employing LC models is first a model-fitting exercise, as with confirmatory factor analysis (CFA), structural equation modeling (SEM; Bollen & Long, 1993), and random effects and multilevel models (Raudenbush & Bryk, 2002; Skrondal & Rabe-Hesketh, 2004). Unlike in null hypothesis testing, where one proposes a straw-argument that one hopes to reject, in model fitting, one tests a model that one hopes to retain as a plausible explanation of the observed data. In null-hypothesis testing, the alternative hypothesis is the desired scientific outcome. We wish to reject the model being tested. However, in model fitting, the alternative hypothesis is not the desired outcome; it is an unspecified more complex model connoting inadequate background theory for an accurate model specification. More classes or other estimates are needed to improve model fit and better account for the data.

The first step in latent variable and random effects models is to get the base model right: the measurement or random effects structure. How many dimensions are needed in a CFA for a given construct? Correspondingly, in mixture models, how many classes are needed to account for the bivariate associations among the class indicators? Very often, there is little existing research guiding the selection of a number of classes for a construct, thus these analyses are commonly exploratory.

LC models are contingency table models, like log-linear models (Bishop et al., 1975; Hagenaars, 1998). In LCA, the proposed model and estimates are used to reproduce the contingency table formed by cross-tabulating all the measured items (i.e., the response patterns). When the data are not sparse (defined below), categorical data fit statistics, such as Pearson's X^2 or the likelihood ratio statistic (G^2) can be used to assess the absolute fit of the model to the data. That is, does the model fit the data well enough that random sampling variation is a plausible explanation for any discrepancies between expected values and the data? If the hypothesized model is the population model, then the distribution of either of these fit statistics (over repeated sampling) is centered on the degrees of freedom (df). The df are equal to the number of cells in the full contingency table – number of estimates – 1.

Just as in CFA and SEM, an overidentified model has at least one df. If we fit a two-class model to four binary items, then the df equals six ($2^4 - 9 - 1$). When data are not sparse, the p value of the statistic can be found by checking its probability against a chi-square distribution with the model's df. A nonsignificant test statistic means the probability of observing a test statistic as or more extreme than the value obtained is relatively large and that the fitted model appears consistent with the data.

Sparse data occur when there are many cells with zero or few observations (Agresti & Yang, 1987; Collins et al., 1993). When data are sparse, the chi-square distribution is not distributed with the nominal degrees of freedom. The mean of the distribution is different but unknown. Therefore, when data are sparse, a Pearson's X^2 or G^2 statistic that appears nonsignificant may indeed be significant. For this reason, many users have stopped reporting these values. However, it is somewhat similar to the use of the chi-square statistic in CFA and SEM. That statistic is not used alone to make decisions about model fit, but it is always reported (Kline, 2015). The same should be done with LC models because the statistics can still be useful. For example, if data are sparse and the G^2 statistic is large, then it is quite likely the model does not fit well.

Relative fit measures, such as information criteria, are currently the most commonly used in LC/LP models. The two most popular information criteria are Akaike's information criteria (AIC; Akaike, 1987) and Bayesian information criteria (BIC; also referred to as *Schwarz information criteria*; Schwarz, 1978). These are penalized quantities that attempt to balance model fit with parsimony. These values do not reflect model fit to the data, but rather they reflect which one model of several appears best given the models' sizes. Lower values reflect better model fit and one simply finds the lowest AIC or BIC among the set to see which model is preferred. Ideally, absolute and relative fit measures point to the same final model (see Burnham & Anderson, 2004, for a good discussion of AIC and BIC).

All other things being equal, parsimony is a desirable characteristic of our models. However, recalling the exploratory nature of most mixture analyses and the logic of model fitting reviewed above, relying on parsimony actually pushes us toward accepting simpler models while the statistical decision process pushes us toward more complexity when our hypothesized model is incorrect and we lack sufficient knowledge about the construct's structure. In real analyses, these countervailing factors on our statistical decision making should be borne in mind. Fit measures frequently disagree, and our knowledge base is frequently lacking with respect to mixture structure. In this case, leaning toward complexity may be preferable, rather than prematurely concluding simplicity (Flaherty, 2015). Given a set of plausible models, such as when determining the appropriate number of classes or profiles in an exploratory analysis, it is imperative to make the best choice for future scientific work.

Entropy (Celeux & Soromenho, 1996) is another useful measure of our model's use, but it is not a measure of fit. Rather, it is a measure of classification accuracy. Entropy ranges from 0 to 1, with 1 meaning perfect classification. Finally, the interpretability of the model is also critical. If a set of estimates makes no sense, what use are they? For example, if several classes in a solution have essentially similar response probabilities, then there are no interesting differences among the classes (e.g., similar to Item 3 in Table 18.1). Alternatively, if an LC proportion is very small, one must decide whether it likely reflects noise in the data or a small substantively interesting group. Essentially, one should scrutinize one's results to ensure that they are substantively meaningful. On the other hand, surprises may also reveal interesting, unanticipated aspects of phenomena under study. Reiterating the trade-off between parsimony and the model fitting statistical decision process, the exploratory nature of most mixture analyses should encourage the researcher to consider more complex, nuanced class structures. There are many other approaches to fit testing and selecting the number of classes, but none have been shown to be generally superior to others. Some approaches have been shown to work well in simulated data, but their general performance in real data remains unclear. See references below for more on these approaches.

This presentation has necessarily been limited. More thorough presentations can be obtained from the citations provided as well as from McCutcheon (1987), Collins and Lanza (2010), Goodman (1974), and Bartholomew et al. (2011). These are presented in order of the authors' opinions about their accessibility to a general psychology audience. Furthermore, both LCA and LPA are types of statistical mixture models (McLachlan & Peel, 2000), so relevant literature may also be found with that term.

LATENT PROFILE MODELS

LCA and LPA are similar models, and most of the LCA discussion applies to LPA too. Rather than conditional response probabilities linking classes and items, conditional means link the profiles and items. Furthermore, residual variances are estimated for the items. Typically, this variance is pooled across the profiles, yielding only one residual variance per item. An important assumption of LPA is that the items are normally distributed conditional on profile membership. The specific normal distribution is determined by the profile item mean and pooled residual variance. As with LCA, assumptions about the structure of the errors in LPA can be tested. LP proportions are interpreted just as in the LCA case. Table 18.2 contains fabricated estimates to illustrate an LPA.

As with the previous example, there are two profiles and three items. Now, however, the items are standardized continuous measures of nicotine dependence. To interpret the LPs, profile means are compared with the overall sample mean as well as across profiles. Item 1 again differentiates the profiles because the profile means are quite different. This result is also reflected in the smaller residual variance for Item 1. Item 2 again does a good job measuring LP 2 but not so much for LP 1. The conditional mean for LP 1 is nearly zero, so it is close to the population mean. Item 3 has almost the same means for both profiles. Item 2 does help us distinguish the profiles, whereas Item 3 does not. Items with a wider range of profile means will have lower residual variance. This is an assessment of how well items are measuring the profiles.

When there are no restrictions among means in an LPA, the number of estimates in the model is straightforward to compute. As with LCA, there are $C - 1$ LP proportions, where C denotes the number of profiles. If there are q items, then $C \times q$ conditional means, and q residual variances are estimated. Unlike LCA, there are no absolute fit statistics for LPA.

TABLE 18.2

Latent Profile (LP) Model Illustration

LP	When you haven't had a cigarette for a while, you feel you need to have one to feel better	Compared with when you started smoking, you now need to smoke more in order to feel the effects	You smoke the same number of cigarettes every day
1 (30%)	−0.50	−0.05	0.10
2 (70%)	0.80	1.20	0.05
Residual variance	0.40	0.60	0.94

Note. Profile means and a residual variance for each item are shown, in standardized scale. Higher scores represent higher dependence.

As discussed above, most LCA and LPA analyses are exploratory, so often researchers run a sequence of models with increasing numbers of classes or profiles and then choose the best model of that set. However, this can be challenging. First, AIC, BIC, and other fit measures often disagree. Second, it is possible that all of the models do not fit the data well. Relative comparisons always point to one model as the best, but it could be the best of several bad choices. Better, generally accepted model selection criteria for both LCA and LPA are needed. Ultimately, the best model should be chosen on the basis of a combination of model fit and estimates, researcher hypotheses and expectations, and the interpretability of the solution (Edwards, 1992; Hu & Bentler, 1995; Marsh et al., 2004).

EMPIRICAL ILLUSTRATION

Nicotine dependence has been conceptualized as both a binary state (addicted or not) and as a continuum (degree of dependence). We use a large, relatively homogeneous sample of U.S. young adults to illustrate both models, specifically data from the Nicotine Dependence Syndrome Scales (NDSS; Shiffman et al., 2004). By narrowing down to a more limited demographic group, we eliminate heterogeneity in our data associated with demographics. The analyses presented here follow on the analyses done with the National Survey on Drug Use and Health (NSDUH) 2004 data for the first edition of this volume (Flaherty & Kiff, 2012).

Sample and Procedures

Data are from the 2014 NSDUH (United States Department of Health and Human Services, 2014) a national survey of U.S. households focused on substance use, abuse, and associated factors. These data are publicly available. For this illustration, we limited the sample to White young adults between 18 and 25 years old who indicated some cigarette smoking in the past 30 days. The sample was nearly 55% male. The total sample size was 2,355.

Measures

Items were selected from the NDSS, which contains five subscales: Drive, Priority, Continuity, Stereotypy, and Tolerance. For each item, participants reported the degree to which the item was true for them on a 5-point Likert scale (ranging from 1 = *not at all true* to 5 = *extremely true*). To form the variables to use in our analysis, we combined the subscale items. Three items measured tolerance, the degree to which individuals have increased their smoking as a result of decreased sensitivity to nicotine. Continuity, also composed of three items, is the degree individuals were smoking consistently across the day. Stereotypy (three items, all were reverse coded) reflects the contextual rigidity of an individual's smoking. The Priority subscale (three items) taps the importance and value placed on smoking. The four-item Drive subscale assesses the avoidance of withdrawal symptoms. Because this scale included more items, and to include an example of multiple indicators, the drive items were split into two sets. Drive 1 reflects irritability or craving experienced when not smoking. Drive 2 captures the sense of control the individual feels over their cigarette smoking. One Drive 2 item was reverse coded.

Data preparation. An LPA was run on the six standardized composite scores just described. For the LCA, we created binary indicators of dependence. Participants received a 0 (no) if they did not endorse any of the dependence items in the item set. Participants received a 1 (yes) for the subscale if they endorsed any level of dependence on any of the corresponding items. For example, to be given a 0 for the binary Continuity indicator, a participant must have replied "not at all true" to all three continuity items.

Data analyses. LCA and LPA models were estimated with Stata version 17 (StataCorp, 2021). We ran 100 sets of random start values (five sets of 20) to assess model estimability. The estimation routine handles missing data via full information maximum likelihood (Schafer & Graham, 2002). For LCA, we fit unrestricted models with one through seven classes. For LPA, we fit one through 15 profiles. Model assessment was based on a combination of estimability, model fit measures, and substantive interpretation.

LCA Results

Table 18.3 presents fit information for models with one to seven LCs. It demonstrates how different fit criteria may disagree. BIC and the G^2 statistic both indicate the two-class model, whereas the AIC points to the six-class model. Besides fit measures, one must check the estimability of the model and if that is good, also check the parameter estimates of any models under consideration. Table 18.3 shows that the two-class model was estimated well. The best log likelihood value was replicated all five times. Larger models were not as well estimated. In practice, many more random start values could be run to better check the estimability, but the current lack of replication of the larger models, including the six-class model, suggests that these data may not be able to distinguish among more complex models. Note, the fact that we cannot reliably estimate a model does not mean the model is not correct in the population. It is a limitation of the data. Once examining a well-estimated model, are the estimates themselves sensible and reasonable? For example, classes with many nearly random response probabilities are probably not very useful, although figuring out why this happened could be important. Are any class sizes very small? Depending upon the sample size in a given problem, small class sizes may only reflect one or a few observations. On the other hand, with a sample of 2,500, a class comprising 1% of the population reflects about 25 people, which could be scientifically worthwhile.

Examining the series of models can also be useful because it shows the relative stability of classes with increasing model size (Arnett & Flaherty, 2022). For example, do classes identified in smaller models (e.g., two or three classes) also appear in more complex models? If so, that suggests the presence of relatively homogeneous classes in the data. On the other hand, seeing a dramatically different solution with five classes, for example, compared with the four-class model, suggests less actual homogeneity in the smaller models. Given the fit statistics and estimability in the current analysis, the two-class model is the safest to report. If more start values indicated better estimability of larger models, they too could be more confidently considered. To create a comparison, we consider the two- and six-class models (Figure 18.1), recognizing that in practice, we would run more start values and perhaps closely examine much more. In other data examples, this two- versus six-class decision could arise with well-estimated models.

The two-class model maps onto a binary conception of nicotine dependence: dependent (LC 1) and not (LC 2). The dependent class is about 71% of the population and has high endorsement probabilities of all the items, except Priority. LC 1 has the highest endorsement probability of Priority, but it is still only

TABLE 18.3

Latent Class Model Fit Statistics and Indices

Class	Best $l(\theta)$	Number of best $l(\theta)$ replications	Number of parameters	G^2	df	p	AIC	BIC	Entropy
1	−6763.93	5	6	2249.669	57	≈ 0	13539.86	13574.44	na
2	−5662.93	5	13	*47.66*	50	0.57	11351.86	*11426.78*	*0.86*
3	−5646.04	1	20	13.88	43	≈ 1.0	11332.08	11447.34	0.75
4	−5632.39	2	27	na	36	na	11314.79	11458.86	0.71
5	−5627.19	0	34	na	29	na	11316.37	11495.03	0.73
6	−5625.28	0	41	na	22	na	*11312.57*	11491.22	0.81
7	−5623.62	0	48	na	15	na	11329.24	11565.52	0.61

Note. Italicized values indicate preferred solutions for each measure of fit. $l(\theta)$ = maximum log likelihood; ≈ means approximately equal; AIC = Akaike's information criteria; BIC = Bayesian information criteria; na = not applicable.

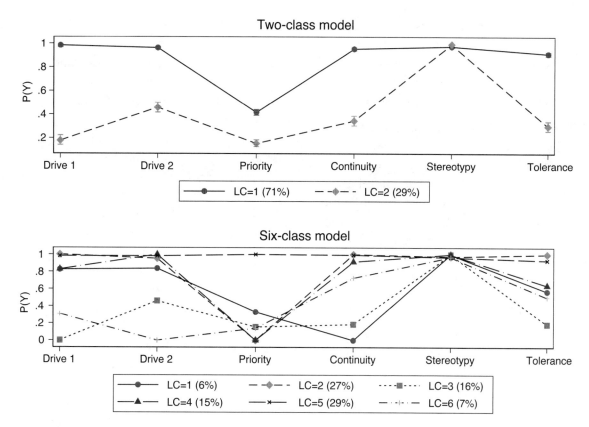

FIGURE 18.1. Two- and six-class models (latent class [LC] analysis) based on six indicators of nicotine dependence from the Nicotine Dependence Syndrome Scale. LC percentages are shown in parentheses in the respective legend. The two-class plot includes 95% confidence intervals. The six-class plot does not because many of the estimates were on the boundary (0 or 1.0).

around 0.40, reflecting the low overall endorsement rate in the sample. Correspondingly, members of LC 2 (29% of the population) have comparably lower endorsement probabilities of all items, except Stereotypy. In these LC analyses, Stereotypy does not distinguish any classes. In this sample, Stereotypy was nearly universally endorsed.

The six-class solution largely parallels the two-class solution. Generally, the dependent class in the two-class model has been broken into four classes. Two of these classes (LCs 2 and 5) comprise almost 60% of the sample and differ on the Priority item. LC 5 is certain to endorse it, LC 2 is virtually certain not to. LCs 1 and 4 largely parallel each other's response probabilities, with the exception of Continuity. Members of these classes are likely to endorse both Drive items; they have moderate rates of endorsement of Tolerance; and members of both are not likely to endorse Priority. LC 4 (15%) is likely to endorse Continuity and LC 1 (6%) is not. LC 3 (16%) and LC 6 (7%) appear to be the two-class model's nondependent class split into two groups. There are some differences between them, but they largely track together, and you can see how the two-class model's estimates are essentially weighted averages of LC 3 and LC 6 response probability estimates.

The choice between the two- and six-class models should be driven by the science and fit measures, not simply by one's preference for one or more fit quantities. Is a class with relatively high dependence item endorsement, except Continuity substantively important? Is breaking out two high dependence classes by Priority important or interesting? In some cases, it could be, perhaps in others, less so. Decisions about models and class structure should take such considerations into account, especially when those analyses are exploratory (Flaherty, 2015).

A frequent concern with models with many classes is that one is just modeling error (for a counterexample, see Flaherty & Shono, 2021). However, the similarity between the six- and two-class solutions suggests this is not the case.

LPA results. Table 18.4 presents the model fit information for unrestricted LP models ranging from one to 10 profiles, although we fit 15. The additional five lines in the table add nothing beyond the first 10. A minimum AIC or BIC was not reached. The lowest value of each occurs for the 15-profile model, and presumably, both would have continued decreasing further. The eight-profile model was estimated well, and the BIC suggested it might be preferable to the nine-profile model. (Note that the highest log likelihood value was not reproduced for the nine-profile model, thus we cannot be confident we've identified a best nine profile model.) However, the eight-profile model included profiles that differed moderately by level only; for example, one profile had means about two times higher than the means in another profile. LPA does not model level well; it models means and residual variances, thus class structure like this may simply be approximating the dimensionality of the original measure. Thus, we looked to a simpler model. The five-profile model, while not being estimated as well as the four-profile model, had the highest entropy of all the models being tested. Given the pattern of AIC and BIC across all the models, any of these models are likely inadequate. We present the five-profile model as an illustration of LPA, but these results are provisional.

Figure 18.2 contains the conditional means of the six standardized indicators for the five nicotine dependence profiles. In Figure 18.2, a conditional mean near 0 denotes a profile mean near the sample average. For reference, the unstandardized sample means were: Drive 1 = 2.6; Drive 2 = 2.6; Priority = 1.3; Continuity = 2.7; Stereotypy = 3.5; and Tolerance = 2.2. The top row of Figure 18.2 are all profiles characterized by higher-than-average nicotine dependence. The first profile (15%) has high Drive, Continuity, and the highest Tolerance of the profiles. Priority is at the sample mean and Stereotypy is below average, which is counterintuitive, but we saw Stereotypy did not work well in the LCA either. Profile 2 is also characterized by high dependence and this small class has very high mean Priority. This is the only group with high Priority. Profile 3 has high Drive and Continuity, albeit lower than the first two profiles, but average Priority, Stereotypy, and Tolerance. They are 17% of the population. The fourth profile (26%) is characterized by

TABLE 18.4

Latent Profile Model Fit Indicators

Profile	Best $l(\theta)$	Number of best $l(\theta)$ replications	Number of parameters	AIC value	BIC value	Entropy
1	−20012.55	na	12	40049.09	40118.25	na
2	−17852.17	5	19	35742.35	35851.85	0.87
3	−17382.73	5	26	34817.45	34967.29	0.83
4	−17045.59	5	33	34157.18	34347.36	0.85
5	−16895.90	2	40	33871.81	34102.33	*0.90*
6	−16798.47	2	47	33690.94	33961.81	0.82
7	−16728.50	5	54	33565.00	33876.20	0.80
8	−16658.00	5	61	33438.01	33789.55	0.80
9	−16468.74	1	68	33073.47	35851.85	0.86
10	−16158.78	1	75	32467.56	32899.78	0.83

Note. Italicized value indicates preferred solution for the measure of fit. $l(\theta)$ = maximum loglikelihood; ≈ means approximately equal; AIC = Akaike's information criteria; BIC = Bayesian information criteria; na = not applicable.

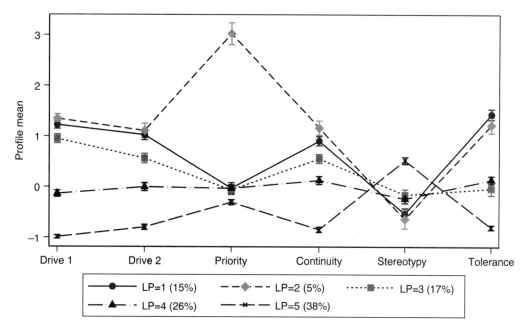

FIGURE 18.2. Five-profile model (latent profile [LP] analysis) based on six indicators of nicotine dependence from the Nicotine Dependence Syndrome Scale. LP percentages are shown in parentheses in the legend. Plotted values are standardized means with 95% confidence intervals.

conditional means near the sample means on all except Stereotypy. Finally, profile five (38%) has the lowest means on all, except Stereotypy, which is higher than average.

The residual variances for the six items measuring the NDSS subscales indicated mixed measurement quality. The first Drive item had the lowest residual variance at 0.17, meaning these five profiles account for 83% of the variance in the first Drive item. The residual variance for Tolerance was 38%. For the second Drive and Continuity items, residual variances were each 49%. Priority was 55% and Stereotypy was 82% since the conditional means for Stereotypy were the most similar.

MODEL SUMMARY

We analyzed the same initial data to emphasize similarities and differences between the models. Both analyses contain examples of good and poor indicators. In the LCA, Drive 1 and Continuity were both examples of good indicators; each having large differences in response probabilities among some or all the classes. Stereotypy and to a lesser degree Priority were both examples of poor indicators. Stereotypy essentially distinguished no classes from one or another. Note that frequently response probabilities near 0.0 or 1.0 are called good measurement in LCA, but when members of all the classes are likely to endorse an item, the item is not actually contributing to LC membership identification. This underscores the pattern-oriented nature of measurement in mixture models. We just pointed to individual items as good or poor, but really, the entire item set matters. This is different from factor analysis, where items are good or poor for everyone in the population; additionally, if there are enough items in a scale, one can usually remove one or two items and not expect measurement to change that much. In the LC and mixture context, sets of items together help distinguish the classes. In the six-class model, Priority distinguishes Class 2 and Class 5, but Drive, Continuity, and Tolerance distinguish Classes 3 and 6 from the Classes 1, 2, and 4. Without the Priority item, we could not differentiate Classes 2 and 5. The importance of this is a scientific decision, not a statistical one. The same measurement perspective applies to the LPA. The pattern of item scores distinguishes the classes. In LPA, we have insight into measurement quality added by the error variance. The first Drive item had the largest spread of profile means across the five-profile model, which correspondingly reduces the residual error.

The results of both analyses are disappointing inasmuch as the two-class model simply parallels a dimension from low to high and the six-class model was not well estimated. Additionally, a reasonably good fitting LP model was not identified. However, this may not mean that these mixture models are poor models for the nicotine dependence construct. It could be that the NDSS is a poor choice for a mixture approach to modeling nicotine dependence. The NDSS, like many psychological scales, was written and developed with a factor analysis model in mind. Items were written to be indicators in a factor analysis. Items were piloted, revised, and rejected based on their performance in factor analysis. This is standard practice in psychology. If the factor model underlies most of our scale construction, should we be surprised when mixture approaches do not perform well or simply recover dimensions? During scale construction, poorly correlated items are revised or dropped. Those very items could be important for distinguishing classes. To make a genuine effort to measure classes, we need to create class-oriented scales from the start.

ADDITIONAL TOPICS

This chapter has introduced LCA and LPA, underscoring their use as measurement models. Some associated topics are introduced or expanded here.

Parameter Restrictions

Two common types of parameter restrictions are parameter fixing and equality restrictions. *Parameter fixing* means that rather than estimate a parameter, one fixes the parameter to a specific value. For example, in the standard LPA model, correlations among residual errors are fixed to zero. Residual correlation between LC indicators is also typically fixed to zero. This is a result of the local independence assumption. *Equality restrictions* constrain two or more estimates to be equal. Two drive items were used to highlight the idea of parallel items in these analyses. With parallel items, one could constrain the item estimates to be equal across two or more classes to test or enforce an assumed parallelism. Furthermore, the standard LPA model pools error variances, which are equality restrictions. Creating scientifically meaningful classes—for example, a reference class for comparison with other classes—can be achieved with parameter restrictions (e.g., Roberts et al., 2018). Parameter restrictions are also commonly used in LCA and LPA to reduce the size of the model to improve estimation. For a review, see Schmiege et al. (2018).

Covariates

Covariate models (Dayton & Macready, 1988) have been developed to explore constructs and characteristics associated with class membership. Logistic (or multinomial logistic) regression models (Hosmer & Lemeshow, 1989) predict class or profile membership as a function of covariates. That is, the LC or LP membership becomes the response. Thorough presentations as well as illustrative examples can be found in Chung et al. (2006) and Reboussin et al. (2006). Others have extended these models to allow covariates to predict item responses as well as LC membership (Pfeffermann et al., 1998). Covariates predicting class membership should have a minimal impact on the interpretation of the classes, but when covariates predict measurement parameters, class interpretations can change substantially.

Consider an LC model with no covariates. The estimated response probabilities are a function of the members expected to be in that class. Assume we have a very good predictor of class membership. With that predictor in the model, the expected members of the class could change appreciably, for example, let's say 10% more observations are expected to be in the class and it grows from 12% without the covariate to 22% with the covariate. As a result of this change in class size, the estimated response probabilities may also change,

In contrast, now consider a predictor of item response. In the LC model without any covariates, the only predictor of item response is the LC variable. Imagine that we had an important predictor of an item response that we add to the model. Now there are two predictors of item response: the LC variable and our covariate. As in regression, the estimates for one predictor can change substantially when a second important predictor is added, this holds here too. Essentially a covariate predicting item response accounts for some variation (information) in the item and the LC variable can only account for a portion of the remaining variation. Thus, in this latter situation, the response probabilities could change substantially, profoundly affecting the class interpretation. This is a type of measurement invariance assessment (Meredith, 1993; Kankaraš et al., 2018).

Longitudinal Models

Thus far, our discussion has involved only cross-sectional models. However, longitudinal LC models allow one to study change over time among class memberships. There are two broad approaches to incorporating LCs into longitudinal analysis: models such as group-based trajectory and growth mixture models treats change continuously, like a growth curve model (Rogosa et al., 1982); on the other hand, models like latent transition analysis model change qualitatively, that is, among discrete states.

Group-based trajectory (Nagin, 2005) and growth mixture models (Muthén & Shedden, 1999) are two mixture approaches to modeling continuous change. Growth mixture models posit a number of trajectory classes within the population, analogous to LC and LPA. Group-based trajectory models use latent classes to approximate an observed distribution, but do not expect to identify "real" classes in a population (Nagin & Odgers, 2010). Groups or classes are comprised of observations with common developmental profiles, but those observations are probabilistically assigned. In these models, the classes summarize the entire pattern of change over time. As an example, if we modeled trajectories of nicotine dependence, we might expect to see one group increasing, another remaining flat and not addicted, and a third, perhaps increasing and then decreasing, representing people who quit.

In contrast, models of discrete change estimate probability of class membership change over time. Latent Markov models (van de Pol & Langeheine, 1990) were originally developed for a single, repeatedly measured item, whereas latent transition models (Collins & Wugalter, 1992) incorporated multiple indicators. These models estimate transition probabilities among the classes between assessment points. Transition probabilities quantify change and stability of the classes over time. For example, suppose someone was a member of a class of nondependent smokers at Time 1. At Time 2, how likely is it that the nondependent smoker became a dependent smoker? What is the probability a Time 1 nondependent smoker is still a nondependent smoker at Time 2?

CONCLUSION

This chapter has focused on two unrestricted categorical latent variable models: the LC and LP models, emphasizing their use as measurement models. In this regard, these models can be viewed in the broader class of latent variable measurement models, including factor and structural equation models. Furthermore, LCA and LPA are two simple mixture models, sharing many similarities with other mixture models. Mixture regression models (DeSarbo & Cron, 1988) embed a regression equation in an LC model, allowing for different regression associations within classes. For example, in one class, depression may predict recent cigarette smoking, but in a second class, depression is not related to recent smoking. Factor mixture models embed a factor model within the LC, where a single categorical latent variable models the different classes, and one or more continuous latent variables model the covariation among observed variables within classes (Lubke & Muthén, 2005). For example, one could imagine a latent class with the expected NDSS factor structure and a second class in which the NDSS items form different factors with potentially different interpretations. Multiple software options fit these models, including the poLCA and mclust packages in R, as well as Stata, Mplus, and LatentGold.

These models are large sample procedures and are often more difficult to estimate than standard factor analytic models. As such, some considerations and precautions may be offered. Sample size requirements are difficult to make because they depend on factors such as class separation (i.e., the *distance* between the class in multivariate space) and measurement quality. A large sample combined with poor measurement may lead to difficulty identifying meaningful classes. On the other hand, if you have very clear response associations with class membership, then a much smaller sample may still yield meaningful classes. All this said, the authors' sense is that 300 to 500 is an absolute minimum sample size without other information (e.g., very strong parameter restrictions or prior information incorporated via a Bayesian approach).

Ideally, this chapter has provided a foundation from which you can work toward incorporating these models in your own work and enables you to consider these models as measurement models therein. Expanding psychological research beyond dimensions to qualitatively different subgroups could prove invaluable to our understanding of behavior.

References

Agresti, A., & Yang, M. (1987). An empirical investigation of some effects of sparseness in contingency tables. *Computational Statistics & Data Analysis*, 5(1), 9–21. https://doi.org/10.1016/0167-9473(87)90003-X

Akaike, H. (1987). Factor analysis and AIC. *Psychometrika*, 52(3), 317–332. https://doi.org/10.1007/BF02294359

Arnett, A. B., & Flaherty, B. P. (2022). A framework for characterizing heterogeneity in neurodevelopmental data using latent profile analysis in a sample of children with ADHD. *Journal of Neurodevelopmental Disorders*, 45. https://doi.org/10.1186/s11689-022-09454-w

Banks, D. E., Bello, M. S., Crichlow, Q., Leventhal, A. M., Barnes-Najor, J. V., & Zapolski, T. C. B. (2020). Differential typologies of current substance use among Black and White high-school adolescents: A latent class analysis. *Addictive Behaviors*, 106, 106356. https://doi.org/10.1016/j.addbeh.2020.106356

Bartholomew, D., Knott, M., & Moustaki, I. (2011). *Latent variable models and factor analysis: A unified approach* (3rd ed.). Wiley. https://doi.org/10.1002/9781119970583

Baumrind, D. (1967). Child care practices anteceding three patterns of preschool behavior. *Genetic Psychology Monographs*, 75(1), 43–88.

Beekman, C., Neiderhiser, J. M., Buss, K. A., Loken, E., Moore, G. A., Leve, L. D., Ganiban, J. M., Shaw, D. S., & Reiss, D. (2015). The development of early profiles of temperament: Characterization, continuity, and etiology. *Child Development*, 86(6), 1794–1811. https://doi.org/10.1111/cdev.12417

Bishop, Y. M. M., Fienberg, S. E., & Holland, P. W. (1975). *Discrete multivariate analysis: Theory and practice*. MIT Press.

Blashfield, R. K., & Aldenderfer, M. S. (1988). The methods and problems of cluster analysis. In J. Nesselroade & R. Cattell (Eds.), *Handbook of multivariate experimental psychology* (pp. 447–473). Plenum Press. https://doi.org/10.1007/978-1-4613-0893-5_14

Bollen, K. A., & Long, J. S. (1993). *Testing structural equation models*. SAGE.

Burnham, K. P., & Anderson, D. R. (2004). Multimodel inference: Understanding AIC and BIC in model selection. *Sociological Methods & Research*, 33(2), 261–304. https://doi.org/10.1177/0049124104268644

Celeux, G., & Soromenho, G. (1996). An entropy criterion for assessing the number of clusters in a mixture model. *Journal of Classification*, 13(2), 195–212. https://doi.org/10.1007/BF01246098

Chung, H., Flaherty, B. P., & Schafer, J. L. (2006). Latent class logistic regression: Application to marijuana use and attitudes among high school seniors. *Journal of the Royal Statistical Society. Series A (Statistics in Society)*, 169(4), 723–743. https://doi.org/10.1111/j.1467-985X.2006.00419.x

Clogg, C. C., & Manning, W. D. (1996). Assessing reliability of categorical measurements using latent class models. In A. von Eye & C. C. Clogg (Eds.), *Categorical variables in developmental research: Methods of analysis* (pp. 169–182).

Academic Press. https://doi.org/10.1016/B978-012724965-0/50011-0

Collins, L. M., Fidler, P. L., Wugalter, S. E., & Long, J. D. (1993). Goodness-of-fit testing for latent class models. *Multivariate Behavioral Research*, 28(3), 375–389. https://doi.org/10.1207/s15327906mbr2803_4

Collins, L. M., & Lanza, S. T. (2010). *Latent class and latent transition analysis: With applications in the social behavioral, and health sciences*. Wiley.

Collins, L. M., & Wugalter, S. E. (1992). Latent class models for stage-sequential dynamic latent-variables. *Multivariate Behavioral Research*, 27(1), 131–157. https://doi.org/10.1207/s15327906mbr2701_8

Cudeck, R., & MacCallum, R. C. (Eds.). (2007). *Factor analysis at 100: Historical developments and future directions*. Psychology Press. https://doi.org/10.4324/9780203936764

Cumsille, P., Darling, N., Flaherty, B. P., & Martínez, M. L. (2006). Chilean adolescents' beliefs about the legitimacy of parental authority: Individual and age-related differences. *International Journal of Behavioral Development*, 30(2), 97–106. https://doi.org/10.1177/0165025406063554

Dayton, C. M., & Macready, G. B. (1988). Concomitant-variable latent-class models. *Journal of the American Statistical Association*, 83(401), 173–178. https://doi.org/10.1080/01621459.1988.10478584

DeSarbo, W. S., & Cron, W. L. (1988). A maximum likelihood methodology for clusterwise linear regression. *Journal of Classification*, 5(2), 249–282. https://doi.org/10.1007/BF01897167

Edwards, A. W. F. (1992). *Likelihood*. Johns Hopkins University Press.

Embretson, S. E., & Reise, S. P. (2000). *Item response theory for psychologists*. Erlbaum.

Flaherty, B. P. (2002). Assessing reliability of categorical substance use measures with latent class analysis. *Drug and Alcohol Dependence*, 68(Suppl. 1), 7–20. https://doi.org/10.1016/S0376-8716(02)00210-7

Flaherty, B. P. (2015). Cigarette smoking patterns as a case study of theory-oriented latent class analysis. In L. M. Scheier (Ed.), *Handbook of adolescent drug use prevention: Research, intervention strategies, and practice* (pp. 437–458). American Psychological Association. https://doi.org/10.1037/14550-025

Flaherty, B. P., & Kiff, C. J. (2012). Latent class and latent profile models. In H. Cooper, P. M. Camic, D. L. Long, A. T. Panter, D. Rindskopf, & K. J. Sher (Eds.), *APA handbook of research methods in psychology, Vol. 3. Data analysis and research publication* (pp. 391–404). American Psychological Association. https://doi.org/10.1037/13621-019

Flaherty, B. P., & Shono, Y. (2021). Many Classes, Restricted Measurement (MACREM) Models for Improved Measurement of Activities of Daily Living. *Journal of Survey Statistics and Methodology*, 9(2), 231–256. https://doi.org/10.1093/jssam/smaa047

Formann, A. K. (1985). Constrained latent class models: Theory and applications. *British Journal of Mathematical & Statistical Psychology*, 38(1), 87–111. https://doi.org/10.1111/j.2044-8317.1985.tb00818.x

Gibson, W. A. (1959). Three multivariate models: Factor analysis, latent structure analysis, and latent profile analysis. *Psychometrika*, 24(3), 229–252. https://doi.org/10.1007/BF02289845

Goodman, L. A. (1974). Exploratory latent structure analysis using both identifiable and unidentifiable models. *Biometrika*, 61(2), 215–231. https://doi.org/10.1093/biomet/61.2.215

Hagenaars, J. (1988). Latent structure models with direct effects between indicators. *Sociological Methods & Research*, 16(3), 379–405. https://doi.org/10.1177/0049124188016003002

Hagenaars, J. A. (1998). Categorical causal modeling: Latent class analysis and directed log-linear models with latent variables. *Sociological Methods & Research*, 26(4), 436–486. https://doi.org/10.1177/0049124198026004002

Hosmer, D. W., & Lemeshow, S. (1989). *Applied logistic regression*. Wiley.

Hu, L., & Bentler, P. M. (1995). Evaluating model fit. In R. H. Hoyle (Ed.), *Structural equation modeling: Concepts, issues, and applications* (pp. 76–99). SAGE.

Jain, A. (2010). Data clustering: 50 years beyond K-means. *Pattern Recognition Letters*, 31(8), 651–666. https://doi.org/10.1016/j.patrec.2009.09.011

Kankaraš, M., Moors, G., & Vermunt, J. (2018). Testing for measurement invariance with latent class analysis. In E. Davidov, P. Schmidt, J. Billiet, & B. Meuleman (Eds.), *Cross-cultural analysis* (2nd ed., pp. 393–419). Routledge. https://doi.org/10.4324/9781315537078-14

Kline, R. B. (2015). *Principles and practice of structural equation modeling* (4th ed.). Guilford Press.

Kohlberg, L. (1963). The development of children's orientation toward a moral order. *Vita Humana*, 6, 11–33.

Lazarsfeld, P. F., & Henry, N. W. (1968). *Latent structure analysis*. Houghton Mifflin.

Lubke, G. H., & Muthén, B. (2005). Investigating population heterogeneity with factor mixture models. *Psychological Methods*, *10*(1), 21–39. https://doi.org/10.1037/1082-989X.10.1.21

Marsh, H. W., Hau, K., & Wen, Z. (2004). In search of golden rules: Comment on hypothesis-testing approaches to setting cutoff values for fit indexes and dangers in overgeneralizing Hu and Bentler's (1999) findings. *Structural Equation Modeling*, *11*(3), 320–341. https://doi.org/10.1207/s15328007sem1103_2

McArdle, J. J. (2001). A latent difference score approach to longitudinal dynamic structural analyses. In R. Cudeck, S. DuToit, & D. Sorbom (Eds.), *Structural equation modeling: Present and future* (pp. 342–380). Scientific Software International.

McCutcheon, A. L. (1987). *Latent class analysis*. SAGE. https://doi.org/10.4135/9781412984713

McLachlan, G., & Peel, D. (2000). *Finite mixture models*. Wiley. https://doi.org/10.1002/0471721182

Meredith, W. (1993). Measurement invariance, factor analysis and factorial invariance. *Psychometrika*, *58*(4), 525–543. https://doi.org/10.1007/BF02294825

Moustaki, I. (1996). A latent trait and latent class model for mixed observed variables. *British Journal of Mathematical & Statistical Psychology*, *49*(2), 313–334. https://doi.org/10.1111/j.2044-8317.1996.tb01091.x

Muthén, B., & Shedden, K. (1999). Finite mixture modeling with mixture outcomes using the EM algorithm. *Biometrics*, *55*(2), 463–469. https://doi.org/10.1111/j.0006-341X.1999.00463.x

Nagin, D. (2005). *Group-based modeling of development*. Harvard University Press. https://doi.org/10.4159/9780674041318

Nagin, D. S., & Odgers, C. L. (2010). Group-based trajectory modeling in clinical research. *Annual Review of Clinical Psychology*, *6*(1), 109–138. https://doi.org/10.1146/annurev.clinpsy.121208.131413

O'Connor, R. M., & Colder, C. R. (2005). Predicting alcohol patterns in first-year college students through motivational systems and reasons for drinking. *Psychology of Addictive Behaviors*, *19*(1), 10–20. https://doi.org/10.1037/0893-164X.19.1.10

Parker, K. E., Salmon, J., Brown, H. L., Villanueva, K., & Timperio, A. (2019). Typologies of adolescent activity related health behaviours. *Journal of Science and Medicine in Sport*, *22*(3), 319–323. https://doi.org/10.1016/j.jsams.2018.08.015

Pfeffermann, D., Skinner, C., & Humphreys, K. (1998). The estimation of gross flows in the presence of measurement error using auxiliary variables. *Journal of the Royal Statistical Society. Series A (Statistics in Society)*, *161*(1), 13–32. https://doi.org/10.1111/1467-985X.00088

Piaget, J. (1960). The general problems of the psychobiological development of the child. In J. M. Tanner & B. Inhelder (Eds.), *Discussions on child development* (Vol. 4, pp. 2–27). International Universities Press.

Racz, S. J., O'Brennan, L. M., Bradshaw, C. P., & Leaf, P. J. (2016). The influence of family and teacher factors on early disruptive school behaviors: A latent profile transition analysis. *Journal of Emotional and Behavioral Disorders*, *24*(2), 67–81. https://doi.org/10.1177/1063426615599541

Raudenbush, S., & Bryk, A. S. (2002). *Hierarchical linear models: Applications and data analysis methods* (2nd ed.). SAGE Publications.

Reboussin, B. A., Song, E. Y., Shrestha, A., Lohman, K. K., & Wolfson, M. (2006). A latent class analysis of underage problem drinking: Evidence from a community sample of 16–20 year olds. *Drug and Alcohol Dependence*, *83*, 199–209. https://doi.org/10.1016/j.drugalcdep.2005.11.013

Roberts, S. T., Flaherty, B. P., Deya, R., Masese, L., Ngina, J., McClelland, R. S., Simoni, J., & Graham, S. M. (2018). Patterns of gender-based violence and associations with mental health and sexual risk behavior among female sex workers in Mombasa Kenya: A latent class analysis. *AIDS and Behavior*, *22*(10), 3273–3286. https://doi.org/10.1007/s10461-018-2107-4

Rogosa, D., Brandt, D., & Zimowski, M. (1982). A growth curve approach to the measurement of change. *Psychological Bulletin*, *92*(3), 726–748. https://doi.org/10.1037/0033-2909.92.3.726

Rost, J. (1988). Rating-scale analysis with latent class models. *Psychometrika*, *53*(3), 327–348. https://doi.org/10.1007/BF02294216

Schafer, J. L., & Graham, J. W. (2002). Missing data: Our view of the state of the art. *Psychological Methods*, *7*(2), 147–177. https://doi.org/10.1037/1082-989X.7.2.147

Schmiege, S., Masyn, K., & Bryan, A. (2018). Confirmatory latent class analysis. *Organizational Research Methods*, *21*(4), 983–1001. https://doi.org/10.1177/1094428117747689

Schwarz, G. (1978). Estimating the dimension of a model. *Annals of Statistics*, *6*(2), 461–464. https://doi.org/10.1214/aos/1176344136

Scott, B. G., Lemery-Chalfant, K., Clifford, S., Tein, J. Y., Stoll, R., & Goldsmith, H. H. (2016). A twin factor mixture modeling approach to childhood temperament: Differential heritability. *Child Development*, *87*(6), 1940–1955. https://doi.org/10.1111/cdev.12561

Shiffman, S., Waters, A., & Hickcox, M. (2004). The nicotine dependence syndrome scale: A multidimensional measure of nicotine dependence. *Nicotine & Tobacco Research*, *6*(2), 327–348. https://doi.org/10.1080/1462220042000202481

Skrondal, A., & Rabe-Hesketh, S. (2004). *Generalized latent variable modeling: Multilevel, longitudinal, and structural equation models*. Chapman & Hall/CRC.

StataCorp. (2021). *Stata Statistical Software: Release 17*.

Thurstone, L. L. (1935). *The vectors of mind: Multiple-factor analysis for the isolation of primary traits*. University of Chicago Press. https://doi.org/10.1037/10018-000

United States Department of Health and Human Services, Substance Abuse and Mental Health Services Administration, & Center for Behavioral Health Statistics and Quality. (2014). *National Survey on Drug Use and Health, 2014*. Inter-university Consortium for Political and Social Research [distributor]. https://doi.org/10.3886/ICPSR36361.v1

van de Pol, F., & Langeheine, R. (1990). Mixed Markov latent class models. *Sociological Methodology*, *20*, 213–247. https://doi.org/10.2307/271087

CHAPTER 19

DECISION TREES AND ENSEMBLE METHODS IN THE BEHAVIORAL SCIENCES

Kevin J. Grimm, Ross Jacobucci, and John J. McArdle

Over the past decade, several *data mining* or *machine learning* techniques have been implemented with greater frequency in the behavioral sciences. Machine learning techniques are a collection of statistical algorithms to generate predictive models based on existing data. These approaches are *exploratory*, in that little to no theory is needed for their implementation, and efficient in their ability to consider a large number of predictors. One of the most popular machine learning algorithms is the *decision trees* algorithm. In this chapter, we review several decision tree algorithms and their extensions to ensemble methods (i.e., Bagging, Random Forests).

A BRIEF HISTORY OF DECISION TREES

Decision trees started when Belson (1959) suggested that person matching could be considered a prediction problem that could be solved through a binary search strategy. In the decade from 1960 to 1970, the stimulus and tools of the current decision tree algorithms were created in the *Automatic Interaction Detector* (AID; Sonquist & Morgan, 1964) programs advocated and used by John Sonquist and John Morgan at the Institute for Social Research at the University of Michigan.

The work reported by Sonquist (1970) is instructive. In his own words,

> This investigation had its origin in what, in retrospect, was a rather remarkable conversation between Professor James Morgan, the author, and several others, in which the topic was whether a computer could ever replace the research analyst himself, as well as replacing many of his statistical clerks. Discarding as irrelevant whether or not the computer could "think," we explored the question whether or not it might simply be programmed to make some of the decisions ordinarily made by the scientist in the course of handling a typical analysis problem, as well as doing computations. . . . This required examining decision points, alternative courses of action, and the logic for choosing one rather than the other; then formalizing the decision procedure and programming it, but with the capacity to handle many variables instead of only a few. (pp. iii–iv)

We thank the National Institute on Aging (Grant AG-07137-20) and the American Psychological Association Science Directorate for funds to support this ongoing research. We also thank our many colleagues for pointing out where these approaches are useful and where they fail.

John J. McArdle passed away before this chapter was published. Jack introduced the field of machine learning, data mining, and statistical learning to us and many behavioral scientists through his teaching and research. We are indebted to Jack for his generosity with his time, his willingness to share his knowledge, and his friendship.—Kevin Grimm & Ross Jacobucci

https://doi.org/10.1037/0000320-019

APA Handbook of Research Methods in Psychology, Second Edition: Vol. 3. Data Analysis and Research Publication, H. Cooper (Editor-in-Chief)
Copyright © 2023 by the American Psychological Association. All rights reserved.

The application of such an approach was applied by Sonquist and Morgan (1964) to an empirical data set of $N = 2,980$ non-farm-working individuals. In this example, the researchers were interested in predicting the item "Do you own a home?" They found 54% of the participants responded *yes*, and Sonquist and Morgan had nine predictor variables to consider. Standard analyses, such as multiple logistic regression, were considered, but these approaches often limit the number of variables included and exclude interesting combinations of variables to examine nonlinear associations and interactions. Sonquist and Morgan took an alternative approach that was revolutionary: They considered each variable in their data set (nine potential predictors) and every possible cutpoint on each of these variables to see which variable and what cutpoint led to the highest prediction accuracy. With their binary outcome, each variable and cutpoint led to the formation of a 2×2 table. That is, participants with values of the predictor variable below the cutoff (i.e., $x_{1i} < c$) versus participants with values of the predictor variable at or above the cutoff (i.e., $x_{1i} \geq c$) crossed with the two levels of the outcome variable. The modal response to the item "Do you own a home?" for participants below the cutoff then served as their predicted response, and the modal response to the item for participants above the cutoff served as the predicted response for these individuals. For each 2×2 table, the chi-square test statistic was calculated. The variable and cutpoint that led to the 2×2 table with the largest chi-square test statistic was chosen to partition the data. It is fairly obvious that this approach is *exploratory* and involves the estimation of many chi-square values. Sonquist and Morgan wrote an algorithm to cycle through the predictors and potential cutpoints.

In these data, the first variable selected to split the data was the age of the head of the household with a value of 35 years. The head of the household age > 35 split partitioned the data into two sets of participants: $n_1 = 2,132$ (72%), of whom 63% owned a home, and $n_2 = 848$ (28%), of whom 30% owned a home. That is, this variable (age of the head of the household), split at this cutpoint (35 years), created the best set of predictions in the outcome for the two resulting groups of participants. As an aside, these researchers did not suggest that we evaluate the probability of the statistical test (Morgan & Sonquist, 1963; Sonquist & Morgan, 1964) because they knew the selection of age of the head of the household in the model was not an a priori selection.

The next radical move they made was to split up or partition the participants based on the selected variable (age of the head of the household) and cutpoint (35 years) into two groups and conduct the search procedure again in each of these groups. That is, for the 35 or older group, they repeated the process and predicted the outcome using all nine variables again (including the possibility of another split with the variable age of the head of the household). Within this group, they found the best variable was the number of people living in the household with the splitting value set at two or more persons. This led to two groups of respondents: (1) respondents where the head of the household was 35 or older with two or more people living in the household, and (2) respondents where the head of the household was 35 or older and living alone. Sixty-nine percent of the former group owned a home, compared with 38% of respondents in the latter group who owned a home.

Sonquist and Morgan (1964) then used the same search procedure in the group of participants where the head of the household was under 35 years of age and found that the best split was on the same variable, number of people living in the household, but at the cutpoint three or more persons. This led to two groups of respondents: (1) respondents where the head of the household was younger than 35 with three or more people living in the household, and (2) respondents where the head of the household was younger than 35 with one or two people living in the household. Forty-five percent in the former group owned a home, compared with 9% of respondents in the latter group. This search procedure was repeated in each subgroup until it was no longer useful in making an accurate prediction. For example, the group of respondents where the head of the household was younger than 35 with one or two people living in the household was not further split because Sonquist and Morgan reported that no other variable could be found to usefully split this group of participants. This group of participants became the first *terminal node* with 355 respondents (12% of the sample). Nine percent of the participants in this terminal node (i.e., age of head of the household < 35 and one or two people living in the house) owned a house. For purposes of later prediction, every member of this group was assigned an expected probability of homeownership equal to .09. Often, a definitive classification is needed and because the predicted probability was less than .50, respondents with these characteristics were predicted to not own a home.

To describe these chosen variables and splits, Sonquist and Morgan (1964) drew the first *classification tree* (reproduced here as Figure 19.1). This tree-like diagram starts out with the box on the left representing the entire sample, where 54% of the sample owned a home. This box is referred to as the *root node* and is followed by additional boxes to the right representing the different groups of participants created through repeated splitting of the data. Each box, or *node*, contains information about the variable and cutpoint used to create the node from the *parent node* to the immediate left. A node that is split is referred to as the *parent node,* and the two nodes created from the parent node are referred to as *child* (or *daughter*) *nodes*. This classification tree is a visual representation of all of the partitions of the data and is read as a series of decision rules. The classification tree highlights the effect of each split of the data on the outcome represented by the percentage of participants in the node who owned a home.

This decision tree approach proposed by Sonquist and Morgan (1964), in addition to providing a clearly defined prediction model, efficiently searches the predictor space inherently searches for nonlinear and interaction effects.

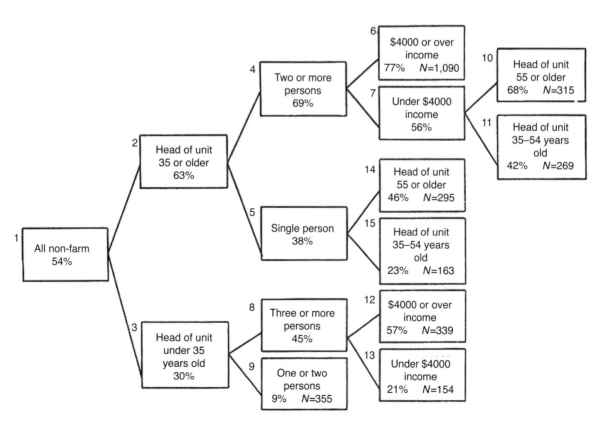

FIGURE 19.1. Decision tree with a binary outcome. From *The Detection of Interaction Effects* (p. 66), by J. Sonquist and J. N. Morgan, 1964, Institute for Social Research. Copyright 1964 by The University of Michigan Press. Reprinted with permission.

The fact that the search algorithm is carried out separately in each child node leads to the possibility that different variables are selected to split the child nodes. Thus, the selection of a variable and its splitting values is conditioned on the variables and splitting values that appear earlier in the decision tree, which is the essence of interactions.

This computer-intensive approach was studied in great detail by Sonquist (1970). He attributed much of the stimulus for this approach to earlier work by others. Sonquist and Morgan (1964; see also Sonquist et al., 1971) developed the automatic interaction detection (AID) computer program, and early extensions of the AID algorithm could predict different types of outcomes (i.e., quantitative vs. categorical) and implemented different criteria for evaluating variables and splitting values. For example, AID handled quantitative outcomes and used the residual sums of squares as the fit index, and CHAID handled nominal or classification problems and used the chi-square (as in Sonquist & Morgan, 1964) value to evaluate fit, and THAID handled classification problems and used the theta index (a measure of classification errors; Messenger & Mandell, 1972; Morgan & Messenger, 1973). A large number of other scientists joined in these efforts (e.g., Bouroche & Tenenhaus, 1970; Hunt et al., 1966), but the decision tree algorithms were not yet popular.

From 1980 to 1990, the Berkeley and Stanford Statistics Departments revived this exploratory approach and used the term *classification and regression trees* (CART). In fact, Breiman et al. (1984) developed several proofs of earlier concepts and developed an original CART program. From 1990 to 2000 there still seemed to be resistance to decision trees, but there were the seeds of growth in respectability among many statisticians (and several publications). From 2001 to 2009, the work of Breiman et al. caught on rapidly, and there was a massive growth of modified decision tree algorithms (e.g., conditional inference trees; Hothorn et al., 2006), extensions of recursive partitioning (e.g., random forests; Breiman, 2001), statistical programs to carry out these algorithms, and applications of these approaches. Very little had changed about the decision tree algorithm in the 40 years since it was defined by Morgan and Sonquist (1963), so something must have changed about the needs of the scientists themselves. It seems researchers were no longer morally opposed to using computer-aided search strategies (see also Leamer, 1978; A. J. Miller, 1990), especially with the increasing amounts of available data (i.e., medical records, internet data, cell phone data), the computers to process the data, and the new-found power of these algorithms to effectively search through hundreds of thousands of variables to create reliable predictive models.

RECURSIVE PARTITIONING ALGORITHMS

There are three commonly implemented recursive partitioning algorithms, including CART (Breiman et al., 1984), Conditional Inference Trees (*ctree*; Hothorn et al., 2006), and Evolutionary Trees (*evtree*; Grubinger et al., 2011). We begin with the CART algorithm before moving on the ctree and evtree algorithms, which were developed to combat limitations of the CART algorithm. The CART algorithm for quantitative outcomes (i.e., regression tree) searches the predictor space for the variable and splitting value that minimizes the residual sums of squares (RSS), where the mean response in each node serves as the predicted value for those participants. Thus, the RSS is

$$RSS = \sum_{j=1}^{J} \sum_{i \in R_j} (y_i - \bar{y}_{R_j})^2 \qquad (19.1)$$

where $\bar{y}_{R_j}$ is the mean for the observations in node j and y_i is the observed outcome score for individual i.

The CART algorithm for categorical (i.e., nominal) outcomes (i.e., classification tree) searches the predictor space for the variable and splitting values that minimizes the weighted sum of the *Gini index*. The Gini index is a measure of impurity or uncertainty. The Gini index is calculated as

$$Gini = 1 - \sum_{c=1}^{C} p_c^2 \qquad (19.2)$$

where p_c is the probability of membership in response category c. For example, say we have data from $N = 500$ participants, and we are trying to predict the classification outcome *sick* versus *healthy*. From this root node, the data are partitioned into two child nodes. In the first node with $N = 200$, the probability of being sick is .30 and the probability of being healthy is .70. In the second node with $N = 300$, the probability of being sick is .80 and the probability of being healthy is .20. The Gini index for the first node is $1 - (.30^2 + .70^2) = .42$ and the Gini index for the second node is $1 - (.80^2 + .20^2) = .32$. A lower Gini index is associated with greater purity or greater confidence in the prediction. Thus, the Gini index is lower for the second node because this node is *purer* because a greater proportion of the participants in this node share the same outcome classification. The weighted average of the Gini indices for this partition is

$$\frac{300}{500}(.42) + \frac{200}{500}(.32) = .38. \quad (19.3)$$

Now that the fit indices to determine which partition of the data is selected are defined, we can discuss *stopping criteria*, which is the second important aspect of CART. A first stopping criterion is the minimum improvement in overall model fit. For example, if the optimal partition of a node does not increase the overall explained variance of the model by more than 1% (for a quantitative outcome), then the node would not be split and would become a terminal node. The second and third stopping criteria relate to sample size. First, a minimum sample size to split a node can serve as a stopping rule. For example, a node must contain data at least 100 participants to be split. Second, a minimum sample size for a terminal node can also serve as a stopping rule. For example, a terminal node must contain data from at least 75 participants. Often, multiple stopping criteria are specified, and different stopping criteria can be breached for different terminal nodes to prevent further tree growth.

Once a stopping criterion is reached for each terminal node, tree growth stops. However, this decision tree structure may not represent the final tree structure. Typically, stopping criteria are set to minimal values to encourage tree growth to ensure that a useful partition of the data is not inadvertently missed. This overgrown tree structure can be used, but it will likely *overfit* the data given the minimal stopping criteria. Thus, the tree structure is often *pruned*, or reduced in size, using *cost-complexity pruning* (Breiman et al., 1984). Cost-complexity pruning leads to a predictable sequence of tree structures that can be evaluated using k-fold cross-validation. After each model is evaluated using k-fold cross-validation, the model with the smallest cross-validated error (e.g., RSS for a quantitative outcome or misclassification rate for a categorical outcome) is typically chosen as the final tree structure; however, researchers have proposed selecting the simplest model that has a cross-validated error within one standard error of the best model (Hastie et al., 2009). This second approach is in line with the logic of Occam's razor.

CART Benefits, Limitations, and Extensions

The CART algorithm has many benefits. First, by examining splits on ordered and quantitative predictor variables, CART is quite resistant to highly skewed distributions, extreme scores, and outliers. That is, because we are simply looking at each variable in a rank-order form, the sensitivity of standard methods to nonnormal distributions and extreme scores simply does not exist. Second, there is no need to dummy (or effect) code categorical predictor variables because CART examines all category combinations for these types of predictors. For example, on a four-level categorical predictor coded A, B, C, D, CART considers the following seven comparisons: (1) A versus B, C, D; (2) B versus A, C, D; (3) C versus A, B, D; (4) D versus A, B, C; (5) A, B versus C, D; (6) A, C versus B, D; and (7) A, D versus B, C. Third, CART inherently searches for nonlinear and interactive effects through its search mechanism (repeatedly splitting the data). Fourth, CART can efficiently handle a large number of variables, even when the number of predictor variables is larger (or much larger) than the sample size. Fifth, CART is robust to collinearity issues among predictors because of its sequential approach to variable testing and selection. Thus, having highly correlated predictors does not negatively impact CART's ability to generate quality predicted values. Sixth, CART easily handles quantitative, ordered, and unordered (categorical) outcomes by simply changing the model fit criteria. Seventh, the interpretation of the resulting decision tree is easy to interpret and follow for non-quantitatively oriented individuals.

While CART has many benefits for creating complex, yet understandable prediction models, it does have limitations. Fortunately, modifications to the CART algorithm have been proposed to tackle these limitations. CART's first limitation is that it is more likely to select variables that have more unique values. For example, an *income* variable measured in thousands of dollars per year is more likely to be selected compared with an *income bracket* variable that indicates the quartile for the participant's yearly income. Variables with more unique values are more likely to be selected because there are more opportunities to partition the data, and the fit index (e.g., RSS) does not take random (baseline) variability into account. The ctree algorithm was developed to combat this issue.

The ctree algorithm uses the *p* value obtained from a permutation test for variable selection in decision trees. Permutation tests repeatedly shuffle the observations with respect to the assigned node to determine a sampling distribution of the test statistic under the null hypothesis. The obtained test statistic can then be compared with this empirical sampling distribution to obtain the *p* value. Selecting the partitioning based on the predictor with the smallest *p* value is a more balanced (fair) approach to variable selection because of the comparison to a sampling distribution. The ctree algorithm can then use a *p* value criterion as a stopping rule, in addition to the two minimum sample size rules described for CART.

A second limitation of the CART algorithm is that it is a *greedy* algorithm. Once a decision to split the data is made, CART never reconsiders this decision. This approach is similar to *forward selection* in regression. That is, the one variable that best predicts the outcome in a univariate regression model is retained in all subsequent models in forward selection, and this selection is never revisited or reconsidered. The evtree algorithm was designed to tackle this limitation of CART.

The evtree algorithm begins by randomly generating decision trees. This process creates a population of decision trees that evolves. The initial population of decision trees (e.g., 100 trees) contain the root node that is split based on a randomly selected variable and randomly selected splitting value. The likelihood that the two child nodes are split is based on a set probability. If a child node is split, then a variable and splitting value are randomly chosen for each node. For each terminal node, the outcome is randomly generated from the outcome distribution. For example, if the outcome were categorical, then a category would be randomly chosen for each terminal node. Next, a *fitness measure* is calculated for each decision tree, where the fitness measure is often a combination of the accuracy of the predictions and a penalty for tree depth (size).

Once the initial population of decision trees is set, the next generation of decision trees is created. There are different algorithms to select decision trees from the current generation as parents for the next generation; however, decision trees that are fittest (based on the fitness measure) are prioritized by having a higher probability of being selected as a parent for each decision tree. In some approaches, the fittest models are also carried to the next generation to ensure the best models are not lost during evolution. Two parent decision trees combine to create an offspring decision tree. The offspring is a combination of the decision trees from the two parents. For example, the left subtree (i.e., part of the decision tree with values less than the split value on the variable selected first) from the first parent decision tree is replaced with the left subtree from the second parent decision tree. In addition to these *cross-over* offspring, there are *mutations*, where a small change is made to a decision tree. For example, the splitting value may change by one.

For each generation, the fittest decision trees are more likely to pass on their structure to the next generation. After a set number of generations, the fittest decision tree is selected. By examining tens of thousands of trees through its evolution process, the evtree algorithm is trying to achieve *global* as opposed to *local* improvement in fit.

A third limitation of CART is its instability (Breiman, 2001; Jacobucci, 2018). The CART algorithm is fairly unstable, and minor perturbations to the data can lead to drastic changes in the tree structure. For example, decision trees fit to bootstrap samples from an empirical data set will often lead to different tree structures. Ensemble methods, such as *bagging* and *random forests*, combine results from multiple machine learning algorithms and were designed to benefit from the instability of decision trees. These ensemble methods have been shown to outperform decision trees in terms of the accuracy of their forecasts.

Bagging (Breiman, 1996) is an ensemble method where the data are bootstrapped and a decision tree (using CART or ctree) is fit to the bootstrapped data. This process is repeated many times (e.g., 5,000), and the predictions from the decision trees are averaged to yield a predicted value for each observation. The number of bootstrap samples in bagging is a *tuning* parameter and can be selected by examining the *out-of-bag* observations. The out-of-bag observations are those observations left out of a bootstrap sample. Approximately one third of observations are not contained within a bootstrap sample because sampling is done with replacement. The out-of-bag observations change every time a new bootstrap sample is drawn. Thus, predictions for these observations can be calculated after the decision tree is fit to the bootstrap sample, and the predictions from this decision tree are averaged with the predictions from the previously fit decision trees. The error rate for the out-of-bag observations is then calculated and examined to determine the optimal number of decision trees. The out-of-bag error rate has been found to approximate the cross-validated error rate obtained through k-fold cross-validation, and this approach is more efficient than k-fold cross-validation.

Random forests (Breiman, 2001) is an extension of bagging and very similar. As with bagging, the data are bootstrapped, a decision tree is fit to each bootstrap sample, and the predictions from each decision tree are averaged to yield a predicted value for each observation. Random forests differs from bagging in the way the decision trees are grown. When splitting a node in random forests, the number of potential splitting variables is less than the total number of predictor variables in the data set. That is, a small number of predictor variables are randomly selected to be considered to split the data at each node. When a small number of variables are randomly selected to potentially split the data for each node, the decision trees are more varied. This forces the decision trees to use more variables, and this additional level of randomness can be beneficial for prediction. This is especially important when predictor variables are highly correlated. For example, say x_{1i} and x_{2i} are highly correlated, but x_{1i} predicts the outcome slightly better than x_{2i}. In bagging, x_{1i} will appear in most of the decision trees, which essentially eliminates x_{2i} from consideration. In random forests, x_{2i} is given a greater chance at being selected because x_{1i} will not be available to partition the data every time that x_{2i} is available to partition the data. In random forests, the number of bootstrap samples and the number of randomly selected predictor variables to partition each node are tuning parameters. As with bagging, the out-of-bag error rates are used to determine the optimal values for the two tuning parameters.

As noted, ensemble models tend to outperform decision tree algorithms in terms of prediction accuracy; however, there are limitations to these approaches. The first limitation is that the straightforward interpretation of the decision tree is gone because there are now hundreds or thousands of decision trees. Instead of a set of decision rules that are easily interpretable, ensemble methods report *variable importance metrics*, which provide comparative information regarding how much each variable contributes to the prediction of the outcome. There are two commonly reported variable importance metrics. These metrics are

(1) the percent increase in the error rate when permuting the variable, and (2) the increase in node purity when the variable was used to partition the data.

The first metric is calculated based on out-of-bag observations. First, the out-of-bag error rate is recorded for the model, which is a collection of decision trees. Next, the values of each variable are permuted, one variable at a time. That is, the values for each variable are shuffled. Next, the out-of-bag observations with the permuted variable are run through the model and the error rate is recorded. The percent increase in this error rate is the first variable importance metric. Permuting the values of variables that are not often used to partition the data, or permuting the values of variables that are not predictive of the outcome, will not lead to an increase in the error rate; however, permuting values of an important variable will increase in the error rate. This metric provides information on how essential each variable is for prediction and is a global measure of variable importance for the model.

The second variable importance metric is the percent increase in node purity when the variable is used to partition the data. This metric uses all the instances in which a given variable is used to split a node and determines the average improvement in prediction accuracy in these situations. This measure of variable importance is a more *local* measure of variable importance because it is conditioned on the variable's selection for splitting.

Variable importance metrics provide a sense of how each variable contributes to the prediction model, but there are two limitations of variable importance metrics. First, variable importance measures can mask the importance of strongly correlated variables. This is particularly true with bagging, but remains relevant with random forests. The second limitation is that variable importance metrics do not provide information about the nature of the association between the predictor variable and the outcome. That is, the variable importance metrics do not indicate if the association was linear versus nonlinear, and they do not indicate the nature of interactive effects. Thus, while knowing which variables are important for prediction is helpful to researchers, the variable importance metrics do not indicate *how* the variables combine to predict the outcomes.

PREDICTING CORONARY HEART DISEASE FROM AGE

In this section, we discuss a simple example of decision tree analyses to illustrate some of the benefits and limitations before moving onto a more complex example. Data for this example are taken from Hosmer and Lemeshow (2000, pp. 2–4). In this example, $N = 100$ people were examined at a hospital for the presence of coronary heart disease. The age of the participant (in years) was measured at the time of the medical evaluation. The question raised by Hosmer and Lemeshow was, "Is age predictive of coronary heart disease?" The R code for this example can be found at GitHub (Grimm et al., 2021a).

One answer to this question is provided by logistic regression, where the binary coronary heart disease variable, *chd*, was predicted by age. Prior to fitting the logistic regression model, a new variable, *age50d*, was calculated by subtracting 50 from age and dividing the difference by 10. This variable makes the intercept from the logistic regression model equal to the predicted log-odds of coronary heart disease for a 50-year-old individual, and the slope for the effect of age is scaled in decades (*age50d*, i.e., a 10-year change in age).

The effect of *age50d* in the logistic regression model was significant with a prediction equation of $\ln\left(\frac{P_i}{1-P_i}\right) = 0.24 + 1.11 \cdot age50d_i$. The slope for *age50d*, 1.11, indicates the log-odds of having coronary heart disease increases 1.11 every 10 years. Exponentiating this parameter leads to the odds ratio, which is 3.03. Thus, participants were approximately 3 times more likely to have coronary heart disease for a 10-year increase in age. This analysis also gives a pseudo-explained variance of $R^2 = .21$. The parameter estimates from the logistic regression model lead to expected probabilities for each value of age, and we plotted these expected probabilities against age in Figure 19.2A. Here, it is clear that the predicted probability of coronary heart disease increases with age.

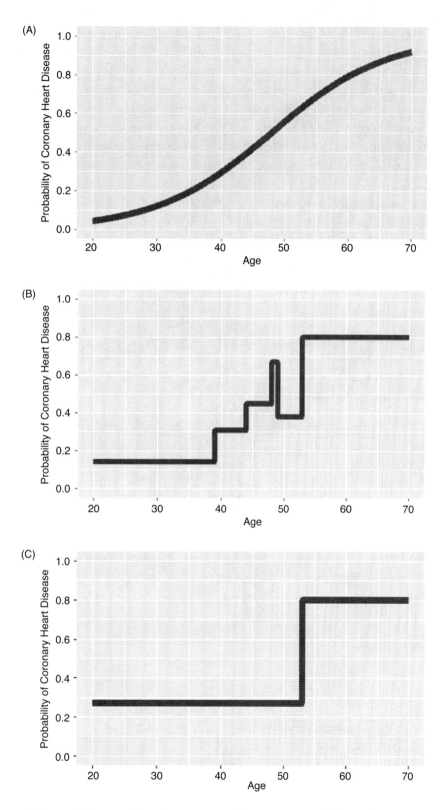

FIGURE 19.2. Predicted associations between age and the probability of having coronary heart disease for the (A) logistic regression model, (B) initial (unpruned) classification tree, and (C) final (pruned) classification tree.

The coronary heart disease data were then run through the CART algorithm using the rpart package (Therneau & Atkinson, 1997). The control parameters of rpart were set to minimal values to encourage tree growth, and the final decision tree was determined through 10-fold cross-validation. The initial decision tree (Figure 19.3A) had six terminal nodes with splitting values on age at 39, 44, 48, 49, and 53. From this model, the proportion of participants with coronary heart disease in each terminal node is interpreted as the predicted probability for those individuals. These predicted probabilities are plotted against age in Figure 19.2B.

The predicted probabilities for coronary heart disease against age follow a step function. The step function highlights how the probability of having coronary heart disease generally increases with age. The changes in the likelihood of having coronary heart disease occur at the splitting values on the age variable; however, there is no association between age and the likelihood of coronary heart disease between the splitting values. The step function highlights how CART can model nonlinear associations by making multiple splits on the same variable. The modeled association between age and the likelihood of

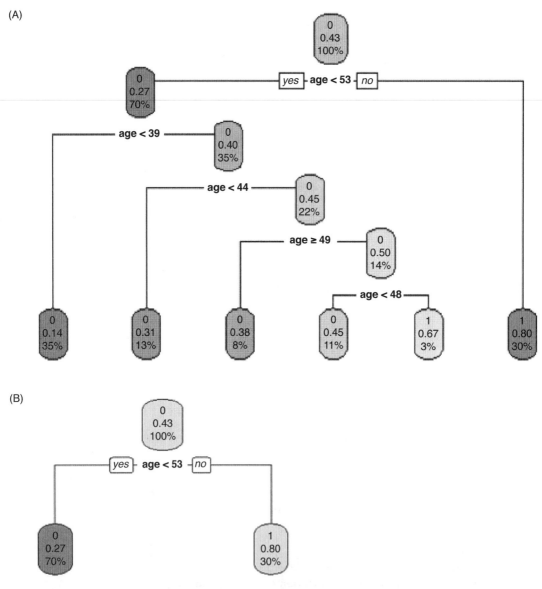

FIGURE 19.3. Decision tree structure for the (A) initial (unpruned) classification tree and (B) final (pruned) classification tree.

coronary heart disease was not monotonic as there was a drop in the predicted probability between the ages of 49 and 53. These estimated likelihoods of having coronary heart disease could also be used to classify individuals.

This initial decision tree structure adequately accounts for the association between age and coronary heart disease in these data; however, the predictions from this model may not generalize to other data sets. That is, the exploratory nature of CART may lead to a model that fits too closely to the analyzed data, and accounts for noise. This model may *overfit* the data. To prevent overfitting, k-fold cross-validation is used to select the final tree structure. The model with the smallest error rate for the 10-fold cross-validation led to a decision tree with a single split of the data at 53 years of age (see Figure 19.3B). Participants younger than 53 years of age were predicted to not have coronary heart disease (predicted probability was .27), whereas participants 53 years old and higher were predicted to have coronary heart disease (predicted probability was .80). These expected values are plotted against age and presented in Figure 19.2C. Here the predicted probability shifts from .27 to .80 at 53 years of age. Having a cutoff at 53 years leads to a pseudo-explained variance of $R^2 = .18$, which is slightly lower than the pseudo-explained variance obtained from the logistic regression. We note that the decision tree is a simpler model than the logistic regression model because there is a single change in the predicted probability. It is also important to note that logistic regression and decision trees have different goals (see Harrell, 2015) with logistic regression modeling the conditional probability and decision tree's goal of classification accuracy. Finally, we note that the final decision tree structure was determined through cross-validation as opposed to optimizing the prediction in these data.

PREDICTING DIABETES DIAGNOSIS USING DECISION TREES AND ENSEMBLES

The empirical data for this example come from the National Institute of Diabetes and Digestive and Kidney Diseases. The data were presented by Smith and colleagues (1988) and downloaded from kaggle.com. Data were collected with the objective of predicting whether an individual had diabetes based on a collection of health indicators and demographic characteristics. All participants were female, at least 21 years old, and of Pima heritage. The predictor variables included (a) the number of pregnancies, (b) glucose level (plasma glucose concentration after 2 hours in an oral glucose tolerance test), (c) diastolic blood pressure, (d) body mass index (BMI), and (e) age. Three decision tree algorithms (CART, ctree, and evtree), bagging, and random forests are used to predict diabetes status from these predictors. The data were cleaned and split into a 70% training data set and 30% *testing* data set. All models were estimated with the training data set where tuning parameters were optimized (through 10-fold cross-validation or out-of-bag error rates). After the final model was selected for each approach, the model was evaluated using the testing data set, and the prediction accuracy of the classification serves as our outcome of interest to compare the performance of the algorithms. The R code for this illustration can be found at GitHub (Grimm et al., 2021b).

Classification and Regression Trees

The CART algorithm was implemented in the rpart package. Stopping criteria were set to minimal values to overgrow the decision tree and 10-fold cross-validation of the error (i.e., misclassification) rate was conducted for model selection. The decision tree with the lowest cross-validated error rate was selected as the final model. The final tree structure is contained in Figure 19.4A. In this figure, the node contains the classification (0 for not-diabetic, 1 for diabetic), the proportion of participants in the node who have diabetes (serves as predicted probability), and the percent of the sample in the node. There were seven terminal nodes with splits on glucose, BMI, and age. Two terminal nodes led to a classification as diabetic and five terminal nodes led to a classification as not-diabetic (with different probabilities). We review the two nodes that led to a classification

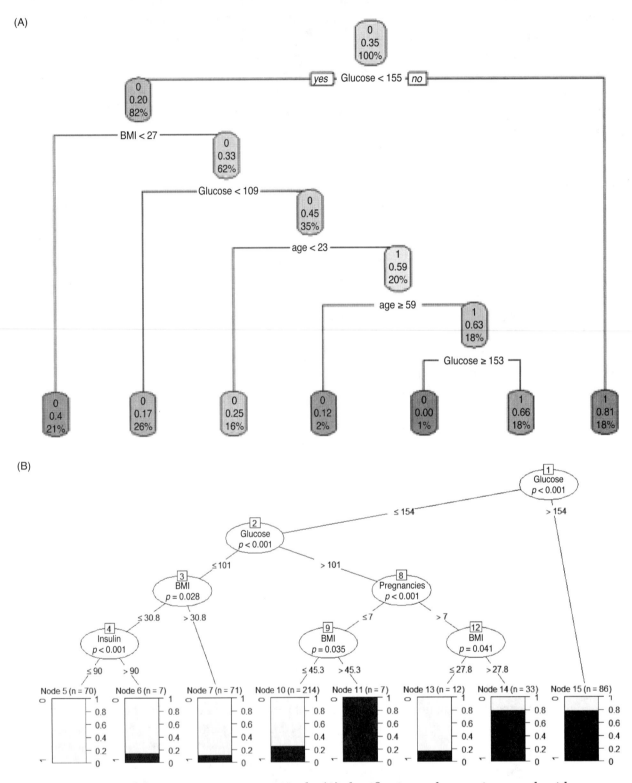

FIGURE 19.4. Final decision tree structure using the (A) classification and regression tree algorithm and (B) conditional inference tree algorithm. BMI = body mass index.

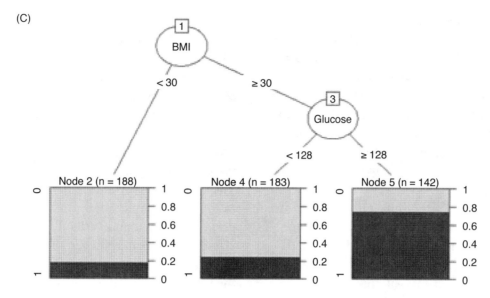

FIGURE 19.4 (*Continued*). Final decision tree structure using the (C) evolutionary tree algorithm.

as diabetic. First, all participants with glucose values greater than or equal to 155 (Node 7) were classified as diabetic. These participants had a predicted probability of having diabetes equal to .80. The second node with a predicted classification as diabetic included participants with glucose values greater than or equal to 109 and less than 153, BMI values greater than or equal to 27, and an age greater than or equal to 29 and less than 59. The predicted probability of having diabetes for this group of participants was .66.

Conditional Inference Trees

The partykit package (Hothorn & Zeileis, 2015) was used to implement the ctree algorithm. A Bonferroni correction was implemented to prevent overfitting. This led to the decision tree contained in Figure 19.4B with seven terminal nodes. In this figure, the splitting variable is contained within the circle along with the *p* value associated with the split of the data. The connections between nodes contain the decision rules with splitting values. Each terminal node indicates the predicted probability of an individual having diabetes based on the participants in the node. Partitioning variables included glucose, BMI, age, and the number of pregnancies. While the tree structure for ctree is notably different than the tree structure for CART, there were several similarities, and the predictions from this model were quite similar. Of the seven terminal nodes, there was only one terminal node that led to a predicted classification as having diabetes. This terminal node included participants with glucose values greater than 154 (i.e., greater than or equal to 155). All other participants were predicted to be non-diabetic with different probabilities.

Evolutionary Trees

The evtree package (Grubinger et al., 2011) was used to implement the evtree algorithm. Several tuning parameters were specified to control the probability of splitting, cross-overs, mutations (both major mutations involving the variable and splitting value, and minor mutations that only involve the splitting value), and pruning the tree at a given node. These probabilities were set to .2, and 200 trees were grown in the initial population. Finally, α was set to its default value of 1, which was associated with the size of the tree.

The resulting decision tree is contained in Figure 19.4C and contains three terminal nodes. The evtree package depends on the partykit package and the decision tree in Figure 19.4C is structured in the same way. That is, the splitting variable is contained within the circle, the connections between nodes contain the decision rules and splitting values, and the terminal nodes indicate the predicted probability of a participant having diabetes based on the mode of the participants in the node. There were only two partitions of the data, with the first split on BMI at a value of 30. Participants with a BMI less than 30 form the first terminal node with a classification of not-diabetic (with a predicted probability of having diabetes equal to 18%). Participants with a BMI greater than or equal to 30 were split by glucose at a value of 128. Participants with a BMI greater than or equal to 30 and a glucose level greater than or equal to 128 were classified as diabetic (with a predicted probability of having diabetes equal to .74). Participants with BMI values greater than or equal to 30 and a glucose level less than 128 were classified as nondiabetic (with a predicted probability of having diabetes equal to .24).

Bagging

Bagging was conducted in the randomForest package (Liaw & Wiener, 2002). Ten-thousand trees were initially grown and the out-of-bag error rate was tracked to determine the optimal number of trees. The out-of-bag error rate reached its minimum after 88 trees. The model was then re-run with this number of decision trees, and the variable importance metrics were output. The variable importance plots are contained in Figure 19.5A. The left plot is based on the permutation test and is the mean decrease in classification accuracy when the variable's values were permuted. The right plot is based on when the variable was used for partitioning and is the average decrease in the Gini index. Glucose was the most important variable, which was followed by BMI. The permutation test indicated the

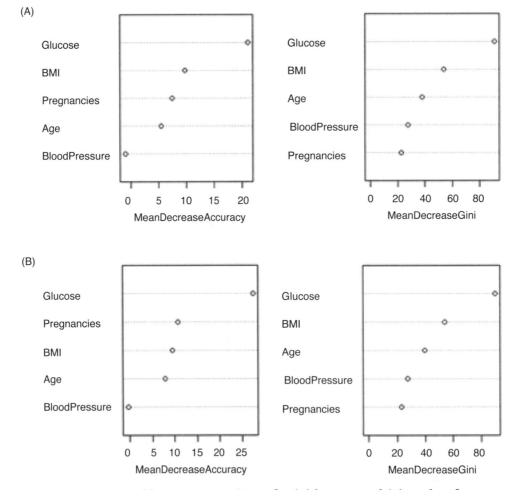

FIGURE 19.5. Variable importance metrics for (A) bagging and (B) random forests. BMI = body mass index.

number of pregnancies and age were the next two most important variables, whereas the average decrease in the Gini index indicated age, followed by diastolic blood pressure, and the number of pregnancies.

Random forests. Random forests was conducted in the randomForest package (Liaw & Wiener, 2002) in R. First, the rfcv function was used to determine an optimal number of randomly selected variables to consider when splitting the data. The optimal number was found to be three variables. The randomForest function was then specified with 10,000 trees with three variables randomly selected for each split. This run was used to determine the optimal the number of trees by examining the out-of-bag error rate. The optimal number of trees was 181, and the randomForest function was run a final time with 181 trees and three variables randomly selected for each split. The variable importance metrics were output from this final model and plots of these metrics are contained in Figure 19.5B. As in Figure 19.5A, the left plot is the mean decrease in classification accuracy when the variable's values were permuted, and the right plot is the average decrease in the Gini index when the variable was used to split the data. The ordering of the variables with respect to the average decrease in the Gini index was the same as bagging, which is because it is a local measure of variable importance. The ordering of variables based on the permutation tests was different, with glucose followed by the number of pregnancies, BMI, age, and diastolic blood pressure. There is a notable drop in this variable importance metric after glucose with the number of pregnancies, BMI, and age having similar variable importance values.

Predictive Comparison

The final predictive model from each machine learning approach was used to generate predicted classifications on the *testing* data set. Additionally, the testing data were bootstrapped to obtain an estimate of the confidence interval for the classification accuracy. Table 19.1 contains the

TABLE 19.1

Performance of the Decision Tree and Ensemble Methods in Predicting Diabetes Status in the Testing Data Set

Algorithm	Classification accuracy	Bootstrap confidence interval
Classification and regression trees	75.8%	70.2%–81.5%
Conditional inference trees	74.9%	69.1%–80.5%
Evolutionary trees	75.3%	69.7%–81.0%
Bagging	73.5%	66.8%–78.8%
Random forests	77.7%	72.0%–83.2%

classification accuracy for each approach and the bootstrapped confidence interval. The models had classification accuracies between .73 and .78. Random forests had the highest classification accuracy and bagging had the lowest classification accuracy with the three decision tree algorithms performing similarly between these two extremes.

RECURSIVE PARTITIONING SUCCESSES AND FAILURES

Exploratory methods, such as the recursive partitioning algorithms and their extensions, can be successfully applied in the behavioral sciences. First, exploratory methods can be used as follow-up analyses to the theoretically driven statistical models. This use of exploratory methods may lead to new hypotheses that can be tested in subsequent studies. The decision tree algorithms are particularly helpful for hypothesis generation of interactive (moderated) and nonlinear effects.

Second, exploratory methods have been successfully applied to empirical data when we do not have a priori theories to rely on for hypothesis testing. One situation where researchers often have little theory to guide analysis is in the context of missing data. Missing data are prevalent in the social and behavioral sciences, and advanced missing data mechanisms, such as multiple imputation, rely on a *missing at random* (MAR) assumption (Rubin, 1976). The MAR assumption is that missingness is associated with measured variables in the data. Often, logistic regression models are fit to predict the likelihood of variable missingness, and these models are often linear and additive (in the log-odds [logit] metric). The causes of missingness are likely to be more complicated and decision tree methods, along with their extensions, can be used to predict variable missingness and impute missing values (see Hayes et al., 2015).

While recursive partitioning is a powerful statistical, they can struggle with small samples (Grimm & Jacobucci, 2021) and when predictor and outcome variables contain a fair amount of measurement error (Jacobucci & Grimm, 2020). The decision tree algorithms can also struggle when effects are linear and interactive effects are not present in the data; however, the ensemble methods can approximate these types of associations. For example, Gonzalez (2021) compared the performance of machine learning algorithms to psychometric models to predict an outcome with data simulated to follow the psychometric approach. The machine learning algorithms struggled when given the item responses to predict the outcome, even though a simple composite score (sum of the item responses) led to good prediction.

Three additional challenges for decision trees are the generalizability of the prediction algorithm, whether variables and/or observations should be weighted, and missing data. The main goal of supervised machine learning algorithms, such as decision trees, is for the predictions from the model to generalize to other data sets. Model selection through k-fold cross-validation can prevent overfitting to the data on-hand, but it does not mean that the predictive model will generalize to samples collected under different circumstances or samples collected from different populations. For example, an algorithm to predict suicide attempt using data from one hospital may not generalize to data collected from another hospital, particularly if the hospitals serve different populations.

Weighting observations, such as using inverse probability weights, can lead to large changes in the variables and splitting values selected. Researchers may weight observations for several reasons, and we highlight two. First, data are weighted to make the sample representative of a particular population, which can aid the generalizability of the resulting predictive model. Second, data are often weighted when analyzing a categorical outcome where the frequencies of outcome categories are very imbalanced. For example, predicting suicide attempt can be difficult with a classification tree because it is a rare event. Baseline accuracy is high in these situations, and classification trees are unlikely to select any variables. Weighting the data based on the relative frequency of the levels of the outcome (increasing the weight for the participants who attempted suicide) is reasonable. Weighting data based on observed frequency leads to issues of weighting *false positives* versus *false negatives* in decision making, and weighting observations affects the resulting predictive models (see Volume 1, Chapter 38, this handbook).

Missing data can lead to biased parameter estimates in standard types of analysis unless the data are missing completely at random, or the data are MAR and analyzed using an advanced missing data technique (e.g., multiple imputation and full information maximum likelihood; see Baraldi & Enders, 2010, and Chapter 2, this volume). Missing data are an issue with decision tree algorithms. If an individual has a missing value on the selected splitting variable, then the algorithm is unable to place the individual in a child node. Advanced missing data approaches, such as multiple imputation and full information maximum likelihood, are not easily implemented with decision trees (Rodgers et al., 2021). Thus, missing data are typically handled using simpler approaches, such as listwise deletion, delete if selected (a form of pairwise deletion), majority rule, and surrogate splits. The surrogate split approach is the default missing data approach in many decision tree algorithms (e.g., rpart) and involves predicting the chosen split of the data with a classification tree using the other predictors in the data set. The variable that predicts the chosen split best (i.e., based on the Gini index) is then used to place the individual into a child node. This variable is referred to as a *surrogate*. If the individual is missing the surrogate variable, then additional surrogate variables are considered. Programs often consider a specified number of surrogates (e.g., 5) and if the individual is missing all of the surrogates, then the observation is placed in the node with the larger sample (following the majority rule approach). Greater research into missing data handling in decision trees is greatly needed given the amount of incomplete data in social and behavioral science data.

MULTIVARIATE EXTENSIONS OF DECISION TREES

Throughout our discussion, we've focused on univariate outcomes—decision tree and ensemble methods to predict a single observed quantitative or categorical variable. Over the past decade, several extensions of decision tree algorithms to predict multivariate outcomes have been proposed. Early work on this topic was initiated by Abdolell et al. (2002), Segal (1992), and Zhang (1997, 1999, 2004; Zhang & Singer, 1999), and focused on repeated measures data with goals of exploring individual change patterns and using person-level variables to predict differences in change. This early work followed the basic logic of survival decision trees (Gordon & Olshen, 1985). For example, Abdolell et al. (2002) proposed the longitudinal recursive partitioning algorithm where a linear mixed-effects model is estimated using the observations in each node. In the root node, the linear mixed-effects model is estimated using the entire sample and the -2 log-likelihood ($-2LL$) is retained. Person-level variables are considered splitting variables, which retain all of the observations for a given person in the same node. For each split of the data, a linear mixed-effects model is estimated in each child node and the summed $-2LL$ for the split is retained. The split of the data that leads to the greatest improvement in the $-2LL$ is made, and the algorithm continues within each child node until a stopping criterion is met. Stopping criteria, such as the previously described criteria based on sample size, are implemented in addition to a minimal improvement in the $-2LL$ when splitting the data.

The work by Abdolell et al. (2002) set the foundation for subsequent research on decision trees for multivariate outcomes. In 2013, Brandmaier et al. published their structural equation modeling trees (SEM trees) algorithm, where a structural equation model is estimated within each node. SEM trees is essentially an exploratory form of multiple group structural equation modeling, where the algorithm is searching for two groups of participants, created based on a split on a measured variable, where the model parameters are most different. As with the work by Abdolell et al. (2002), the variable and splitting value are chosen based on the improvement in the $-2LL$ (or using p values based on permutation tests). As with multiple group modeling, parameter constraints can be imposed to search for groups of participants who are most different on a specific set of model parameters (e.g., factor means).

Given the generality of structural equation modeling, SEM trees has opened the door for decision trees to be applied to many types of models (e.g., latent curve models, confirmatory factor models, item response models, path models, survival models). For example, SEM trees can be implemented to examine measurement invariance in latent variable measurement models (e.g., confirmatory factor models). This changes the nature of examining measurement invariance from planned partitions of the data (e.g., low vs. high socioeconomic status) to exploratory partitions of the data (e.g., low versus high verbal ability), and from partitions based on categorical variables (e.g., females vs. males) to partitions based on quantitative (e.g., verbal ability) as well as categorical variables. Additionally, the SEM trees approach also searches for combinations of groups that have different model parameters (e.g., females with high verbal ability vs. males with high verbal ability) given the repeated splits of the data. The exploratory nature of SEM trees for examining measurement invariance is similar to the exploratory approach of finite mixture models applied to measurement models (De Ayala et al., 2002);

however, the search process in SEM trees relies on measured variables as opposed to latent classes (see Jacobucci et al., 2017). The research on SEM trees has led to further extensions to more complex statistical models (see Fokkema et al., 2017; Stegmann et al., 2018) and computational machinery (Serang et al., 2021).

In addition to these model-based decision tree approaches, the decision tree approaches for multivariate data have been applied to raw scores (De'ath, 2002) and covariance matrices (P. J. Miller et al., 2016). For example, De'ath (2002) proposed the *mvpart* algorithm for multivariate partitioning to search for groups of participants who are most different based on a multivariate distance metric. P. J. Miller et al. (2016) proposed the *mvtboost* algorithm, which uses the boosted regression tree algorithm (Friedman, 2001) to identify variables that create splits of the data where the covariance structure of the outcome variables is most different.

CONCLUSION

Sonquist (1970) proposed the underlying principles of decision trees (embodied in the AID algorithm and program) and illustrated how this approach is useful for dealing with nonadditive and nonlinear relations. The number of applications of decision trees has increased dramatically over the past two decades. The increased interest has been spurred by the demonstrated potential of these algorithms and their extensions (e.g., boosting) to find the signal in data collected in a variety of fields (e.g., consumer behavior, medicine, sports).

The increased interest in these algorithmic approaches to prediction has been slower in the social and behavioral sciences. Overall, the application of decision trees and tree ensemble methods, along with generalizations that incorporate latent variables, have seen limited application in the social and behavioral sciences. Further, the application of decision trees and ensembles have been mainly applied for predictive, as opposed to explanatory, purposes. These points relate to a central perceived limitation of these machine learning methods, namely, that they can only be applied for exploratory or atheoretical predictive purposes. We view this as primarily stemming from a relatively narrow view of *confirmatory* research (e.g., from a hypothetico-deductive perspective), and see it as more productive to place these machine learning methods in the context of theory generation, development, and appraisal (Haig, 2014). While most machine learning algorithms are not appropriate for theory appraisal, they can and have been used for both theory generation and development. For both generation and development, this can involve identifying novel relationships, evaluating whether the functional form is linear or nonlinear, assessing potential interactions between variables, efficiently incorporate a large number of potential confounding variables to a previously validated model, among many other avenues. In short, we encourage researchers to overcome their feelings of guilt when they do not have concrete hypotheses (McArdle, 2014) and use decision trees and their extensions for theory generation and development.

In conclusion, there is much work left to be done to deal effectively with multivariate outcomes, missing data, and small samples with decision tree methods and their extensions. Also, research is needed on understanding the strengths and limitations of applying decision tree methods in psychology. We look forward to seeing this work come to fruition.

References

Abdolell, M., LeBlanc, M., Stephens, D., & Harrison, R. V. (2002). Binary partitioning for continuous longitudinal data: Categorizing a prognostic variable. *Statistics in Medicine*, 21(22), 3395–3409. https://doi.org/10.1002/sim.1266

Baraldi, A. N., & Enders, C. K. (2010). An introduction to modern missing data analyses. *Journal of School Psychology*, 48(1), 5–37. https://doi.org/10.1016/j.jsp.2009.10.001

Belson, W. A. (1959). Matching and prediction on the principle of biological classification. *Applied Statistics*, 8(2), 65–75. https://doi.org/10.2307/2985543

Bouroche, J. M., & Tenenhaus, M. (1970). Quelques méthodes de segmentation. Revue française d'informatique et de recherche opérationnelle [Some methods of Segmentation. French Journal of Computer Science and Operational Research]. *RAIRO Operations Research*, *4*, 29–42. https://doi.org/10.1051/ro/197004V200291

Brandmaier, A. M., von Oertzen, T., McArdle, J. J., & Lindenberger, U. (2013). Structural equation model trees. *Psychological Methods*, *18*(1), 71–86. https://doi.org/10.1037/a0030001

Breiman, L. (1996). Bagging predictors. *Machine Learning*, *24*(2), 123–140. https://doi.org/10.1007/BF00058655

Breiman, L. (2001). Random forests. *Machine Learning*, *45*(1), 5–32. https://doi.org/10.1023/A:1010933404324

Breiman, L., Friedman, J., Olshen, R., & Stone, C. (1984). *Classification and regression trees*. Wadsworth & Brooks/Cole.

De Ayala, R. J., Kim, S. H., Stapleton, L. M., & Dayton, C. M. (2002). Differential item functioning: A mixture distribution conceptualization. *International Journal of Testing*, *2*(3), 243–276. https://doi.org/10.1080/15305058.2002.9669495

De'ath, G. (2002). Multivariate regression trees: A new technique for modeling species–environment relationships. *Ecology*, *83*(4), 1105–1117. https://doi.org/10.1890/0012-9658(2002)083[1105:MRTANT]2.0.CO;2

Fokkema, M., Smits, N., Zeileis, A., Hothorn, T., & Kelderman, H. (2017). Detecting treatment-subgroup interactions in clustered data with generalized linear mixed-effects model trees. *Behavior Research Methods*, *50*(5), 2016–2034. https://doi.org/10.3758/s13428-017-0971-x

Friedman, J. H. (2001). Greedy function approximation: A gradient boosting machine. *Annals of Statistics*, *29*(5), 1189–1232. https://doi.org/10.1214/aos/1013203451

Gonzalez, O. (2021). Psychometric and machine learning approaches for diagnostic assessment and tests of individual classification. *Psychological Methods*, *26*(2), 236–254. https://doi.org/10.1037/met0000317

Gordon, L., & Olshen, R. A. (1985). Tree-structured survival analysis. *Cancer Treatment Reports*, *69*(10), 1065–1069. https://europepmc.org/article/med/4042086

Grimm, K. J., & Jacobucci, R. (2021). Reliable trees: Reliability informed recursive partitioning for psychological data. *Multivariate Behavioral Research*, *56*(4), 595–607. https://doi.org/10.1080/00273171.2020.1751028

Grimm, K. J., Jacobucci, R., & McArdle, J. J. (2021a). American Psychological Association research methods—recursive partitioning [code]. GitHub. https://github.com/kevin-j-grimm/ApaDecisionTrees/blob/main/Appendix20.1.Rmd

Grimm, K. J., Jacobucci, R., & McArdle, J. J. (2021b). Recursive partitioning—empirical example [code]. GitHub. https://github.com/kevin-j-grimm/ApaDecisionTrees/blob/main/Appendix20.2.Rmd

Grubinger, T., Zeileis, A., & Pfeiffer, K. P. (2011). evtree: Evolutionary learning of globally optimal classification and regression trees in R (No. 2011-20). *Working Papers in Economics and Statistics*. EconStor. https://www.econstor.eu/handle/10419/73524

Haig, B. D. (2014). *Investigating the psychological world: Scientific method in the behavioral sciences*. MIT Press. https://doi.org/10.7551/mitpress/9780262027366.001.0001

Harrell, F. E., Jr. (2015). *Regression modeling strategies: With applications to linear models, logistic and ordinal regression, and survival analysis*. Springer. https://doi.org/10.1007/978-3-319-19425-7

Hastie, T., Tibshirani, R., & Friedman, J. (2009). *The elements of statistical learning: Data mining, inference, and prediction* (2nd ed.). Springer Science & Business Media. https://doi.org/10.1007/978-0-387-84858-7

Hayes, T., Usami, S., Jacobucci, R., & McArdle, J. J. (2015). Using classification and regression trees (CART) and random forests to analyze attrition: Results from two simulations. *Psychology and Aging*, *30*(4), 911–929. https://doi.org/10.1037/pag0000046

Hosmer, D. W., & Lemeshow, S. (2000). *Applied logistic regression*. Wiley. https://doi.org/10.1002/0471722146

Hothorn, T., Hornik, K., & Zeileis, A. (2006). Unbiased recursive partitioning: A conditional inference framework. *Journal of Computational and Graphical Statistics*, *15*(3), 651–674. https://doi.org/10.1198/106186006X133933

Hothorn, T., & Zeileis, A. (2015). partykit: A modular toolkit for recursive partytioning in R. *Journal of Machine Learning Research*, *16*(118), 3905–3909. https://www.jmlr.org/papers/volume16/hothorn15a/hothorn15a.pdf

Hunt, E. B., Marin, J., & Stone, P. J. (1966). *Experiments in induction*. Academic Press.

Jacobucci, R. (2018, January 18). Decision tree stability and its effect on interpretation. *PsyArXiv* [preprint]. https://doi.org/10.31234/osf.io/f2utw

Jacobucci, R., & Grimm, K. J. (2020). Machine learning and psychological research: The unexplored effect of measurement. *Perspectives on Psychological Science*, *15*(3), 809–816. https://doi.org/10.1177/1745691620902467

Jacobucci, R., Grimm, K. J., & McArdle, J. J. (2017). A comparison of methods for uncovering sample heterogeneity: Structural equation model trees and finite mixture models. *Structural Equation Modeling*, *24*(2), 270–282. https://doi.org/10.1080/10705511.2016.1250637

Leamer, E. E. (1978). *Specification searches: Ad hoc inferences with nonexperimental data*. Wiley.

Liaw, A., & Wiener, M. (2002). Classification and regression by randomForest. *R News*, *2*, 18–22. https://cogns.northwestern.edu/cbmg/LiawAndWiener2002.pdf

McArdle, J. J. (2014). Exploratory data mining using decision trees in the behavioral sciences. In J. J. McArdle & G. Ritschard (Eds.), *Contemporary issues in exploratory data mining* (pp. 3–47). Taylor & Francis.

Messenger, R., & Mandell, L. (1972). A modal search technique for predictive nominal scale multivariate analysis. *Journal of the American Statistical Association*, *67*(340), 768–772. https://doi.org/10.1080/01621459.1972.10481290

Miller, A. J. (1990). *Subset selection in regression*. Chapman & Hall.

Miller, P. J., Lubke, G. H., McArtor, D. B., & Bergeman, C. S. (2016). Finding structure in data using multivariate tree boosting. *Psychological Methods*, *21*(4), 583–602. https://doi.org/10.1037/met0000087

Morgan, J. N., & Messenger, R. C. (1973). *THAID: A sequential search program for the analysis of nominal scale dependent variables*. Institute for Social Research, University of Michigan.

Morgan, J. N., & Sonquist, J. A. (1963). Problems in the analysis of survey data, and a proposal. *Journal of the American Statistical Association*, *58*(302), 415–434. https://doi.org/10.1080/01621459.1963.10500855

Rodgers, D. M., Jacobucci, R., & Grimm, K. J. (2021). A multiple imputation approach for handling missing data in classification and regression trees. *Journal of Behavioral Data Science*, *1*(1), 127–153. https://doi.org/10.35566/jbds/v1n1/p6

Rubin, D. B. (1976). Inference and missing data. *Biometrika*, *63*(3), 581–592. https://doi.org/10.1093/biomet/63.3.581

Segal, M. R. (1992). Tree-structured methods for longitudinal data. *Journal of the American Statistical Association*, *87*(418), 407–418. https://doi.org/10.1080/01621459.1992.10475220

Serang, S., Jacobucci, R., Stegmann, G., Brandmaier, A. M., Culianos, D., & Grimm, K. J. (2021). Mplus Trees: Structural equation model trees using Mplus. *Structural Equation Modeling*, *28*(1), 127–137. https://doi.org/10.1080/10705511.2020.1726179

Smith, J. W., Everhart, J. E., Dickson, W. C., Knowler, W. C., & Johannes, R. S. (1988). Using the ADAP learning algorithm to forecast the onset of diabetes mellitus. In *Proceedings of the Annual Symposium on Computer Application in Medical Care* (p. 261). American Medical Informatics Association. https://www.ncbi.nlm.nih.gov/pmc/articles/PMC2245318/

Sonquist, J. (1970). *Multivariate model building*. Institute for Social Research.

Sonquist, J., & Morgan, J. N. (1964). *The detection of interaction effects*. Institute for Social Research.

Sonquist, J. A., Baker, E. L., & Morgan, J. N. (1971). *Searching for structure: An approach to analysis of substantial bodies of micro-data and documentation for a computer program*. Institute for Social Research, University of Michigan.

Stegmann, G., Jacobucci, R., Serang, S., & Grimm, K. J. (2018). Recursive partitioning with nonlinear models of change. *Multivariate Behavioral Research*, *53*(4), 559–570. https://doi.org/10.1080/00273171.2018.1461602

Therneau, T. M., & Atkinson, E. J. (1997). *An introduction to recursive partitioning using the RPART routines* (Vol. 61, p. 452) [Technical report]. Mayo Foundation.

Zhang, H. (1999). Analysis of infant growth curves using multivariate adaptive splines. *Biometrics*, *55*(2), 452–459. https://doi.org/10.1111/j.0006-341X.1999.00452.x

Zhang, H. (2004). Mixed effects multivariate adaptive splines model for the analysis of longitudinal and growth curve data. *Statistical Methods in Medical Research*, *13*(1), 63–82. https://doi.org/10.1191/0962280204sm353ra

Zhang, H., & Singer, B. (1999). *Recursive partitioning in the health sciences*. Springer. https://doi.org/10.1007/978-1-4757-3027-2

Zhang, H. (1997). Multivariate adaptive splines for longitudinal data. *Journal of Computational and Graphical Statistics*, *6*(1), 74–91. https://doi.org/10.2307/1390725

SECTION 6

DYADIC AND SOCIAL NETWORK DATA

CHAPTER 20

USING THE SOCIAL RELATIONS MODEL TO UNDERSTAND INTERPERSONAL PERCEPTION AND BEHAVIOR

P. Niels Christensen, Deborah A. Kashy, and Katelin E. Leahy

Many psychological phenomena are inherently tied to an interpersonal context. In developmental psychology, both peer and family interactions play critical roles in a child's development. In group psychotherapy, a group member's improvement may depend on their own insight as well as the insight of the other group members. Likewise, being an effective team member might depend not only on one's own skills but also the strengths and weaknesses of the other team members. In each of these examples a person's outcomes are, at least to some degree, dependent on others. Given this naturally occurring interdependence, studies of interpersonal phenomena require methods designed to examine individual behavior embedded within the social context. In this chapter, we introduce the social relations model (SRM; Kenny, 1994) as one such methodological approach.

Developed by Kenny and colleagues (2020; Warner et al., 1979), the SRM provides a general framework from which interpersonal behavior can be studied. The generative nature of the SRM is well illustrated by its use in more than 320 research articles and chapters, and in more than 70 master's theses and dissertations. Indeed, over 100 research articles and book chapters using the SRM or elaborating on it have been published since the first edition of this handbook was published in 2012.

The most basic assumption of the SRM is that a person's behavior with a particular partner may reflect (a) aspects of the larger group to which the two individuals belong, (b) aspects of the individual enacting the behavior, (c) aspects of the partner with whom the behavior occurs, and (d) qualities unique to the two individuals' relationship with one another. Consider an example of mother–daughter conflict. Such conflict could reflect family-level norms (e.g., everyone in the family is contentious, and so conflict is common), qualities of the daughter (e.g., she may be low in trait agreeableness, and so she fights with all family members), qualities of the mother (e.g., she makes heavy demands from everyone in the family, so everyone fights with her), and unique attributes of the mother–daughter relationship (e.g., their similarity to one another makes them highly competitive).

As is perhaps clear from the complexity of this initial example, the SRM provides a means for examining interpersonal behavior that is multiply determined. We begin this chapter by defining the components of the model, including the data structures typically used to extract the model components. Next, we provide examples of previous SRM research to illustrate the types of questions that can be addressed using the model. Third, we outline methodological issues central to SRM research, including procedural and measurement considerations. The chapter concludes with a brief introduction to select issues involved in analyzing SRM data, and readers are referred to other sources for more specific guidance in this area.

THE SRM COMPONENTS

Consider as an example a study of texting communication in roommate relationships. In this fictitious study, we include residents living in 20 four-person dormitory suites, and we measure how many texts each person sends to each of the other roommates. One observation we obtain is that Ava sends a lot of texts to Sue. Why might this occur? It might be that Ava, Sue, and their other two roommates are all very close friends who communicate frequently, and so Ava's particular texting with Sue might simply reflect a group-level norm. However, Ava's behavior with Sue might also be driven by something about Ava—she might be the kind of person who sends texts to anyone and everyone. Alternatively, Sue might be a very outgoing person who tends to elicit text updates from everyone, and so Ava's behavior with Sue could reflect something about Sue. Finally, it might be that Ava's level of texting with Sue is uniquely high, higher than Ava typically texts to others, higher than others typically text to Sue, and higher than their group-level norm. This unique element of Ava's texting with Sue might occur if Ava and Sue are especially close friends.

This example highlights the fact that interpersonal behavior between two individuals within a group can reflect group-level, individual-level, and dyad-level effects (Table 20.1). The *group effect* measures the average level of the behavior across all group members. In the example, it might be that some groups of roommates experience significant interpersonal conflict and therefore no one in the suite texts much to any of their roommates, whereas other groups (like Ava and Sue's) become quite close. The two individual-level factors that might contribute to the particular behavior within a dyad are called actor effects and partner effects. *Actor effects* refer to the degree to which a person's behavior toward others is consistent across all partners. In our example, Ava would have a strong actor effect if she texts a great deal to all of her roommates. *Partner effects* refer to the degree to which everyone who interacts with a person behaves in the same way with that person. If Sue has a tendency to elicit communication from everyone in her suite, then she would have a strong partner effect.

The labels *actor* and *partner effects* are typically used in reference to behaviors (e.g., texting,

TABLE 20.1

Social Relations Model Components for Rating Measures and Behavioral Measures

Score	=	Group mean	+	Ava's actor effect	+	Sue's partner effect	+	Ava's relationship effect with Sue
				Behavioral measure				
Ava's texting with Sue	=	Group mean for texting	+	Ava's tendency to text all partners	+	Sue's tendency to receive texts from all partners	+	Ava's unique amount of texts to Sue
Score	=	Group mean	+	Ava's perceiver effect	+	Sue's target effect	+	Ava's relationship effect with Sue
				Rating measure				
Ava's rating of Sue's friendliness	=	Group mean for friendliness	+	Ava's rating of all partners' friendliness	+	Sue's rating as friendly by all partners	+	Ava's unique rating of Sue's friendliness

smiling, touching). However, the SRM is often used to study interpersonal perception, and in this domain the individual-level effects are typically described as *perceiver* and *target effects*. For instance, if we also measure Ava's perception of Sue's warmth, Ava's perceiver effect would be her tendency to see all of her roommates as warm. Likewise, Sue's target effect would measure the degree to which everyone in the suite thinks that Sue is warm. To summarize, actor or perceiver effects describe causes due to the person *performing* the action or perception. Partner or target effects describe causes due to the *recipient* of the action or perception.

Finally, as we have noted, Ava's behavior with Sue might also be unique to their specific relationship. This is the dyad-level effect, which is termed the *relationship effect* in the SRM. The relationship effect indicates whether the behavior (or perception) might be due to aspects of the dyad that go beyond the group-level and individual-level components. So even if Ava texts frequently with all of her roommates (a strong actor effect) and Sue receives many texts from all of her roommates (a strong partner effect), we might still find *especially* high numbers of texts from Ava to Sue. As discussed in greater detail below, one can think of the actor and partner effects as analogous to main effects in a random effects analysis of variance (ANOVA) context, whereas the relationship effect is akin to an interaction of the two. That is, relationship effects indicate especially strong (or weak) connections between particular types of actors and particular types of partners.

Data Structures for the SRM

The fundamental data requirement for an SRM analysis is that each person must be paired with (i.e., interact with or rate) multiple partners. The SRM was designed to consider data that are generally asymmetric across partners (e.g., Ava sends more texts to Sue than vice-versa) rather than shared experiences across pairs of partners (e.g., the total number of texts Ava and Sue send each other). In some designs participants serve as both raters and targets of ratings by other participants. In other designs, some participants might only serve as raters, whereas other participants only serve as targets. Regardless of the specific approach, it is the requirement of multiple interactions or ratings that allows the SRM to separate the group-, individual-, and dyad-level effects. Here we describe the two types of data structures that have most often been used in SRM research: round-robin designs and block designs.

Round-robin designs. As shown in Table 20.2, in round-robin data structures every member of the group interacts with or rates every other individual in the group; the key requirement is that each dyadic combination provides an outcome score from both members. Consider a different suite of four roommates in our fictitious study: Armando (A), Bakari (B), Chuck (C), and Dev (D). In a typical round-robin design, we have observations of Armando's texting to Bakari (AB), Armando's texting to Chuck (AC), and so on. Moreover, we would also measure how frequently Bakari and Chuck text Armando (BA and CA). In this way, each dyad actually generates two scores (i.e., AB and BA).

The diagonal of a round-robin design would be self data (e.g., Armando rates himself on warmth), although such measures are optional. For behavioral measures, self data are relatively rare because, for example, one rarely texts oneself. However, for rating data, researchers often collect self-reports for the variables. Because self-ratings can differ in systematic ways from ratings of others (e.g., they may be subject to self-enhancement biases), these scores are typically not included in the estimation of the basic SRM parameters. Instead, they are treated as individual-level covariates that may relate to the actor and partner effects (discussed in greater detail in the section on Types of Research Questions). It is possible, however, to collect "dyadic" self-ratings. For example, one might want to investigate whether self-perceptions of competence vary across interaction partners (i.e., Do I feel more competent when I'm around Armando versus when I am with Bakari?). For such analyses, self-perceptions would be measured across partners and treated like any other dyadic rating (see Christensen et al., 2003, for an example).

TABLE 20.2

Common Data Structures That Can Be Analyzed Using the Social Relations Model

Round robin		\multicolumn{4}{c}{Partners (targets)}				
		Armando	Bakari	Chuck	Dev				
Actors (perceivers)	Armando		AB	AC	AD				
	Bakari	BA		BC	BD				
	Chuck	CA	CB		CD				
	Dev	DA	DB	DC					

Full block						Partners (targets)			
		Armando	Bakari	Chuck	Dev	Eduardo	Frank	Genji	Hal
Actors (perceivers)	Armando					AE	AF	AG	AH
	Bakari					BE	BF	BG	BH
	Chuck					CE	CF	CG	CH
	Dev					DE	DF	DG	DH
	Eduardo	EA	EB	EC	ED				
	Frank	FA	FB	FC	FD				
	Genji	GA	GB	GC	GD				
	Hal	HA	HB	HC	HD				

Block designs. The block design is actually a family of designs including the full-block, half-block, and asymmetric-block. In the full-block design, a group is broken into two subgroups and individuals interact with only those in the other subgroup. So if the group includes eight individuals, A through H, persons A, B, C, and D interact with or rate persons E, F, G, and H. Thus, as indicated in Table 20.2, the full-block design results in two sets of observations: the upper-right section and the lower-left section. As was true in the round-robin design, in the full-block design each dyad produces two scores (e.g., A with E and E with A).

Sometimes data are collected from only one half of the block design, such that A, B, C, and D rate E, F, G, and H, but not vice-versa. This is called a half-block design. Coesens et al. (2010) used a half-block design to examine eating behavior in families composed of two parents and two children. Parents reported on their children's eating behavior, but children did not report on their parents' behavior. Finally, the asymmetric-block design is similar to the full-block design with the exception that persons A through D can be distinguished from persons E through H on a meaningful variable. For example, in a study of romance perceptions (Eastwick & Hunt, 2014), subgroups of men rated subgroups of women and vice-versa. In the asymmetric block, separate SRM parameter estimates are computed for the subgroups (e.g., men's perceptions of women and women's perceptions of men).

Finally, the round-robin and block designs can be combined. This approach was taken by Boldry and Kashy (1999) in a study of intergroup perception. Members of high- and low-status groups rated every member of their own group *and* every member of the other group. This approach resulted in two round-robins for the *within*-group data: one for high-status groups and another for low-status groups. In addition, the study included an asymmetric block design for the *between*-group data (i.e., high-status group members rated members of the low-status group, and low-status group members rated members of the high-status group). In essence, the authors collected data in a giant round-robin format but also recorded indicators of group identity so that each participant's ratings could be segmented as either between-group or within-group. Combining these different SRM designs permitted the researchers to test hypotheses about ingroup bias and outgroup homogeneity.

The SRM Variances

An important focus of a basic SRM study is on estimating the degree to which a particular behavior or rating reflects group-level, individual-level, and dyad-level effects. To address this question, SRM analyses estimate the amount of variance in dyadic scores that is due to these different effects, and so the SRM is often described as variance decomposition model. To illustrate the variance decomposition, Table 20.3 presents fictitious data from a single half-block design in which eight perceivers rate the perceived friendliness of seven targets. The final column in the top panel of the table shows the average ratings made by each perceiver, and the bottom row shows the average ratings received by each target.

The *perceiver (actor) variance* measures whether there is variation from perceiver to perceiver in their average ratings of the targets' friendliness. Thus, this variance is based on the row main effect. In studies of interpersonal perception, the perceiver variance is often considered a measure of the degree of *assimilation*. For the friendliness example, perceiver variance suggests that some participants rated all of the targets as high in friendliness (e.g., Perceiver G), whereas other participants rated all of the targets as unfriendly (e.g., Perceiver F). For behavioral variables, actor variance could be considered an indicator of trait-like tendencies because it represents a person's behavioral consistency across partners. For example, if the behavior being observed is self-disclosure, significant actor variance might suggest that some individuals are consistently high-disclosers and others are consistently low-disclosers.

The *target (partner) variance* measures the degree to which some individuals are consistently seen by others as high in friendliness (e.g., Target 2), whereas others are seen by everyone as low in friendliness (e.g., Target 6). Therefore, the estimate of target variance is based on the *variability among the column means* after averaging across perceivers. In interpersonal perception data the target variance measures *consensus* (the degree to which all individuals agree that some targets are high on a trait whereas other targets are low on the trait).

TABLE 20.3

The Social Relations Model Variances

Perceiver	Target 1	Target 2	Target 3	Target 4	Target 5	Target 6	Target 7	Perceiver *M*
A	5	6	5	6	5	4	7	5.428
B	3	5	4	7	3	3	6	4.428
C	4	7	6	6	4	4	4	5.000
D	4	8	6	8	8	4	5	6.142
E	3	7	5	7	4	2	6	4.857
F	3	6	4	5	3	2	5	4.000
G	6	8	7	7	6	5	8	6.714
H	5	6	5	5	4	4	6	5.000
Target *M*	4.125	6.625	5.525	6.375	4.625	3.500	5.875	5.196

Source of Variation	Expected Mean Square or E(MS)	Estimated MS
Perceiver	$\sigma_e^2 + \sigma_{PT}^2 + t\sigma_P^2$	5.467
Target	$\sigma_e^2 + \sigma_{PT}^2 + p\sigma_T^2$	10.994
Perceiver * Target	$\sigma_e^2 + \sigma_{PT}^2$	.776

Note. In the E(MS), $t = 7$, the number of targets; $p = 8$, the number of perceivers. The estimated MS are from a mixed model analysis of variance treating Target as a within-subjects factor and Perceiver as a between-subjects factor. Equating the E(MS) to the estimated values provides estimates of the perceiver variance, $\sigma_P^2 = .670$, target variance, $\sigma_T^2 = 1.277$, and relationship (plus error) variance $\sigma_e^2 + \sigma_{PT}^2 = .776$.

With behavioral measures, the partner variance assesses whether individuals vary in the degree to which they elicit similar behavior from others. For self-disclosure, some individuals might elicit a great deal of self-disclosure, whereas other individuals are rarely the recipients of self-disclosure.

The *relationship variance* measures the degree to which dyadic scores vary depending upon the specific individuals in the dyad, after partialing out variance due to those individuals' perceiver and target effects (or actor and partner effects if the variable is a behavior). That is, the relationship variance is the *variability in the cells*, after the row marginal means and the column marginal means have been removed. For example, in Table 20.3, Perceiver B's rating of Target 7 is a "6," which is a high value relative to this perceiver's other ratings, and it is high relative to other perceivers' ratings of Target 7. Relationship variance might be especially likely for variables like romantic attraction. In such an example, people are attracted to specific others beyond any perceiver and target effects.

The bottom section of Table 20.3 presents the expected mean squares or E(MS) for the half-block design, which is analogous to a random effects ANOVA. These formulas show that observed variation in the row means, which is the estimated mean square (MS) for the effect of Perceiver in ANOVA terms, reflects three sources of variance: error variance (σ_e^2), variance due to the perceiver by target interaction—which is relationship variance (σ_{PT}^2), and perceiver variance (σ_P^2). The variance of the column means, which is the estimated mean square for the effect of Target in ANOVA terms, is similarly comprised of error variance (σ_e^2), relationship variance (σ_{PT}^2), and target variance (σ_T^2). With this single half-block design, we can actually use ANOVA to estimate the mean squares, and then with simple algebra, solve for these values. The one constraint is that with only one rating per cell (i.e., each perceiver rates each target's friendliness once), true relationship variance cannot be separated from error variance. Finally, note that although these calculations can be relatively simple in a half-block design, in other SRM designs, these calculations are more complex and are generally conducted using specialized programs (e.g., SOREMO, Kenny, 1996b), or specific codes in standard statistical packages (see Kenny, 2016).

Developing an SRM Study: Types of Research Questions

The SRM can address a variety of research questions; we offer only select examples here (see Kenny, 2021, for an extensive list of articles and chapters that either use or extend the SRM). Some important research questions can be addressed by simply examining the amount of actor, partner, or relationship variance. For example, theories of leadership might be informed by asking the basic question: Do people agree on who is a good leader? SRM studies on both leadership and personality reveal that target variance for both leadership and extraversion is considerably larger than perceiver variance (de Vries, 2010; Livi et al., 2008). This finding suggests that there is consensus about who is a good leader and who is an extravert within groups of acquainted individuals. Conversely, other research suggests that ratings of agreeableness among unacquainted college students have more perceiver variance than target variance (Graziano & Tobin, 2002). This result suggests that people assimilate their ratings of agreeableness for new acquaintances: Some individuals see new acquaintances as agreeable, but others tend to see new acquaintances as disagreeable.

More complex research questions examine associations between individual-level (i.e., actor and/or partner) effects or between dyad-level (i.e., relationship) effects across variables. For example, actor–actor correlations can investigate whether a person's behavior on one variable is related to their behavior on another variable. Similarly, partner–partner correlations indicate whether a person's ability to elicit one type of response is related to eliciting another response. Examples of these correlations can be found in the Schrodt, Soliz, and Braithwaite (2008) study on communication within stepfamilies. They found evidence that stepparents—but not the biological parents or children—who talk more with their family also report more relational satisfaction across all members of their family (actor–actor correlation). In contrast, the children demonstrated a partner–partner correlation: Children with whom other family members reported greater relationship satisfaction tended to elicit more talking from those family members.

Correlating the SRM effects with each other can also test for reciprocity (i.e., if I see others a particular way, do they see me the same way?). Reciprocity in the SRM can be examined two ways: generalized and dyadic. *Generalized reciprocity* is the correlation between perceiver and target effects, which determines whether a general response with others elicits a similar response from most others. So, if I generally report liking others (strong perceiver effect), do most other people report liking me (strong target effect)? For example, Pylyser et al. (2020) found that when stepparents believed they mattered to family members, their family members (parents, children, and stepchildren) also believed that they mattered to the stepparent. On the other hand, *dyadic reciprocity* is the correlation between individuals' relationship effects. This tests the more specific question of: If I particularly like you, do you particularly like me? Interestingly, these two approaches to reciprocity can yield different patterns of results. In the Eastwick et al. (2007) study of speed dating with individuals identifying as heterosexual, reciprocity correlations for romantic interest were *positive* at the dyadic level but *negative* at the generalized level. This suggests that if Azad particularly likes Ellen, Ellen is likely to feel especially positive about Azad. However, if Azad reports high romantic interest for all women (e.g., Ellen, Frances, Gabriela, and Hana), those women are *less* likely to be interested in him.

Other research questions can be based on correlations between the actor or partner effects and individual differences (e.g., self-ratings or personality data). For example, one could correlate self-perceptions with target effects to investigate *self-accuracy*, or *self-other agreement*. Such correlations estimate whether seeing oneself in a particular way is related to how a person is actually seen by others. Studying employees from a non-profit organization, Doeze Jager et al. (2017) found evidence for self–other agreement on need for achievement and need for power, but not on need for affiliation. That is, these employees' views of their own motivations generally matched how their colleagues viewed them, except on the affiliation dimension. Self-perceptions can also be used to predict perceiver effects, which provides an estimate of *assumed similarity*. For example, does seeing oneself as likeable mean that one will see others as likeable too? Mahaffey and Marcus (2006) measured assumed similarity in sex offenders and found that those with higher scores on psychopathy also believed that other offenders had higher psychopathy.

Fles and Lakey (2017) provided an example of correlating personality variables with the SRM individual-level effects. Specifically, Big Five traits were used to predict the degree to which participants were consensually seen as supportive. That is, they correlated target effects for supportiveness with participant's self-ratings on the Big Five factors of personality. This analysis allowed them to demonstrate that people rated by others as supportive were generally higher in agreeableness, extraversion, and emotional stability. Using a comparable SRM analytic strategy, Marcus et al. (2019) examined perceptions of externalizing behavior and psychopathy in well-acquainted student groups. These researchers found that self-reports of psychopathy were associated with target effects on perceptions of a variety of negative social behaviors (e.g., cheating).

Finally, experimental manipulations can be included in SRM studies. Such manipulations can occur either within or between groups. Within-group manipulations would be treated as individual-difference variables and could be used to predict actor or partner effects. By using a between-group manipulation, researchers can evaluate whether the variance or the relationships among the SRM components are different across the manipulated variable. Details about experimental manipulations in SRM studies are included in the Experimental Manipulations section later.

Developing an SRM Study: Procedural Considerations

Number of participants per group. In a social relations analysis the variances for the three central components (actor, partner, and relationship) are estimated for each group, and then these variances are pooled across groups. Therefore, statistical power is a joint function of the size of the groups and number of groups, although group size has a stronger effect on power (see Lashley & Kenny, 1998, for details about power in SRM research). Group size is important because larger groups generate more precise estimates of the SRM variances and, in turn, more power for statistical tests. Indeed, a single large group can have more power than several smaller groups (although one or few groups would also mean no opportunity to model variability across groups). Also, power is lower in block designs than round-robin designs with the same group size because fewer dyadic data points are collected in block designs (i.e., not everyone rates or interacts with everyone else). Thus, the number of groups needed depends on the group size, the design, and the size of the effects the researchers are seeking to detect. For example, one might need only two 12-person groups to reach .80 power for larger effects in a round-robin design, whereas over 1,000 four-person groups would be needed with a small effect in an asymmetric block design (Lashley & Kenny, 1998). In sum, from a purely statistical standpoint, larger groups and round-robin designs will have more power, whereas smaller groups and block designs will have less statistical power.

Despite the statistical benefits of larger groups, they are not always practical due to participant fatigue. For example, consider a study of self-disclosure in one-on-one interactions among previously unacquainted students. If the study were conducted as a round-robin design with 10 students per group, each participant would have nine interactions. Even if the interactions are relatively brief this would likely result in substantial participant fatigue. This time burden would be even more problematic if the participants were required to complete questionnaires following each interaction.

Given the statistical benefits and practical limitations of large groups, researchers need to balance the burden they place on participants against the number of groups that they will need to include. Studies that include simple and easy tasks for participants (e.g., ratings of romantic interest at zero acquaintance) can benefit from having a larger group. As participant burden increases, researchers will need to use larger numbers of smaller groups to achieve sufficient power.

The minimum group size (round-robin design) or subgroup size (block design) is three participants. However, this minimum is only possible for round-robin studies if the researcher assumes that no dyadic reciprocity exists. For some research contexts, such as a study of interpersonal perception with unacquainted group members, it may be reasonable to expect that the unique way person A sees B has no relation to B's unique perception of A. However, some variables, such as liking, and some research contexts, such as studies of well-acquainted individuals, make such a restriction untenable. In these cases, researchers should plan to include groups of four or more participants.

In most round-robin designs there is a minimum of four participants in each group. The maximum number of participants in a group or subgroup is theoretically unlimited, although practical constraints will typically limit this size. Note that some SRM-specific software (i.e., the SOREMO and BLOCKO programs) limit group size to 25 in round-robin designs and subgroup size to 20 in block designs.

Timing of the interactions. Dyadic interactions among unacquainted participants can occur *simultaneously* in the presence of the entire group or *sequentially* in a series of one-on-one interactions. Using the simultaneous approach, Armando, Bakari, Chuck, and Dev would be seated in the same room and asked to interact with each other. In an example of simultaneous interactions, Christensen and Kashy (1998) had four undergraduates participate in each session. After completing self-rating measures of loneliness, the individuals were seated around a table to work together on a problem-solving task. In this case, the task was merely a tool to get the participants interacting with one another. Following the task, each participant provided perception ratings about each other participant (i.e., a round-robin design). This approach allowed us to evaluate whether the lonely people were seen differently by others, which was tested by the correlation between participants' loneliness scores and their target effects on the perception ratings.

Alternatively, a sequential procedure would have Armando and Bakari interact in one location while Chuck and Dev interact in another. After the first set of interactions, half of the partners switch locations so that A and C interact while B and D interact, and so on. This sequential approach was used to study dyadic negotiations in four- and five-person groups (Elfenbein et al., 2008) as well as in a "speed-dating" study of positive affect (Berrios et al., 2015). In these studies, students engaged in a series of tasks (negotiation or dating conversation, respectively) with other members of their group one at a time. Whereas Elfenbein et al. (2008) were able to use a round-robin design, speed-dating studies like Berrios et al. (2015) have used heterosexual dyads and so are typically conducted as asymmetric block designs.

The simultaneous interaction approach has the benefit of efficiency but might limit the expression of partner-specific responses (behavioral data) or the discrimination among the different partners (rating data). These problems would be expected to increase with the size of the group. Conversely, the sequential approach is potentially more time-consuming, but participants need only attend to one partner at a time. Decisions about which approach to use are often determined by the variables to be measured. Some behavioral data (e.g., smiling at specific others) would be difficult for experimenters to record for many participants simultaneously, especially in a large group. Similarly, complex rating data (e.g., assessments of each member's personality along multiple dimensions) will be challenging for participants if they don't have enough information to distinguish between the group members. In both cases, one would find mostly actor variance and little partner variance: If participants cannot make clear distinctions among the other group members, their behavior and perceptions will be driven by their own attributes. That is, they may report liking everyone in the group, or they may smile frequently at everyone in the group. Other types of data are more amenable to collection in large groups. For example, Lönnqvist et al. (2008) had cadets rate the performance of every other member of their platoon in a round-robin fashion. Even though the platoons ranged in size from 14 to 21 cadets, the round-robin design could be used because the cadets were familiar with each other, and the ratings were relatively simple.

Researchers who are deciding between a sequential or simultaneous approach must also consider practical issues related to space. Simultaneous interactions can usually be conducted in one large room. However, having interactions in sequence typically requires multiple, adjoining lab rooms where each dyad can be seated. In a round-robin study with a group size of four participants, a researcher could conduct the study with as few as two rooms. Armando would interact with Bakari in one room while Chuck interacts with Dev in the other room. After the first interaction, Bakari and Dev switch rooms for the second interaction, then Chuck and Dev switch rooms for the final interaction. If one were conducting a block design with four participants in each subgroup, four rooms would be required (A with E, B with F, C with G, and D with H). Finally, researchers must also consider whether participants will need privacy while completing ratings of their interaction partners. If so, one would need as many spaces or computers as there are participants in the group.

Roles. Thus far in our discussion, we have treated individuals within groups as indistinguishable or interchangeable (e.g., four roommates, five unacquainted individuals). However, the SRM can also be used when groups are composed of individuals who can be identified with particular roles. The most common type of study that uses a SRM with roles are studies of family members, although this type of design could also be used when group members are randomly assigned to roles within the group. The key idea is that within a family (or other group), each individual can be distinguished by their role (e.g., mother, father, older child, younger child), and outcomes may differ across roles. That is, the SRM uses dyadic data based on each pairing of roles to estimate separate actor and partner effects for each role and separate relationship effects for each combination of roles.

For example, Ackerman et al. (2011) examined positive interpersonal behavior in family conflict resolution interactions with four-person families. Families were videotaped while trying to resolve a difficult family problem, and then coders rated how warm and supportive each person was with every other family member. Thus, in this research 12 data points were coded in each interaction (Mother's support of Father or MF, Mother's support of Older child or MO, Mother's support of Younger child or MY, as well as FM, FO, FY, OM, OF, OY, and YM, YF, and YO).

The SRM for families then partitions the variance in these ratings into a family mean effect, actor effects for each role, partner effects for each role, and relationship effects for each dyadic combination of roles. In the Ackerman et al. (2011) study, results suggested that there is a strong family-level component to positive interpersonal behavior. Beyond this, there was substantial actor variance for each role, suggesting that individual differences are a key determinant of warm and supportive behavior in families (i.e., some people are warm to all family members, but others are not). Finally, there was evidence of relationship variance—especially for mothers' and fathers' communication with one another. Notably, because the data set used in the study by Ackerman et al. (2011) was early data from a long-term longitudinal study, these researchers were able to examine correlates of the SRM components of warm and supportive behavior in the family of origin with marital relationship outcomes for the children 20 years later (Ackerman et al., 2013). This work showed that individuals reared in warm and supportive families reported more positive marital relationships, and their partners also reported more positive relationships.

Cook et al. (2018) also used four-person families and found that, on average, families were fairly responsive to each other. Yet within family roles, the perceiver effects revealed that mothers saw their families as more responsive, whereas younger children saw their families as less responsive. Similarly for target effects, mothers were seen by others as especially responsive compared with other roles in the family. Finally, their data only found that two of the 12 specific relationships yielded uniquely different ratings: Especially low scores on responsiveness were found for mothers perceiving the younger child and fathers perceiving mothers.

Experimental manipulations. As noted earlier, experimental manipulations can either be within-group or between-groups. *Within-group* manipulations could occur at the individual- or dyad-level. Individual-level manipulations could be treated like measured individual difference variables and used to predict actor/perceiver effects or partner/target effects. In a hypothetical study on self-disclosure, half the participants could be given bogus information that their interaction partner is especially friendly. Each individual's expectation would then be treated as an individual difference variable. Alternatively, if each group member were assigned to a particular condition (e.g., leader, manager, senior worker, trainee), an SRM with roles approach could be taken, treating the manipulation as the "role" variable.

Dyad-level manipulations within groups could be designed to influence sets of interaction partners in different ways. For example, Back et al. (2008) randomly assigned students to different seats on the first day of a class and, a year later, the students indicated their strength of friendship with each other student. In this way, the researchers manipulated the physical distance between members of each dyad. This approach allowed the researchers to demonstrate that physical proximity predicted dyadic friendship intensity beyond perceiver and target effects.

Between-group manipulations could occur in either a round-robin or block design. In a round-robin, each group would be assigned to one level of the independent variable. When analyzing the data, SRM effects and variances are generated separately for the groups at each level of the independent variable and then compared across groups. In a similar approach, Loignon et al. (2017) randomly assigned whether teams received "frame of reference" training, which has been shown to increase the quality peer evaluations in a management context. Using a round-robin design, each team member evaluated every other team member on their performance following the training manipulation. The researchers then compared target effects (consensus) for peer evaluations across trained and untrained groups.

In a block design, each subgroup could be assigned to one level of the independent variable. For example, members of one subgroup could be given access to important resources for a task, and members of the other subgroup could be denied access to such resources. With such an approach, one could compare perceptions of poorly resourced individuals with perceptions of individuals who are well-resourced. That is, an asymmetric-block design would be used to compare results across the subgroups. Because these designs use two subgroups, the independent variable would generally be limited to two levels.

Although we discuss examples of experimental designs above, it should be noted that the same principles apply to quasi-experimental or measured differences between groups. The Boldry and Kashy (1999) study of intergroup bias compared high-status and low-status groups, with status as an observed variable (year in school). To test some of their hypotheses, the researchers ran separate round-robin analyses for high-status group members rating one another and for low-status group members rating one another. They also analyzed the high-status individuals' ratings of the low-status group members and vice versa. A key hypothesis that was tested using this approach was whether there was greater target variance for ingroup ratings relative to outgroup ratings.

Developing an SRM Study: Measurement Considerations

As noted in the section on developing research questions, the type of questions that can be addressed with the SRM have few limits. However, the researcher must measure some dyadic variable and the participants must make multiple ratings. These requirements can be met in different ways.

Measuring perception data. One consideration is the timing of the measures. In the *variable fastest-moving* approach, participants rate several characteristics for each target at once. After making all of the ratings for one target, participants then make the same ratings for the next target. It is also possible to collect data with the *person fastest-moving*. With this strategy, the participants rate all targets on one variable, then all targets on a second variable, and so on.

Although variable fastest-moving is more common, researchers should reflect on the implications of each approach. The benefit of the variable-fastest moving approach is that participants can focus on their assessments or memories of a single target. This is especially helpful when participants have sequential interactions with targets and can make ratings immediately after each dyadic interaction while the experience is fresh in their minds. Yet problems can arise if participants rely on halo effects from the target's personality. If so, "central characteristics" (e.g., warmth, physical attractiveness) have the potential to bias other ratings of that target (Asch, 1946). In this way target–target correlations might be inflated due to the method of data collection.

Conversely, the person fastest-moving approach can make it easier for participants to contrast among targets on a given variable and, in turn, avoid reliance on target halo effects. This approach is most practical when participants are involved in a simultaneous interaction. However, the person fastest-moving approach might be challenging for participants if they must constantly switch between memories or schemas for different targets. This effort could result in greater participant fatigue, which could have two practical consequences. Some fatigued participants might begin to respond haphazardly, increasing overall error variance. Other fatigued participants might begin relying on a response set (i.e., not discriminating among targets), which would inflate perceiver variance.

Measuring behavior data. Collecting behavioral data can be challenging in an SRM study because multiple participants must be coded or recorded simultaneously. Although it is possible for researchers to code participant behaviors in situ, they will often want a video record of the participants' actions. The number of cameras required depends on the type of behaviors the researcher wants to study. Macro-level behaviors (e.g., leaning forward, proportion of time talking) can be recorded for two participants using a single camera that captures them in profile. However, coding smaller behaviors (e.g., smiling, eye gaze) will often require a separate camera facing each participant. If so, the number of participants in each group will be limited by the number of cameras unless the researchers stagger the interactions, which would require more participant time.

Measuring behavioral data is more feasible in studies that use sequential interactions than in studies using simultaneous interactions. The main limitation of simultaneous interactions is the difficulty of accurately determining the target of most behaviors. That is, if one is smiling, talking, or leaning forward in a group, to whom is the person directing the behavior? In some cases, it is possible to identify the specific targets of behaviors with an elaborate methodological approach. One such study trained individual cameras on each of four participants who were completing a group decision-making task (Krause et al., 2014). After the recording stage, the researchers coded social behaviors directed by each participant toward each other participant, which allowed for an SRM analysis of behavioral data using the simultaneous interaction approach.

After the SRM Study: Analysis Considerations

Data from an SRM study typically have been analyzed using one of two specialized statistical programs (SOREMO and BLOCKO; downloadable at https://davidakenny.net/srm/srmp.htm; Kenny, 1996a, 1996b). More recently researchers have developed an R package, TripleR (Schönbrodt et al., 2012) that can conduct SRM analyses. In addition, the SRM can be analyzed using variants of multilevel models in standard statistical packages (e.g., SAS, SPSS; Kenny, 2016). These programs generate estimates of the variances, correlations among the SRM effects, and correlations between the SRM effects and individual difference data.

One interesting analysis option following an SRM method is to estimate perceiver and target effects for each individual in a study and then use these outputs to test more complex mediation or moderation hypotheses. For example, Christensen et al. (2003) evaluated whether the relationship between social anxiety and meta-perceptions (i.e., perceptions of how one is viewed by others) was mediated by self-perceptions, whereas Christensen et al. (2012) analyzed whether ethnic identification moderated perceptions of interaction partners for members of majority versus minority ethnic groups

In sum, conducting SRM research can be relatively complex as compared with an online survey study or other methods. However, the challenges involved in conducting research that requires multiple participants interacting or rating multiple partners are typically compensated by rich and interesting data that speak to the nuanced nature of human interaction. With its ability to address a wide variety of research questions, the SRM is a useful tool for researchers interested in social relationships.

CONCLUSION

In the 40 years since the first publication of an SRM analysis, Kenny's model has proven itself to be a useful tool for studying dyadic phenomena in many fields of psychology and beyond. Although most widely utilized in social psychology, the

SRM has been used to address wide-ranging research questions about development (e.g., Buist et al., 2008), intrafamily communication (Schrodt et al., 2008), dance coordination (Carlson et al., 2018), food sharing (Koster & Leckie, 2014), psychopathology (Mahaffey & Marcus, 2006), and listening on work teams (Kluger et al., 2021). The SRM has even been used to examine interactions between pairs of fish (Dunlap, 2002) and between humans and dogs (Kwan et al., 2008). We hope this chapter will entice even more scientists to consider an SRM approach for their own research questions.

References

Ackerman, R. A., Kashy, D. A., Donnellan, M. B., & Conger, R. D. (2011). Positive-engagement behaviors in observed family interactions: A social relations perspective. *Journal of Family Psychology*, 25(5), 719–730. https://doi.org/10.1037/a0025288

Ackerman, R. A., Kashy, D. A., Donnellan, M. B., Neppl, T., Lorenz, F. O., & Conger, R. D. (2013). The interpersonal legacy of a positive family climate in adolescence. *Psychological Science*, 24(3), 243–250. https://doi.org/10.1177/0956797612447818

Asch, S. E. (1946). Forming impressions of personality. *Journal of Abnormal Psychology*, 41(3), 258–290. https://doi.org/10.1037/h0055756

Back, M. D., Schmukle, S. C., & Egloff, B. (2008). Becoming friends by chance. *Psychological Science*, 19(5), 439–440. https://doi.org/10.1111/j.1467-9280.2008.02106.x

Berrios, R., Totterdell, P., & Niven, K. (2015). Why do you make us feel good? Correlates and interpersonal consequences of affective presence in speed-dating. *European Journal of Personality*, 29(1), 72–82. https://doi.org/10.1002/per.1944

Boldry, J. G., & Kashy, D. A. (1999). Intergroup perception in naturally occurring groups of differential status: A social relations perspective. *Journal of Personality and Social Psychology*, 77(6), 1200–1212. https://doi.org/10.1037/0022-3514.77.6.1200

Buist, K. L., Reitz, E., & Dekovic, M. (2008). Attachment stability and change during adolescence: A longitudinal application of the social relations model. *Journal of Social and Personal Relationships*, 25(3), 429–444. https://doi.org/10.1177/0265407508090867

Carlson, E., Burger, B., & Toiviainen, P. (2018). Dance like someone is watching: A social relations model study of music-induced movement. *Musicae Scientiae*, 1, 1–16. https://doi.org/10.1177/2059204318807846

Christensen, P. N., Duangdao, K., Isaacs, H., & Alfonso-Reese, L. (2012). Projection and mirror effects in cross-group interactions: A social relations model study of similarity perceptions. *Self and Identity*, 11(1), 36–50. https://doi.org/10.1080/15298868.2010.501684

Christensen, P. N., & Kashy, D. A. (1998). Perceptions of and by lonely people in initial social interaction. *Personality and Social Psychology Bulletin*, 24(3), 322–329. https://doi.org/10.1177/0146167298243009

Christensen, P. N., Stein, M. B., & Means-Christensen, A. (2003). Social anxiety and interpersonal perception: A social relations model analysis. *Behaviour Research and Therapy*, 41(11), 1355–1371. https://doi.org/10.1016/S0005-7967(03)00064-0

Coesens, C., De Mol, J., De Bourdeaudhuij, I., & Buysse, A. (2010). The role of interpersonal influence in families in understanding children's eating behavior: A social relations model analysis. *Journal of Health Psychology*, 15(8), 1267–1278. https://doi.org/10.1177/1359105310369187

Cook, W. L., Dezangré, M., & De Mol, J. (2018). Sources of perceived responsiveness in family relationships. *Journal of Family Psychology*, 32(6), 743–752. https://doi.org/10.1037/fam0000411

de Vries, R. E. (2010). Lots of target variance: An update of SRM using the HEXACO Personality Inventory. *European Journal of Personality*, 24(3), 169–188. https://doi.org/10.1002/per.764

Doeze Jager, S., Born, M., & Van der Molen, H. (2017). Self-other agreement between employees on their need for achievement, power, and affiliation: A social relations study. *Scandinavian Journal of Work and Organizational Psychology*, 2(1), 9. https://doi.org/10.16993/sjwop.29

Dunlap, K. D. (2002). Hormonal and body size correlates of electrocommunication behavior during dyadic interactions in a weakly electric fish, *Apteronotus leptorhynchus*. *Hormones and Behavior*, 41(2), 187–194. https://doi.org/10.1006/hbeh.2001.1744

Eastwick, P. W., Finkel, E. J., Mochon, D., & Ariely, D. (2007). Selective versus unselective romantic desire: Not all reciprocity is created equal. *Psychological Science*, 18(4), 317–319. https://doi.org/10.1111/j.1467-9280.2007.01897.x

Eastwick, P. W., & Hunt, L. L. (2014). Relational mate value: Consensus and uniqueness in romantic evaluations. *Journal of Personality and Social Psychology*, 106(5), 728–751. https://doi.org/10.1037/a0035884

Elfenbein, H. A., Curhan, J. R., Eisenkraft, N., Shirako, A., & Baccaro, L. (2008). Are some negotiators better than others? Individual differences in bargaining outcomes. *Journal of Research in Personality*, 42(6), 1463–1475. https://doi.org/10.1016/j.jrp.2008.06.010

Fles, E., & Lakey, B. (2017). The personality traits of consensually supportive people. *Personality and Individual Differences*, 104, 87–91. https://doi.org/10.1016/j.paid.2016.07.032

Graziano, W. G., & Tobin, R. M. (2002). Agreeableness: Dimension of personality or social desirability artifact? *Journal of Personality*, 70(5), 695–728. https://doi.org/10.1111/1467-6494.05021

Kenny, D. A. (1994). *Interpersonal perception: A social relations analysis*. Guilford Press.

Kenny, D. A. (1996a). BLOCKO [Computer software]. https://davidakenny.net/srm/srmp.htm

Kenny, D. A. (1996b). SOREMO [Computer software]. https://davidakenny.net/srm/srmp.htm

Kenny, D. A. (2016). *Estimation of SRM using specialized software*. https://davidakenny.net/doc/srmsoftware.pdf

Kenny, D. A. (2020). *Interpersonal perception: The foundation of social relationships* (2nd ed.). Guilford Press.

Kenny, D. A. (2021). *SRM references*. https://davidakenny.net/srm/srm.htm

Kluger, A. N., Malloy, T. E., Pery, S., Itzchakov, G., Castro, D. R., Lipetz, L., Sela, Y., Turjeman-Levi, Y., Lehmann, M., New, M., & Borut, L. (2021). Dyadic listening in teams: Social relations model. *Applied Psychology: An International Review*, 70(3), 1045–1099. https://doi.org/10.1111/apps.12263

Koster, J. M., & Leckie, G. (2014). Food sharing networks in lowland Nicaragua: An application of the social relations model to count data. *Social Networks*, 38, 100–110. https://doi.org/10.1016/j.socnet.2014.02.002

Krause, S., Back, M. D., Egloff, B., & Schmukle, S. C. (2014). Implicit interpersonal attraction in small groups: Automatically activated evaluations predict actual behavior toward social partners. *Social Psychological & Personality Science*, 5(6), 671–679. https://doi.org/10.1177/1948550613517723

Kwan, V. S. Y., Gosling, S. D., & John, O. P. (2008). Anthropomorphism as a special case of social perception: A cross-species social relations model analysis of humans and dogs. *Social Cognition*, 26(2), 129–142. https://doi.org/10.1521/soco.2008.26.2.129

Lashley, B. R., & Kenny, D. A. (1998). Power estimation in social relations analysis. *Psychological Methods*, 3(3), 328–338. https://doi.org/10.1037/1082-989X.3.3.328

Livi, S., Kenny, D. A., Albright, L., & Pierro, A. (2008). A social relations analysis of leadership. *The Leadership Quarterly*, 19(2), 235–248. https://doi.org/10.1016/j.leaqua.2008.01.003

Loignon, A. C., Woehr, D. J., Thomas, J. S., Loughry, M. L., Ohland, M. W., & Ferguson, D. M. (2017). Facilitating peer evaluation in team contexts: The impact of frame-of-reference rater training. *Academy of Management Learning & Education*, 16(4), 562–578. https://doi.org/10.5465/amle.2016.0163

Lönnqvist, J., Leikas, A., Verkasalo, M., & Paunonen, S. V. (2008). Does self-enhancement have implications for adjustment. *Basic and Applied Social Psychology*, 30(4), 377–386. https://doi.org/10.1080/01973530802502374

Mahaffey, K. J., & Marcus, D. K. (2006). Interpersonal perception of psychopathy: A social relations analysis. *Journal of Social and Clinical Psychology*, 25(1), 53–74. https://doi.org/10.1521/jscp.2006.25.1.53

Marcus, D. K., Robinson, S. L., & Eichenbaum, A. E. (2019). Externalizing behavior and psychopathy: A Social Relations Analysis. *Journal of Personality Disorders*, 33(3), 310–325. https://doi.org/10.1521/pedi_2018_32_343

Pylyser, C., Loncke, J., Loeys, T., De Mol, J., & Buysse, A. (2020). Perceived mattering in stepfamilies: A social relations model analysis. *Personal Relationships*, 27(2), 366–384. https://doi.org/10.1111/pere.12318

Schönbrodt, F. D., Back, M. D., & Schmukle, S. C. (2012). TripleR: An R package for social relations analyses based on round-robin designs. *Behavior Research Methods*, 44(2), 455–470. https://doi.org/10.3758/s13428-011-0150-4

Schrodt, P., Soliz, J., & Braithwaite, D. O. (2008). A social relations analysis model of everyday talk and relational satisfaction in stepfamilies. *Communication Monographs*, 75(2), 190–217. https://doi.org/10.1080/03637750802023163

Warner, R. M., Kenny, D. A., & Stoto, M. (1979). A new round robin analysis of variance for social interaction data. *Journal of Personality and Social Psychology*, 37(10), 1742–1757. https://doi.org/10.1037/0022-3514.37.10.1742

Chapter 21

DYADIC DATA ANALYSIS

Richard Gonzalez and Dale Griffin

The study of interdependence contributes to a rich understanding of social life. Does one partner's depression predict their spouse's depression? Does one partner's depression predict their spouse's marital satisfaction? How similar are the partners' level of depression, and does that similarity predict other variables such as marital satisfaction? What predicts the degree of similarity in depression across marital partners? Research questions such as these involve data that connect two individuals, so we say the units are *interdependent*. To add complexity, such research questions frequently include multiple variables and can involve longitudinal data collection. What makes these research questions psychologically interesting is that they focus on interpersonal processes. Of course, when studying interpersonal processes, it would be useful to collect data and use analytic procedures that permit the assessment and testing of those interpersonal processes.

The analysis of interdependent data presents special issues because the connections across individuals within a dyad need to be addressed in the analyses. Failure to account for these interpersonal correlations can introduce bias into an analysis, but more important, consideration of these interpersonal correlations allows one to assess interesting interpersonal psychological processes. Thus, the violation of independence is the ugly pebble that can be transformed into the pearl of interdependence theory. In this chapter, we illustrate a few analytic techniques that go beyond correcting data for independence "violations" to providing richer models that permit the researcher to assess psychological processes of interdependence. Interdependence is not treated as a nuisance that needs to be corrected but rather as one of the key psychological parameters to model. We view this chapter as introductory, focusing on the special case of dyads, and we review a few of the basic analysis techniques that are currently available.

The analysis of dyadic data can become complex in that there are several issues that need to be addressed in the analytic model, such as whether dyad members are exchangeable or distinguishable, whether dyadic data are cross-sectional or longitudinal, whether the analysis is framed as a multilevel model or a structural equation model (SEM), whether one takes a latent variable approach to partition individual and dyadic variance or whether one's theoretical model focuses on direct relations across people and across variables on observed data, whether data are normally distributed or categorical, and so on. As with any data analysis exercise, these different design features and priorities yield many combinations that are too numerous to review in a short introductory chapter. We refer the reader to a comprehensive treatment by Kenny et al. (2006),

https://doi.org/10.1037/0000320-021
APA Handbook of Research Methods in Psychology, Second Edition: Vol. 3. Data Analysis and Research Publication, H. Cooper (Editor-in-Chief)
Copyright © 2023 by the American Psychological Association. All rights reserved.

which covers many of these different combinations, and the edited volume by Card et al. (2008).

Our goal for this chapter is to highlight some simple concepts so researchers can develop an intuition and an appreciation for the procedures that are possible when one includes both individuals from a dyad in the same analyses. We discuss some of our favorite issues surrounding dyadic analyses and review a handful of the available data analytic techniques, taking a more intuitive and basic approach rather than presenting a general framework in which the various analytic approaches are special cases.

MODELING INTERDEPENDENCE VERSUS CORRECTING VIOLATIONS OF INDEPENDENCE

We initially became interested in dyadic data analysis because as social psychologists we wanted to study dyadic processes but recognized that the standard analytic techniques were too limiting. It seemed strange to us that researchers who studied dating couples, for example, often collected data from only one individual in the couple, or only examined the mean score across both members of a couple, and threw away the individual variation. These practices occurred because they provided a way to bypass the violation of statistical independence. One automatically has independent data when only one member of each couple is represented in the data set, or when a couple is boiled down to a single number. But can a researcher who is interested in studying dating couples make claims about the couple from data from only one person? Rather than go down the road of "one hand clapping" philosophical-type arguments, we decided instead to work on analytic procedures that allowed the study of the couple.

A study that assesses only one dating partner from each dyad gathers information about the relationship as indexed by that single subject. One can learn about the predictors of one partner's marital satisfaction but not how each dyad member influences the other's marital satisfaction. A study that assesses both members of the couple can examine how one person influences another, can examine the similarity or dissimilarity of the couple members, can examine whether the degree of similarity predicts some other variable, and so on. The potential for testing richer psychological questions increases when the researcher collects data from both individuals. One can now study the dyad—as an interdependent unit—in a deeper way.

The analysis of dyadic data has gone through an identity crisis over the past 2 decades. In the early days, methodologists warned about the dangers of failing to account for dependency in data when observations are made on both members of a dyad. The basic idea was that when members of the same dyad are analyzed together, their data are dependent on each other in much the same way that two observations in a pretest/posttest repeated measures design are related to each other. We understand well what happens to statistical inference if we ignore temporal dependence in a repeated measures analysis, and the early literature on dyadic data analysis focused on the analogous effects of ignoring nonindependence in dyadic research (e.g., Kenny, 1990; Kenny & Judd, 1986). This early literature made use of the intraclass correlation (ICC) as a tool to model the effects of violating independence. The ICC can be used to show how classic analysis of variance (ANOVA) and regression designs go awry in the presence of nonindependent data, such as how parameter estimates are biased or how p values can become either too liberal or too conservative.

Concern about the violation of independence seems to be a small piece of the larger puzzle. If one wants to study couples, then interdependence comes with the territory. Interdependence is part of the phenomenon, not a statistical flaw in one's data. The problem of violating independence is not with the data or the research question, but it is merely a symptom that one is using an inappropriate analytic technique for the research question. A researcher of dyadic processes should not have to adjust their interdependent data, or their interdependent research question, to conform to a statistical model of *independence*.

Instead, the statistical tools should allow the researcher to model interdependence directly in much the same way that a researcher has standard tools for analyzing data that are temporally dependent. The tools should provide ways to assess and measure interdependence, and they should provide ways to test theories of interdependence. In short, statistical techniques should facilitate the goals of the researcher, not provide roadblocks that get in the way of testing theory and understanding process.

Fortunately, the field of dyadic data analysis has moved away from primarily being concerned about the bias introduced through violations of the independence assumption. The current focus is on developing methods that facilitate the testing of research questions about interdependence. We next turn to a general introduction to types of association in data, which will provide a grounding for understanding dyadic data analysis.

TEMPORAL, MULTIVARIATE, AND INTERPERSONAL COVARIATION

There are three common types of associations that occur in psychological data. One type is temporal association, which occurs when data from the same participant are collected multiple times. We do not treat those observations as independent because we want to capture the temporal association, and in many cases, the temporal association is the key focal point. We do not merely use repeated measures or longitudinal designs because they provide more statistical power; we use repeated measurements because they provide unique information about change processes. A second type of association is due to interrelations among multiple variables. Such associations across variables are what multiple regression and SEMs assess. What is the relation between marital satisfaction and depression? We use multivariate techniques to study the association between variables. The third type of association is interpersonal association as seen in dyadic designs. Observations may have interpersonal associations because they come from the same members of a social unit, such as the two members of a dyad or students in the same classroom. We use dyadic techniques because we are interested in studying interpersonal processes.

These three kinds of associations between observations are not mutually exclusive, with one, two, or all three possibly occurring in the same study. For example, if there is a single dependent variable for each member of the dyad, then the observations are correlated by virtue of the interpersonal relations. If those same observations are also repeated for each dyad member, now there are associations both interpersonally and temporally in the data. If the dyad members are each measured once but on several variables, then both multivariate and interpersonal associations exist in the data. If both dyad members are observed repeatedly over time across several variables, then the observations exhibit associations temporally, interpersonally, and across variables. Analyses should account for all types of associations present in the data set.

Fortunately, there is a single basic idea that captures all three types of associations. Different models such as repeated measures analyses, multilevel analyses, and SEM provide similar ways of capturing the associations that occur between observations. A relatively easy way to conceptualize these associations is through the covariance matrix between all observations combining people, time, and variables. We begin with a simple description and build up the elements. Suppose we have 20 individuals measured once on a single variable and we want to estimate the mean across the 20 individuals. These data can be modeled as $Y_i = \mu + \varepsilon_i$ (i.e., a constant intercept for all 20 participants, which in this case will be the mean μ, and an error term ε). The usual assumption is that the error terms are independent and identically distributed. In other words, these 20 error terms are modeled as a 20×20 covariance matrix having a special structure. The diagonal contains a constant number, which is the variance of the residuals (the "identically distributed" part yields the same error variance across all observations). The off-diagonal terms are all zero because the residuals are assumed to be independent. Thus, this model imposes a theoretical covariance structure on the observations Y (also a 20 × 20 covariance matrix) such that any two observations are independent, and there is a common variance across all observations.

It may seem like overkill to explain so much detail for the simple model of the mean of 20 observations, but this is the basic structure we need to illustrate the three types of association. The different types of association impose structure on the covariance matrix of observations, and it is helpful to take this view to gain insight into the issues surrounding interdependent data.

Now we turn to the case of temporal association by considering two observations for the same person, that is, the 20 individuals are measured twice, so there are a total of 40 observations. The model for comparing the difference between the mean at each time becomes $Y_{ti} = \mu + \beta_t + \alpha_i + \varepsilon_{ti}$ with grand mean μ, a time fixed-effects factor β, a subject main effect treated as a random-effect factor α, and error term ε. This results in 40 error terms, which can be placed in a 40 × 40 covariance matrix.[1] The random effect terms α introduce a covariance across the 40 observations: Two observations from the same person, that is, two observations having the same α, are now associated relative to other observations even though the residuals remain independent. So, in the 40 × 40 covariance matrix of observations Person 1's Time 1 and Time 2 scores have a nonzero entry, Person 2's Time 1 and Time 2 scores have the same nonzero entry, and so on. We typically assume homogeneity of covariance, so each of the nonzero entries in the off-diagonal are constrained to be equal.

This framework can be extended to dyads. Suppose the 40 observations came from 20 heterosexual dating couples. A covariance is introduced between two members of the same dyad (interpersonal association) in just the same way as a covariance is introduced by two observations from the same person (temporal association). Similarly, the covariance between individuals from different dyads is zero, just as the covariance between observations of two different people in the case of repeated measurement is zero.

Appropriate methods for analysis of dyadic data are designed to take proper account of the temporal, interpersonal, and multivariate associations across observations. For example, a multilevel modeling approach to dyadic data takes the information supplied by the user that two individuals are nested in the same dyad and internally constructs a covariance matrix that has the proper structure. Likewise, other approaches to dyadic data analysis, such as SEM, also establish a covariance matrix with the proper structure. It is for this reason that different approaches can be used to analyze dyadic data—the key feature is how the analytic approach structures the covariance between observations. Different analytic frameworks like multilevel models and SEMs merely become the user interface by which the user can communicate the proper structure of the covariance matrix.

In the remaining sections of this chapter, we build on this basic intuition that design features in dyadic data require particular analytic elements. Readers familiar with multilevel modeling will recognize that we treat individuals as nested within dyads. Readers familiar with SEMs will recognize that we create latent variables to model shared dyadic variance. Dyadic data analysis can be discussed in terms of either multilevel models or SEMs. We switch back and forth between both representations freely because both offer unique insights into dyadic data analysis and some problems are easier to specify in one representation than the other. The covariance representation presents a common language to discuss these different analytic strategies. We first present the simple case of a single dependent variable collected from dyad members, and then we explore other design features involving temporal and multivariate elements.

---

[1] In this introductory chapter, we take liberties with notation. For example, we frequently switch between two subscripts t and i to denote time (e.g., 1 or 2) and person (e.g., 1–20), and a single subscript i to denote time and person (e.g., 1–40). We also do not carefully distinguish population and sample parameters.

THE BASIC INTERDEPENDENCE MODEL: ONE DEPENDENT VARIABLE, TWO PEOPLE

A key distinction is whether dyad members are distinguishable or exchangeable (e.g., Griffin & Gonzalez, 1995). Dyad members are distinguishable when the individuals can be identified on the basis of a theoretically meaningful variable such as gender in the case of heterosexual dating couples. Dyad members are exchangeable when the individuals cannot be distinguished on the basis of a theoretically meaningful variable, such as in the case of same-sex dating couples. In this chapter, we mostly focus on the distinguishable case. For details on the exchangeable case, see Griffin and Gonzalez (1995) and Kenny et al. (2006).

Interdependence between interval scaled data in the context of linear models is captured by the ICC. The basic intuition for the ICC is that it measures similarity in terms of the percentage of variance associated with between-couple—versus within-couple—variance. One standard formulation takes the variance associated with a dyad-level parameter and normalizes it by the sum of that dyad-level variance plus the variance of the individual-level error term. In the context of the general linear model, the underlying structural model for an observation Y for the jth person in the ith dyad is

$$Y_{ij} = \mu + \beta_j + \alpha_i + \varepsilon_{ij}, \quad (21.1)$$

where the μ is the fixed-effect constant, β_j is the fixed-effect term for the jth subject in a dyad (e.g., husband and wife), α_i is a random effect for dyad that is assumed to be normally distributed with mean zero and variance, σ_α^2 and the usual error term ε with variance σ_ε^2. (As mentioned earlier, in this chapter we focus on distinguishable dyads so we have a fixed-effect term to denote couple member (β_j); in an exchangeable dyad the individuals cannot be identified by a fixed-effect term so it is not included in the model.) Note the similarity of this model and the model for the two-time repeated measures presented earlier in the chapter. There are slightly different estimation formulas for the ICC depending on whether one uses maximum likelihood or restricted maximum likelihood (the latter accounts for degrees of freedom as in an ANOVA) estimation, but the basic logic is similar. The ICC becomes the ratio

$$\frac{\sigma_\alpha^2}{\sigma_\alpha^2 + \sigma_\varepsilon^2}. \quad (21.2)$$

Some people like to represent this framework in the context of a multilevel model with the first level representing data at the individual level and the second level representing dyads. This model can be written in two parts:

$$Y_{ij} = \gamma_i + \beta_j + \varepsilon_{ij} \text{ and} \quad (21.3)$$

$$\gamma_i = \mu + \alpha_i, \quad (21.4)$$

where β is a fixed effect term that estimates, say, the difference between the two distinguishable dyad members, γ is a random effect dyad term, and the ε is the usual error term. If one substitutes Equation 21.4 into Equation 21.3, then the result is the same as Equation 21.1. The two approaches are the same.

A third way to conceptualize the ICC is as an SEM with two indicators, one latent factor, and a specific set of restrictions. If one sets the variance of the latent factor to one, the two indicator paths to the observed variables for each dyad member equal to each other, and the error variances equal to each other, then the indicator paths are equal to the square root of the ICC (Figure 21.1). The rationale for equating the two indicator paths is because the interpretation of the latent variable is one of *shared variance* in which both individuals (regardless of whether they are exchangeable or distinguishable) contribute equally. This is a different parameterization and interpretation than the usual latent factor in which indicators of different variables can have different path estimates and so can relate differentially to the latent variable.

Thus, there are several ways to conceptualize the logic of interdependence as indexed by the ICC, and they all lead to the same result. One can model the intraclass correlation as a linear mixed

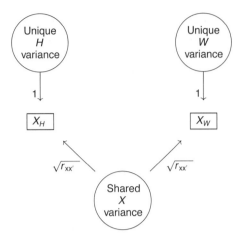

FIGURE 21.1. Illustration of the structural equations approach to estimating the intraclass correlation between husband (X_H) and wife (X_W) data in the distinguishable case.

model, as a multilevel model, or as an SEM. The results will be the same as long as the same estimation procedure is used (e.g., maximum likelihood) and the proper constraints on the parameters are imposed throughout. All three approaches impose the identical structure on the relevant covariance matrix. There is no conceptual reason to favor one statistical framework over the other when it comes to dyadic data analysis. It is not necessary to limit oneself to using, say, multilevel modeling programs when one has nested data of the type seen in dyadic research. We find that other considerations, such as the ability to relax some constraints or the ability to handle missing data in sensible ways, turn out to be important in choosing one statistics package or modeling framework over another. For example, it may be easier to test some constraints, such as the equality of error variance across individuals, or to generalize the model to allow for differential error variance in one approach rather than another. The interdependence issue present in dyadic data analysis does not by itself force an analyst into one specific type of statistical representation.

Throughout this chapter, we focus on normally distributed interval scale data. Given that we operate in the context of a linear mixed model (i.e., a general linear model with random effects), it is relatively straightforward to test these models within the generalized linear mixed model (GLMM). This generalization includes extensions to regression models on various distributions such as the binomial, the negative binomial, and the Poisson. These extensions may turn out to be relatively straightforward for simple models, but as we introduce more complicated multivariate dyadic models, the GLMM approach needs to be studied more carefully given that some distributions impose some challenging restrictions on some parameters, for example, the definition of the ICC in the context of binomial data is tricky because the usual GLMM logit link function imposes a constraint on the error variance (e.g., Snijders & Bosker, 1999). The generalization of dyadic models to nonnormal distributions remains an open area of research.

A MULTIVARIATE INTERDEPENDENT MODEL: TWO DEPENDENT VARIABLES, TWO PEOPLE

Latent Variable Model

Our discussion of the ICC so far has focused on one variable (Figure 21.1). We extend this framework to the case of two variables observed on each member of the dyad (Figure 21.2). For instance, we collect data on depression and marital satisfaction for each member of the distinguishable couple. In addition to two ICCs, one for each variable X (depression) and Y (satisfaction), the model adds two new terms that span the two variables. One term is the dyad-level covariance, which is interpreted as the covariance between two latent variables, or the dyadic relation between dyadic depression and dyadic satisfaction. In the context of dyadic data analysis, the latent variable estimated under the constraints shown in Figure 21.2 represents the shared variance between husband and wife within each respective variable. So the covariance is the covariance between the shared variance on depression and the shared variance on marital satisfaction. The dyad correlation is not equivalent to the correlation between the dyad means (Griffin & Gonzalez, 1995). The individual-level covariance is the covariance between the

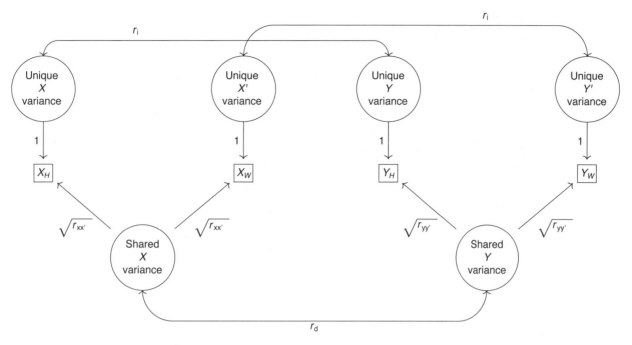

FIGURE 21.2. Illustration of the structural equations approach to estimating the intraclass correlation between husband and wife on two variables X and Y, the dyad level correlation r_d and the individual level correlation r_i.

individual factor variance on each variable (denoted as r_i in Figure 21.2). That is, the husband and wife each have idiosyncratic error variance remaining after accounting for the shared dyadic variance on each variable. The individual-level covariance represents the covariance across those individual-level error terms (e.g., the covariance between the husband's individual error term on depression and his individual error term on marital satisfaction). When couple members are distinguishable, it is possible to test the assumption of equal individual-level covariances by allowing the two r_i terms to be freely estimated and comparing the free model to the constrained model using the likelihood ratio test (i.e., Gonzalez & Griffin, 2001).

The model depicted in Figure 21.2 can be equivalently estimated in the context of a multilevel model. Unfortunately, the description of the multivariate model is not straightforward because multilevel models are typically expressed for a single variable with a single residual term ε at level 1. But we need separate error terms for each of the two variables. As we show later in this section, to fit the multilevel model to the multivariate example in Figure 21.2, it is necessary to express the multilevel model in a way that allows for different residual variances for each variable. We present one method to model multiple variables in the multilevel model using a switching regression technique.

The variables are represented in a single long column of data, which we denote **Y**. That is, we have a single column of data that includes the husband's depression, the wife's depression, the husband's marital satisfaction, and the wife's marital satisfaction. So, if there are 20 dyads, there are a total of 80 observations because each dyad member contributes two scores. It may seem strange to place data from different people and different variables into the same column, but by using proper codes, the model can account for data associated with different variables and different people. The approach constructs the appropriate 80 × 80 covariance matrix for the 80 observations. One way to account for the dependence of multiple variables is to use the repeated measures option common in multilevel model programs (e.g., depression and marital satisfaction would be treated as a repeated measures with an unconstrained covariance matrix, including heterogeneous variances, because we would not necessarily require that the variance for depression equal the variance for marital satisfaction). This approach is described in Kenny et al. (2006).

An equivalent representation of the multivariate framework in a multilevel model involves a *switching regression* approach, and we briefly review it here because it illuminates key points about the multivariate dyadic latent model (see Gonzalez & Griffin, 2001). First, as before place all observations from both partners and from both variables into a single long column Y. Second, create two columns of dummy codes. One dummy code D1 assigns a one to all depression scores and a zero for all marital satisfaction scores. The other dummy code D2 assigns a zero to all depression scores and a one to all marital satisfaction scores. The dummy codes perfectly partition the long column of observations into depression data and into marital satisfaction data. The first-level equation is written as follows, does not include an error variance at Level 1 (this can be easily implemented in the MLwiN multilevel modeling program) and does not include a fixed-effect intercept:

$$Y = \beta_d D1 + \beta_s D. \tag{21.5}$$

These two βs from Level 1 are modeled as random effects. The error terms for each variable can be modeled separately for each variable because they will be attached to different βs at the second level. The intercept and the error term are omitted at this first level to estimate them separately for each variable at the higher level; otherwise, the model will inappropriately estimate a pooled error variance and a pooled intercept across both variables.

The second level of regression equations are as follows:

$$\beta_d = \text{intercept}_d + v_{dg} + u_{di} \text{ and} \tag{21.6}$$

$$\beta_s = \text{intercept}_s + v_{sg} + u_{si}, \tag{21.7}$$

where v and u are random effects that code group and individual terms (respectively), each equation has its own fixed effect intercept term, the subscripts d, s, g, and i refer to depression, satisfaction, group, and individual, respectively. The random effect v assesses group-level variance, and the random effect u assesses individual-level variance. In short, the switching regression (Level 1) isolates the two variables depression and marital satisfaction, and the next two levels capture the dyadic structure. This can be implemented as a three-level model as far as the statistical program is concerned, but some researchers would call this a two-level model given that there is no error variance in the first level with the switching regression (Equation 21.5).

Now comes the important part of this particular formulation, which provides some new intuition. We formulate a covariance structure on each of the random effects v (group level) and u (individual level). Let the two group-level vs be bivariate normally distributed with covariance matrix,

$$\Omega_v = \begin{bmatrix} \sigma_{vd}^2 & \\ \sigma_{vds} & \sigma_{vs}^2 \end{bmatrix}, \tag{21.8}$$

where d and s denote depression and satisfaction, respectively. This means that the random effect v associated with depression has variance σ_{vd}^2, random effect v associated with satisfaction has variance σ_{vs}^2, and the two have covariance σ_{vds}. Similarly, an analogous covariance is formulated on the two individual-level us,

$$\Omega_u = \begin{bmatrix} \sigma_{ud}^2 & \\ \sigma_{uds} & \sigma_{us}^2 \end{bmatrix}. \tag{21.9}$$

This covariance matrix gives the variances and covariance between depression and satisfaction at the individual level. In this formulation, we require equality of all individual-level correlations (i.e., referring to Figure 21.2, this particular multilevel model implementation forces the two individual-level correlations for husband and wife to be identical).

These two covariance matrixes contain information about group-level and individual-level variance for each variable and information about group-level and individual-level covariance between the two variables. They provide all the information necessary to compute the terms in the latent group model as well as each of the two ICCs. Using the terms in those two covariance matrixes, we have

intraclass correlation for depression: $\dfrac{\sigma_{vd}^2}{\sigma_{vd}^2 + \sigma_{ud}^2}$,

intraclass correlation for satisfaction: $\dfrac{\sigma_{vs}^2}{\sigma_{vs}^2 + \sigma_{us}^2}$,

individual level correlation between depression and satisfaction: $\dfrac{\sigma_{uds}}{\sqrt{\sigma_{ud}^2 \sigma_{us}^2}}$, and

dyad level correlation between depression and satisfaction: $\dfrac{\sigma_{vds}}{\sqrt{\sigma_{vd}^2 \sigma_{vs}^2}}$.

The two intraclass definitions are identical to what we presented in a previous section. The form of the individual- and dyad-level correlations is the usual correlation (a covariance divided by the square root of a product of variances). The individual-level correlation uses terms from the individual-level covariance matrix u and the group-level correlation uses terms from the group-level covariance matrix v. Thus, these two covariance matrixes yield the ICCs, the variances of the individual- and group-level latent variables, and the individual- and group-level correlations, and the matrixes are identical to the SEM represented in Figure 21.2. This framework sets up the same structure on the 80 × 80 covariance matrix as the SEM in Figure 21.2.

The basic dyadic structure for the two variable latent model can be extended to more variables and to more complicated models. For example, one can take the two-variable model described in Figure 21.2 and use those variables (depression and marital satisfaction) to predict a third variable, say, parenting quality. The prediction can be modeled at both the individual level and the dyad level so that the prediction of parenting quality can occur at two levels. Does the shared variance of depression (dyad level) predict parental quality? Does the shared variance of marital satisfaction predict parental quality? Does the individual-level variance of the husband's depression predict his individual-level variance of parenting?

The take-home message of this type of modeling is that the variances and covariances are each partitioned into individual-level and dyad-level terms. Once the partition is performed, research questions can be tested at each level. It is in this way that the analysis of dyadic data goes beyond "correcting" data for violations of independence and instead directly models interdependence. We can see how partitioning the analysis into separate individual-level and dyad-level covariance matrixes provides useful terms, such as ICCs, to illuminate the study of interpersonal processes. Gonzalez and Griffin (2001) discuss research questions that lead naturally to such models and Iida et al. (2018) discuss different interpretations each model provides.

Actor–Partner Model

The *actor–partner model* (APM) depicted in Figure 21.3 provides an alternative model for the case of multiple variables over dyad members. The difference between the two models is how the interdependence is modeled—the latent variable model uses unmeasured causes or latent variables, whereas the APM uses observed variables directly. Is the wife's marital satisfaction predicted by both the husband's and the wife's depression? In this research question, there are no latent variables representing dyadic- and individual-level variance. Instead, we have two actor paths (a and d) that represent the influence of one individual's depression on the same individual's level of marital satisfaction. There are two cross-person cross-variable paths (b and c) that represent the effect of the wife's depression on her husband's marital satisfaction and the effect of the husband's depression on his wife's satisfaction (these are regression coefficients so are interpreted as the

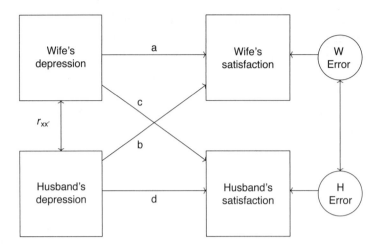

FIGURE 21.3. Actor–partner model for depression and marital satisfaction.

effect of one variable controlling for the linear effect of the other variable). The two exogenous predictors (depression from each couple member) are correlated, and the residuals associated with satisfaction as the dependent variable are correlated.

The model fits from the latent variable model in Figure 21.2 and the APM in Figure 21.3 are equivalent under some special restrictions. When two equality constraints are placed on the path coefficients ($a = d$ and $b = c$), the two residual variances are constrained to be equal, and the variances of the two predictors are constrained to be equal, then the models yield identical measures of fit. It is possible to generalize the models in different ways by relaxing equality constraints, and this is what makes each of them differentially useful as models. In general, a good use of the latent variable model formulation is when one wants to partition individual- and dyad-level variance and understand shared versus unique relations between variables; a good use of the APM is when one wants to examine the interrelations of individuals (in particular, how one couple member's data predicts the other member's data). Research questions involving similarity of dyad members are naturally tested with the latent variable model, whereas research questions of interpersonal influence are naturally tested with the APM (Gonzalez & Griffin, 2001). In some literatures the APM is known as a *seemingly unrelated regression* (SUR).

The traditional APM can be represented graphically as two planes in a three-dimensional representation. In our running example, the two predictors, wife's and husband's depression, are used to define two of the axes. The third axis is the outcome variable satisfaction and includes data from both dyad members. The a and b coefficients define one plane representing the relation between the partners' depression and the actor's (wife's) satisfaction; the c and d coefficients define a second plane representing the relation between the partners' depression and the actor's (husband's) satisfaction. This three-dimensional representation was used by Schoenbrodt et al. (2018) to implement the study of similarity within dyad members as proposed by Edwards and Parry (1993) and Griffin et al. (1999).

THE LONGITUDINAL INTERDEPENDENCE MODEL: A SINGLE VARIABLE, TWO TRAJECTORIES, TWO PEOPLE

There has been much progress on models of longitudinal data, such as latent growth curve analysis (e.g., Singer, 1998). We can combine advances from latent growth modeling with those in dyadic models. Within our framework, these hybrid designs produce data with both temporal and interpersonal association. For simplicity in exposition, we assume a relatively simple example in which the investigator has three time-points, and each member of the couple provides depression data at each of those three time-points. There are several ways one can approach the modeling of this situation. One is to focus on the latent growth curve to model a curve for each person. This places priority on the temporal association. To deal with the interpersonal association, or interdependence, one could allow covariances across key terms in the latent growth curve. Suppose we fit both a random intercept and a random slope to the three waves of depression data with separate trajectories for the wife and for the husband. To model the interdependence attributable to couples, we estimate additional covariances between the husband and wife's random effect intercept, a covariance between the husband and wife's random effect slope, and cross-covariances spanning one person's intercept with the other's slope. The model assesses, for instance, the relation between latent parameters of the growth model, the intercept and slope, across dyad members, and additional temporal structure can be modeled in the residuals (see next section).

A second way to model these data is to take the latent variable dyadic model as primary and apply it three times, once for each time-point. So there are three V-style diagrams, as in Figure 21.1—one for each time the depression variable is assessed. This portion of the model accounts for the interpersonal association. To account for temporal association, one can estimate covariance terms across individual- and dyadic-level variances, or instead of covariances, one could estimate an autoregressive model having regression paths across time predicting the individual- and dyad-level variances. This model can be used to assess the stability of the dyadic- and individual-level variances.

These two model frameworks differ in their focus or priority. The first model places priority on the trajectories over time and addresses interdependence over the parameters of the trajectory. The second model places priority on the interdependence between dyad members and addresses temporal association over the interdependence parameters. Both models can yield identical model fits depending on how they are parameterized and the nature of constraints that are imposed. That is, they both can imply the same covariance structure on the observations by properly accounting for both temporal and interpersonal association in the observations. They can also be relaxed and generalized in different ways and so can be used to test different models with different psychological implications. Both of these frameworks can be specified in the context of multilevel models. For an example of a longitudinal design in the multilevel framework for couple research using a single dependent variable, see Barnett et al. (1995). We prefer to conceptualize latent growth models in the context of SEM because it is sometimes easier to generalize the temporal part of the model, such as being able to specify unconstrained error variances at each time. But we recognize that both the multilevel and structural equation modeling approaches to latent growth modeling have their merits and can be reduced to identical underlying models depending on how the constraints are imposed within each framework.

A LONGITUDINAL, MULTIVARIATE INTERDEPENDENT MODEL: TWO DEPENDENT VARIABLES, TWO TRAJECTORIES, TWO PEOPLE

This design contains all three types of association: temporal, multivariate, and interpersonal. It arises when the research design measures couples on multiple variables such as depression and marital satisfaction over multiple time-points. For example, husband and wife dyad pairs are assessed on both depression and marital satisfaction at each of three time points. We describe one way to model these three associations simultaneously. Conceptually, we can estimate the latent group model (i.e., the model depicted in Figure 21.2) separately at each time. But rather than estimating three separate submodels (one for Time 1, a second for Time 2, and a third for Time 3), it is appropriate to estimate the entire model simultaneously (i.e., the latent group model at all three times together). This simultaneous model permits, among other things, the estimation of stability of the latent variable terms. This can be accomplished either by estimating covariances between all time i latent variables and all time $i + 1$ latent variables or by estimating regression paths between two adjacent time-points for different terms in the multivariate interdependent model. This representation gives priority to interdependence, then models the cross-variable association and the temporal association.

Other frameworks are possible too, such as placing priority on the temporal part and estimating trajectories for each person on each variable. Once the latent trajectories are estimated, then the multivariate and interpersonal associations are added across the relevant trajectory parameters. This produces, typically, a random intercept and random slope for each dyad member and these can be linked at the dyad level by estimating covariances across these random effects. Extensions of this approach include adding an APM structure to the residuals to model the correlated error over time within the same person as well as cross-person (Berry & Willoughby, 2017; Hamaker et al., 2015). There are many exciting new developments in modeling dyadic change (e.g., Bringmann et al., 2018; Gistelinck & Loeys, 2019; Gray & Ozer, 2019).

One can also perform additional analyses (e.g., moderation, mediation) to gain a deeper understanding of the contributors to the different elements of this general model, such as examining the predictors of group-level stability or individual-level stability, or examining interesting combinations such as cross-variable individual-level stability, for example, examining the correlation between the error for husbands' depression at Time 1 with the error of husbands' marital satisfaction at Time 2. This model can also be implemented in a multilevel framework.

STRUCTURAL EQUATION MODELING, MULTILEVEL MODELS, AND GENERALIZATIONS

Our general formulation of temporal, multivariate, and interpersonal association is useful for organizing many of the dyadic models that have been discussed in the literature. We see that different implementations, such as in an SEM approach or in a multilevel modeling approach, offer advantages and disadvantages. Sometimes it is easier to work with an SEM program such as when dyads are distinguishable, there are multiple variables, or one wants to test mediation and moderation. Sometimes a multilevel model approach is easier to implement, such as when dyads are exchangeable, there are missing data, or one is primarily concerned with partitioning dyad and individual random effect variance. Some generalizations or tests of constraints are easier within one framework than another, but many features can be implemented with either approach. For example, exchangeable and distinguishable dyads can be modeled with either multilevel models or with SEMs (e.g., Woody & Sadler, 2005).

The analysis of the latent dyad model can be conducted even when some groups have data from only one member (e.g., Snijders & Bosker, 1999). Multilevel techniques permit *units* of unequal sizes. So, if the unit is the individual with, say, four time-points, then one way to handle missing data would be to treat the missingness as something that yields unequal-size units. The general multilevel framework can thus handle missing observations in a longitudinal design as well as groups of unequal sizes (as would be encountered, for example, in research in which a family is the unit of analysis and families vary in size); for a complete discussion, see Raudenbush and Bryk (2002). For a discussion on extensions of the models reviewed in this chapter to groups, see Gonzalez and Griffin (2001), where the principle of a dyad extends to all possible pairs (e.g., a group of four has six possible dyadic relations).

We view the close connection to both structural equation and multilevel modeling frameworks as a plus rather than a negative, as providing insight rather than a source of confusion. As new methods become available in either framework, the dyadic researcher can easily switch back and forth to take advantage of new developments. For example, recent advances in growth mixture modeling techniques for simultaneously estimating trajectories and identifying different classes of individuals exhibiting different trajectory patterns could be extended to dyadic research.

SOFTWARE IMPLEMENTATIONS

The dyadic researcher has a broad array of software choices. Major statistical programs (e.g., SPSS, SAS, R, Stata) can run the procedures described in this chapter. The user must be mindful of the particular defaults in any statistical program they use. Researchers preferring an SEM framework can use any SEM program, including EQS, LISREL, AMOS, lavaan, and Mplus. Those who prefer a multilevel modeling approach can use programs such as HLM, MLwiN, nlme or lme4, and Mplus. Bayesian estimation of these models can be implemented either in traditional SEM programs such as Mplus or special packages such as BRMS in R. Again, careful attention to defaults in any statistical program one uses is important.

Some statistical programs such as Mplus and SAS NLMIXED make estimating and testing general models relatively easy. We welcome such flexible software. At the same time, we caution researchers that as new procedures are created by mixing and matching diverse elements (e.g., a dyadic longitudinal growth mixture model on binary data; for a discussion on dyadic categorical data, see Loeys & Molenberghs, 2013), it becomes even more important to understand the statistical underpinnings of one's model. It is common to see strange behavior in such novel hybrid models, such as negative error variances. The researcher should seek methodological advice when exploring new modeling territory. It is not advisable to use quick fixes, such as setting a negative error variance to zero, or setting a particular equality constraint, merely because that makes the program converge or run without error. Rather, when a new hybrid model produces strange output, it is best to consult a methodologist and understand the theoretical—as well as the statistical— implications. Further, the growing interest in the use of Bayesian estimation in the case of dyadic data analysis in some ways makes fitting complex models easier (e.g., use of binary, count, and normally distributed data within the same model); however, other modeling aspects may be more difficult due to the additional attention needed to evaluate convergence, choice of prior distributions and the hierarchical nature of parameters.

We recommend that the dyadic researcher maintain an open mind when choosing among different statistical packages. There is probably no single statistics package, or framework, that will serve all research needs. The dyadic researcher will also need to be flexible in setting up the data in different ways for different analyses. Sometimes dyadic analyses can be done in wide format, such that each row represents a couple and data from both members of the couple appear on the same row of the data matrix (as when using an SEM framework). Other times analyses are easier in long format, such that each row represents a person, so data from a couple spans two rows in the data matrix, as when using a multilevel framework. Each of those two data formats requires careful use of couple codes; data for distinguishable individuals is coded by individual codes in the long format but automatically by columns in the wide format. Sometimes data need to be entered twice, in the sense that one column contains data from Harry and Sally (separate rows), whereas a second column contains the same data for the same variable but in reverse order (i.e., Sally and Harry). This type of data entry can be used for the pairwise approach to dyadic data analysis (Griffin & Gonzalez, 1995) and in the APM (Kenny et al., 2006).

CONCLUSION

Dyadic designs provide researchers an exciting route to study interpersonal processes. The inclusion of both individuals from the dyad in the data set provides the opportunity to study interdependence. Interdependence is not a problem with the data but is a limitation of the standard statistical techniques psychologists tend to use. By framing interdependence in the language of associations, we showed that it is possible to discuss temporal, interpersonal, and multivariate associations together. The richness of dyadic data analysis is such that sometimes it is longitudinal, sometimes multivariate, and sometimes both. So it is necessary to take into account three sources of association that may be present in a dyadic design. We hope this chapter has convinced the reader to study dyadic processes.

References

Barnett, R. C., Raudenbush, S. W., Brennan, R. T., Pleck, J. H., & Marshall, N. L. (1995). Change in job and marital experiences and change in psychological distress: A longitudinal study of dual-earner couples. *Journal of Personality and Social Psychology*, 69(5), 839–850. https://doi.org/10.1037/0022-3514.69.5.839

Berry, D., & Willoughby, M. T. (2017). On the practical interpretability of cross-lagged panel models: Rethinking a developmental workhorse. *Child Development*, 88(4), 1186–1206. https://doi.org/10.1111/cdev.12660

Bringmann, L. F., Ferrer, E., Hamaker, E. L., Borsboom, D., & Tuerlinckx, F. (2018). Modeling nonstationary emotion dynamics in dyads using a time-varying vector-autoregressive model. *Multivariate Behavioral Research*, 53(3), 293–314. https://doi.org/10.1080/00273171.2018.1439722

Card, N., Selig, J., & Little, T. (2008). *Modeling dyadic and interdependent data in the developmental and behavioral sciences*. Routledge.

Edwards, J., & Parry, M. (1993). On the use of polynomial regression equations as an alternative to difference scores in organizational research. *Academy of Management Journal*, 36, 1577–1613.

Gistelinck, F., & Loeys, T. (2019). The actor-partner interdependence model for longitudinal dyadic data: An implementation in the SEM framework. *Structural Equation Modeling*, 26(3), 329–347. https://doi.org/10.1080/10705511.2018.1527223

Gonzalez, R., & Griffin, D. (2001). A statistical framework for modeling homogeneity and interdependence in groups. In M. Clark & G. Fletcher (Eds.), *Handbook of social psychology: Vol. 2. Interpersonal processes* (pp. 505–534). Blackwell.

Gray, J., & Ozer, D. (2019). Comparing two models of dyadic change: Correlated growth versus common fate. *Social Psychological & Personality Science*, 10(7), 957–965. https://doi.org/10.1177/1948550618799066

Griffin, D., & Gonzalez, R. (1995). The correlational analysis of dyad-level data: Models for the exchangeable case. *Psychological Bulletin*, 118(3), 430–439. https://doi.org/10.1037/0033-2909.118.3.430

Griffin, D., Murray, S., & Gonzalez, R. (1999). Difference score correlations in relationship research: A conceptual primer. *Personal Relationships*, 6(4), 505–518. https://doi.org/10.1111/j.1475-6811.1999.tb00206.x

Hamaker, E. L., Kuiper, R. M., & Grasman, R. P. (2015). A critique of the cross-lagged panel model. *Psychological Methods*, 20(1), 102–116. https://doi.org/10.1037/a0038889

Iida, M., Seidman, G., & Shrout, P. (2018). Models of interdependent individuals versus dyadic processes in relationship research. *Journal of Social and Personal Relationships*, 35(1), 59–88. https://doi.org/10.1177/0265407517725407

Kenny, D. A. (1990). Design issues in dyadic research. In C. Hendrick & M. S. Clark (Eds.), *Review of personality and social psychology: Vol. 11. Research methods in personality and social psychology* (pp. 164–184). Sage.

Kenny, D. A., & Judd, C. M. (1986). Consequences of violating the independence assumption in the analysis of variance. *Psychological Bulletin*, 99(3), 422–431. https://doi.org/10.1037/0033-2909.99.3.422

Kenny, D. A., Kashy, D. A., & Cook, W. L. (2006). *Dyadic data analysis*. Guilford Press.

Loeys, T., & Molenberghs, G. (2013). Modeling actor and partner effects in dyadic data when outcomes are categorical. *Psychological Methods*, 18(2), 220–236. https://doi.org/10.1037/a0030640

Raudenbush, S., & Bryk, A. (2002). *Hierarchical linear models: Applications and data analysis methods* (2nd ed.). SAGE.

Schoenbrodt, F., Humberg, S., & Nestler, S. (2018). Testing similarity effects with dyadic response surface analysis. *European Journal of Personality*, 32(6), 627–641. https://doi.org/10.1002/per.2169

Singer, J. (1998). Using SAS PROC MIXED to fit multilevel models, hierarchical models and individual growth models. *Journal of Educational and Behavioral Statistics*, 23(4), 323–355. https://doi.org/10.3102/10769986023004323

Snijders, T., & Bosker, R. (1999). *Multilevel analysis: An introduction to basic and advanced multilevel modeling*. SAGE.

Woody, E., & Sadler, P. (2005). Structural equation models for interchangeable dyads: Being the same makes a difference. *Psychological Methods*, 10(2), 139–158. https://doi.org/10.1037/1082-989X.10.2.139

SECTION 7

USING DATA COLLECTED BY OTHERS

CHAPTER 22

THE DATA OF OTHERS: NEW AND OLD FACES OF ARCHIVAL RESEARCH

Sophie Pychlau and David T. Wagner

Rummaging through a dusty basement or searching through stacks of files, archival researchers piece together the past like archeologists uncovering a lost civilization. Yet archival research well into the 21st century is anything but dusty or outdated. Instead, the recent explosion of data allows modern researchers to study most anything with data that are pervasive, inclusive, high-fidelity, and often free. Archival research is an umbrella term for research using data that were acquired for other purposes than addressing the current researcher's questions and encompasses a dazzling diversity of data types and methods. This approach to research promises to address some of the most troubling issues in contemporary psychology that have led to a "crisis of confidence" (Baumeister, 2016) in the discipline.

Several issues have contributed to this crisis of confidence. First, concerted replication efforts have revealed that a large share, if not the majority, of findings published in psychology cannot be replicated, despite using original material, sufficient power, and advance reviews of methodological fidelity (Open Science Collaboration, 2015). The failure to replicate published findings has been attributed to the traditional reliance on null-hypothesis significance testing in social science, which leads to the biased reporting of a small set of significant research findings whereas other, nonsignificant findings are doomed to the file drawer. However, since p values inevitably vary between samples, there is always a chance that significant findings merely represent false positives that, in conjunction with publication bias, might create whole literatures of false effects (Cumming, 2014; Open Science Collaboration, 2015). As we will show, archival research offers ways to easily and cost-effectively replicate and complement laboratory findings by the same, or different, research team but in a different context.

A second issue reducing confidence in psychological research concerns the lack of representativeness in the samples that researchers use. Samples that appear in the major psychology journals tend to be WEIRD—that is, they are **W**estern and **e**ducated and come from **i**ndustrialized, **r**ich, and **d**emocratic countries (Henrich et al., 2010). In other words, participants in psychological research, often psychology undergraduates, only represent a minor share of the target population. In contrast, archival research draws on samples from a much wider population, and sometimes entire populations, promising to mitigate the lack of representative samples in psychology research.

Third, when researchers do not recruit their own students for research, they often recruit online survey takers who are financially rewarded for their time and effort. However, inquiries into recent decrements in data quality acquired through crowdsourcing platforms such as Amazon

https://doi.org/10.1037/0000320-022
APA Handbook of Research Methods in Psychology, Second Edition: Vol. 3. Data Analysis and Research Publication, H. Cooper (Editor-in-Chief)
Copyright © 2023 by the American Psychological Association. All rights reserved.

Mechanical Turk have revealed that an increasing number of survey takers participate under false pretenses (Chmielewski & Kucker, 2020; Kennedy et al., 2020). In contrast, archival research often includes data that were collected unobtrusively for purposes other than research, and therefore it does not lure fraudulent responders.

In this chapter, we argue that archival research can strengthen confidence in psychology as a science and holds potential to be part of most, if not all programs of research. While only a trivial portion of the total research published relies on archival data, research increasingly uses archival approaches, as our trend analysis in Figure 22.1 shows. This increased use is made possible by the expanding availability of information as well as the proliferation of methods for analyzing large quantities of diverse data. In this chapter, we argue that archival approaches offer substantial value, and we hope to spur more research relying on archival data. The beauty—and challenge—of archival research is that "almost any artifact can become the basis for archival research" (Stewart, 2012, p. 481). Mindful of the potential for informational overload that such abundance presents, in this chapter, we offer a typology of archival data to point researchers who are interested in conducting archival research to data types and methods of analysis that might fit their needs. As we do so, we highlight less commonly used forms of data, such as pictures and videos, with the aim of broadening the sight of researchers interested in making an impact on the field through the use of novel and reliable data sources.

As said, archival data describe data that were originally collected for other purposes than testing the researchers' specific hypotheses. The intention behind the original data collection distinguishes archival data from data gathered in laboratory experiments or survey studies. The terms *primary* and *secondary* data for research summarize that distinction: Whereas primary data are collected by researchers to answer a specific research question, archival (i.e., secondary) data

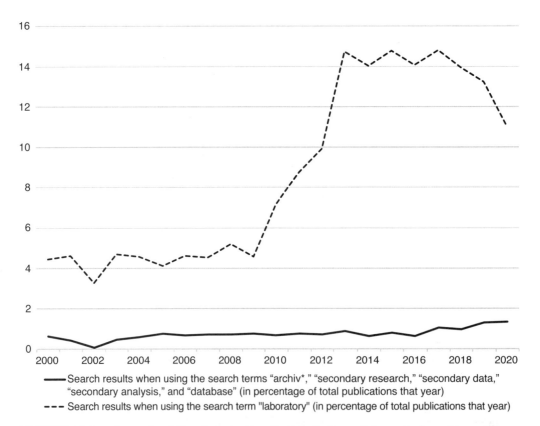

FIGURE 22.1. Annual publications in Google Scholar's top 20 psychology journals, based on Web of Science literature searches.

might speak to a particular research question but were not specifically collected to address it. Throughout this chapter, we use the terms *archival* and *secondary* interchangeably. The pair of primary and secondary research is particularly helpful when discussing the crisis of confidence because primary and secondary research complement each other; for example, secondary research can strengthen the external validity of findings from primary research.

Archival data are often *big data*, yet big data is not always archival but instead is defined through its granularity (George et al., 2014). The intention of the original data collection defines archival data, whereas the scope of the data and the methods used to analyze it broadly define big data. The exact origin and meaning of the term remain contested (George et al., 2014; Lohr, 2013), and big data, like archival research, is an umbrella term that encompasses different kinds of data. The possibly most popular definition of big data refers to its volume (number of observations or variables), velocity (number of repeated measurements), and variety (big data can come in various forms that psychology researchers might not be familiar with; Borgman, 2015). Although different dimensions can make data highly granular or big, there is no clear cutoff point for deeming data "big" and the dimension of "bigness" remain somewhat ambiguous (Adjerid & Kelley, 2018). In practice, big data describes all "data sets where manually inspecting each case (i.e., observation by variable) is so cumbersome it becomes practically impossible" (Braun et al., 2018, p. 636). Archival research often employs large data sets because the amount of available information is growing rapidly, and researchers are continually examining new kinds of information. Although estimates vary, it appears that the digital universe—the digital data created, replicated, and consumed annually—contains now about as many digital bits as the universe contains stars (Chute et al., 2008). Big data is here to stay and might likely become an indispensable part of psychology science. In this chapter, we aim to provide a rough roadmap for researchers to use secondary research, including big data.

In the following section, we elaborate upon the opportunities that archival research holds for addressing the crisis of confidence in psychology, specifically the opportunities for external validity and transparency. Subsequently, we describe five ideal types of archival data in detail, outlining their different advantages and disadvantages as well as providing a brief overview of methods used to analyze each type. Furthermore, we provide examples for each ideal type of secondary data. As others before us (Heng et al., 2018), we illustrate how archival data can be used for true, natural, and quasi-experiments as well as correlational studies. Table 22.1 presents an overview of our typology. We discuss methodological challenges that many if not all types of archival data share and their remedies. A section on ethics concludes our chapter.

ADDRESSING THE CRISIS OF CONFIDENCE THROUGH SECONDARY RESEARCH

Archival research possesses several strengths that can help ameliorate the crisis of confidence in psychology. First, archival research bolsters the external validity of research findings precisely because the data were collected for other than the researchers' purposes. External validity tends to be higher in archival research because archival research is often equivalent to the study of naturally occurring behavior of non-WEIRD people and therefore promises to make psychology more egalitarian by including people who are typically underrepresented in research. In many cases, archival data stem from natural settings and behaviors, such as when an online search engine stores users' search entries (e.g., Barnes et al., 2015) or government agencies record the number of traffic accidents or interracial marriages (Galinsky et al., 2013; Yam et al., 2020). Hence, archival data allow researchers to study the whole range of naturally occurring behaviors, not just attitudes, beliefs, or a narrow set of behaviors that bear little resemblance to real-world behaviors. Moreover, archival research allows studying nonmanipulable causes such as socially sensitive circumstances through either direct

TABLE 22.1

Five Types of Secondary Data

Type	Opportunities and advantages	Challenges and disadvantages	Exemplary sources
Statistical records and archives	■ External validity ■ Temporal nature of data ■ Replication	■ Threat to construct validity ■ Absence of direct measures of beliefs or attitudes ■ Limited to the aggregate level	■ U.S. Bureau of Labor Statistics ■ National Center for Health Statistics ■ U.S. Census Bureau
Panel studies and survey programs	■ External validity ■ Individual-level data ■ Temporal nature of data ■ Direct measures of beliefs and attitudes	■ Threat to ecological validity ■ Limited set of panel studies and measures	■ American Time Use Survey ■ German General Social Survey ■ Mexican-origin families in the US (California Families Project)
Verbal records and language	■ Ecological validity and unobtrusive measurement ■ Omnipresence of language ■ Many methods for analysis available	■ Threat to construct validity ■ Representativeness in mass communications low ■ Access to personal communications difficult	■ Google Books Ngram Viewer (https://books.google.com/ngrams) ■ Linguistic Data Consortium at University of Pennsylvania (https://www.ldc.upenn.edu/)
Images and video	■ Ecological validity and unobtrusive measurement ■ Omnipresence of pictures and movies	■ Threat to construct validity ■ Analysis effortful ■ Fewer and less wide-spread methods for analysis	■ Video interviews with business leaders in Africa, Asia, Latin America and the Middle East (https://www.hbs.edu/creating-emerging-markets/) ■ Prints & Photographs Online Catalog of the Library of Congress ■ Calisphere (digital collections of the University of California)
Digital footprints	■ Ecological validity and unobtrusive measurement ■ Behavioral data	■ Threat to construct validity ■ Proprietary nature of data ■ Participants' privacy	■ Google Trends (https://trends.google.com/) ■ Search for Call Detail Records on https://dataverse.harvard.edu/ ■ myPersonality project (Facebook app)

or proxy measures. For example, using archival data across dozens of world languages reveals that genderedness of language has the ability to shape, not just reflect, prejudice against women (DeFranza et al., 2020).

When sampling naturally occurring behaviors, archival research offers unique opportunities to incorporate the context of phenomena. This is valuable because context is often overlooked in research (Johns, 2018) even though "much social behavior is not organized beyond a 'local,' or situation-specific level" (Thorngate, 1976, p. 134). Using archival data, researchers can build theory around context (Leavitt et al., 2020) and build more realistic models of behavior as the interaction of person and situation (Lewin et al., 1936). In particular, archival data can help examine the role of time.

Many phenomena are dynamic, but it can be difficult to examine the role of time in the laboratory. By contrast, archival data are often longitudinal, making it possible to study the ebbs and flows of focal constructs.

Furthermore, in contrast to primary data, which often consist of experimentally elicited behaviors or explicitly gathered survey responses of a small sample of WEIRD study participants, secondary data generalize to a larger number and diversity of people. Specifically, archival data commonly originate in non-WEIRD samples. Some samples used in archival research are highly representative of the population, such as samples originating in U.S. Census data or phone records. Other samples, such as Twitter users (Mislove et al., 2011), may have their own sampling bias yet still be more representative and capture a larger share of the population than WEIRD samples. Together, sampling naturally occurring behaviors of participants representative of the larger population strengthens the external validity and generalizability of research findings from archival data.

A second strength of archival research lies in its potential to spur replicable results and replication efforts. Due to its higher representativeness of different populations and contexts, archival data offer more precise estimates of effect sizes than laboratory experiments, which can both deflate and inflate effect sizes (Baumeister, 2016). Laboratory experiments deflate effect sizes because the set of manipulable causes is more limited in a controlled context, and they inflate effect sizes because the controlled environment reduces noise. The presence of demand characteristics in laboratory experiments can further bias findings. By contrast, archival research often employs very large sample sizes, yielding high power to detect effects. Moreover, large samples yield more reliable point estimates than do studies based on small sample sizes. In consequence, archival research enables researchers to practice the "new statistics" (Cumming, 2014). The upshot is that by incorporating archival studies into their programs of research, scientists are likely to arrive at more accurate and replicable effect sizes. In an institutional environment that rewards novelty instead of replication, the importance of complementing novel primary research through secondary research and trying to replicate findings with archival data cannot be understated. Archival research offers an often cost-effective opportunity to replicate one's findings from primary research in a different sample and at a larger scale.

A third strength of archival research that scientists can use to mitigate the crisis of confidence rests in its potential for transparency of both data and procedures for its analysis. A few prominent cases of HARKing (hypothesizing after results are known) and outright fabrication of data have contributed to the erosion of confidence in psychology as a science; these cases involved primary data that can be manipulated or even fabricated more easily (e.g., Levelt et al., 2012).

In contrast, archival data are often publicly available and the syntax to analyze them can be made available as well. Hence, the very nature of the secondary or archival data combined with the community-verifying aspect of science bolsters confidence in the veracity of findings based on archival data. In this way, enabling others to replicate one's findings is more than a symbolic gesture to improve trust (Simonsohn, 2013).

In consequence, using secondary data allows researchers to sample large populations and naturally occurring behavior, arriving at more precise point estimates and externally valid findings. These strengths enable researchers to replicate their own and others' findings in new contexts. Furthermore, analyses and the data themselves are transparent, strengthening replicability specifically and trust into psychology science generally. Hence, we recommend psychology researchers use secondary data to overcome the crisis of confidence in the field.

Five Types of Secondary Data

In order to help researchers interested in archival data to comprehend the diversity of more and less conventional archival data sets and identify data sets for their own use, we developed a typology of archival data. We delineated five types of archival data: statistical records and archives, panel studies and research survey archives, verbal records and language as data, images and video as data, and behavioral traces from digital interactions. Our typology is the result of reviewing psychology and social science studies that use secondary data; it is inductively generated, and we make no claims to presenting an exhaustive list of types. Furthermore, we describe *ideal* types—that is, we establish distinct types of data so that readers can see the forest for the trees. However, the types are not mutually exclusive, and data sets can contain several types simultaneously. For example, researchers can develop applications that social media users download (e.g., Bail et al., 2017; Greenberg et al., 2015). Such applications can give researchers access to users' nonpublic data as well as administer research surveys to users; they therefore draw on both primary and secondary data, on data as language (e.g., posts and messages) as well as behavioral traces from online interactions (e.g., likes and shares). By presenting ideal types, we hope to maximize comprehensibility of diverse sources of archival data and to highlight the potential inherent in different types, yet we encourage combining several types of data in the same study when that is a sensible possibility.

Statistical Records and Archives

Records kept in physical or digital archives present the archetype of archival data. Data kept in statistical records tend to come from "paper traces" (or digital traces) of nonresearch interactions that citizens have with the record-keeping institution. For example, filing one's taxes or getting married creates paper traces that, when recorded and aggregated, become statistical data. Both public and private institutions maintain statistical records, although for different purposes. Information collected by government agencies such as the U.S. Census Bureau tends to be publicly available. However, researchers might gain access to proprietary data sets when they are able to collaborate with the private institutions owning data and relying on scientists to analyze them (Hartmann & Henkel, 2020).

Advantages of using statistical records and archives concern the representativeness of samples and the longitudinal nature of the records. The Census of Population and Housing conducted by the U.S. Census Bureau every decade generates the very data necessary to understand which parameters make a sample representative of the population, and census data itself presents an excellent source of secondary data. Furthermore, as records tend to be kept over long periods of time, statistical records are often longitudinal and may contain enough time points so that researchers can examine the role of time regarding a specific phenomenon. Such possibilities are particularly helpful when the temporal nature of a phenomenon is unknown (Spector & Meier, 2014).

A disadvantage of statistical records is the absence of measures of beliefs or attitudes. Statistical archives often measure only information relevant for the record-keeping institution itself or when legal regulations require record keeping. Therefore, statistical records might appear to be of little use to psychologists interested in granular phenomena at the individual level. However, if researchers can link beliefs or attitudes of interest to behaviors recorded in statistical archives, they have the opportunity to extend findings from laboratory studies to the larger population. For example, while Galinsky and his colleagues (2013) investigated the presence and content of racial stereotypes in surveys and laboratory experiments, they were able to show that these stereotypes were consistent with interracial marriage patterns recorded in the U.S. Census.

Besides using statistical records in correlational studies to complement primary research, researchers can also use them for conducting natural or quasi-experiments. If a researcher is able to (a) identify an external event that mimics random assignment and functions as a direct or proxy measure of the researcher's theoretical construct, and (b) identify statistical records that are longitudinal and contain theoretically relevant outcome measures, then the researcher can conduct a natural experiment by comparing statistical records from before with records from after the event occurred. For example, a comparison between the number of workplace injuries on Mondays after the switch to daylight saving time and the number of workplace injuries on other days presents a natural experiment (Barnes & Wagner, 2009). The authors used the clock change as an intervention and identified the pre- and postintervention outcome variable in records from the National Institute for Occupational Safety and Health. Similarly, researchers can use statistical records to conduct quasi experiments when an event concerns a nonrandom subset of participants, such as parents who were ordered to attend a divorce education program (deLusé & Braver, 2015).

Researchers who use statistical data for correlational studies may want to account for the lower internal validity, that is, the difficulty of making causal inferences from nonexperimental data (Shadish et al., 2002). Strengthening internal validity through the appropriate statistical methods is important when the correlational study is a stand-alone study and not accompanied by experimental evidence. Fortunately, econometricians have developed tools to eliminate other possible explanations for covariation and account for the lack of random assignment. One set of such methods allows researchers to account for selection bias, which is the confounding of population differences with treatment effects (Shadish et al., 2002). propensity score matching (Dehejia & Wahba, 1999; Morgan & Winship, 2015) and the more recently developed coarsened exact matching (Iacus et al., 2012) allow researchers to mimic treatment and control groups by pairing observations that differ only in regard to the independent variable of interest but match on a number of chosen control variables. Instrumental variables, variables that influence the independent variable but do not have a direct effect on the outcome variable, present another method to control for selection bias since they control for confounding variation and isolate the independent variable's effect on the outcome variable (Murnane & Willett, 2010), but they can be notoriously difficult to identify.

Another set of statistical methods allows researchers to account for lagged effects in longitudinal data. When analyzing data stretching over several years or decades, it is possible to confound effects of the independent variable with effects of specific but unaccounted events or maturation effects in general. Again, methods that help account for lagged effects are particularly important if the archival study is not complemented by experimental evidence. Autoregressive models, in which earlier values of the dependent variable serve themselves as predictors (Brandt & Williams, 2006), allow researchers to account for lagged effects. Additionally, if researchers analyze time series data at the individual level, they might employ growth curve modeling techniques where subjects are nested within themselves, effectively serving as their own control groups (Collins, 2006; Preacher et al., 2008).

Panel Studies and Survey Programs

In contrast to statistical archives, panel studies, survey programs, and research study archives[1] involve data collected through questionnaires or interviews. Both panel studies and survey programs represent concerted research efforts, often over several decades. Distinct from most empirical studies published in journal articles, panel studies and survey programs are expansive in the range of variables assessed, allowing for inquiry beyond the questions that initially motivated data collection. Whereas panel studies repeatedly survey the same sample of respondents, survey programs administer the same (or similar) surveys to respondents newly sampled for each survey wave. Panel studies and survey programs tend to be conducted by researchers since survey administration presupposes research experience. For example, the National Opinion Research Center at the University of Chicago conducts the General Social Survey (GSS). However, some government agencies collect data through surveys if such data do not leave a paper trace but are more easily collected by directly asking participants. For example, the U.S. Census Bureau annually conducts the American Community Survey that contains questions such as whether grandparents take responsibility for children in one's household.

Advantages of panel studies and survey programs concern their representativeness, measurements of attitudes and beliefs, and longitudinal nature. As with statistical records and archives, panel studies and survey programs benefit from their representative samples. For example, the GSS involves stratified random sampling of households. In contrast to statistical records, panel studies and survey programs often

---

[1] Research study archives, that is, physically or digitally stored empirical research studies, involve direct interactions with respondents for the purpose of data collection. Although originally collected for the primary researchers' purposes, if other researchers later draw on those data for their own purposes, such data become secondary data. Research study archives as secondary data are mostly used in meta-analyses and present a prime example of the usefulness of secondary research to address replicability issues. Because meta-analyses are discussed elsewhere (e.g., Cooper et al., 2019; Moreau & Gamble, 2020) and present a rather well-known case of secondary research, we do not further discuss meta-analyses in this chapter.

contain measures of attitudes and beliefs. For example, the GSS contains several questions about respondents' views on abortion. The presence of such measures makes panel studies and survey programs uniquely useful as a type of archival data for social scientists. Furthermore, by combining time series and cross-sectional design, panel studies provide longitudinal data for the same set of participants and therefore allow following attitudes and beliefs at the individual level over time. In contrast, survey programs allow following attitudes and beliefs at the aggregate level; for example, the GSS has been conducted since 1972.

Disadvantages of panel studies and survey programs involve their smaller samples (relative to some other forms of secondary data) and the possibility of demand characteristics. Due to the high effort of survey administration, sample sizes in panel studies and survey programs are smaller than those of statistical records. For example, the GSS conducts in-person interviews that average 90 minutes in length. While sample sizes in panel studies and survey programs still tend to be higher than in many stand-alone research surveys, the final sample size can fall short of the full sample when examining measures that were only administered to a random subsample of respondents. Furthermore, because respondents are aware of participating in the collection of data, the presence of demand characteristics cannot be ruled out.

Despite these disadvantages, panel studies and survey programs offer the unique opportunity to examine attitudes and beliefs in highly representative samples over time. Similar to statistical records and archives, data from survey programs are often used in correlational studies and frequently allow researchers to replicate effects found in smaller samples, but at a larger scale. For example, Stamos and colleagues (2019) analyzed GSS data to replicate the finding from a cross-sectional survey that childhood socioeconomic status predicts social trust in adulthood. Using a larger sample and responses from different points in time as well as other measures of socioeconomic status and trust, their replication provided strong support for the impact of childhood socioeconomic status on adulthood trust. Furthermore, since panel studies and survey programs tend to contain a large number of measures at the individual level, researchers might be able to identify mediators and moderators of theorized cause-effect relationships. Moreover, as with data from statistical archives, the potential for natural or quasi-experiments exists with panel and survey program data if researchers can identify an external event separating observations into treatment and control conditions. For example, using data from the American Time Use Survey that is conducted by the U.S. Bureau of Labor and Statistics, Barnes and Wagner (2009) showed that people do indeed sleep less on days after the switch to daylight saving time, effectively conducting a natural experiment.

Many methods used for analyzing data from panel studies and survey programs are identical to the methods used to analyze statistical records because those two types of data differ mainly in the availability of measures of attitudes and beliefs. However, the presence of such measures in panel studies and survey programs allows researchers to conduct mediation analyses (e.g., Stamos et al., 2019), which are less common when using data from archives or statistical records. Mediation is a particularly enticing possibility in panel studies when researchers survey the same respondents at different time points and can therefore ensure that the assumed cause precedes the assumed effect. Furthermore, given that attitudes and beliefs are often measured as latent constructs, researchers are able to test for longitudinal measurement invariance (i.e., whether the structure of latent constructs is the same across time points; Liu et al., 2017).

Verbal Records and Language as Data

Language is the most direct medium of personal and mass communication. In our digitalized world, recordings of the spoken or written word offer an inexhaustible source of secondary data. Researchers can freely access language records in the form of articles in newspapers or magazines, radio or television shows, as well as social media or blogs posts. Even personal communication channels such as email or text messages can function as rich sources of secondary data.

Language as secondary data has considerable advantages for psychology research since it is "the ever-present context of our cognitions" (DeFranza et al., 2020, p. 7) and, therefore, offers countless ways to measure attitudes and beliefs without directly probing respondents. The unobtrusive measurement of attitudes and beliefs through language records is particularly desirable when researchers want to analyze cognitions without social desirability when studying socially sensitive behavior or hindsight bias when conducting retrospective research. For example, analyzing meeting transcripts from the years leading up to the financial crisis, Fligstein et al. (2017) argued that regulators and experts were slow to react to the impending collapse of the financial system because the macroeconomic frame through which they interpreted market anomalies obscured critical links between financial system and economy.

A further advantage concerns the longitudinal nature of data such as newspaper articles that originate in sustained communications between senders and recipients. Such data can offer stronger evidence for causal inferences. For example, positive thinking in *USA Today* newspaper articles predicted declines in the Dow Jones index both 1 week and 1 month after an article was published, lending support to the detrimental impact of positive thinking about the future on performance (Sevincer et al., 2014).

Disadvantages of using language as secondary data are the possibly weak construct validity of measures and possibly less representative samples than in the previously described types of archival data. Dependent on the methods used to analyze language as data, construct validity can be weak when operationalizing behaviors, beliefs, attitudes, or emotions through specific words or word patterns. We discuss construct validity in more detail later in this chapter. Furthermore, language as secondary data results in possibly biased samples when certain groups or individuals are particularly vocal or constitute the majority of a medium's user base. For example, Wikipedia contributors are overwhelmingly male (Bear & Collier, 2016).

Language records stemming from personal communication allow researchers to study communication in dyads or networks, which is a noteworthy exception to the aggregate or individual-level data discussed throughout this chapter. Therefore, researchers studying constructs at dyadic or network levels may stand to benefit the most from using personal communication as secondary data. However, such data are more difficult to access because private communications tend to remain private. An exception is the Enron email corpus, which contains over 600,000 emails from Enron senior management. The corpus was created during the legal investigation following the company's collapse and later made available for wider use by researchers.[2] The corpus is a uniquely useful source of data to study networks and corporations committing fraud.

Other exceptions to privacy restricting researchers' access to personal communication occur when communicators themselves decide to share their data with researchers. For example, apps that social media users download can give researchers access to private messages exchanged through the social media platform (e.g., Bail et al., 2017; Greenberg et al., 2015). The decision to share one's private messages with researchers involves some degree of direct contact between researchers and participants. Therefore, researchers have the possibility to combine primary and secondary research within the same study. For example, Markowitz and Hancock (2018) studied deception in online dating by asking participants to upload messages they exchanged with their dating partners as well as rate the extent of deception in the messages they received.

In contrast, mass communication is easily accessible as a source of secondary data and yet allows insights into constructs of a personal nature. Whereas some mass communication media such as newspaper articles, SEC filings,

---

[2] Interested readers can download the gzipped data set (https://www.cs.cmu.edu/~enron/enron_mail_20150507.tar.gz) or browse through the data online (http://www.enron-mail.com/).

or presidential inaugural speeches (Sevincer et al., 2014) are highly edited and may therefore limit constructs that researchers can study, social media offer a vast number of people an unmediated platform to communicate with known and unknown others. Social media profiles reflect users' actual rather than idealized personalities (Back et al., 2010) and have accordingly gained considerable traction as data in personality research (e.g., Park et al., 2015). Remarkably, spatial aggregation of social media language even allows insights into well-being and personality patterns of populations on a large scale since social media posts can be traced back to specific geographical locations (Jaidka et al., 2020).

Social media are an omnipresent form of secondary data with high external validity, but, in contrast to more conventional forms of language as data such as newspaper articles, its acquisition requires some technical skills. Researchers interested in using social media data can either use data sets built and made available by other researchers (e.g., Barberá's Twitter data; Barberá, 2015) or build their own data sets through web scraping—that is, using algorithms to find and extract data from online sources. Web scraping algorithms take advantage of the hierarchical structure of web-based content with HTML being the basic scripting language of all content displayed in web browsers that ensures cohesive user experiences across different websites. Both user-generated content and metadata, such as date and time of a post or the location of a user, can be scraped (see Landers et al., 2016, for an instructional overview of web scraping; see Kern et al., 2016, for how to process both textual and nontextual data from social media). Since social media offer both language recordings as well as behavioral traces such as "likes," we resume our discussion of social media when describing behavioral traces as data.

Whereas methods used to acquire and clean social media data might be less familiar to psychologists, a vast number of methods are available to analyze language as data once such data have been acquired. In general, closed and open-vocabulary approaches can be distinguished for the quantification of language as data (for an overview, see Kern et al., 2016). When using closed-vocabulary approaches, text analysis programs sort words into preestablished and topic-specific lexica or categories. The programs then count the number of words in each category relative to other categories, thereby quantifying the data. Perhaps the most widely known closed-vocabulary text analysis program is the Linguistic Inquiry and Word Count program that contains several dozen lexica, covering, for example, cognitive processes, core drives and needs, and affect words (e.g., Tausczik & Pennebaker, 2010). More recently, open-vocabulary approaches have become increasingly common in which text analysis programs create data-specific lexica. Such bottom-up approaches "allow the data to tell their own stories" (Kern et al., 2016, p. 514). Researchers then simply interpret the found word clusters and attach labels to them. However, researchers might want to limit the number of word clusters to strike a balance between precision (a high number of clusters means that cluster are small and easy to interpret) and redundancy (a high number of clusters also means that some clusters are probably redundant; see Kern et al., 2016, for an overview).

Visual Data: Images and Video

Researchers have traditionally used static and moving pictures in primary and particularly in qualitative research. Anthropologists have long relied on photographing and videotaping the foreign cultures of their interest, but psychologists have less experience with images or video as data (although exceptions exist; cf. Carrère & Gottman, 1999; Ekman, 1973; Frese et al., 2003). However, with the tremendous growth of the digital universe, visual content has become increasingly available online and psychologists might consider it as a type of secondary data.

Advantages of visual content as secondary data concern its ecological validity and the unobtrusive measurement of core constructs. Facial expressions and other nonverbal modes of communication promise insight into the depicted person's unedited cognitions and emotions, as Ekman (1973) has shown in his research on facial expressions as involuntary responses. Furthermore, an advantage of video over other types of data presented here is that video content constitutes multimodal and context-rich data, comprising audio content (that can be transcribed and analyzed as described above) as well as images, capturing both sights and sounds, verbal and nonverbal expressions. Video furthermore contains dynamic content and allows scientists to address process-oriented research questions. Given these advantages, researchers can draw on video as secondary data for a variety of uses and approaches, both quantitative and qualitative.

However, the advantages of unobtrusive measurement and multimodality of visual content come with certain caveats since the richness of such data needs to be systematically processed for research purposes. The analysis of images or video is effortful when the data have to be coded manually. Only a handful of researchers in the social sciences have drawn on artificial intelligence for this purpose, yet the rapid progress of machine learning promises to result in more widespread adoption by social scientists. Furthermore, given that visual content as secondary data is still unconventional and psychology journals have a tradition of text-based scholarship, readers should be aware that such data might hold a certain liability of newness.

When coded and quantified, images from secondary sources can be used in correlational studies just like other data yet with the unique advantages that visual content presents. For example, the coding of gravestone imagery and inscriptions offers unobtrusive measurement of religion and longevity at the individual level across a wide spectrum of the population, using an online database of cemetery records (findagrave.com) that contains over 80 million pictures of gravestones (Zelinsky, 2007). Besides its external validity (everyone dies!), space on gravestones is limited and only the most valued characteristics of a person are inscribed there. Therefore, religious imagery and inscriptions on gravestones promise evidence of religiosity that is arguably unaffected by response bias. Combining gravestone analysis with information from the U.S. religion census, Ebert and colleagues (2020) found that—contrary to a staple in social sciences—religiosity does not confer universal benefits for longevity but does so only in predominantly religious counties. Theoretically, such data could be used in natural or quasi-experiments as well if researchers can identify causal variables that they can link to the data provided through gravestones.

Another example highlights the ecological validity that video as secondary data promises. Carroll and Russell's (1997) analysis of actors' facial expressions in Hollywood movies stands in stark contrast to the static images of facial expressions on which Ekman's (1973) research is based. Students and trained coders rated actors' emotions and facial expressions in four movies that won awards for acting. The results show that the emotions that actors conveyed were rarely associated with specific facial expressions; only happiness was uniquely associated with the Duchenne smile. The fact that raters were nevertheless able to identify specific emotions casts doubt on the theory that an emotion is necessarily accompanied by a specific facial expression.

In both these examples, coders had to manually code the data, an effortful and costly process. In contrast, Choudhury and colleagues (2019) used machine learning to analyze data from an archive of video interviews with star CEOs. Specifically, they employ a supervised machine learning algorithm that, using static facial images as input, assigns weights along eight facial expressions to each image. Combining the analysis of facial expressions with both open and closed-dictionary analyses of the interview transcripts, the authors establish five distinct communication styles that they subsequently link to specific firm outcomes.

Readers interested in manually coding images or video are referred to Bock et al.'s (2011) overview of quantitative content analysis. Regarding the qualitative analysis of videos, LeBaron et al. (2018) presented several points to consider in the introduction to a special issue on video methods. They lauded the richness and possibilities of video as data but advised researchers to "not try to analyze everything because you cannot" (LeBaron et al., 2018, p. 247). Readers interested in using machine learning algorithms for coding visual content may consult Leavitt and colleagues' (2020) overview of several approaches to machine learning and might consider collaborating with researchers from other disciplines who have the necessary expertise.

Digital Footprints: Behavioral Traces From Digital Interactions

Worldwide, each day people spend several hours online. The increasing digitalization of everyday life creates a wealth of behavioral data that holds largely untapped potential for secondary research: "Individuals online can . . . up-vote/down-vote stories, share and consume various content (articles, videos, movies, etc.), search for certain things, and peruse various products then decide to purchase (or not) . . . The ability to capture all of these interactions makes even nonevents equally interesting (e.g., what a user *did not* click)" (Adjerid & Kelley, 2018, p. 902, italics in original).

If researchers are able to identify usable "data breadcrumbs" from such online activities, they gain longitudinal data of behavior with high external validity. Digital footprints are left by naturally occurring online behavior of a large number of people, every minute leaving countless digital bits, generating big data with large numbers of observations, variables, and time points (Adjerid & Kelley, 2018). Perhaps most important, digital footprints, in distinction to the other types of data presented in this chapter, represent concrete behavior, allowing researchers to unobtrusively measure naturally occurring behavior at a minute-by-minute level. As we discuss in the next section, the wealth of unobtrusively recorded data from online interactions questions the meaning of informed consent when conducting research with human subjects.

However, the disadvantages of digital breadcrumbs as secondary data are considerable. First and foremost, not all digital footprints are usable for research, nor are they always accessible—such data tend to be proprietary, generated on specific websites and owned by website operators. Furthermore, when psychologists can access such data, their methodological training in graduate school is unlikely to have prepared them for wrangling such big data that require substantial processing before they are usable for analysis.

However, some digital footprints are accessible for researchers. Interested readers should be familiar with several contexts in which online interactions leave behavioral traces to identify opportunities for research. Clickstream and keyword data are prominent in consumer and marketing research and of direct interest to website operators themselves, yet often proprietary and less used in psychology. A clickstream or click path is the pathway that a user takes on a certain website; keywords are the terms internet users search for online. A noteworthy example of freely available keyword data is Google Trends, providing information about the frequency of specific search terms over the course of several years. Keyword data provide a rough insight into users' collective mind in a given moment and researchers can use such data as proxy measures of behaviors or even cognitions. For example, supporting the argument that sleep deprivation increases cyberloafing, people search for more entertainment-related terms following the change to daylight saving time than on other days (Wagner et al., 2012).

Social media platforms store a wealth of digital traces left by social interactions, making them a uniquely valuable online environment to study social dynamics. Besides the language data generated by user activities on social media platforms discussed above, platforms also provide users with options of nonverbal interactions such as liking, sharing, or following other users' posts or content from external websites. Some behavioral data from social media platforms is proprietary (e.g., Facebook Likes used to be public but can now be hidden if users opt to do so) but publicly visible behaviors can be web scraped. An example of a scraped and now freely available data set is a Twitter data set that contains estimates of users' political ideologies based on the political accounts they follow (Barberá, 2015).³ When such data are not publicly available, researchers can source them with users' permission. For example, myPersonality was a Facebook app that asked people to donate their Facebook data when taking a personality questionnaire, resulting in a data set of millions of responders that the developers of the app shared with noncommercial researchers (e.g., Greenberg et al., 2015). Bail and colleagues (2017) developed a similar application for their primary research on whether advocacy organizations should use emotional appeals or rational arguments to stimulate public discussion. Researchers might consider inquiring about data sets built through the use of such applications or even develop their own applications to harvest data for a whole program of primary research.

Smartphones are another source of secondary behavioral data. Smartphone usage generates a variety of behavioral traces. Whereas data from smartphones' built-in sensors tend to be proprietary and are more often used in primary research when researchers themselves develop apps (e.g., Bush et al., 2019), call detail records—records of incoming and outgoing calls, time and duration of the call as well as the approximate location of the phone—might be more accessible. Using an anonymized billing data set of six million mobile phone users that was recorded by a mobile provider as required by law and billing purposes, González et al. (2008) found that human mobility follows highly regular spatial and temporal patterns. Furthermore, service providers sometimes invite researchers to big data challenges using anonymized call detail records and subsequently publish the data sets.⁴

Due to the largely proprietary nature of digital footprint data, collaborations between researchers and corporations are a noteworthy possibility for gaining access to such data. When partnering with corporations, researchers can even conduct primary and secondary true experiments. An example of a secondary true experiment is the study of emotional contagion through social networks even in the absence of nonverbal cues, as when manipulating the amount of emotional content in the Facebook News Feed (Kramer et al., 2014). An example for a primary true experiment comes from manipulating whether users of an online dating site who were able to anonymously browse through other users' profiles—effectively providing them with a one-way mirror—experienced more or better matching outcomes (they did not; Bapna et al., 2016). Although there are only few examples in the literature of such collaborations between researchers and corporations, researchers should be aware of the increasing interest that corporations have in such research. Although basic corporate research has been declining (e.g., Arora et al., 2018), many corporations are interested in using artificial intelligence and machine learning to gain insights from the big data they own and that might provide them with strategic advantages over competitors if only they are able to extract the knowledge inherent in the data (Hartmann & Henkel, 2020).

Methodologically, many challenges with data from digital footprints are similar to other types of big data discussed above. Yet first, in distinction to other types of data, researchers need to convert the raw data into usable data sets for storing and analysis by creating user-footprint matrices (Kosinski et al., 2016). Analysis further often requires reducing the dimensionality of data since big data from digital footprints often contains more variables than there are users (Kosinski et al., 2016), making analysis problematic.

Methodological Challenges and Remedies

Throughout this chapter, we have pointed at the methodological challenges and remedies specific to certain types of secondary data. However, most of the types share several challenges that we have not discussed yet. Specifically, secondary research and data are prone to suffer from HARKing, overfitting, and weak construct validity. There are no easy one-size-fits-all remedies

---

³The code to generate the data as well as the final data set can be found on a GitHub repository (https://github.com/pablobarbera/twitter_ideology/).
⁴For example, readers can find one such data set here: https://doi.org/10.7910/DVN/EGZHFV.

for these issues; hence, we discuss them at greater length.

HARKing becomes a concrete threat in secondary research because of the large sample sizes of secondary data. Large samples and high power mean that even effects without theoretical importance are likely to be statistically significant. In many cases, secondary data sets allow researchers to cherry-pick results that fit their purpose—a troubling possibility in a field unsettled by a crisis of confidence. Preregistering one's study, the increasingly used remedy to prevent HARKing in primary research, is a possibility with secondary research as well. However, with secondary research, data are already generated or collected at the time of preregistration, and it is possible that researchers possess some knowledge about the data, shaping the generation of research questions and hypotheses. Seeing that a certain knowledge of the data set is necessary to determine whether it is useful for one's research purposes at all, a "pure" preregistration is impossible. As a remedy, Heng and colleagues (2018) recommended that researchers transparently report any iterations between exploration of the data and the formulation of research questions or hypotheses. Furthermore, research teams can prevent HARKing procedurally by assigning the roles of research question generator and data analyst to different people in the team (Heng et al., 2018).

Another challenge when conducting secondary research is the possibility of overfitting one's model. Overfitting occurs when a model perfectly predicts variance because its parameters include both essential variables and noise. Secondary data are vulnerable to overfitting because they frequently contain a large number of variables. Overfitted models are of limited scientific value because they blur the difference between local significance and universal meaning of their variables and cannot be applied to other contexts.

Both HARKing and overfitting can be prevented when researchers explicitly ground their research questions and hypotheses in theory, thereby taking theory, not results, as their starting point and concentrating only on theoretically relevant variables. However, we do not suggest that secondary data should only be used to test theoretically grounded hypotheses that were formulated prior to data analysis. Due to their frequently longitudinal nature, the measurement of naturally occurring and sometimes socially sensitive behaviors, as well as their high external validity, secondary data—particularly when big—hold considerable potential for exploratory and theory-generating research. For example, when using machine learning algorithms that analyze big secondary data, researchers might make serendipitous discoveries that question, supplement, or stretch known theories. In contrast to human researchers, algorithms are not affected by blinders such as gap spotting or academic siloes (Leavitt et al., 2020).

Some of these serendipitous discoveries or data-driven theories might be "local but perishable" as they are built around a specific context (Leavitt et al., 2020). Local theories, similar to overfitted models, do not translate well to other contexts, but can be of immediate practical relevance. The COVID-19 pandemic is a powerful reminder of the importance of finding scientific solutions that are locally effective rather than universally true. For example, rather than developing a grand theory about people's acceptance of governmental restrictions of public life in order to curb the spread of a virus, psychologists might instead examine which appeals are effective in a specific local context.

However, secondary data can also assist in the generation or modification of grand theories. To assure that data-driven theories extend beyond their local contexts, Harlow and Oswald (2016) suggested to "develop theories and hypotheses on an initial training set of data and then verify those findings with other validation data sets, either from a hold-out sample of the original data or from separate, independent data" (p. 448) (for details on developing theory through big data, see Landers et al., 2016). As an example of how theorists can learn from secondary and big data, consider Stanley and Byrne's (2016) study of Twitter hashtags and posts tags on Stack Overflow, a website where users can post and answer programming questions. Framing the choice of hashtags or post tags as a memory retrieval task, the authors improved two models of memory retrieval by applying them to the two big data sets and exploring several modifications to them.

A further challenge many forms of secondary data share concerns construct validity because secondary data commonly do not contain validated measures of psychological constructs. Weak construct validity is a considerable threat in secondary research, separating empirical studies from literatures they aim to inform. Comparing measures' role within research studies to the role of stilts for beach houses, poor measures present fatal flaws: Like a single faulty stilt can make the whole house fall into the sea, one poor measure is enough to endanger the whole study (Ketchen et al., 2013). Since most secondary data are byproducts of recording and storing data for other purposes than research, variables in secondary data may not accurately represent the theoretical constructs in which researchers are interested. Instead, constructs may be measured by only one item, which is frequently the case in panel studies, or only indirectly measured through surrogate measures or proxies, such as framing the choice of a specific hashtag as a declarative memory retrieval task (Stanley & Byrne, 2016). The weak construct validity is further exacerbated by the lack of means to evaluate measurement reliability because only "few archival databases will have multi-item measures that allow for typical measurement of reliability" (Barnes et al., 2018, p. 1466).

However, researchers have developed several approaches to validate surrogate measures. For example, researchers can establish construct equivalence by complementing a secondary study with primary research in which the validated measure and its surrogate are administered concurrently (Payne et al., 2003). If statistical properties suggest that both measures assess the same construct, the measures are said to be equivalent and can be used interchangeably. The principle of linking validated and surrogate measures can be achieved in many ways. For example, regarding the problem of construct validity with digital footprints (e.g., what constructs does a "like" on Facebook represent?), Braun and Kuljanin (2015) suggested using subject matter experts that rate the relevance of specific digital footprints.

Ethical Issues in Archival Research

Lastly, researchers should consider the ethical issues that accompany the use of secondary data. Technological possibilities have outpaced the societal discourse on what is and what isn't ethical and novel kinds of secondary data complicate the interpretation of existing ethical guidelines. Issues arise particularly in the context of data generated through participants' daily-life internet usage and the expectations of such data remaining private. As a community, we have to reinterpret the principles underlying ethical research conduct when dealing with such data.

In primary research with human subjects, informed consent presents the standard. To obtain participants' informed consent researchers provide potential participants with the information necessary to make an informed decision whether to participate or not. The American Psychological Association's (2017) *Ethical Principles of Psychologists and Code of Conduct* state that archival research does not require informed consent as long as confidentiality is protected and disclosure of responses would not harm participants. However, researchers might not be able to effectively protect participants' confidentiality by stripping data from direct identifiers because the unique patterns of indirect identifiers can allow third parties to reidentify individuals in the data set. This possibility emerges when data encompass granular information at the individual level such as with social media content as secondary data (e.g., Zimmer, 2010). Hence, "it is almost impossible to completely de-identify people" for such data (Kern et al., 2016, p. 521). To account for this difficulty, researchers can report data only in aggregate. Although this is certainly a possibility for researchers who deal with highly granual secondary data, it contradicts efforts to make research more transparent, accessible, and thereby replicable.

If confidentiality cannot be guaranteed, do researchers have to obtain informed consent? For secondary research, particularly using big data, obtaining informed consent poses severe challenges. First, it could be prohibitively costly and therefore impractical if not impossible. For example, researchers analyzing Twitter posts cannot be expected to contact every user to elicit their consent before including their posts in the sample. Second, although websites' terms and conditions could function as the equivalent of informed consent, users rarely read them and are therefore unaware of which data are captured, stored, and maybe sold or passed on to others. In one study, the vast majority of participants conceded the naming rights of their first-born child when they agreed to terms and conditions they apparently had not read (Maronick, 2014; ProPrivacy, 2020).

If confidentiality cannot be guaranteed but informed consent is practically impossible to obtain, we argue that researchers must consider users' expectations of confidentiality. However, the nature of these expectations can be elusive. Most internet users are likely to understand that the data generated through their browsing behavior might be used for marketing purposes; "Amazon knew we were pregnant before our parents did," as one user comments (Wienberg & Gordon, 2015). Despite the knowledge that their browsing behavior in general might not be private, expectations of confidentiality arguably vary. For example, internet users likely have very different expectations of privacy if they are browsing a dating platform marketed to people in relationships or comparing different vacuum cleaners online.

Expectations of confidentiality are not uniform for explicitly public online activities either. Internet users often publicly share details of their private life. For example, bloggers who publicly document their life for family members or friends understand that strangers can access their blogs but show surprise—both positive and negative—that academic researchers might use their blogs as data (Wienberg & Gordon, 2015). Therefore, expectations of confidentiality appear to be fluid and contextual even when users' behavior is public.

The matter of contextual confidentiality expectations is further complicated by the possibilities of unobtrusively measuring personality traits and attitudes online. As described above, researchers can infer personality traits through language analyses of Twitter posts (e.g., Jaidka et al., 2020). However, users are unlikely to expect researchers to subject their posts to language analyses. Therefore, while users know that their posts are public, they might be unaware of the effectively public display of their personality in these posts. Hence, "it is questionable what users understand public to mean" when they engage with others online (Kern et al., 2016, p. 521). For the academic community, the question remains to be answered how ethical the possibilities of unobtrusive measurement are, and it is "currently unclear if psychologists have a responsibility to obtain consent in such cases" (Landers et al., 2016, p. 487).

Due to the highly contextual nature of online privacy and the heterogeneity of online activities, no single principle can protect the privacy of internet users and the confidentiality of their data (Nissenbaum, 2009). The internet is not a single social realm for which a single set of privacy standards applies but the totality of very heterogenous experiences and activities. Publicly available data do not fall under the purview of internal review boards since they are exempt from policies protecting human subjects in research (Protection of Human Subjects, 2017). Absent institutional guidelines, the burden to evaluate the ethicality of secondary research lies with researchers and their audience.

To aid researchers and their audience in evaluating the ethicality of secondary research that draws on data generated online, we suggest considering *contextual privacy* (Nissenbaum, 2011). The notion of contextual privacy refers to expectations about privacy that are specific to the local context in which the data were generated because "the contexts in which activities are grounded shape expectations that, when unmet, cause anxiety, fright, and resistance"

(Nissenbaum, 2011, p. 38). Again, the diversity of secondary data defies a single approach and identifying users' privacy expectations may not always be straightforward. Yet, absent a societal consensus or institutional procedures, the burden lies with researchers to carefully consider individuals' privacy expectations and ensure their ethical treatment.

CONCLUSION

In this chapter, we have argued why and how secondary or archival data can help ameliorate the crisis of confidence in psychology. Secondary data can offer high external validity, measures of socially sensitive and naturally occurring behaviors as well as cognitions, beliefs, and attitudes, and maximum transparency. We present a typology of secondary data, encompassing both conventional and novel types. Discussing advantages, disadvantages, examples, and methods associated with each type, as well as challenges and remedies that most types of secondary data share and the ethical questions associated with some types of secondary data, we hope this chapter will encourage researchers to use secondary data more often and equip them with the basic knowledge of what to consider and where to start.

References

Adjerid, I., & Kelley, K. (2018). Big data in psychology: A framework for research advancement. *American Psychologist, 73*(7), 899–917. https://doi.org/10.1037/amp0000190

American Psychological Association. (2017). *Ethical principles of psychologists and code of conduct*. https://www.apa.org/ethics/code

Arora, A., Belenzon, S., & Patacconi, A. (2018). The decline of science in corporate R&D. *Strategic Management Journal, 39*(1), 3–32. https://doi.org/10.1002/smj.2693

Back, M. D., Stopfer, J. M., Vazire, S., Gaddis, S., Schmukle, S. C., Egloff, B., & Gosling, S. D. (2010). Facebook profiles reflect actual personality, not self-idealization. *Psychological Science, 21*(3), 372–374. https://doi.org/10.1177/0956797609360756

Bail, C. A., Brown, T. W., & Mann, M. (2017). Channeling hearts and minds: Advocacy organizations, cognitive-emotional currents, and public conversation. *American Sociological Review, 82*(6), 1188–1213. https://doi.org/10.1177/0003122417733673

Bapna, R., Ramaprasad, J., Shmueli, G., & Umyarov, A. (2016). One-way mirrors in online dating: A randomized field experiment. *Management Science, 62*(11), 3100–3122. https://doi.org/10.1287/mnsc.2015.2301

Barberá, P. (2015). Birds of the same feather tweet together. Bayesian ideal point estimation using twitter data. *Political Analysis, 23*(1), 76–91. https://doi.org/10.1093/pan/mpu011

Barnes, C. M., Dang, C. T., Leavitt, K., Guarana, C. L., & Uhlmann, E. L. (2018). Archival data in micro-organizational research: A toolkit for moving to a broader set of topics. *Journal of Management, 44*(4), 1453–1478. https://doi.org/10.1177/0149206315604188

Barnes, C. M., Gunia, B. C., & Wagner, D. T. (2015). Sleep and moral awareness. *Journal of Sleep Research, 24*(2), 181–188. https://doi.org/10.1111/jsr.12231

Barnes, C. M., & Wagner, D. T. (2009). Changing to daylight saving time cuts into sleep and increases workplace injuries. *Journal of Applied Psychology, 94*(5), 1305–1317. https://doi.org/10.1037/a0015320

Baumeister, R. F. (2016). Charting the future of social psychology on stormy seas: Winners, losers, and recommendations. *Journal of Experimental Social Psychology, 66*, 153–158. https://doi.org/10.1016/j.jesp.2016.02.003

Bear, J. B., & Collier, B. (2016). Where are the women in Wikipedia? Understanding the different psychological experiences of men and women in Wikipedia. *Sex Roles, 74*(5-6), 254–265. https://doi.org/10.1007/s11199-015-0573-y

Bock, A., Isermann, H., & Knieper, T. (2011). Quantitative content analysis of the visual. In E. Margolis & L. Pauwels (Eds.), *The SAGE handbook of visual research methods* (pp. 265–282). SAGE Publications. https://doi.org/10.4135/9781446268278.n14

Borgman, C. L. (2015). *Big data, little data, no data: Scholarship in the networked world*. MIT Press. https://doi.org/10.7551/mitpress/9963.001.0001

Brandt, P. T., & Williams, J. T. (2006). *Multiple time series models* (Vol. 148). SAGE.

Braun, M. T., & Kuljanin, G. (2015). Big data and the challenge of construct validity. *Industrial and Organizational Psychology: Perspectives on Science and Practice, 8*(4), 521–527. https://doi.org/10.1017/iop.2015.77

Braun, M. T., Kuljanin, G., & DeShon, R. P. (2018). Special considerations for the acquisition and wrangling of big data. *Organizational Research Methods, 21*(3), 633–659. https://doi.org/10.1177/1094428117690235

Bush, N. E., Armstrong, C. M., & Hoyt, T. V. (2019). Smartphone apps for psychological health: A brief state of the science review. *Psychological Services, 16*(2), 188–195. https://doi.org/10.1037/ser0000286

Carrère, S., & Gottman, J. M. (1999). Predicting divorce among newlyweds from the first three minutes of a marital conflict discussion. *Family Process, 38*(3), 293–301. https://doi.org/10.1111/j.1545-5300.1999.00293.x

Carroll, J. M., & Russell, J. A. (1997). Facial expressions in Hollywood's portrayal of emotion. *Journal of Personality and Social Psychology, 72*(1), 164–176. https://doi.org/10.1037/0022-3514.72.1.164

Chmielewski, M., & Kucker, S. C. (2020). An MTurk crisis? Shifts in data quality and the impact on study results. *Social Psychological & Personality Science, 11*(4), 464–473. https://doi.org/10.1177/1948550619875149

Choudhury, P., Wang, D., Carlson, N. A., & Khanna, T. (2019). Machine learning approaches to facial and text analysis: Discovering CEO oral communication styles. *Strategic Management Journal, 40*(11), 1705–1732. https://doi.org/10.1002/smj.3067

Chute, C., Manfrediz, A., Minton, S., Reinsel, D., Schlichting, W., & Toncheva, A. (2008). The diverse and exploding digital universe. *IDC White Paper*. https://www.idc.org/idc-white-papers

Collins, L. M. (2006). Analysis of longitudinal data: The integration of theoretical model, temporal design, and statistical model. *Annual Review of Psychology, 57*(1), 505–528. https://doi.org/10.1146/annurev.psych.57.102904.190146

Cooper, H., Hedges, L. V., & Valentine, J. C. (Eds.). (2019). *The handbook of research synthesis and meta-analysis*. Russell Sage Foundation. https://doi.org/10.7758/9781610448864

Cumming, G. (2014). The new statistics: Why and how. *Psychological Science, 25*(1), 7–29. https://doi.org/10.1177/0956797613504966

DeFranza, D., Mishra, H., & Mishra, A. (2020). How language shapes prejudice against women: An examination across 45 world languages. *Journal of Personality and Social Psychology, 119*(1), 7–22. https://doi.org/10.1037/pspa0000188

Dehejia, R. H., & Wahba, S. (1999). Causal effects in nonexperimental studies: Reevaluating the evaluation of training programs. *Journal of the American Statistical Association, 94*(448), 1053–1062. https://doi.org/10.1080/01621459.1999.10473858

deLusé, S. R., & Braver, S. L. (2015). A rigorous quasi-experimental design to evaluate the causal effect of a mandatory divorce education program. *Family Court Review, 53*(1), 66–78. https://doi.org/10.1111/fcre.12131

Ebert, T., Gebauer, J. E., Talman, J. R., & Rentfrow, P. J. (2020). Religious people only live longer in religious cultural contexts: A gravestone analysis. *Journal of Personality and Social Psychology, 119*(1), 1–6. https://doi.org/10.1037/pspa0000187

Ekman, P. (1973). Cross-cultural studies of facial expression. In P. Ekman (Ed.), *Darwin and facial expression: A century of research in review* (pp. 169–222). Academic Press.

Fligstein, N., Stuart Brundage, J., & Schultz, M. (2017). Seeing like the Fed: Culture, cognition, and framing in the failure to anticipate the financial crisis of 2008. *American Sociological Review, 82*(5), 879–909. https://doi.org/10.1177/0003122417728240

Frese, M., Beimel, S., & Schoenborn, S. (2003). Action training for charismatic leadership: Two evaluations of studies of a commercial training module on inspirational communication of a vision. *Personnel Psychology, 56*(3), 671–698. https://doi.org/10.1111/j.1744-6570.2003.tb00754.x

Galinsky, A. D., Hall, E. V., & Cuddy, A. J. (2013). Gendered races: Implications for interracial marriage, leadership selection, and athletic participation. *Psychological Science, 24*(4), 498–506. https://doi.org/10.1177/0956797612457783

George, G., Haas, M. R., & Pentland, A. (2014). Big data and management. *Academy of Management Journal, 57*(2), 321–326. https://doi.org/10.5465/amj.2014.4002

González, M. C., Hidalgo, C. A., & Barabási, A. L. (2008). Understanding individual human mobility patterns. *Nature, 453*(7196), 779–782. https://doi.org/10.1038/nature06958

Greenberg, D. M., Baron-Cohen, S., Stillwell, D. J., Kosinski, M., & Rentfrow, P. J. (2015). Musical preferences are linked to cognitive styles. *PLOS ONE, 10*(7), e0131151. https://doi.org/10.1371/journal.pone.0131151

Harlow, L. L., & Oswald, F. L. (2016). Big data in psychology: Introduction to the special issue. *Psychological Methods, 21*(4), 447–457. https://doi.org/10.1037/met0000120

Hartmann, P., & Henkel, J. (2020). The rise of corporate science in AI: Data as a strategic resource. *Academy of Management Discoveries, 6*(3). https://doi.org/10.5465/amd.2019.0043

Heng, Y. T., Wagner, D. T., Barnes, C. M., & Guarana, C. L. (2018). Archival research: Expanding the methodological toolkit in social psychology. *Journal of Experimental Social Psychology, 78*, 14–22. https://doi.org/10.1016/j.jesp.2018.04.012

Henrich, J., Heine, S. J., & Norenzayan, A. (2010). Most people are not WEIRD. *Nature*, *466*(7302), 29. https://doi.org/10.1038/466029a

Iacus, S. M., King, G., & Porro, G. (2012). Causal inference without balance checking: Coarsened exact matching. *Political Analysis*, *20*(1), 1–24. https://doi.org/10.1093/pan/mpr013

Jaidka, K., Giorgi, S., Schwartz, H. A., Kern, M. L., Ungar, L. H., & Eichstaedt, J. C. (2020). Estimating geographic subjective well-being from Twitter: A comparison of dictionary and data-driven language methods. *Proceedings of the National Academy of Sciences of the United States of America*, *117*(19), 10165–10171. https://doi.org/10.1073/pnas.1906364117

Johns, G. (2018). Advances in the treatment of context in organizational research. *Annual Review of Organizational Psychology and Organizational Behavior*, *5*(1), 21–46. https://doi.org/10.1146/annurev-orgpsych-032117-104406

Kennedy, R., Clifford, S., Burleigh, T., Waggoner, P. D., Jewell, R., & Winter, N. J. (2020). The shape of and solutions to the MTurk quality crisis. *Political Science Research and Methods*, *8*(4), 614–629. https://doi.org/10.1017/psrm.2020.6

Kern, M. L., Park, G., Eichstaedt, J. C., Schwartz, H. A., Sap, M., Smith, L. K., & Ungar, L. H. (2016). Gaining insights from social media language: Methodologies and challenges. *Psychological Methods*, *21*(4), 507–525. https://doi.org/10.1037/met0000091

Ketchen, D. J., Jr., Ireland, R. D., & Baker, L. T. (2013). The use of archival proxies in strategic management studies: Castles made of sand? *Organizational Research Methods*, *16*(1), 32–42. https://doi.org/10.1177/1094428112459911

Kosinski, M., Wang, Y., Lakkaraju, H., & Leskovec, J. (2016). Mining big data to extract patterns and predict real-life outcomes. *Psychological Methods*, *21*(4), 493–506. https://doi.org/10.1037/met0000105

Kramer, A. D., Guillory, J. E., & Hancock, J. T. (2014). Experimental evidence of massive-scale emotional contagion through social networks. *Proceedings of the National Academy of Sciences of the United States of America*, *111*(24), 8788–8790. https://doi.org/10.1073/pnas.1320040111

Landers, R. N., Brusso, R. C., Cavanaugh, K. J., & Collmus, A. B. (2016). A primer on theory-driven web scraping: Automatic extraction of big data from the internet for use in psychological research. *Psychological Methods*, *21*(4), 475–492. https://doi.org/10.1037/met0000081

Leavitt, K., Schabram, K., Hariharan, P., & Barnes, C. M. (2020). Ghost in the machine: On organizational theory in the age of machine learning. *Academy of Management Review*. Advance online publication. https://doi.org/10.5465/amr.2019.0247

LeBaron, C., Jarzabkowski, P., Pratt, M. G., & Fetzer, G. (2018). An introduction to video methods in organizational research. *Organizational Research Methods*, *21*(2), 239–260. https://doi.org/10.1177/1094428117745649

Levelt, W. J., Drenth, P. J. D., & Noort, E. (2012). *Flawed science: The fraudulent research practices of social psychologist Diederik Stapel*. Commissioned by the Tilburg University, University of Amsterdam, and the University of Groningen. https://pure.mpg.de/rest/items/item_1569964_8/component/file_1569966/content

Lewin, K., Heider, F., & Heider, G. M. (1936). *Principles of topological psychology*. McGraw-Hill. https://doi.org/10.1037/10019-000

Liu, Y., Millsap, R. E., West, S. G., Tein, J. Y., Tanaka, R., & Grimm, K. J. (2017). Testing measurement invariance in longitudinal data with ordered-categorical measures. *Psychological Methods*, *22*(3), 486–506. https://doi.org/10.1037/met0000075

Lohr, S. (2013, February 1). The origins of 'Big Data': An etymological detective story. *The New York Times*. https://archive.nytimes.com/bits.blogs.nytimes.com/2013/02/01/the-origins-of-big-data-an-etymological-detective-story/

Markowitz, D. M., & Hancock, J. T. (2018). Deception in mobile dating conversations. *Journal of Communication*, *68*(3), 547–569. https://doi.org/10.1093/joc/jqy019

Maronick, T. J. (2014). Do consumers read terms of service agreements when installing software? A two-study empirical analysis. *International Journal of Business and Social Research*, *4*(6), 137–145.

Mislove, A., Lehmann, S., Ahn, Y. Y., Onnela, J. P., & Rosenquist, J. (2011, July). Understanding the demographics of Twitter users. In *Proceedings of the International AAAI Conference on Web and Social Media*, *5*(1), 554–557. https://ojs.aaai.org/index.php/ICWSM/article/view/14168

Moreau, D., & Gamble, B. (2022). Conducting a meta-analysis in the age of open science: Tools, tips, and practical recommendations. *Psychological Methods*, *27*(3), 426–432. https://doi.org/10.1037/met0000351

Morgan, S. L., & Winship, C. (2015). *Counterfactuals and causal inference*. Cambridge University Press.

Murnane, R. J., & Willett, J. B. (2010). *Methods matter: Improving causal inference in educational and social science research*. Oxford University Press.

Nissenbaum, H. (2009). *Privacy in context: Technology, policy, and the integrity of social life*. Stanford University Press. https://doi.org/10.1515/9780804772891

Nissenbaum, H. (2011). A contextual approach to privacy online. *Daedalus, 140*(4), 32–48. https://doi.org/10.1162/DAED_a_00113

Open Science Collaboration. (2015). Estimating the reproducibility of psychological science. *Science, 349*(6251), aac4716. https://doi.org/10.1126/science.aac4716

Park, G., Schwartz, H. A., Eichstaedt, J. C., Kern, M. L., Kosinski, M., Stillwell, D. J., Ungar, L. H., & Seligman, M. E. P. (2015). Automatic personality assessment through social media language. *Journal of Personality and Social Psychology, 108*(6), 934–952. https://doi.org/10.1037/pspp0000020

Payne, S. C., Finch, J. F., & Tremble, T. R., Jr. (2003). Validating surrogate measures of psychological constructs: The application of construct equivalence to archival data. *Organizational Research Methods, 6*(3), 363–382. https://doi.org/10.1177/1094428103254455

Preacher, K. J., Wichman, A. L., MacCallum, R. C., & Briggs, N. E. (2008). *Latent growth curve modeling*. SAGE.

ProPrivacy. (2020). *Privacy complacency: The hidden dangers lurking beneath today's surface-level data protection*. https://proprivacy.com/privacy-news/privacy-complacency-ebook

Protection of Human Subjects. 45 CFR § 46 (2017). https://www.hhs.gov/ohrp/regulations-and-policy/regulations/45-cfr-46/revised-common-rule-regulatory-text/index.html#46.104(a)

Sevincer, A. T., Wagner, G., Kalvelage, J., & Oettingen, G. (2014). Positive thinking about the future in newspaper reports and presidential addresses predicts economic downturn. *Psychological Science, 25*(4), 1010–1017. https://doi.org/10.1177/0956797613518350

Shadish, W. R., Cook, T. D., & Campbell, D. T. (2002). *Experimental and quasi-experimental designs for generalized causal inference*. Houghton Mifflin.

Simonsohn, U. (2013). Just post it: The lesson from two cases of fabricated data detected by statistics alone. *Psychological Science, 24*(10), 1875–1888. https://doi.org/10.1177/0956797613480366

Spector, P. E., & Meier, L. L. (2014). Methodologies for the study of organizational behavior processes: How to find your keys in the dark. *Journal of Organizational Behavior, 35*(8), 1109–1119. https://doi.org/10.1002/job.1966

Stamos, A., Altsitsiadis, E., & Dewitte, S. (2019). Investigating the effect of childhood socio-economic background on interpersonal trust: Lower childhood socioeconomic status predicts lower levels of trust. *Personality and Individual Differences, 145*, 19–25. https://doi.org/10.1016/j.paid.2019.03.011

Stanley, C., & Byrne, M. D. (2016). Comparing vector-based and Bayesian memory models using large-scale datasets: User-generated hashtag and tag prediction on Twitter and Stack Overflow. *Psychological Methods, 21*(4), 542–565. https://doi.org/10.1037/met0000098

Stewart, D. W. (2012). Secondary analysis and archival research: Using data collected by others. In H. Cooper, P. M. Camic, D. L. Long, A. T. Panter, D. Rindskopf, & K. J. Sher (Eds.), *APA handbook of research methods in psychology: Vol. 3. Data analysis and research publication* (pp. 473–484). American Psychological Association. https://doi.org/10.1037/13621-024

Tausczik, Y. R., & Pennebaker, J. W. (2010). The psychological meaning of words: LIWC and computerized text analysis methods. *Journal of Language and Social Psychology, 29*(1), 24–54. https://doi.org/10.1177/0261927X09351676

Thorngate, W. (1976). Possible limits on a science of social behavior. In L. H. Strickland, F. E. Aboud, & K. J. Gergen (Eds.), *Social psychology in transition* (pp. 121–139). Springer. https://doi.org/10.1007/978-1-4615-8765-1_9

Wagner, D. T., Barnes, C. M., Lim, V. K. G., & Ferris, D. L. (2012). Lost sleep and cyberloafing: Evidence from the laboratory and a daylight saving time quasi-experiment. *Journal of Applied Psychology, 97*(5), 1068–1076. https://doi.org/10.1037/a0027557

Wienberg, C., & Gordon, A. S. (2015). Insights on privacy and ethics from the web's most prolific storytellers. *The 7th Annual ACM Web Science Conference (WebSci '15)*. Oxford, UK: Association for Computing Machinery. https://doi.org/10.1145/2786451.2786474

Yam, K. C., Jackson, J. C., Lau, J., Qin, X., Barnes, C. M., & Chong, J. K. (2020). Association of high profile football matches in Europe with traffic accidents in Asia: Archival study. *BMJ, 371*, m4465. https://doi.org/10.1136/bmj.m4465

Zelinsky, W. (2007). The Gravestone Index: Tracking personal religiosity across nations, regions, and periods. *Geographical Review, 97*(4), 441–466. https://doi.org/10.1111/j.1931-0846.2007.tb00406.x

Zimmer, M. (2010). "But the data is already public": On the ethics of research in Facebook. *Ethics and Information Technology, 12*(4), 313–325. https://doi.org/10.1007/s10676-010-9227-5

CHAPTER 23

SOCIAL NETWORK ANALYSIS IN PSYCHOLOGY: RECENT BREAKTHROUGHS IN METHODS AND THEORIES

Wei Wang, Tobias Stark, James D. Westaby, Adam K. Parr, and Daniel A. Newman

"Everything is related to everything else" (Tobler, 1970, p. 240), the very first law of geography, has not only profoundly impacted the geographic scientific inquiry, but its relational focus of thinking and theorization has also inspired many psychologists. However, although psychology has a long history of acknowledging and studying relatedness as part of human nature—for example, self-determination theory (Deci & Ryan, 2000) identifies relatedness as one of the three basic, universal, and innate psychological needs—yet properly utilizing social network analysis (SNA), the formal method that specifically studies relations, is still uncommon in psychological research, partially due to its methodological complexity and analytical obscurity for many psychologists. Indeed, as a standalone method and analytical technique, SNA necessitates a different research design and data collection method that are not often covered in a typical research methods textbook in psychology. In addition, unlike many classic statistical methods such as analysis of variance (ANOVA) and regression that are readily available in SPSS, a predominant statistical computer program that has been taught in almost every psychology program, SNA requires totally different analytical tools that are traditionally beyond the access for many psychologists. As such, although SNA is increasingly interesting for psychological research, its application in psychology is still uncommon.

Fortunately, thanks to the free R statistical programming language (R Core Team, 2021) and its increasing popularity in the psychology community, the analytical barrier for SNA is gradually fading away. More important, as R becomes the main statistical tool for many psychologists for data management and statistical analyses, integrating SNA into mainstream psychological research can be seamless. As a result, with the powerful R statistical programming, we believe now is the right time to reintroduce SNA to the psychology community through an R approach—and to rethink incorporating SNA in our methodological and analytical toolbox to advance psychological research.

Thus, this chapter serves as an SNA primer, with a goal of familiarizing psychologists with basic SNA methodological concepts and the corresponding analytical techniques in R. We also introduce some advanced SNA methods and showcase examples of recent applications of SNA in advancing theoretical development across multiple psychological research domains.

The data sets, R code, and color versions of figures used in this chapter are available on https://osf.io/3wtby/.
https://doi.org/10.1037/0000320-023
APA Handbook of Research Methods in Psychology, Second Edition: Vol. 3. Data Analysis and Research Publication, H. Cooper (Editor-in-Chief)
Copyright © 2023 by the American Psychological Association. All rights reserved.

SOCIAL NETWORK CONCEPTS AND METHODOLOGICAL FOUNDATIONS

Before moving on, we first elaborate on the foundations of SNA, including the philosophy, research design, data collection, and management.

Philosophy of Social Network Analysis

Classic statistical analyses in psychology often focus on the effects of individuals' attributes (e.g., personality traits, intelligence, sociodemographic characteristics, psychological status) and effects of environments in the individuals are nested (e.g., parenting or teaching style, team cohesion, organizational climate). Although both individual and environmental characteristics play an important role in shaping behaviors and psychological states, such an approach focuses on the research unit in isolation, overlooking the relationships among the research entity. Indeed, ignoring the relational structure and focusing solely on the isolated individuals may result in missing out on the whole picture of our research questions and may even unintentionally lead to biased findings and conclusions (Brass, 2012).

Unlike classic statistical analyses, SNA primarily focuses on the relationships—particularly, relational structure—among individuals, maintaining that a network determines constraints and opportunities that an individual may encounter, which in turn affect the actor's outcomes of our research interest (Borgatti et al., 2018). Accordingly, it is critical to understand the interconnected *network* environments that an actor is embedded in addition to the attributes of isolated individuals and environmental entities. Moreover, SNA also provides a unique perspective to study the formation and resolution of social relations, which itself is of great research interest in psychology, given the relatedness of human nature (Deci & Ryan, 2000).

In SNA, the network entity often refers to an "actor," "node," or "vertex" (Figure 23.1a provides an illustration). Although in psychology, actors are typically individual persons such as students, employees, and so forth, they can be any research

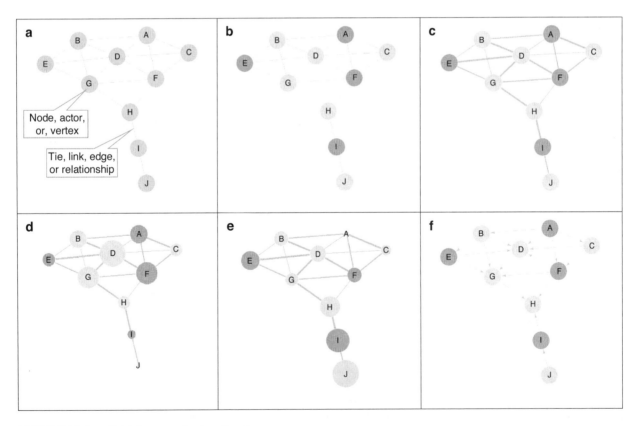

FIGURE 23.1. Social network visualization.

entities, including both individual entities, such as persons, animals, or objects, and collective entities, such as teams, organizations, countries, etc. The relationship among nodes refers to "tie," "link," or "edge" (see Figure 23.1a). Although SNA also studies dyadic links (e.g., A is linked to B, C is linked to D, etc.), it is the interlinks and indirect connected paths that make SNA unique and powerful. For instance, A is linked to B, and B is linked C and D; thus, A is indirectly linked to C and D. From this perspective, a network is a connected web with directly or indirectly linked nodes, and SNA goes beyond the dyad level that focuses on pairwise relationships to the node level and network level analyses, which will be elaborated in this chapter.

Social Network Research Design

Psychologists are well equipped with research design with respect to experiment, quasi-experiment, and nonexperiment. However, the research design for social network studies is different, requiring a set of unique considerations regarding network types, relationships, as well as network boundary and sampling.

Whole-networks versus ego-networks. The first consideration is to decide on whole-networks versus ego-networks, which are two different types of networks with respect to research design, data collection, and data analysis. Although whole-networks are more commonly used in psychology, ego-networks can be particularly valuable for certain research questions.

Whole-networks. Whole-network research often explores how the social structure or certain types of connections affect people. For instance, research has shown that direct and indirect relationships with members of other racial or ethnic groups are related to less prejudice (Wölfer et al., 2016, 2017) and the development of adolescents' ethnic identity (Leszczensky et al., 2016). Whole-network data are also often employed to study the opposite causal relationship, asking which processes lead to the development of a tie between people. For example, research has shown that prejudice and ethnic identities predict the development of interethnic or interracial ties (Jugert et al., 2018; Leszczensky & Pink, 2019; Stark, 2015).

Ego-networks. Ego-network (aka egocentric networks) studies concern people's perception of their immediate social contacts, their "core personal networks" (Marsden, 2011). Egocentric network studies are used in both qualitative and quantitative research. These studies typically explore how people's characteristics affect their network (structure) and how perceptions of their social connections affect them, their behavior, or their decisions. For instance, qualitative research found that conversations about HIV preexposure prophylaxis (PrEP) between women who inject drugs and their network members depend on the type of relationship they have, perceptions of benefits of such conversations for the given network member, and feelings of obligations (Felsher et al., 2021). Previous quantitative research found that the structure of people's core personal networks is affected by the Big Five personality traits. For instance, people scoring higher on neuroticism tend to have more triadic structures in their network, and people scoring high on extraversion have more strong ties (Rapp et al., 2019). The structure of people's egocentric networks (gender composition, density, structural holes) is also associated with college students' self-reported physical, emotional, and sexual violence victimization, showing that risk-factors are not only on the individual level but also in people's social context (Patterson et al., 2020). Other work found that people who have a dense representation of their social support network (meaning that they perceive their alters to be close) feel more support from their network (Lee et al., 2020) and those with a larger support network report higher well-being (Cheyne et al., 2021).

Note that ego-networks can also be derived from a whole network by using either the function `make_ego_graph()` from the igraph (Csardi & Nepusz, 2006) R package or the function `ego.extract()` function from the sna R package (Butts, 2008). We demonstrated the extraction of ego-networks for nodes D and H from the kite network in Figure 23.1f are plotted in Figures 23.2a and 23.2b, respectively.

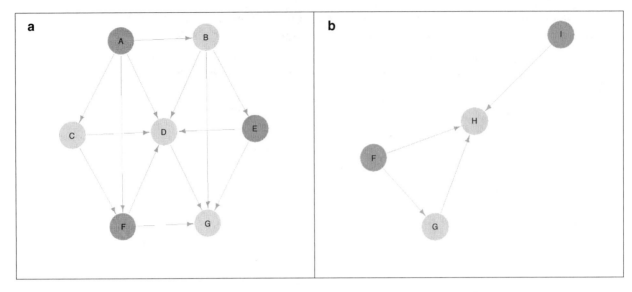

FIGURE 23.2. Ego-networks extracted from Figure 23.1 for Nodes D (a) and H (b).

Relationships. To design a network study, we also need to consider what relationship ties to focus on and how to measure them. Types of relationships vary dramatically based on the research questions. In psychology, the common relationships include social roles (friend of, supervisor of, kinship), social interactions (talk to, help, give advice to or seek advice from), emotional reactions (like, trust, hate, jealous), and flows (information, workflows). Similarity is a different relationship that is understudied in psychology— for example, coming from the same location, holding the same membership, attending the same events, possessing the same attributes such as gender or attitudes. Another perspective to classify social network relationships is instrumental versus expressive (Porter et al., 2019). Previous research has shown that instrumental (e.g., advice, workflow) and expressive (e.g., friendship, emotional reactions) networks differentially influence outcomes such as gossip flow (Grosser et al., 2010) and turnover behavior (Vardaman et al., 2015).

To measure relationship ties, we consider both quantification and directionality. *Quantification* refers to the numeric values we assign to represent the presence or absence of a tie as well as tie strength. If we only care to distinguish the presence and absence of a tie, we take a binary network approach, in which only 1 and 0 are used. However, we may also use a graded scale (e.g., 0, 1, 2, 3) to quantify tie strength, where 0 indicates no relationship and 3 indicates a close relationship.

A network tie can be either directed or undirected, depending on the nature of a relationship. For example, an advice-seeking network is directed—when A seeks advice from B, the relationship is established from actor A to actor B. Typically, most relationships based on social roles, social interactions, emotion reactions and flows are directed. In contrast, whereas similarity-based relationships are undirected.

Network boundary and sampling. *Network boundary* refers to actors' membership in a study. Note that the network boundary does not imply a network per se needs a boundary. Instead, it means that a network *study* requires appropriate restricting actor membership. That is, bounding a network is largely determined by the nature of our network research question. For example, if we are interested in how smoking behaviors among adolescents in a high school are reciprocally influenced by their social network peers, all students in that selected high school will be the actors (egos and alters) to survey in the study, thus the high school bounds the network. However, we should clarify that restricting a network boundary within a high school does not mean there are no social ties or peer influence existing outside the high school, but rather, it means that the current research question focuses only on the social ties and peer influence within the high school.

Appropriately specifying the network boundary is critical to social network research, as different boundaries may result in different findings. One famous example of this was demonstrated by Brass (1984): While centrality within departments was positively related to power and promotions, the relationship for centrality within the entire organization was negative.

For whole-network studies, the network boundary is often clear and formal, and the set of egos is also the same set of alters. However, this is not the case for ego-network studies. Each ego in an ego-network study may have their own set of alters, thus the network boundary varies from ego to ego. As a result, the strategy to randomly sample participants (i.e., egos) from a population for an ego-network study is similar to other psychological studies.

Social Network Data Collection and Management

Whole-network data collection. In a whole-network study, each member of a social network reports to which other network members they are connected. This requires that (a) the social network has a meaningful boundary that determines who belongs to the network (e.g., a school cohort or a department in a company), (b) every member of the social network is known by the researcher in advance, and (c) all network members can be invited to participate in the study. As large quantities of data are collected by interviewing each network member, whole network studies tend to use quantitative techniques for data analysis.

Survey questions to collect whole-network data include a roster format and a name-generator format. Whereas the former requires an entire set of names and asks respondents to respond to each name, the latter simply asks respondents to list contact names based on their recall. We recommend the roster format because it is less subject to recall error and potential biases than the name-generator format. Because the names of the network members are typically known before data are collected in a whole-network study, these names can be displayed in the questionnaire and participants can simply indicate to whom they are related (Marsden, 2011; Stark, 2018). Nowadays, whole network studies can be implemented in most commercial survey software (e.g., Qualtrics), which facilitates both data collection and coding. Privacy or practical concerns force researchers sometimes to conduct such studies with paper-and-pencil questionnaires. For instance, the CILS4EU project collected social network data among more than 18,000 students in 958 classrooms in four countries with printed questionnaires (Kalter et al., 2019). Participants received a name list that associated a number with each classmate and were asked to copy the number of, for instance, their friends onto the questionnaire.

Ego-network data collection. For ego-networks, participants (called *egos*) are first asked to name their contacts (called *alters*) in name-generator questions. Most widely used is a question that asks for names of people with whom one has discussed important matters (Burt, 1984). In name-interpreter questions, the participant subsequently reports characteristics of these contacts (e.g., their gender). The structure of the social network among these contacts is either assessed by asking whether each pair of alters is connected (e.g., "Does Jon know Amanda?") or by having the participant draw lines between alters in a graphical representation of the network (e.g., Birkett et al., 2021; Stark & Krosnick, 2017). Because the alters are typically not interviewed (but see Pearcy et al., 2008; Stark & Stocké, 2021), egocentric network questions can be implemented in regular surveys (e.g., they are regularly part of the U.S. General Social Survey).

Egocentric network studies typically rely on software for the data collection because the names of network contacts that a participant enters can then be copied into follow-up questions about these contacts. Early software developed for the collection of network data, such as EgoNet, EgoWeb (2.0) and C-IKNOW, translated what was done in paper-and-pencil questionnaires into computer programs (McCarty & Govindaramanujam, 2005). The central innovation was that these programs could present a picture of the network that researchers used during the interview to discuss the network structure with the participant. More recent applications, such as ANAMIA (Tubaro et al., 2014) and Vennmaker (Borucki, 2017), allow researchers to cocreate a visual representation of a social network in an interactive participatory way together with their participants.

The latest generation of software for the collection of egocentric network data makes full use of graphical interfaces to collect information on network contacts and the network structure. The program Network Canvas (Birkett et al., 2021) was designed solely for qualitative research and it requires the program to be installed on the computer or tablet on which the participant responds to questions (Figure 23.3). It provides not only a graphical user interface to program a questionnaire but also tools to safely transfer the collected data to a central server, making data backup easy, even for remote data collections. The programs GENSI (Stark & Krosnick, 2017) and OpenEddi (Eddens et al., 2017) can be used for both qualitative and quantitative studies as network questionnaires can be completed in a regular browser. All of these programs allow participants to create a visual representation of their social network in real time and answer questions about their network contacts by interacting with the picture of their network. Because a visual representation of a social network can become unclear when the network increases in size, OpenEddi offers alternative response formats such as sorting the names of contacts into piles (Eddens & Fagan, 2018). The software GENSI (see Figure 23.3) has been extended to declutter the visual representation and now allows the collection of data on larger (~25 contacts) networks (Stulp, 2021). The program formr (Reins et al., 2021) does not use graphical tools but allows simple programming of an egocentric network questionnaire in R. Network graphics can be added by implementing a GENSI

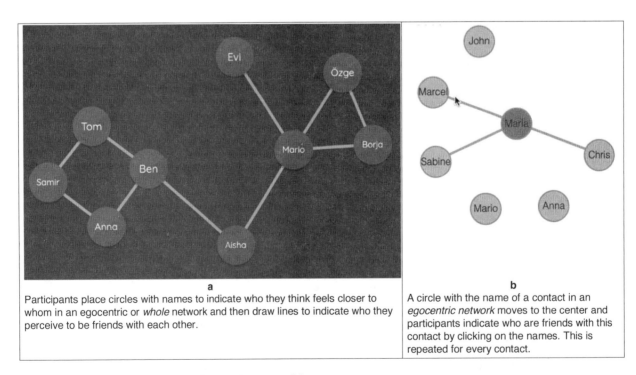

a	b
Participants place circles with names to indicate who they think feels closer to whom in an egocentric or *whole* network and then draw lines to indicate who they perceive to be friends with each other.	A circle with the name of a contact in an *egocentric network* moves to the center and participants indicate who are friends with this contact by clicking on the names. This is repeated for every contact.

FIGURE 23.3. Network Canvas (a) and GENSI (b).

questionnaire in formr. All of these programs are open-source freeware.

Data management. The collected social network data can be organized in two formats for network analysis in the next step: edge-list format and matrix format. The edge-list format typically consists of three columns, specifying the "from" and "to" nodes and the values of the tie strength. More information, if any, about the ties may be stored with additional columns. Each row in an edge-list data represents a specific link. In contrast, the matrix format stores all the link information in an $N \times N$ matrix, where N denotes the network size, and rows represent egos and columns represent alters. Besides the edge-list and matrix data to store the link data, we may also include node information to store in a separate data file. For example, we may include demographic information for individual nodes. Taking a kite structured network (Krackhardt, 1990) for an example, we have made toy data for a kite network to demonstrate both data formats with hypothetical link weights and node demographic information in Figure 23.4. In R, the two data formats can be easily converted to each other by using functions as_adjacency_matrix() and graph_from_adjacency_matrix().

Node Data

ID	Gender	Age
A	M	8
B	F	22
C	F	16
D	F	25
E	M	28
F	M	22
G	F	20
H	F	31
I	M	35
J	F	40

Edge Data

From	To	Weight
A	B	2
A	C	3
A	D	1
A	F	2
B	D	3
B	E	1
B	G	1
C	D	1
C	F	2
D	G	3
E	D	3
E	G	2
F	D	3
F	G	2
F	H	1
G	H	3
I	H	3
J	I	2

Matrix Format With a Binary Scale

	A	B	C	D	E	F	G	H	I	J
A	0	1	1	1	0	1	0	0	0	0
B	0	0	0	1	1	0	1	0	0	0
C	0	0	0	1	0	1	0	0	0	0
D	0	0	0	0	0	0	1	0	0	0
E	0	0	0	1	0	0	1	0	0	0
F	0	0	0	1	0	0	1	1	0	0
G	0	0	0	0	0	0	0	1	0	0
H	0	0	0	0	0	0	0	0	0	0
I	0	0	0	0	0	0	0	1	0	0
J	0	0	0	0	0	0	0	0	1	0

Matrix Format With a Graded Scale

	A	B	C	D	E	F	G	H	I	J
A	0	2	3	1	0	2	0	0	0	0
B	0	0	0	3	1	0	1	0	0	0
C	0	0	0	1	0	2	0	0	0	0
D	0	0	0	0	0	0	3	0	0	0
E	0	0	0	3	0	0	2	0	0	0
F	0	0	0	3	0	0	2	1	0	0
G	0	0	0	0	0	0	0	3	0	0
H	0	0	0	0	0	0	0	0	0	0
I	0	0	0	0	0	0	0	3	0	0
J	0	0	0	0	0	0	0	0	2	0

FIGURE 23.4. Social network data organization.

BASIC SOCIAL NETWORK MEASURES AND ANALYTICAL STRATEGIES

According to Brass (2012), there exist four approaches to social network analyses, with four respective research foci: structure, relationships, resources, and cognition. The structural approach is the most common in psychology, and we introduce it in this section. Psychological research with respect to the other three approaches is elaborated in the next section on the advanced social network analysis.

From a purely structural perspective, the structural approach to SNA primarily focuses on the structural position of a node in a network, arguing that "an actor's position in a network determines in part the constraints and opportunities that he or she will encounter, and therefore identifying that position is important for predicting actor outcomes such as performance, behavior, or beliefs" (Borgatti et al., 2018, p. 1). Taking a kite structured network (Krackhardt, 1990) shown in Figure 23.1 for an example, one may notice that node D is in the most central position in the network, as it has the most connected alters. To better understand social network effects, social network researchers have developed various measures to quantify structural differences among nodes, the most popular of which is centrality. Centrality characterizes how central a node is in a network, through the definition of "central" is operationalized with various versions, including degree centrality, closeness centrality, betweenness centrality, etc. In addition to the node-level network measures, there are also network-level measures to characterize an entire network—for example, network size, density, centralization, reciprocity, transitivity, etc. We list these common measures, along with their definitions and R code to compute, in Table 23.1.

Visualizing Social Networks

Visualizing social networks, as a vital step in social network analysis, is perhaps the best way to intuitively understand a social network. In practice, we often first visualize social networks before computing network measures and conducting further inferential statistical analyses.

With R package igraph (Csardi & Nepusz, 2006), visualizing a social network visualization is straightforward, with three easy steps: (1) inputting edge-list data as illustrated in Figures 23.4a and 23.4b; (2) creating an igraph network object with the input data, typically using the `graph_from_data_frame()` function; and (3) visualizing the created igraph network object with `plot()` function. In addition, both edge attributes (e.g., weight/tie strength and directionality) and node attributes (e.g., gender and age) can be visualized in a network plot. We demonstrate the visualization of the same hypothetical kite network with various versions in Figure 23.1. The corresponding R code is provided in Appendix 23.1.

Social Network Analytical Strategies

In general, there are two approaches to analyzing social networks, depending on how network variables are used in the analysis. The first approach is to analyze network variables as explanatory variables, in which we try to explain outcomes by network theories indexed by relevant network variables (e.g., degree centrality, ego-network density, see Table 23.1). The outcomes to be predicted can be any variables of our research interest, primarily lying in two categories, achievements (e.g., job performance) and behavioral styles (e.g., drug use) (Borgatti et al., 2018). This approach basically focuses on the consequences of network variables, and it can be conveniently incorporated into classic statistical models (e.g., regression, HLM, SEM) that are familiar to psychologists.

In contrast, the second approach focuses on the antecedents of networks—treating network variables as outcome variables. In this approach, network researchers are mainly interested in how extraneous variables such as homophily, personality, culture, balance, and so on, are associated with network variables. For example, previous research found that individuals with high monitoring were more likely to occupy structural holes in a network (Mehra et al., 2001; Oh & Kilduff, 2008). One dominant research area in this analysis approach is to study factors predicting

TABLE 23.1
Common Social Network Structural Measures

Measure	Definition	R function to calculate
Node-level measures (characterizing individual nodes)		
Degree	Total number of direct links/edges a node has; the simplest measure of degree	`igraph::degree(inet,mode="all")` `sna::degree(mnet,cmode="freeman")`
In-degree	Number of directional links to the actor from other actors	`igraph::degree(inet,mode="in")` `sna::degree(mnet,cmode="indegree")`
Out-degree	Number of directional links from the actor to other actors	`igraph::degree(inet,mode="out")` `sna::degree(mnet,cmode="outdegree")`
Strength	Sum of the weights of all incident edges (for weighted/graded networks)	`strength(inet)` `graph.strength(inet)`
Closeness	How close an actor is to all the other actors in a network; a central node has the least steps to reach to other nodes (a lower score)	`igraph::closeness(inet,mode="total")` `sna::closeness(mnet,gmode="graph")`
Betweenness	Number of shortest paths going through a node, indicating the brokerage or gatekeeping potential	`igraph::betweenness(inet)` `sna::betweenness(mnet)`
Eigenvector	Similar to degree centrality but takes into account alters' power; for undirected network only	`sna::evcent(mnet)` `igraph::evcent(inet)$vector` `eigen_centrality(inet)$vector`
PageRank	Aka Google's PageRank; the probability that any message will arrive to a particular node; a variant of Eigenvector for directed network	`authority_score(inet)$vector`
Constraint	Burt's (2005) constraint scores, aka structural holes; higher for egos with less redundant alters	`constraint(inet)`
Ego-network density	The density of each node' ego-network; works only for ego with more than 2 alters	`g.comb<-ego.extract(mnet,neighborhood="combined")` `ego.size<-sapply(g.comb,NROW)` `if(any(ego.size>2)){sapply(g.comb[ego.size>2],` `  function(x){gden(x[-1,-1])})}`
Node-level measures (characterizing an entire network)		
Size density	Total number of nodes/actors a network has Proportion of the number of actual links/edges out of the number of possible links/edges	`dim(mnet)[1]` `sna::gden(mnet)` `edge_density(inet)` `graph.density(inet)`
Centralization	Extent to which centrality scores differ among the nodes in a network: 0 = all nodes are equally central; 1 = one node is maximally central while all others are minimally central	`centr_degree(inet)$centralization`
Reciprocity	Probability of two nodes to be a mutual connected (i.e., if A is connected to B, B is also connected to A)	`reciprocity(inet)`
Transitivity	Probability that two neighbors of a node are connected (i.e., the ratio of the triangles and connected triples in the graph)	`gtrans(mnet)` `transitivity(inet)`
Diameter	Number of paths of the longest path between any two nodes	`diameter(inet)`

Note. In the R function, inet represents an igraph network object, whereas mnet represents a matrix-formatted network.

the formation of different network ties or network patterns. This type of research requires a special set of models—for example, the exponential random-graph model (ERGM; Hunter, Handcock, et al., 2008)—that will be introduced in the next section.

ADVANCED SOCIAL NETWORK ANALYSIS FOR PSYCHOLOGICAL RESEARCH

Going beyond typical SNA analytics of a given system for descriptive metrics such as density and centrality, Borgatti and Halgin (2011) specified that network frameworks can also test the association between social network phenomena and nonnetwork phenomena, where an antecedent social network variable, such as the occurrence of structural holes or weak ties, is used to explain nonnetwork outcomes, such as the attitudes, beliefs, and behaviors of actors in those networks. To illustrate, Levitan and Visser (2009) used network methods to examine the association between network composition and individuals' attitude strength on political beliefs. A name-generator approach was used in which participants were asked to list five members of their social networks with whom they interact regularly and discuss important matters and report on the attitudes of those listed with respect to a target topic. A network variable illustrating attitudinal congruence was created by subtracting the strength of the perceived attitudes for each of the listed network members from the participant's attitude on the topic, and these scores were averaged to form an index indicating network heterogeneity, or the attitudinal diversity of each participant's social network with respect to the target political topic. Network heterogeneity, in terms of attitudinal diversity of participants' social networks on a topic, was then used to predict the strength of participants' attitudes, in terms of malleability, finding that personal networks with increased attitudinal diversity were associated with lower levels of attitude strength. Levitan and Visser (2009) inferred that political beliefs were more likely to be responsive to change for individuals who were situated in more attitudinally diverse social networks.

Recently, Agneessens and Labianca (2022) specified four elements involved in testing hypotheses and conducting social network research in organizational settings, which can be adapted to the study of psychological phenomena more broadly, including (a) defining the research question and determining the target population, (b) discerning the network boundary and identifying the sample, (c) collecting relational data, and (d) using the appropriate social network analysis technique and inferential statistical test to examine the research question. It is also critical to consider the level of analysis appropriate for the given research question. Social network analysis can examine outcomes at the dyadic (tie), individual (actor), and/or group (network) levels (Agneessens, 2021). Propositions generated to test psychological phenomena at each of these levels of analysis correspond to dyadic, nodal, and network-level hypotheses, as well as mixed dyadic-monadic hypotheses (Borgatti et al., 2013).

Throughout this chapter, it becomes clear that social networks are inherently multilevel data objects. And in terms of some ego-centric systems, "it is standard to regard ties as nested within the respondent (ego), who in turn may by nested within a group" (Brass & Borgatti, 2019, p. 5). Hence, perceptions, attitudes, and behaviors are often presumed to depend on the nature of the social relationships and broader social structures in which individuals are situated, and therefore, care must be taken in determining the boundary of the network, referring to which actors, or types of actors ought to be included in the study, as well as which types of relationships among those actors are relevant to examining the particular research question of interest (Laumann et al., 1992, p. 62). Care must also be taken to deal with missing entities in a network because the summary of structural properties of the system can be greatly distorted, for example, if data were not collected on a very central figure to the system (Kossinets, 2006). On sociocentric designs, social networks are often bounded on naturally occurring units, such as a group, team, school, classroom, or organization, whereas, on egocentric/personal network designs, the social network is bounded by the participant and represents a perception, or cognitive social network, indicating the unique social world in which that individual is situated and perceives (McCarty et al., 2019).

Furthermore, the research question often helps inform the relevant method. For example, psychological research based on the similarity-attraction hypothesis (e.g., Byrne, 1971) suggests that homophily (McPherson et al., 2001) leads individuals to form social relationships with others that have similar attributes as themselves. To test this hypothesis, researchers could use dyadic sampling on a whole network where the outcome of interest is the strength of a dyadic relation between two randomly sampled individuals in a specific group. The researcher can also collect data on relational similarities (e.g., age, gender, extroversion) and use the attributes of actors to predict the strength of a dyadic relationship between two randomly sampled individuals, where the outcome variable is at the dyadic level of analysis.

Alternatively, a researcher may examine whether certain types of relationships between actors increase the probability that a certain type of attitude or behavior will be expressed in a given social group. For example, a researcher may examine if people are more likely to get a vaccine if others in their social network are also vaccinated. This is an example of a diffusion hypothesis, which according to Borgatti et al. (2013), "is the idea that people's beliefs, attitudes, and practices come about in part because of interaction with others who already have those beliefs" (p. 152). To test such a notion, researchers could use a random sample to examine whether the actors in the network are vaccinated and have them generate a list of those individuals in their personal networks with whom they know, discuss important matters, or regularly interact, and have them report on whether or not those other network members (alters) are vaccinated, as well as specify the types of social relationships they have with those alters. In contrast, a snowball sampling design, could be used to have participants send the network survey to those they listed as part of the name-generator question to collect data on both the vaccination status, as well as the type of relationships with the other participants included in the study to construct network variables, such as the proportion of alters vaccinated (a network-level variable), and the types of dyadic relationships between alters and the participant (a dyadic-level variable), to predict participants' vaccination status and/or intention to get vaccinated (a nonnetwork outcome at the individual level).

Analytically, various statistical techniques are needed to account for dependencies among observations inherent in the nested structure of network data. Permutation and nonparametric techniques such as the quadratic assignment procedure (QAP; Krackhardt, 1988), ERGM (Hunter, Handcock, et al., 2008) and stochastic actor-oriented longitudinal model (SAOM; Kalish, 2020) are the most commonly used to either control for or model the statistical dependencies and autocorrelation resulting from the nested structure of social network data.

The Quadratic Assignment Procedure

The quadratic assignment procedure (QAP) handles dependencies in network data by treating it essentially "as a nuisance that needs to be corrected for rather than as an interesting feature that can be modeled." The QAP is most commonly used on sociocentric data sets and allows researchers to model dyadic-level dependent variables using one or multiple dyadic-level, antecedent variables (see Borgatti et al., 2013, for a more detailed overview). Psychologists can also use the MRQAP to measure associations between two or more nonnetwork variables, such as relational similarities at the individual-level of analysis by converting a column of attribute data representing variable information (e.g., gender or age) for each actor, n, where n denotes the number of actors in the network, into a set of dyadic variables suitable for QAP correlation and regression. This is done using the conversion method, to transform attribute data into an $n \times n$ matrix, where each cell (other than the diagonal) in the adjacency matrix contains a 1 if both individuals are of the same gender, and a 0 if those two individuals are of different genders, converting attributes of individuals into dyadic relations representing similarities between two actors in the social network on the same attribute (Borgatti et al., 2013).[1] This can be executed in the UCINET VI using the Data|Attribute-to-Matrix routine to create a node-by-node adjacency matrix depicting similarities in gender or age differences.

The resulting matrices can be correlated with each other, and with other matrices of the same size and symmetry, including matrices representing dyadic relations, such as friendships, using the MRQAP routine in UCINET VI (Borgatti et al., 1999) for Windows, as well as across platforms in R using the netlm, g.cor, and qaptest functions in the sna package (Butts, 2008). The QAP approach allows researchers to test dyadic and mixed dyadic-monadic hypotheses in which the antecedent and outcome variables are either both at the individual level or one or more individual-level variables are being correlated with variables at the dyadic level, such as social relations. The QAP preserves unique contingencies and dependencies contributed by the structure and configuration of the network in which attributes of individuals are embedded as a function of the network boundary imposed on the data during the data collection process. Statistical inference on egocentric network data, on the other hand, tend to use hierarchical linear regression or hierarchical logistic regression models (Vacca, 2018), and multiple membership multiple classification models to account for additional nesting structures such as time and egos nested in overlapping group memberships. Such methods of statistical inference enable psychologists to use a "falsifiable methodology" for studying the influence of social systems on psychological outcomes, where the assumption of independence among observations is violated (Laumann et al., 1992, p. 61).

The Exponential Random-Graph Model

In SNA, both the ERGM (or p^* model) and the SAOM are widely used to account for the endogenous dependencies in a social network[2]—the former was originally developed for the analysis of cross-sectional data (Lusher et al., 2013), and the latter is suited for the longitudinal analysis of change in networks (see the next section). In this and the next section, we give an intuitive introduction to these models without mathematical connotations. The cited literature provides more technical introductions for the interested readers.

ERGMs address the problem that social networks violate the assumption of independence of observations that underlies most regression models. To do so, ERGMs consider ties in the network to be conditionally independent by explicitly modeling the existing dependency through local network configurations (Frank & Strauss, 1986; Robins et al., 2007). These local configurations can represent interdependence on the dyadic level (e.g., reciprocity), between triads (e.g., a friend of a friend is a friend, or stars structures), and even between more nodes. The focus on local configurations implies that ties are conditionally independent of ties that are far away in the network.

The estimation process of an ERGM describes the probability that the graph (network) transitions from its current state to an adjacent graph state; that is, for each tie how likely it is to change (be created or broken) given how the rest of the network looks. The idea is that the network is made up of local configurations such as reciprocated ties or triads and the coefficients represent the probability that each configuration contributed to the observed network structure. Next to accounting for these endogenous network processes, researchers can add variables representing actor characteristics to the model to test if ties are

---

[1] For continuous attributes, such as age similarities, each cell in the matrix indicates the age differences as a dyadic variable, which is calculated by subtracting the age of the row actor from the age of a column actor.
[2] Although mainly for whole network data, extensions are also available for the statistical analysis of egocentric network data, but these go beyond the scope of this chapter.

more likely to change if they involve an actor with a certain value on the variable (e.g., higher age) or if they form between two actors with similar values (e.g., similar age). Coefficients from an ERGM are interpreted as general tendencies in the network, conditional on the rest of the network structure, and not as preferences of the actors in the network.

ERGMs are conducted by Markov chain Monte Carlo maximum likelihood estimation (Hunter, 2007). Intuitively, the estimation works as follows: A series of new networks are simulated based on initial guesses for the weight of each parameter (representing local configuration and actor characteristics) in the model. A sample from the simulated networks is then compared with the observed data. If the simulated networks look very different, the parameters are adjusted accordingly for the next simulation run. If they look similar, the parameters get slowly refined until the difference between the simulated and the observed network meets some predefined criterion. The simulated networks are then used to infer the probability of certain ties and local network structures in the network. Such analyses are possible in the R package suite statnet (Krivitsky et al., 2020) and the stand-alone program PNet (Wang et al., 2009). See Appendix 23.2 for R code for an example of ERGM analysis.

Goodness-of-fit statistics can be calculated by comparing how well the simulated networks resemble the observed network with regard to auxiliary statistics that were *not* explicitly modeled in the evaluation function (Hunter, Goodreau, & Handcock, 2008). Goodness-of-fit analysis can guide the model development as it indicates which additional parameters might improve the fit of the model to the data (for an illustration of the approach, see Goodreau et al., 2009). ERGMs also provide the AIC and BIC of an analysis indicating how well the model fits the data. Because simulating networks from scratch is quite complex, ERGMs often do not converge, or they experience model degeneracy, meaning that networks with no ties or all possible ties are simulated. Goodness-of-fit analyses do not help in these situations, but the available software provides diagnosis tools of the simulation algorithm that can help to identify problems in the model.

ERGMs have been used to show how group boundaries and social status in an organization explain about whom people gossip (Ellwardt et al., 2012). Other studies found that obesity is socially shared (for an overview, see Zhang et al., 2018), that information exchange between organizations depends on their distance and location (Sohn et al., 2020), and that hormones are related to social behavior (higher cortisol levels were related to fewer friendships; see Kornienko et al., 2014).

Multilevel and longitudinal ERGMs. More recently, extensions of ERGMs have been presented for multilevel applications (Wang, Robins, Pattison, & Lazega, 2016). These models allow for complex data structures that go beyond traditional multilevel structures in which observations are nested within higher level units (e.g., students in schools). Such models can have different sets of nodes that each define a level and there can be ties between the nodes of the same level and between nodes of different levels. For instance, researchers can have advice ties with each other in their own and other labs, and there can be collaboration ties between the labs at which the researchers work (Lazega et al., 2008). Multilevel ERGMs can also be used to analyze two-mode (bipartite) networks in which there are no relations between nodes of the higher level (Wang et al., 2013; Wang, Robins, & Matous, 2016).

Although ERGMs were developed for crosssectional analyses, different extensions have been presented that allow the modeling of change in social networks over time. Examples are the tERGM (Hanneke et al., 2010), the longitudinal ERGM (Snijders & Koskinen, 2013), and the separable temporal ERGM (Krivitsky & Handcock, 2014). However, empirical applications of longitudinal ERGMs are rare because longitudinal analyses of change in social networks over time are typically conducted with stochastic actor-oriented models.

The Stochastic Actor-Oriented Model

SAOMs (Snijders, 2017), are often referred to as RSiena-analyses because they can be conducted in the R-package RSiena (Ripley et al., 2022). SAOMs are "actor-oriented" because they do not predict ties based on the structure of the entire network as ERGMs do, but the process through which focal actors (nodes) in the network decide to create or break ties (for a comparison of the two models, see Block et al., 2019). The assumption is that the actors adjust their social relationships to maximize the satisfaction (utility) they receive from their position in the social network (Snijders, 2001; Snijders et al., 2010). For instance, actors who have a preference for reciprocated friendships would derive more satisfaction from creating friendships with others who also nominated them as friends than from a friendship with someone else. Thus, an SAOM analysis would reveal a preference for reciprocity in the network if reciprocated friendships were more likely to develop over time and/or more likely to be maintained than nonreciprocated friendships.

Such preferences are modeled in the so-called "evaluation function" from which tendencies of tie formation and maintenance can be inferred. Researchers can add effects that are of theoretical importance for the assumed process underlying the change in the network. These can be endogenous network effects such as reciprocity or transitivity but also preferences of actors such as their age (e.g., younger people form more friendships than older people) or their preferences for network contacts (e.g., people prefer friends of a similar age). The SAOM allows testing whether these assumed effects can explain the change that was observed between two observations of the same network.

SAOMs assume that the observed stages of the network are representations of a continuous change process. This is modeled in a stochastic simulation process in which actors are randomly chosen at each "microstep" to either create a new tie, break an existing tie, or do nothing at all, depending on which decision maximizes the actors' satisfaction with their network given the assumed effects in the evaluation function (Snijders et al., 2010). The first observation of the network forms the starting point, and the simulation models possible changes over time through a sequence of microsteps, similar to agent-based simulation models, trying to create networks that resemble the empirical observed network at the next time point. This simulation process is repeated thousands of times and the differences between the observed network at the next time point and the thousands of simulated networks are used to estimate how well the effects included in the evaluation function can create the observed change between the time points.

Different indicators are available to assess the model fit of a SAOM. First, t-ratios indicate whether the simulation process successfully converged, and the estimated coefficients are trustworthy. Convergence of SAOMs tends to be more easily achieved than of ERGMs because SAOMs only simulate the change between two observations of a network, whereas ERGMs need to simulate the development of a network from scratch. Second, goodness-of-fit statistics can be calculated based on auxiliary statistics similar to the approach for ERGMs (Lospinoso & Snijders, 2019). See Appendix 23.3 for R code for an example of SAOM analysis with RSiena.

Statistical inference: Selection versus influence. Given the longitudinal approach, SAOMs are particularly suited to explore which processes underlie network autocorrelation. That is, a multitude of research has found that people who have a social tie (e.g., a friendship) often are similar in their behaviors, attitudes, and background characteristics. SAOMs allow testing whether network autocorrelation is because people tend to select friends who are similar or that friends become similar over time. For such an analysis, one or more additional dependent variables can be added to the evaluation function (Steglich et al., 2010). These "behavioral" dependent variables can be any kind of changeable attribute. Next to changing the network in each micro-step of the simulation process, the actors can now also change their value in each of the behavioral dependent variables in order to maximize their satisfaction given the values of their network contacts on this variable. Such analyses have shown that adolescents both select friends with similar levels of cigarette smoking and influence their friends' behaviors (McMillan et al., 2018; Mercken et al., 2010). Other studies have explored whether social selection or social influence is the cause of friends' similarity with regard to antisocial behavior (for an overview, see Sijtsema & Lindenberg, 2018), educational expectations (e.g., Lorenz et al., 2020), or academic engagement (e.g., Stark et al., 2017; Zhang et al., 2019). SAOMs have also been used to show that a preference for friends with similar tastes in music can be mistaken for a preference for friends of the same ethnicity (Stark & Flache, 2012). See Appendix 23.4 for R code for an example of coevolution of networks and behavior SAOM analysis with RSiena.

Multilevel and multiplex SAOMs. Because many social network studies have a multilevel structure (e.g., networks of children in multiple schools), SAOMs have been extended to allow the combined estimation of change in multiple networks in three ways (Snijders, 2016). First, each network can be estimated separately, and the results are then combined in a meta-analysis (e.g., Leszczensky & Pink, 2019). Second, all networks can be analyzed simultaneously in a "multigroup" analysis (e.g., Zingora et al., 2020). This approach is more suited for small networks that often lead to convergence problems, but it makes the problematic assumption that the same processes take place in all networks. Third, recently developed Bayesian random-coefficient multilevel SAOMs allow simultaneous estimation without this assumption (Koskinen & Snijders, 2020). Moreover, it is possible to include between-networks effects in the estimation process such as the school track to which each network belongs (e.g., Lorenz et al., 2020) or the popularity of a school subject in each network (e.g., Raabe et al., 2019).

Next to having multiple behavioral dependent variables in the model, SAOMs also allow the simultaneous estimation of change in multiple networks and their effects on each other (Snijders et al., 2013). Examples are two social networks such as friendship and bullying (Hooijsma et al., 2020; Rambaran et al., 2020); social networks and networks of perceptions such as peers' ethnicity (Boda et al., 2020; Kisfalusi et al., 2020); or social networks and networks of similar behavior such as co-citation or similar language use (Stark et al., 2020). A multiplex SAOM allows disentangling to what extent change in one network leads to change in another network. Also, two-mode (bipartite) networks can be included in SAOMs. Such models allow testing whether an affiliation in a two-mode network leads to the creation of a social tie in a one-mode network or whether existing social ties lead to joining one's contacts affiliations (Fujimoto et al., 2018; Lomi & Stadtfeld, 2014; Raabe et al., 2019).

Network Perception Research

Both sociocentric and egocentric designs are able to test various psychological (e.g., Shea et al., 2015) research on cognitive social structures (CSS; Krackhardt, 1987), which offers another level of network analysis that focuses on how people perceive their social networks—in terms of the perceived social network structure and perception accuracy (Casciaro et al., 2015). Participants report not only on social relationships between themselves and others in the network, but also on the perceived social relationships between every set of individuals in the social network, which is then used to calculate accuracy in perceiving social network structure. Psychological research on social cognition and perception is also starting to interface more with research on *network perception*—conceptualized as a "cognitive representation" of those individuals that are perceived as belonging to one's social environment, indicating that other people are not stored in memory "on the basis of individual attributes such as gender, age, or education," but rather as "clusters of social groups, contexts, or roles, and *'chunked substructures'*" (McCarty et al., 2019, pp. 74–75). This research suggests that cognition and social intelligence evolved in response to pressures and demands of living in complex social environments, in which the ability to accurately perceive social relations between oneself and others, as well as between others in one's social world, confers a selective advantage in primate species (Brashears & Quintane, 2015).

How social relationships are stored in memory and how they are retrieved when people are asked to generate their social network (Smith et al., 2020) have been shown to be shaped by individual differences, such as by gender (Brashears et al., 2016) and personality (Selden & Goodie, 2018), which are often situated in positive or negative social relationships (Marineau et al., 2018) and situational and positional effects, such as being isolated, excluded, or ostracized in a network (O'Connor & Gladstone, 2015). Various research on network perception has been grounded on the *functional specificity hypothesis,* suggesting that "social interaction is goal-directed," where people "engage in selective and purposive activation of ties" (Perry & Pescosolido, 2010, p. 346). Psychological research demonstrates that one's goals shape not only which individuals come to mind in name-generator methods (Shea & Fitzsimons, 2016) but also evaluations of the closeness and strength of social relations with other individuals (Fitzsimons & Shah, 2008) and which people in one's social environment are worth forming a social relationship with (Finkel & Eastwick, 2015). In this way, the idea of functional specificity is an important consideration in the methodological design of egocentric network studies, as a participant's own goals may shape which members of their social network will be activated by name-generator questions (Perry et al., 2018), and in turn, impact the data used to make inferences about visualized networks and related network statistics. Concerning network visualization, there are also numerous choices today for researchers in terms software. Beyond UCINET, the following programs have been employed in various setting: GEPHI, EgoNet, NodeXL, Kumu, and R programming packages such as igraph and VisNetwork. R programming continues to grow in popularity among network scientists given its flexibility in analyzing research questions.

There are other new advances employing network concepts to cognitive-motivational psychological phenomena, such as research examining goal systems (Kung & Scholer, 2021). While network perception research examines how cognitive social structures are encoded and represented in the mind, goal systems theories view goals as forming a "mentally represented network" of goals and associated means for attaining them (Kruglanski et al., 2002, pp. 333–334; Orehek & Forest, 2016). Research on network perception can also shed light on the "social side" of self-regulation involved in shared, parallel, and personal goal pursuits, where people (two or more) are thought of as being as part of a single self-regulating system, called a *transactive goal system,* for which thought and action is shaped and coordinated by "a shared constellation of goals, pursuits, and outcomes" (Fitzsimons et al., 2015, pp. 648–649). However, we presume, as was indicated by Kung and Scholer (2021), that this line of work could further benefit from social network theorizing by incorporating social actors as means to attaining goals through mechanisms suggested by dynamic network theory, to which we turn next.

Network Goal Analysis: A Framework Integrating Psychology and Social Networks

A modern metatheory and method developed to address the gap between psychological approaches of human motivation and social network analysis is dynamic network theory (DNT; Westaby et al., 2014) and its corresponding method of network goal analysis (NGA) to study single and multiple goal systems (Westaby, 2012; Westaby & Parr, 2020). In this ground-breaking approach, goal nodes are inserted into social networks with theoretical logic, which allows the method to comprehensively model and explain how and why social networks pivot around human goal pursuits. According to the theory, two overarching types of "social network role" behaviors exist and can be methodologically measured and modeled: person-to-goal relations and person-to-person relations involved with those same corresponding goals.

For person-to-goal relations, the roles are independently involved with that target goal pursuit. First, actors engaged in goal striving arcs (G) are those independently *striving* to attain a goal, such as Actor 1 and 2 in a special forces unit reporting that they are independently working on different parts of a mission on their own (see Part B of Figure 23.5). This concept accounts for the powerful predictive power of intentions and goals on behavior and performance in psychology, respectively (Ajzen & Kruglanski, 2019; Fishbein & Ajzen, 2010). Second, actors engaged in *goal preventing* arcs (P) are independently involved in obstructing a given system goal, such as Actor 3, a military enemy, who is trying to sabotage the target system goal behind the scenes. The third person-to-goal role (a reciprocating arc) is direct *task feedback* (FB) about the goal pursuit examined in the network, such as Actors 1 and 2 seeing how their direct efforts are proceeding in real time on the ground as well as other actors in the network that may learn about the pursuits, such as Actor 5, an officer, and Actor 4, an intelligence operation officer for enemy forces. FB arcs integrate validated self-regulation and goal pursuit principles from psychology (Locke & Latham, 2019; Westaby, 2012).

For person-to-person relations, four relational concepts are necessary and presumed sufficient to explain how the social actors interface with one another to facilitate or obstruct a given goal or behavioral pursuit. First, *system support* arcs (S) represent support mechanisms involved in promoting the focal goal and conceptually subsumes a host or powerful empirically supported concepts in psychology, such as (a) the importance of tactical assistance with goals (instrumental support), (b) love, care or concern for others in the pursuits (emotional support), and (c) advice and resource mechanisms related to goal striving (e.g., material, financial, logistical, etc.). In Figure 23.5, Actors 5, 6, and 7 are providing tactical and resource support to Actors 1 and 2 through a chain of command. Second, *supportive resistance* arcs (V) illustrate ties or social relationships that jointly hinder, obstruct, or aim to prevent the goal pursuit under examination, such as Actor 4, who is supporting Actor 3's enemy resistance to the focal goal. Third, *system negation* arcs (N) occur when an actor is upset with how others are involved in the goal pursuit, or feelings of dislike or prejudice in the given context, such as Actor 4 being particularly aware of and upset with Actor 5's leadership actions on the other side of the conflict. Last, DNT specifies that *system reactance* arcs demonstrate actors that are trying to constructively solve a problem or conflict with others in relation to the goal. In Figure 23.5, Actor 5 is trying to promote constructive solutions to the larger conflict impacting this mission. This concept uniquely integrates conflict resolution into SNA, which has received little attention among network scientists, despite its critical importance for psychological health and well-being (Westaby & Redding, 2014).

By looking at the multiplex nature of the relations in an NGA, considerable new meaning may be ascertained in some settings. For example, when an N link between two actors is jointly seen in a multiplex set with R as well (i.e., $P(N \cup R) = 1$), it illustrates potential optimism in the system to recover from the given conflict because some actors are working on a solution. In our example, Actor 5 may be trying to send communications to Actor 4 that attempt to look for a solution to this broader goal conflict so that the mission can be modified or regulated with less loss of life (e.g., informing them that civilians may need to leave a location at a certain period of time). When many P, V, and N links occur in a system without any R, it could suggest a much more intractable system with poor predicted macro-outcomes. In all, including conflict linkages within network analytics is often helpful as well, given the host of new findings that show how conflict arcs can demonstrate different network dynamics (Labianca & Brass, 2006).

Past research contrasting SNA links to NGA links has also revealed surprising counter-intuitive results that sometimes can change the fundamental meaning about positive and negative arcs in social networks (Westaby & Redding, 2014). For example, in Part A of Figure 23.5, Actor 4 has a positive relation (+) with Actor 3, thus intuitively tempting a network scientist to infer that this positive relation is like all the other

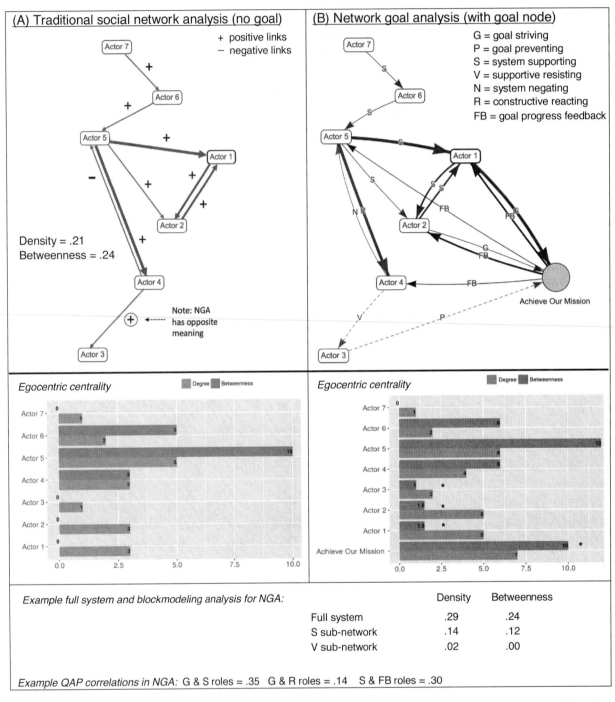

FIGURE 23.5. Comparing social network approaches in the same complex system. NGA = Network goal analysis. *The exclusive non-zero betweenness centrality in NGA manifest among Actors 1, 2, and 3 and "Achieve Our Mission" goal node illustrates that the goal node is attracting connections from independent G links and P links. And the FB, in turn, is reaching/connecting with other actors in unique ways about goal progress information.

positive relations (+) in the system. However, when one contextualizes these same actors in the context of the target mission goal in this system, a shift of meaning occurs for this arc. That is, according to the NGA, Actor 3 is actually helping Actor 4 to prevent the other side's mission success, which means that the relationship between Actors 3 and 4 is actually a supportive resistance (V) conflict/negative arc working against the mission goal under study. Thus, SNA and NGA portrayed the opposite meaning for this arc, which is fully explained by the framed target goal under study. In terms of methodological design, this indicates that researchers need to be mindful of not only the functional specificity of goal-directed social networks but also the types of arcs being assessed and drawing upon methodologically grounded theory, particularly when examining social networks involved in goals, target behaviors, or human striving contexts that may have conflict or competition. This is especially relevant in organizational research because organizations are often primarily created to pursue business objectives within competitive environments. Furthermore, this approach has broad applications in interorganizational network contexts, where multiple organizations may both collaborate and compete to accomplish common goals that are beyond the scope of a single organization (e.g., Raab & Kenis, 2009).

There are also important peripheral and emergent processes that can be uniquely understood through psychological theorizing in DNT. For example, observers may be inspired by watching another's goal pursuit (i.e., a person-to-person observation behavior) and thus decide to become goal strivers themselves (i.e., an emergent person-to-goal behavior). Moreover, with goals accounted for in social networks, researchers can examine predicted affect-based contagion effects, such as the network rippling of positive emotions across social networks based on goal progression: Goal progression (at the actor, dyadic, or network levels) is predicted to result in positive emotions for actors in G and S roles while cascading negative emotions to actors in P and V roles, if they exist (i.e., envy effects modeled in NGA).

For example, in Figure 23.5, Actors 3 and 4 would be predicted to experience negative emotions if the other side's focal mission is achieved.

Methodologically, NGA can be readily applied at the individual level of single-goal pursuits, such as by using an egocentric design to examine how people perceive the influence of their social network's complex behavior on efforts to attain their goal, such as in the illustration above or to get a job, to lose weight, or complete a work project. NGA can map all of the perceived networks relations in those systems. Given its methodological grounding in psychology, conducting an NGA has been primarily executed via an advanced Qualtrics survey of at least one key actor in the focal goal system, who makes judgments about all potential person-to-goal and person-to-person relations. Researchers can download the survey for scientific purposes (see https://www.tc.columbia.edu/dnl/). Once a survey of a system is complete, an R *shiny* program transforms the outputted CSV file from the Qualtrics survey into NGA visuals (and metrics) of the full system as well as subsystem dynamics, such as viewing the G, P, S, V, N and R subnetworks separately. Example subnetwork metrics are illustrated on the bottom of Figure 23.5 in the simple example for both SNA and NGA. Subsystem visuals and metrics become helpful when the complexity of a full, multiplex system becomes very saturated with linkages. Technically, the program automatically converts the person-to-goal attributes into relevant dyadic variables, thus allowing for correlations to be run across the social network roles in DNT using QAP, and for example, to examine the degree to which G arcs are correlated with S arcs as predicted in DNT (see Westaby & Parr, 2020, for a fuller application). QAP is a particularly attractive metric in outputted NGA results for psychologists because only one Qualtrics survey from one case study network is needed to generate each correlation matrix for each system. When multiple networks are examined from a broader sample (e.g., from a key goal actor or goal striver of each separate system in a population of interest to a researcher), meta-analyses can combine the correlation matrices from the separate systems. Qualtrics surveys and R shiny programs are made available for the research community (see https://www.tc.columbia.edu/dnl/), including an HTML full report for the example in Figure 23.5. Underlying R code can be requested, when publications require the code for transparency and accountability or to follow APA guidelines. In the spirit of open-source programming promoted through R programming, programming edits and partnerships are encouraged to continue to develop (and/or further debug) the in-progress programming for the broader scientific community.

Although DNT is presumed to explain the most critical network behaviors involved in social and organizational goal pursuits and unpacks rich complexities of full systems that include competition and conflict, some researchers may decide to focus on only the positive NGA subelements, such as examining only G, S, and FB arcs in an organizational system. This may be relevant or justified when survey time is constrained or there are concerns about the data collection in real-world settings, such as sensitivities about public reports showing conflict arcs for specific actors. For scientific projects with anonymous data collection on target goals or behavioral pursuits, this concern is likely less problematic. However, researchers need to be careful when considering providing reports on negative/conflict arcs even when actor names are deidentified in reports. This is because readers may be able to strongly infer an actor's identity even though the data are technically deidentified. For example, in an organizational context, if "Employee X" is shown to have several negative in-bound system negation (N) arcs in a report and some people in the organization know that only one employee is known to receive many complaints, Employee X would likely be easily identified even though not named in analyses, which could have additional real-world consequences for the employee, unintended by the researcher. In all, researchers need to be vigilant in their ethics involved with SNA in real-world settings.

Complex Observable Systems and Massive Online Behavior

Other highly complex systems can be modeled with SNA and NGA as well, including the modeling and computer simulation of networks involved in goal pursuits over time or the lifespan (Westaby & Shon, 2017), which has relevance for counseling and coaching contexts, and the modeling of group discussions from observable behavior instead of self-reports. For example, the latter builds from Westaby et al.'s (2016) proposal that social network interactions can be understood by measuring how much actors are independently introducing and discussing a topic (i.e., a G arc toward topic node X) and then measuring other group members' support of the goal strivers, such as through head nods or statements of agreement (S). Moreover, conflict relations associated with goal strivers' comments can also be assessed, such as a system negation arc (N) coded when Person X demonstrates that they are upset with Person Y's goal striving commentary. In this way, a richer understanding about how the social network is engaging in various topics is captured as well as how actors respond to one another in discussing the various topics. Hence, the approach allows researchers to uniquely visualize how different actors are focusing on different topics in the context of their person-to-person network reactions.

Lastly, NGA can also be applied to understanding behavior in massive online platforms, such as discussion boards, YouTube, and Stack Overflow (Westaby, 2020). For example, when topical questions, such as those entered into search boxes, are framed as goal nodes, the online users striving to answer them become automatically coded as actors with G links to the question goal node and those that comment or support those trying to answer are automatically coded as showing system support (S) arcs toward the actors engaged in the answering G. In this way, the behavior of the entire system can be uniquely visualized and analyzed by person-to-goal answering behavior and person-to-person support relations. Advantageously, because these relations can be specified from how people are using the program, there is no need for subjective coding or surveys, and thus massive systems can be modeled easily, given computational power. Substantively, this method can unpack the potential actors considered to be super influencers on S network structure, like traditional SNA, but also uniquely unpack which topics (i.e., goal node questions) are super influential in the given system in conjunction with social relations, which cannot be as deduced through person-to-person relations in SNA alone, even with compared with multigraph SNA architecture. Future research is needed to further compare the methods and their implications for understanding super influencing mechanisms in massive online systems and applications to artificial intelligence (AI) programs that can use such information to make inferences and predictions about future behavior, being fully mindful of associated ethics.

Attitudinal and Behavioral Contagion: An Example in Turnover Research

A *contagion effect* is defined as the tendency for the affect, cognition, and/or behavior of individuals to impact the corresponding affect, cognition, and/or behavior of connected others (Levy & Nail, 1993; see also Festinger, Schachter, & Back, 1950; Salancik & Pfeffer, 1978). Contagion effects are sometimes also referred to as a ripple effect, spillover, snowballing, diffusion, or simply social influence. Conceptually and methodologically, a contagion effect can be indicated by a positive relationship between individual employees' scores on a variable, and the aggregate of the employees' direct contacts'/peers' scores on the same variable (e.g., Burt & Janicik, 1996; Christakis & Fowler, 2008; Ibarra & Andrews, 1993). For instance, in one study (described by Burt & Janicik, 1996; based on Heinz et al., 1993), lobbyists listed the names of fellow lobbyists whom they identified as willing to assist them if requested, and results suggested a strong relationship between one's own liberal/conservative beliefs and the beliefs of their advisers (i.e., a result consistent with the interpretation of contagion of ideology beliefs).

Social contagion effects are pervasive. Among the phenomena for which social scientists have claimed contagion effects are group emotion (Barsade, 2002), depression (Joiner, 1994), leader charisma attributions (Pastor et al., 2002), organizational philanthropy (Galaskiewicz & Burt, 1991), burnout (Bakker & Schaufeli, 2000), loneliness (Cacioppo et al., 2009), obesity (Christakis & Fowler, 2007), smoking (Christakis & Fowler, 2008), happiness (Fowler & Christakis, 2008), and unethical behavior in organizations (Brass et al., 1998). In general, such direct contagion effects are theorized to be mediated in two ways: (a) an unconscious, automatic mimicry by the target person of the attitudes, behaviors, or cognitions of others in the social situation (Chartrand & Bargh, 1999); and/or (b) conscious contagion (Hsee et al., 1990), such as when the target individual becomes aware of behaviors, feelings, or cognitions of others and then engages in discussion with these others, empathizes with them, or compares their own situation with these others.

Traditional nonnetwork approach: Individual mediation model. Over the past 50 years of studying voluntary turnover, management researchers have primarily focused on the individual microlevel predictors of the turnover decision, particularly through an individual's attitudinal responses to the job role. The basic *satisfaction-intention-turnover mediation model* is rooted in the work of Porter and Steers (1973, p. 153) and Ajzen and Fishbein (1980). The model is straightforward: It specifies a path from job satisfaction to turnover intentions (and withdrawal cognitions) and then a subsequent path from turnover intentions to actual turnover behavior. Such a model has been well-supported by meta-analytic data (Tett & Meyer, 1993, p. 277) and is thus characterized here as the classic satisfaction-intention-turnover model.

The classic satisfaction-intention model is not the only sequential model of voluntary turnover proposed to date. One notable alternative sequential model is the *unfolding model of voluntary turnover* (Lee & Mitchell, 1994)—which emphasizes the roles of shocks/events and decision frames/scripts, in addition to job satisfaction in the turnover process. We agree with the notion set forth in the unfolding model that some individuals may not follow the traditional path and may decide to leave despite being satisfied with their jobs. Nonetheless, as summarized by Mitchell and Lee (2001), "Most people leave via paths 3 and 4b, which are the more 'traditional' paths. While path 3 involves a shock and path 4b does not, both paths result in some relative job dissatisfaction, which in turn leads to searching for alternatives and a fairly rational, comparative, decision process" (p. 229). Indeed, as noticed by Felps et al. (2009), "In virtually all other traditional models, various factors influence turnover through their impact on organizational commitment and job satisfaction, which in turn influence intent to leave, which then leads to voluntary turnover." (p. 546). We also note that job satisfaction can be considered the dominant precursor to turnover intentions because in Tett and Meyer's (1993) meta-analytic review, a proposed model that emphasized job satisfaction showed much better empirical fit than did an alternative model in which organizational commitment was the dominant precursor to turnover intentions, revealing little empirical role for organizational commitment once job satisfaction and turnover intentions are both accounted for (p. 277, Model 3).

A novel network approach to turnover research: Turnover network contagion. We use the contagion metaphor, which depicts how dissatisfaction and the intention to leave a job can spread within a social network like a virus might spread and cluster within groups of actors in a social network (Leenders, 2002). The contagion metaphor provides a useful and potentially insightful framework for understanding and investigating social structural and attitudinal antecedents of turnover. Turnover and its antecedents (including negative affect and beliefs) are easily transmittable, concrete, and readily interpreted by others; attributes that appear readily conducive to contagion effects (Barsade, 2002). Contagion effects also seem more likely to occur when coworkers develop a shared attitude or belief conducive to turnover (e.g., Mauno et al., 2014, found that turnover intentions and associated work-related attitudes were shared at the departmental level of analysis, providing indirect evidence for contagion of turnover intentions). Other research suggestive of contagion effects for withdrawal behavior comes from Eder and Eisenberger (2008), who found significant relations between the average tardiness of the work group and the tardiness of individual employees as well as between the work group average on a measure of withdrawal behavior and individual scores on the same withdrawal measure.

Particularly relevant to the turnover contagion, Bartunek et al. (2008) conducted a series of three qualitative case studies (in a computer company, a sales organization, and a doctoral student cohort) to inductively derive a coherent theory of collective turnover. Bartunek et al. (2008) defined *collective turnover* as "the turnover of two or more organization members in close temporal proximity based on shared social processes and decisions to leave an organization" (p. 6). According to the collective turnover theory, events (e.g., unsatisfactory supervisor response) trigger dissatisfaction, which further leads to complaints and group conversations. As such, negative emotions may spread from one employee to another, and the ongoing dissatisfaction intensifies through social comparison for cohesive groups, escalates over time, and eventually leads to intentions to leave the organization for some employees.

For network contagion, the aggregate of the perceptions, attitudes, or behavior of the social network connected peers shapes the corresponding perception, attitude, or behavior of the focal person (i.e., the ego). This type of contagion was also referred to as cohesion contagion (Burt et al., 2013) and social influence (Feeley & Barnett, 1997). At this point, we should clarify an important theoretical distinction between turnover network contagion versus job embeddedness. *Job embeddedness* refers to the number and depth of the employee's connections to other people in the organization and community, and the individual's fit to the job (Mitchell et al., 2001). Employees who are more embedded are "stuck" and less likely to voluntarily leave the organization than those who are less embedded, over and beyond the effects of job satisfaction (Mitchell et al., 2001; Mitchell & Lee, 2001). Felps et al. (2009) found that turnover of bank employees was associated with the average job search and job embeddedness of their coworkers in the bank branch. Yet job embeddedness is not the same thing as network contagion. As described by Felps et al., "Like the contagion of illness, the process involves the transmission of something from one individual to another. For us, the 'something' is the tendency to leave a job" (p. 546). In essence, Felps et al. used network contagion as a theoretical rationale beneath their finding of cross-level job embeddedness effects—i.e., the finding that group-level job embeddedness predicts individual turnover. Combining the novel network approach and the traditional individual mediation model, Wang, Newman, and Dipboye (2016) proposed an integrative model as presented in Figure 23.6.

Further advancing turnover network contagion further: Contingent network contagion. Beyond network turnover, we are also able to examine a moderating effect by leveraging on ego network density. To intuitively demonstrate different ego network structures, we illustrate two actors (i.e., Actors A and B) in the upper panel of Figure 23.7. Although both actors have the same number of alters (i.e., three), the ego network structures of the two actors differ due to the distinct network connections among their alters. Actor A's alters are all disconnected, whereas Actor B's are all connected. Such different connections among alters have important theoretical implications for ego's experience in the group.

In particular, Coleman (1988) conceptualized network closure, which is a form of social capital characterized by mutual obligations and trustworthiness, enforcement of norms, and shared information and resources; and this notion of network closure is often operationalized as ego network density (Zaheer et al., 2010). Interestingly, both Putnam (2000) and Burt (2001, 2005) have highlighted the importance of dense networks/network closure for social capital but use different labels. Using the term *bonding capital*, Putnam argued that strong and close-knit ties and dense social networks generate trust, cooperation, mutual support, and a sense of solidarity and belonging, which yield benefits and advantages for success. Similarly, Burt (2001) endorsed network closure as the essence of social capital and proposed that high-closure networks (a) provide reliable communication channels and (b) offer a supporting and trusting environment. Burt (2001) suggested that in a dense or high-closure network, one's noncooperation would be quickly detected and punished severely due to the rapid spread of bad reputation. The attempt of group members to avoid a bad reputation reinforces a strong supporting and trusting environment, and strengthens the group's solidarity and esprit de corps.

We assert that when a coworker quits from a cohesive network, it is more damaging to trust, cohesion, perceived support, and individual social capital compared with when a coworker departs a sparse network. Indeed, when a

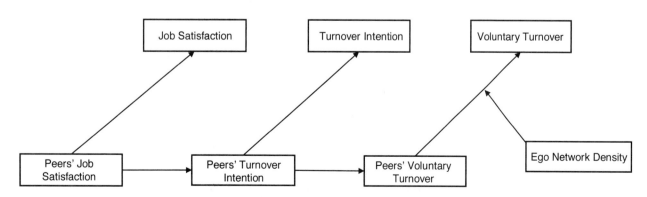

FIGURE 23.6. Social network contagion in the job satisfaction-intention-turnover model.

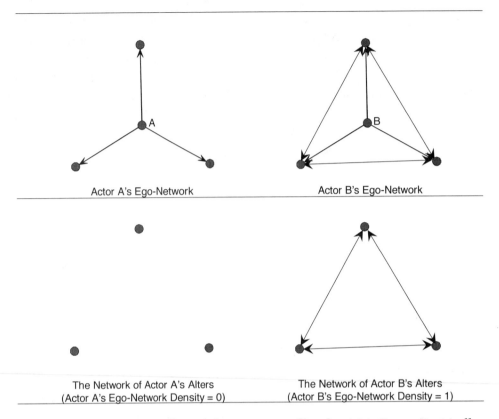

FIGURE 23.7. Ego-networks and their corresponding densities. Egos are typically removed when analyzing ego network properties.

coworker leaves a cohesive or closed network, we contend there is a greater loss of social capital (Coleman, 1988). Indeed, such a loss of network social capital/bonding capital might also be interpreted as a network-based analog for the loss of job embeddedness (Mitchell et al., 2001). Consistent with this interpretation, Morrison (2002) showed that advice ego network density was related to positive features of individual task mastery and role clarity (network density also relates to well-defined performance expectations; Podolny & Baron, 1997), which implies that these valued aspects of work could be lost if coworkers departed a high-closure network, leaving only a sparse network behind.

By drawing on the bonding capital/network closure concept from social capital theory, we may advance the network turnover contagion by proposing contingent network contagion. That is, ego network density moderates the turnover contagion effect, such that the turnover contagion effect is stronger for actors with a dense ego network than for those with a less dense ego network. For the two actors illustrated in Figure 23.7, according to contingent network contagion, peers' voluntary turnover influences Actor B's turnover more strongly than it would influence Actor A's. That is, Actor B is more likely to quit their job than Actor A, given the same number of alters quitting their jobs—because Actor B has suffered a greater loss of social capital (Coleman, 1988).

Analyzing social networks for contagion research. There are at least two distinct analytical strategies to study network contagion effects. One is to utilize spatial lag models such as the network autocorrelation model (Anselin, 1988), the other is to compute network contagion indices, which are then integrated into regression models or structural equation models. We briefly discuss the two strategies next.

Network autocorrelation model. The network autocorrelation model is also known as the spatial lag model or network effects model, which explicitly deals with the nonindependence inherent in social network autocorrelation/contagion effects (Anselin, 1988; Doreian, 1980). This model has the form $Y = \rho WY + X\beta + \varepsilon$, where W is the social network matrix, the parameter ρ is the strength of contagion in the dependent variable Y (i.e., the W network matrix is row-standardized, so that ρ is specified as the relationship between each person's score on Y and the *average* of that person's peers' scores on Y; Leenders, 2002), and the error term ε follows a Gaussian distribution $N(0, \sigma^2 H)$. This model has also been used previously for analyzing contagion effects in organizational and managerial studies (e.g., Ibarra & Andrews, 1993; Mizruchi & Stearns, 2006).

Wang, Newman, and Dipboye (2016) ran three network autocorrelation models with the dependent variables being job satisfaction, intention to quit, and voluntary turnover, respectively; all three models included age and sex as control variables, and they found that ρ estimates were statistically significant for job satisfaction ($\rho_{job\ sat} = .15; p < .05$) and voluntary turnover ($\rho_{voluntary\ turnover} = .23; p < .05$), and not statistically significant for intention to quit ($\rho_{intention\ to\ quit} = .06; p > .05$, n.s.). Thus, Wang, Newman, and Dipboye (2016) demonstrated network job satisfaction contagion and network turnover contagion.

Network contagion indices. According to Leenders (2002) and Wang, Newman, and Dipboye (2016), an ego's network contagion index may be computed by averaging the directly connected alters' attribute scores. For example, Ego A's network job satisfaction contagion is indexed by the mean job satisfaction of the Ego A's alters. Similarly, Ego A's network turnover contagion is indexed by the number of turnovers among the alters divided by Ego A's total number of alters. Analytically, the contagion index is computed by WY, where W is the standardized social network matrix (i.e., each row is divided by the sum of the row), and Y represents contagion attributes (e.g., job satisfaction, turnover). Once the contagion index is calculated, it can be further analyzed with other variables in common statistical models such as regression and structural equation models. For example, Wang, Newman, and Dipboye (2016) computed the network turnover contagion, network job satisfaction contagion, and network turnover intention contagion, and ran SEM models to holistically examine the contagion effects on ego's turnover, job satisfaction, and turnover intentions, respectively. More recently, Wang et al. (2021) combined the network turnover contagion effect and ego network centrality to examine a contingent network contagion, suggesting that network turnover contagion only occurs to egos who reside in a dense (vs. sparse) ego network.

CONCLUSION

This chapter introduces social network analysis—a formal method to study relationships—to the psychology community and highlights in the recent breakthroughs in methods and theories. With the increasing utilization of the R statistical programing language in psychological research, the analytical barrier of SNA has become minimal for many psychologists. In this chapter, we have elaborated on the methodological foundations of social network research, introduced both basic and advanced social network analytical techniques, also showcased applications of SNA in various psychological domains for advancing theoretical research. It is our hope this chapter will help energize more social network research in psychology.

APPENDIX 23.1: R CODE TO VISUALIZE NETWORKS DEMONSTRATED IN FIGURE 23.1

```r
# Load library
library(sna)
library(igraph)

# Input data
edges <- read.csv("KiteEdgeData.csv",header=T)
nodes <- read.csv("KiteNodeData.csv",header=T)

# Build an igraph object
inet <- graph_from_data_frame(d=edges, vertices=nodes, directed=F)

# Specify network layout
layout1 <- layout_with_kk(inet)

# Add network attributes
ages <- V(inet)$Age
colors <- ifelse(V(inet)$Gender=="M", "skyblue", "pink")
deg <- degree(inet, mode="all")*7
weights <- E(inet)$Weight*2

# Figure 23.1a
plot(inet, vertex.frame.color = "white" ,
     edge.arrow.size=.7, edge.width = 1,
     vertex.color = "gray", vertex.size=25, layout=layout1)

# Figure 23.1b: Specifying gender by colors
plot(inet, vertex.frame.color = "white" ,
     edge.arrow.size=.7, edge.width = 1,
     vertex.color = colors, vertex.size=25, layout=layout1)

# Figure 23.1c: Specifying gender and tie strength
plot(inet, vertex.frame.color = "white" ,
     edge.arrow.size=.7, edge.width = weights,
     vertex.color = colors, vertex.size=25, layout=layout1)

# Figure 23.1d: Specifying gender, tie strength, and degree centrality
plot(inet, vertex.frame.color = "white",
     edge.arrow.size=.7, edge.width = weights,
     vertex.color = colors, vertex.size=deg, layout=layout1)

# Figure 23.1e: Specifying gender, tie strength, and age
plot(inet, vertex.frame.color = "white" ,
     edge.arrow.size=.7, edge.width = weights,
     vertex.color = colors, vertex.size=ages, layout=layout1)

# Figure 23.1f: Specifying gender and relation direction
inet <- graph_from_data_frame(d=edges, vertices=nodes, directed=T)
plot(inet, vertex.frame.color = "white" ,
     edge.arrow.size=.7, edge.width = 1,
     vertex.color = colors, vertex.size=25, layout=layout1)
```

APPENDIX 23.2: ILLUSTRATION OF AN ERGM ANALYSIS WITH STATNET IN R

```
# the package ergm belongs to the statnet suite
library(ergm)
library(RSiena)

# For this example, we load the first observation of the s50 data set of
# friendships among 50 high school girls that is part of the RSiena package
# (see below)

# We tell statnet that the data contain a directed network
network <- as.network(s501, directed = TRUE)

# Inspect the network object to see that it was correctly loaded
network

# Run an ERGM model with the basic parameters
# Note: edges is degree distribution, mutual is reciprocity, and
# ttriple is transitive triples

model1 <- ergm(network ~ edges + mutual+ ttriple)

# Retrieve and inspect your result
summary(model1)
```

APPENDIX 23.3: ILLUSTRATION OF A SAOM ANALYSIS WITH RSiena IN R

```
# Load the RSiena package
library(RSiena)

# Check s50 dataset of friendships among 50 highschool girls from RSiena
s501        # The friendship network at T1 is a 50x50 adjacency matrix

# We create a network object that contains the friendship networks of T1
# and T2 and tells RSiena that it consists of 50 actors and 2 waves
friendship <- sienaDependent(array( c(s501, s502), dim = c( 50, 50, 2 )))

# Create a constant covariate of the girls alcohol consumption at T1
alcoholT1 <- coCovar(s50a [,1])

# We create an RSiena object that combines the dependent network object
# and the independent actor covariate
mydata<- sienaDataCreate(friendship, alcoholT1)

# To specify which effects should be included in the evaluation function,
# we first need to create an effects object
myeff <- getEffects(mydata )

# Model specification: outdegree and reciprocity are included by default
# we add two effects to capture triadic closure (transTrip and cycle3)
myeff <- includeEffects(myeff, transTrip, cycle3)

# add a covariate effect, testing if girls who drink more are popular
myeff <- includeEffects(myeff, altX, interaction1 = "alcoholT1")

# Analysis
# First, create an object with the algorithm settings (here the defaults)
myalgorithm <- sienaAlgorithmCreate(projname = 'test')

# Run the SAOM
result1 <- siena07(myalgorithm, data = mydata, effects = myeff)

# Inspect your result
summary(result1)
```

APPENDIX 23.4: ILLUSTRATION OF A COEVOLUTION OF NETWORKS AND BEHAVIOR SAOM WITH RSiena IN R

```
# Instead of only considering T1 of alcohol consumption, we now add the
# First two waves as a behavioral dependent variable to the model
alcoholT1T2 <- sienaDependent (s50a [,1:2], type = "behavior")

# To set up the model, we have to repeat the steps from above
# Create the data file with both two dependent variables
mydata2<- sienaDataCreate(friendship, alcoholT1T2)

# Model specification:
myeff2 <- getEffects(mydata2)
myeff2 <- includeEffects(myeff2, transTrip, cycle3)

# To test for selection, we add the similarity effect for alcohol drinking
myeff <- includeEffects(myeff2, altX, egoX, simX,
          interaction1 = "alcoholT1T2")

# Finally, we add an social influence effect to the model
myeff2 <- includeEffects(myeff2, avSim, name="alcoholT1T2",
          interaction1 = "friendship")

# Run the co-evolution SAOM
result2 <- siena07(myalgorithm, data = mydata2, effects = myeff2)
summary(result2)   #inspect your result
```

References

Agneessens, F. (2021). Dyadic, nodal and group-level approaches to study the antecedents and consequences of networks: Which social network models to use and when? In R. Light & J. Moody (Eds.), *The Oxford handbook of social networks* (pp. 188–218). Oxford University Press.

Agneessens, F., & Labianca, G. (2022). Collecting survey-based social network information in work organizations. *Social Networks, 68*, 31–47. https://doi.org/10.1016/j.socnet.2021.04.003

Ajzen, H., & Fishbein, M. (1980). *Understanding attitudes and predicting social behavior*. Prentice-Hall.

Ajzen, I., & Kruglanski, A. W. (2019). Reasoned action in the service of goal pursuit. *Psychological Review, 126*(5), 774–786. https://doi.org/10.1037/rev0000155

Anselin, L. (1988). *Spatial econometrics: Methods and models*. Kluwer Academic.

Bakker, A. B., & Schaufeli, W. B. (2000). Burnout contagion processes among teachers 1. *Journal of Applied Social Psychology, 30*(11), 2289–2308.

Barsade, S. G. (2002). The ripple effect: Emotional contagion and its influence on group behavior. *Administrative Science Quarterly, 47*(4), 644–675. https://doi.org/10.2307/3094912

Bartunek, J. M., Huang, Z., & Walsh, I. J. (2008). The development of a process model of collective turnover. *Human Relations, 61*(1), 5–38. https://doi.org/10.1177/0018726707085944

Birkett, M., Melville, J., Janulis, P., Phillips, G., II, Contractor, N., & Hogan, B. (2021). Network Canvas: Key decisions in the design of an interviewer assisted network data collection software suite. *Social Networks, 66*, 114–124. https://doi.org/10.1016/j.socnet.2021.02.003

Block, P., Stadtfeld, C., & Snijders, T. A. B. (2019). Forms of dependence: Comparing SAOMs and ERGMs from basic principles. *Sociological Methods & Research, 48*(1), 202–239. https://doi.org/10.1177/0049124116672680

Boda, Z., Néray, B., & Snijders, T. A. B. (2020). The dynamics of interethnic friendships and negative ties in secondary school: The role of peer-perceived ethnicity. *Social Psychology Quarterly, 83*(4), 342–362. https://doi.org/10.1177/0190272520907594

Borgatti, S. P., Everett, M. G., & Freeman, L. C. (1999). *Ucinet for Windows: Software for social network analysis*. Analytic Technologies.

Borgatti, S. P., Everett, M. G., & Johnson, J. C. (2013). *Analyzing social networks*. SAGE.

Borgatti, S. P., Everett, M. G., & Johnson, J. C. (2018). *Analyzing social networks* (2nd ed.). SAGE.

Borgatti, S. P., & Halgin, D. S. (2011). On network theory. *Organization Science*, 22(5), 1168–1181. https://doi.org/10.1287/orsc.1100.0641

Borucki, I. (2017). A visual data collection method: German local parties and associations. *Connections*, 37(1–2), 45–52. https://doi.org/10.21307/connections-2017-003

Brashears, M. E., Hoagland, E., & Quintane, E. (2016). Sex and network recall accuracy. *Social Networks*, 44, 74–84. https://doi.org/10.1016/j.socnet.015.06.002

Brashears, M. E., & Quintane, E. (2015). The microstructures of network recall: How social networks are encoded and represented in human memory. *Social Networks*, 41, 113–126. https://doi.org/10.1016/j.socnet.2014.11.003

Brass, D. J. (1984). Being in the right place: A structural analysis of individual influence in an organization. *Administrative Science Quarterly*, 29(4), 518–539. https://doi.org/10.2307/2392937

Brass, D. J. (2012). A social network perspective on organizational psychology. In S. W. J. Kozlowski (Ed.), *The Oxford handbook of organizational psychology* (Vol. 1, pp. 667–695). Oxford University Press. https://doi.org/10.1093/oxfordhb/9780199928309.013.0021

Brass, D. J., & Borgatti, S. P. (2019). Multilevel thoughts on social networks. In S. E. Humphrey & J. M. LeBreton (Eds.), *The handbook of multilevel theory, measurement, and analysis* (pp. 187–200). American Psychological Association. https://doi.org/10.1037/0000115-009

Brass, D. J., Butterfield, K. D., & Skaggs, B. C. (1998). Relationships and unethical behavior: A social network perspective. *Academy of Management Review*, 23(1), 14–31. https://doi.org/10.5465/amr.1998.192955

Burt, R. S. (1984). Network items and the general social survey. *Social Networks*, 6(4), 293–339. https://doi.org/10.1016/0378-8733(84)90007-8

Burt, R. S. (2001). Structural holes versus network closure as social capital. In N. Lin (Ed.), *Social capital: Theory and research* (pp. 30–56). Aldine de Gruyter.

Burt, R. S. (2005). *Brokerage and closure: An introduction to social capital*. Oxford University Press.

Burt, R. S., & Janicik, G. A. (1996). Social contagion and social structure. In D. Iacobucci (Ed.), *Networks in marketing* (pp. 32–49). SAGE Publications. https://doi.org/10.4135/9781483327723.n4

Burt, R. S., Kilduff, M., & Tasselli, S. (2013). Social network analysis: Foundations and frontiers on advantage. *Annual Review of Psychology*, 64(1), 527–547. https://doi.org/10.1146/annurev-psych-113011-143828

Butts, C. (2008). Social network analysis with sna. *Journal of Statistical Software*, 24(6), 1–51. https://doi.org/10.18637/jss.v024.i06

Byrne, D. E. (1971). *The attraction paradigm*. Academic Press.

Cacioppo, J. T., Fowler, J. H., & Christakis, N. A. (2009). Alone in the crowd: The structure and spread of loneliness in a large social network. *Journal of Personality and Social Psychology*, 97(6), 977–991. https://doi.org/10.1037/a0016076

Casciaro, T., Barsade, S. G., Edmondson, A. C., Gibson, C. B., Krackhardt, D., & Labianca, G. (2015). The integration of psychological and network perspectives in organizational scholarship. *Organization Science*, 26(4), 1162–1176. https://doi.org/10.1287/orsc.2015.0988

Chartrand, T. L., & Bargh, J. A. (1999). The chameleon effect: The perception-behavior link and social interaction. *Journal of Personality and Social Psychology*, 76(6), 893–910. https://doi.org/10.1037/0022-3514.76.6.893

Cheyne, T., Smith, M. A., & Pollet, T. V. (2021). Egocentric network characteristics of persons with Type 1 diabetes and their relationships to perceived social support and well-being. *Health Psychology and Behavioral Medicine*, 9(1), 662–680. https://doi.org/10.1080/21642850.2021.1951272

Christakis, N. A., & Fowler, J. H. (2007). The spread of obesity in a large social network over 32 years. *The New England Journal of Medicine*, 357(4), 370–379. https://doi.org/10.1056/NEJMsa066082

Christakis, N. A., & Fowler, J. H. (2008). The collective dynamics of smoking in a large social network. *The New England Journal of Medicine*, 358(21), 2249–2258. https://doi.org/10.1056/NEJMsa0706154

Coleman, J. S. (1988). Social capital in the creation of human capital. *American Journal of Sociology*, 94, S95–S120. https://doi.org/10.1086/228943

Crossley, N., Bellotti, E., Edwards, G., Everett, M. G., Koskinen, J., & Tranmer, M. (2015). *Social network analysis for ego-nets*. SAGE Publications.

Csardi, G., & Nepusz, T. (2006). The igraph software package for complex network research. *InterJournal: Complex Systems*, 1695. https://igraph.org

Deci, E. L., & Ryan, R. M. (2000). The "what" and "why" of goal pursuits: Human needs and the self-determination of behavior. *Psychological*

Inquiry, 11(4), 227–268. https://doi.org/10.1207/S15327965PLI1104_01

Doreian, P. (1980). Linear models with spatially distributed data: Spatial disturbances or spatial effects? *Sociological Methods & Research, 9*(1), 29–60. https://doi.org/10.1177/004912418000900102

Eddens, K. S., & Fagan, J. M. (2018). Comparing nascent approaches for gathering alter-tie data for egocentric studies. *Social Networks, 55*, 130–141. https://doi.org/10.1016/j.socnet.2018.05.009

Eddens, K. S., Fagan, J. M., & Collins, T. (2017). An interactive, mobile-based tool for personal social network data collection and visualization among a geographically isolated and socio-economically disadvantaged population: Early-stage feasibility study with qualitative user feedback. *JMIR Research Protocols, 6*(6), e124. https://doi.org/10.2196/resprot.6927

Eder, P., & Eisenberger, R. (2008). Perceived organizational support: Reducing the negative influence of coworker withdrawal behavior. *Journal of Management, 34*(1), 55–68. https://doi.org/10.1177/0149206307309259

Ellwardt, L., Labianca, G. J., & Wittek, R. (2012). Who are the objects of positive and negative gossip at work? A social network perspective on workplace gossip. *Social Networks, 34*(2), 193–205. https://doi.org/10.1016/j.socnet.2011.11.003

Feeley, T. H., & Barnett, G. A. (1997). Predicting employee turnover from communication networks. *Human Communication Research, 23*(3), 370–387. https://doi.org/10.1111/j.1468-2958.1997.tb00401.x

Felps, W., Mitchell, T. R., Hekman, D. R., Lee, T. W., Holtom, B. C., & Harman, W. S. (2009). Turnover contagion: How coworkers' job embeddedness and job search behaviors influence quitting. *Academy of Management Journal, 52*(3), 545–561. https://doi.org/10.5465/amj.2009.41331075

Felsher, M., Koku, E., Lankenau, S., Brady, K., Bellamy, S., & Roth, A. M. (2021). Motivations for PrEP-related interpersonal communication among women who inject drugs: A qualitative egocentric network study. *Qualitative Health Research, 31*(1), 86–99. https://doi.org/10.1177/1049732320952740

Festinger, L., Schachter, S., & Back, I. (1950). *Social pressures in informal groups.* Stanford University Press. https://doi.org/10.2307/3707362

Finkel, E. J., & Eastwick, P. W. (2015). Interpersonal attraction: In search of a theoretical Rosetta Stone. In M. Mikulincer, P. R. Shaver, J. A. Simpson, & J. F. Dovidio (Eds.), *APA handbook of personality and social psychology: Vol. 3. Interpersonal relations* (pp. 179–210). American Psychological Association. https://doi.org/10.1037/14344-007

Fishbein, M., & Ajzen, I. (2010). *Predicting and changing behavior: The reasoned action approach.* Psychology Press.

Fitzsimons, G. M., Finkel, E. J., & vanDellen, M. R. (2015). Transactive goal dynamics. *Psychological Review, 122*(4), 648–673. https://doi.org/10.1037/a0039654

Fitzsimons, G. M., & Shah, J. Y. (2008). How goal instrumentality shapes relationship evaluations. *Journal of Personality and Social Psychology, 95*(2), 319–337. https://doi.org/10.1037/0022-3514.95.2.319

Fowler, J. H., & Christakis, N. A. (2008). Dynamic spread of happiness in a large social network: Longitudinal analysis over 20 years in the Framingham Heart Study. *BMJ, 337*. https://doi.org/10.1136/bmj.a2338

Frank, O., & Strauss, D. (1986). Markov graphs. *Journal of the American Statistical Association, 81*(395), 832–842. https://doi.org/10.1080/01621459.1986.10478342

Fujimoto, K., Snijders, T. A. B., & Valente, T. W. (2018). Multivariate dynamics of one-mode and two-mode networks: Explaining similarity in sports participation among friends. *Network Science, 6*(3), 370–395. https://doi.org/10.1017/nws.2018.11

Galaskiewicz, J., & Burt, R. S. (1991). Interorganization contagion in corporate philanthropy. *Administrative Science Quarterly, 36*(1), 88. https://doi.org/10.2307/2393431

Goodreau, S. M., Kitts, J. A., & Morris, M. (2009). Birds of a feather, or friend of a friend? Using exponential random graph models to investigate adolescent social networks. *Demography, 46*(1), 103–125. https://doi.org/10.1353/dem.0.0045

Grosser, T. J., Lopez-Kidwell, V., & Labianca, G. (2010). A social network analysis of positive and negative gossip in organizational life. *Group & Organization Management, 35*(2), 177–212. https://doi.org/10.1177/1059601109360391

Hanneke, S., Fu, W., & Xing, E. P. (2010). Discrete temporal models of social networks. *Electronic Journal of Statistics, 4*, 585–605. https://doi.org/10.1214/09-EJS548

Heinz, J., Laumann, E., Nelson, R., & Salisbury, R. (1993). *The hollow core.* Harvard University Press.

Hooijsma, M., Huitsing, G., Kisfalusi, D., Dijkstra, J. K., Flache, A., & Veenstra, R. (2020). Multidimensional similarity in multiplex networks: Friendships between same- and cross-gender bullies and same- and cross-gender victims. *Network Science, 8*(1), 79–96. https://doi.org/10.1017/nws.2020.1

Hsee, C. K., Hatfield, E., Carlson, J. G., & Chemtob, C. (1990). The effect of power on susceptibility to emotional contagion. *Cognition and Emotion*, *4*(4), 327–340. https://doi.org/10.1080/02699939008408081

Huitsing, G., & Monks, C. P. (2018). Who victimizes whom and who defends whom? A multivariate social network analysis of victimization, aggression, and defending in early childhood. *Aggressive Behavior*, *44*(4), 394–405. https://doi.org/10.1002/ab.21760

Huitsing, G., Snijders, T. A. B., Van Duijn, M. A. J., & Veenstra, R. (2014). Victims, bullies, and their defenders: A longitudinal study of the coevolution of positive and negative networks. *Development and Psychopathology*, *26*(3), 645–659. https://doi.org/10.1017/S0954579414000297

Hunter, D. R. (2007). Curved exponential family models for social networks. *Social Networks*, *29*(2), 216–230. https://doi.org/10.1016/j.socnet.2006.08.005

Hunter, D. R., Goodreau, S. M., & Handcock, M. S. (2008). Goodness of fit of social network models. *Journal of the American Statistical Association*, *103*(481), 248–258. https://doi.org/10.1198/016214507000000446

Hunter, D. R., Handcock, M. S., Butts, C. T., Goodreau, S. M., & Morris, M. (2008). ERGM: A package to fit, simulate, and diagnose exponential-family models for networks. *Journal of Statistical Software*, *24*(3), a54860. https://doi.org/10.18637/jss.v024.i03

Ibarra, H., & Andrews, S. B. (1993). Power, social influence, and sense making: Effects of network centrality and proximity on employee perceptions. *Administrative Science Quarterly*, *38*(2), 277–303. https://doi.org/10.2307/2393414

Joiner, T. E., Jr. (1994). Contagious depression: Existence, specificity to depressed symptoms, and the role of reassurance seeking. *Journal of Personality and Social Psychology*, *67*(2), 287–296. https://doi.org/10.1037/0022-3514.67.2.287

Jugert, P., Leszczensky, L., & Pink, S. (2018). The effects of ethnic minority adolescents' ethnic self-identification on friendship selection. *Journal of Research on Adolescence*, *28*(2), 379–395. https://doi.org/10.1111/jora.12337

Kalish, Y. (2020). Stochastic actor-oriented models for the co-evolution of networks and behavior: An introduction and tutorial. *Organizational Research Methods*, *23*(3), 511–534. https://doi.org/10.1177/1094428118825300

Kalter, F., Kogan, I., & Dollmann, J. (2019). Studying integration from adolescence to early adulthood: Design, content, and research potential of the CILS4EU-DE data. *European Sociological Review*, *35*(2), 280–297. https://doi.org/10.1093/esr/jcy051

Kisfalusi, D., Pál, J., & Boda, Z. (2020). Bullying and victimization among majority and minority students: The role of peers' ethnic perceptions. *Social Networks*, *60*, 48–60. https://doi.org/10.1016/j.socnet.2018.08.006

Kornienko, O., Clemans, K. H., Out, D., & Granger, D. A. (2014). Hormones, behavior, and social network analysis: Exploring associations between cortisol, testosterone, and network structure. *Hormones and Behavior*, *66*(3), 534–544. https://doi.org/10.1016/j.yhbeh.2014.07.009

Koskinen, J., Jones, P., Medeuov, D., Antonyuk, A., Puzyreva, K., & Basov, N. (2020). Analysing networks of networks. *ArXiv Preprint*. https://doi.org/10.48550/arXiv.2008.03692

Koskinen, J., & Snijders, T. A. B. (2020). *Random-effect multilevel stochastic actor-oriented models* [Unpublished manuscript]. University of Melbourne, Australia.

Kossinets, G. (2006). Effects of missing data in social networks. *Social Networks*, *28*(3), 247–268. https://doi.org/10.1016/j.socnet.2005.07.002

Krackhardt, D. (1987). Cognitive social structures. *Social Networks*, *9*(2), 109–134. https://doi.org/10.1016/0378-8733(87)90009-8

Krackhardt, D. (1988). Predicting with networks: Nonparametric multiple regression analysis of dyadic data. *Social Networks*, *10*(4), 359–381. https://doi.org/10.1016/0378-8733(88)90004-4

Krackhardt, D. (1990). Assessing the political landscape: Structure, cognition, and power in organizations. *Administrative Science Quarterly*, *35*(2), 342. https://doi.org/10.2307/2393394

Krackhardt, D., & Kilduff, M. (1999). Whether close or far: Social distance effects on perceived balance in friendship networks. *Journal of Personality and Social Psychology*, *76*(5), 770–782. https://doi.org/10.1037/0022-3514.76.5.770

Krivitsky, P. N., & Handcock, M. S. (2014). A separable model for dynamic networks. *Journal of the Royal Statistical Society. Series B, Statistical Methodology*, *76*(1), 29–46. https://doi.org/10.1111/rssb.12014

Krivitsky, P. N., Handcock, M. S., Hunter, D. R., Butts, C. T., Klumb, C., Goodreau, S. M., & Morris, M. (2020). *statnet: Software tools for the Statistical Modeling of Network Data*. https://statnet.org

Krohn, M. D., Massey, J. L., & Zielinski, M. (1988). Role overlap, network multiplexity, and adolescent deviant behavior. *Social Psychology Quarterly*, *51*(4), 346. https://doi.org/10.2307/2786761

Kruglanski, A. W., Shah, J. Y., Fishbach, A., Friedman, R., Chun, W. Y., & Sleeth-Keppler, D.

(2002). A theory of goal systems. In M. P. Zanna (Ed.), *Advances in experimental social psychology* (Vol. 34, pp. 331–378). Emerald Publishing.

Kung, F. Y. H., & Scholer, A. A. (2021). Moving beyond two goals: An integrative review and framework for the study of multiple goals. *Personality and Social Psychology Review, 25*(2), 130–158. https://doi.org/10.1177/1088868320985810

Labianca, G., & Brass, D. J. (2006). Exploring the social ledger: Negative relationships and negative asymmetry in social networks in organizations. *Academy of Management Review, 31*(3), 596–614. https://doi.org/10.5465/amr.2006.21318920

Laumann, E., Marsden, P., & Prensky, D. (1992). The boundary specification problem in network analysis. In L. C. Freeman, D. R. White, & A. K. Romney (Eds.), *Research methods in social network analysis* (pp. 61–87). Routledge.

Lazega, E., Jourda, M. T., Mounier, L., & Stofer, R. (2008). Catching up with big fish in the big pond? Multi-level network analysis through linked design. *Social Networks, 30*(2), 159–176. https://doi.org/10.1016/j.socnet.2008.02.001

Lee, D. S., Stahl, J. L., & Bayer, J. B. (2020). Social resources as cognitive structures: Thinking about a dense support network increases perceived support. *Social Psychology Quarterly, 83*(4), 405–422. https://doi.org/10.1177/0190272520939506

Lee, T. W., & Mitchell, T. R. (1994). An alternative approach: The unfolding model of voluntary employee turnover. *Academy of Management Review, 19*(1), 51–89. https://doi.org/10.2307/258835

Leenders, R. T. A. J. (2002). Modeling social influence through network autocorrelation: Constructing the weight matrix. *Social Networks, 24*(1), 21–47. https://doi.org/10.1016/S0378-8733(01)00049-1

Leszczensky, L., & Pink, S. (2019). What drives ethnic homophily? A relational approach on how ethnic identification moderates preferences for same-ethnic friends. *American Sociological Review, 84*(3), 394–419. https://doi.org/10.1177/0003122419846849

Leszczensky, L., Stark, T. H., Flache, A., & Munniksma, A. (2016). Disentangling the relation between young immigrants' host country identification and their friendships with natives. *Social Networks, 44*, 179–189. https://doi.org/10.1016/j.socnet.2015.08.001

Levitan, L. C., & Visser, P. S. (2009). Social network composition and attitude strength: Exploring the dynamics within newly formed social networks. *Journal of Experimental Social Psychology, 45*(5), 1057–1067. https://doi.org/10.1016/j.jesp.2009.06.001

Levy, D. A., & Nail, P. R. (1993). Contagion: A theoretical and empirical review and reconceptualization. *Genetic, Social, and General Psychology Monographs, 119*(2), 233–284. https://pubmed.ncbi.nlm.nih.gov/8405969/

Locke, E. A., & Latham, G. P. (2019). The development of goal setting theory: A half century retrospective. *Motivation Science, 5*(2), 93–105. https://doi.org/10.1037/mot0000127

Lomi, A., & Stadtfeld, C. (2014). Social networks and social settings: Developing a coevolutionary view. *KZfSS Kölner Zeitschrift Für Soziologie Und Sozialpsychologie, 66*(S1), 395–415. https://doi.org/10.1007/s11577-014-0271-8

Lorenz, G., Boda, Z., Salikutluk, Z., & Jansen, M. (2020). Social influence or selection? Peer effects on the development of adolescents' educational expectations in Germany. *British Journal of Sociology of Education, 41*(5), 643–669. https://doi.org/10.1080/01425692.2020.1763163

Lospinoso, J., & Snijders, T. A. (2019). Goodness of fit for stochastic actor-oriented models. *Methodological Innovations, 12*(3). https://doi.org/10.1177/2059799119884282

Lusher, D., Koskinen, J., & Robins, G. (2013). *Exponential random graph models for social networks. Theory, methods, and applications.* Cambridge University Press.

Marineau, J. E., Labianca, G., Brass, D. J., Borgatti, S. P., & Vecchi, P. (2018). Individuals' power and their social network accuracy: A situated cognition perspective. *Social Networks, 54*, 145–161. https://doi.org/10.1016/j.socnet.2018.01.006

Marsden, P. V. (2011). Survey methods for network data. In J. Scott & P. J. Carrington (Eds.), *The SAGE handbook of social network analysis* (pp. 370–388). SAGE.

Mauno, S., De Cuyper, N., Tolvanen, A., Kinnunen, U., & Mäkikangas, A. (2014). Occupational well-being as a mediator between job insecurity and turnover intention: Findings at the individual and work department levels. *European Journal of Work and Organizational Psychology, 23*(3), 381–393. https://doi.org/10.1080/1359432X.2012.752896

McCarty, C., & Govindaramanujam, S. (2005). Modified elicitation of personal networks using dynamic visualization. *Connections, 26*(2), 9–17.

McCarty, C., Lubbers, M. J., Vacca, R., & Molina, J. L. (2019). *Conducting personal network research: A practical guide.* Guilford Press.

McMillan, C., Felmlee, D., & Osgood, D. W. (2018). Peer influence, friend selection, and gender: How network processes shape adolescent smoking, drinking, and delinquency. *Social Networks, 55*, 86–96. https://doi.org/10.1016/j.socnet.2018.05.008

McPherson, M., Smith-Lovin, L., & Cook, J. M. (2001). Birds of a feather: Homophily in social networks. *Annual Review of Sociology, 27*(1), 415–444. https://doi.org/10.1146/annurev.soc.27.1.415

Mehra, A., Kilduff, M., & Brass, D. J. (2001). The social networks of high and low self-monitors: Implications for workplace performance. *Administrative Science Quarterly, 46*(1), 121–146. https://doi.org/10.2307/2667127

Mercken, L., Snijders, T. A. B., Steglich, C. E. G., Vartiainen, E., & De Vries, H. (2010). Dynamics of adolescent friendship networks and smoking behavior. *Social Networks, 32*(1), 72–81. https://doi.org/10.1016/j.socnet.2009.02.005

Mitchell, T. R., Holtom, B. C., Lee, T. W., Sablynski, C. J., & Erez, M. (2001). Why people stay: Using job embeddedness to predict voluntary turnover. *Academy of Management Journal, 44*(6), 1102–1121.

Mitchell, T. R., & Lee, T. W. (2001). The unfolding model of voluntary turnover and job embeddedness: Foundations for a comprehensive theory of attachment. *Research in Organizational Behavior, 23*, 189–246. https://doi.org/10.1016/S0191-3085(01)23006-8

Mizruchi, M. S., & Stearns, L. B. (2006). The conditional nature of embeddedness: A study of borrowing by large U.S. firms, 1973–1994. *American Sociological Review, 71*(2), 310–333. https://doi.org/10.1177/000312240607100207

Morrison, E. W. (2002). Newcomers' relationships: The role of social network ties during socialization. *Academy of Management Journal, 45*(6), 1149–1160. https://doi.org/10.5465/3069430

O'Connor, K. M., & Gladstone, E. (2015). How social exclusion distorts social network perceptions. *Social Networks, 40*, 123–128. https://doi.org/10.1016/j.socnet.2014.09.002

Oh, H., & Kilduff, M. (2008). The ripple effect of personality on social structure: Self-monitoring origins of network brokerage. *Journal of Applied Psychology, 93*(5), 1155–1164. https://doi.org/10.1037/0021-9010.93.5.1155

Orehek, E., & Forest, A. L. (2016). When people serve as means to goals: Implications of a motivational account of close relationships. *Current Directions in Psychological Science, 25*(2), 79–84. https://doi.org/10.1177/0963721415623536

Pastor, J.-C., Meindl, J. R., & Mayo, M. C. (2002). A networks effects model of charisma attributions. *Academy of Management Journal, 45*(2), 410–420.

Patterson, M. S., Prochnow, T., Nelon, J. L., Spadine, M. N., Brown, S. E., & Lanning, B. A. (2020). Egocentric network composition and structure relative to violence victimization among a sample of college students. *Journal of American College Health*, 1–9. Advance online publication. https://doi.org/10.1080/07448481.2020.1841777

Pearcy, R., Waldron, D., O'Boyle, C., & MacDonagh, R. (2008). Proxy assessment of quality of life in patients with prostate cancer: How accurate are partners and urologists? *Journal of the Royal Society of Medicine, 101*(3), 133–138. https://doi.org/10.1258/jrsm.2008.081002

Perry, B., Pescosolido, B., & Borgatti, S. (2018). *Egocentric network analysis: Foundations, methods, and models.* Cambridge University Press. https://doi.org/10.1017/9781316443255

Perry, B. L., & Pescosolido, B. A. (2010). Functional specificity in discussion networks: The influence of general and problem-specific networks on health outcomes. *Social Networks, 32*(4), 345–357. https://doi.org/10.1016/j.socnet.2010.06.005

Podolny, J. M., & Baron, J. N. (1997). Resources and relationships: Social networks and mobility in the workplace. *American Sociological Review, 62*(5), 673. https://doi.org/10.2307/2657354

Porter, C. M., Woo, S. E., Allen, D. G., & Keith, M. G. (2019). How do instrumental and expressive network positions relate to turnover? A meta-analytic investigation. *Journal of Applied Psychology, 104*(4), 511–536. https://doi.org/10.1037/apl0000351

Porter, L. W., & Steers, R. M. (1973). Organizational, work, and personal factors in employee turnover and absenteeism. *Psychological Bulletin, 80*(2), 151–176. https://doi.org/10.1037/h0034829

Putnam, R. D. (2000). *Bowling alone: The collapse and revival of American community.* Simon & Schuster.

Raab, J., & Kenis, P. (2009). Heading toward a society of networks: Empirical developments and theoretical challenges. *Journal of Management Inquiry, 18*(3), 198–210. https://doi.org/10.1177/1056492609337493

Raabe, I. J., Boda, Z., & Stadtfeld, C. (2019). The social pipeline: How friend influence and peer exposure widen the STEM gender gap. *Sociology of Education, 92*(2), 105–123. https://doi.org/10.1177/0038040718824095

Rambaran, J. A., Dijkstra, J. K., & Veenstra, R. (2020). Bullying as a group process in childhood: A longitudinal social network analysis. *Child Development, 91*(4), 1336–1352. https://doi.org/10.1111/cdev.13298

Rapp, C., Ingold, K., & Freitag, M. (2019). Personalized networks? How the Big Five personality traits influence the structure of egocentric networks. *Social Science Research*, 77, 148–160. https://doi.org/10.1016/j.ssresearch.2018.09.001

R Core Team. (2021). *R: A language and environment for statistical computing.* R Foundation for Statistical Computing. https://www.R-project.org

Reins, L. M., Arslan, R. C., & Gerlach, T. M. (2021). Assessing ego-centered social networks in formr: A tutorial. *Advances in Methods and Practices in Psychological Science*, 4(1). https://doi.org/10.1177/2515245920985467

Repke, L., & Benet-Martínez, V. (2018). The (diverse) company you keep: Content and structure of immigrants' social networks as a window into intercultural relations in Catalonia. *Journal of Cross-Cultural Psychology*, 49(6), 924–944. https://doi.org/10.1177/0022022117733475

Ripley, R. M., Snijders, T. A. B., Boda, Z., Vörös, A., & Preciado, P. (2022, June 1). *Manual for RSiena (Version 1.3.11).* University of Oxford Department of Statistics (Nuffield College); University of Groningen Department of Sociology. https://www.stats.ox.ac.uk/~snijders/siena/RSiena_Manual.pdf

Robins, G., Pattison, P., Kalish, Y., & Lusher, D. (2007). An introduction to exponential random graph (p^*) models for social networks. *Social Networks*, 29(2), 173–191. https://doi.org/10.1016/j.socnet.2006.08.002

Salancik, G. R., & Pfeffer, J. (1978). A social information processing approach to job attitudes and task design. *Administrative Science Quarterly*, 23(2), 224–253. https://doi.org/10.2307/2392563

Selden, M., & Goodie, A. S. (2018). Review of the effects of Five Factor Model personality traits on network structures and perceptions of structure. *Social Networks*, 52, 81–99. https://doi.org/10.1016/j.socnet.2017.05.007

Shea, C., & Fitzsimons, G. M. (2016). Personal goal pursuit as an antecedent to social network structure. *Organizational Behavior and Human Decision Processes*, 137, 45–57. https://doi.org/10.1016/j.obhdp.2016.07.002

Shea, C. T., Menon, T., Smith, E. B., & Ennich, K. (2015). The affective antecedents of cognitive social network activation. *Social Networks*, 43, 91–99. https://doi.org/10.1016/j.socnet.2015.01.003

Sijtsema, J. J., & Lindenberg, S. M. (2018). Peer influence in the development of adolescent antisocial behavior: Advances from dynamic social network studies. *Developmental Review*, 50, 140–154. https://doi.org/10.1016/j.dr.2018.08.002

Simpson, B., Markovsky, B., & Steketee, M. (2011). Power and the perception of social networks. *Social Networks*, 33(2), 166–171. https://doi.org/10.1016/j.socnet.2010.10.007

Skvoretz, J., & Agneessens, F. (2007). Reciprocity, multiplexity, and exchange: Measures. *Quality & Quantity: International Journal of Methodology*, 41(3), 341–357. https://doi.org/10.1007/s11135-006-9005-y

Smith, E. B., Brands, R. A., Brashears, M. E., & Kleinbaum, A. M. (2020). Social networks and cognition. *Annual Review of Sociology*, 46(1), 159–174. https://doi.org/10.1146/annurev-soc-121919-054736

Snijders, T. A. B. (2001). The statistical evaluation of social network dynamics. *Sociological Methodology*, 31(1), 361–395. https://doi.org/10.1111/0081-1750.00099

Snijders, T. A. B. (2016). The multiple flavours of multilevel issues for networks. In E. Lazega & T. A. B. Snijders (Eds.), *Multilevel network analysis for the social sciences: Theory, methods, and applications* (pp. 15–46). Springer. https://doi.org/10.1007/978-3-319-24520-1_2

Snijders, T. A. B. (2017). Stochastic actor-oriented models for network dynamics. *Annual Review of Statistics and Its Application*, 4(1), 343–363. https://doi.org/10.1146/annurev-statistics-060116-054035

Snijders, T. A. B., & Koskinen, J. (2013). Longitudinal models. In D. Lusher, J. Koskinen, & G. L. Robins (Eds.), *Exponential random graph models for social networks: Theories, methods and applications* (pp. 130–140). Cambridge University Press.

Snijders, T. A. B., Lomi, A., & Torló, V. J. (2013). A model for the multiplex dynamics of two-mode and one-mode networks, with an application to employment preference, friendship, and advice. *Social Networks*, 35(2), 265–276. https://doi.org/10.1016/j.socnet.2012.05.005

Snijders, T. A. B., Van de Bunt, G. G., & Steglich, C. E. G. (2010). Introduction to stochastic actor-based models for network dynamics. *Social Networks*, 32(1), 44–60. https://doi.org/10.1016/j.socnet.2009.02.004

Sohn, C., Christopoulos, D., & Koskinen, J. (2020). Borders moderating distance: A social network analysis of spatial effects on policy interaction. *Geographical Analysis*, 52(3), 428–451. https://doi.org/10.1111/gean.12218

Stark, T. H. (2015). Understanding the selection bias: Social network processes and the effect of prejudice on the avoidance of outgroup friends. *Social Psychology Quarterly*, 78(2), 127–150. https://doi.org/10.1177/0190272514565252

Stark, T. H. (2018). Collecting Social Network Data. In D. L. Vannette & J. A. Krosnick (Eds.), *The Palgrave handbook of survey research* (pp. 241–254). Palgrave Macmillan. https://doi.org/10.1007/978-3-319-54395-6_31

Stark, T. H., & Flache, A. (2012). The double edge of common interest: Ethnic segregation as an unintended byproduct of opinion homophily. *Sociology of Education*, 85(2), 179–199. https://doi.org/10.1177/0038040711427314

Stark, T. H., & Krosnick, J. A. (2017). GENSI: A new graphical tool to collect ego-centered network data. *Social Networks*, 48, 36–45. https://doi.org/10.1016/j.socnet.2016.07.007

Stark, T. H., Leszczensky, L., & Pink, S. (2017). Are there differences in ethnic majority and minority adolescents' friendships preferences and social influence with regard to their academic achievement? *Zeitschrift für Erziehungswissenschaft*, 20(3), 475–498. https://doi.org/10.1007/s11618-017-0766-y

Stark, T. H., Rambaran, J., & McFarland, D. (2020). The meeting of minds: Forging social and intellectual networks within universities. *Sociological Science*, 7, 433–464. https://doi.org/10.15195/v7.a18

Stark, T. H., & Stocké, V. (2021). Predicting data quality of proxy reports in egocentric network studies. *Social Networks*, 66, 38–49. https://doi.org/10.1016/j.socnet.2021.01.007

Steglich, C. E. G., Snijders, T. A. B., & Pearson, M. (2010). Dynamic networks and behavior: Separating selection from influence. *Sociological Methodology*, 40(1), 329–393. https://doi.org/10.1111/j.1467-9531.2010.01225.x

Stulp, G. (2021). Collecting large personal networks in a representative sample of Dutch women. *Social Networks*, 64, 63–71. https://doi.org/10.1016/j.socnet.2020.07.012

Tett, R. P., & Meyer, J. P. (1993). Job satisfaction, organizational commitment, turnover intention, and turnover: Path analyses based on meta-analytic findings. *Personnel Psychology*, 46(2), 259–293. https://doi.org/10.1111/j.1744-6570.1993.tb00874.x

Tobler, W. R. (1970). A computer movie simulating urban growth in the Detroit region. *Economic Geography*, 46, 234–240. https://doi.org/10.2307/143141

Tubaro, P., Casilli, A. A., & Mounier, L. (2014). Eliciting personal network data in web surveys through participant-generated sociograms. *Field Methods*, 26(2), 107–125. https://doi.org/10.1177/1525822X13491861

Vacca, R. (2018). Multilevel models for personal networks: Methods and applications. *Statistica Applicata—Italian Journal of Applied Statistics*, 30(1), 59–97. https://doi.org/10.26398/IJAS.0030-003

Vardaman, J. M., Taylor, S. G., Allen, D. G., Gondo, M. B., & Amis, J. M. (2015). Translating intentions to behavior: The interaction of network structure and behavioral intentions in understanding employee turnover. *Organization Science*, 26(4), 1177–1191. https://doi.org/10.1287/orsc.2015.0982

Wang, P., Robins, G., Pattison, P., & Koskinen, J. (2009). *PNet: Program for the simulation and estimation of exponential random graph models*. Melbourne School of Psychological Sciences, The University of Melbourne. https://www.melnet.org.au/pnet

Wang, P., Robins, G., Pattison, P., & Lazega, E. (2013). Exponential random graph models for multilevel networks. *Social Networks*, 35(1), 96–115. https://doi.org/10.1016/j.socnet.2013.01.004

Wang, P., Robins, G., Pattison, P., & Lazega, E. (2016). Social selection models for multilevel networks. *Social Networks*, 44, 346–362. https://doi.org/10.1016/j.socnet.2014.12.003

Wang, P., Robins, G. L., & Matous, P. (2016). Multilevel network analysis using ERGM and its extension. In E. Lazega & T. A. B. Snijders (Eds.), *Multilevel network analysis for the social sciences: Theory, methods and applications* (p. 125). Springer. https://doi.org/10.1007/978-3-319-24520-1_6

Wang, W., Newman, D. A., & Dipboye, R. L. (2016). Social network contagion in the job satisfaction-intention-turnover model. *Academy of Management Proceedings*, 2016(1), 17930. https://doi.org/10.5465/ambpp.2016.82

Wang, W., Newman, D. A., Hom, P. W., Dipboye, R. L., & Zheng, X.-M. (2021). *Breaking up the band: Turnover network contagion* [Unpublished manuscript].

Westaby, J. D. (2012). *Dynamic network theory: How social networks influence goal pursuit*. American Psychological Association. https://doi.org/10.1037/13490-000

Westaby, J. D. (2020). Modeling massive social network problem solving via network goal analysis vs. social network analysis [abstract]. *Academy of Management Proceedings*, 2020(1). https://doi.org/10.5465/AMBPP.2020.14393abstract

Westaby, J. D., & Parr, A. K. (2020). Network goal analysis of social and organizational systems: Testing dynamic network theory in complex social networks. *The Journal of Applied Behavioral Science*, 56(1), 107–129. https://doi.org/10.1177/0021886319881496

Westaby, J. D., Pfaff, D. L., & Redding, N. (2014). Psychology and social networks: A dynamic network theory perspective. *American Psychologist*, *69*(3), 269–284. https://doi.org/10.1037/a0036106

Westaby, J. D., & Redding, N. (2014). Social networks, social media, and conflict resolution. In P. T. Coleman, M. Deutsch, & E. C. Marcus (Eds.), *The handbook of conflict resolution: Theory and practice* (3rd ed., pp. 998–1022). Jossey-Bass.

Westaby, J. D., & Shon, D. (2017). Simulating the social networks in human goal striving. In R. R. Vallacher, S. J. Read, & A. Nowak (Eds.), *Computational models in social psychology* (pp. 231–257). Psychology Press. https://doi.org/10.4324/9781315173726-11

Westaby, J. D., Woods, N., & Pfaff, D. L. (2016). Extending dynamic network theory to group and social interaction analysis: Uncovering key behavioral elements, cycles, and emergent states. *Organizational Psychology Review*, *6*(1), 34–62. https://doi.org/10.1177/2041386614551319

Wölfer, R., Jaspers, E., Blaylock, D., Wigoder, C., Hughes, J., & Hewstone, M. (2017). Studying positive and negative direct and extended contact: Complementing self-reports with social network analysis. *Personality and Social Psychology Bulletin*, *43*(11), 1566–1581. https://doi.org/10.1177/0146167217719732

Wölfer, R., Schmid, K., Hewstone, M., & van Zalk, M. (2016). Developmental dynamics of intergroup contact and intergroup attitudes: Long-term effects in adolescence and early adulthood. *Child Development*, *87*(5), 1466–1478. https://doi.org/10.1111/cdev.12598

Zaheer, A., Gözübüyük, R., & Milanov, H. (2010). It's the connections: The network perspective in interorganizational research. *The Academy of Management Perspectives*, *24*(1), 62–77. https://doi.org/10.5465/amp.24.1.62

Zhang, S., de la Haye, K., Ji, M., & An, R. (2018). Applications of social network analysis to obesity: A systematic review. *Obesity Reviews*, *19*(7), 976–988. https://doi.org/10.1111/obr.12684

Zhang, X., Pomerantz, E. M., Qin, L., Logis, H., Ryan, A. M., & Wang, M. (2019). Early adolescent social status and academic engagement: Selection and influence processes in the United States and China. *Journal of Educational Psychology*, *111*(7), 1300–1316. https://doi.org/10.1037/edu0000333

Zingora, T., Stark, T. H., & Flache, A. (2020). Who is most influential? Adolescents' intergroup attitudes and peer influence within a social network. *Group Processes & Intergroup Relations*, *23*(5), 684–709. https://doi.org/10.1177/1368430219869460

Chapter 24

META-ANALYSIS

Jeffrey C. Valentine, Therese D. Pigott, and Joseph Morris

Imagine that you read about a recent study in your favorite media outlet. The study assesses the effectiveness of a psychosocial intervention designed to increase participation rates for a preventive screening procedure and claims to have found a statistically significant and positive increase in screenings after exposure to the intervention. A friend administers a program that provides the screening procedure and asks your advice about whether she should try the intervention. Many might be tempted to point to the study that found the statistically significant and positive benefit and say "yes." However, the study that appeared in the media is unlikely to be the only study ever conducted examining the effectiveness of the intervention, and when collected together, the studies examining the intervention are unlikely to paint a clear picture of the intervention's effectiveness. These are the primary problems that are addressed by meta-analysis. In the sections that follow, we introduce systematic reviewing and meta-analysis, describe what effect sizes are and how they are used in meta-analysis, and then provide an overview of many of the main decision points in a meta-analysis. We close this chapter with a brief discussion of some extensions to meta-analysis.

SYSTEMATIC REVIEWING AND META-ANALYSIS

What Is a Systematic Review?

On reflection, it seems obvious that if there are multiple studies addressing a research question of interest—for example, the effectiveness of an intervention, or the direction and strength of a relationship, or what it is like to live with some physical or mental condition—then all of the relevant studies ought to be considered when arriving at a conclusion. It does not make sense to use arbitrary decision rules to limit studies for review, such as relying on the most recent study, or the studies that appear in the peer-reviewed academic literature, or the most famous study. That all relevant studies ought to be located and considered is the primary principle underlying systematic reviews. The goal of a systematic review is to limit bias in the identification, evaluation, and synthesis of a body of relevant studies that address a specific research question. In support of this goal, systematic reviewers aim to use explicit, reproducible methods to identify, extract information from, and analyze studies. Introductions to systematic reviewing can be found in Cooper (2017), Lipsey and Wilson (2001), and Littell et al. (2008).

Many systematic reviews are conducted—and certainly, almost all should be conducted—using a publicly available protocol that specifies, in as much detail as possible and before actually doing the work, the methods that will be used when conducting the systematic review. For example, a good protocol will operationally define the literature search procedures, including the exact keywords that will be used, the databases that will be searched, and the individuals and organizations that will be contacted when looking for potentially relevant unpublished studies; doing so increases both transparency and reproducibility. The main benefit of a protocol is that it helps protect the consumers of systematic reviews, and the systematic reviewers themselves, from methodological decisions that mainly serve to advance the interests of the systematic reviewers, for example, by dredging the data and reporting only statistically significant relationships (Valentine & Konstantopoulos, 2016). An additional benefit of a protocol is that it forces systematic reviewers to think deeply, before data collection, about important aspects of the review. For example, it is likely that interventions will be implemented at least slightly differently across studies. Some might last longer (say five sessions) while others might be shorter (say, one session). Or some might sample nurses while others might sample physicians. As a result, decisions need to be made regarding boundary conditions—that is, what characteristics an intervention must have (or alternatively, not have) to be included in the review. Usually, addressing these boundary questions is among the more interesting and intellectually rewarding aspects of doing a systematic review in part because usually there are no simple answers to these questions. It should be clear that deep substantive expertise is needed for the systematic review team to reach defensible decisions regarding boundary criteria. Consider the case of studies that are aimed at nurses and doctors. The systematic reviewers need to be able to make a judgment about whether the intervention's effects are likely to differ across these populations, or if they are expected to be similar enough that they can be combined.

We note here—and reinforce later—that the number of studies that are ultimately expected to be included in the review is an important additional consideration. If the expected number of studies is large, then it often makes more sense to be inclusive if one is unsure about the boundary conditions. Inclusivity is defensible in this case because a large number of studies will allow the reviewers to conduct moderator, subgroup, or sensitivity analyses, and perhaps to control for study characteristics in the analysis. If the expected number of studies is small, then there will be few or no such analysis opportunities, making inclusion decisions much more consequential.

WHAT IS A META-ANALYSIS?

Whereas the methods of systematic reviewing address how studies are identified and appraised for potential inclusion in a literature synthesis, the methods of meta-analysis address how the information in the identified studies is integrated and summarized. In contrast to the methods for synthesizing study results that many scholars would be tempted to use, meta-analysis is more transparent and reproducible and has generally better inferential properties. Comparing meta-analysis to vote counting is a good way to illustrate these benefits. Vote counting usually involves tallying the statistical significance decisions across studies. The category with the most votes wins. While this is an intuitively appealing, transparent, reproducible strategy that is relatively easy to implement, it has serious limitations. Among these are that it counts the wrong thing (statistical significance decisions) and that it only addresses the question of whether a relationship exists, not whether the relationship is strong enough to be important. Even more concerning, Hedges and Olkin (1985) demonstrated that if statistical power in the underlying studies is not high—a common situation in the medical and social sciences—then vote counting actually has less statistical power as the number of studies increases.

Effect Sizes

In contrast, meta-analysis involves combining effect sizes. Effect sizes are statistics that describe the magnitude of the relationships observed in the studies. Questions of magnitude are extremely important. One cannot do a benefit/cost analysis of an intervention's effect without an effect size (the benefit), for example, and importantly, statistical significance itself tells us nothing about whether the effect size is trivial or meaningful. Like all statistics, effect sizes have variances associated with them. Most meta-analyses involve weighting effect sizes by the inverse of their variances and, as we describe later, effect size variances are closely related to sample size (effect sizes drawn from larger samples will tend to have smaller variances). Because effect size variances are closely related to sample size, inverse variance weighting gives proportionally more weight to larger studies. Hence, meta-analysis involves computing a weighted average effect size from studies that address the same research question.

There are three basic types, or families, of effect sizes that are used in most meta-analyses. These are the mean difference, correlation, and odds ratio effect sizes. The choice of effect size metric is usually governed by issues related to the nature of the research question and the nature of the dependent variable, but in reality, all of the common effect sizes and effect size variances can be transformed from one version to another (see Chapter 6, this volume, for a description of how to do this and the conditions under which it is sensible to do so). Starting with the mean difference family, we provide computational details for computing each effect size and effect size variance commonly used in meta-analysis.

The Mean Difference Family

One way to analyze data from a two-group experiment with a continuous dependent variable is an independent groups t test. This t test is closely related to the mean difference family of effect sizes and as a result, a mean difference effect size is often used to analyze the results of experiments when the dependent variable is measured continuously. There are types of effect sizes in the mean difference family, one common the other uncommon. The mean difference effect size that is most common is the standardized mean difference, sometimes known as Cohen's d. Using sample notation, this effect size can be defined as

$$d = \frac{\bar{Y}_1 - \bar{Y}_2}{s_p}, \quad (24.1)$$

where $\bar{Y}_1$ and $\bar{Y}_2$ are the means for Group 1 and Group 2. Note that the numerator of the standardized mean difference is identical to the numerator for an independent groups t test. The denominator, s_p, is the pooled standard deviation. When $n_1 = n_2$, the pooled standard deviation is just the square root of the mean of the two variances,

$$s_p = \sqrt{\frac{s_1^2 + s_2^2}{2}}, \quad (24.2)$$

and when groups are not equal in size, the pooled standard deviation is the square root of the weighted variance for Group 1 and the weighted variance for Group 2,

$$s_p = \sqrt{\frac{(n_1-1)s_1^2 + (n_2-1)s_2^2}{(n_1-1)+(n_2-1)}}. \quad (24.3)$$

Thus, the standardized mean difference expresses the difference between two group means (the numerator) in terms of their common (pooled) standard deviation (the denominator). It is equivalent to the difference between means that would have been observed if the data had first been standardized using the pooled standard deviation.

The standardized mean difference effect size is known to be biased in small samples (Hedges, 1981). This bias is quite strong at very small sample sizes but decreases rapidly as sample size increases. To illustrate this point, if $n_1 = n_2 = 3$, then d overstates the population effect size by 20%, but if $n_1 = n_2 = 30$, then d overstates the population effect size by less than 3%, and if $n_1 = n_2 = 300$, then d overstates the population effect size by less than 0.25%. Due to this bias, it is common to apply a correction to the effect size and its variance; the resulting effect size is often referred to as Hedges' g,

$$g = \left(1 - \frac{3}{4df - 1}\right)d, \quad (24.4)$$

where d is the standardized mean difference effect size and df refers to the degrees of freedom used to estimate the pooled standard deviation (i.e., $n_1 + n_2 - 2$). The variance of d is defined as

$$var_d = \frac{n_1 + n_2}{n_1 n_2} + \frac{d^2}{2(n_1 + n_2)}, \quad (24.5)$$

and the variance of g is defined as

$$var_g = var_d \times \left(1 - \frac{3}{4df - 1}\right). \quad (24.6)$$

The standardized mean difference effect size is so common because it addresses a common problem, which is how to express study results when the dependent variable is measured on different scales in different studies. In a collection of studies assessing the effectiveness of a treatment for depression, for example, it is likely that different measures of depression symptomatology will be used. Because they are scaled differently, 1 point on one scale does not mean the same thing as 1 point on another scale, and therefore the means cannot be compared directly across studies. This is exactly why the standardized mean difference effect size is so handy. At the same time, few researchers and consumers of research have a good feel for how to interpret standardized effect sizes (see Valentine et al., 2019, for suggestions), so there is a cost associated with using these effect sizes.

Because of this cost, it is advisable to use the unstandardized mean difference effect size if all of the studies that will be meta-analyzed use either the same outcome measure, for example the same depression inventory, or use measures that are scaled the same way. The unstandardized mean difference effect size can be defined as

$$D = \bar{Y}_1 - \bar{Y}_2, \quad (24.7)$$

which is the numerator from the standardized mean difference effect size. The variance of D is defined as

$$var_D = \frac{n_1 + n_2}{n_1 n_2} s_p^2 \quad (24.8)$$

with all terms defined as above. Assume that the data shown in Table 24.1 were obtained from a study. If all studies to be meta-analyzed used the same scale, or measures that were scaled in the same way, we could use the unstandardized mean difference effect size, which here would be computed as

$$D = \bar{Y}_1 - \bar{Y}_2 = 12 - 10 = 2. \quad (24.9)$$

Recall that when sample sizes are equal, the pooled variance is just the average of the group variances, so for these data, the pooled variance is 16,

$$s_p^2 = \frac{s_1^2 + s_2^2}{2} = \frac{4^2 + 4^2}{2} = \frac{32}{2} = 16, \quad (24.10)$$

and, therefore, the pooled standard deviation is 4 (the square root of 16). The variance of the unstandardized mean difference effect size would then be

$$var_D = \frac{n_1 + n_2}{n_1 n_2} s_p^2 = \frac{20 + 20}{20 \times 20} 16 = \frac{40}{400} 16$$

$$= .1(16) = 1.6. \quad (24.11)$$

TABLE 24.1

Data Illustrating the Mean Difference Family of Effect Sizes

Group	Mean	Standard deviation	Sample size
1	12	4	20
2	10	4	20

D (+2.0) and its variance (1.60) would then be used in a meta-analysis to represent this study.

If multiple scales were used in the studies that will be meta-analyzed, we would use the standardized mean difference effect size. Recall that we have already computed the pooled standard deviation (which was 4.0). Therefore, the standardized mean difference effect size would be computed as

$$d = \frac{\bar{Y}_1 - \bar{Y}_2}{s_p} = \frac{12-10}{4} = +0.50. \quad (24.12)$$

Hedges' g is computed as

$$g = \left(1 - \frac{3}{4df-1}\right)d = \left(1 - \frac{3}{(4\times 38-1)}\right).50$$

$$= \left(1 - \frac{3}{151}\right).50 = .98(.50) = 0.49. \quad (24.13)$$

The variance of d would be

$$var_d = \frac{n_1+n_2}{n_1 n_2} + \frac{d^2}{2(n_1+n_2)} = \frac{20+20}{20\times 20} + \frac{.50^2}{2(20+20)}$$

$$= .1 + .003125 = .10313, \quad (24.14)$$

and, therefore, the variance of g would be

$$var_g = var_d \times \left(1 - \frac{3}{4df-1}\right) = .1031\times .98 = .1011.$$

$$(24.15)$$

Hedges' g (+0.49) and its variance (.1011) would represent this study in a meta-analysis.

The Correlation Family

As an effect size for meta-analysis, correlation coefficients have several attractive properties. Primary among these is that they are familiar to a broad range of researchers and research consumers. Because many people believe they understand what correlation coefficients mean, this lowers one barrier to communicating the results of a synthesis. An additional benefit is that correlation coefficients can be used in a variety of research situations. Because of the way that most people learn about correlation coefficients, most researchers think about them in the context of a sample assessed with two continuous measures, for example, a measure of depressive symptomatology and a measure of anxiety, or a measure of job satisfaction and a measure of the extent to which a manager is viewed as promoting autonomy. However, correlation coefficients can also be used to assess the effects of an experiment (when used this way, it is referred to as the point-biserial correlation) and can be used with two binary measures as well (when used this way, it is referred to as Φ, or phi). Regardless of which version is used, the math used to calculate the correlation is the same. For example, the correlation coefficient can be computed from z-scores:

$$r = \frac{\sum z_x z_y}{n} \quad (24.16)$$

where z_x and z_y are the z-scores for individual i on measures x and y, and n is the sample size. The variance of r is not constant across all values so by convention most meta-analyses involving correlations use Fisher's z for analysis, which is a variance stabilizing transformation of the correlation coefficient and is computed as

$$z_r = .5 ln \frac{1+r}{1-r}, \quad (24.17)$$

where ln is the natural log of the righthand term in the formula. Most spreadsheet applications have built-in functionality to compute this value (often, `=fisher(r)` will return the value of Fisher's z for value r). For example, assume data from an experiment are analyzed using a point-biserial correlation. A total of 40 participants were equally allocated to one of two groups, and the resulting correlation was +0.237. Fisher's z transformation would yield a value of +0.243, and the variance of Fisher's z is approximately

$$var_{Fisher's\ z} = \frac{1}{n-3} = \frac{1}{40-3} = .0270. \quad (24.18)$$

The formula for the (approximate) variance of Fisher's z is quite simple and reinforces the relationship between the sample size and the effect size variance. Fisher's z (+0.243) and its variance (.0270) would be used in a meta-analysis to represent this study.

The Odds Ratio Family

In the previous section, we mentioned that the Φ correlation coefficient can be used to analyze two binary variables, for example, group status (e.g., treatment vs. control) and graduation status (e.g., graduated vs. did not graduate). The use of Φ is relatively uncommon. More common in this case is using the odds ratio. Odds ratios have the benefit of being well-named (the odds ratio is, literally, a ratio of odds). There are two main downsides to odds ratios. One is that most people do not think in terms of odds, so the metric is not intuitively appealing. Another is that, like the correlation coefficient, the odds ratio has a complex distribution. Like the correlation coefficient, by convention most meta-analyses involving the odds ratio are actually done on a transformed version of the odds ratio: the log odds ratio.

Imagine an experiment in which 175 participants are randomly assigned to one of two conditions (treatment vs. control; 100 of the students are assigned to the treatment condition) and are assessed on whether they graduate from high school. A total of 130 students graduated high school: 80 from the treatment group and 50 from the control group. These data can be displayed in a 2 × 2 table (Table 24.2).

TABLE 24.2

Data Illustrating the Odds Ratio

Group	Graduated	Did not graduate
Treatment	80 a	20 b
Control	50 c	25 d

The odds ratio can be computed as

$$OR = \frac{a/b}{c/d} = \frac{80/20}{50/25} = \frac{4}{2} = 2.0, \quad (24.19)$$

where a, b, c, and d refer to cells in a 2 × 2 table. The quantities in the numerator and denominator of the fraction are odds, so the odds ratio is the ratio of the odds in one group to the odds in another group. In this case, the odds of graduation in the treatment group (4.0) were two times greater than the odds of graduation in the control group (2.0), leading to an odds ratio of 2.0. A common but incorrect interpretation of the odds ratio is to take the position that treatment group students were twice as likely to graduate. That interpretation is actually known as a risk ratio or a success ratio, depending on whether lower rates are better (risk ratio) or higher rates are better (success ratio). In this case, higher rates are better for graduation. The success rate in the treatment group was 80% (i.e., 80% of treatment students graduated) and the success rate in the control group was 66.7%, so treatment students were .80/.667 = 1.20, or 20% more likely to graduate than control students.

By convention, most meta-analyses involving odds ratios are conducted on the natural log of the odds ratio. Like with the r to Fisher's z transformation, this transformation serves as a variance stabilization technique. Most spreadsheet applications have built-in functionality to compute this value (often, =ln(OR) will return the natural log for value OR); in base R, the ln function will return the natural log. The natural log of 2.0 is +0.693. The variance of the logged odds ratio is defined as

$$var_{logOR} = \frac{1}{a} + \frac{1}{b} + \frac{1}{c} + \frac{1}{d}, \quad (24.20)$$

where, again, a, b, c, and d refer to cells in a 2 × 2 table. For the example above,

$$var_{logOR} = \frac{1}{a} + \frac{1}{b} + \frac{1}{c} + \frac{1}{d}$$

$$= \frac{1}{80} + \frac{1}{20} + \frac{1}{50} + \frac{1}{25} = .1225. \quad (24.21)$$

The logged odds ratio (+0.693) and its variance (.1225) would then be used in a meta-analysis to represent this study.

Meta-Analysis

Meta-analysis is the statistical combination of studies that address a similar research question, for example, the effects of cognitive-behavioral therapy on measures of depressive symptomatology. We have already made the point that effect sizes are weighted by the inverse of their variances to arrive at the statistics of interest in a meta-analysis. One of the primary benefits of this weighting scheme is that it allows more precise estimates to contribute more to the meta-analytic average, and computing this average is often one of the primary goals of a meta-analysis. But inverse-variance weighting has another advantage. Homoscedasticity is one of the assumptions of the general linear model, and it occurs when all observations have the same variance. As we have seen, however, effect size variances depend on the sample sizes used to estimate them—which is why we cannot analyze effect sizes from different studies using a simple technique like ordinary least squares regression. Effect sizes are rarely, if ever, estimated with the same sample size across studies (if they were, it would be possible to take a simple average of the effect sizes to estimate the mean effect size). Before delving into the mechanics of a meta-analysis, we need to discuss the important considerations in the choice of meta-analytic models.

Model choice in meta-analysis. Often, one of the primary goals of a meta-analysis is to estimate a mean effect size. To do this, we have to choose an analytic model. We will discuss two analytic models: fixed effects models and random effects models. Note that many users of meta-analysis allow a statistical test, the homogeneity test that we describe below, to dictate the decision of whether to use a fixed effects or random effects model. Specifically, they will adopt a fixed effects model if they fail to reject the null hypothesis of effect size homogeneity, and a random effects model if they do reject this null hypothesis. In contrast, experts recommend that model choice be treated as a conceptual question that is guided either by the synthesist's beliefs about the state of the world or their goals for meta-analysis (Hedges & Vevea, 1998), not by the results of a statistical test.

Fixed effects models. Meta-analysts should use a fixed effects model when either (a) they believe that all effect sizes are estimating the same population parameter (when used this way, the model is sometimes referred to as a fixed effect model or a common effect model) or (b) their interest is in estimating the effect size in the studies that are available for review. In either case, inferences arising from fixed effects models are said to be conditioned on the studies in the meta-analytic data set. Meta-analysis using the fixed effects model is straightforward: Effect sizes are weighted by the inverse of their conditional variances (as defined above), and then a weighted average of the effect size is computed.

The common effect assumption can be hard to defend. If true, it implies that sampling error is the only reason that effect sizes differ from one another, and therefore, if all of the studies used infinitely large samples, they would all have the same effect size. This means that all differences in study characteristics, such as how the dependent variable was measured, how the intervention was implemented, and the nature of the sample, are immaterial in that they do not affect the effect size. This might be defensible if the studies being meta-analyzed are very tight replications of one another, for instance if they were all tests of an intervention that was delivered at different times of the year but were otherwise identical. A slightly less strong version of the common effect assumption allows for moderators. That is, even if all the effect sizes are drawn from infinitely large studies, they might have different characteristics that lead them to have different effect sizes, but once these characteristics are taken into account, for example via regression adjustment, all of the residual effect sizes would be the same. This version of the fixed effects assumption is also hard to defend in most meta-analyses conducted in the social and medical sciences, because even when they are testing the same hypothesis, different studies tend to differ from one another in at least some potentially important respects—and probably in multiple unknown respects too—and it is usually impossible to identify all of the study characteristics that lead to differences in effect size (Valentine et al., 2011).

Fixed effects assumptions are more defensible when the reviewers' stated intention is to summarize the results of the studies available for meta-analysis. That is, the reviewers might be interested in making inferences about the studies in hand (and those studies that are highly similar to them). For example, a funding agency might be interested in meta-analyzing the results of a similar set of interventions that share the same funding stream. Another reason that meta-analysts might choose to summarize the results of the available studies is that there are too few studies to support random effects estimation. As will be seen below, random effects models are generally more defensible in the kinds of reviews that are typical for the social and medical sciences. But if the number of studies available for review is small, then the meta-analytic estimate of the variance of the true effect sizes will be imprecise and among other things, this means that the actual Type I error rate could either exceed or be smaller than the nominal Type I error rate. Therefore, invoking fixed effects assumptions is one potential solution to the problem of having a small number of studies in the meta-analysis, though at the cost of limiting the generalizability of the findings.

Random effects model. Whereas the inferences arising from fixed effect assumptions are conditional, inferences arising from the random effects model are unconditional in the sense that they refer to a population of studies from which the observed studies are considered to be a random sample. Treating the observed studies as a random sample from a population of studies implies that even if all studies were infinitely large and if all known study differences affecting the effect size were taken into account, the effect sizes observed in different studies would still not be the same (perhaps due to unknown differences in study characteristics driving effect size estimates). Random effects assumptions are almost certainly more believable than fixed effects assumptions in most meta-analyses done in the social and medical sciences because, as we articulated earlier, studies addressing the same research question tend not to be very tight replications of one another but instead might be characterized as ad hoc replications. Therefore, the studies will tend to vary in multiple known and unknown ways, making random effects assumptions more defensible.

Assuming a random effects model slightly complicates meta-analysis. The fixed effects model assumes that there is only one source of error (sampling error), so the variance of the effect size estimate only has to reflect this one source of error. The random effects model has to accommodate multiple sources of error (between study differences and sampling error). This is done by estimating the variance of the distribution of true effect sizes (τ^2) and incorporating this estimate into each effect size's estimated variance.

A Running Example

For the rest of this chapter, we illustrate the concepts of meta-analysis using the studies reported in Valentine et al. (2022). These authors collected 104 studies that examine the direct and indirect effects on depression of two theoretically important cognitive constructs, dysfunctional attitudes and negative automatic thinking, using a meta-analytic structural equation modeling framework. Of the 104 studies in the data set, 26 gave at least two measures of depressive symptomatology to participants and of these, 19 gave the Beck Depression Inventory and one other measure of depressive symptomatology to participants. Our running example involves these 19 studies. The meta-analysis will explore how strongly related these measures of depressive symptomatology are, how much variation there is in the observed effect sizes, and how much of a threat publication bias might be. The studies, along with their sample sizes, effect sizes (correlation coefficients and Fisher's z transformed correlations), and all of the information needed to conduct the analyses reported below, are available in Table 24.3. R code (R Core Team, 2020) for these analyses is available in Appendix 24.1.

Meta-Analysis

TABLE 24.3
Example Data and Supporting Calculations

Study	n	r	r_z	v	w	w × ES	w²	wtsqdev	τ²	v*	w*	w* × ES
Column a	Column b	Column c	Column d	Column e	Column f	Column g	Column h	Column i	Column j	Column k	Column l	Column m
berle_2012	134	0.650	0.775	0.0076	131	101.564	17161	2.005	0.046	0.054	18.529	14.366
bernholtz_2013	66	0.809	1.124	0.0159	63	70.820	3969	3.193	0.046	0.062	16.075	18.070
ciesla_2007	126	0.740	0.950	0.0081	123	116.909	15129	0.326	0.046	0.054	18.360	17.451
dagostino_2016	132	0.680	0.829	0.0078	129	106.956	16641	0.630	0.046	0.054	18.489	15.329
haeffel_2005	237	0.590	0.678	0.0043	234	158.574	54756	11.464	0.046	0.051	19.759	13.390
hankin_2001	233	0.702	0.871	0.0043	230	200.408	52900	0.176	0.046	0.051	19.730	17.192
hughes_2008	364	0.650	0.775	0.0028	361	279.595	130321	5.596	0.046	0.049	20.364	15.772
hundt_2011	299	0.810	1.127	0.0034	296	333.601	87616	15.391	0.046	0.050	20.115	22.670
lutz_1984 (dep)	36	0.590	0.678	0.0303	33	22.363	1089	1.617	0.046	0.077	13.048	8.842
lutz_1984 (non-dep)	37	0.530	0.590	0.0294	34	20.065	1156	3.243	0.046	0.076	13.202	7.791
margolis_1982	54	0.620	0.725	0.0196	51	36.975	2601	1.544	0.046	0.066	15.165	10.994
mayer_2004	80	0.581	0.664	0.0130	77	51.149	5929	4.243	0.046	0.059	16.857	11.198
mccarron_1980	19	0.890	1.422	0.0625	16	22.751	256	4.375	0.046	0.109	9.188	13.065
quiggle_2001	240	0.820	1.157	0.0042	237	274.166	56169	15.753	0.046	0.051	19.780	22.882
randolph_1998	246	0.500	0.549	0.0041	243	133.481	59049	29.716	0.046	0.050	19.821	10.888
schwartz-stav_2006	48	0.896	1.449	0.0222	45	65.206	2025	13.614	0.046	0.069	14.586	21.136
syzmanski_1997	247	0.761	0.999	0.0041	244	243.796	59536	2.448	0.046	0.050	19.828	19.811
wong_2008	868	0.790	1.071	0.0012	865	926.788	748225	25.718	0.046	0.047	21.056	22.560
you_2007	306	0.520	0.576	0.0033	303	174.631	91809	31.546	0.046	0.050	20.147	11.611
sums					3715.0	3339.798	1406337.0	172.596			334.101	295.020

Note. n = sample size; r = correlation coefficient; r_z = Fisher's z transformed correlation coefficient; w = fixed effects weight (i.e., $1/v$); $w \times ES$ = fixed effects weight × the effect size (Fisher's z); wtsqdev = the weighted squared deviation of the effect size about the mean effect size; τ^2 = random effects variance component; v^* the random effects variance (i.e., $v + \tau^2$); w^* = random effects weight (i.e., $1/v^*$); $w^* \times ES$ is the random effects weight × the effect size ($w^* \times$ Fisher's z); dep = depressed.

Estimating a mean effect size using fixed effects.
After extracting information from studies, including the effect sizes and their variances, and choosing a meta-analytic model, the next step usually involves computing a mean effect size. A weighted mean effect size can be computed by

$$\overline{ES} = \frac{\sum(w_i ES_i)}{\sum w_i}. \quad (24.22)$$

In words, a weighted mean effect size is computed by summing the product of each study's effect size and its associated weight, and then dividing that quantity by the sum of the weights. The information needed to compute the mean effect size is given in columns f and g in Table 24.3. The last row in the table provides the needed sums: the sum of each effect size times its weight and the sum of the weights. For these 19 studies, these sums are 3339.798 (column g) and 3715 (column f), so the mean effect size is 3339.798/3715 = .899. Recall that this is a Fisher's z transformed correlation coefficient, so we need to back transform into r so we can interpret it more easily. This can be done many ways, for example by using =fisherinv in most spreadsheet applications. Here, Fisher's z of .899 transforms into a correlation coefficient of .72, meaning that under fixed effects assumptions the mean correlation between the Beck Depression Inventory and another measure of depressive symptomatology in these 19 studies was +.72.

Estimating a mean effect size using random effects. As we mentioned earlier, random effects meta-analysis is slightly more complicated because we have to account for multiple sources of differences potentially affecting effect sizes. We do this by estimating the variance of the true effect sizes, τ^2. Estimating this variance requires a reasonable number of studies, so if there are few studies available for meta-analysis, random effects estimation might not be feasible. Estimation is best done iteratively using statistical software (restricted maximum likelihood estimation is common), but we can illustrate what is happening using some elementary statistics. We start by computing Q, the homogeneity statistic, about which we will have more to say later. Q is simply a weighted sum of the squared deviations of each effect size from the meta-analytic mean effect size

$$Q = \sum w_i \left(ES_i - \overline{ES}\right)^2. \quad (24.23)$$

After computing Q, we can compute τ^2, the estimated variance of the true effect sizes—also known as the random effects or the between-studies variance component—as

$$\tau^2 = \frac{Q - k - 1}{\sum w_i - \frac{\sum w_i^2}{\sum w_i}}, \quad (24.24)$$

where k is the number of studies and w_i refers to each effect size's weight. The numerator of τ^2 represents total variability (in square units) minus expected variability (represented by the number of studies). This quantity is provided in the last row of column i from Table 24.3, 172.596. Because there are 19 estimates, the numerator for τ^2 is 172.596 − (19 − 1) = 154.596. The denominator for τ^2 looks complicated, but it is just the sum of the weights minus this quantity: the sum of the weights squared divided by the sum of the weights. The denominator serves to put τ^2 back into the original units of measurement (here, Fisher's z squared). The values needed for computation are provided in Table 24.3's column f (the sum of the weights) and column h (the sum of the squared weights), so the denominator is 3715 − (1406337/3715) = 3336.444. Therefore, τ^2 = 154.596/3336.444 = .046.

The mean effect size under random effects assumptions is computed the same way that the mean effect size for fixed effects assumptions is computed: divide the sum of the product of each study's random effects weight and its effect size by the sum of the weights. Here, the sum of the weights is 334.101 (column l), and the sum of the product of each study's weight and its effect size is 295.02 (column m). Hence, the mean effect size assuming random effects is 115.835/132.180 = .878, which, transformed back into a correlation coefficient, is +.71.

Table 24.4 illustrates one last point. For each study, it shows the fixed effects and the random effects weights, and also shows the relative contribution of each study to the overall mean (i.e., the relative weight for each study). The relative weight is expressed as a percentage of the total weight. As can be seen in the table, one consequence of choosing the random effects model is that the weights will tend to be more equal than they were in the fixed effects model. The rank ordering of the weights is the same in both models, for example, Wong (2008) has the largest portion of the fixed effect weight (23.3%) and the random effects weight (6.3%), but the difference in relative weight between Wong (2008) and the next largest study, Hughes et al. (2008), is much larger under fixed effects assumptions than under random effects assumptions (the relative weights for Hughes et al. were 9.7% assuming fixed effects and 6.1% assuming random effects). This occurs because, as we demonstrated, the random effects variance involves adding a constant representing the variance of the true effect sizes to the conditional (fixed effects) variance, and the larger this constant, the more equal the relative weights under random effects assumptions.

Inferential test and confidence intervals for the mean effect size. Regardless of whether fixed effects or random effects assumptions are invoked, the null hypothesis significance test and confidence interval are produced the same way. Meta-analysis is a large sample technique, so hypothesis testing is usually done using the z-distribution. Assume we have chosen a Type I error rate of $\alpha = .05$ and want to conduct a two-tailed (nondirectional) test. The variance of a mean effect size is

$$var_{\overline{ES}} = \frac{1}{\sum w_i}. \qquad (24.25)$$

TABLE 24.4

Relative Weights Under Fixed Effects and Random Effects Assumptions

Study	N	w	Relative weight (fixed effects)	w*	Relative weight (random effects)
berle_2012	134	131	3.5%	18.529	5.5%
bernholtz_2013	66	63	1.7%	16.075	4.8%
ciesla_2007	126	123	3.3%	18.360	5.5%
dagostino_2016	132	129	3.5%	18.489	5.5%
haeffel_2005	237	234	6.3%	19.759	5.9%
hankin_2001	233	230	6.2%	19.730	5.9%
hughes_2008	364	361	9.7%	20.364	6.1%
hundt_2011	299	296	8.0%	20.115	6.0%
Lutz_1984 (dep)	36	33	0.9%	13.048	3.9%
Lutz_1984 (non-dep)	37	34	0.9%	13.202	4.0%
margolis_1982	54	51	1.4%	15.165	4.5%
mayer_2004	80	77	2.1%	16.857	5.0%
mccarron_1980	19	16	0.4%	9.188	2.8%
quiggle_2001	240	237	6.4%	19.780	5.9%
randolph_1998	246	243	6.5%	19.821	5.9%
schwartz-stav_2006	48	45	1.2%	14.586	4.4%
syzmanski_1997	247	244	6.6%	19.828	5.9%
wong_2008	868	865	23.3%	21.056	6.3%
you_2007	306	303	8.2%	20.147	6.0%
Sums		3715.0	100%	334.101	100%

Note. N = sample size; w = fixed effects weight (i.e., 1/v); w* = random effects weight (i.e., 1/v*); dep = depressed.

From Table 24.3, the sum of the fixed effects weights was 3715. Therefore, the variance of the mean effect size under fixed effects assumptions was 1/3715 = .0003 and the standard error is the square root of the variance, or .0164. From Table 24.3, the sum of the random effects weight was 334.101. Therefore, the variance of the mean effect size under random effects assumptions was 1/334.101 = .003 and the standard error is the square root of the variance, or .0547.

The null hypothesis significance test for the mean effect size is

$$z = \frac{|\overline{ES}|}{SE_{\overline{ES}}}. \quad (24.26)$$

The numerator is the absolute value of the mean effect size, and the denominator is the standard error of the mean effect size. Recall that expressed in Fisher's z, the meta-analytic mean under fixed effects assumptions was 0.899 and that under random effects assumptions, it was 0.878. Therefore, the obtained value of z is .899/.0164 = 54.8 for the fixed effects estimate and .878/.0547 = 16.1 for the random effects estimate. The critical value of z at $\alpha = .05$ two-tailed is 1.96; because the obtained value of z is greater than the critical value of z for both estimates, we can reject the null hypothesis that all effect sizes are estimating the same population parameter under both fixed effects and random effects models. Exact p values can be found using many spreadsheet applications, using = 2 * (1 – NORMSDIST(ABS(z))), and in base R using 2 * (pnorm(z, lower.tail = FALSE)), where z is the observed value of z.

The 95% confidence interval for a mean effect size is

$$95\% \, CI = \overline{ES} \pm 1.96(SE_{\overline{ES}}). \quad (24.27)$$

Therefore, for fixed effects assumptions, the 95% confidence interval is $0.90 \pm 1.96(.0164) = 0.90 \pm .03$, and for random effects assumptions, the 95% confidence interval is $0.88 \pm 1.96(.0547) = 0.88 \pm 0.10$. To assist interpretation, we can convert all of these Fisher z values back into correlation coefficients. Recall that we did this earlier for the mean effect sizes and obtained values of +.72 for the fixed effects mean and +.71 for the random effects mean. These estimates are quite close to one another and suggest a strong average correlation between the Beck Depression Inventory and other measures of depressive symptomatology, but the confidence interval for the random effects mean is much wider than it is for the fixed effects mean. For fixed effects, the lower and upper values of the 95% confidence interval are .70 and .73 while for the random effects model, the lower and upper values of the 95% confidence interval are .65 and .75. This pattern of results is expected and illustrates an important point: confidence intervals under random effects assumptions will usually be wider, and will never be narrower, than confidence intervals under fixed effects assumptions.

Assessing Heterogeneity

Most meta-analyses include a homogeneity test. The null hypothesis of this test is that each effect size is estimating the same population parameter, for example, that $\rho_1 = \rho_2 = \ldots \rho_i$ for the correlation coefficient. We introduced the homogeneity test, Q, when describing how to compute a mean effect size under random effects assumptions. Recall that Q is simply a weighted sum of squares. It approximately follows the χ^2 distribution with $k-1$ degrees of freedom, where k is the number of effect sizes. The last row in column i from Table 24.3 shows that the sum of the squared deviations of each effect size from the mean effect size was 172.6. The critical value of χ^2 at 18 df using a Type I error rate of $\alpha = .05$ is 28.87, so we can reject the null hypothesis that all effect sizes are estimating the same population parameter.

A statistic that often accompanies the homogeneity test is I^2, which is an estimate of the percentage of the variability in effect sizes that is due to true variability as opposed to sampling error. It can be computed as

$$I^2 = \frac{Q-k-1}{Q}. \quad (24.28)$$

This statistic is usually incorrectly interpreted as an absolute measure of heterogeneity. Meta-analysts who take the position that, for example, heterogeneity is large because I^2 is large are interpreting I^2 as an absolute measure. But this is a mistake. One way to think about I^2 is that it represents the ratio of variability in the true effect sizes to total variability in effect sizes. Total variability in effect sizes depends in part on the expected sampling error. Therefore, the value of I^2 depends in part on the expected sampling error. The same amount of true variability might be small or large depending on whether sampling error is large or small (Borenstein et al., 2017).

A better approach to thinking about how much heterogeneity is present is to examine the width of a prediction interval. Whereas confidence intervals convey information about the likely range of the population effect, prediction intervals describe the likely range within which some future observation might fall (e.g., the next study). If the number of studies in the meta-analysis is not small, a 95% prediction interval can be computed by

$$PI = \bar{Y} \pm 1.96\tau, \quad (24.29)$$

where τ is the square root of the between-studies variance component. Earlier, we computed the between-studies variance component as .046, and the square root of this value is 0.214. Recall that the meta-analytic mean Fisher's z was +0.88 under random effect assumptions. Therefore, the prediction interval ranges from a low of 0.88 − 1.96(.21) = .47 and a high of .88 + 1.96(.21) = 1.29 in Fisher z units and a low of .43 and a high of .86 when expressed as correlation coefficients. This prediction interval is quite large: One way to think about this range is that in the population represented by these studies the proportion of variance shared between the Beck Depression Inventory and another measure of depressive symptomatology ranges between 18% and 74%, suggesting a great deal of true heterogeneity.

Nonindependent effect sizes. Our discussion so far has assumed that each study contributed only one effect size to the meta-analysis. But in fact, it is common for studies to provide multiple effect sizes relevant to a particular meta-analysis. For example, in the set of studies we used to illustrate the principles of meta-analysis, Hankin (2001) and Mayer (2004) assessed the relationship between the Beck Depression Inventory and another depression inventory on the same people at two different points in time. Because effect sizes based on the same people are highly correlated, ignoring this dependence results in several undesirable consequences, including (a) studies contributing multiple effect sizes will have too much influence on the statistical analyses and (b) the estimated meta-analytic standard error will be spuriously precise (resulting in p values that are too small). Therefore, meta-analysts need a strategy for handling multiple effect sizes when they are present in a study.

There are two general approaches for addressing effect size dependence. These might be termed "reductionist" and "integrative" approaches. Reductionist approaches include (a) randomly selecting one effect size to represent the study, (b) using decision rules to choose one effect size (e.g., because it is believed to better represent the constructs of interest—any such rules are articulated in a protocol that was made public prior to data collection), and (c) simply averaging the effect sizes within a study. Reductionist approaches are easy to implement, but this comes at a cost: they all result in a loss of information. Integrative approaches better preserve the available information but are harder to implement. These include multilevel meta-analysis (Van den Noortgate et al., 2013), full multivariate meta-analysis (Jackson et al., 2011), robust variance estimation (Hedges et al., 2010), and averaging effect sizes in a way that takes into account the correlation among them (What Works Clearinghouse, 2020).

Due to their ease of implementation, reductionist approaches are, by far, the most common strategies for addressing the problems presented by having multiple effect sizes available in studies, but integrative approaches are becoming more common as software supporting their use becomes more available (for example, robust variance estimation is supported in multiple R packages including robumeta; Fisher et al., 2017). In addition, integrative approaches have advantages when used in combination with meta-regression to explore why effect sizes vary from one another. We have more to say on this point later.

Publication bias. It is a near certainty that statistically significant findings are overrepresented in the published research literature. One reason this occurs is that researchers might believe that because their study did not achieve a statistically significant result, they did not find anything worthwhile. This mistaken belief might cause them to lose interest and to be reluctant to write up and submit the study for publication consideration. All else being equal, smaller effect sizes will have larger p values, so smaller effect sizes are less likely to be statistically significant than larger effect sizes. This means that the published literature probably overrepresents larger effect sizes (because they will be more likely to be statistically significant) and underrepresents smaller effect sizes (because they will be less likely to be statistically significant). The problem is that systematic reviewers will find it easier to locate and include relevant published studies than relevant unpublished studies and therefore, the studies included in a meta-analysis might under-represent studies that have smaller effect sizes. This phenomenon is known as *publication bias*. It is sometimes also referred to as "small study effects" because the small studies that happen to observe large enough effects will tend to get published, while studies that do not observe large enough effects will tend to go unpublished.

The best defense against publication bias is a vigorous search that aims to uncover all relevant studies regardless of their publication status. At the same time, most meta-analyses should involve a formal assessment of how likely publication bias appears to be and if it appears likely to be operating, how much bias it might cause. Several statistical tests have been developed to help meta-analysts do this. Unfortunately, these tests must be interpreted cautiously because none are very good in the sense that they perform well in the kinds of conditions routinely found in meta-analyses in the social and medical sciences. In particular, these tests (a) require a relatively large number of studies and (b) do not perform well in the presence of heterogeneity. For this reason, many experts (e.g., Kepes & McDaniel, 2015; Vevea et al., 2019) propose treating publication bias tests as sensitivity analyses and triangulating the evidence about publication bias using multiple statistical tests.

Before discussing the statistical tests for publication bias, part of the formal assessment of the plausibility that publication bias has influenced the makeup of the retrieved studies requires the expert judgment of the meta-analysts and the consumers using their work. This judgment can focus on several different aspects: here we address three. Perhaps the most important of these pertains to the likely presence of external factors that are related to both sample size and effect size. For example, assume that better intervention implementation leads to larger effect sizes, and that the intervention is easier to implement well in small studies. This will lead to effect sizes that are larger in smaller studies. All publication tests will interpret this as potential evidence of publication bias, even though it is not. Therefore, meta-analysts need to think carefully about these possible external influences prior to running publication bias tests.

In addition, judgments need to be made about the likelihood that publication bias is operating on the research hypothesis relevant to the meta-analysis. If the meta-analytic hypothesis tends to be the focus of the underlying studies—such as when the interest is in testing the effects of some intervention for depression—then it seems likely that publication bias might have influenced the makeup of the retrieved studies for the reasons that we articulated earlier. However, if the meta-analytic hypothesis tends to be of secondary interest in the primary research papers then publication bias is less likely to influence the makeup of the retrieved studies. Our example data illustrate this point: The focus of the underlying studies was never on assessing the degree of overlap between the Beck Depression Inventory and another measure of depressive symptomatology. Instead, these studies focused on other hypotheses such as the relationship among other constructs related to cognitive models of depression (like attribution style and rumination). Therefore, the studies in our meta-analytic data set were unlikely to have been selected for publication based on results relevant to the meta-analytic hypothesis.

Finally, the proportion of published versus unpublished studies contributing to a meta-analysis is relevant to the likelihood of publication bias. Unless there is strong reason to believe otherwise, a meta-analysis based solely or largely on published studies ought to be assumed to be affected by publication bias. In our example data set, two thirds of the studies were unpublished dissertations, and dissertation approval typically is not contingent on the observed results. This is another reason why we would expect publication bias to be less likely in the example data set.

Funnel plots. The funnel plot is a graphical tool for exploring whether publication bias might be operating. Sometimes, funnel plots serve as informal publication bias tests, but few experts recommend that they be used this way. The funnel plot for the example data set is in Figure 24.1. Each filled-in circle represents a study effect size. By convention, the scale of measurement (i.e., the effect size metric) is presented on the x-axis and a measure of precision (usually the standard error) is presented on the y-axis. Note that a standard error of 0 (which would indicate an infinitely large sample) is not at the graph's origin. Instead, it is at the top of the graph. This has the effect of placing the largest studies at the top of the graph. Sample sizes decrease as one moves down the y-axis, so smaller studies, for which the effect size estimate is less precise, will tend to scatter more than larger studies. The plot's diagonal lines represent this in that they can be thought of as indicating the expected range within which effect

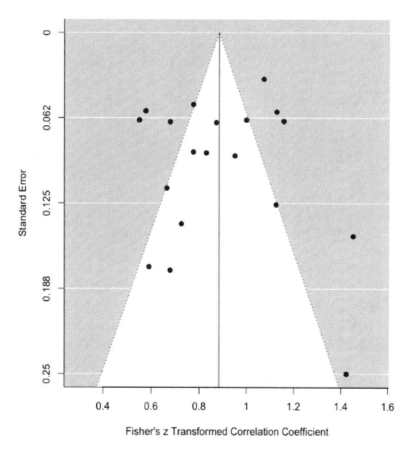

FIGURE 24.1. Funnel plot.

sizes are expected to lie depending on sample size. The vertical line bisecting the plot represents the meta-analytic mean effect size.

As long as no other factors causing a relationship between sample size and effect size exist, if all studies relevant to the meta-analysis are included then the funnel plot should be symmetric. Typically, researchers look for gaps in the plot that indicate asymmetry. Examining Figure 24.1, there appears to be a gap in the lower righthand side of the scatter plot. However, this gap is not where it would be expected to be if publication bias is operating. In general, we expect that publication bias will result in censoring studies with effects that are closer to zero (because they are less likely to be statistically significant, all else being equal). Because the mean effect size in this plot is positive, we would expect to see any publication bias operating to the left of the mean (i.e., on the smaller effect sizes) but in this case, the gap, if there really is a gap, is to the right (meaning that the gap might suggest that studies with larger correlations between the Beck Depression Inventory and other measures of depressive symptomatology have been censored or at least, unlocated).

This discussion highlights two problems with using a funnel plot as a publication bias test. One is that if the number of studies is not large and/or if heterogeneity is present, funnel plots will often be ambiguous. The other problem is related to the first: reading funnel plots can be a highly subjective exercise. Formal statistical tests offer an alternative to informal funnel plot assessment of publication bias. As we mentioned, these tests are not perfect. As typically used, they are not even very good. Still, when used with their limitations in mind, they are useful as sensitivity analyses to help assess the likelihood and potential impact of publication bias.

Statistical tests for publication bias. There are a large number of publication bias tests. As of this writing, the R package metafor (Viechtbauer, 2010) provides four: trim and fill (Duval & Tweedie, 2000), the regression test (Egger et al., 1997; Rodgers & Pustejovsky, 2021), the rank correlation test (Begg & Mazumdar, 1994), and the Henmi-Copas approach to meta-analysis (Henmi & Copas, 2010). All four of these publication bias tests, and most others, involve assessing the relationship between effect size and some measure of study size (e.g., a standard error) and interpret any identified relationship as possible evidence of publication bias. Recall that because none of the publication bias tests are very good given the conditions in most meta-analyses, most experts recommend running multiple tests and triangulating the evidence. For the example data, none of the four publication bias tests identified potential publication bias. The trim and fill procedure did not detect funnel plot asymmetry, neither the regression test nor the rank correlation test identified a relationship between effect size and precision, and the Henmi-Copas approach yielded results highly similar to those obtained from the random effects meta-analysis. These results, combined with our judgment that publication bias is unlikely for this particular research question, provide some level of comfort that publication bias is probably not operating on these data.

Meta-Regression

Researchers often conduct meta-analyses not only to estimate a mean effect size from a set of studies but also to explore effect size variation across studies. Meta-regression is one way to explore effect size variation. Meta-regression is analogous to ordinary least squares regression models but uses weighted least squares to account for heteroscedasticity among effect sizes. Meta-regression allows for multiple categorical and continuous moderators, and should be used, when possible, instead of single-variable models (Tipton et al., 2019), which fail to account for likely overlap (and therefore confounding) among variables. For example, many researchers use study quality indicators (e.g., randomized controlled trials vs. quasi-experiments) as control variables in meta-regression to examine how study quality relates to effect size magnitude. Meta-regression can also reduce concerns about Type I error rate inflation associated with conducting several univariate tests (Polanin & Pigott, 2015).

At the same time, the statistical power requirements for meta-regression are very high, and therefore Type I error inflation is usually not an important concern. The number of studies required for reasonable statistical power for individual regression coefficients depends on several factors, including the number of studies, the magnitude of the effects being estimated, and the assumptions about the structure of the effect size data set. It is therefore not possible to provide a robust rule of thumb for the minimum number of studies required to support meta-regression. We can relate that in our experience, researchers greatly underestimate the number of studies required and that greater awareness of the ubiquity of low statistical power for these types of analyses is needed (see Hedges & Pigott, 2004). Using an integrative approach to dependent effect sizes as discussed earlier increases the number of effect sizes available for the meta-regression, allowing for more flexibility in exploring heterogeneity.

Finally, researchers should choose moderators to include in a meta-regression a priori to avoid bias associated with making data-driven decisions. When developing a protocol for a systematic review, researchers hypothesize about why studies observe different effect sizes, and these hypotheses drive what study characteristics are coded and explored as moderators. When interesting hypotheses arise during the analysis, unanticipated moderator tests should be labeled as exploratory. No matter how moderators are chosen for a meta-regression, care should be taken in making inferences from the analysis. Meta-regression models examine how study characteristics relate to study effect size estimates, and any inferences made from these models are correlational in nature and at the level of the study (Cooper, 2017). Moderator analysis can provide clues as to why effect sizes differ, but they do not offer definitive explanations.

CONCLUSION

In this chapter, we set out to provide a framework for systematic reviewing focusing on the conceptual and statistical issues pertinent to meta-analysis. Although some aspects of meta-analysis can be quite complex mathematically, most involve straightforward extensions, motivated by the need to account for heteroscedasticity, of the statistical procedures familiar to most scholars. We attempted to clearly communicate not only the technical framework on which meta-analysis is based, but also the relevant conceptual considerations like the choice of the analytic model and the trouble with publication bias tests in an understandable and accessible manner. In doing this, we barely scratched the surface of the range of applications for meta-analysis, including Bayesian meta-analysis (Turner & Higgins, 2019), psychometric meta-analysis (Schmidt et al., 2019), network meta-analysis (Salanti et al., 2008), and meta-analysis of single case design research (Pustejovsky & Ferron, 2017). Our hope is that this chapter provides a good springboard for learning about these and other interesting extensions of meta-analysis.

APPENDIX 24.1: R CODE FOR EXAMPLE DATA

```
# Data for Valentine, Pigott, & Morris, 2023 running example
# Note that there are slight differences, due to rounding,
# between the metafor results and those reported from hand
# calculations in the chapter.

# installs and loads required metafor package, uncomment if needed
# install.packages("metafor")
library(metafor)
# data for the chapter's running example
author_year <-
c("berle_2012","bernholtz_2013","ciesla_2007","dagostino_2016",
"haeffel_2005","hankin_2001","hughes_2008","hundt_2011","lutz_1984_dep",
"lutz_1984_nondep","margolis_1982","mayer_2004","mccarron_1980",
"quiggle_2001","randolph_1998","schwartz-stav_2006",
"syzmanski_1997","wong_2008","you_2007")
r <-
c(0.65,0.809,0.74,0.68,0.59,.702,.650,0.81,0.59,0.53,0.62,.581,0.89,0.82,0.5,
0.8955,.761,0.79,0.52)
n <-
c(134,66,126,132,237,233,364,299,36,37,54,80,19,240,246,48,247,868,306)
apa_meta <- data.frame(author_year, r, n)
#View(apa_meta)
# converts the correlation coefficients to Fisher's z
dat <- escalc(measure="ZCOR", ri = r, ni = n, data = apa_meta)
# fixed effects meta-analysis
res <- rma(yi, vi, method = "FE", data=dat, slab = paste(apa_meta$author_year))
res
# random effects meta-analysis with the Dersimonian-Laird estimator
res <- rma(yi, vi, method = "DL", data=dat, slab = paste(apa_meta$author_year))
res
# prediction intervals
pi <-predict(res)
pi
# transform all Fisher's z results back into correlations
mean_corr <- (2.71828^(2*pi$pred)-1)/(2.71828^(2*pi$pred)+1)
corr_ci_lb <- (2.71828^(2*pi$ci.lb)-1)/(2.71828^(2*pi$ci.lb)+1)
corr_ci_ub <- (2.71828^(2*pi$ci.ub)-1)/(2.71828^(2*pi$ci.ub)+1)
corr_pi_lb <- (2.71828^(2*pi$cr.lb)-1)/(2.71828^(2*pi$cr.lb)+1)
corr_pi_ub <- (2.71828^(2*pi$cr.ub)-1)/(2.71828^(2*pi$cr.ub)+1)
# publication bias assessments
trimfill(res)
ranktest(res)
regtest(res)
hc(res)
# produces plots
funnel(res)
forest(res, header = TRUE)
```

References

The asterisk (*) indicates studies used in the meta-analysis.

Begg, C. B., & Mazumdar, M. (1994). Operating characteristics of a rank correlation test for publication bias. *Biometrics, 50*(4), 1088–1101. https://doi.org/10.2307/2533446

*Berle, D., & Starcevic, V. (2012). Preliminary validation of the Nepean dysphoria scale. *Australasian Psychiatry, 20*(4), 322–326. https://doi.org/10.1177/1039856212447966

*Bernholtz, B. (2013). *The client's and therapist's vocal qualities in CBT and PE-EFT for depression* (Order No. 1764221250) [Doctoral dissertation, University of Toronto]. ProQuest Dissertations & Theses.

Borenstein, M., Higgins, J. P., Hedges, L. V., & Rothstein, H. R. (2017). Basics of meta-analysis: I^2 is not an absolute measure of heterogeneity. *Research Synthesis Methods, 8*(1), 5–18. https://doi.org/10.1002/jrsm.1230

*Ciesla, J. A. (2004). *Rumination, negative cognition, and their interactive effects on depressed mood* (Order No. 3141263) [Doctoral dissertation, State University of New York at Buffalo]. ProQuest Dissertations & Theses.

Cooper, H. (2017). *Research synthesis: A step-by-step approach* (5th ed.). SAGE.

*D'Agostino, A., Manganelli, E., Aportone, A., Rossi Monti, M., & Starcevic, V. (2016). Development, cross-cultural adaptation process and preliminary validation of the Italian version of the Nepean Dysphoria Scale. *Journal of Psychopathology, 22*(2), 149–156. https://www.jpsychopathol.it/issue/issue-2-2016/

Duval, S. J., & Tweedie, R. L. (2000). A nonparametric "trim and fill" method of accounting for publication bias in meta-analysis. *Journal of the American Statistical Association, 95*(449), 89–98.

Egger, M., Davey Smith, G., Schneider, M., & Minder, C. (1997). Bias in meta-analysis detected by a simple, graphical test. *BMJ, 315*(7109), 629–634. https://doi.org/10.1136/bmj.315.7109.629

Fisher, Z., Tipton, E., & Hou, Z. (2017). *robumeta: Robust variance meta-regression*. R package version 2.0. https://CRAN.R-project.org/package=robumeta

*Haeffel, G. J. (2005). *Cognitive vulnerability to depression: Distinguishing between implicit and explicit cognitive processes* (Order No. 3186167) [Doctoral dissertation, University of Wisconsin–Madison]. ProQuest Dissertations & Theses.

*Hankin, B. L. (2001). *Cognitive vulnerability-stress theories of depression: A 2-year prospective study to predict depressive symptoms and disorder* (Order No. 3020729) [Doctoral dissertation, University of Wisconsin–Madison]. ProQuest Dissertations & Theses.

Hedges, L. V. (1981). Distribution theory for Glass's estimator of effect size and related estimators. *Journal of Educational Statistics, 6*(2), 107–128. https://doi.org/10.3102/10769986006002107

Hedges, L. V., & Olkin, I. (1985). *Statistical methods for meta-analysis*. Academic Press.

Hedges, L. V., & Pigott, T. D. (2004). The power of statistical tests for moderators in meta-analysis. *Psychological Methods, 9*(4), 426–445. https://doi.org/10.1037/1082-989X.9.4.426

Hedges, L. V., Tipton, E., & Johnson, M. C. (2010). Robust variance estimation in meta-regression with dependent effect size estimates. *Research Synthesis Methods, 1*(1), 39–65. https://doi.org/10.1002/jrsm.5

Hedges, L. V., & Vevea, J. L. (1998). Fixed-and random-effects models in meta-analysis. *Psychological Methods, 3*(4), 486–504. https://doi.org/10.1037/1082-989X.3.4.486

Henmi, M., & Copas, J. B. (2010). Confidence intervals for random effects meta-analysis and robustness to publication bias. *Statistics in Medicine, 29*(29), 2969–2983. https://doi.org/10.1002/sim.4029

*Hughes, M. E., Alloy, L. B., & Cogswell, A. (2008). Repetitive thought in psychopathology: The relation of rumination and worry to depression and anxiety symptoms. *Journal of Cognitive Psychotherapy, 22*(3), 271–288. https://doi.org/10.1891/0889-8391.22.3.271

*Hundt, N. E. (2011). *Reinforcement sensitivity, cognitive biases, stressful life events, and depression symptoms* (Order No. 3473465) [Doctoral dissertation, University of North Carolina at Greensboro]. ProQuest Dissertations & Theses.

Jackson, D., Riley, R., & White, I. R. (2011). Multivariate meta-analysis: Potential and promise. *Statistics in Medicine, 30*(20), 2481–2498. https://doi.org/10.1002/sim.4172

Kepes, S., & McDaniel, M. A. (2015). The validity of conscientiousness is overestimated in the prediction of job performance. *PLOS ONE, 10*(10), e0141468. https://doi.org/10.1371/journal.pone.0141468

Lipsey, M. W., & Wilson, D. B. (2001). *Practical meta-analysis*. SAGE.

Littell, J. H., Corcoran, J., & Pillai, V. (2008). *Systematic reviews and meta-analysis*. Oxford University Press. https://doi.org/10.1093/acprof:oso/9780195326543.001.0001

*Lutz, R. W. (1984). *Mood and the selective recall and evaluation of naturally occurring pleasant and unpleasant events (depression)* (Order No. 8415476) [Doctoral dissertation, Arizona State University]. ProQuest Dissertations & Theses.

*Margolis, M. F. (1982). *The use of exercise and group cognitive therapy in the treatment of depression* (Order No. 8212763) [Doctoral dissertation, Hofstra University]. ProQuest Dissertations & Theses.

*Mayer, J. L. (2004). *Postpartum mood disturbance in first time mothers: Application of cognitive diathesis-stress models of depression* (Order No. 3131331) [Doctoral dissertation, Idaho State University]. ProQuest Dissertations & Theses.

*McCarron, J. A. (1980). *The relative efficacy of cognitive therapy and chemotherapy for the treatment of depression among the retired elderly* (Order No. 8028693) [Doctoral dissertation, California School of Professional Psychology]. ProQuest Dissertations & Theses.

Polanin, J. R., & Pigott, T. D. (2015). The use of meta-analytic statistical significance testing. *Research Synthesis Methods*, *6*(1), 63–73. https://doi.org/10.1002/jrsm.1124

Pustejovsky, J. E., & Ferron, J. M. (2017). Research synthesis and meta-analysis of single-case designs. In J. M. Kaufmann, D. P. Hallahan, & P. C. Pullen (Eds.), *Handbook of special education* (2nd ed., pp. 168–186). Routledge. https://doi.org/10.4324/9781315517698-15

*Quiggle, N. L. (2001). *The relation between childhood abuse and adult depression: Negative cognitions as a mediator* (Order No. 3038832) [Doctoral dissertation, Vanderbilt University]. ProQuest Dissertations & Theses.

R Core Team. (2020). *R: A language and environment for statistical computing*. R Foundation for Statistical Computing. https://www.R-project.org

*Randolph, J. J., & Dykman, B. M. (1998). Perceptions of parenting and depression-proneness in the offspring: Dysfunctional attitudes as a mediating mechanism. *Cognitive Therapy and Research*, *22*(4), 377–400. https://doi.org/10.1023/A:1018761229824

Rodgers, M. A., & Pustejovsky, J. E. (2021). Evaluating meta-analytic methods to detect selective reporting in the presence of dependent effect sizes. *Psychological Methods*, *26*(2), 141–160. https://doi.org/10.1037/met0000300

Salanti, G., Higgins, J. P. T., Ades, A. E., & Ioannidis, J. P. (2008). Evaluation of networks of randomized trials. *Statistical Methods in Medical Research*, *17*(3), 279–301. https://doi.org/10.1177/0962280207080643

Schmidt, F. L., Le, H., & Oh, I.-S. (2019). Correcting for the distorting effects of study artifacts in meta-analysis and second order meta-analysis. In H. Cooper, L. V. Hedges, & J. C. Valentine (Eds.), *The handbook of research synthesis and meta-analysis* (3rd ed., pp. 315–338). Russell Sage Foundation. https://doi.org/10.7758/9781610448864.18

*Schwartz-Stav, O., Apter, A., & Zalsman, G. (2006). Depression, suicidal behavior and insight in adolescents with schizophrenia. *European Child & Adolescent Psychiatry*, *15*(6), 352–359. https://doi.org/10.1007/s00787-006-0541-8

*Szymanski, J. B. (1997). *Investigating the underlying factor structure of measures of depressive symptomatology and correlates of depression using structural equation modeling* (Order No. 9733545) [Doctoral dissertation, Northern Illinois University]. ProQuest Dissertations & Theses.

Tipton, E., Pustejovsky, J. E., & Ahmadi, H. (2019). A history of meta-regression: Technical, conceptual, and practical developments between 1974 and 2018. *Research Synthesis Methods*, *2*(10), 161–179. https://doi.org/10.1002/jrsm.1338

Turner, R. M., & Higgins, J. P. T. (2019). Bayesian meta-analysis. In H. Cooper, L. V. Hedges, & J. C. Valentine (Eds.), *The handbook of research synthesis and meta-analysis* (3rd ed., pp. 299–314). Russell Sage Foundation. https://doi.org/10.7758/9781610448864.17

Valentine, J. C., Aloe, A. M., & Wilson, S. J. (2019). Interpreting effect sizes. In H. Cooper, L. V. Hedges, & J. C. Valentine (Eds.), *The handbook of research synthesis and meta-analysis* (3rd ed., pp. 433–452). Russell Sage Foundation. https://doi.org/10.7758/9781610448864.22

Valentine, J. C., Biglan, A., Boruch, R. F., Castro, F. G., Collins, L. M., Flay, B. R., Kellam, S., Mościcki, E. K., & Schinke, S. P. (2011). Replication in prevention science. *Prevention Science*, *12*(2), 103–117. https://doi.org/10.1007/s11121-011-0217-6

Valentine, J. C., Cheung, M. W.-L., Smith, E. J., Alexander, O., Hatton, J. M., Hong, R. Y., Huckaby, L. T., Patton, S. C., Pössel, P., & Seely, H. D. (2022). A primer on meta-analytic structural equation modeling: The case of depression. *Prevention Science*, *23*(3), 346–365. https://doi.org/10.1007/s11121-021-01298-5

Valentine, J. C., & Konstantopoulos, S. (2016). *Using systematic reviews and meta-analyses to inform public policy decisions*. The National Academies of Sciences, Engineering and Medicine. https://sites.nationalacademies.org/cs/groups/dbassesite/documents/webpage/dbasse_171853.pdf

Van den Noortgate, W., López-López, J. A., Marín-Martínez, F., & Sánchez-Meca, J. (2013). Three-level meta-analysis of dependent effect sizes. *Behavior Research Methods, 45*(2), 576–594. https://doi.org/10.3758/s13428-012-0261-6

Vevea, J. L., Coburn, K., & Sutton, A. (2019). Publication bias. In H. Cooper, L. V. Hedges, & J. C. Valentine (Eds.), *The handbook of research synthesis and meta-analysis* (3rd ed., pp. 383–430). Russell Sage Foundation. https://doi.org/10.7758/9781610448864.21

Viechtbauer, W. (2010). Conducting meta-analyses in R with the metafor package. *Journal of Statistical Software, 36*(3), 1–48. https://doi.org/10.18637/jss.v036.i03

What Works Clearinghouse. (2020). *Supplement to the WWC procedures handbook, version 4.1*. Institute of Education Sciences. https://ies.ed.gov/ncee/wwc/Docs/referenceresources/WWC-41-Supplement-508_09212020.pdf

*Wong, K. C. (2008). *Psychometric investigation into the construct of neurasthenia and its related conditions: A comparative study on Chinese in Hong Kong and mainland China* (Order No. 3348888) [Doctoral dissertation, The Chinese University of Hong Kong]. ProQuest Dissertations & Theses.

*You, S. (2007). *A gender comparison of cognitive vulnerability as a function of moderation and mediation between negative life events and depressive mood* (Order No. 3291219) [Doctoral dissertation, Purdue University]. ProQuest Dissertations & Theses.

PART II

PUBLISHING AND THE PUBLICATION PROCESS

CHAPTER 25

RESEARCH DATA MANAGEMENT AND SHARING

Katherine G. Akers and John A. Borghi

Research data are an important scholarly product and should be treated as such. Though journal articles remain the primary way in which research findings are communicated and evaluated, access to underlying data is necessary to fully assess, reproduce, and build upon the conclusions of a given article. Data sets may also be standalone research products; used, combined, and even cited on their own. But it is important to draw a distinction between data sets that are available and those that are actually usable—meaning that they can be accessed and understood by both the original research team and anyone with whom they have been shared. Ensuring the usability of research data requires addressing a broad set of activities related to how data are stored, organized, and described throughout the entire research process (Borghi et al., 2018; Briney et al., 2020). Such activities are often grouped together under the umbrella term research data management (RDM). Table 25.1 provides a summary of other important terms used in this discussion.

One approach to understanding RDM is through the FAIR guiding principles (Wilkinson et al., 2016). Initially developed to describe data repositories and other technical infrastructure, the acronym FAIR is now colloquially used to describe individual data sets that are findable, accessible, interoperable, and reusable. In this context, "findable" refers to data that are clearly indexed or identified (generally using a persistent identifier such as a digital object identifier [DOI]), "accessible" to data that are available through a clearly defined process, "interoperable" to data that are structured in a standard way so they can be easily combined with other similarly structured data sets, and "reusable" to data that are well described following relevant community standards and have clearly defined conditions for reuse. However, while the FAIR principles have been widely adopted, the exact steps that need to be taken to meet them are often ambiguous (Mons et al., 2017).

For a more immediate demonstration of the importance of RDM, consider the following three questions in the context of your own research:

1. If another researcher were to ask for the data and other materials associated with one of your studies, would you be able to easily find and make them available?
2. If another researcher who works in the same research area as you were to access a copy of the data and other materials associated with one of your studies, would they be able to use them without asking you too many questions?
3. Do you think you would be able to find and use the data from one of your current studies 10 years from now?

https://doi.org/10.1037/0000320-025
APA Handbook of Research Methods in Psychology, Second Edition: Vol. 3. Data Analysis and Research Publication, H. Cooper (Editor-in-Chief)
Copyright © 2023 by the American Psychological Association. All rights reserved.

TABLE 25.1
Definitions of Key Terms

Data	Observations or measurements, usually quantified and obtained in the course of research. In a data management context, information needed to make use of data (e.g., documentation) should be considered as part of that data.
Research data management	An umbrella term that encompasses activities related to the storage, organization, description, and dissemination of data as well as related research materials (e.g., documentation, code and software).
Data sharing	The release of data for use by others. Includes "open" data sharing, where a data set and related research materials are made publicly available, and more restricted forms of sharing where materials are made available only to specific groups, for specific purposes, or for specific amounts of time.

Each of these questions touches on an aspect of RDM. The first question concerns how well data are organized, the second concerns how well data are documented, and the third how well data are stored and preserved. If you are not able to answer "yes" to each question, you and your research team may want to reconsider how you are managing your data.

Although it is not frequently included in research methods-related coursework (Tenopir et al., 2016), RDM is an important component of good research practice. Proper RDM prevents data sets and other important materials, which in psychology often represent the efforts of both researchers and research participants, from becoming lost or unusable. RDM also facilitates collaboration within and between research groups by enabling team members to efficiently find and use the data they need. Data management is also an important precursor to data sharing. According to the American Psychological Association's (2017) "Ethical Principles of Psychologists and Code of Conduct" (section 8.14),

> *Psychologists do not withhold the data on which their conclusions are based from other competent professionals who seek to verify the substantive claims through reanalysis and who intend to use such data only for that purpose, provided that the confidentiality of the participants can be protected and unless legal rights concerning proprietary data preclude their release.*

Proper RDM is foundational to adhering to this practice and, when appropriate, effectively sharing data more broadly with other reusers or for other purposes. When data are properly organized and analytic procedures are well-documented, the process of evaluating, replicating, and tracing the effects of study-related decisions is greatly simplified.

The lack of availability of psychology research data has been a point of discussion for more than half a century (Ceci & Walker, 1983; Craig & Reese, 1973; Wicherts et al., 2006; Wolins, 1962) and is often a consequence of data and other materials being lost, becoming inaccessible to the research team, or saved in a form that would require a considerable time investment to make usable (Houtkoop et al., 2018; Vanpaemel et al., 2015). All of these situations can be avoided with the implementation of proper RDM practices. But psychology research also poses special challenges for RDM. Data are collected in a wide variety of forms using an immensely diverse array of methods and tools. Data are often collected from human participants, whose privacy must be protected. Data often need to be preserved alongside a host of other materials (e.g., surveys, stimuli, computer code, statistical program output), and there is little consensus about how study procedures and analysis steps should be recorded and communicated. As a result, different research groups, and even different researchers within the same group, may have markedly different RDM practices.

This chapter covers the basic principles of RDM within the context of psychology. Although RDM often involves the use of specific tools and technologies, the focus of this chapter is on good general RDM practices—behaviors and activities that should be employed during the day-to-day course of doing research. Though the following sections cover different components of RDM, good practice typically involves standardization, meaning that everyone on the research team follows the same set of RDM procedures, and documentation, meaning that information and instructions related to the team's RDM procedures are recorded, kept up-to-date, and made accessible to everyone on the research team.

DATA MANAGEMENT PLANNING

RDM is an iterative and continuous process, with decisions made in the early stages substantially affecting what can be done later. Thus, it is generally most efficient to properly manage your data as you are collecting and analyzing it rather than trying to reconstruct everything after your analysis is complete. For example, if you conduct human subjects research and plan to share your data through a data repository at the conclusion of a study, language related to data sharing should be included in participant informed consent forms (Meyer, 2018). Similarly, maintaining good documentation about the content and context of specific variables in a data set will make it easier to use that same data set if you return to it after several days, weeks, or even years. Perhaps the most important step in managing research data is the creation, maintenance, and communication of documentation that prospectively outlines RDM-related procedures for a given study. This documentation is often referred to as a data management plan (DMP).

Many research funding agencies require that DMPs be submitted as part of the grant application process. For example, the National Science Foundation enacted a DMP requirement in 2011, and similar requirements exist or are being developed for many other national research funding bodies in and outside the United States. Requirements for DMPs can vary substantially between and even within different funding agencies (Williams et al., 2017), but free tools like DMPTool (https://dmptool.org/) and DMPOnline (https://dmponline.dcc.ac.uk/) provide templates and guidance for meeting the specific requirements of particular funders.

There is a small but growing body of literature about the efficacy of DMPs created as part of grant proposals (Hudson-Vitale & Moulaison-Sandy, 2019; Smale et al., 2018), but such plans should really just be the beginning. Whether or not you create a plan as part of a grant proposal, you should also maintain a much more expansive document for your research team's internal use. A DMP created and maintained by your team for your own use should be more like a set of standard operating procedures that outline your approach to RDM activities. Your plan should be descriptive and instructive, including details of how data should be managed during and after completion of the study, that team members can refer to whenever necessary. While your DMP should be in place before you begin data collection, you should also ensure that the plan is kept up to date when practices change over time.

Table 25.2 outlines several questions to ask yourself while creating a DMP, with subsequent

TABLE 25.2

Questions to Ask Yourself While Planning for Data Management

Element	Questions to ask yourself
Collection	What data do you plan to collect/generate? Includes type(s) of data (e.g., questionnaires, behavioral data) as well as file formats.
Storage	How will you store and manage access to your data?
Documentation	What information will be needed to ensure your data can be read, interpreted, and used in the future?
Sharing	How will you share your data with others? Are there restrictions on what you can share?
Preservation	What data should be retained, archived, or preserved for the long term?
Compliance	How will you handle any ethical and/or legal issues related to your data?
Responsibilities	Who is responsible for ensuring that data are well managed? What resources will you/they require?

sections of this chapter delving deeper into specific practices related to most of these questions. However, as covering every relevant practice for every type of data set in psychology is beyond the scope of a single chapter, we also urge you to seek out assistance from your colleagues or institution.

DATA COLLECTION AND STORAGE

As soon as you begin collecting data, it is important to start implementing rules for organizing your data—both within and across files—and safely storing them to prevent data loss. Although shortcutting these rules is all too easy, adhering to them will save you time in the long run by increasing the likelihood that your data are complete, error-free, and easy to analyze by you, members of your research team, and others with whom you may eventually share your data.

Although some data collection software may automatically produce clean, well-structured data files, files that are manually compiled by researchers, such as spreadsheets, are often rife with inconsistencies and errors that can egregiously impact subsequent analyses and interpretations (Panko, 1998). Consider the example data set shown in Table 25.3, in which the columns do not have descriptive names, the "Var002" column contains both numeric and text values, the "Var004" column contains an empty cell, and the "Var005" column appears to contain two observations. If you were not intimately familiar with this data set, you would likely not be able to understand or use it.

Therefore, when working with spreadsheets, you should take several actions to guard against introducing errors. First, ensure that your data are tidy; each column should be a single variable with a unique descriptive name, each row should be a single observation, and each table should consist of observations made at a single level of analysis (Wickham, 2014). Second, consistency is critical; use consistent data layouts across files, consistent codes for categorical variables, and consistent date formats (Broman & Woo, 2018). Regarding date formats, be especially aware of the assumptions that your software may be making that could lead to errors that are difficult to reverse, such as Excel's automatic conversion of some gene symbols into dates (Ziemann et al., 2016). Furthermore, it is good practice to fill in all cells in a spreadsheet and maintain consistency in the use of symbols to represent values that are either truly missing or intentionally absent. Third, rather than using text color or highlighted cells to indicate meaning (e.g., the presence of outliers), consider creating a separate column to more clearly convey this meaning (e.g., a column named "outlier" with possible values of "true" or "false"). Fourth, to protect your raw data from being inadvertently erased or overwritten, consider write-protecting raw data files and using separate files to hold processed data, perform calculations, or prepare graphs (Broman & Woo, 2018; Hart et al., 2016). Taking these actions results in spreadsheets that are tidier and more likely to be understood by you or others in the future, such as the better-managed version of our example data set shown in Table 25.4.

To help you keep track of your data during and after a study, organize the data, documentation, and related research materials (e.g., surveys, stimuli, computer code, statistical program output) within folders and subfolders using a logical system that makes the most sense for the particular study. Regarding file naming, one approach is to include approximately three pieces of important information in the name of each file, such as the study name, experiment, run, date, or version number. File names should be unique, kept reasonably short, should not contain special characters, and

TABLE 25.3

An Unmanaged Data Set, data.csv

Var001	Var002	Var003	Var004	Var005
001	1	0.95	1169	18,25
003	2	0.75		55,62
004	Low	0.85	798	28,38
005	High	0.90	938	67,75

Note. In its current state, what can you say about the contents of this data set or the study that it came from?

TABLE 25.4

A Better-Managed Version of the Example Data Set

participant_id	group	accuracy	rt_ms	stai_s	stai_t
001	1	0.95	1169	18	25
003	2	0.75	NA	55	62
004	1	0.85	798	28	38
005	2	0.90	938	67	75

Note. This reformatted version of our data set, examplestudy_combined_version01.csv (formerly data.csv), is easier to understand and use.

should employ dashes or underscores rather than spaces, which are incompatible with some software and operating systems (Briney et al., 2020). As you are working with your data, it is a good idea to periodically save new versions of files with different version numbers or dates in the file name to allow you to return to an earlier version of files in case of human error or technical failure without having to start from scratch. Furthermore, using the label "final" in a file name is generally not recommended, as it is almost certainly the case that the "final" version of your file is not indeed final but will undergo further changes (Briney et al., 2020).

As any hard drive or server can fail, it is critical to back up your data, documentation, and related research materials to protect against their loss. A good rule to follow is the "3-2-1 rule": have at least three copies of the data in two geographically separate locations using more than one type of storage device (Briney et al., 2020). For example, you may want to store two copies of data files locally (e.g., computer and external hard drive) and one copy off-site (e.g., cloud storage), which would allow you to circumvent unexpected problems such as natural disasters, theft, or cloud storage outages. Ideally, you should set up a system in which your data back-ups occur automatically at regular intervals and periodically check that this system is functioning as intended (Briney et al., 2020; Hart et al., 2016).

DATA DOCUMENTATION

Even when your data are well organized and properly stored, ensuring usability requires the creation and maintenance of documentation (Freedland & Carney, 1992). Documentation is generally divided into two categories: study-level documentation, which details practices, procedures, and processes implemented throughout the course of a given study; and data-level documentation, which details the structure and contents of individual data files. Though documentation is perhaps most immediately useful in collaborative research (Ellis & Leek, 2018), maintaining good documentation will help you understand your own work when you return to it days, weeks, or years in the future.

Exactly how you should create and maintain documentation over the course of a study will depend on the type(s) of data you are working with, the details of your data collection and analysis workflow or pipeline, and your expectations for sharing the data after study completion. However, certain best practices can be applied to most types of data and most situations. The examples in Table 25.5 are not meant to be an exhaustive list but rather to illustrate the type of information you should document.

We have already discussed one example of study-level documentation: the DMP. Another common type of study-level documentation is a study protocol, which is a detailed specification of your hypotheses, methods, and analyses (Klein et al., 2018). Like a DMP, a research protocol should be as detailed as possible. Some elements of a DMP and a research protocol may overlap. However, while a DMP includes information and instructions related to how data should be organized, stored, and documented, a research protocol describes the details of a study's overall design and analysis workflow. Within the context of RDM, a protocol helps you document what steps you took to collect and analyze your data and how the data were transformed over time, from "raw" data to a form more appropriate for analysis and sharing.

In psychology, preregistration of study protocols has been discussed as a method for increasing

TABLE 25.5

Information to Be Included in Study- and File-Level Documentation

Study-level documentation	File-level documentation
Details of the data collection process.	Information about the variables appearing in a file.
How files are organized and saved.	Definitions of codes, classification schemes, and acronyms used in a file.
How data are validated or how quality assurance checks are performed.	How missing values are coded in a file (and why they are missing).
How data are manipulated or transformed during the data analysis process.	Details about the processes used to transform the contents of a file.
Mention of software tools (and their versions) used to collect, analyze, and visualize data.	Information about how a file is connected to other files (e.g., files related to a single participant).
Description of the roles and responsibilities of individual research team members.	If applicable, details about when the contents of a file were changed and by whom.

transparency and preventing publication bias (Nosek et al., 2019; Szollosi et al., 2020), and registered reports—a publication pathway in which a protocol is submitted to a journal, undergoes peer review, and is subsequently granted in-principle acceptance for publication—have grown in popularity. However, unlike clinical trials (e.g., Chan et al., 2013; De Angelis et al., 2004), there are presently no formal guidelines for creating or registering protocols in psychology (Hardwicke & Ioannidis, 2018). Therefore, like with a DMP, you should make a distinction between a protocol submitted as part of a registered report or other mechanism and a research protocol used internally by your research team. Common elements for a research protocol include but are not limited to: study name (and other administrative details), rationale, objectives, design, methodology, statistical analysis, and expected outcomes. No matter what form it takes, your research protocol should be sufficiently detailed so that another researcher working in your area would be able to read it and understand exactly how your research team is conducting your study.

Your description of study design and methodology should include precisely how you and your team plan to recruit participants and (when appropriate) assign them to groups, how you plan to collect data (including specific details about interventions, tasks, and/or experimental paradigms), and how you will perform statistical analyses.

Regarding file-level documentation, perhaps the most ubiquitous form is a data dictionary or codebook. Data dictionaries can come in many formats, but all include information about the structure and contents of a data file (Horstmann et al., 2020). Some data dictionaries are designed to be machine-readable, meaning that their contents can be read and automatically acted upon by computer programs during the data analysis process. Other data dictionaries are human-readable, meaning their contents are presented in such a way that a researcher with some familiarity with the subject matter is able to read and understand the information provided. At a minimum, you should maintain a human-readable data dictionary that is consistent, meaning that the same structure is used throughout. Like a protocol, there are no formal guidelines for what information a data dictionary should contain, but common elements include

- variable names and descriptions
- data types (e.g., categorical, continuous)
- explanation of codes (e.g., group identifiers)
- explanation of symbols reflecting missing data

To demonstrate the value of file-level documentation, let us return to our example data set, which we have renamed *examplestudy_combined_version01.csv*. Previously we discussed giving data files and variables unique and descriptive names. Although the variable names in our example data set do indeed give important information about the contents of each column, additional information is still necessary to understand the content of this data set as how the data were collected and analyzed. This kind of information is included in our data dictionary (Table 25.6).

Two additional forms of documentation are ReadMe files and lab notebooks. We previously discussed keeping study-related materials in an

TABLE 25.6

Rudimentary Data Dictionary[a]

Variable	Full name	Data type	
participant_id	Participant ID number	Categorical	Assigned based on date of enrollment.
group	Group assignment	Categorical	1 = Low anxiety group
			2 = High anxiety group
			Group assignment was based on State-Trait Anxiety Inventory-Y (STAI) State Subscale score. Participants with a score greater than 40 are assigned to the high anxiety group.
acc_percent	Response accuracy	Continuous	Overall accuracy on the stop signal task. Units are correct responses over the total number of trials.
rt_ms	Reaction time (ms)	Continuous	Average reaction time for correct trials only. Units are milliseconds.
stai_s	STAI-Y (state subscale)	Continuous	Total score. Individual items are coded (separately) as follows:
			1 = Not at all
			2 = Somewhat
			3 = Moderately so
			4 = Very much so
			Missing values are coded as "NA."
stai_t	STAI-Y (trait subscale)	Continuous	Total score. Individual items are coded (separately) as:
			1 = Almost never
			2 = Sometimes
			3 = Often
			4 = Almost always
			Missing values are coded as "NA."

[a]Dictionary for the file examplestudy_combined_version01.csv.

organized file structure. A ReadMe file, which is often a text file or word processing document, contains human-readable information about how to navigate the file structure and a description of each item contained therein. A ReadMe file should be placed at the top of the file structure so it is the first document seen when a study data set is opened.

A lab notebook is a complete record of the research process, including why experiments were initiated, how they were performed, and the results. While not all branches of psychology have a culture of maintaining formal lab notebooks like other fields, you should still maintain contemporaneous notes you can refer back to and pass along to future collaborators. Referring back to our example data set (Table 25.3), information about why there is no participant with the ID number 002 or why the reaction time data for participant 003 are missing would be first recorded in a lab notebook and also possibly in a data dictionary.

Electronic lab notebooks (ELNs) are computer programs designed to replace (or complement) paper notebooks. Due to their features related to data organization, data storage, and access control, you may consider an ELN as a central component of a team's RDM system. However, an ELN may not be necessary or even preferred in every circumstance. Whatever system you choose, even if it is paper-based, remember the characteristics emphasized in the introduction: standardization and documentation. You and your team should document your work using the same methods and maintain documentation about how everyone should document their work. In general, a good rule of thumb is to document more than you think is necessary.

Data Sharing

After completing your study, you may want or be expected to share the data that you collected or generated for a variety of different reasons. For example, you may be required to share your data by your funding agency or a journal that requires data sharing (e.g., *PLOS ONE*). You may want to earn an Open Data badge on a journal article (Kidwell et al., 2016) or benefit from the citation advantage associated with articles with publicly available data sets (Colavizza et al., 2020; Piwowar & Vision, 2013). Or perhaps you wish to provide access to your data to bolster the rigor and reproducibility of your findings or enable future analyses that combine data sets to glean new insights (Martone et al., 2018). Regardless of your reasons for data sharing, your primary decision at this point may be how to provide access to the data, as several different approaches exist that vary in their degree of openness.

The least open approach is indicating in a journal article or other research report that the data will be made available upon request. This approach is also the least effective, as only a small proportion of researchers can actually be contacted or choose to provide access to their data when requested by email (Vanpaemel et al., 2015; Vines et al., 2014; Wicherts et al., 2006). Moreover, if the data are not already prepared for sharing at the point of request, this approach may end up being more work for both the requestor, who may need to exert effort into deciphering the data set and asking questions, and the requestee, who may need to retroactively construct file-level documentation to answer those questions.

Another approach to data sharing is to include data files as supplemental materials accompanying a journal article. However, this approach does not treat data sets as stand-alone research products and may not adequately meet FAIR guidelines, as supplemental materials are difficult for others to find independently of a journal article, may be subject to journal copyright restrictions, and may not be maintained by journals in the long term (Caetano & Aisenberg, 2014; Merrill, 2015; Towse et al., 2021).

The most open approach is to deposit data into an online data repository, which allows others to more easily find your data and access them without your mediation. There are presently four major types of repositories that can hold and provide access to research data: disciplinary repositories, funder-sponsored repositories, general repositories, and institutional repositories. Disciplinary repositories are designed for data within particular disciplines or subdisciplines, such as OpenNeuro (https://openneuro.org/) for brain imaging data. Funder-sponsored repositories are designed for data from studies that rely on grants from specific funding agencies, such as the National Institute of Mental Health Data Archive (https://nda.nih.gov/) or the National Institute of Aging's National Archive of Computerized Data on Aging (https://www.icpsr.umich.edu/web/pages/NACDA/index.html). General repositories, such as Dryad (https://datadryad.org/), figshare (https://figshare.com/), or the Open Science Framework (https://osf.io/), are designed to hold many different types of research materials, including data, from any discipline. Finally, institutional repositories are hosted by specific universities or research institutions, such as the University of Michigan's Deep Blue Data (https://deepblue.lib.umich.edu/data). Some of these repositories are fully open, meaning that anyone can freely download data without constraints, whereas other repositories restrict data access to specific users who meet certain requirements when the data contain identifying or protected information.

Out of these repository options, we generally recommend depositing data and file-level documentation into a disciplinary or funder-sponsored repository when one is available, as these repositories may be more likely to make your data findable, accessible, and interoperable by other researchers in your area of study. Above all, however, be sure to select a repository that demonstrates trustworthiness by assigning permanent identifiers, such as DOIs, to data sets; requiring adequate documentation and metadata about data sets; and performing active curation practices to increase the chances that data sets will be findable, accessible, interoperable, and reusable into the reasonable future (Goodman et al., 2014).

Although depositing your data in a repository goes a long way toward meeting the FAIR guidelines (Wilkinson et al., 2016), special attention must still be paid to ensuring that your data are reusable. Indeed, an evaluation of open data sets linked from psychology journals showed that 51% of data sets were incomplete (i.e., unable to be understood independently of the article or did not support reproducibility of the article's findings) and 68% had limited reusability (i.e., data files were not machine-readable, relied on proprietary software, or were not well described by documentation) (Towse et al., 2021). Therefore, to increase the likelihood that your data can be understood and used by others, it is important to deposit robust file-level documentation (e.g., data dictionary or codebook, ReadMe file) alongside the data files.

Upon choosing to deposit your data and documentation in a data repository, you may also consider publishing a "data article" (or "data paper," "data descriptor," etc.). Different from a research article, which analyzes data with the aim of drawing conclusions, a data article provides a brief but detailed description of an available data set with the aim of enabling its use by others. Some journals can be considered "data journals" that exist primarily to publish data articles (e.g., *Journal of Open Psychology Data*, *Data in Brief*, *Scientific Data*), whereas other journals publish data articles as one possible article type (e.g., *Brain and Behavior*, *Neuroinformatics*). Not only do data articles further enhance the findability and reusability of data, they also typically undergo peer review and thus can be listed on your curriculum vitae to boost your research productivity (Candela et al., 2015).

Data Preservation

Even if you do not plan to make your data available to others, you should still take steps to ensure that data are properly archived and preserved. In the United States, federal regulations require the retention of research data collected from human participants for at least 3 years following the conclusion of a study (U.S. Department of Health and Human Services, 2021). Many research institutions have similar requirements, often as part of a broader set of data policies (Briney, 2015). However, many researchers preserve their data for far longer, often in locked filing cabinets or closets. When preserving data for long periods, consider the potential usability of your data. Data preservation is an active process involving, at a minimum, the migration of data and other materials to locations and formats that ensure they are not only still accessible but also still usable over time (Hodge, 2000). When taking steps to preserve data over the long term, it is important to think through both how and where you want to store your data.

Exactly how you should preserve your data depends on their format when they were collected and analyzed. For digital data, certain file formats may become obsolete or inaccessible over time (Rosenthal, 2010). For example, text documents and spreadsheets originally created in Microsoft Works (1987–2007) may not be open in Microsoft Word or Excel today. One way to address situations like this is to migrate data and other materials to open file formats. Open (i.e., nonproprietary) file formats are those that can be used and implemented by anyone. In practice, this means that files stored in open formats can be opened and used by a variety of proprietary, free, and open-source software tools rather than just a single piece of software. For this reason, open formats are far more likely to remain usable over the long term, even if the software that created them is not available or no longer functional.

Another factor to consider when migrating digital file formats is the loss or manipulation of information that can occur with compression and other forms of processing (Cromey, 2012). For example, when images are encoded into a "lossy" format, such as JPEG, some of the original image information is lost and cannot be restored. Though this may result in a smaller file size, the quality of the image may be affected. By contrast, "lossless" image formats, such as TIFF, generally have larger file sizes. This particular example is notable because TIFF is a proprietary format, maintained by Adobe Inc. Thus, preservation means making a complex decision about how to maximize the likelihood of continued accessibility of your data into the future. To help with such decisions, we synthesize recommendations from the U.S. Library of Congress (Library of Congress, 2020) with a list of open file types in Table 25.7.

TABLE 25.7

File Types for Data Preservation

Type	Library of Congress recommended formats	Open formats
Text	XML-based markup formats (e.g., EPUB, BITS), PDF, XML-based document formats (e.g., DOCX, ODF)	Plain text (TXT), HTML, Markdown, ePub, LaTeX, Open Office XML, PDF
Images	TIFF, PNG, JPEG2000	PNG, SVG, JPEG2000, GIF
Video	MOV, MPEG-2	Matroska (MKV)
Audio	PCM, WAVE	WAVE, FLAC, MP3, OGG
Data sets	Formats using well-known schemas with public validation tool available, line-oriented formats (e.g., TSV, CSV, fixed-width), any proprietary format that is a de facto standard for a profession or supported by multiple tools (e.g., XLS, XLSX)	TSV, CSV

Note. This is not meant to be an exhaustive list but highlights common file formats and data types. Note that "open" file formats are not necessarily lossless.

In addition to the file types used to preserve your data, you should also consider the storage medium. Consider the obsolescence of media such as floppy disks and even CD-Rs and DVD-Rs. Information stored on these media are increasingly inaccessible as the number of computers sold with disk drives decreases. A solid-state hard drive has a lower rate of failure than a USB flash drive, but every form of digital data storage has a rate of failure. When possible, therefore, you should preserve data in multiple locations. You should also take steps to ensure the integrity of your data. In the realm of digital preservation, this means ensuring its fixity, or that it has remained unchanged over time. As many trustworthy data repositories actively employ long-term preservation strategies, sharing data through a repository often means that it will be effectively preserved over the long term. If you cannot or choose not to share your data in this manner, university libraries and information technology departments are sources of expertise and often offer services related to long-term digital preservation.

Compliance

RDM-related compliance issues may arise at multiple points of the research process due to funding agency and journal policies, regulations concerning the management and sharing of data from human subjects research, and the potential need to determine how others can and cannot reuse your data in the future.

As we previously mentioned, both public and private funding agencies increasingly require DMPs or data sharing plans as components of grant applications (Williams et al., 2017), requiring researchers to formulate plans for managing and providing access to their data even before a study commences. In addition, peer-reviewed journals are increasingly adopting data sharing policies that encourage or require authors to make the data underlying their results available in an effort to increase research rigor and reproducibility. For some of these journals, the data may undergo peer review along with the manuscript, and manuscript acceptance is not granted until the precondition of data sharing is met (Resnik et al., 2019). However, while funding agency and journal policies push researchers to make their data more accessible to other researchers or the general public, it is at the same time important to guard against violating the privacy or confidentiality of human research participants (Zook et al., 2017). These opposing expectations regarding data sharing are also reflected by research participants themselves, who are often supportive of data sharing for "the common good" but harbor concerns about being identified or having their data misused, such as by insurance companies or for commercial purposes (Cummings & Day, 2019; Kalkman et al., 2022).

The good news is that data from human participants can be safely shared if you take certain precautions. The first critical steps should occur when you develop an informed consent form and apply for institutional review board

(IRB) approval. If you intend to share your data with other researchers or the public, do not promise participants in the informed consent form that their data will not be shared outside the research team. Instead, incorporate language into the informed consent form that describes why the data will be shared, with whom it will be shared, and how information that could identify them will be removed from the data before sharing (Alter & Gonzalez, 2018; Meyer, 2018). In your IRB protocol, do not promise to destroy the data after study completion. Rather, explain how participants will be informed about data sharing, describe how you will make adequate provisions to protect data containing private or confidential information (U.S. Department of Health and Human Services, 2021), and lay out your strategies for providing an appropriate level of data access to relevant stakeholders during and after the study. If your data are already collected and you did not proactively obtain consent from participants to share their data, data sharing might still be possible under certain circumstances (Meyer, 2018). However, planning ahead to avoid roadblocks to data sharing is always the best approach.

During the data collection and analysis stages, you should take care to safely store human subjects data and manage access to these data by other members of your research team, especially if the data contains sensitive, private, or protected health information. These procedures should be thoroughly described in your IRB protocol and research protocol and followed by all members of the research team. Depending on the nature of your study, the following questions may need to be answered:

- Should data containing identifying information be stored separately from the rest of the data?
- Should certain data files be password-protected or stored in an encrypted manner?
- Who will have access to the data during the collection and/or analysis stages?
- Will new research team members receive training or onboarding related to data security?
- How will the data be securely shared among research team members at different institutions?
- What happens when someone on the research team leaves or changes institutions?
- Should certain parts of the data be destroyed or discarded after study completion?

As different institutions may have different requirements and systems for secure data storage, we advise consulting with staff at your institution for further guidance and resources (Briney et al., 2020).

Before sharing data collected from human research participants, you should assess the risks of revealing their identities and perform sufficient data deidentification or anonymization to minimize those risks (Alter & Gonzalez, 2018; Meyer, 2018). Multiple deidentification approaches exist, including the Health Insurance Portability and Accountability Act's (HIPAA's) "safe harbor" method (i.e., removing 18 specific identifiers), converting continuous demographic variables into categories, masking original data values, using open-source "de-facing" tools such as those offered by OpenfMRI (https://openfmri.org/de-identification/), or taking advantage of expert de-identification services offered by some disciplinary and funder-sponsored repositories. It is important to recognize that even when direct identifiers (e.g., name, birthdate, Social Security number) are stripped from data, participants can still potentially be reidentified using combinations of indirect identifiers. Therefore, it is the researcher's responsibility to thoroughly interrogate the data before sharing to reduce the risks of participant reidentification as much as possible (Zook et al., 2017).

When choosing how to share human subjects data, depositing the data into a trustworthy data repository is still preferable to making the data available upon request (American Psychological Association's Data Sharing Working Group, 2015). However, if the data cannot be fully de-identified or anonymized without losing its value, you should select a data repository that provides suitable options for restricting access to specific individuals who meet certain qualifications, such as collaborators or academic researchers with an approved IRB protocol. Even the most highly sensitive data can be shared through a virtual or physical data enclave, which allows specific researchers to analyze data within a secure environment but blocks the removal of data from that environment. When allowing specific individuals to access data containing personal or identifying information, it is advisable to use a legally binding data-use agreement that delineates what reusers can and cannot do with the data and outlines expectations for appropriately handling the data to protect participants' identities (Alter & Gonzalez, 2018).

Regardless of whether your research involves human participants, when making your data available to the general public, it is important to understand, and in some cases define, how others can reuse the data. "Raw" observational or experimental data are typically considered "facts" and are thus not protected by copyright (Carroll, 2015). However, you can apply a Creative Commons (CC) license (https://creativecommons.org/) to data to impose certain conditions on its reuse. The most permissive CC license (CC0) places a work in the public domain, which allows others to distribute, remix, adapt, or build upon it in any medium or format with no conditions. By contrast, a more restrictive CC license (CC BY-NC) allows others to remix, adapt, and build upon your work, but only for noncommercial purposes and only when acknowledging the creator. Note that your choice of a CC license may be dictated by your institution, funding agency, or other relevant regulatory body, and some data repositories automatically apply certain CC licenses to data sets (Figueiredo, 2017).

CONCLUSION

Data are the backbone of your research. Therefore, a considered approach to managing your data throughout the entirety of your study is critical for good research practice and serves to increase the rigor and reproducibility of your findings. In this chapter, we argue that proper data management begins before you begin collecting data and can even extend beyond study completion. Before data collection, it is important to formulate a DMP and, if performing human subjects research, describe your RDM practices in your IRB protocol and incorporate language about RDM and data sharing into your informed consent form. While collecting and analyzing your data, keep your data tidy and well-organized, create data dictionaries or other file-level documentation, and back up your data to prevent loss. After study completion, adhere to the FAIR guiding principles by using a trustworthy data repository to share your data to the broadest extent possible, and take appropriate steps to ensure that your data files are preserved in a way that allows them to be reopened and reused in the future. Above all, we cannot emphasize enough the importance of being consistent in your own RDM practices, of standardizing RDM practices among members of your research team, and thoroughly documenting your practices so they can be understood by you, your collaborators, and other potential reusers in the future.

As your data can have enduring value after the completion of your study, we recommend performing RDM with the ultimate goal of sharing your data with others, as data sharing not only encourages a culture of openness and accountability but also enables secondary data analyses and meta-analyses, thereby increasing research efficiency and accelerating scientific progress (American Psychological Association's Board of Scientific Affairs, 2015). However, psychologists may still have several concerns about data sharing, such as the time and effort needed to prepare data for sharing, the possibility of mistakes being exposed, and the potential for data to be misinterpreted or misused (Abele-Brehm et al., 2019; Houtkoop et al., 2018). We do not discount the fact that good RDM certainly takes time and effort, but we argue that carefully managing your data throughout the entirety of your study and choosing an appropriate method of data sharing can lessen these concerns by ensuring that your data and analyses are error-free, that your documentation adequately describes the content of your data files, that your data and accompanying documentation are already in a nearly shareable state upon study completion, and that, if needed, reuse of your data is restricted to specific individuals for certain purposes. Furthermore, concerns about not receiving appropriate credit for your data can be balanced by greater community acceptance of collaborative approaches to data sharing and synthesis (Hunt, 2019; Perrino et al., 2013) and data citation practices (Crosas, 2014) as well as the recognition that studies with data available in public repositories receive more citations (Piwowar & Vision, 2013).

Finally, we urge you to take full advantage of RDM support offered by your institution, such as RDM training, services, and resources provided by your library; secure data storage options provided by your information technology department; and guidance on de-identifying and sharing human subjects data provided by your institution's statistical core and IRB or research compliance offices (Briney et al., 2020; Meyer, 2018).

References

Abele-Brehm, A. E., Gollwitzer, M., Steinberg, U., & Schönbrodt, F. D. (2019). Attitudes toward open science and public data sharing: A survey among members of the German Psychological Society. *Social Psychology, 50*(4), 252–260. https://doi.org/10.1027/1864-9335/a000384

Alter, G., & Gonzalez, R. (2018). Responsible practices for data sharing. *American Psychologist, 73*(2), 146–156. https://doi.org/10.1037/amp0000258

American Psychological Association. (2017). *Ethical principles of psychologists and code of conduct* (2002, amended effective June 1, 2010, and January 1, 2017). https://www.apa.org/ethics/code/index.aspx

American Psychological Association's Data Sharing Working Group. (2015). *Data sharing: Principles and considerations for policy development.* https://www.apa.org/science/leadership/bsa/data-sharing-report.pdf

Borghi, J. A., Abrams, S., Lowenberg, D., Simms, S., & Chodacki, J. (2018). Support your data: A research data management guide for researchers. *Research Ideas and Outcomes, 4,* e26439. https://doi.org/10.3897/rio.4.e26439

Briney, K. A. (2015). *Data management for researchers: Organize, maintain and share your data for research success.* Pelagic Publishing.

Briney, K. A., Coates, H., & Goben, A. (2020). Foundational practices of research data management. *Research Ideas and Outcomes, 6,* e56508. https://doi.org/10.3897/rio.6.e56508

Broman, K. W., & Woo, K. H. (2018). Data organization in spreadsheets. *The American Statistician, 72*(1), 2–10. https://doi.org/10.1080/00031305.2017.1375989

Caetano, D. S., & Aisenberg, A. (2014). Forgotten treasures: The fate of data in animal behaviour studies. *Animal Behaviour, 98,* 1–5. https://doi.org/10.1016/j.anbehav.2014.09.025

Candela, L., Castelli, D., Manghi, P., & Tani, A. (2015). Data journals: A survey. *Journal of the Association for Information Science and Technology, 66*(9), 1747–1762. https://doi.org/10.1002/asi.23358

Carroll, M. W. (2015). Sharing research data and intellectual property law: A primer. *PLOS Biology, 13*(8), e1002235. https://doi.org/10.1371/journal.pbio.1002235

Ceci, S. J., & Walker, E. (1983). Private archives and public needs. *American Psychologist, 38*(4), 414–423. https://doi.org/10.1037/0003-066X.38.4.414

Chan, A.-W., Tetzlaff, J. M., Gøtzsche, P. C., Altman, D. G., Mann, H., Berlin, J. A., Dickersin, K., Hróbjartsson, A., Schulz, K. F., Parulekar, W. R., Krleža-Jerić, K., Laupacis, A., & Moher, D. (2013). SPIRIT 2013 explanation and elaboration: Guidance for protocols of clinical trials. *BMJ, 346.* https://doi.org/10.1136/bmj.e7586

Colavizza, G., Hrynaszkiewicz, I., Staden, I., Whitaker, K., & McGillivray, B. (2020). The citation advantage of linking publications to research data. *PLOS ONE, 15*(4), e0230416. https://doi.org/10.1371/journal.pone.0230416

Craig, J. R., & Reese, S. C. (1973). Retention of raw data: A problem revisited. *American Psychologist, 28*(8), 723. https://doi.org/10.1037/h0035667

Cromey, D. W. (2012). Digital images are data: And should be treated as such. In D. J. Taatjes & J. Roth (Eds.), *Cell imaging techniques* (Vol. 931, pp. 1–27). Humana Press. https://doi.org/10.1007/978-1-62703-056-4_1

Crosas, M. (2014). The evolution of data citation: From principles to implementation. *IASSIST Quarterly, 37*(1-4), 62. https://www.semanticscholar.org/paper/The-Evolution-of-Data-Citation:-From-Principles-to-Crosas/de5db00dc64c88ddc8b2729745a89a3ec8fe264b

Cummings, J. A., & Day, T. E. (2019). But what do participants want? Comment on the "Data Sharing in Psychology" special section (2018). *American Psychologist, 74*(2), 245–247. https://doi.org/10.1037/amp0000408

De Angelis, C., Drazen, J. M., Frizelle, F. A., Haug, C., Hoey, J., Horton, R., Kotzin, S., Laine, C., Marusic, A., Overbeke, A. J. P. M., Schroeder, T. V., Sox, H. C., Van Der Weyden, M. B., & the International Committee of Medical Journal Editors. (2004). Clinical trial registration: A statement from the International Committee of Medical Journal

Editors. *The New England Journal of Medicine*, *351*(12), 1250–1251. https://doi.org/10.1056/NEJMe048225

Ellis, S. E., & Leek, J. T. (2018). How to share data for collaboration. *The American Statistician*, *72*(1), 53–57. https://doi.org/10.1080/00031305.2017.1375987

Figueiredo, A. S. (2017). Data sharing: Convert challenges into opportunities. *Frontiers in Public Health*, *5*, 327. https://doi.org/10.3389/fpubh.2017.00327

Freedland, K. E., & Carney, R. M. (1992). Data management and accountability in behavioral and biomedical research. *American Psychologist*, *47*(5), 640–645. https://doi.org/10.1037/0003-066X.47.5.640

Goodman, A., Pepe, A., Blocker, A. W., Borgman, C. L., Cranmer, K., Crosas, M., Di Stefano, R., Gil, Y., Groth, P., Hedstrom, M., Hogg, D. W., Kashyap, V., Mahabal, A., Siemiginowska, A., & Slavkovic, A. (2014). Ten simple rules for the care and feeding of scientific data. *PLOS Computational Biology*, *10*(4), e1003542. https://doi.org/10.1371/journal.pcbi.1003542

Hardwicke, T. E., & Ioannidis, J. P. A. (2018). Mapping the universe of registered reports. *Nature Human Behaviour*, *2*(11), 793–796. https://doi.org/10.1038/s41562-018-0444-y

Hart, E. M., Barmby, P., LeBauer, D., Michonneau, F., Mount, S., Mulrooney, P., Poisot, T., Woo, K. H., Zimmerman, N. B., & Hollister, J. W. (2016). Ten simple rules for digital data storage. *PLOS Computational Biology*, *12*(10), e1005097. https://doi.org/10.1371/journal.pcbi.1005097

Hodge, G. M. (2000). Best practices for digital archiving: An information life cycle approach. *D-Lib Magazine*, *6*(1). https://doi.org/10.1045/january2000-hodge

Horstmann, K. T., Arslan, R. C., & Greiff, S. (2020). Generating codebooks to ensure the independent use of research data: Some guidelines. *European Journal of Psychological Assessment*, *36*(5), 721–729. https://doi.org/10.1027/1015-5759/a000620

Houtkoop, B. L., Chambers, C., Macleod, M., Bishop, D. V. M., Nichols, T. E., & Wagenmakers, E.-J. (2018). Data sharing in psychology: A survey on barriers and preconditions. *Advances in Methods and Practices in Psychological Science*, *1*(1), 70–85. https://doi.org/10.1177/2515245917751886

Hudson Vitale, C., & Moulaison-Sandy, H. (2019). Data management plans: A review. *DESIDOC Journal of Library and Information Technology*, *39*(6), 322–328. https://doi.org/10.14429/djlit.39.06.15086

Hunt, L. T. (2019). The life-changing magic of sharing your data. *Nature Human Behaviour*, *3*(4), 312–315. https://doi.org/10.1038/s41562-019-0560-3

Kalkman, S., van Delden, J., Banerjee, A., Tyl, B., Mostert, M., & van Thiel, G. (2022). Patients' and public views and attitudes towards the sharing of health data for research: A narrative review of the empirical evidence. *Journal of Medical Ethics*, *48*(1), 3–13. https://doi.org/10.1136/medethics-2019-105651

Kidwell, M. C., Lazarević, L. B., Baranski, E., Hardwicke, T. E., Piechowski, S., Falkenberg, L.-S., Kennett, C., Slowik, A., Sonnleitner, C., Hess-Holden, C., Errington, T. M., Fiedler, S., & Nosek, B. A. (2016). Badges to acknowledge open practices: A simple, low-cost, effective method for increasing transparency. *PLOS Biology*, *14*(5), e1002456. https://doi.org/10.1371/journal.pbio.1002456

Klein, O., Hardwicke, T. E., Aust, F., Breuer, J., Danielsson, H., Mohr, A. H., IJzerman, H., Nilsonne, G., Vanpaemel, W., & Frank, M. C. (2018). A practical guide for transparency in psychological science. *Collabra: Psychology*, *4*(1), 20. https://doi.org/10.1525/collabra.158

Library of Congress. (2020). *Library of Congress Recommended Formats Statement—2020–2021*. https://www.loc.gov/preservation/resources/rfs/index.html

Martone, M. E., Garcia-Castro, A., & VandenBos, G. R. (2018). Data sharing in psychology. *American Psychologist*, *73*(2), 111–125. https://doi.org/10.1037/amp0000242

Merrill, E. (2015). A word about supplemental materials. *The Journal of Wildlife Management*, *79*(7), 1039–1040. https://doi.org/10.1002/jwmg.926

Meyer, M. N. (2018). Practical tips for ethical data sharing. *Advances in Methods and Practices in Psychological Science*, *1*(1), 131–144. https://doi.org/10.1177/2515245917747656

Mons, B., Neylon, C., Velterop, J., Dumontier, M., da Silva Santos, L. O. B., & Wilkinson, M. D. (2017). Cloudy, increasingly FAIR; Revisiting the FAIR Data guiding principles for the European Open Science Cloud. *Information Services & Use*, *37*(1), 49–56. https://doi.org/10.3233/ISU-170824

Nosek, B. A., Beck, E. D., Campbell, L., Flake, J. K., Hardwicke, T. E., Mellor, D. T., van't Veer, A. E., & Vazire, S. (2019). Preregistration is hard, and worthwhile. *Trends in Cognitive Sciences*, *23*(10), 815–818. https://doi.org/10.1016/j.tics.2019.07.009

Panko, R. R. (1998). What we know about spreadsheet errors. *Journal of Organizational and End User*

Computing, 10(2), 15–21. https://doi.org/10.4018/joeuc.1998040102

Perrino, T., Howe, G., Sperling, A., Beardslee, W., Sandler, I., Shern, D., Pantin, H., Kaupert, S., Cano, N., Cruden, G., Bandiera, F., Brown, C. H., & the NIMH Collaborative Data Synthesis for Adolescent Depression Trials Study Team including. (2013). Advancing science through collaborative data sharing and synthesis. *Perspectives on Psychological Science*, 8(4), 433–444. https://doi.org/10.1177/1745691613491579

Piwowar, H. A., & Vision, T. J. (2013). Data reuse and the open data citation advantage. *PeerJ*, 1, e175. https://doi.org/10.7717/peerj.175

Resnik, D. B., Morales, M., Landrum, R., Shi, M., Minnier, J., Vasilevsky, N. A., & Champieux, R. E. (2019). Effect of impact factor and discipline on journal data sharing policies. *Accountability in Research*, 26(3), 139–156. https://doi.org/10.1080/08989621.2019.1591277

Rosenthal, D. S. H. (2010). Format obsolescence: Assessing the threat and the defenses. *Library Hi Tech*, 28(2), 195–210. https://doi.org/10.1108/07378831011047613

Smale, N., Unsworth, K., Denyer, G., & Barr, D. (2018 Preprint). The history, advocacy and efficacy of data management plans. *bioRxiv*, 443499. https://doi.org/10.1101/443499

Szollosi, A., Kellen, D., Navarro, D. J., Shiffrin, R., van Rooij, I., Van Zandt, T., & Donkin, C. (2020). Is preregistration worthwhile? *Trends in Cognitive Sciences*, 24(2), 94–95. https://doi.org/10.1016/j.tics.2019.11.009

Tenopir, C., Allard, S., Sinha, P., Pollock, D., Newman, J., Dalton, E., Frame, M., & Baird, L. (2016). Data management education from the perspective of science educators. *International Journal of Digital Curation*, 11(1), 232–251. https://doi.org/10.2218/ijdc.v11i1.389

Towse, J. N., Ellis, D. A., & Towse, A. S. (2021). Opening Pandora's box: Peeking inside psychology's data sharing practices, and seven recommendations for change. *Behavior Research Methods*, 53(4), 1455–1468. https://doi.org/10.3758/s13428-020-01486-1

U.S. Department of Health and Human Services. (2021). *Electronic Code of Federal Regulations: Title 45: Public Welfare, PART 46-Protection of Human Subjects*. https://www.ecfr.gov/cgi-bin/text-idx?SID=30784bd520020b10713a01f87a1e98d3&mc=true&node=pt45.1.46&rgn=div5

Vanpaemel, W., Vermorgen, M., Deriemaecker, L., & Storms, G. (2015). Are we wasting a good crisis? The availability of psychological research data after the storm. *Collabra: Psychology*, 1(1), 3. https://doi.org/10.1525/collabra.13

Vines, T. H., Albert, A. Y. K., Andrew, R. L., Débarre, F., Bock, D. G., Franklin, M. T., Gilbert, K. J., Moore, J.-S., Renaut, S., & Rennison, D. J. (2014). The availability of research data declines rapidly with article age. *Current Biology*, 24(1), 94–97. https://doi.org/10.1016/j.cub.2013.11.014

Wicherts, J. M., Borsboom, D., Kats, J., & Molenaar, D. (2006). The poor availability of psychological research data for reanalysis. *American Psychologist*, 61(7), 726–728. https://doi.org/10.1037/0003-066X.61.7.726

Wickham, H. (2014). Tidy data. *Journal of Statistical Software*, 59(10), 1–23. https://doi.org/10.18637/jss.v059.i10

Wilkinson, M. D., Dumontier, M., Aalbersberg, I. J., Appleton, G., Axton, M., Baak, A., Blomberg, N., Boiten, J. W., da Silva Santos, L. B., Bourne, P. E., Bouwman, J., Brookes, A. J., Clark, T., Crosas, M., Dillo, I., Dumon, O., Edmunds, S., Evelo, C. T., Finkers, R., . . . Mons, B. (2016). The FAIR Guiding Principles for scientific data management and stewardship. *Scientific Data*, 3(1), 160018. https://doi.org/10.1038/sdata.2016.18

Williams, M., Bagwell, J., & Nahm Zozus, M. (2017). Data management plans: The missing perspective. *Journal of Biomedical Informatics*, 71, 130–142. https://doi.org/10.1016/j.jbi.2017.05.004

Wolins, L. (1962). Responsibility for raw data. *American Psychologist*, 17(9), 657–658. https://doi.org/10.1037/h0038819

Ziemann, M., Eren, Y., & El-Osta, A. (2016). Gene name errors are widespread in the scientific literature. *Genome Biology*, 17(1), 177. https://doi.org/10.1186/s13059-016-1044-7

Zook, M., Barocas, S., Boyd, D., Crawford, K., Keller, E., Gangadharan, S. P., Goodman, A., Hollander, R., Koenig, B. A., Metcalf, J., Narayanan, A., Nelson, A., & Pasquale, F. (2017). Ten simple rules for responsible big data research. *PLOS Computational Biology*, 13(3), e1005399. https://doi.org/10.1371/journal.pcbi.1005399

CHAPTER 26

QUESTIONABLE PRACTICES IN STATISTICAL ANALYSIS

Rex B. Kline

Questionable data analysis practices are a major part of the larger concept of *questionable research practices*, which is broadly defined by Gerrits et al. (2019) as the intentional or unintentional reporting of "conclusions or messages that may lead to incorrect inferences and do not accurately reflect the objectives, the methodology or the results of the study" (p. 2). How the data are collected and analyzed and how analysis results are interpreted can obviously affect what is communicated. Incomplete, distorted, or opaque postanalysis reporting is thus another crucial aspect of questionable research practices. There are now several guidelines for reporting analysis results, including newly revised journal article reporting standards (JARS) for quantitative, qualitative, and mixed-methods studies—respectively, JARS-Quant, JARS-Qual, and JARS-Mixed—by the American Psychological Association (APA; Appelbaum et al., 2018; Levitt et al., 2018). Analysis-related issues feature prominently in APA and other reporting standards (e.g., EQUATOR network[1]) in terms of *what* should be reported, but there is less guidance about *how* to analyze data. In contrast, this chapter more directly concerns the "how," or in this case dubious or poor practices in statistical analysis to avoid.

HARD VERSUS SOFT QUESTIONABLE PRACTICES

Wasserman (2013) differentiated between "hard" and "soft" instances of questionable research practices. The hard case involves outright scientific fraud, including the fabrication or falsification of data with the overt intention to deceive, and also plagiarism, or falsely taking credit for the ideas or work of others. There are notorious cases of fraud in various scientific disciplines, including fake stem cell lines in cloning research (Saunders & Savulescu, 2008) and data falsification in research on organic semiconductors published in prestigious journals such as *Science*, *Nature*, and *Physics Review* (Service, 2003). Psychology has its own infamous examples, including three researchers who faked data for publications in some of the most prominent journals in social psychology, including *Personality and Social Psychology Bulletin* (Funder & Task Force on Publication and Research Practices, 2014; Simonsohn, 2013).

In a meta-analysis of 18 prior surveys on scientific misconduct among researchers in pharmacology, nursing, medicine, and health education, among other disciplines, Fanelli (2009)

---

[1]https://www.equator-network.org/reporting-guidelines/

https://doi.org/10.1037/0000320-026
APA Handbook of Research Methods in Psychology, Second Edition: Vol. 3. Data Analysis and Research Publication, H. Cooper (Editor-in-Chief)
Copyright © 2023 by the American Psychological Association. All rights reserved.

reported that about 2% of scientists admitted to data falsification or modification on at least one occasion. Over the 18 surveys, admission rates varied by format of the survey, wording of the questions, and profession. Specifically, lower rates of self-disclosed misconduct were reported in mailed surveys or when questions included the words "fabrication" or "falsification," and admission rates were generally higher among medical or pharmacological researchers. Fanelli suggested that the actual rate of scientific misconduct could be even higher than 2%, given the sensitive nature of the subject and limitations of self-report questionnaires.

Soft misconduct corresponds more closely to the term "questionable" in that such practices do not generally involve the explicit motivation to cheat or deceive through fabricated data. Instead, questionable practices, although not necessarily wrong, raise doubts about the study (Gerrits et al., 2019). They arise out of what Simmons et al. (2011) called *researcher degrees of freedom*, or the relatively broad latitude that science authors have when writing or presenting their results. Such discretion refers to the wide range of decisions that can be made about how (a) target variables are operationalized or measured, (b) cases are selected including the sample size, (c) data are screened or processed before or during the analysis, (d) selections are made among multiple covariates or alternative measures of predictors or outcomes, and (e) inference criteria are applied in deciding whether the hypotheses are supported by the data, among other kinds of decisions that can affect the results.

Soft misconduct occurs when researchers intentionally or unintentionally "spin" their results by (a) making decisions of the kind mentioned in the previous paragraph that skew the results in favor of the hypotheses while (b) failing to disclose just how those decisions affected the results. It is a form of propaganda that ranges from misreporting by "beautification" of analysis results to misinterpretation of those results that gives readers a false impression (Boutron & Ravaud, 2018). It also involves overinterpretation, or the use of overly optimistic language in the text, or the drawing of conclusions based on self-curated—and, thus, overly favorable—analysis results, perhaps as a way to disguise or distract from shortcomings in design, sampling, or procedures (Ochodo et al., 2013).

There are two levels of questionable data analysis practices: specific and general. Specific dubious practices concern technical shortcomings in the application of a particular analytical method, such as regression techniques in single-outcome analyses or structural equation modeling (SEM) in analyses with multiple predictors or outcomes. It is beyond the scope of this chapter to address questionable practices for the myriad of statistical techniques. Fortunately, there are publications about best statistical practices for specific methods—examples include Aguinis and Gottfredson (2010) about estimating interaction effects in multiple regression, Morrison et al. (2017) about using SEM in psychology research, and Schreiber (2021) about best practices in exploratory factor analysis—and an article search by the reader may turn up something helpful for a particular statistical technique.

General questionable practices can occur over a wide range of analyses, that is, they are not specific to the use of any particular analysis method. An example is the inference method that determines whether the results are interpreted as supporting or not supporting the hypotheses. Among psychology researchers, classical null hypothesis significance testing that generates p values is the best known and most widely used method. There are other inference methods, including Bayesian estimation and interval estimation with effect sizes (Calin-Jagemen & Cumming, 2019; Rougier, 2019), but the reporting of p values is predominant in the psychology research literature. Thus, it is no surprise that many, if not most, questionable data analysis practices involve the misuse or misinterpretation of p values.

TYPES AND RATES OF QUESTIONABLE PRACTICES

Dozens of general questionable data analysis or reporting practices have been described in the literature. For instance, Gerrits et al. (2019)

constructed a checklist of 35 such practices in the area of health services research, and Boutron and Ravaud (2018) described a total of 13 different ways to "spin" (i.e., misreport) about methods, results, or generalizability in biomedical research. John et al. (2012) surveyed 2,155 research psychologists (36% response rate) about 10 different questionable practices using novel incentives for honest reporting. The respondents were told that contributions to charities of their choice would be made by John et al. based on the truthfulness of the respondents' answers. Half the respondents were also (honestly) told that the amount of the contribution was determined by a Bayesian statistical algorithm that checks for truthful responding (i.e., the more truthful, the greater the donation). John et al. reported that conditions just described boosted proportions of respondents who admitted engaging in questionable practices, especially those seen as more unacceptable or flagrant.

Listed in Table 26.1 in descending order by self-admission rates are the questionable practices endorsed by respondents in John et al.'s (2012) survey who received the two truth-telling incentives just described. These results are summarized next: Most psychology researchers admitted to failing to report results for all outcomes (67%) as well as to deciding whether to collect more data after checking if a desired result is significant (58%). The latter practice is a kind of *p-hacking* closely related to stopping data collection because a significant result was obtained—also called *testing to a foregone conclusion* (Steward & Balice-Gordon, 2014)—which was endorsed by 23% of the respondents in John et al.'s sample (see Table 26.1). A problem with this tactic is that the p value can increase again to above $p = .05$ as more data are collected (Nuzzo, 2014). Other ways to hack p values are considered later.

Near-majorities of psychology researchers surveyed by John et al. (2012) selectively reported results from other studies consistent with their hypotheses (50%), decided whether to exclude data after checking the impact of doing so on the results (43%), or described an unexpected finding

TABLE 26.1

Types and Rates of Questionable Practices Among Psychology Researchers

Practice	Rate (%)
1. Failed to report results for all outcome variables	67
2. Decided to collect more data after checking whether results are statistically significant	58
3. Selectively reported findings from other studies that supported hypotheses	50
4. Decided whether to exclude data after checking the impact of doing so on the results	43
5. Described unexpected findings as though they were predicted from the beginning of the study	35
6. Failed to report results from all conditions in the study	27
7. Rounded off $p > .05$, such as .053, in order to report as $p < .05$	23
8. Stopped data collection after checking whether a result is significant	23
9. Claimed that results were unaffected by demographic characteristics either when either uncertain or knowing the claim is false	5
10. Falsified data	2

Note. Adapted from "Measuring the Prevalence of Questionable Research Practices With Incentives for Truth Telling," by L. K. John, G. Loewenstein, and D. Prelec, 2012, *Psychological Science*, 23(5), p. 525 (https://doi.org/10.1177/0956797611430953). Copyright 2020 by SAGE Publications. Adapted with permission.

as predicted from the start (35%; Table 26.1). The presentation of a post-hoc hypothesis informed by data analysis as if it were a prior prediction is *HARKing*, or hypothesizing after the results are known (Kerr, 1998). There are a few basic variations, including (a) *HARKing by subtraction*, where results that are smaller in magnitude or not significant are omitted or minimized by paying them little attention; and (b) *HARKing by addition*, where larger or significant effects are emphasized and thus made more prominent (Bosco et al., 2016). Related forms include (c) *cherry-picking*, where the researcher selects among results from different subgroups or variables that all estimate the same relation between two constructs; and (d) *question trolling*—also called *data dredging* or *data snooping*—which is the unplanned search among heterogeneous effects for multiple constructs to find the strongest results, such as those that are significant, that become the focus of the paper (Murphy & Aguinis, 2019). There is also (e) *JARKing*, or justifying after results are known (Nuzzo, 2015), which happens when researchers present results that are not significant as though they actually support the hypotheses. An example of JARKing is the use of the hackneyed phrase about results "trending" toward significance, but they are not really so (e.g., $.05 \leq p \leq .10$).

About a quarter of research psychologists in John et al.'s (2012) sample failed to report findings from all conditions in the study (27%) or "rounded off" a p value just above .05, such as $p = .053$ rounded to $p < .05$, in order to present the result as significant (23%; Table 26.1). This form of cheating may reflect *dichotomania*, or the obsession to dichotomize continuous p values based on arbitrary thresholds, such as $p < .05$, and the associated compulsion to hype significant results while bemoaning, ignoring, or discounting findings that are not significant (Greenland, 2017).

It is no surprise that even harder forms of misconduct were admitted at lower rates in John et al.'s (2012) study, including the willfully blind or false claim that results were unaffected by demographic characteristics (5%) or falsification of data (2%; Table 26.1), a self-admitted rate among psychology researchers similar to the corresponding rate among biomedical researchers surveyed by Fanelli (2009). Altogether, about 94% of the psychology researchers who received full truth-telling incentives in the John et al. survey admitted to engaging in one or more questionable practices—and in this sense, such practices may be the norm, not the exception. However, Fiedler and Schwarz (2016) criticized the methods and interpretation of John et al. and suggested that rates of questionable practices could be overstated.

There is other evidence that rates of questionable practices of the kind just considered are disturbingly high in the research literature for psychology and other areas. Head et al. (2015) used both meta-analytic and text-mining methods to analyze *p*-curves, or distributions of *p* values over sets of open-access empirical studies in biology, chemistry, engineering, medicine and health sciences, and psychology and cognitive sciences. Evidence for widespread *p*-hacking was indicated by relatively excessive occurrences of p values just below .05, or the conventional level of statistical significance, and thus exactly at the point where *p*-hacking may be the strongest. A caveat is that the degree of expected bias due to the *p*-hacking, or the reporting of inflated effects sizes, was not so strong that it would radically alter conclusions in meta-analytic summaries, at least among the particular articles analyzed by Head et al.

Masicampo and Lalande (2012) reported similar results in their analyses of articles published in 2007 and 2008 in three respected psychology research journals, *Journal of Experimental Psychology: General*, *Journal of Personality and Social Psychology*, and *Psychological Science*. Distributions of over 3,500 p values collected from a total of 36 journal issues were analyzed with curve estimation procedures including residuals analysis. Over all articles, relative frequencies of p values in the range .045 to .050 were unexpectedly high, given numbers of p values in other ranges. Bruns and Ioannidis (2016) cautioned that analysis of *p*-curves in observational research can be misleading when estimating the extent of *p*-hacking unless those curves are calibrated to control for omitted-variables bias, which can mimic effects of *p*-hacking in uncorrected distributions. They also noted that violations of randomization can potentially distort *p*-curves for experimental studies.

The issue of HARKing is a little more complicated because sometimes it is reviewers or journal editors who request the post-hoc addition of hypotheses during the peer review process. Thus, HARKing does not always reflect author misconduct because reviewers and editors are *expected* to ask for revisions, some of which may involve testing new hypotheses (Murphy & Aguinis, 2019). It is also generally true that neither reviewers nor journal editors take kindly to reporting of results that do not support hypotheses (Bosco et al., 2016). There is actually a positive role in science for post-hoc analyses of data that corresponds to what Hollenbeck and Wright (2017) referred to as *Tharking*, or transparently HARKing in the Discussion section. They argued that the Discussion section in scientific papers is in fact the proper place for reporting on post hoc, more exploratory data analyses. Doing so leverages available data in a way that does not necessarily bias parameter estimates reported in the Results section while explicitly acknowledging uncertainty associated with nonreplicated results from any particular study. The potential benefit of Tharking may be even greater in research areas where data are scarce or difficult to collect. In contrast, Hollenbeck and Wright (2017) emphasized that the greater threat to science is *Sharking*, or secretly HARKing in the introduction.

Another challenge is that it is difficult to estimate the extent of HARKing without authors themselves admitting that certain hypotheses were based on inspecting the data. Kerr (1998) described indirect evidence from a survey of about 160 researchers in psychology and sociology. The researchers were asked about the frequency with which they had *personally* observed HARKing versus the testing of a priori hypotheses—that is, the classical hypothetico-deductive (HD) approach—among scholarly peers. Although the HD method was the modal response, various forms of HARKing were mentioned at basically the same rates, or just as common as the prescribed method (HD). When the same scholars were asked about the frequency of HARKing they *suspected* in their disciplines, it was rated both as the modal strategy and as occurring more often than the HD approach.

More recent indirect evidence about HARKing was described by Bosco et al. (2016), who analyzed correlation effects sizes for predicting job performance from factors such as extraversion and emotional stability in about 140 studies published from between 1980 and 2000 in *Journal of Applied Psychology* and *Personnel Psychology*. About 40% of authors for studies published since 2005 surveyed by Bosco et al. (2016) indicated that one or more hypotheses had changed between completion of data analysis and publication, with about half attributing the change to the review process and the rest to the authors themselves. Bosco et al. also analyzed effect sizes from a meta-analytic study in the same general area (Judge et al., 2001).

Article text was analyzed by Bosco et al. (2016) for results described as "hypothesized" (predicted) versus "nonhypothesized" (not predicted). Some of the hypothesized findings could be the result of HARKing by addition, that is, they are significant or larger effects "discovered" after analyzing the data. In contrast, some nonhypothesized results may reflect HARKing by subtraction, or postanalysis discounting or minimization of nonsignificant or smaller effect sizes. There is no direct way through text analysis alone to discern whether any result is the product of HARKing. Instead, Bosco et al. treated the status of results as hypothesized versus nonhypothesized as a fallible indicator of HARKing. Over all articles and after controlling for possible confounding factors such as publication year, score reliability, research design, and setting (e.g., laboratory vs. field study), Bosco et al. found that absolute effect sizes for results classified as hypothesized were up to .20 correlation units greater than for nonhypothesized findings. In other words, population correlation effect sizes *may* be appreciably overstated due to HARKing, within the limitations about indirect evidence mentioned earlier.

Murphy and Aguinis (2019) conducted computer simulation studies based on meta-analytic results in the areas of applied psychology and management to estimate how HARKing might bias effect size estimates. Two types of HARKing were simulated, cherry-picking and question trolling—or, respectively, selecting among different results that give the strongest support for a particular hypothesis versus the empirical search for results that seem noteworthy and thus provide a post-analysis rationale for the study. Effects of varying rates of both kinds of HARKing just described (base rates = .20–.80 in steps of .20) were studied under conditions already known to affect bias, including sample size (N = 100–280 in steps of 20 cases), the total number of results from which to select (2–10), and heterogeneity of population correlation effect sizes (ρ = .20 with standard deviations of .05, .10, and .15).

Simulation results by Murphy and Aguinis (2019) indicated relatively little bias associated with cherry-picking except when it occurred at the highest rate (.80) in the smallest samples with the largest pool of findings from which to select. In the combination just mentioned, estimates of the population correlation were positively biased by up to .10 in correlation units. The degree of bias was greater for question trolling when it occurred at the highest rates (.60, .80) along with a larger pool of sample results (6–10) and more heterogeneous population effect sizes. In this case, estimates of the population correlation were positively biased by up to .20 in correlation units, or a 100% inflation in sample correlations when $\rho = .20$. But when the rate of question trolling was < .60, there was relatively little bias. Of the two kinds of HARKing simulated by Murphy and Aguinis, question trolling presented the greater threat, especially when studying effects of smaller magnitude. For larger effects, though, the impact of cherry-picking might be less, such as when the true effect is $\rho = .55$ and the cherry-picked sample estimate is $r = .65$: The effect may be so strong, and thus more obvious, that the consequences of overestimation may not be all that serious.

Banks et al. (2016) used a triangulation approach in their review of 64 studies based on four different methods to estimate rates of questionable research practices in organizational science, education, political science, and accounting. These methods include (a) behavioral observations, where unpublished studies, such as dissertations, are compared with later published versions for the same works. The aim is to determine whether unsupported results in unpublished studies are reported in the final version or whether other changes occurred, such as adding or removing covariates, turned nonsignificant results into significant ones. Other methods included (b) researcher self-report surveys, (c) observer-report surveys, and (d) sensitivity analysis, where statistical methods are used to estimate whether the data are so improbable that distortion or falsification seems a more likely explanation (Simonsohn, 2013).

Results from about 90% of the works reviewed by Banks et al. (2016) indicated evidence for questionable research practices. Estimates of practices considered by Banks et al. as "ugly" (data falsification) ranged from about 2% to 27% with reports from observers exceeding those from self-reports. The majority of poor practices considered as "bad" involved *p*-hacking, or the manipulation of the analysis to generate significant results. Evidence from both survey and nonsurvey-based methods, including behavioral observations or sensitivity analysis, were generally consistent in supporting the widespread nature of *p*-hacking. Engagement in questionable practices did not vary by academic rank.

WHY QUESTIONABLE PRACTICES MATTER

A natural question is, Does "soft" misconduct—those questionable research practices—really matter? That is, should we really care that some—well, okay, maybe even most—researchers bend the rules a bit by presenting the very best of their results, rounding off some *p* values here and there, or self-promoting their own hypotheses through a little *p*-hacking to get a few more significant results? I believe the answer is "yes," for the reasons listed next:

1. Questionable research practices are unethical (Panter & Sterba, 2011).
2. Such practices can fill the research literature with false positive results, translating Type I errors into hard-to-eradicate theory (Kerr, 1998). Longford (2005) warned that the uncritical use of significance testing would lead to a "junkyard of unsubstantiated confidence" (p. 471), and Simmons et al. (2011) used the term *false-positive psychology* to describe the same problem.
3. Poor practices lead to the wasting of perhaps most of the research funding in psychology and medicine, among other disciplines, especially if replication is not valued (Chalmers & Glasziou, 2009; Gelman, 2018; Szucs & Ioannidis, 2017).
4. They can discredit entire disciplines or areas of research. Earp and Trafimow (2015) outlined

a crisis of confidence in social psychology owing to data falsification and lack of replication. Once an insider's phrase, "*p*-hacking" has now entered popular culture as slang for cheating by manipulation of the facts (Aschwanden, 2019). This development reflects poorly on researchers in psychology and other areas.

5. Dubious practices matter in the statistical education of new graduate students—and future scholars—specifically, students should be made aware of the problem and encouraged to follow data analysis best practices (Kline, 2020b).

6. Questionable research practices can hurt or even kill people. A tragic example was *p*-hacking in clinical trials of rofecoxib (Vioxx) to hide evidence of increased risk for heart attack. Vioxx was later withdrawn from the market, but only after thousands of patients died (Graham et al., 2005). Another example is *marketing-based medicine*, or the deviation from *evidence-based medicine* characterized by the suppression or spinning of negative results for the sake of product sales (Spielmans & Parry, 2010). For example, marketing of opioids to physicians in the United States was associated with higher rates of prescribing and, in turn, with greater mortality due to overdoses (Hadland et al., 2019).

Most readers in psychology would be familiar with the "Ethical Principles of Psychologists and Code of Conduct" of the APA (2017). Many of these principles concern the delivery of professional or consulting services in schools, clinics, or other applied settings, but there is an entire section (Section 8) about research and publication. For example, Sections 8.10 to 8.11 specifically call out data fabrication and plagiarism as unethical, and Section 8.14 specifies that psychologists are obliged to share data on which conclusions in research reports are based. There is a similar requirement for researchers funded by the National Institutes of Health (NIH) in the United States (NIH, 2020) to make data available for verification of results and additional use. Unfortunately, research psychologists do not always comply. For example, Wicherts et al. (2006) requested data sets from authors of 141 studies published in APA journals, and the positive response rate after 6 months and hundreds of email messages was only 26%.

Ethical guidelines for statistical analysis by the Committee on Professional Ethics of the American Statistical Association (2018, p. 1) are intended not just for professional statisticians, but also for all practitioners "regardless of job title or field of degree . . . who utilize and report statistical analyses and their implications." The guidelines remind researchers of their obligations for accountability in their use of statistical methods and transparency in reporting the results. For example, they should address assumptions made in the analysis, report limitations of statistical inference, and refrain from any overinterpretation or distortion of the results. Ziliak (2016) extended these principles in his call for granting agencies in the United States to explicitly define the misuse of significance testing as a form of scientific misconduct. The comprehensive volume by Panter and Sterba (2011) deals with the range of ethical issues in statistical analysis for researchers in psychology and related fields.

WAYS TO LIMIT *p*-HACKING

Because many, if not most, forms of statistical misconduct in psychology research involve *p*-hacking, I next deal with ways to limit the extent of this practice and, one hopes, reduce its potential biasing effects on the research literature. This discussion is based on the following assumptions:

1. Classical significance testing should *not* be viewed as the default method of inference by researchers in the social, behavioral, or medical sciences (Wasserstein et al., 2019).
2. If significance testing is used, then (a) its assumptions and requirements must be taken seriously and (b) safeguards against *p*-hacking should be applied; otherwise, the results may not be trustworthy (Kline, 2013).
3. Researchers and graduate students should be aware of reforms to significance testing that

may reduce the potential for its misuse (Hurlbert et al., 2019; Kline, 2013, 2020b). These reforms include no significance testing at all. However, calls to ban on its use (Amrhein et al., 2019) or actual prohibitions in journal policy (Trafimow & Marks, 2015) are not supported by all researchers (Ioannidis, 2019).

4. The strongest—but not foolproof—way to guard against *p*-hacking is preregistration of the analysis plan (Nosek et al., 2018).

5. Although the various safeguards and alternatives just listed may prevent abuses, there can still remain appreciable variation of results from complex data sets over different researchers who make transparent, justifiable, and honest decisions about the analysis (Silberzahn et al., 2018).

A fundamental principle of statistical analysis is that results can be very untrustworthy, if basic requirements for the use of a particular method are untenable. It is regrettable, then, that significance testing is too often applied in quite ritualized, mechanical ways with relatively little thought about its assumptions and perhaps even less about alternatives. For the outcomes of significance testing, or *p* values, to be reasonably correct, the "big nine" requirements listed in Table 26.2 should be met (Kline, 2020a). To summarize, the essential logic of significance testing is frequentist, which assumes random sampling from known populations. With few exceptions, most samples in human studies are ad hoc or convenience samples selected because they happen to be available. Unless convenience samples are representative—that is, they resemble probability samples—*p* values can be very distorted. As Berk (2004) put it, "frequentist statistical inference formally does not apply" (p. 51) to unrepresentative convenience samples.

Basic significance tests in analysis of variance (ANOVA) and regression assume that the only source of error is sampling error and, specifically, that sources of what the statistician William Gosset called "real error"—such as measurement, specification error, or implementation error, among other kinds—are all zero (Table 26.2).

TABLE 26.2

Requirements for Getting Accurate Results in Significance Testing

Condition	Explanation
1. Study probability samples	Convenience samples should be representative
2. Minimize error other than sampling error	Measurement, specification, or implementation error can contaminate estimates of error variance
3. Verify distributional or other assumptions	Explicitly evaluate assumptions and describe corrective actions, if any
4. Intelligently specify level of α, if any	State rationale for choice that balances Type I and Type II errors
5. Estimate a prior power, if α is specified	Disqualifying if omitted; observed power is not an acceptable substitute
6. Test plausible null hypotheses	Explicitly justify nil hypothesis; otherwise, state rationale for non-nil hypothesis
7. Do not misinterpret the results	Avoid common false beliefs about results that are significant versus not significant
8. Replicate the results	Qualify claims based on unreplicated results or, even better, conduct explicit replications
9. Preregister the analysis plan	With no prior plan, explain how results were not subject to *p*-hacking

Note. Adapted from *Becoming a Behavioral Science Researcher: A Guide to Producing Research That Matters* (2nd ed., pp. 134–135), by R. B. Kline, 2020a, Guilford Press. Copyright 2020 by Guilford Press. Adapted with permission.

For example, significance testing in multiple regression assumes that reliabilities for all predictors equal 1.0, but (a) this stringent requirement is seldom mentioned, and (b) *p* values in tests for individual coefficients can be greatly distorted even by relatively modest amounts of measurement error in large samples (Westfall & Yarkoni, 2016; Williams et al., 2013). Violation of distributional or other assumptions, such as homoscedasticity, can also severely distort *p* values, but too few researchers address these requirements or other aspects of data screening that can distort the results (Osborne, 2013).

"Dumb α" refers to the specification of the default—and arbitrary—level of statistical significance without considering whether $\alpha = .05$ provides the proper balance of Type I and Type II errors in a particular study. An alternative is to specify a "smart α" that achieves such a balance, even if that level is quite different from the conventional .05, such as $\alpha = .30$ in a study where Type II error is more serious than Type I error (see Table 26.2). For example, Mudge et al. (2012) described methods and freely available computer syntax for establishing optimal levels of α that minimize the combination of Type I and Type II error at hypothesized effect sizes or reflect a priori probabilities of the null and alternative hypotheses, among other variations. Aguinis et al. (2010) described a similar capability for "smart α" based on Bayesian principles.

In my experience, many—and perhaps most—students and established researchers are surprised to learn that it is not strictly necessary in significance testing to specify a criterion level of statistical significance at all. This "no α" option means that (a) p values are not dichotomized against an arbitrary (nor any) standard and, consequently, (b) results are not classified as either "significant" or "not significant" because these terms are not used at all nor are any special typographical symbols, such as asterisks, that designate "significant" p values (Hurlbert & Lombardi, 2009). Instead, exact p values are reported, such as $p = .065$, but the whole obsolete, hoary, outdated, and cognitive distortion-inducing practice of touting the awesomeness of the "significant" findings while bemoaning, discounting, or ignoring their embarrassing, unwashed kin, the "nonsignificant" results, vanishes. The call for researchers to stop using the term "significant" is now issued increasingly often (Hurlbert et al., 2019). For example, Wasserstein et al. (2019) advised researchers to draw no conclusion about scientific or practical importance based on statistical significance, or lack thereof, especially if the level of α is arbitrary Instead, researchers should describe whether their results are large and precise enough (i.e., effect sizes with confidence intervals) to be of substantive significance, given the research aim and context.

"No α" also means that (a) there is no explicit control over Type I error and (b) the concept of statistical power does not apply because power requires the rejection of null hypotheses, and there is no such thing here. Specification of arbitrary values of α for individual significance tests or some kind of equally arbitrary value that supposedly controls for multiplicity—such as Bonferroni corrections where the criterion level for each separate test is α/c and c is the total number of tests—provide illusory control over phantom errors, especially with no consideration about effects on Type II error (Hurlbert et al., 2019; Ziliak, 2016). An alternative to power analysis is *precision for planning*, or the estimation of minimum sample sizes required to estimate population effect size within a target margin of error (Rothman & Greenland, 2018). This means that target sample sizes are based on confidence intervals widths instead of on the probability of correctly rejecting a null hypothesis over random replications (i.e., traditional power analysis). The R package MBESS (Kelley, 2022) has precision for planning capabilities.

If a level of α is specified (intelligently, please), then report the results of an a priori power analysis (Table 26.2). Without estimates of power, there are two confounded interpretations of results that are not significant: (a) If power is low, then such results are expected because the sample size is too small for accurate statistical inference. If power is as low as .50, then there is no point in conducting the study at all from the perspective of significance testing. This is because flipping a coin as the way to decide whether to reject the null hypothesis has the same likelihood of detecting a true effect over replications compared with actually collecting data. Unfortunately, only about 15% of researchers who use significance testing report a priori power (Osborne, 2013). (b) But if power is actually high, such as .90 or so, then nonsignificant results provide evidence against the alternative hypothesis. For reasons explained by Hoenig and Heisey (2001), estimating retrospective (observed, post hoc) power after the data are collected is fundamentally flawed and no substitute for a priori power. In my view, the failure to estimate power in studies where outcomes of significance testing are central to the presentation is disqualifying. Anderson et al. (2017) offered good advice about estimating population effect size in power analysis.

Almost all null hypotheses tested in published studies are nil hypotheses, where a population effect, difference, or association is predicted to equal zero (Table 26.2). Although nil hypotheses may be justifiable in new research areas where it is unknown whether relations of interest even exist, such hypotheses are typically strawman arguments in more established areas. That is, nil hypotheses are known to be false before any data are collected, and p values for data under implausible nil hypotheses are generally too low (Anderson et al., 2000). Although it is possible to test non-nil hypotheses by hand for basic t tests of mean differences, it is more difficult to do so in other kinds of analyses, such as in ANOVA. This is because noncentral distributions for test statistics like F that assume nonzero population effect sizes are generally needed, but computer tools for general statistical analyses, such as SPSS, do not typically allow the specification of non-nil hypotheses.

There is ample evidence that false interpretation of outcomes in significance testing—those p values—is the rule instead of the exception in psychology and other disciplines (Amrhein et al., 2019; Kline, 2013, Chapter 4). It does not help that widely used introductory psychology textbooks are full of errors about the meaning of significant versus nonsignificant results (Cassidy et al., 2019). Thus, a requirement for significance testing should be the absence of misinterpretations about p values (Table 26.2); specifically, mention of the odds-against-chance, inverse-probability, or replicability fallacies, among other cognitive errors, should be disqualifying. An even stronger antidote to the worst foibles in significance testing is replication, or the empirical demonstration that a result is consistent over variations in participants or animals, settings or laboratories, particular sets of stimuli, or variation in geography or demographic variables, among others. Most readers are probably aware of the replication crisis in psychology, so it unnecessary to further explain the problem, but overreliance on significance testing in single samples is a contributing factor (Maxwell et al., 2015).

The last requirement listed in Table 26.2 concerns preregistration of the analysis plan. Researcher degrees of freedom in significance testing are so numerous and flexible that *any* effect can be presented as significant (Simmons et al., 2011). This includes nil results, such as $M_1 - M_2 = 0$, which could be presented as significant through an undisclosed, HARKing-based switch from the nil hypothesis:

$$H_0: \mu_1 - \mu_2 = 0$$

to a non-nil hypothesis such as

$$H_0: \mu_1 - \mu_2 = 10.0$$

Just as p values can be hacked down (e.g., < .05) in situations where significant results favor the researcher's hypotheses, they can also be hacked up (increased), especially if statistical significance does not support the hypotheses. An example is the widely reported model chi-square test in SEM, where it is *nonsignificant* results that support retaining the model (among other considerations; Kline, 2016). Thus, there is the possibility in SEM for *model-hacking*, where the p value in the chi-square test can be increased simply by adding to the model free parameters, or additional effects that require estimates, even if those modifications have little theoretical rationale. Just as in more standard significance testing where the goal to get low p values, model-hacking in SEM to get higher p values is a form of confirmation bias.

Nosek et al. (2018) described what they called the *preregistration revolution*, where more extensive—and honest—use of preregistration could more transparently differentiate between postdiction and prediction in the analysis. In its purest form, the researcher files an analysis plan with an independent, publicly accessible registry before the data are collected.[2] The plan specifies hypotheses, predictor and outcome variables, and statistical analyses to be conducted when the data are available. Appreciable departures from the preregistered plan in the eventual empirical study could indicate HARKing or *p*-hacking. For example, Goldacre et al. (2016) tracked switched outcomes in preregistered clinical trials, including outcomes registered but not reported and new, unregistered outcomes added but with little or no mention in the final article. Letters are sent to journal editors when outcomes are unreported or added, and outcomes of those communications are summarized on a website. In this way, reporting biases might be more readily detected (Nosek et al., 2018).

Preregistration can be adapted for situations that depart from the purest form just described. For example, preregistration of an *analysis decision tree* that anticipates analysis options or courses of action following later discovery of assumption violations during the analysis is possible and helps to more clearly separate prediction from postdiction. When the data are extant, such as when an archival data set will be analyzed, a more unalloyed form of preregistration could be preserved if the data are not yet inspected. Some form of a partial lack of awareness could help, such as when the analysis plan is registered by a member of the research team who has not yet seen the data or at least not for variables of interest. Nosek et al. (2018) noted that it is more challenging to separate prediction and postdiction for existing data, but the alternative, no preregistration at all, offers little, if any, transparency. Other potential challenges to preregistration are considered by Nosek et al. (2018), but they all depend on honesty. For example, preregistration can be potentially hacked by collecting and analyzing the data before filing an analysis plan that matched what was done while giving the false impression that the plan is a priori (Kline, 2020a).

Wicherts et al. (2016, p. 3) described a total of 34 degrees of freedom that researchers have in the hypothesis generation, design, data collection, analysis, and reporting phases of conducting empirical studies. These areas for discretion also correspond to potential opportunities for *p*-hacking. Wicherts et al.'s (2016) degrees of freedoms are summarized in Table 26.3 as a 20-item list of ways to guard against *p*-hacking other than study preregistration. Many of the suggestions in Table 26.3 have already been mentioned, but they summarized altogether in the table. Examples of recommendations in the table include differentiating between exploratory and confirmatory predictions (hypothesis phase); stating rationales for specifying variables as covariates, mediator, or moderators and disclosing reasons for changes in variable status (design phase); description of how cases were sampled or recruited and how the sample size was determined (data collection phase); reporting on data screening and integrity and detailing inference methods and criteria for making decisions about hypotheses (analysis phase); and making data, computer syntax, and materials or stimuli publicly available (reporting phase), which supports replication.

Journal article reporting standards, checklists of best practices, and *transparency and openness promotion* (TOP) guidelines and journal policies about data accessibility, sharing of research materials, and mandatory pledges by authors that reporting is complete (Chambers, 2018; Nosek et al., 2015) are all intended to reduce distorting effects of questionable research or data analysis practices. There is also evidence that awarding open-science badges by journals actually increases rates of the sharing of data and research materials (Kidwell et al., 2016).

But even in an ideal world where all researchers put the interests of science ahead of all else—that is, there is no HARKing, *p*-hacking, or other means of self-promoting researcher's hypotheses,

---

[2] Examples include https://clinicaltrials.gov/ and https://osf.io/.

TABLE 26.3

Checklist to Avoid *p*-Hacking

Context and hypotheses
1. Clearly differentiate between exploratory and confirmatory research, state hypotheses and expected directions of effects

Design
2. Disclose dropping of conditions or pooling of data over conditions in experimental studies, and outline the selection or calculation of predictor variables in nonexperimental studies
3. State operational definitions for outcomes and whether outcomes were measured in several alternative ways (e.g., justify choices among different variations)
4. Disclose measurement of additional variables that enable post hoc exclusion of cases, such as manipulation checks
5. Describe the rationale for specifying variables as covariates, mediators, or moderators
6. Conduct a reasoned a priori power analysis and state assumptions, such as population effect size and how such was estimated
7. Specify the sampling plan including whether data were pooled over multiple small samples

Data collection
8. Specify how cases were assigned to groups or conditions
9. Explain how cases (participants, animals) were excluded, especially if those decisions were post hoc; explain how different selection criteria could change the results
10. Describe blinding procedures for researchers or participants or used to exclude cases during data collection
11. State the stopping rule for data collection (e.g., power analysis, resource limits)

Analysis
12. Explain the treatment of missing data, outliers, or the pre-processing of data, including normalization or smoothing, in unplanned ways
13. Outline distributional or other assumptions evaluated and corrective actions taken
14. Justify the statistical method, especially if there are alternatives, and also the use of a particular computer tool with default versus user-specified options
15. Give a rationale for the chosen method to estimate standard errors, especially if (a) significance testing is emphasized and (b) the results vary appreciably over methods
16. Outline the inference criteria, such as Bayes factors, effect sizes, confidence intervals, or *p* values with reference to hypotheses

Reporting
17. Check accuracy of numerical results in text, tables, and graphics
18. Make data and computer syntax available
19. Follow relevant journal article reporting standards, given the type of research (e.g., quantitative vs. qualitative) or topic (e.g., treatment outcome)
20. Make stimuli, materials, or instructions available (enable replication)

Note. Adapted from "Degrees of Freedom in Planning, Running, Analyzing, and Reporting Psychological Studies: A Checklist to Avoid *p*-Hacking," by J. M. Wicherts, C. L. S. Veldkamp, H. E. M. Augusteijn, M. Bakker, R. C. M. van Aert, and M. A. L. M. van Assen, 2016, *Frontiers in Psychology*, 7, Article 1832, p. 3 (https://doi.org/10.3389/fpsyg.2016.01832). CC BY 4.0.

intentional or not—analysis results can still be affected by good-faith but subjective decisions made by researchers who have little, if any, stake in the outcome. This is especially true when data sets are complex with many potential covariates and there is no single, clear-cut, "best" statistical technique that should be applied. That is, even after eliminating questionable practices, analysis results still depend on a range of decisions about the analysis. Such decisions should be both transparent and defensible, but there may be no way to avoid appreciable variation in results even when analyses all involve the same data.

Silberzahn et al. (2018) assembled a large data set on over 2,000 male soccer players in Europe and the interactions of those players with over 3,000 referees concerning the number of red cards issued to each player by each referee. A red card signals an offense so serious that the player must immediately leave the game. Some violations, such as assaulting or spitting on another player, are obvious and egregious, but otherwise red cards are issued at the discretion of referees for perceived offenses that can be more ambiguous. The data set was presented to a total 23 different teams consisting of 61 analysts of various academic ranks, disciplines, and countries of residence with 62% holding PhD degrees. The teams were asked to determine whether soccer players with darker skin tone were more likely to receive red cards from referees. The selection of statistical techniques and covariates was left up to each team.

After the first round of data analysis, reports from each team (with identity removed) were reviewed both by other teams and other researchers who were familiar with the data set (Silberzahn et al., 2018). Thus, each team received anonymous peer reviews, and then teams had the opportunity to modify their approach in a second analysis round. Finals reports written in the style of the Methods and Results sections of a journal article were then submitted. The 29 teams used 21 different combinations of covariates, including none (three teams). Effect sizes varied appreciably over the teams. For example, values of odds ratios for the relative odds of players with darker skin tones receiving a red card against those for lighter skin-tone players ranged from .89 to 2.93, and 69% of the teams reported significant effects while 31% did not observe such effects. Results over teams did not vary strongly with choice of statistical method (e.g., logistic vs. linear regression, single-level vs. multi-level analysis), peer ratings of analysis quality, nor with the level of initial belief in the truth of the main research hypothesis.

A lesson from Silberzahn et al. (2018) is that even when researchers are not motivated by publication nor receiving grant monies, analysis results are still subject to reasoned, but still subjective, decisions by those who analyze data. There is no "defense" against the reality of analysis-dependent findings in complex data sets due to neither *p*-hacking nor other questionable forms of manipulating the analysis in favor of the researcher's hypotheses except transparency in data, methods, and decisions. Silberzahn et al. also suggested that a *crowdsourcing data analysis*, which is conducted by multiple independent researchers or teams without incentives to find publishable results, could estimate the range of variation in results over different decisions about statistical techniques or covariates. Such an approach is probably unrealistic in many, and perhaps most, studies. But to paraphrase a well-known adage from Brandeis (1914, p. 42), transparency (instead of sunlight) is the best of disinfectants, especially in science.

CONCLUSION

The science blogger Neuroskeptic (2012) described the Nine Circles of Scientific Hell, a variation of the Nine Circles of Hell as described in Dante Alighieri's *Inferno*, the first book in his *Divine Comedy* trilogy. Neuroskeptic's version is a humorous take on the fates that await scientists who transgress against best practices. The Ninth Circle is reserved for researchers who fake data, the very worst of scientific sinners. They can expect to spend eternity trapped in solid ice along with Satan, who is holding a paper based on fabricated data that says Hell cannot freeze over. The Sixth, Seventh, and Eighth Circles are for, respectively, plagiarizers, researchers who hide entire data sets, and researchers who publish partial results. They are tormented in various ways that involve inaccessible information that could free them or being exposed to undisclosed side effects of being prodded with spears as incentive to exercise.

Researchers who were HARKers, *p*-hackers, or who "cleaned" data by creative removal of outliers in Neuroskeptic's (2012) scientific Hell are sent to, respectively, the Third, Fourth, and Fifth Circles to suffer various indignities related to their sins. For example, *p*-hackers must fish for their food after selecting from a bewildering variety of tackle (rods, reels, lures, etc.), but only one fish in 20 is edible, so hunger is never-ending. The Second Circle is for scientists who oversold the importance of their results, and they are trapped in sludge up to their necks while being promised a breakthrough method to escape that never materializes. Finally, the First Circle is a Limbo for researchers who themselves committed no scientific sin, but they stood by while others did.

They must watch the suffering of their colleagues below, knowing that they are partly responsible because they remained silent or actually encouraged the questionable practices of their condemned colleagues.

Of course, there is no actual divine judgment, nor punishment, for questionable statistical or reporting practices. Instead, there is basically an honor system for researchers that involves not just the commitment to best practices, but also walking the talk through (a) taking reporting standards seriously by providing accurate and complete descriptions of the results; (b) making data sets, syntax, and other research materials accessible and, thus, verifiable; and (c) not only supporting replication as scientific gold standard, but actually doing it. Yes, there are perverse incentives to HARK, p-hack, or oversell in the form of publish-or-perish economies for researchers in academic or other settings. There are also ethical codes for researchers and data analysts that specify, nay, demand eschewing shoddy, poor, or deceptive practices. As noted by Eich (2014), enduring reform of analysis and reporting must come more from the ground up—individual researchers and related stakeholders—than come from the top, or codes and standards from professional associations. Top-down guidelines and statements, although important, can only encourage scientific integrity. You have to do the rest.

References

Aguinis, H., & Gottfredson, R. K. (2010). Best-practice recommendations for estimating interaction effects using moderated multiple regression. *Journal of Organizational Behavior*, 31(6), 776–786. https://doi.org/10.1002/job.686

Aguinis, H., Werner, S., Abbott, J. L., Angert, C., Park, J. H., & Kohlhausen, D. (2010). Customer-centric science: Reporting significant research results with rigor, relevance, and practical impact in mind. *Organizational Research Methods*, 13(3), 515–539. https://doi.org/10.1177/1094428109333339

American Psychological Association. (2017). *Ethical principles of psychologists and code of conduct* (2002, amended effective June 1, 2010, and January 1, 2017). https://www.apa.org/ethics/code/index.aspx

Amrhein, A., Greenland, S., & McShane, B. (2019). Retire statistical significance. *Nature*, 567, 305–307. https://doi.org/10.1038/d41586-019-00857-9

Anderson, D. R., Burnham, K. P., & Thompson, W. L. (2000). Null hypothesis testing: Problems, prevalence, and an alternative. *The Journal of Wildlife Management*, 64(4), 912–923. https://doi.org/10.2307/3803199

Anderson, S. F., Kelley, K., & Maxwell, S. E. (2017). Sample-size planning for more accurate statistical power: A method adjusting sample effect sizes for publication bias and uncertainty. *Psychological Science*, 28(11), 1547–1562. https://doi.org/10.1177/0956797617723724

Appelbaum, M., Cooper, H., Kline, R. B., Mayo-Wilson, E., Nezu, A. M., & Rao, S. M. (2018). Journal article reporting standards for quantitative research in psychology: The APA Publications and Communications Board task force report. *American Psychologist*, 73(1), 3–25. https://doi.org/10.1037/amp0000191

Aschwanden, C. (2019, November 26). We're all "p-hacking" now. *Wired*. https://www.wired.com/story/were-all-p-hacking-now/

Banks, G. C., Rogelberg, S. G., Woznyj, H. M., Landis, R. S., & Rupp, D. E. (2016). Editorial: Evidence on questionable research practices: The good, the bad, and the ugly. *Journal of Business and Psychology*, 31(3), 323–338. https://doi.org/10.1007/s10869-016-9456-7

Berk, R. A. (2004). *Regression analysis: A constructive critique*. SAGE.

Bosco, F. A., Aguinis, H., Field, J. G., Pierce, C. A., & Dalton, D. R. (2016). HARKing's threat to organizational research: Evidence from primary and meta-analytic sources. *Personnel Psychology*, 69(3), 709–750. https://doi.org/10.1111/peps.12111

Boutron, I., & Ravaud, P. (2018). Misrepresentation and distortion of research in biomedical literature. *Proceedings of the National Academy of Sciences of the United States of America*, 115(11), 2613–2619. https://doi.org/10.1073/pnas.1710755115

Brandeis, L. D. (1914). *Other people's money and how the bankers use it*. Stokes.

Bruns, S. B., & Ioannidis, J. P. A. (2016). p-Curve and p-hacking in observational research. *PLOS ONE*, 11(2), Article e0149144. https://doi.org/10.1371/journal.pone.0149144

Calin-Jageman, R. J., & Cumming, G. (2019). The new statistics for better science: Ask how much, how uncertain, and what else is known. *The American Statistician*, 73(Suppl. 1), 271–280. https://doi.org/10.1080/00031305.2018.1518266

Cassidy, S. A., Dimova, R., Giguère, B., Spence, J. R., & Stanley, D. J. (2019). Failing grade: 89% of introduction-to-psychology textbooks that define or explain statistical significance do so incorrectly.

Advances in Methods and Practices in Psychological Science, 2(3), 233–239. https://doi.org/10.1177/2515245919858072

Chalmers, I., & Glasziou, P. (2009). Avoidable waste in the production and reporting of research evidence. *Lancet, 374*(9683), 86–89. https://doi.org/10.1016/S0140-6736(09)60329-9

Chambers, C. D. (2018). Introducing the transparency and openness promotion (TOP) guidelines and badges for open practices at *Cortex*. *Cortex, 106*, 316–318. https://doi.org/10.1016/j.cortex.2018.08.001

Committee on Professional Ethics of the American Statistical Association. (2018, April 14). *Ethical guidelines for statistical practice*. https://www.amstat.org/asa/files/pdfs/EthicalGuidelines.pdf

Earp, B. D., & Trafimow, D. (2015). Replication, falsification, and the crisis of confidence in social psychology. *Frontiers in Psychology, 6*, Article 621. https://doi.org/10.3389/fpsyg.2015.00621

Eich, E. (2014). Business not as usual. *Psychological Science, 25*(1), 3–6. https://doi.org/10.1177/0956797613512465

Fanelli, D. (2009). How many scientists fabricate and falsify research? A systematic review and meta-analysis of survey data. *PLOS ONE, 4*(5), e5738. https://doi.org/10.1371/journal.pone.0005738

Fiedler, K., & Schwarz, N. (2016). Questionable research practices revisited. *Social Psychological & Personality Science, 7*(1), 45–52. https://doi.org/10.1177/1948550615612150

Funder, D., & Task Force on Publication and Research Practices, Society for Personality and Social Psychology. (2014). Notice: PSPB articles by authors with retracted articles at PSPB or other journals: Stapel, Smeesters, and Sanna. *Personality and Social Psychology Bulletin, 40*(1), 132–135. https://doi.org/10.1177/0146167213508152

Gelman, A. (2018). The failure of null hypothesis significance testing when studying incremental changes, and what to do about it. *Personality and Social Psychology Bulletin, 44*(1), 16–23. https://doi.org/10.1177/0146167217729162

Gerrits, R. G., Jansen, T., Mulyanto, J., van den Berg, M. J., Klazinga, N. S., & Kringos, D. S. (2019). Occurrence and nature of questionable research practices in the reporting of messages and conclusions in international scientific Health Services Research publications: A structured assessment of publications authored by researchers in the Netherlands. *BMJ Open, 9*(5), Article e027903. https://doi.org/10.1136/bmjopen-2018-027903

Goldacre, B., Drysdale, H., Powell-Smith, A., Dale, A., Milosevic, I., Slade, E., Hartley, P., Marston, C., Mahtani, K., & Heneghan, C. (2016). *Tracking switched outcomes in clinical trials*. https://compare-trials.org/

Graham, D. J., Campen, D., Hui, R., Spence, M., Cheetham, C., Levy, G., Shoor, S., & Ray, W. A. (2005). Risk of acute myocardial infarction and sudden cardiac death in patients treated with cyclo-oxygenase 2 selective and non-selective non-steroidal anti-inflammatory drugs: Nested case-control study. *Lancet, 365*(9458), 475–481. https://doi.org/10.1016/S0140-6736(05)17864-7

Greenland, S. (2017). Invited commentary: The need for cognitive science in methodology. *American Journal of Epidemiology, 186*(6), 639–645. https://doi.org/10.1093/aje/kwx259

Hadland, S. E., Rivera-Aguirre, A., Marshall, B. D. L., & Cerdá, M. (2019). Association of pharmaceutical industry marketing of opioid products with mortality from opioid-related overdoses. *JAMA Network Open, 2*(1), Article e186007. https://doi.org/10.1001/jamanetworkopen.2018.6007

Head, M. L., Holman, L., Lanfear, R., Kahn, A. T., & Jennions, M. D. (2015). The extent and consequences of *p*-hacking in science. *PLOS Biology, 13*(3), Article e1002106. https://doi.org/10.1371/journal.pbio.1002106

Hoenig, J. M., & Heisey, D. M. (2001). The abuse of power: The pervasive fallacy of power calculations for data analysis. *The American Statistician, 55*(1), 19–24. https://doi.org/10.1198/000313001300339897

Hollenbeck, J. R., & Wright, P. M. (2017). Harking, sharking, and tharking: Making the case for post hoc analysis of scientific data. *Journal of Management, 43*(1), 5–18. https://doi.org/10.1177/0149206316679487

Hurlbert, S. H., Levine, R. A., & Utts, J. (2019). Coup de grâce for a tough old bull: "Statistically significant" expires. *The American Statistician, 73*(Suppl. 1), 352–357. https://doi.org/10.1080/00031305.2018.1543616

Hurlbert, S. H., & Lombardi, C. M. (2009). Final collapse of the Neyman–Pearson decision theory framework and rise of the neoFisherian. *Annales Zoologici Fennici, 46*(5), 311–349. https://doi.org/10.5735/086.046.0501

Ioannidis, J. P. A. (2019). The importance of predefined rules and prespecified statistical analyses: Do not abandon significance. *Journal of the American Medical Association, 321*(21), 2067–2068. https://doi.org/10.1001/jama.2019.4582

John, L. K., Loewenstein, G., & Prelec, D. (2012). Measuring the prevalence of questionable research practices with incentives for truth telling. *Psychological Science, 23*(5), 524–532. https://doi.org/10.1177/0956797611430953

Judge, T. A., Thoresen, C. J., Bono, J. E., & Patton, G. K. (2001). The job satisfaction-job performance relationship: A qualitative and quantitative review. *Psychological Bulletin*, *127*(3), 376–407. https://doi.org/10.1037/0033-2909.127.3.376

Kelley, K. (2022). *MBESS: The MBESS R package* (R package 4.9.0). https://CRAN.R-project.org/package=MBESS

Kerr, N. L. (1998). HARKing: Hypothesizing after the results are known. *Personality and Social Psychology Review*, *2*(3), 196–217. https://doi.org/10.1207/s15327957pspr0203_4

Kidwell, M. C., Lazarević, L. B., Baranski, E., Hardwicke, T. E., Piechowski, S., Falkenberg, L.-S., Kennett, C., Slowik, A., Sonnleitner, C., Hess-Holden, C., Errington, T. M., Fiedler, S., & Nosek, B. A. (2016). Badges to acknowledge open practices: A simple, low-cost, effective method for increasing transparency. *PLOS Biology*, *14*(5), e1002456. https://doi.org/10.1371/journal.pbio.1002456

Kline, R. B. (2013). *Beyond significance testing: Statistics reform in the behavioral sciences* (2nd ed.). American Psychological Association. https://doi.org/10.1037/14136-000

Kline, R. B. (2016). *Principles and practice of structural equation modeling* (4th ed.). Guilford Press.

Kline, R. B. (2020a). *Becoming a behavioral science researcher: A guide to producing research that matters* (2nd ed.). Guilford Press.

Kline, R. B. (2020b). Post p value education in graduate statistics: Preparing tomorrow's psychology researchers for a postcrisis future. *Canadian Psychology*, *61*(4), 331–341. https://doi.org/10.1037/cap0000200

Levitt, H. M., Bamberg, M., Creswell, J. W., Frost, D. M., Josselson, R., & Suárez-Orozco, C. (2018). Journal article reporting standards for qualitative primary, qualitative meta-analytic, and mixed methods research in psychology: The APA Publications and Communications Board task force report. *American Psychologist*, *73*(1), 26–46. https://doi.org/10.1037/amp0000151

Longford, N. T. (2005). Editorial: Model selection and efficiency: Is "which model . . . ?" the right question? *Journal of the Royal Statistical Society. Series A (Statistics in Society)*, *168*(3), 469–472. https://doi.org/10.1111/j.1467-985X.2005.00366.x

Masicampo, E. J., & Lalande, D. R. (2012). A peculiar prevalence of p values just below .05. *Quarterly Journal of Experimental Psychology: Human Experimental Psychology*, *65*(11), 2271–2279. https://doi.org/10.1080/17470218.2012.711335

Maxwell, S. E., Lau, M. Y., & Howard, G. S. (2015). Is psychology suffering from a replication crisis? What does "failure to replicate" really mean? *American Psychologist*, *70*(6), 487–498. https://doi.org/10.1037/a0039400

Morrison, T. G., Morrison, M. A., & McCutcheon, J. M. (2017). Best practice recommendations for using structural equation modelling in psychological research. *Psychology*, *8*(9), 1326–1341. https://doi.org/10.4236/psych.2017.89086

Mudge, J. F., Baker, L. F., Edge, C. B., & Houlahan, J. E. (2012). Setting an optimal α that minimizes errors in null hypothesis significance tests. *PLOS ONE*, *7*(2), Article e32734. https://doi.org/10.1371/journal.pone.0032734

Murphy, K. R., & Aguinis, H. (2019). HARKing: How badly can cherry-picking and question trolling produce bias in published results? *Journal of Business and Psychology*, *34*(1), 1–17. https://doi.org/10.1007/s10869-017-9524-7

National Institutes of Health. (2020, October 29). *Final NIH policy for data management and sharing*. https://grants.nih.gov/grants/policy/data_sharing/

Neuroskeptic. (2012). The nine circles of scientific hell. *Perspectives on Psychological Science*, *7*(6), 643–644. https://doi.org/10.1177/1745691612459519

Nosek, B. A., Alter, G., Banks, G. C., Borsboom, D., Bowman, S. D., Breckler, S. J., Buck, S., Chambers, C. D., Chin, G., Christensen, G., Contestabile, M., Dafoe, A., Eich, E., Freese, J., Glennerster, R., Goroff, D., Green, D. P., Hesse, B., Humphreys, M., . . . Yarkoni, T. (2015). Promoting an open research culture. *Science*, *348*(6242), 1422–1425. https://doi.org/10.1126/science.aab2374

Nosek, B. A., Ebersole, C. R., DeHaven, A. C., & Mellor, D. T. (2018). The preregistration revolution. *Proceedings of the National Academy of Sciences of the United States of America*, *115*(11), 2600–2606. https://doi.org/10.1073/pnas.1708274114

Nuzzo, R. (2014). Scientific method: Statistical errors. *Nature*, *506*(7487), 150–152. https://doi.org/10.1038/506150a

Nuzzo, R. (2015). How scientists fool themselves—And how they can stop. *Nature*, *526*(7572), 182–185. https://doi.org/10.1038/526182a

Ochodo, E. A., de Haan, M. C., Reitsma, J. B., Hooft, L., Bossuyt, P. M., & Leeflang, M. M. G. (2013). Overinterpretation and misreporting of diagnostic accuracy studies: Evidence of "spin." *Radiology*, *267*(2), 581–588. https://doi.org/10.1148/radiol.12120527

Osborne, J. W. (2013). *Best practices in data cleaning*. SAGE.

Panter, A. T., & Sterba, S. K. (Eds.). (2011). *Handbook of ethics in quantitative methodology*. Routledge. https://doi.org/10.4324/9780203840023

Rothman, K. J., & Greenland, S. (2018). Planning study size based on precision rather than power. *Epidemiology*, *29*(5), 599–603. https://doi.org/10.1097/EDE.0000000000000876

Rougier, J. (2019). *p*-values, Bayes factors, and sufficiency. *The American Statistician*, *73*(Suppl. 1), 148–151. https://doi.org/10.1080/00031305.2018.1502684

Saunders, R., & Savulescu, J. (2008). Research ethics and lessons from Hwanggate: What can we learn from the Korean cloning fraud? *Journal of Medical Ethics*, *34*(3), 214–221. https://doi.org/10.1136/jme.2007.023721

Schreiber, J. B. (2021). Issues and recommendations for exploratory factor analysis and principal component analysis. *Research in Social & Administrative Pharmacy*, *17*(5), 1004–1011. https://doi.org/10.1016/j.sapharm.2020.07.027

Service, R. F. (2003). Scientific misconduct. More of Bell Labs physicist's papers retracted. *Science*, *299*(5603), 31. https://doi.org/10.1126/science.299.5603.31b

Silberzahn, R., Uhlmann, E. L., Martin, D. P., Anselmi, P., Aust, F., Awtrey, E., Bahník, Š., Bai, F., Bannard, C., Bonnier, E., Carlsson, R., Cheung, F., Christensen, G., Clay, R., Craig, M. A., Dalla Rosa, A., Dam, L., Evans, M. H., Flores Cervantes, I., . . . Nosek, B. A. (2018). Many analysts, one data set: Making transparent how variations in analytic choices affect results. *Advances in Methods and Practices in Psychological Science*, *1*(3), 337–356. https://doi.org/10.1177/2515245917747646

Simmons, J. P., Nelson, L. D., & Simonsohn, U. (2011). False-positive psychology: Undisclosed flexibility in data collection and analysis allows presenting anything as significant. *Psychological Science*, *22*(11), 1359–1366. https://doi.org/10.1177/0956797611417632

Simonsohn, U. (2013). Just post it: The lesson from two cases of fabricated data detected by statistics alone. *Psychological Science*, *24*(10), 1875–1888. https://doi.org/10.1177/0956797613480366

Spielmans, G. I., & Parry, P. I. (2010). From evidence-based medicine to marketing-based medicine: Evidence from internal industry documents. *Journal of Bioethical Inquiry*, *7*(1), 13–29. https://doi.org/10.1007/s11673-010-9208-8

Steward, O., & Balice-Gordon, R. (2014). Rigor or mortis: Best practices for preclinical research in neuroscience. *Neuron*, *84*(3), 572–581. https://doi.org/10.1016/j.neuron.2014.10.042

Szucs, D., & Ioannidis, J. P. A. (2017). When null hypothesis significance testing is unsuitable for research: A reassessment. *Frontiers in Human Neuroscience*, *11*, Article 390. https://doi.org/10.3389/fnhum.2017.00390

Trafimow, D., & Marks, M. (2015). Editorial. *Basic and Applied Social Psychology*, *37*(1), 1–2. https://doi.org/10.1080/01973533.2015.1012991

Wasserman, R. (2013). Ethical issues and guidelines for conducting data analysis in psychological research. *Ethics & Behavior*, *23*(1), 3–15. https://doi.org/10.1080/10508422.2012.728472

Wasserstein, R. L., Schirm, A. L., & Lazar, N. A. (2019). Moving to a world beyond "$p < 0.05$." *The American Statistician*, *73*(Suppl. 1), 1–19. https://doi.org/10.1080/00031305.2019.1583913

Westfall, J., & Yarkoni, T. (2016). Statistically controlling for confounding constructs is harder than you think. *PLOS ONE*, *11*(3), Article e0152719. https://doi.org/10.1371/journal.pone.0152719

Wicherts, J. M., Borsboom, D., Kats, J., & Molenaar, D. (2006). The poor availability of psychological research data for reanalysis. *American Psychologist*, *61*(7), 726–728. https://doi.org/10.1037/0003-066X.61.7.726

Wicherts, J. M., Veldkamp, C. L. S., Augusteijn, H. E. M., Bakker, M., van Aert, R. C. M., & van Assen, M. A. L. M. (2016). Degrees of freedom in planning, running, analyzing, and reporting psychological studies: A checklist to avoid *p*-hacking. *Frontiers in Psychology*, *7*, Article 1832. https://doi.org/10.3389/fpsyg.2016.01832

Williams, M. N., Grajales, C. A. G., & Kurkiewicz, D. (2013). Assumptions of multiple regression: Correcting two misconceptions. *Practical Assessment, Research & Evaluation*, *18*(11), Article 11. https://doi.org/10.7275/55hn-wk47

Ziliak, S. T. (2016). Statistical significance and scientific misconduct: Improving the style of the published research paper. *Review of Social Economy*, *74*(1), 83–97. https://doi.org/10.1080/00346764.2016.1150730

CHAPTER 27

ETHICAL ISSUES IN MANUSCRIPT PREPARATION AND AUTHORSHIP

Jennifer Crocker

Publishing in the scientific literature makes one a member of a community of scholars in a way that simply reading the scientific literature cannot. By publishing in scientific journals, one becomes a contributor to, as well as a consumer of, science. Publishing scholarly work is perhaps the most important sign that one is truly a scientist, whose research contributes knowledge based on data and careful inference and adds to our collective understanding of phenomena of theoretical and practical significance. Of the many research studies that are conducted, only those that are published become widely available and enduring. Scientific publications live on in libraries, journal archives, bookshelves, and computer hard drives long after the date of publication. The insights they contribute may become part of the established understanding, or they may be debunked, or rendered outdated by subsequent research, but they remain in the research literature.

Scientists have many reasons to conduct research and publish their findings in scientific journals. Sharing knowledge gleaned from research with other scientists advances scientific understanding and perhaps improves the world in some way; this may be the noblest goal of publication. But there are other very real and practical consequences of publishing in scientific journals. Publications that have successfully made it through the peer review process have credibility that non-peer-reviewed papers and publications lack. Publication is the main route by which scientists obtain job offers and advance their own careers and those of their students and collaborators. Granting agencies who fund research rely in part on applicants' previous publication records when making decisions about what projects to fund. Academic and other research institutions rely on publication track records to evaluate candidates for promotions. Publications are the primary basis for various awards and honors given by scientific societies. They are the "coin of the realm."

Usually, the goals of contributing to understanding of phenomena and advancing one's own career or those of one's students are well-aligned. But tensions between these goals can sometimes arise. The pressure to publish more articles before going on the job market, coming up for a tenure or promotion review, or applying for research funding can create incentives to take ethical shortcuts. This pressure can subtly or overtly affect the choices researchers make in the research and publication process. Many of those decisions fall in a gray area where the ethical choice is debatable, or the unethical choice can be justified to oneself or others. Norms regarding acceptable practices can vary from laboratory to laboratory, and year to year, adding to ambiguity about ethical practices.

Despite the tension that researchers may feel in specific situations, the goal of having a successful scientific career can be compatible with the goal of doing research with integrity. Research and publication done with integrity are more likely to advance scientific understanding, and also more likely to enhance the researcher's reputation as a careful scientist whose work can be trusted. Certainly, a reputation for taking ethical shortcuts— or worse—can derail a scientific career and undermine the impact of the scientist's research. Awareness of evolving ethical standards and guidelines for publishing scientific research can help scientists avoid unintentionally damaging their own reputations.

To address a range of ethical issues in the research and publication process, scientific societies and other organizations have developed guidelines to help researchers stay within ethical boundaries when they make decisions or confront dilemmas in the research and publication process. For example, the American Psychological Association (APA) has published ethical principles and a code of conduct for psychologists, including ethical guidelines for research and publication (https://www.apa.org/ethics/code). In addition, the Publications and Communications Board at APA considers and sometimes adopts new policies and guidelines for topics such as open science, replication, plagiarism, and authorship. Many scientific journal editors and publishers, including APA, subscribe to guidelines of the Committee on Publishing Ethics (COPE; https://publicationethics.org/guidance). These guidelines continue to evolve to provide clearer and more consistent advice that helps researchers, editors, and publishers avoid ethical pitfalls.

GENERAL ETHICAL PRINCIPLES OF PSYCHOLOGISTS

The general ethical principles articulated by APA provide an aspirational guide rather than a specific code of conduct (which APA also has). These general principles, reprinted in abbreviated form here, can serve as a moral and ethical compass for researchers, teachers, and practitioners.

1. *Beneficence and nonmaleficence.* Psychologists strive to benefit those with whom they work and take care to do no harm.
2. *Fidelity and responsibility.* Psychologists establish relationships of trust with those with whom they work.
3. *Integrity.* Psychologists seek to promote accuracy, honesty, and truthfulness in the science, teaching, and practice of psychology.
4. *Justice.* Psychologists recognize that fairness and justice entitle all persons to access and benefit from the contributions of psychology and to equal quality in the processes, procedures, and services being conducted by psychologists.
5. *Respect for people's rights and dignity.* Psychologists respect the dignity and worth of all people, and the rights of individuals to privacy, confidentiality, and self-determination.

This chapter discusses ethical considerations regarding some of the major decisions researchers make in the process of preparing their work for publication, and even after it is published. When psychologists think about ethical principles as applied to research, what comes to mind first may be ethical principles with regard to the treatment of human and animal research participants. Most human subjects research in the United States and many other countries cannot be conducted until it has been reviewed and approved by an institutional review board. Because psychologists who conduct research already receive training in ethical treatment of human or animal participants, that topic will not be covered in this chapter. However, there are ethical considerations in research both before and after the data are collected that receive less attention; the focus here is on ethical considerations that arise after data have been collected. A more complete discussion of these and other ethical issues in conducting and publishing research is available in Cooper (2016).

In the stages of analysis, writing, and publication, researchers may commit many types of misconduct, including data fabrication, falsification, or fraud, using questionable research practices such as selective reporting that misrepresents the findings of the research, intellectual theft, plagiarism, redundant publication, authorship misconduct, and undeclared conflicts of interests. This chapter considers the ethical issues at stake, and what to do if you suspect or know of unethical behavior in the conduct or reporting of research.

RESEARCH IN CRISIS?

The primary goal of science, if not of every scientist at every moment, is to contribute to scientific understanding of phenomena. Scientists aim to create, individually and collectively, a body of knowledge based on scientific methods that can be replicated, extended, and used by other researchers, policy makers, and consumers of research. Although specific manifestations of phenomena may change over time, researchers ideally aim to discover underlying facts and principles that are relatively enduring, and therefore help build a stable foundation of knowledge. These principles and facts may be challenged, overturned, and ultimately discarded, but the scientific process by which this happens helps to uncover more enduring facts and principles.

This idealistic view of science has been challenged by three phenomena, one that is (one hopes) quite rare, and the others less so: falsification of data, failures to replicate, and questionable research practices (see Spellman et al., 2018, for a discussion).

Fabrication and Falsification of Data

APA's Ethical Standard 8.10 regarding reporting research findings states that "psychologists do not fabricate data." Fabricating and falsifying data, whether making it up entirely (fabrication), editing it to obtain desired results (falsification), or altering figures depicting the results, represents cheating in the research process at its most extreme, and clearly undermines the scientific enterprise. Yet, contravening this first principle of research ethics, an unknown number of researchers sometimes cheat by making up or manipulating their data, in whole or in part, to get the results they want. We know this occurs because of a few widely publicized cases, such as that of Diederik Stapel, an award-winning Dutch social psychologist who confessed to fabricating data, and 58 of whose publications have been retracted according to Retraction Watch (https://retractionwatch.com/2015/12/08/diederik-stapel-now-has-58-retractions/). Although fabrication of data is not limited to psychology and has likely occurred almost as long as science has existed, a flurry of incidents in the past two decades increased the prominence of this issue (Spellman et al., 2018).

Data fabrication and falsification result from the conflict between career advancement and advancement of science. Fabricating data can be much easier than scientific discovery, at least in the short term. The rewards of data fabrication may seem great, and researchers who are completely confident in their ideas may find ways to justify this ethical breach (Bhattacharjee, 2013). However, the costs of data fabrication are many. First and foremost is the cost to scientific understanding— false findings take the research literature farther from, rather than closer to, the truth. They mislead other scientists, whose work may be based on or influenced by the false findings. They undermine the public's trust in scientific information and advice based on it. They consume journal pages and funding resources that could be allocated to more sound results. They taint the reputations of coauthors and others affiliated with the researcher or the project. And once discovered, they spoil the reputations and careers of the very researchers who had hoped to advance their careers through data fabrication. The fall from grace is very big when data fabrication is discovered; academics found to have fabricated data may lose their academic positions and often cannot find new ones. The career risks of data fabrication are increasing; the likelihood that fraud will be uncovered has increased with statistical tools that check for anomalies in data structure and bots such as Statcheck that crawl the web checking for errors in statistical tests.

Given these many costs, it is important to create a context in one's own program of research and research training program that firmly discourages this behavior, by providing training in ethical conduct, setting norms, and developing practices that make it less likely. For many years, Stapel "collected" his own data, rather than having his graduate or undergraduate students involved in data collection. When others asked to see his original data, he had excuses for not providing it. Establishing routine practices in which collection of original data is shared and transparent, and data are shared with collaborators and archived along with code used in analyses (SPSS syntax, etc.) so results can be replicated can go a long way toward discouraging data fabrication.

Failures to Replicate

A second crisis in research is the increasing occurrence of failures to replicate published research findings. Science has long been viewed as self-correcting, because findings that cannot be replicated become discredited in the literature. However, replicating others' research findings has generally been considered less innovative and important than coming up with novel findings, so replication for its own sake was not prioritized by scientists or their institutions. As a result, scientists attempt to replicate less often than this self-correction assumption would require. Furthermore, when scientists do attempt to replicate others' work and cannot, it is often assumed that they did something wrong, or that subtleties in the methods required to obtain an effect were not communicated in the published article reporting the original study. Fabrication of data obviously contributes to this problem, but it is mainly due to other, more common practices.

In 2005, John Ioannidis published a paper provocatively titled, "Why Most Published Research Findings Are False." Ioannidis's conclusions were based on logical arguments and simulations, not an attempt to replicate published studies. His arguments inspired researchers to begin systematically evaluating whether published studies in psychology could be replicated. Efforts such as the Many Labs projects (Ebersole et al., 2016; Klein et al., 2014, 2018), Registered Replication Reports (Simons et al., 2014), and the Reproducibility Project: Psychology (Open Science Collaboration, 2015) attempted to quantify the percentage of established findings that could be replicated in highly powered studies conducted in laboratories around the world, with methods and materials that had been reviewed in advance or approved by the original authors (see Spellman et al., 2018, for a discussion). The results of these efforts have, for the most part, been disappointing; often less than half, and sometimes far less, of statistically significant findings replicated (but see Gilbert et al., 2016, for a more optimistic interpretation). There are many reasons why attempts to replicate previous findings might fail, and failures to replicate do not necessarily imply misconduct on the part of the original researchers.

Some researchers are not convinced that science has a replication "crisis," arguing that replication and failures to replicate are "just how science works" (Feldman Barrett, 2015). They are skeptical that evidence of replication projects is as dismal as some have concluded (Gilbert et al., 2016), raising the possibility that focusing on an overblown replication crisis itself undermines trust in science. Failures to replicate have become national news, receiving coverage in *The New York Times*, for example (e.g., Van Bavel, 2016), providing ammunition to politicians and policy makers who prefer that policy be based on grounds other than science.

Those who are convinced that science has a replication crisis acknowledge the risk to the reputation of science and scientists, but argue that attempting to minimize a real problem also does damage to trust in science, and we can know how real the problem is only through empirical tests of replicability.

This debate is likely to continue before a consensus emerges about just how serious the replication crisis is. In the meantime, regardless of the prevalence of failures to replicate, the costs of publishing research that cannot be replicated remain. When feasible, researchers could mitigate these costs by conducting highly powered replications (ideally, preregistered) of their own findings before publishing them to ensure that significant results are not due to chance alone (more on preregistration later). Researchers are ethically obligated to provide complete and transparent descriptions of their methods so that other scientists can conduct high-fidelity replications of their work. APA's Journal Article Reporting Standards (https://apastyle.apa.org/jars) provide guidelines for what to report to facilitate evaluation and replication of research.

Questionable Research Practices

One reason many research findings fail to replicate is that researchers have considerable flexibility when analyzing and writing up their research findings. This flexibility, sometimes referred to as "researcher degrees of freedom," means that researchers can "find" support for almost any hypothesis. As Simmons et al. (2011) elegantly put it when pointing out this problem:

> In the course of collecting and analyzing data, researchers have many decisions to make: Should more data be collected? Should some observations be excluded? Which conditions should be combined and which ones compared? Which control variables should be considered? Should specific measures be combined or transformed or both? It is rare, and sometimes impractical, for researchers to make all these decisions beforehand. Rather, it is common (and accepted practice) for researchers to explore various analytic alternatives, to search for a combination that yields "statistical significance," and to then report only what "worked." The problem, of course, is that the likelihood of at least one (of many) analyses producing a falsely positive finding at the 5% level is necessarily greater than 5%. This exploratory behavior is not the byproduct of malicious intent, but rather the result of two factors: (a) ambiguity in how best to make these decisions and (b) the researcher's desire to find a statistically significant result. (p. 1359)

A detailed description of questionable research practices in statistical analysis of data, including those related to data collection and preparation, misuse of statistical significance testing and lack of transparent reporting can be found in Kline (Chapter 26, this volume).

The ethical problem with researcher flexibility is that when researchers consciously or unconsciously make decisions that favor finding and reporting significant results, or not finding or not reporting nonsignificant results, their work distorts the degree of support for their hypothesis, and this can distort the research literature, misleading other scientists, policy makers, and other consumers. These distortions also make it difficult for others to replicate those findings, both because the results may be false positives and because other researchers may make decisions that do not favor, or even that contradict, the original researcher's hypothesis.

It is important to clarify that the ethical issue with researcher flexibility is *not* that researchers thoroughly analyze their data, combine or transform variables, test whether inclusion of control variables strengthens or weakens findings, examine whether effects hold for different dependent measures, and so on. All of these choices can be appropriate, justifiable, and ethical. Careful researchers often conduct many analyses because they want to know how strongly their data support their hypotheses, and whether there are any weaknesses in the results or aspects of the findings that would lead them to temper their conclusions. For example, researchers may include covariates in their analyses not because they are seeking a covariate that yields a significant predicted finding where before there was none, but rather because they want to know if any of those covariates can explain (away) a significant finding, which would reduce its importance. Researchers may try to anticipate questions or objections to their conclusions and be prepared with the answers prior to submitting for publication. The ethical issue arises when the researchers' choices consistently favor finding their preferred result, and they report supportive but not unsupportive findings.

TRANSPARENCY AND OPENNESS AS AN ETHICAL PRINCIPLE IN PUBLISHING

One way to address problems with fabrication, replication, and questionable research practices is open science. Open science is a set of practices that increase the transparency and accessibility of the research process by making research relevant information findable, accessible, and usable by other researchers. Sharing data, analysis code, materials, experimental scripts and protocols, a priori hypotheses, and design and analysis choices with other scientists, preferably in a publicly available location, all exemplify open science practices (see Spellman et al., 2018, for a review and discussion).

Transparency and openness encourage ethical behaviors and discourage misconduct by making more of the scientific process visible and verifiable. Other researchers can evaluate the decisions researchers have made, verify the effects of those decisions on results and conclusions, test the effects of making different analytic decisions, and more easily replicate the research. Decisions that bias results in favor of the researcher's hypotheses or conclusions are more easily identified, as are errors or inappropriate analytic assumptions. To avoid having their decisions and results called into question, researchers who practice transparency and openness are likely to be careful that their decisions are not only defensible but also optimal.

Openness and transparency are ethical practices for other reasons as well (Martone et al., 2018; Ross et al., 2018). Most important, transparency and openness speed the advancement of science because allowing errors, faulty analytic decisions, and sometimes fraud to be caught more quickly reduces the influence of inaccurate or misleading conclusions on the research literature. They facilitate replications and extensions of the research because methods and materials are easily available, which advances scientific inquiry. They permit other researchers to use the data to test novel hypotheses in existing data sets, increasing the benefits of the data to scientific understanding; this may especially benefit researchers at underresourced institutions who lack access to research equipment, space, or participant populations. Open data and analytic code also facilitate syntheses of areas of research through meta-analysis. Thus, transparency and openness are ethical practices because they are good for scientific understanding and the scientific community.

Researchers may worry that openness and transparency will mean that any imperfections in their data—variables that do not show the predicted effect, marginally significant results, and so on—will be held against them when their research undergoes the peer review process. When researchers are no longer free to use their flexibility to conceal imperfect or nonsignificant findings, their manuscripts may be rejected for publication because of flaws in the support for hypotheses or conclusions. Reviewers and editors accustomed to seeing only "perfect" patterns of results due to researcher flexibility to present the strongest evidence may judge imperfections harshly. If researchers are to be open and transparent about the research process, reviewers and editors must also be open to the idea that support for a hypothesis or conclusion should be based on an overall pattern of results, even if some of the specific findings are not conventionally significant, and should not reject manuscripts because a measure or a study yields results that might be due to chance. Openness requires that reviewers, editors, and readers accept imperfection in scientific results. Indeed, manuscripts reporting research with occasionally unsupportive results may be more credible than manuscripts that report many studies or measures all of which (perhaps barely) reach the $p < .05$ level of statistical significance (Simonsohn et al., 2015). Accepting and even welcoming nonperfect patterns of results requires a culture shift among researchers, reviewers, and editors that is just getting underway.

Transparent and open science is not always more ethical than "cloaked" science in which the data are not publicly available (Ross et al., 2018). Although sharing materials, experimental protocols, and analysis scripts from one's own research is usually risk-free, sharing data can be another story. Many ethical issues must be considered prior to sharing data, whether privately (with another researcher) or publicly (in a data repository or open science website). As Ross et al. (2018) noted, these considerations include human participant protections, regulatory constraints, laws, contractual agreements, data ownership and many others. Whereas some data can be easily de-identified and pose minimal risk to participants, other data may involve risk of disclosure of sensitive information. Even de-identified data, from which names, birth dates, Social Security numbers, addresses (including IP addresses), and other identifying information have been stripped, may be identifiable through geolocation information and other particularities or combinations of variables in the data (Ross et al., 2018). Established data repositories such as the Inter-university Consortium for Political and Social Research have methods for sharing data that protect participants' and others' rights (Alter & Gonzalez, 2018). Although openness and transparency are generally good for science, researchers must carefully consider any legal or regulatory constraints and harms that may result from sharing their data.

Some researchers have expressed concern that open science practices have costs for research productivity and advancing one's career as a researcher (Baumeister, 2016; Stroebe & Strack, 2014; but see Hesse, 2018, for a discussion). For example, requirements for adequately powered statistical tests, openness and transparency in data and analyses, providing detailed codebooks to make data and analysis code usable to others, and full reporting of materials, methods and results consume researchers' limited time and resources. Thus, rather than speeding the advancement of science, open science practices could slow it down by burdening researchers with increasing demands. Open science practices may also result in inefficient use of resources, as graduate students and faculty spend their time creating, checking, and uploading these materials. Time and resources devoted to these efforts can negatively affect researchers' productivity and career prospects.

It is true that open science practices can be time-consuming, especially when researchers first begin to adopt them (Vazire, 2018). Learning the ropes of preregistration, preparing one's data sets so they are reusable, and preparing supplementary materials to make them accessible online to provide detailed explanations of materials, methods, and findings can all be time-consuming. However, as norms change and more researchers adopt these practices as a part of their scientific routines, these costs are likely to diminish, and the benefits for advancement of both science and researchers' careers are likely to increase. Other scientists are likely to have more confidence in findings that are transparently shared, and can easily answer questions about findings by delving into the data themselves (see Spellman et al., 2018, for a discussion).

Another objection to open science is based in concerns that one's research ideas will be "scooped" as researchers who put no effort into collecting the data can easily download it and use it to write their own manuscripts. Although many small data sets from experiments that were designed to test a specific hypothesis are unlikely to be used this way, some researchers collect large data sets that take a great deal of time, money, and effort to gather and many months or years to fully analyze. Some longitudinal research costs many millions of dollars and researchers invest years of their careers into collection of a single data set. Given the effort and expense of collecting the data, researchers often assess many variables because it is not feasible to run a new study to rule out alternative explanations, for example. These researchers, in particular, may find ethical or other requirements to make all of the data they collected available immediately to be particularly unreasonable as it both slows their own scientific productivity and allows others to exploit their work.

A number of solutions have been proposed, from embargoing data for a period of time to allow the data collector to write up the results, to including the data collectors as authors on subsequent manuscripts by data users, to creating citable digital object identifiers for data sets so data collectors receive credit when their data are used by others. When other researchers publish from an open data set, should the original data collector have any rights regarding how the data are used or what conclusions are drawn? Ethical guidelines for the use of other people's data continue to evolve, and it is unlikely that a "one size fits all" solution exists.

Preregistration

A second, related solution to fabrication, failures to replicate, and questionable research practices is preregistration, or specifying a research plan and submitting it to a registry prior to data collection or analysis. Preregistration encourages ethical practices and discourages misconduct by constraining researcher flexibility, specifically the tendency to present exploratory findings as confirmatory, or hypothesizing after the results are known, or HARKing (Kerr, 1998). It clearly distinguishes between exploratory research, in which the researcher examines the data to develop new hypotheses, and confirmatory research conducted to test an a priori hypothesis. Exploratory research and digging into data to "uncover" the story the data tell can yield significant results by capitalizing on chance findings and increase the prevalence of "false positive" results in the literature, particularly when sample sizes are small and statistical power is low. These false positive results distort the research literature, misleading other scientists, policy makers, and consumers of research.

Preregistration can also protect others' work and ideas when they practice open science. The fear that one's ideas or hypotheses will be scooped by others who have access to one's data can be reduced by preregistering hypotheses. Preregistration sites such as the Open Science Framework can date-stamp and lock preregistrations, so researchers can point to the site where their hypothesis was preregistered if another researcher subsequently publishes a paper testing that hypothesis. This practice should help researchers avoid intellectual theft of their idea, an issue discussed later.

Preregistration efforts have varied, and a wide variety of preregistration templates are available, resulting in inconsistencies in what information is preregistered. Complete preregistration involves a public declaration of a precise research question, hypotheses, sample size or stop rules for data collection, methods, and data analysis plan prior to conducting the research, or prior to analyzing data in the case of archival data (Spellman et al., 2018). Recently, several organizations including the APA, the British Psychological Society, and the German Psychological Society partnering with the Center for Open Science and the Leibniz Institute for Psychology, have collaborated to develop field-wide standards for preregistration. They created a preregistration template (https://osf.io/46qc8) that allows for a flexible degree of detail that can be adapted for a variety of research projects (Sokol-Chang & Oswald, 2021). The amount of information requested may seem daunting at first, but it is a useful document for planning a project in detail. Simpler templates are also available. Other preregistration forms and templates can be found at the Open Science Framework and the Leibniz Institute for Psychology.

In the context of widespread encouragement to preregister research, it is worth noting that "exploratory" is not a four-letter word. Exploratory and confirmatory analyses can be reported in the same manuscript, as long as they are appropriately identified. Exploratory data analysis is not unethical or even a questionable research practice. Analyzing data thoroughly and from every angle is a useful research practice. Often, the hypothesis that motivated a research project is not confirmed, and researchers want to know why, and whether the data support an alternative account. Exploratory research can be the source of important discoveries. Misconduct involves presenting exploratory research as confirmatory.

Of course, discoveries that result from data mining, or simply putting a statistical trowel in the data to see what one can dig up, could easily be due to chance. In general, discoveries made this way should be replicated in a preregistered study before the researcher and others have confidence in findings. Some data sets that are very large and involve years of data collection or great expense cannot be replicated, or at least not easily or promptly. Findings can still be informative if the effect size and/or sample size are large enough to indicate that the results are not simply due to chance. The generalizability of the finding to other samples may still be in doubt, however.

It is also worth noting that the line between exploratory and confirmatory research is not always bright and clean. Many studies fall somewhere between exploratory and confirmatory, as when researchers speculate based on theory and previous findings, yet are unsure of the precise conditions that will show an effect, how to successfully manipulate their independent variables, how strong an effect will be, what measures will be sensitive to the predicted effects, and what the effects of including covariates might be. In this situation, the research is not data mining, but not sufficiently confirmatory to commit to a thorough preregistration of hypotheses, analyses, and so on. Researchers who wonder if their study is exploratory could ask themselves whether findings that deviate from expectations on a particular measure or in a particular comparison of means would lead them to doubt their hypothesis, or instead think they haven't tested it well. In the latter case, the research is clearly exploratory. In the current climate, it seems wise to treat such research as informed exploration and follow up significant results with a preregistered study.

Writing the Manuscript

Once a study has been run and the data have been analyzed, it is time to write a manuscript reporting the results. Ethical considerations continue to emerge at every stage of manuscript preparation and in every section of the manuscript.

In writing a manuscript, authors should be sure to give credit to others where it is due for their ideas, words, data, and contributions to the research. Authors who submit their work to APA journals are asked to certify that they have complied with APA's ethical standards, including Standard 8.11, which states, "Psychologists do not present portions of another's work or data as their own, even if the other work or data source is cited occasionally" (APA, 2017).

Copyright infringement. In writing manuscripts, authors must take care to respect copyrights to information and materials they want to describe in their research. Authors should be sure to check whether the information they want to use is copyrighted, and obtain permission to reprint it if it is.

Plagiarism. Plagiarism is a form of using others' work or words without giving appropriate credit. Most of us are familiar with the idea of plagiarism, but less familiar with the different forms it can take. The most familiar form of plagiarism is unaltered copying of text from others' work, whether that work is published or unpublished, copyrighted or not. It is not unethical to use others' words if the fact that one has done so is acknowledged by putting those words in quotation marks with the appropriate citation. This becomes plagiarism when the fact that the words are a direct quote is not acknowledged.

It is easy to plagiarize by copying and pasting text from documents; it is almost as easy to detect such plagiarism using software created for that purpose. Many journals routinely run submitted manuscripts through programs that report the degree of overlap with other documents available on the internet. These reports indicate precisely what aspects of those documents are duplicates and the documents they overlap with. Journal editors will reject manuscripts that have an unacceptable degree of overlap. Authors can avoid this by running their own manuscripts prior to submission, to ensure that none of their material has intentionally or unintentionally been plagiarized. Most universities have licensed software that can be used for this purpose.

Changing a few words or phrases in copied text without crediting others also constitutes plagiarism (Roig, 2003). This type of plagiarism may be more difficult to detect but can still result in unacceptably high levels of overlap in software checks. A graduate student whose essay exam yielded an unusually high degree of overlap with information available on the web once explained, "There were no complete sentences that were word-for-word identical to material on the web."

This student wrongly assumed that changing a word here and there was either acceptable or at least would escape detection.

Researchers also sometimes summarize others' work in their own writing. To avoid plagiarism, summaries should be the summarizers' own words, and cite the work that is summarized.

What about reusing one's own writing in a new document? Doing so without acknowledgement constitutes self-plagiarism. It is problematic when that writing has been copyrighted by someone else. When articles are accepted for publication, authors are required to sign over the copyright to their work to the publisher, who then owns the rights to the work.

Publishers may allow authors a bit of leeway in using their own work in subsequent papers, depending on the extent of overlap and where it occurs in the manuscript. Authors sometimes labor to find the best way to express an idea or describe a method or data analysis strategy, and may object to rewriting in less clear form to avoid overlap with their own published work. How objectionable this is considered depends on the particular reviewers, editors, and publishers who consider the work. Newly submitted work should be original. Authors should keep any overlap with their own previous writing to the bare minimum, and preferably restrict it to the methods and results sections where they cannot improve on their past writing, and include appropriate citations.

Intellectual theft. Another way authors may present another's work as their own is by taking their ideas, but not their words, without appropriate credit. Because ideas cannot be copyrighted, and are often freely shared among communities of scholars, researchers might think there is nothing unethical about putting those ideas to the test. But such behavior constitutes intellectual theft and violates the ethical principle that psychologists establish relationships of trust with those with whom they work (see Cooper, 2016, for a discussion).

Scientists with similar interests will often discuss their ideas with others at conferences and other research presentations, or conclude their manuscripts and presentations with ideas for future studies. Many a researcher has rued sharing their ideas with others who proceeded to test and publish them without crediting the person who originated the idea. This is particularly upsetting when the person who takes the idea and claims ownership of it is in a position of authority over the originator of the idea, such as a research advisor.

Taking others' ideas without crediting the source has many costs. First, it can damage relationships if the person who shared the idea believes they were taken advantage of. Second, it can make scientists reluctant to share ideas for future research or talk about what they are currently working on for fear of having their ideas stolen. This can hinder the research process, as the back and forth of ideas and criticism of them stalls. Third, being known as a person who steals ideas is bad for the reputations and careers of scientists.

It is easy to head off these difficulties by mentioning to the originator of the idea that one would like to follow it up, and asking whether the originator would like to collaborate, and if not, would object. This allows the person who would like to follow up the idea to discover if other efforts are currently underway. A cooperative approach can foster trust, collaboration, and even friendship, instead of mistrust, hoarding of ideas, and damaged relationships and reputations.

Honesty about exploratory and confirmatory research. In writing a research report, ethical principles indicate that authors should be honest in describing the origins of their ideas. This principle extends to being honest about whether the research is exploratory or confirmatory. Psychologist Norbert Kerr (1998) coined the term HARKing (hypothesizing after the results are known) to describe writing the introduction to an article as if the results had been hypothesized in advance when they were not. Researchers often—usually—encounter unexpected findings, which prompt them to rethink their ideas. This is appropriate and the source of many scientific discoveries. However, as noted previously, presenting exploratory findings as confirmatory can distort the research literature because it can increase the false positive findings in the literature. Accordingly, the introduction section to articles should honestly describe research as exploratory if it is.

Some researchers may object that this leads to poor writing. Psychologist Daryl Bem has been criticized for his advice to tell a good story when writing an article, even to the extent of throwing out the ideas that motivated the research (e.g., Spellman et al., 2018). But this does not mean that ethical writing requires describing all of one's wrong-headed predictions and then presenting the evidence that they were wrong-headed. Introductions can honestly state that one prediction would be this, but another prediction would be that, and the present study explores these possibilities. The ethical issue is in pretending that one hypothesized unexpected results.

Sometimes research does not provide a good test of an idea for reasons the researcher did not foresee—the focal dependent measures turned out to be unreliable, for example. Yet there may still be something potentially interesting or important in the findings. In this case, Bem's advice to throw out one's initial hypotheses might be valid. Researchers can write an article about the important finding, including a review of relevant literature. However, they should not present the findings as hypothesized in advance if they were not. And as always when conducting research that yields unexpected findings, it is a good idea to conduct a replication study, ideally one that is preregistered, to be sure the finding is not merely due to chance.

What studies to include in a manuscript.
In addition to the many decisions researchers make when analyzing their data, they also decide which studies to include in the manuscript. Should "failed" studies be included in addition to those that yield significant results? What about pilot studies conducted to determine whether an experimental manipulation works as intended, or if the methods are feasible? If a researcher has replicated a study several times, should all of those replications be reported in the manuscript? And if a study can address several unrelated or only loosely related research questions, should all findings be included in a single manuscript?

These can be difficult decisions with no clear right or wrong answer. For the sake of full transparency, researchers may want to report every study, every measure, and every analysis they have conducted or could conduct on their data. However, overly long manuscripts with huge numbers of analyses can result in lack of clarity and coherence, making it difficult for readers to "digest" the findings and undermining rather than enhancing the contribution to scientific knowledge.

Further discouraging researchers from including all studies, analyses, and results associated with their project are the page or word limits many journals impose on manuscripts. Page limits are, by and large, a good thing. They encourage authors to be concise in their writing, which usually means the writing is clearer and therefore better. Excessively long articles also use up more of the limited number of pages allocated to a journal, decreasing the space available for other manuscripts. Indeed, journal editors have been known to ask authors to remove studies from their manuscripts to reduce page length.

However, page limits also encourage or require authors to be selective in what they report, creating opportunities for ethically questionable decisions. The emergence of a type of article called "short reports" with very strict page or word limits exacerbated this problem (Ledgerwood & Sherman, 2012). If an article can be no longer than 2,000 or 4,000 words, researchers must be selective in what they report. Authors may reasonably respond to these constraints by including the studies, measures, and analyses that "worked," and omitting those that did not. The short report format seems designed to encourage researchers to take advantage of researcher flexibility, and bias their report in favor of findings they like.

Fortunately, most journals permit authors to include links to supplementary online materials, where they can more completely report the results of their research, including pilot studies and replications. To ensure that they remain available, those supplemental materials should be deposited in a permanent location at the journal or a repository like the Open Science Framework—not on the authors' own websites, which tend to be unstable over time as authors change universities, revamp their sites, retire, and so on.

Studies with failed manipulations are a gray area. It can be useful to other researchers to know that a particular manipulation failed, so sharing this information can be helpful, especially if the manipulation has been published in the literature so is assumed to "work." However, in the initial stages of a research project, researchers may explore new or different ways to manipulate a construct that has not been manipulated previously; many of these efforts may fail. Although this point may be debatable, it is probably not unethical to exclude these initial efforts from a research report, because they do not afford adequate tests of the hypothesis and so are uninformative regarding the research question. Researchers should report all studies that test their hypotheses (i.e., those that successfully manipulated their independent variable, whether the results were as predicted or not), either in the manuscript itself or in supplementary materials.

What variables (independent or dependent) to report in a manuscript. Transparency and openness require that researchers do not conceal aspects of their study from readers, even if the researchers think those aspects are not relevant to the research question at hand. This means, at a minimum, that researchers should report all experimental conditions and all measures included in the research. If it makes sense to combine two or more experimental conditions, that should be reported. Likewise, readers should know what measures were included in a study, even if they are not relevant to the research question at hand. Researchers can list all variables measured or even include a complete copy of their research materials and measures in an online supplement or open science repository.

Simmons et al. (2012) proposed that researchers who have determined their sample size in advance, reported all their variables, and not dropped any experimental conditions in their report of their research say so, in a simple 21-word statement: "We report how we determined our sample size, all data exclusions (if any), all manipulations, and all measures in the study." This statement can be supported with supplemental materials to assure readers that it is accurate.

Increasingly, journals have adopted policies that encourage or require greater openness and transparency. Some journals award badges to articles that have open data, open materials, or preregistered studies. Many publishers and have signed onto the Transparency and Openness Promotion (TOP) Guidelines (Nosek et al., 2015), which specify differing levels of openness required by journals. Table 27.1 summarizes different levels of TOP guidelines for eight different domains, including citation, analytical methods, research design, preregistration, data transparency, research materials, transparency, preregistration, and replication. APA Journals now requires TOP Level 1 adoption for each of the eight TOP domains across its core titles, and strongly encourages the adoption of TOP Level 2 for each of the eight TOP domains except for data transparency and replication.

Duplicate publication. In light of the importance of publications to a scientist's career, it is not surprising that some scientists want to publish as many articles as they can. This creates incentives for duplicate publication (publishing the same findings more than once, usually in different journals). The Ethics Code of the APA expressly prohibits misrepresenting data as original when they have been published before. Duplicate publication distorts the research literature by overrepresenting a finding, which misleads other scientists, policy makers, and consumers of research. When journals were available only in print, authors would sometimes want to make their findings available to researchers in a different discipline by publishing them in another journal.

TABLE 27.1

Transparency and Openness Promotion (TOP) Guidelines Summary Table

	Not implemented	Level I	Level II	Level III
Citation standards	No mention of data citation.	Journal describes citation of data in guidelines to authors with clear rules and examples.	Article provides appropriate citation for data and materials used consistent with journal's author guidelines.	Article is not published until providing appropriate citation for data and materials following journal's author guidelines.
Data transparency	Journal encourages data sharing, or says nothing.	Article states whether data are available, and, if so, where to access them.	Data must be posted to a trusted repository. Exceptions must be identified at article submission.	Data must be posted to a trusted repository, and reported analyses will be reproduced independently prior to publication.
Analytic methods (code) transparency	Journal encourages code sharing, or says nothing.	Article states whether code is available, and, if so, where to access it.	Code must be posted to a trusted repository. Exceptions must be identified at article submission.	Code must be posted to a trusted repository, and reported analyses will be reproduced independently prior to publication.
Research materials transparency	Journal encourages materials sharing or says nothing.	Article states whether materials are available, and, if so, where to access them.	Materials must be posted to a trusted repository. Exceptions must be identified at article submission.	Materials must be posted to a trusted repository, and reported analyses will be reproduced independently prior to publication.
Design and analysis transparency	Journal encourages design and analysis transparency, or says nothing.	Journal articulates design transparency standards.	Journal requires adherence to design transparency standards for review and publication.	Journal requires and enforces adherence to design transparency standards for review and publication.
Study preregistration	Journal says nothing.	Article states whether preregistration of study exists, and, if so, where to access it.	Article states whether preregistration of study exists, and, if so, allows journal access during peer review for verification.	Journal requires preregistration of studies and provides link and badge in article to meeting requirements.
Analysis plan preregistration	Journal says nothing.	Article states whether preregistration of study with analysis plan exists, and, if so, where to access it.	Article states whether preregistration with analysis plan exists, and, if so, allows journal access during peer review for verification.	Journal requires preregistration of studies with analysis plans and provides link and badge in article to meeting requirements.
Replication	Journal discourages submission of replication studies, or says nothing.	Journal encourages submission of replication studies.	Journal encourages submission of replication studies and conducts results blind review.	Journal uses Registered Reports as a submission option for replication studies with peer review prior to observing the study outcomes.

Note. More information is available at https://www.cos.io/initiatives/top-guidelines. From "Summary Table," by the Center for Open Science, 2015 (https://www.cos.io/initiatives/top-guidelines). CC BY 4.0.

This has never been acceptable, because the journal that published the article first typically owns the copyright, but now that journals are available online, there is no reason that researchers in other disciplines cannot find relevant research.

Duplicate publication may be acceptable under some circumstances (see the *Publication Manual of the American Psychological Association* [APA, 2020], for a discussion); for example, if the findings have been published as an abstract, in a publication that is not widely available (e.g., a dissertation), or as a preprint. Scientists increasingly post preprints of manuscripts in online repositories both to get information out to other scientists quickly and to get feedback on their manuscript before it is submitted for peer review. Most manuscripts are substantially revised during the peer review process, so the final published version differs from the preprint. Whether posting a preprint precludes publication in a journal is a decision typically made by journal editors. Editors may consider how widely available the manuscript is, how frequently it has been downloaded and cited, and so on, in judging the contribution and originality of the submitted manuscript. Duplicate publication may also be acceptable if a manuscript reports reanalyses of previously published data, yielding new findings or new insights into a phenomenon. In any case, previously published versions of the findings, including abstracts and preprints, should be acknowledged.

Piecemeal publication. Piecemeal publication involves splitting the results of a single study into many publications when they could reasonably be combined into a single manuscript. According to the *Publication Manual of the American Psychological Association* (APA, 2020), "authors are obligated to present work as parsimoniously and completely as possible within the space constraints of journal articles" (p. 19).

Piecemeal publication distorts the research literature if multiple reports based on the same underlying data introduce findings into the literature multiple times. Even when the primary research questions and findings of one manuscript differ from the primary questions and findings of another, secondary findings such as descriptive statistics and correlations among measures may be reported in both manuscripts. Researchers who want to understand the literature or synthesize those findings in a meta-analysis must be able to tell which findings appear in other papers. To avoid introducing such distortions, researchers should acknowledge with complete citations any previous publications based on the same underlying data.

Some large data sets include hundreds or thousands of variables, and because collecting those data can be expensive in terms of both time and money, they may be designed to answer many different questions. And after data collection is completed, the richness of the data set may allow researchers to address research questions they did not anticipate in advance. In such cases, a single report of the findings would be excessively long and theoretically unfocused for a journal article.

Researchers in this situation should consider using data reduction strategies that might help them more parsimoniously present their findings. For example, if a study includes many different variables related to well-being, does factor analysis indicate that those variables measure the same underlying construct, or are they empirically distinct? Do analyses of those variables yield highly similar or quite different results? When other findings have been published from the same data set, are the new findings truly unique, or are they essentially the same finding revealed in different measures? Highly correlated measures that yield similar results can easily be combined into a single manuscript.

When data reduction strategies do not simplify presentation, large data sets may be "carved up" according to the research questions they answer, always keeping in mind the goals of completeness and parsimony, and the importance of citing previous papers based on the same underlying data.

Authorship: Responsibility and Credit for Research

One gratifying aspect of scientific publication is seeing one's name in print (or on screen) as the author of an article, after what may have been a years-long journey from idea to publication. Authorship signifies credit and responsibility for the work reported in the article. Authorship decisions therefore involve ethical considerations.

Credit. Order of authorship signifies who should get more credit and who should get less. Authorship serves as an important indicator of research contributions and productivity, and can be an important consideration in hiring, promotion, and salary decisions. Perhaps it should not be surprising that authorship issues can be a major source of dissatisfaction and conflict among members of research teams. Conflicts regarding who is an author and who is not, and where researchers are placed in the list of authors can be emotional and difficult to resolve. In some cases, they lead to damaged or broken relationships, and those negative effects can be long-lasting. In one recent case, a researcher complained about not being included as an author on a paper published 35 years ago!

Underlying many authorship conflicts is a human tendency for people to be more aware of and value more highly their own efforts and contributions than those of others, and therefore to believe that they are more responsible for, and deserve more credit for, joint projects (Ross & Sicoly, 1979). When asked what percentage of the credit for the work they deserve, coworkers' estimates added up to more than 100% of the credit. This phenomenon can easily occur among authorship teams, where members are each more aware of the time, effort, knowledge, and creativity they contributed than they are of others' contributions. And researchers may disagree about what contributions matter most for the final product—the idea, the methods, the data analysis, or the writing. Add to this general human tendency to believe we deserve more credit than others would give us and the consequences of authorship for one's career, and it is not surprising that disagreements arise at the point of assigning authorship.

Further contributing to the potential for conflict is the ambiguity in defining what contributions merit authorship in the first place, and conflicting norms regarding the meaning of being listed as first, last, or in the middle of the list of authors. Many scientific disciplines reserve the first position for the person who was most responsible for getting the actual research completed, and the last position for the senior member of the research team, who often guides the research and its interpretation. The APA Ethics Code states that authors should be listed in order of their relative contributions, with the person who contributed the most listed first. Even within psychology departments, researchers who publish in different scientific journals may follow different rules for assigning authorship. Researchers are strongly encouraged to talk about authorship expectations early in a research project, and to continually revisit those expectations as the research proceeds and contributions may diverge from initial expectations (APA, 2020). Conflicts about authorship are less likely to arise when roles and responsibilities are discussed early and often.

Sometimes people are listed as authors when they do not want to be. Forged authorship occurs when people who made no contribution to the work are listed as authors without their knowledge or consent, in hopes of increasing the chances that the paper will be accepted for publication. This practice is obviously unethical. Alternatively, people who actually did contribute to the research may be listed as authors against their wishes. For example, when data collected by a graduate student are used in a later paper written by the advisor, the student (or former student) may be listed as an author. This occasionally happens without the knowledge or consent of the person listed on the paper, who discovers they have been listed as an author when asked to sign a copyright form on acceptance of the manuscript for publication. People cannot be forced to be an author against their wishes, according to the Committee for Publication Ethics (n.d.a) guidelines (https://doi.org/10.24318/cope.2018.1.1).

If a listed author contributed to a manuscript but does not want to be listed or does not want their contribution (e.g., data) used in the manuscript, publication may delayed while the parties involved try to resolve the disagreement. This is extremely frustrating to the authors whose manuscript has been accepted, and also to the person who did not know and does not want to be included as an author. To prevent these issues, journals increasingly ask all authors to acknowledge their contribution when the paper is submitted for publication. In this case, the peer review process does not proceed until all authors have agreed to their roles as listed with the submission.

Responsibility. Authors often focus on who gets credit for research contributions and pay less attention to the responsibilities of authorship. Journal editors, publishers, and professional societies differ in their views of authors' responsibilities. APA journals require authors to state in writing that they have complied with APA ethical standards in the treatment of their sample. Authors also have responsibility for other ethical aspects of their work, specifically with regard to not fabricating data, taking reasonable steps to correct errors in published articles, avoiding plagiarism, ensuring that authorship accurately reflects contributions, avoiding duplicate publication, and sharing their research data with other scientists for the purposes of verification (APA, 2017). They must also declare any conflicts of interest, such as a connection to an entity that could be financially affected by the results of the work. Thus, authorship carries significant responsibilities.

To increase transparency and integrity regarding authorship and research contributions, publishers and scientific societies have begun to adopt more informative standards for authorship. Several publishers, societies, and journals including some APA journals have adopted the Contributor Roles Taxonomy (CRediT) to specify each author's contributions to published articles. Authors are encouraged to use Open Researcher and Contributor Identity (ORCID) identifiers to avoid confusion with other authors who have the same name. McNutt et al. (2018) also proposed that editors and publishers endorse the following statement about authorship credit and responsibilities, which has been adopted by APA journals:

Each author is expected to have made substantial contributions to the conception or design of the work; or the acquisition, analysis, or interpretation of data; or the creation of new software used in the work; or have drafted the work or substantively revised it; AND to have approved the submitted version (and any substantially modified version that involves the author's contribution to the study); AND to have agreed both to be personally accountable for the author's own contributions and to ensure that questions related to the accuracy or integrity of any part of the work, even ones in which the author was not personally involved, are appropriately investigated, resolved, and the resolution documented in the literature. (McNutt et al., 2018, p. 258)

Many people may contribute to research projects in ways that do not substantially affect the direction of the work (that is, they have no input into the design, conceptualization, analysis, interpretation, or writing of the project), yet nonetheless are important to acknowledge. For example, research assistants may collect or code data, statistical consultants may provide advice on data analysis, or researchers from other laboratories may provide critical feedback on a draft. These contributions should be recognized in an acknowledgment note in the published manuscript.

Disagreements about authorship credit and responsibility should be raised as early as possible in the research process, so they can be resolved ethically and amicably. As with any difficult conversation, it is best to keep in mind that you may not be aware of others' contributions, and approach the topic as an exploration, rather than an accusation or demand (e.g., Stone et al., 1999). The Committee on Publishing Ethics provides advice for new researchers on how to deal with authorship disputes (COPE, n.d.a).

SUSPICIONS AND ALLEGATIONS OF MISCONDUCT

Those who suspect misconduct on the part of another researcher are ethically obligated to pursue it, particularly if they are a part of the research team. Allegations of misconduct are fraught, as they threaten the reputation and career of the accused, and can damage important relationships of the accused and the accuser. When concerns or suspicions about misconduct arise, it is important to distinguish facts or evidence that imply misconduct from gossip or rumors about misconduct. Gossip lacking any evidentiary basis should not be repeated, because false accusations can be very damaging to both accuser and accused. People who believe they have evidence of misconduct should document it, while keeping in mind that there may be innocent explanations for apparent misconduct. The possibility of misconduct should be treated as a question to be explored, not a foregone conclusion.

If feasible, those who believe misconduct has occurred should approach the possible offender and have a conversation about apparent anomalies without explicitly or implicitly making accusations. For example, if the data on which analyses are based differ from the raw data, instead of accusing someone of data fabrication, it would be more fruitful to ask about it in a factual way. For example, one might say, "I noticed some differences between the raw data we collected and the data that were used in analyses, and I wanted to be sure there were no mistakes and that we report any omissions or corrections accurately. Can we talk about this?"

In the best case, there is a compelling and ethical explanation for what might have appeared to be misconduct, and the matter is resolved, or there was a mistake that can be corrected. If, however, a satisfactory explanation is not forthcoming, then the person with suspicions needs to take further action to avoid being complicit in the misconduct. At this point, it would be wise to consult other members of the research team with any concerns; they may have additional facts that shed light on the situation, and may be able to help with further steps. Then, one can consult with trusted authorities such as a department chair, Office of Research, or the research funder. These inquiries may trigger an investigation, usually done by the funder or the accused researcher's institution. Once this step is taken, the investigation and resolution may be out of the accuser's hands.

If a manuscript has been submitted to or published by a scientific journal, people with concerns about misconduct can contact the journal's editor, who will advise about next steps. The Committee on Publishing Ethics guidelines state that "journals should have a clearly described process for handling allegations, however they are brought to the journal's or publisher's attention. Journals must take seriously allegations of misconduct pre-publication and post-publication. Policies should include how to handle allegations from whistleblowers" (COPE, n.d.b).

Journal editors will attempt to resolve issues amicably when they can. If an article has been published, the publisher may issue a correction or a retraction of the article, preferably with the agreement of the authors. If an institution has investigated and made a finding of misconduct, the investigating body will issue a report and an article may be retracted without the consent of the authors.

Ideally, all researchers are sufficiently aware of publication ethics to avoid any behaviors that result in accusations of misconduct. Those who do find themselves accused of misconduct are likely to find the accusation upsetting. Although it might be tempting to either issue a blanket denial or even to lash out at the accuser, these behaviors are unlikely to result in a positive resolution. Instead, those who are (or feel) accused should be as transparent and nondefensive as possible. Willingness to acknowledge errors and mistakes will lead to a quicker and potentially more constructive outcome.

CONCLUSION

Researchers usually have at least two goals when analyzing and writing up their research for publication—advancing scientific understanding of phenomena and advancing their own careers and those of their students and collaborators. These two goals are usually well-aligned, but tensions between them can sometimes arise, creating incentives to take ethical shortcuts in the data analysis and publication process. The pressure these incentives create can subtly or overtly affect the choices researchers make in the publication process. By becoming aware of ethical pitfalls and dilemmas in advance, researchers can identify and avoid them. This will ultimately be good for their own careers and the people they work with, and good for science.

References

American Psychological Association (APA). (2020). *Publication manual of the American Psychological Association* (7th ed.). https://doi.org/10.1037/0000165-000

Alter, G., & Gonzalez, R. (2018). Responsible practices for data sharing. *American Psychologist, 73*(2), 146–156. https://doi.org/10.1037/amp0000258

American Psychological Association. (2017). *Ethical principles of psychologists and code of conduct* (2002, amended effective June 1, 2010, and January 1, 2017). https://www.apa.org/ethics/code/index.aspx

Baumeister, R. F. (2016). Charting the future of social psychology on stormy seas: Winners, losers, and recommendations. *Journal of Experimental Social Psychology, 66*, 153–158. https://doi.org/10.1016/j.jesp.2016.02.003

Bhattacharjee, Y. (2013, April 26). The mind of a con man. *The New York Times*. https://www.nytimes.com/2013/04/28/magazine/diederik-stapels-audacious-academic-fraud.html

Committee on Publication Ethics. (n.d.a). *How to handle authorship disputes: A guide for new researchers*. https://doi.org/10.24318/cope.2018.1.1

Committee on Publication Ethics. (n.d.b). *Allegations of misconduct*. https://publicationethics.org/misconduct

Cooper, H. (2016). *Ethical choices in research: Managing data, writing reports, and publishing results in the social sciences*. American Psychological Association. https://doi.org/10.1037/14859-000

Ebersole, C. R., Atherton, O. E., Belanger, A. L., Skulborstad, H. M., Allen, J. M., Banks, J. B., Baranski, E., Bernstein, M. J., Bonfiglio, D. B. V., Boucher, L., Brown, E. R., Budiman, N. I., Cairo, A. H., Capaldi, C. A., Chartier, C. R., Chung, J. M., Cicero, D. C., Coleman, J. A., Conway, J. G., . . . Nosek, B. A. (2016). Many Labs 3: Evaluating participant pool quality across the academic semester via replication. *Journal of Experimental Social Psychology, 67*, 68–82. https://doi.org/10.1016/j.jesp.2015.10.012

Feldman Barrett, L. (2015, September). Psychology is not in crisis. *The New York Times*, A23. https://www.nytimes.com/2015/09/01/opinion/psychology-is-not-in-crisis.html

Gilbert, D. T., King, G., Pettigrew, S., & Wilson, T. D. (2016). Comment on "Estimating the reproducibility of psychological science." *Science, 351*(6277), 1037. https://doi.org/10.1126/science.aad7243

Hesse, B. W. (2018). Can psychology walk the walk of open science? *American Psychologist, 73*(2), 126–137. https://doi.org/10.1037/amp0000197

Ioannidis, J. P. A. (2005). Why most published research findings are false. *PLOS Medicine, 2*(8), e124. https://doi.org/10.1371/journal.pmed.0020124

Kerr, N. L. (1998). HARKing: Hypothesizing after the results are known. *Personality and Social Psychology Review, 2*(3), 196–217. https://doi.org/10.1207/s15327957pspr0203_4

Klein, R. A., Ratliff, K. A., Vianello, M., Adams, R. B., Jr., Bahník, S., Bernstein, M. J., Konrad Bocian, K., Brandt, M. J., Brooks, B., Brumbaugh, C. C., Cemalcilar, Z., Chandler, J., Cheong, W., Davis, W. E., Devos, T., Eisner, M., Frankowska, N., Furrow, D., Galliani, E. M., . . . Nosek, B. A. (2014). Data from investigating variation in replicability: A "Many Labs" Replication Project. *Journal of Open Psychology Data, 2*(1), e4. https://doi.org/10.5334/jopd.ad

Klein, R. A., Vianello, M., Hasselman, F., Adams, B. G., Adams, R. B., Jr., Alper, S., Aveyard, M., Axt, J. R., Babalola, M. T., Bahník, Š., Batra, R., Berkics, M., Bernstein, M. J., Berry, D. R., Bialobrzeska, O., Binan, E. D., Bocian, K., Brandt, M. J., Busching, R., . . . Nosek, B. A. (2018). Many Labs 2: Investigating variation in replicability across samples and settings. *Advances in Methods and Practices in Psychological Science, 1*(4), 443–490. https://doi.org/10.1177/2515245918810225

Ledgerwood, A., & Sherman, J. W. (2012). Short, sweet, and problematic? The rise of the short report in psychological science. *Perspectives on Psychological Science, 7*(1), 60–66. https://doi.org/10.1177/1745691611427304

Martone, M. E., Garcia-Castro, A., & VandenBos, G. R. (2018). Data sharing in psychology. *American Psychologist, 73*(2), 111–125. https://doi.org/10.1037/amp0000242

McNutt, M. K., Bradford, M., Drazen, J. M., Hanson, B., Howard, B., Jamieson, K. H., Kiermer, V., Marcus, E., Pope, B. K., Schekman, R., Swaminathan, S.,

Stang, P. J., & Verma, I. M. (2018). Transparency in authors' contributions and responsibilities to promote integrity in scientific publication. *Proceedings of the National Academy of Sciences of the United States of America, 115*(11), 2557–2560. https://doi.org/10.1073/pnas.1715374115

Nosek, B. A., Alter, G., Banks, G. C., Borsboom, D., Bowman, S. D., Breckler, S. J., Buck, S., Chambers, C. D., Chin, G., Christensen, G., Contestabile, M., Dafoe, A., Eich, E., Freese, J., Glennerster, R., Goroff, D., Green, D. P., Hesse, B., Humphreys, M., . . . Yarkoni, T. (2015). Promoting an open research culture. *Science, 348*(6242), 1422–1425. https://doi.org/10/gcpzwn

Open Science Collaboration. (2015). Estimating the reproducibility of psychological science. *Science, 349*(6251), aac4716. https://doi.org/10.1126/science.aac4716

Roig, M. (2003). Avoiding plagiarism, self-plagiarism, and other questionable writing practices: A guide to ethical writing. *The Office of Research Integrity.* https://bsc.ua.edu/wp-content/uploads/2017/07/plagiarism-1.pdf

Ross, M., & Sicoly, F. (1979). Egocentric biases in availability and attribution. *Journal of Personality and Social Psychology, 37*(3), 322–336. https://doi.org/10.1037/0022-3514.37.3.322

Ross, M. W., Iguchi, M. Y., & Panicker, S. (2018). Ethical aspects of data sharing and research participant protections. *American Psychologist, 73*(2), 138–145. https://doi.org/10.1037/amp0000240

Simmons, J. P., Nelson, L. D., & Simonsohn, U. (2011). False-positive psychology: Undisclosed flexibility in data collection and analysis allows presenting anything as significant. *Psychological Science, 22*(11), 1359–1366. https://doi.org/10.1177/0956797611417632

Simmons, J. P., Nelson, L. D., & Simonsohn, U. (2012). A 21 word solution. *Dialogue: The Official Newsletter of the Society for Personality and Social Psychology, 26*(2), 4–7. https://ssrn.com/abstract=2160588

Simons, D. J., Holcombe, A. O., & Spellman, B. A. (2014). An Introduction to Registered Replication Reports at Perspectives on Psychological Science. *Perspectives on Psychological Science, 9*(5), 552–555. https://doi.org/10.1177/1745691614543974

Simonsohn, U., Simmons, J. P., & Nelson, L. D. (2015). Better P-curves: Making P-curve analysis more robust to errors, fraud, and ambitious P-hacking, a Reply to Ulrich and Miller (2015). *Journal of Experimental Psychology: General, 144*(6), 1146–1152. https://doi.org/10.1037/xge0000104

Sokol-Chang, R., & Oswald, F. L. (2021). International open science: A preregistration template for quantitative research in psychology. *The Score.* https://www.apadivisions.org/division-5/publications/score/2021/01/international-open-science

Spellman, B. A., Gilbert, E. A., & Corker, K. S. (2018). Open science. *Stevens' handbook of experimental psychology and cognitive neuroscience* (Vol. 5, pp. 1–47). https://doi.org/10.1002/9781119170174.epcn519

Stone, D., Patton, B., & Heen, S. (1999). *Difficult conversations: How to discuss what matters most.* Penguin Books.

Stroebe, W., & Strack, F. (2014). The alleged crisis and the illusion of exact replication. *Perspectives on Psychological Science, 9*(1), 59–71. https://doi.org/10.1177/1745691613514450

Van Bavel, J. (2016, May 27). Why do so many studies fail to replicate? *The New York Times.* https://www.nytimes.com/2016/05/29/opinion/sunday/why-do-so-many-studies-fail-to-replicate.html

Vazire, S. (2018). Implications of the credibility revolution for productivity, creativity, and progress. *Perspectives on Psychological Science, 13*(4), 411–417. https://doi.org/10.1177/1745691617751884

Index

Abdolell, M., 445
Abell, R. A., 389
Absorbing states, in event history analysis, 271
Academic engagement studies, 515
Accelerated research design, 260
Accessibility of data, 563
Ackerman, R. A., 460
Actor effects, in SRM, 452, 460
Actor-partner model (APM), 473–474
Actors, in SNA, 502, 510, 523
Actor variance, 455, 458
ACT (American College Testing) scores, 133
Actuarial method, in event history analysis, 278
Addictions, 152
Additive models, generalized, 193, 194
Additivity of data, 59–60
Adobe Illustrator, 106
Adobe InDesign, 78
Adolescent delinquency example, 251–252
Adolescent relationships example, 269–278
Advisor (software), 106
Age group, as multicategorical value, 117
Aggregate data, 495
Aggregation, disaggregation vs., 221
Agneessens, F., 510
Agnostic imputation, 40, 41, 43, 45
Agresti, A., 217
Aguinis, H., 580, 583–584, 587
AI (artificial intelligence), 491, 492, 494
AIC (Akaike information criteria), 398, 415, 417, 513
AID (Automatic Interaction Detector), 429, 432, 446

Aiken, L. S., 232–233
Air traffic controllers example, 206–207
Aitkin, M., 217
Ajzen, H., 521
Akaike information criteria (AIC), 398, 415, 417, 513
Akers, Katherine G., 563–577
Alcohol consumption examples, 91, 95, 257, 259–260
Allison, P., 291
Alpha, smart vs. dumb, 586–587
Alpha factor analysis, 385
Alters, in SNA, 523
Amazon Mechanical Turk, 482
American College Testing (ACT) scores, 133
American Community Survey, 487
American Psychological Association (APA), 579, 598, 604
 data Sharing Working Group, 573
 "Ethical Principles of Psychologists and Code of Conduct," 495, 564, 585, 599, 611–612
 journals, 605, 608, 612
 Publication Manual of the American Psychological Association, 610
 Publications and Communications Board, 598
 publications of, 107
 Task Force on Statistical Inference, 27, 185
American Statistical Association, 585
American Time Use Survey, 488
AMOS (software), 477
Amount data, re-expression of, 63
Analysis, appropriate level of, in longitudinal data analysis, 254
Analysis decision trees, 589

Analysis of covariance (ANCOVA), 55, 255, 258
Analysis of variance (ANOVA), 169–186, 251, 255, 258
 analysis of mean differences, 171–173
 assumptions about error, 586
 effect size, indexes of, 185
 in exploratory data analysis, 65–69
 family-wise error rates in, 183–185
 framework for, 173–179
 in generalized linear models, 214
 group equivalence, assertion of, 185–186
 model-based analysis, 170–171
 robust alternatives to, 182–183
 violations of model assumptions and outliers, 180–183
Analytic rotations of factors, 389
ANAMIA (software), 506
Anastasi, A., 298
Anchor-based methods, 151
Anchoring, in graphics, 86, 89, 90
ANCOVA (analysis of covariance), 55
Anderson, D. R., 588
Anderson, R. B., 81
Andresen, R., 157
Annotation, of graphics, 88
Anonymization of personal data, 495, 573, 603
ANOVA. *See* Analysis of variance
Antagonistic interactions, 114
Antisocial behavior studies, use of SNA for, 515
Ant-vis/G2, 106
APA. *See* American Psychological Association
APM (actor-partner model), 473–474
Appelbaum, M., 181

Index

A priori contrasts, in ANOVA, 179
A priori hypothesis testing, 583
A priori power, 587
Archival research, 481–500
   and "crisis of confidence," 481–485
   digital interactions, traces from, 484–485, 492–493
   ethical issues in, 495–497
   methodological challenges and remedies, 493–495
   panel studies and survey programs, 484–485, 487–488
   statistical records and archives, 484–487
   verbal records and language as data, 484–486, 488–490
   visual data, 484–485, 490–492
Archives, 486–487
Arminger, G., 400
Arrindell, W. A., 154
Article retraction, 599, 613
Artificial intelligence (AI), 491, 492, 494
Asimov, Isaac, 54
Assessment intervals, in LGC modeling, 319
Assessment timing, 259
Assimilation, in SRM, 455
Assistant professor income example, 171–173, 185
Assumed similarity, 457
Assumption(s)
   in inferential methods, 5–6
   in LGC modeling, 319–320
   violations of, 180–181
Atheoretical partialing, in multiple regression, 193
Attitudes toward psychological counseling example, 99–100
Augusteijn, H. E. M., 590
Authorship credit, 605, 610–611
Authorship responsibility, 610–612
Automatic Interaction Detector (AID), 429, 432, 446
Autoregressive models, 339, 487
Auxiliary values, 36–38
Auxiliary variables, 31–32, 42, 46
Axis-parallel projections, 83

Back, M. D., 460
Backup of data, 567
Backward-stepping, forward-stepping vs., 228
Bad data and inadequate models, 5–25
   bootstrap methods, 16–17
   effect size, 19–20
   hypothesis testing vs. decision making, 9
   nonnormal distributions, 9–10
   normal distributions, 6–9
   outliers, 10–12
   plots, 13–16
   rank-based methods, 19
   regression, 20–22
   robust methods, 17–18
   skewed distributions, 12–13
Bagging, 435, 442–443
Bail, C. A., 493
Bailey, Russell J., 147–165
Baker, R. J., 216
Bakker, M., 590
Balances data, re-expression of, 63
Bandwidth, 92
Banks, G. C., 584
BAP (bone alkalizing phosphatase) example, 103
Bar graphs, 89, 90
Barnett, A., 217
Barnett, R. C., 472
Bartunek, J. M., 522
Baseline differences, in longitudinal data analysis, 255
Baseline models, in LST models, 305
Basic models, in MLM, 222
Batholomew, D., 415
Bauer, D. J., 190
Baumrind, D., 411
Bayesian generalized linear models, 216
Bayesian imputation, full, 40
Bayesian information criterion (BIC), 398, 417
   in LC/LP models, 415
   in SNA, 513
Bayesian statistics
   and clinical significance, 156–157, 161
   CRAN Task View on, 217
   in imputation, 40
   and margins of error, 173n2
Bayesian structural equation modeling (BSEM), 404
BDI. *See* Beck Depression Inventory
Bechtoldt, H. P., 391–394, 399–400
Beck Depression Inventory (BDI), 150, 156, 546, 550, 551, 553, 554
Becoming a Behavioral Science Researcher (Kline), 586
Beginning times, in event history analysis, 274
Behavior data measurement, in SRM, 462
Bell, R. Q., 260
Belson, W. A., 429
Belzak, W. C. M., 190
Bem, Daryl, 607
Benchmarks, for treatment response, 158
Beneficence and nonmaleficence, 598
Benevolence, 367–368, 370–373
Beniger, J. R., 77, 79
Bentler, Peter M., 318, 387, 398
Bergin, 148
Berk, R. A., 586
Berlin, J. A., 140
Bernoulli distributions, 207
Berra, Yogi, 54
Berry, D., 255
Bertin, J., 81
Best, L. A., 77
Best practices, checklists of, 589
Between-group comparisons, 158
Between-group data relationships, in SRM, 454
Between-group manipulations, in SRM, 461
Between-person differences, stable, in LST models, 297
Beutler, L. E., 149
Bible, feelings about (example), 103
Bible, King James translation, 102
BIC. *See* Bayesian information criterion
Big Data
   in archival research, 483, 494
   in EDA, 53
   graphic displays of, 103–106
Big Five personality factors, 379, 457, 503
Bilinear interaction, 190
Binary data, effect-size indexes based on, 139–143
Binomial data with overdispersion, 213–215
Binomial distribution, 203
Bipolar disorder, 157
Bishop, J., 306
Bitmap file formats, 106
Blanchard, E. B., 151
Blanchard's method, 152
Blimp (software), 43
Block designs, in SRM, 454, 458, 461
BLOCKO (software), 458, 462
Blossfeld, H.-P., 278
Bo, Ai, 169–199
Bock, A., 491
Boker, Steven M., 331, 337–350
Boldry, J. G., 454, 461
Bolger, N., 236, 240–241

Bonding capital, 523
Bone alkalizing phosphatase (BAP) example, 103
Bonett, D. G., 387
Bonferroni method, 587
Bonferroni method, modified, 175, 179, 183, 195–196
Boosted regression tree algorithm, 446
Bootstrap methods, 435
 for bad data and inadequate models, 16–17, 21
 bootstrap-t method, 17
 in graphics, 103
 for trimmed means, 182
Borenstein, Michael, 129–146
Borgatti, S. P., 510, 511
Borghi, John A., 563–577
Borner, Katy, 101
Borrowing strength, 62n2
Bosco, F. A., 583
Bostock, Mike, 106
Boundary conditions, in systematic reviews, 540
Boutron, I., 581
Box, G. E. P., 194
Boxplot(s), 14
 in EDA, 57, 60, 62
 and outside values, 93
 rules of, 10–11
Box problem, Thurstone's, 388
Brain and Behavioral Informatics, 571
Braithwaite, D. O., 456
Brandeis, L. D., 591
Brandmaier, Andreas, 445
Breadcrumbs, 492–493
Breakdown points of estimators, 18
Breiman, L., 432
British Psychological Society, 604
Broström, G., 271, 278
Browne, M. W., 400
Brunner, E., 19
Bryk, A. S., 222, 225, 230, 234, 352, 362, 476
BSEM (Bayesian structural equation modeling), 404
Budescu, D. V., 181, 192
Buffering effect, in MMR, 113–114, 117
Burn-in period, 41
Burt, R. S., 523
Byrne, M. D., 494

CAIC (consistent Akaike information criterion), 398
Cameron, A. C., 217
Campbell, D. T., 403–404

Campbell & Fiske rules, 403
Canonical factor analysis, 385
CAR (cortisol awakening response), 13, 15, 21–23
Card, N., 465
Car data example, 86–87
Carling, K., 11
Carr, D. B., 88
Carroll, J. B., 379
Carroll, J. M., 491
Carswell, C. M., 82
CART (classification and regression trees), 432–436, 439, 441
Castro-Schilo, L., 256, 403
Categorical-by-continuous variable display, 92–93
Categorical data, for generalized linear models, 217
Categorical values, 93
Categorical variables, in graphics, 89
Categories, in graphics, 83
Cattell, R. B., 379, 386, 400
Cattell-Horn-Carroll (CHC) model of mental ability domain, 379
Causal processes, 338
CBT (cognitive behavior therapy), 150, 175
CC (Creative Commons) licenses, 574
CEFA (Comprehensive Exploratory Factor Analysis), 389
Cell means approach, 174
 in ANOVA, 179, 183
 to contrasts, 177
Cemetery records, in archival research, 491
Censoring, in event history analysis, 269, 271, 277, 281
Census of Population and Housing, 486
Centered within clusters (CWC) predictors, in MLM, 229
Center for Epidemiologic Studies Depression (CESD) Scale, 21–22
Center for Open Science, 604, 609
Centering
 in longitudinal data analysis, 256
 in MLM, 229, 238–239
 in MMR, 123–124
Center of the distribution
 in event history analysis, 277
CESD (Center for Epidemiologic Studies Depression) Scale, 21–22
CFA. *See* Common factor analysis; Confirmatory factor analysis
Chambers, J. M., 217
Chance findings, 147

Change, within-person, 254
Change models, in LST models, 297
Chartjunk, 82
Chartrand, J. M., 99–100
CHC (Cattell-Horn-Carroll) model of mental ability domain, 379
Checklists
 of best practices, 589
 for EDA, 69–72
Cherry-picking, 581, 583–584
Cheung, G. W., 400
Chicago school children example, 390–394
Child nodes, 431, 445
Children's Wisconsin Trauma Center, 292
Choudhury, P., 491
Christensen, P. Niels, 451–464
Chronic pain and psychosocial disability example, 28–31, 34–35, 38–39, 43–44, 47
Ciesla, Jeffrey A., 317–335
C-IKNOW, 506
CILS4EU project, 505
Circular plots, 101
CIs. *See* Confidence intervals
Classical test theory (CTT), 156
Classification and regression trees (CART), 432–436, 439, 441
Classification trees, 126, 431
Cleveland, William, 77–81, 86, 95
Cleveland's hierarchy, 80, 90
Clickstream, 492
Cliff, N., 19
Clinical significance, 147–165
 advantages of, 157–158
 alternative methods for assessment of, 154–155
 as concept, 148–150
 extensions of research on, 155–157
 Jacobson-Truax method for assessment of, 152–156
 limitations of, 159–161
 research, future directions for, 160–161
 traditional assessment of, 147–148
Closed-vocabulary approaches, in archival research, 490
Closure, in graphics, 80
Cluster analysis, 411
Clustered bar charts, 97–99
Cluster models, in generalized linear models, 216
Clutter, in graphics, 81
Coarsened exact matching, 487

Coding, in MMR, 115
Coefficient(s)
    comparison of, 238
    correlation, 143, 543
    fixed, 231–232
    interaction, 115
    level-1, 222
    in MLM, 222, 231–232, 238
    nonrandomly varying, 232
    of predictor variables, 64
    randomly varying, 231
    regression, 123, 186
    significance tests of, 191
    standardized, 192, 235
Cognition and graphics, 81
Cognitive behavior therapy (CBT), 150, 175
Cognitive function tests, 60
Cognitive science, 79
Cohen, J., 19–20, 115, 187, 194, 195, 398
Cohen's d, 185
Cohesion contagion, 522
Cohort-sequential designs, 260
Coin-flipping analogy, 183
Cole, David A., 311, 317–335
Coleman, J. S., 523
Collective turnover, 522
Collett, D., 278
Collins, B. M., 77
Collins, L. M., 260, 416
Collins, S. E., 255
Committee for Professional Ethics of the American Statistical Association, 585
Committee on Publication Ethics (COPE), 598, 611–613
Common factor analysis (CFA), 379–380
Common factor analysis, principal component analysis vs., 394
Common latent state variables, 304, 307, 309–310
Common latent trait variables, 304
Communication function of charts, 79
Comparison of groups, 5–6
Competing models, in EDA, 72
Competing-risk models, in event history analysis, 289–290
Complex observable systems, 520–521
Compliance, in research data management and sharing, 572–574
Component term exclusion, in multiple regression, 190

Composite link functions, in generalized linear models, 216
Comprehension tests example, 391
Comprehensive Exploratory Factor Analysis (CEFA), 389
Comrey, A. L., 404
Conditional inference trees, 441
Conditional Inference Trees (ctree), 432, 441
Conditional response profiles, in LC, 412
Confidence intervals (CIs), 7–8
    in ANOVA, 181
    computation of, 144
    displaying in graphics, 91
    in effect-size estimation, 129, 131
    in graphics, 95
    for mean effect sizes, 549–550
    and measures of central tendency, 12
    in MMR, 122
    for the population mean, 8
    widths of, 587
Confidentiality, 496
Configural effects, in graphics, 80
Configural invariance, 261
Confirmatory factor analysis (CFA), 395–405
    advanced forms of, 399–404
    estimation in, 397
    evaluation of fit in, 397–398
    in generalized linear models, 216
    in LC models, 414
    readjustment in, 398–399
    recent extensions of, 404
    selection of manifest variables in, 396
    selection of observations in, 395–396
    specification in, 396–397
Confirmatory research, 446
Conflicts of interest, in authorship, 612
Confounds with curvilinearity, 190
Consistency, in LST models, 299
Consistent Akaike information criterion (CAIC), 398
Constant variance, 59–60
Construct validity, in archival research, 493, 495
Contagion, contingent network, 523
Contagion effects, 521
Contagion research, 524
Contextual privacy, 496
Contingency table models, LC models as, 415
Contingent network contagion, 523
Continuous latent variable models, 411
Continuous moderator variables, 190–191

Continuous time, discrete time vs., 272
Continuous-time methods, in event history analysis, 269–270
Continuous variables
    in graphics, 91, 95
    in MMR, 115
    moderator, 190–191
Contouring of graphics, 99
Contrast parameterization, 309–310
Contrasts, in cell means approach, 174
Contrast strategies, for single degree of freedom, in ANOVA, 186
Contributor Roles Taxonomy (CRediT), 612
Convenience samples, 586
Convergence
    information, 48
    in longitudinal data analysis, 260
    in MLM, 233–234
Cook, W. L., 460
Cooper, H., 536, 598
Cooper, M. L., 257
COPE (Committee on Publication Ethics), 598, 611–613
Copyright infringement, 605
Coren, S., 83
Coronary heart disease example, 436–439
Correlated trait-correlated method (CT-CM) model, 403
Correlation coefficient, 143, 543, 550
Correlation family, of effect sizes, 543–544
Correlations, 129
Cortisol awakening response (CAR), 13, 15, 21–23
Cost-complexity pruning, 433
Count data, for generalized linear models, 217
Count data, re-expression of, 63
Counted fraction data, re-expression of, 63
Count variable prediction, 210–211
Covariance
    analysis of (ANCOVA), 55
    coverage, 44, 46
    coverage tables, 43
    in dyadic data analysis, 467–468, 470–471
    in three-level data, 361–365
Covariate inclusion, theoretically guided, 193
Covariate models, in LCA/LPA, 422–423
Covariates, use of, 193–194
COVID-19 pandemic, 494

Cox, D. R., 194, 217, 278
Cox proportional hazards model, in event history analysis, 280
CRAN Task View on Bayesian statistics, 217
Creative Commons (CC) licenses, 574
Credible intervals, 173n2
CRediT (Contributor Roles Taxonomy), 612
Credit for research, 610–612
Cressie, N. A. C., 180
"Crisis of confidence," and archival research, 481–485
Critical ratios
 for contrasts, 178
 in general linear model, 187
 for mean differences, 173
Crocker, Jennifer, 597–615
Cronbach's alpha, 153
Cross-classified analyses, in MLM, 225–226
Cross-level interactions, in MLM, 232
Crossover interactions, in MMR, 114
Cross-over offsprings, mutations in decision trees, 434
Crowdsourcing data analysis, 590–591
CT-CM (correlated trait-correlated method) model, 403
Ctree (Conditional Inference Trees), 432, 441
CTT (classical test theory), 156
Cubic functions, in multiple regression, 194
Cudeck, R., 387
Cultural group study example, in MLM, 227
Curran, Patrick J., 351–376
Curvature, in regression surface, 121, 124
Curve of factors models
 factor of curves model vs., 324
 in LST models, 306
Curvilinearity, confounds with, 190
Cutoff(s)
 criteria, 158, 159
 functional distribution, 159
 scores, 153
CWC (centered within clusters) predictors, in MLM, 229

d. See Standardized mean difference
d, computation of
 Hedges' g and δ vs., 135
 in studies of matched groups, 134–135
 in studies with independent groups, 135–137
 in studies with matched groups, 137–138
D3 (Data Driven Documents), 106
Dante Aligheri, 591
Darlington, R. B., 192
DASS-21 (Depression Anxiety Stress Scales), 155
Data
 accessibility of, 563
 additivity of, 59–60
 archival, types of, 485–493
 bad. See Bad data and inadequate models
 breadcrumbs, 492
 collection and storage of, 505, 566–567
 considerations in dynamical systems and differential equations, 348
 documentation of, 567–569
 fabrication and falsification of, 485, 579–580, 582, 584, 585, 599–600
 findability of, 563
 hierarchically nested, 220
 personal, deidentification of, 495, 573, 603
 preservation of, 571–572
 sharing of, 569–571
 storage media for, 572
 as term, 564
 transformation, in EDA, 12–13, 59
 trimming of, 16
 use agreements, 574
 variables, documentation of, 565
 Winsorizing of, 12
Data accessibility policies of journals, 589
Data analysis
 crowdsourcing of, 590–591
 questionable practices in, 580
Data articles, 571
Data collection software, 566
Data Desk (software), 58
Data dictionaries, 568–569
Data displays, in EDA, 55–58
Data dredging, 581
Data Driven Documents (D3), 106
Data elements, common, 568
Data files, as article supplements, 570
Data in Brief, 571
Data-ink ratio, 81–82
Data-level documentation, 567–568, 570
Data management, in SNA, 507
Data management plans (DMPs), 565, 572
Data privacy, in archival research, 495
Data reduction strategies, 610
Data repositories, 570
Data sets
 archival, 485–493
 creation of imputed, 40–44
 determining multilevel structure of, 224–228
 embargoes of, 603
 longitudinal, 253
 nonrectangular, 101–102
 requirements for LGC modeling, 318
Data sharing, 564, 602–603
Data snooping, 581
Data structures
 multilevel, 220
 for SRM, 453–455
Daughter nodes, 431
De'ath, G., 446
Death rates, birth rates vs., 99
Decibels, 59
Decimal logs, 84
Decision making, hypothesis testing vs., 9
Decision rules, theory-driven, in ANOVA, 182
Decision trees
 analytic, 589
 in multiple regression, 193
Decision trees and ensemble methods, 429–448
 coronary heart disease example, 436–439
 diabetes prediction, 439–443
 history of decision trees, 429–432
 multivariate extensions of decision trees, 445–446
 recursive partitioning algorithms, 432–436, 443–445
Deeks, J. J., 140
Deep Blue Data, 570
Degrees of freedom (*df*), 203, 204, 208, 211, 215, 415
"Degrees of Freedom in Planning, Running, Analyzing, and Reporting Psychological Studies" (Wicherts), 590
De-identification of personal data, 495, 573, 603
Delay-discounting measures, 252

De Leeuw, J., 219
Delinquency of adolescents example, 251–252
Delta
  d and Hedges' g vs., 135
  risk difference, 139–141
Demographic variables, unnecessary, 193
Depression, 150
  in adolescents example, 329
  and marital satisfaction example, 470–475
  measurement of symptoms of, 5, 20–22
  and social support in females examples, 116–117
Depression Anxiety Stress Scales (DASS-21), 155
Design function of charts, 79
De Smet, M. M., 155
The Detection of Interaction Effects (Sonquist and Morgan), 431
Deteriorated (patient category), 153, 158, 159
Developmental curves, 351
Deviance statistics, 208
De Vries, R. M., 156
df (degrees of freedom), in LC/LP models, 415
DFBETA, 64
DFFITS (difference in fits), 64
Diabetes prediction example, 439–443
Diaconis, P., 62
Diagnostic plots, and multiple regression models, 64
Diagnostic statistics, 64
Diary study example, 221, 223, 225, 234, 236, 237
Dichotomania, 582
Dichotomous variables, in MMR, 116
Diener, E., 403
Difference in fits (DFFITS), 64
Difference Limen experiment, 65–67
Differential equations, 337, 339–341
Differential structural equation modeling (dSEM), 331–332
Diffuse MNAR mechanism, 32
Diffusion hypotheses, 511
Digital interactions, traces of, 492–493
Digital object identifiers (DOIs), 563, 570, 603
Dimensionality, in graphics, apparent vs. effective, 83
Dipboye, R. I., 523, 525
Directionality, of relationship ties, 504

Disaggregation, aggregation vs., in MLM, 221
Disciplinary data repositories, 570, 573
Discrete-event time distributions, 273
Discrete-event time models, in event history analysis, 282–286
Discrete time, continuous time vs., 272
Discrete-time event history models, 278–291
Discrete-time methods, in event history analysis, 269, 278
Discrete-time survival models (DTSMs), 278
Disordinal interactions, in MMR, 114
Distribution-based methods, 150–151
Distributions, 7
  binomial, 203
  contaminated, 9
  heavy-tailed, 9
  marginal, 46
  mixed normal, 10, 18
  nonnormal, 9–10, 19
  normal, 6–9, 20
  sampling, 7
  skewed, 10, 12–13, 16
  Student's t, 17–18
  unconditional, 46
Divine Comedy (Dante), 591
DMPOnline, 565
DMPs (data management plans), 565, 572
DMPTool, 565
DNT (dynamic network theory), 516, 520
Dobson, A. J., 217
Documentation of data variables, 565
Doeze Jager, S., 457
Doherty, M. E., 81
DOIs (digital object identifiers), 563, 570, 603
Dominance analysis, in multiple regression, 192–193
Dot-box plot, 93
Dot histograms, 93
Dot plots, 90, 96
Draper, N., 195
Drop-out of participants, in longitudinal data analysis, 250–251
The Drunkard's Walk (Mlodinow), 54
Dryad (data repository), 570
DSEM (differential structural equation modeling), 331–332
DTSMs (discrete-time survival models), 278
Dumenci, L., 310

Dummy variables
  in dyadic data analysis, 472
  in event history analysis, 279–280, 282–283, 286, 292–293
  in MMR, 115–118, 187
  in multilevel data, 221
  in multivariate growth curve modeling, 356–360, 364
Duncan, T. E., 324
Duplicate publications, 608
Duration models, 269
Dyadic data analysis, 465–478
  in archival research, 489
  covariation in, 467–468
  interdependence and independence, 466–467
  interdependence model, longitudinal, 474–475
  interdependence model, longitudinal multivariate, 475–476
  interdependence model, multivariate, 470–474
  interdependence models, 469–476
  multilevel models, 476–477
  software implementations, 477
  structural equation modeling, multilevel models, and generalizations, 476–477
Dyadic interactions, in SRM, 458
Dyadic links, in SNA, 503
Dyadic reciprocity, 457
Dyad-level effects, in SRM, 456
Dyad-level manipulations, in SRM, 460–461
Dynamical systems and differential equation models of change, 337–350
  data considerations, 348
  LDEs (linear differential equations), 339–343
  other differential equation models, 345–348
  specifying LDE models, 343–345
Dynamic network theory (DNT), 516, 520

Eastwick, P. W., 457
Ebert, T., 491
ECharts, 106
Ecological fallacy, in MLM, 221
EDA. *See* Exploratory data analysis
Eder, P., 522
Edges, in SNA, 503
Educational expectations studies, 515
EFA. *See* Exploratory factor analysis

Effects-based ANOVA model, 173–174
Effect sizes and effect size estimation, 129–146
　averaging of, 551
　for bad data and inadequate models, 19–20
　and clinical significance, 148, 152
　conversion among indexes, 144–145
　correlation family in, 543–544
　dependence of, 551–552
　estimation of, in multilevel modeling, 236–237
　indexes based on binary data, 139–143
　indexes based on means, 132–135, 145
　indexes based on two continuous variables, 143–144
　indexes of, 185
　mean difference family in, 541–543
　and meta-analyses, 132
　odds ratio family in, 543–545
　parameters, statistics, and precision, 130
　and p values, 130–132
　selection of indexes, 132
　and standardized mean difference, 135–139
　treatment effect vs., 129–130
Efron, B., 53
EgoNet, 516
Ego networks, 523
　density of, 524
　in SNA, 503, 505–506, 510
Eid, M., 298, 310, 311, 403
Eigendecomposition, 105
Eigenvalues, 386, 391
Eisen, S. V., 151, 154
Eisenberger, R., 522
Ekman, P., 491
Electronic lab notebooks, 569
Elfenbein, H. A., 458
Embargoes, of data sets, 603
Emerson, J. D., 71n5
EMF (Extended Windows Metafiles), 106
Emotional reactions, in SNA, 504
Employee turnover example, 521–525
E(MS) (expected mean squares), 455
Encapsulated PostScript (EPS) files, 106
Enders, Craig K., 27–51, 229
Enron email corpus, 489
Ensemble methods. See Decision trees and ensemble methods
Entropy, in LC/LP models, 415

EPS (Encapsulated PostScript) files, 106
Epsilon squared, as index of effect size, 185
EQS (software), 477
Equality restrictions, in LCA/LPA, 422
Equal-tailed bootstrap-t, 17
Equamax criterion, 389
Equilibrium values, 340–342
Equivalence testing, 149, 151, 152
ERGM (exponential random-graph model), 512–513, 527
Ergonomics, 79
Error(s)
　assumptions, in ANOVA, 586
　estimated standard, 171, 172, 186
　false negative. See Type II errors
　false positive. See Type I errors
　indexes of magnitude of, in ANOVA, 170–171
　rates, 183–184
　representation, 102, 103
ESEM (exploratory structural equation modeling), 404
Estimability, of LCA models, 414
Estimated standard errors, 171, 172, 186
Estimators, breakdown points of, 18
Eta squared, 171, 185
Ethical issues. See also Ethical issues in authorship
　in archival research, 495–497
　in exploratory data analysis, 62–63
　in psychology, 598–599
　in statistical analysis, 585
Ethical issues in authorship, 597–615
　authorship responsibility and credit for research, 610–612
　data fabrication and falsification, 599–600
　general ethical issues in psychology, 598–599
　manuscripts, writing of, 605–610
　misconduct, allegations of, 613
　preregistration of data management plan, 604–605
　questionable research practices, 601
　replication failures, 600–601
　transparency and openness, 602–604
"Ethical Principles of Psychologists and Code of Conduct" (APA), 495, 564, 585
European Social and World Values Surveys, 235

Evaluation functions, 514
Event history analysis, 215, 269–295
　adolescent relationships example, 270–272
　applicability of, 272
　describing event time distribution, 272–278
　discrete-time event history models, 278–291
　syntaxes for data conversion, 292–295
　as term, 271
Events, in studies, 143
Event-time distribution
　describing, 272–278
　estimation of, 273
Evidence-based medicine, 585
Evtree (Evolutionary Trees), 432, 434, 441–442
Example studies
　adolescent delinquency, 251–252
　adolescent relationships, 269–278, 280–294
　air traffic controllers, 206–207
　alcohol consumption, 91, 95, 257, 259–260
　anxiety treatment, 117–118
　assistant professor income, 171–173, 185
　attitudes toward psychological counseling, 99–100
　Bible, feelings about, 103
　bone alkalizing phosphatase (BAP), 103
　car data, 86–87
　Chicago school children, 390–394
　chronic pain and psychosocial disability, 28–31, 34–35, 38–39, 43–44, 47
　comprehension tests, 391
　coronary heart disease, 436–439
　cultural group study example, 227
　death rates vs. birth rates, 99
　depression and disability, 43–45
　depression and marital satisfaction, 470–475
　depression in adolescents, 329
　depressive symptomatology, 546–554, 556
　diabetes prediction, 439–443
　diary study, 221, 223, 225, 234, 236, 237
　disability and depression, 43–45
　employee turnover, 521–525
　factorial analysis of variance, 176

Example studies (continued)
  Graduate Record Examination Advanced Psychology Test score, 96
  Home ownership, 430–432
  jurors, 175–178, 184
  learning disabilities, 202–206
  literacy and foreign-born residents, 221
  Mathematics placement test, 208–210
  McDonald's restaurants, 84
  Morse code signals, 84
  music preference, 208
  nicotine dependence, 417–423
  Olympic gold medal, 91
  patent data, 95–96
  roommate, 451–454, 458–459
  Scholastic Aptitude Test (SAT), 129–130, 132, 135–136, 138
  self-esteem and social anxiety, 193
  sex differences, social support, and depression, 116–118
  sexual partners, 13, 15, 89, 93–94, 97–98, 182
  sleep and exercise, 115–116, 119–121, 123
  smokers, 15–16
  social support and depression in females, 116–117
  spirit consumption, 91, 95
  student math success, 231
  students in classes, 222–223, 225
  study time, 215
  texting, 451–453
  thermoregulation, 331
  third graders, behavior of, 210–212
  USMA cadet example, 367–371
Excel, 566
Expected mean squares, 455
Experimental manipulations, in SRM, 460–461
Explanatory power, 20
Explanatory variables, network variables as, 508
Exploratory data analysis (EDA), 53–73
  ANOVA (analysis of variance), 65–69
  checklists for, 69–72
  competing models, 72
  data displays, 55–58
  ethics of, 62–63
  measurement scales, 63
  process of, 69–72
  re-expression, 59–62
  regression, 63–64
  traditional statistics vs., 54–55

Exploratory Data Analysis (Tukey), 57
Exploratory factor analysis (EFA), 380–395, 580
  empirical example for, 390–394
  estimation in, 383–385
  factor scores in, 390
  in generalized linear models, 216
  interpretation in, 389–390
  key equations in, 380–381
  number of factors in, 385–388
  PCA (principal component analysis) vs., 394–395
  recent extensions of, 404
  rotation of factors in, 388–389
  selection of MVs (manifest variables) in, 382–383
  selection of observations in, 381–382
  theory of, 380
Exponential random-graph model (ERGM), 512–513
Exponential random-graph model (ERGM) analysis, 527
Extended Windows Metafiles (EMF), 106
External validity, 150
Extra dependent variables (extra DVs), 37, 39, 43

Fabrication and falsification of data, 485, 579–580, 582, 584, 599–600
Fabrigar, L. R., 404
Facebook data, in archival research, 493
Facial expressions, in archival research, 490, 491
Factor analysis models, 411
Factored regression models, 38–39
Factorial analysis of variance example, 176
Factorial designs, 65
Factorial invariance models, in CFA, 401
Factor models, 411
Factor of curves model, curve of factors approach vs., 324
Factor score indeterminacy, 390
Fahrmeir, L., 217
"Failed" study, inclusion in manuscript, 607–608
Failure time analysis, 215
Failure time models, 269
Failure to replicate, 481, 600–601
FAIR principles, 563, 570
False negatives. *See* Type II errors
False positives. *See* Type I errors
Falsifiable methodology, 512

Falsification of data. *See* Fabrication and falsification of data
Family means effects, in SRM, 460
Family roles, in SRM, 460
Family-wise error rates, 183, 188–189
Fanelli, D., 579–580
Faraway, J. J., 217
Farmus, L., 255–256
FCS (fully conditional specification) procedure, 41
Felps, W., 523
Ferrer, E., 403
Ferrer, R., 151
Few, S., 81
Fidelity and responsibility, 598
Fiedler, K., 582
Figure-ground effects, in graphics, 80–81
File formats, migration of, 571
File-level documentation, 570
File naming conventions, 566–567
FIML (full information maximum likelihood), 35–37, 45, 46, 318–319, 444
Findability of data, 563
Findagrave.com, 491
Finite mixture models, 216
First-order differential equations, 339–341
Fishbein, M., 521
Fisher's r-z transform, 227
Fisher's z score, 143–144, 543–544, 546–548, 550
Fiske, D. W., 403–404
Fit measures. *See* Model fit testing
Fitness measure, 434
Fixed effects models, in meta-analysis, 545–546, 548–549
Flaherty, Brian P., 411–427
Fleeson, W., 297
Fleiss, J. L., 145
Fles, E., 457
Flood, N., 156
Flows, in SNA, 504
Floyd, F. J., 404
FMI (fraction of missing information) values, 42–43
Focused MNAR mechanism, 30
FOLDE (fourth-order latent differential equation) model, 347–348
Follow-up tests, in ANOVA, 170
Force-directed methods, 101
Forged authorship, 611
Forms of interaction, in MMR, 113–114
Forward selection regression, 434

Forward-stepping, backward-stepping vs., 228
Fourth-order latent differential equation (FOLDE) model, 347–348
Fox, J., 195, 217
Fraction of missing information (FMI) values, 42–43
Frailty, in event history analysis, 290
"Frame of reference" training, 461
F ratios, 174, 227
Fraud, scientific, 579
Freed-loading LGC, 320
Freese, J., 217
Frequency sorting, 85
Frequentists, 216
Friedman's test, 19
Frigge, M., 11
Frontiers in Psychology, 590
F tests, in ANOVA, 179–182
Full information maximum likelihood (FIML), 35–37, 45, 46, 318–319, 444
Fully Bayesian imputation, 40
Fully conditional specification (FCS) procedure, 41
Functional specificity hypothesis, in SNA, 516
Funder-sponsored data repositories, 570, 573
Funkhouser, H. G., 77
Funnel plots, 553–554
Fuzzy error representation, 103

Gain score approach, in longitudinal data analysis, 255–256
Galinsky, A. D., 486
Gamma distributions, 215
Gamma-mixed Poisson distribution, 212–213
Ganzach, Y., 190
Gaussian data, 57
Gender identity, as multicategorical value, 117
Generalizations, in dyadic data analysis, 476–477
Generalized additive models, for generalized linear models, 217
Generalized least squares (GLS), 385
Generalized linear mixed models (GLMMs), 470
Generalized linear models (GLMs), 201–218. *See also* General linear model
  binomial data with overdispersion, 213–215
  count variable prediction, 210–211
  extensions, 215–216
  general linear model vs., 201
  logistic regression, 205–210
  logit models, 202–204
  log-linear models, 202, 205
  overdispersion and the negative binomial model, 211–213
  software for, 216–217
  time to an event, 215
Generalized local linear approximation (GLLA), 338
Generalized reciprocity, 457
General linear model, 187, 201. *See also* Multiple regression framework and general linear model
General population norms, 159
General Social Survey (GSS), 89, 93–94, 96, 103, 487–488
GENSI, 506
Geodesic distances, 101
GEPHI, 516
German Psychological Society, 604
Gerrits, R. G., 579, 580
Gestalt principles, 80–81
Ggplot2, 106
Gill, J., 217
Gillan, D. J., 82
Gini index, 432–433, 442–444
Girgus, J. S., 83
GitHub, 436, 439
GLLA (generalized local linear approximation), 338
GLMMs (Generalized linear mixed models), 470
GLMs. *See* Generalized linear models
Global Assessment of Functioning Scale, 154
Global improvement in fit, 435
Global Symptom Index, 154
GLS (generalized least squares), 385
Goal progression, 517
Gogola, G. R., 56
Goldacre, B., 588
Goldstein, H. I., 222, 356
Gonnelli, S., 103
González, M. C., 493
Gonzalez, O., 444
Gonzalez, Richard, 465–478
Goodman, L. A., 415
Goodness of fit
  in event history analysis, 284, 286–287
  in SNA, 513, 514
Google Trends, 492
Gorsuch, R. L., 405
Gosset, William, 586
Gottfredson, R. K., 383, 580
Grade data, re-expression of, 63
Graham, J. W., 37–38, 260, 262
The Grammar of Graphics (Wilkinson), 100, 106
Grand-means centered predictors, in MLM, 229–231
Grant proposals, 565, 572
Graphic displays of data, 77–110
  with one variable, 89–93
  with two variables, 93–97
  with three variables, 97–99
  with many variables, 99–101
  Big data, 103–106
  black-and-white, 81
  guidelines for chart construction, 78–89
  nonrectangular data sets, 101–102
  software for, 106–107
  uncertainty in, 102–103
Gravestone analysis, in archival research, 491
Grayson, D., 12
Greedy algorithms, 434
Green, B. F., Jr, 65n4, 66–68
Greene, W. H., 188
Gregory, R. L., 83
Grid lines, in graphics, 88
Griffin, Dale, 465–478
Grimm, Kevin J., 256, 383, 429–448
Group-based trajectory models, in LCA/LPA, 423
Group comparisons, 5–6
Group-data method, for estimating event time distribution, 273–278
Group effects, in SRM, 452
Group equivalence assertion, in ANOVA, 185–186
Group-level change, 151, 160
Group-level data relationships, 220
Group-mean-centered predictors, in MLM, 229, 237
Group means in ANOVA, 171
Groups, comparison of, 5–6
Groups, in MLM, 221
Group size, 458
Growth curves, 351
Growth-mixture modeling, 156, 161, 423
Growth models, 327–329, 351
Growth trajectories, 351

GSS (General Social Survey), 487–488
Guilford, J. P., 404
Guttman, Louis, 101, 383
Guttman's bounds, 385, 391

Habituation of response, 252
Hageman, W. J., 154
Hageman and Arrindell method (HA), for calculating RCI, 154
Hairballs, 101
Hakstian, A. R., 389
Halgin, D. S., 510
Hamaker, E. L., 222, 235, 297
HA (Hageman and Arrindell) method, for calculating RCI, 154
Hancock, G. R., 400, 403
Hancock, J. T., 489
Hankin, B. L., 551
Hannan, M. T., 271
Hansen, N. B., 149
Hardin, J. W., 217
Hard misconduct, 579–580, 582
HARKing (hypothesizing after results are known)
  in archival research, 485, 493–494
  and exploratory vs. confirmatory research, 606
  and preregistration, 604
  as questionable practice, 581–583
Harlow, L. L., 494
Harman, H. H., 405
Harris-Kaiser orthoblique rotations, 389, 393
Hartigan, J. A., 99
Hastie, T. J., 217
Hayes, A. F., 117
Hayes, Timothy, 27–51
Hazard functions, in event history analysis, 278–279
Hazard models, 269
Hazard rates, 145
HD (hypothetical-deductive approach), to research, 583
Head, M. L., 582
Headaches, 152
Health Insurance Portability and Accountability Act (HIPAA), 573
Health psychology behavioral targets, 152
Heart attack risk, 585
Heart disease example, 436–439
Heavy-tailed distributions, 9–10
Hebrew University, 54
Hedges, L. V., 145, 540

Hedges' g. See also Standardized mean difference
  computation of, 135–138
  d and delta vs., 135
Heiser, J., 81
Heisey, D. M., 587
Hell, 591–592
Helm, Jonathan Lee, 379–410
Hertzog, C., 297
Heterogeneity
  in meta-analysis, 550–551
  of population subgroups, 412
  unobserved, in event history analysis, 290
Heteroscedasticity, 16, 19–21, 554. See also Homoscedasticity
Hexagonal bins, 104
Hierarchically nested data, 220
Hierarchical models, in LST, 310
Higgins, J. P. T., 140
Higher-order effects, in MMR, 112
Highest correlation in row (MAXR), 383
"High School Yearbooks" (Meehl), 256
Hilbe, Joseph M., 217
Hiller, W., 151
Hintz, F., 312
HIPAA (Health Insurance Portability and Accountability Act), 573
HIPAA safe harbor method of deidentification, 573
Histograms
  appropriate uses of, 14, 91–92
  in EDA, 55, 56, 60
  for Large-N data, 104
HLM (software)
  for dyadic data analysis, 477
  in MLM, 241
  and random effects modeling, 232
Hoaglin, David C., 53–73
Hoenig, J. M., 587
Hoffmann, J. P., 217
Hollenbeck, J. R., 582, 583
Homeostatic systems, in longitudinal data analysis, 254
Home ownership example, 430–432
Homogeneity, 56–57
Homogeneity testing, in meta-analysis, 550–551
Homoscedasticity, 20, 21, 181, 540, 545. See also Heteroscedasticity
Honesty in research, 606–607
Horn, J., 379, 386, 403
Hosmer, D. W., 217, 436
Hotelling, Harold, 105, 337–338, 349

Hotelling's classical method, 105
Howard, W. J., 38
Hox, J. J., 240
Hsu, L. M., 159
Hu, L., 398
Human factors psychology, 79
Human research participants, 572
Human subjects research, 496, 598, 603
Humphreys, L. G., 386
Hyperplanes, 388
Hypotheses, diffusion, in SNA, 511
Hypothesis testing, decision making vs., 9
Hypothesized results, non-hypothesized vs., 583
Hypothetical-deductive approach (HD), to research, 583

ICCs. See Intraclass correlations
Ideal fourths, 11
Imipramine, 150
Improved (patient category), 153
"Improving Present Practices in the Visual Display of Interactions" (McCabe, Kim, and King), 122–123
Impulsivity of subjects, 252
Imputation-analysis model alignment, 40
Imputation and pooling estimate analysis, 41–43
Imputed data sets, creation of, 40–41
Inadequate research models. See Bad data and inadequate models
Inclusivity, in systematic reviews, 540
Independence
  and homoscedasticity, 540
  violation of, 466
Independent groups t tests, 541
Indexes, of effect sizes, 132–135, 139–145
Indiana University, 101
Indicator-specific effects, in LST models, 306
Individual differences in within-person change, 254
Individual-level change, 148–149, 152, 158
Individual-level covariance, in dyadic data analysis, 470–471
Individual-level data relationships, 220
Individual task mastery, 524
Inferential methods, 5–6
Inferno (Dante), 591
Information indices, 398

Information technology professionals, 572, 575
Informed consent, 496
Inhomogeneity, 56
Input data construction, 280
Institute for Social Research, 429
Institutional data repositories, 570
Institutional review boards (IRBs), 496, 572–573, 598
Integrative approaches, to effect size dependence, 551–552
Integrity, 367–373, 598
Intellectual theft, 606
Interaction analysis
　in ANOVA, 184–185
　examples of, 114–118
　in multiple regression, 189–191
Interaction(s)
　antagonistic, 114
　beyond MMR context, 125
　coefficients, 115
　contrast, 177
　effects, 175, 580
　in MLM, 232
Intercept, inferences about, 20
Intercept-only model, in LGC modeling, 320–322, 327
Intercept-slope covariation, in LGC modeling, 323
Interdependence, 451, 466–467
Interdependence data. *See* Dyadic data analysis
Interdependence models, in dyadic data analysis, 469–476
Internal consistency reliability estimates, 159
International contexts, of clinical significance, 157
Interoperability of data, 563
Interpersonal associations, in dyadic data analysis, 467, 475
Interpersonal behavior, 451
Interpersonal psychotherapy (IPT), 150
Interpretability, of LC/LP models, 415
Interrelations among variables, 467
Inter-university Consortium for Political and Social Research, 603
Interval measurement scales, 63
Interval scaled data, 469
Intraclass correlations (ICCs)
　in dyadic data analysis, 465, 469–470
　in MLM, 226
Ioannidis, John, 600
IPT (interpersonal psychotherapy), 150

IRBs (institutional review boards), 496, 572–573, 598
IRT (item response theory), 156, 161
Irwin, H. J., 310
Isometric projections, 83
Item response theory (IRT), 156, 161
Iteration, in EDA, 53
Iterative optimization algorithms, 34

Jabrayilov, R., 156
Jaccard, James, 169–199
Jackson, K. M., 260
Jacobson, N. S., 150–156
Jacobson-Truax method
　and clinical significance, 151
　research, future directions for, 160–161
　weaknesses of, 159
Jacobucci, Ross, 429–448
Jags (software), 217
Janse, P. D., 154
JARKing (justifying after the results are known), 582
JARS (journal articles reporting standards), 579
Java programming, 106
Jebsen Large Heavy Object Test, 56
J-N (Johnson-Neyman technique), 118–120
Job embeddedness, 522–524
Job satisfaction, 521–522
John, L. K., 581–582
Johnson, J., 192, 193
Johnson, P. O., 65n4, 191
Jöreskog, K. G., 384, 399, 403
Journal article reporting standards, 589
Journal of Applied Psychology, 583
Journal of Consulting and Clinical Psychology, 153–154
Journal of Experimental Psychology: General, 582
Journal of Open Psychology Data, 571
Journal of Personality and Social Psychology, 582
Journal policies, on research sharing, 589
Journals article reporting standards (JARS), 579
Joyce, James, 102
Judd, C. M., 186, 192, 195
Juran, J. M., 90
Juror example, 175–178, 184
Justice, 598
Justifying after the results are known (JARKing), 582

Kaggle.com, 439
Kahneman, Daniel, 54
Kalbfleisch, J., 271
Kalman filtering, 338
Kaplan-Meier estimation, of event time distribution, 273
Karin, E., 151
Kashy, Deborah A., 451–464
Kelly, P. J., 155
Kenny, D. A., 311, 332, 403, 462, 465, 472
Kernel density, 91–92
Kernel density plots, 15
Kernel regression, 95
Kerr, Norbert L., 583, 606
Keselman, H. J., 180
Keyword data, in archival research, 492
K-fold cross-validations, 439, 444
Kiff, Cara J., 411–427
Kim, D. S., 122–123
Kim, S. B., 255
Kimball, A. W., 318
King, Kevin M., 111–128, 189, 254
Kirk, J., 155
Kirk, R., 174, 183, 186
Kite networks, 503, 508
Kline, Rex B., 579–595, 601
Kmeans clustering, 105
Koenker, R., 188
Kohlberg, L., 411
Kosslyn, S. M., 81
Kreft, I., 219
Kruskal-Wallis test, 19
Kulinskaya, E., 19
Kumu, 516
Kung, F. Y. H., 516
Kurtosis, in ANOVA, 181

Labianca, G., 510
Lab notebooks, 568–569
Lagged effects in longitudinal data, 487
Lakey, B., 457
Lalande, D. R., 582
Lambert, Michael J., 147–165
Language as data, 484–486, 488–490
Lanza, Stephanie T., 415
Laplace, Pierre-Simon, 7
"Large N" data, 104–105, 181
"Large p" data, 105
Latent class analysis (LCA), 216, 413
Latent class and latent profile models, 411–427
　additional topics, 422–423
　latent class models, 412–416

Latent class and latent profile models (continued)
  latent profile models, 416–417
  nicotine dependence example, 417–422
  overview, 411–412
Latent difference score analyses, 330–331
Latent differential equations (LDEs), 338, 343–348
  coupled second-order, 345–346
  first-order univariate, 343
  fourth-order, 347–348
  multilevel second-order, 346–347
  multivariate second-order, 345
  second-order univariate, 344–345
LatentGold (software), 424
Latent growth curves, modified, in longitudinal data analysis, 257
Latent growth modeling, multivariate, 324–329
Latent intercepts, 324
Latent probit method, 45
Latent profile models, 416–417
Latent quadratic random variables, 321–322
Latent quadratic trend, 324
Latent slopes, 324
Latent state change models, 302, 305
Latent state residual variables, in LST models, 299
Latent state self-regulation, 338
Latent state-trait (LST), 297–316
  basic concepts of, 298–299
  implications of definitions, 299–300
  models of, 301–312
  theory of, 297
Latent state variables, 299
Latent trait change models, 302, 306
Latent trait variables, 299
Latent trajectories, 351
Latent variable modeling
  in dyadic data analysis, 470–474
  for generalized linear models, 217
Latent variable modeling of continuous growth, 317–335
  applications of, 317–324
  multivariate latent growth modeling, 324–329
  new directions in, 329–333
  univariate and multivariate approaches, 329–330
Latent variable models, in generalized linear models, 216
Latent variables, in LST models, 304
LaTeX, 106–107

Laurenceau, J.-P., 236, 240–241
Lavaan (latent variable analysis), 43, 48n5
Lavaan (software), 477
Lawless, J. E., 218
LCA (latent class analysis), 413
LCA/LPA. See Latent class and latent profile models
LC (latent class) models, 412–416
LCS models, 257–258
LDEs. See Latent differential equations; Linear differential equations
LDEs (linear differential equations), 339–345
Leahy, Katelin E., 451–464
Learning disabilities example, 202–206
Leavitt, K., 492
LeBaron, C., 491
LeBreton, J., 192, 193
Lee, T. W., 522
Leenders, R. T. A. J., 525
Left-censoring, 271
Left out variable error (LOVE)
  in multiple regression framework, 187–188
  and use of covariates, 193
Legends, on graphic displays, 97–98
Leibniz Institute for Psychology, 604
Lemeshow, S., 436
Lenz, A. S., 152
Level-1 coefficients, in MLM, 222
"Level robust" methods, 18
Leverage, 64
Leverage point, bad, 21
Levitan, L. C., 510
Levy, R., 400
Lewandowsky, S., 81
Lewis, C., 387
Lexical sorting, 84
LGC analysis, univariate vs. multivariate approaches to, 329–330
Librarians, 572, 575
Library of Congress, 571–572
Life-table method, for estimating event time distribution, 273–278
Likelihood function, in event history analysis, 282
Likelihood ratio (LR) tests
  in event history analysis, 285
  and ML estimation, 385
Likelihoods, 32–33
Likert scales, 382–383
Lim, H. J., 292
Lind, J. C., 387
Linear growth curve models, in LST models, 302, 305–306

Linearity of data, 59–61
Linear mixed model, in dyadic data analysis, 469–470
Linear second-order differential equations, 341–342
Link function
  in generalized linear models, 201
  in logistic regression, 206
  in logit models, 203
  in log-linear models, 205
Links, in SNA, 503
Lipsey, M. W., 145, 539
LISREL (software), 477
Literacy and foreign-born residents example, 221
Littell, 539
Little, R. J. A., 216, 262
Little, T. D., 400
Liu, Qimin, 317–335
Lme4 (software), 477
Local improvement in fit, 435
Loess smoothers, 95, 99
Loewenstein, G., 581
Logarithms, in generalized linear models, 205
Logistic regression, 45, 205–210, 217
Logit models, 202–204
Log-linear models, 202, 205
Loignon, A. C., 461
Long, J. S., 217
Longitudinal coverage validity, 258–259
Longitudinal data, 489
Longitudinal data, for generalized linear models, 217
Longitudinal data analysis
  attrition and selectivity bias, 250–252
  sample selection and generalizability of findings, 247–250
Longitudinal factor models, in CFA, 402–403
Longitudinal models, in LC, 423
Longitudinal study designs, 260
Lönnqvist, J., 459
Lord, F. M., 255, 257
Lord's paradox, 255, 257
"Lossless" image formats, 571
Loßnitzer, Christiane, 297–316
Loss of data, 571
LOVE (left out variable error), 187–188, 193
Lower-order effects, in MMR, 112
LPA (latent profile analysis), 416–417
LR (likelihood ratio) test, 385
LST-R theory, 298
Luo, H., 106

MacCallum, R. C., 356, 358, 382
MAD (median absolute deviation)
    -median rule, 11–13
Mahaffey, K. J., 457
Mahalanobis distance, 35–36
Manifest variables (MVs), 392
Manual coding, in archival research, 491
Manual dexterity test, 56–60, 62
Manuscripts, writing, 605–610
Many Labs project, 600
Many-variable data, graphic displays for, 99–101
MAP (minimum average partial) correlation procedures, 385
Maps, 79
MAR (missing at random), 28–30, 45, 443–444
Marcotte LGL Project, 101
Marcus, D. K., 457
Mare, R. D., 291
Marginal distributions, 46
Marginal means differences, 175
Margins of error (MOEs), 172–173, 180–181
Marketing-based medicine, 585
Markov chain Monte Carlo (MCMC) algorithms, 40–41, 513
Markov models, latent, 423
Markowitz, D. M., 489
Marsh, H. W., 403
Masicampo, E. J., 582
Mason, R., 399
Mass communication, in archival research, 489
Massive online behavior, 520–521
Mathematica, 106
Mathematics placement test example, 208–210
MATLAB, 23
Mauro, R., 188
Maximum likelihood estimations (MLEs), 32–39, 397, 414
    algorithms, in MLM, 233
    in EFAs, 384–385
    in event history analysis, 282–285
    in LGC modeling, 320
    in MLM, 222
MAXR (highest correlation in row), 383
Maxwell, S. E., 180, 183, 186, 191
Mayer, J. L., 551
Maze tasks, 60
MCAR (missing completely at random), 25, 28–29, 47, 444
McArdle, John J., 257, 399, 400, 403, 429–448

McCabe, Connor J., 111–128, 189
McClelland, G. H., 192
McCoach, D. B., 232, 240
McConathy, D., 81
McCormick, Ethan M., 351–376
McCullagh, P., 201, 217, 218
McCutcheon, A. L., 415
McDonald, R. P., 405
McDonald's restaurants example, 84
McGinley, James S., 351–376
McGlinchey, J. B., 149, 159
McHorney, C. A., 151
McLaughlin, D. H., 12
MCMC (Markov chain Monte Carlo) algorithms, 40–41, 513
MCMC convergence diagnostics, 41
McNamara, T. P., 81
McNutt, M. K., 612
mdmb (software), 43
MDS (multidimensional scaling), 85, 99, 101
Mean centering, 189
Mean difference(s)
    analysis of, 171–173
    family of effect sizes, 541–543
    in MMR, 117
Mean-level change, 254
Means, effect-size indexes based on, 132
Measurement error compounding, 151
Measurement errors, in LST models, 299
Measurement items, in LC, 413
Measurement model, in LGC modeling, 324–327
Measurement scales, in EDA, 63
Measures of central tendency, 11–12
    outlier-resistant, 182
    robust, 182–183
Measures of uncertainty, in MMR, 122
Measure-specific components in LST models, 306
Median, 11–12, 182
Median absolute deviation (MAD) -median rule, 11–13
Median splits, in multiple regression framework, 189–190
Median survival time, in event history analysis, 277
Mediation, in MLM, 238
Meehl, P. E., 193, 256–257
Memory, for graphs, 81
Memory for social relationships, 516
Menu systems, for graphics, 106
Meredith, W., 399, 400, 403
M estimation, in ANOVA, 182

M estimators, in multiple regression framework, 188
Meta-analysis, 539–559
    defined, 540
    depressive symptomatology example in, 546–554, 556
    and effect sizes, 131, 132, 144, 148, 541–545
    full multivariable, 551
    meta-regression, 554–555
    model choice in, 545–546
    multilevel, 551
    systematic reviews, 539–540
Meta-regression, 554–555
Method factors, in LST models, 306–310
Method SB, 17
Metric invariance, 261
Metric transformations, in ANOVA, 180–181
Meyer, J. P., 522
Microsoft powerBI, 106
Microsoft Word, 107
Migration of digital file formats, 571
Miller, G. A., 83
Miller, P. J., 446
Millsap, R. E., 400
Minimally sufficient identification (MSI) constraints, 396
Minimum average partial (MAP) correlation procedures, 385
Misconduct
    allegations of, 598–599, 612, 613
    of researchers, 62
    self-disclosed, 580
Missing-at-random (MAR) mechanisms, 28–30, 45, 262, 443–444
Missing-completely-at-random (MCAR) mechanisms, 28–29, 47, 262, 444
Missing data, 443–444
    for LGC modeling, 318
    misconceptions about, 46
    in multilevel modeling (MLM), 234–235
    prevalence of, 46
    problems, in generalized linear models, 216
Missing data handling, 27–51. *See also* Missing-at-random (MAR) mechanisms; Missing-completely-at-random (MCAR) mechanisms; Missing-not-at-random (MNAR) mechanisms
    disability and depression example, 43–45
    maximum likelihood estimation, 32–39

Missing data handling (continued)
  mechanisms of, 28–32
  multiple imputation, 39–43
  results reporting of, 46–49
Missing entities, in SNA, 510
Missing-not-at-random (MNAR) mechanisms, 28–31, 36, 45–47, 262
Mitchell, T. R., 522
Mixed normal distributions, 10, 18
Mixed Poisson regression, 217
Mixtures of categorical and continuous variables, 38
MLEs (maximum likelihood estimations), 32–39, 384–385, 397, 414
ML (maximum likelihood) factor analysis, 387
MLM. See Multilevel modeling
MLMs (multilevel linear models), 351
Mlodinow, Leonard, 54
MLwiN (software), 477
MMR. See Moderated multiple regression, interaction analysis of
MNAR. See Missing-not-at-random (MNAR) mechanisms
MNAR-by-omission mechanism, 31, 36, 47
MNLFA (moderated nonlinear factor analysis), 156, 161
Moby Dick (Melville), 101
Modal regression, 103
Model-based analysis, 170–171
Model-based frameworks, in ANOVA, 171
Model-based imputation, 40
Model diagnostics and fits, in MLM, 233–234
Model fit testing
  in LC/LP models, 414–418
  in LPA, 420
Modeling and conditional predictions
  in ANOVA, 170–171
  of complex observable systems, 520–521
Model misspecification, 252
Model misspecification, in multiple regression framework, 187
Model population parameters, 171
Model(s)
  with autoregression, 311
  comparisons, in ANOVA, 171, 186
  competing, in EDA, 72
  competing-risk, in event history analysis, 289–290
  of discrete change, in LCA/LPA, 423
  hierarchical, in LST, 310
  inadequate. See Bad data and inadequate models
Models of missingness. See Missing-at-random (MAR) mechanisms; Missing-completely-at-random (MCAR) mechanisms; Missing-not-at-random (MNAR) mechanisms
Model specification, 252
Moderated effects, 111
Moderated multiple regression, interaction analysis of, 111–128
  applications in larger contexts, 125–126
  estimation and probing of, 112–114
  (J-N) Johnson-Neyman technique for, 118–120
  misconceptions about, 123–125
  plotting of, 120–123
Moderated nonlinear factor analysis (MNLFA), 156, 161
Moderation, in MLM, 232
Moderation hypothesis, 111
Moderator variables, 175
Modes, in EDA, 56
Modified Bonferroni methods, 175, 179, 183, 195–196
MOEs (margins of error), 172–173, 180–181
Moleiro, C., 149
Montanelli, R. G., Jr., 386
Monte Carlo methods, 385, 387, 398
Montoya, A. K., 117
Morgan, John, 429–432
Morris, Joseph, 539–559
Morrison, E. W., 524
Morrison, T. G., 580
Morse code signals example, 84
Mosaic plot, 93–94
Mosteller, F., 63, 194
Moulder, Robert G., 337–350
Mouse-running-maze tasks, 60
MPG (miles per gallon), 59
Mplus (software), 48n5
  for dyadic data analysis, 477
  for LCA/LPA, 424
  for LST models, 312
  in MLM, 236, 241
Mplus 8 (software), 43
Mroziński, B., 236
MSI (minimally sufficient identification) constraints, 396
MTMM (multitrait-multimethod analysis), 298, 403–404
Mudge, J. F., 587
Mulaik, S. A., 405
Mullen, T., 19
Multicategorical variable interactions, in MMR, 117
Multiconstruct LST models, 298
Multiconstruct models, in LST, 298
Multidimensional nature of change, 155
Multidimensional scaling (MDS), 85, 99, 101
Multigroup analysis, in SNA, 515
Multilevel analyses, in dyadic data analysis, 467–468
Multilevel data objects, in SNA, 510
Multilevel linear models (MLMs), 351
Multilevel meta-analysis, 551
Multilevel modeling (MLM), 219–242
  alternatives to, 226
  basic models of, 221–224
  coefficients in, 238
  conducting, 228–234
  defining, 220–221
  effect size estimation of, 236–237
  mediation in, 238
  missing data in, 234–235
  multilevel structure of data sets, 224–228
  nonlinear analyses of, 237
  and papers for publication, 238–239
  power analysis of, 236
  and reading papers about, 239–240
  reliability of, 237–238
  software for, 240
  standardization of, 235
  weighted analyses of, 235
Multilevel models
  in dyadic data analysis, 471, 476–477
  in LC, 414
Multilevel structure of data sets, determining, 224–228
Multimethod designs, in LST models, 312
Multiple comparisons, in ANOVA, 179
Multiple-group CFA, 399
Multiple imputation, 46, 48, 443, 444
  for LGC modeling, 318
  in missing data handling, 39–43
Multiple-indicator extension of the trait-state model, 311
Multiple membership analyses, in MLM, 225–226
Multiple regression approach, in longitudinal data analysis, 257

Multiple regression framework and general linear model, 186–195
  interaction analysis in, 189–191
  model testing perspective on, 194
  predictor importance, indexes of, 191–193
  use of covariates in, 193–194
  violations of model assumptions in, 186–187
Multiplot panels, in graphics, 86
Multistate models, in LST, 301–302
Multitrait-multimethod analysis (MTMM), 298, 403–404
Multivariate approaches, to latent variable modeling of continuous growth, 329
Multivariate associations, in dyadic data analysis, 475
Multivariate extensions of decision trees, 445–446
Multivariate growth curve model for three-level data, 351–376
  three-level growth models, 361–367
  two-level growth models, 352–361
Multivariate intercept-only, 327–329
Munzel, U., 19
Munzner, Tamara, 101
Murphy, K. R., 583–584
Music preference example, 208
Muthén, B., 45, 222, 235
mvpart algorithm, 446
MVs (manifest variables), 392
mvtboost algorithm, 446
MyPersonality, 493

Name data, re-expression of, 63
National Archive of Computerized Data on Aging, 570
National Institute for Occupational Safety and Health (NIOSH), 486
National Institute of Aging, 570
National Institute of Diabetes and Digestive and Kidney Diseases (NIDDK), 439
National Institutes of Health (NIH), 585
National Opinion Research Center, 487
National Science Foundation, 565
National Survey on Drug Use and Health (NSDUH), 417
Nature (journal), 579
N-dimensional aggregation algorithm, 104
NDSS. *See* Nicotine Dependence Syndrome Scales

Necker cube, 83
Negative binomial models, 211–213, 217
Neighbor models, in LST, 305
Nelder, J. A., 201, 216, 217
Nesselroade, J. R., 297
Nested data, 214–217, 220, 361
Nested models, in event history analysis, 285
Nested sorting, 84
Nested tables, of graphics, 86
Network autocorrelation model, 524–525
Network boundary and sampling, in SNA, 504–505
Network Canvas, 506
Network closure, 523
Network contagion, 523–525
Network goal analysis (NGA), 516–520
Network level, in SNA, 510
Network perception research, in SNA, 515–516
Neuroskeptic (blogger), 591
Newman, Daniel A., 501–537
Newman, M. E. J., 101
Newnham, E. A., 159
Newspaper articles, 489
New York Times, 600
Neyman, J., 191
Nezlek, John B., 219–242
NGA (network goal analysis), 516–520
Nicotine dependence example, 417–423
Nicotine Dependence Syndrome Scales (NDSS), 417, 419, 421–422, 424
NIDDK (National Institute of Diabetes and Digestive and Kidney Diseases), 439
NIH (National Institutes of Health), 585
NIH Collaborative Depression Project, 150
Nil hypothesis, 588
NIMH Data Archive, 570
Nine Circles of Scientific Hell, 591
NIOSH (National Institute for Occupational Safety and Health), 486
Nmle (software), 477
No change (patient category), 159
Nodes, in SNA, 502
NodeXL, 516
Nominal measurement scales, 63
Nominal response scales, 208
Nonevents, in studies, 143
Nonlinear analyses, in MLM, 237
Nonlinear mapping, 105–106
Nonlinear outcomes analyses, in MLM, 237
Nonlinear regression, 193

Nonmaleficence, 598
Nonnormality tests, 181
Nonnormal distributions, 9–10, 19
Nonorthogonal contrasts, 184
Nonparametric regression estimators, 22
Nonrectangular data sets, 101–102
Nonverbal communication, in archival research, 490, 492
Normal distributions, 6–9, 20
Normality
  variation, in ANOVA, 180–181
  variation, in multiple regression framework, 187
Normality assumptions, in ANOVA, 180
Normalization of data, 59
Normal probability plots, in EDA, 58
Normative comparisons, 151–152, 158
Normative data, 159
Nosek, B. A., 588–589
Notched box plots, 96
NSDUH (National Survey on Drug Use and Health), 417
Null hypothesis, 588
  in ANOVA, 173
  in effect-size estimation, 130–131
Number needed to treat, 145
Numerical facility, in EFA, 390
Numerical sorting, 84
Nutger, M. A., 155
Nyman-Carlsson, E., 149
Nyquist limits, 343

Oakes, D., 217
Oblique rotations of factors, 389
Observed effect sizes, 130
Occam's razor, 433
Occasion-specificity models, 311
Odds ratio (ω), 139–140, 142–143
Odds ratio family, of effect sizes, 544–545
Offsets, in GLM, 211
Offspring decision trees, 434
Ogles, Benjamin M., 147–165
Olivera-Aguilar, M., 398
Olkin, I., 145, 540
OLS. *See* Ordinary least squares
Olympic gold medal example, 91
Omega squared, as index of effect size, 185
Omnibus tests, 118
  F tests, 174–175, 179
  for one-way and complex factorial designs, 183
  of squared multiple correlations, 188

Index

One-variable data, graphic displays for, 89–93
Online survey takers, 481
Open Data badges, 570
OpenEddi, 506
Open file formats, 571
OpenfMRI, 573
OpenMx, 343
Openness of research process, 602–604
OpenNeuro (data depository), 570
Open Office, 107
Open Researcher and Contributor Identity (ORCID), 612
Open Science Framework, 570, 604, 608
Opioid marketing, 585
Optimization algorithms, in ML, 34
OQ-45 (Outcome Questionnaire 45.2), 149
ORCID (Open Researcher and Contributor Identity), 612
Ordinal data, 208–210
Ordinal interactions, in MMR, 113–114
Ordinal measurement scales, 63
Ordinary least squares (OLS), 187, 236
　analysis, 229
　analysis, vs. MLM, 226
　analysis vs. MLM, 222
　in multiple regression framework, 188
　regressions, 194
Orientation, in graphics, 85
Orthoblique rotations, Harris-Kaiser, 389, 393
Orthogonal contrasts, in ANOVA, 179, 184
Orthogonal rotations of factors, 388–389
Orthogonal transformation, in multiple regression, 193
Oswald, F. L., 494
Outcome measure reliability, 153
Outcome Questionnaire 45.2 (OQ-45), 149
Outcome variability, 148
Outcome variables
　in LGC modeling, 320
　network variables as, 508
Outlier rules, in EDA, 57
Outliers, 20–21
　in ANOVA, 181–182
　in bad data and inadequate models, 10–13
　downweighting of, 182
　in EDA, 54, 56–57
　in multiple regression, 187–191
　in multiple regression framework, 188
Out-of-bag observations, 435–436, 442
Out-of-range parameter estimations, 327–328
Outside values, 93
Overdispersion, 211–215
Overextraction of factors, in EFA, 390
Overfitting of data, in archival research, 439, 493–494
Overinterpretation of results, 580

PA extraction of factors using prior commonality estimates, 384–385, 391
Page limits, 607
Paired t tests, 257
Paneling, in graphics, 99
Panel model, cross-lagged, 254–255
Panel studies and survey programs, 487–488
Panter, A. T., 585
Papers for publication, 238–239
Parallel analysis, 386
Parallel-coordinate plots, in EDA, 58–59, 62
Parameter fixing, in LCA/LPA, 422
Parameterization, contrast, 309–310
Parameters, in effect-size estimation, 130
Pardo, A., 151
Parent decision trees, 434
Parent nodes, 431
Pareto charts, 85
Parr, Adam K., 501–537
Parsimony, 415, 610
Partial boxplots, in EDA, 55
Partialing, atheoretical, in multiple regression, 193
Partialing out, in EDA, 55
Partial regression plots, 55, 64
Participant drop-out, in longitudinal data analysis, 250–251
Participant fatigue, in SRM, 462
Participant informed consent, 565
Partikit package, 441
Partitioning of participants, 430
Partner effects, in SRM, 452, 460
Partner variance, 455–456, 458
PAs (principal axes), 383
Patent data example, 95–96
Path diagrammatic notation, 37n2
Pattern mixture models, 45

PCA. *See* Principal component analysis
p-curves, 582
PDF (portable document format), 106
Pearson's correlation, 18, 20
Pediatric firearms victims, 292
Perceiver effects, 453, 455, 460
Percentage change from baseline, 151
Percentage improvement, 152
Percentile bootstrap, 12, 16–17, 20–21
Perception data measurement, in SRM, 461–462
Perception of statistical graphics, 79
Pernet, C. R., 23
Persistent identifiers, 563
Personal communications, 489
Personality and Social Psychology Bulletin, 579
Personality domains, factor analysis for, 379
Personality factors, Big Five, 379, 457, 503
Person fastest-moving approach, 461–462
Person-in-a-situation, in LST models, 298
Personnel Psychology, 583
Person-oriented data set, 280–281, 292
Person–period data sets, 280–282, 286, 288, 290, 292
Person-to-goal relations, 516–517
Person-to-person relations, 517
Persuasion function of charts, 79
Pfaff, D. L., 520
p-hacking, 580–582, 584–591
Phone records, 484
Physics Review, 579
p_i (probability density), 32–33
Piaget, Jean, 411
Pick-a-point method, in MMR, 115, 118, 119
Piecemeal publications, 610
Pie charts, 89–90
Pierce, D. A., 218
Pigott, Therese D., 539–559
Pinker, S., 79
Plagiarism, 579, 585, 605
Playfair, William, 77
Plot(s)
　for bad data and inadequate models, 13–16
　brushing, in EDA, 58
　kernel density, 15
Plotting, of interactions in moderated multiple regression, 120–123
Point equilibrium, 339

Poisson distributions, 84
    and GLM, 125–126
    in log-linear models, 205, 210–211
    and overdispersion, 211–213
Poisson generalized linear model, 125
poLCA (software), 424
Policy decisions, 158
Political polls, 172
polr (proportional odds logistic regression), 209
Polynomial
    effects, in MMR, 124–125
    models, 22
    regression, 193
    specification of time period, 286
Pooling estimate analysis, 41–43
Population-based strategies, in longitudinal data analysis, 248–249
Population median estimation, 19
Porter, L. W., 521
Post hoc contrasts, 184
Post-hoc tests, in ANOVA, 170
Potthoff, R. F., 191
Power, 9
Power analysis, in MLM, 236
Preacher, K. J., 238, 371
Pre- and post-scores, 137–138
Precision
    in effect-size estimation, 130
    for planning, 587
Prediction errors, in ANOVA, 170
Predictor importance indices, in multiple regression, 191–193
Predictors
    centered within clusters, in MLM, 229
    in event history analysis, 278
    in MLM, 222–223
Prefuse (software), 106
Pregibon, D., 218
Prelec, D., 581
Prenoveau, J. M., 311
Prentice, R., 271
Preregistration of research plan, 494, 586, 588–589, 604–605
Preservation of research data, 571
Presidential inaugural speeches, 490
Pre-whitening of time series, 340
Primary data, 482
Primary mental abilities, 379
Principal axes (PAs), 383
Principal component analysis (PCA)
    common factor analysis vs., 394
    and EFA, 386–387, 394–395

and Large *p* data, 105
    and many-variable data, 99
Probability density (p_i), 32–33
Probability distribution, in GLM, 205
Probing of interaction effects, in MMR, 115
Probit, 204
Production systems, for graphics, 106
Product vs. interaction, in MMR, 125
Programming systems, for graphics, 106
Projections
    axis-parallel, 83
    in graphics, 99
Project MATCH, 259
Promax rotations, 389
Propensity score matching, 487
Proportionality assumption, of discrete-event time models, 289
Proportional models of change, 151
Proportional odds logistic regression (*polr*), 209
Proportional odds model, 209, 280
Proportions, effect-size indexes based on, 139–143, 145
Protocols, for systematic reviews, 540
Proximity, in graphics, 80–81
Pruning of tree structures, 433
Pseudo-3D bar charts, 83
Psychological Science, 582
Psychosocial disability model. *See* Chronic pain and psychosocial disability example
Psychotherapy outcome research, 158
PTSD (posttraumatic stress disorder), 160
Publication bias in meta-analysis, 552–554
Publication Manual of the American Psychological Association, 610
Publishers, 78
Putnam, R. D., 523
p values
    and effect sizes, 130–132
    misuse or misinterpretation of, 9, 580
    rounding of, 582
Pychlau, Sophie, 481–500
Pylyser, C., 457
Python Graphics, 106

QAP (quadratic assignments procedure), 511–512, 517
Q-Q (quantile-quantile) plots, 13–14, 55
Quadratic assignments procedure (QAP), 511–512, 517

Quadratic functions, in multiple regression, 194
Qualtrics surveys, 519–520
Quantification, of relationship ties, 504
Quantile analysis, 183
Quantile-quantile (Q-Q) plots, 13–14, 55
Quantile regression, in multiple regression framework, 188
Quark Express, 78
Quasi-likelihood functions, for GLM, 218
Questionable practices in statistical analysis, 579–595
    hard vs. soft misconduct, 579–580
    importance of, 584–585
    p-hacking, limitation of, 585–591
    types and rates of, 580–584
Questionnaires, paper-and-pencil, 506
Question-trolling, 581, 583–584

R (programming language), 7, 43, 93
    for decision trees, 436, 439
    for dyadic data analysis, 477
    for generalized linear models, 209, 212, 216, 217
    for Johnson-Neyman technique, 118
    for LCA/LPA, 424
    for MLM, 236, 240, 241
    packages, 23
    and percentile bootstrapping, 16
    precision for planning capability of, 587
    for publication bias, 554, 556
    randomForest package, 442–443
    R CRAN, 101
    R data table, 104
    R Lattice package, 86
    in SNA, 501, 503, 506–508, 512–515, 526–528
    for SRM, 462
Rabash, J., 225
Rabe-Hesketh, S., 216
Race/ethnicity
    in juror example, 175–178
    as multicategorical value, 117
Ramm & Grinum, 254
Random effects, and unobserved heterogeneity, 291
Random effects models
    in LC, 414
    in meta-analysis, 545–546, 548–549
Random error modeling, in MLM, 231
Random error terms
    and alternatives to MLM, 227
    in MLM, 223
    nonsignificant, 231–232

Random experiments, in LST models, 298
RandomForest (software), 442
Random forests, 435, 442
Random noise, 39
Random sampling, 20
Rank-based methods, for bad data and inadequate models, 19
Ranked data, re-expression of, 63
Rank-order consistency, 254
Ratio measurement scales, 63
Raudenbush, S. W., 222, 225, 230, 234, 352, 362, 476
Ravaud, P., 581
Raw differences, 129
Raw mean difference, 132–135
Raykov, T., 32
RCI (reliable change index), 153–154, 159
Reading abilities in children, estimation of, 21–22
ReadMe files, in research data management, 568–569
Reciprocals, 60
Reciprocity, generalized, 457
Recovered (patient category), 153, 158, 159
Recovery of variance-covariance matrices, in LGC modeling, 318–319
Recovery-oriented measures, 155–157
Rectangle areas, 93
Recurrent events, in event history analysis, 271
Recursive partitioning algorithms, 126, 432–436, 443–445
Red cards in soccer, 590–591
Reductionist approaches, to effect size dependence, 551–552
Redundancy
  in ANOVA, 179
  in graphics, 82
Re-expression, 53–54
  in EDA, 59–61
  in exploratory data analysis, 59–62
  for various types of data, 63
Regions of significance, for continuous moderator variables, 190–191
Registered Replication Reports, 600
Regression coefficients, 123, 186
Regression estimators, robust, 21
Regression(s)
  assumptions about error in, 586
  for bad data and inadequate models, 20–22
  in exploratory data analysis, 63–64
  in generalized linear models, 214
  model building, 71
  outliers in, 21
  stepwise, 191–192
  toward the mean, 54, 154, 159
Regression trees, 126. *See* Classification and regression trees (CART)
Regulative ideal, 62
Reise, S. P., 400, 404
Relational structure among individuals, in SNA, 502
Relationship effects, in SRM, 453, 460
Relationships, in SNA, 504
Relationship variance, 456, 460
Relative fit measures, in LC/LP models, 415
Reliability
  in LST models, 299
  of multilevel modeling (MLM), 237–238
Reliable change, 149
Reliable change index (RCI), 153–154, 159
Religion census, in archival research, 491
Remission of symptoms, 149, 151
Rensvold, R. B., 400
Repeated measures analyses, in dyadic data analysis, 467, 471
Replication failures, 600–601
Replication of studies, 588, 600–601
Reporting biases, 589
Reproducibility Project: Psychology, 600
Research
  honesty, 606
  practices, questionable, 579, 601
  transparency and openness in, 602–604
Research data management and sharing, 563–577
  compliance, 572–574
  data collection and storage, 566–567
  data documentation, 567–569
  data preservation, 571–572
  data sharing, 569–571
  planning stage, 565–566
  RDM, as term, 564
  transparency and openness in, 602–604
Research design, accelerated, 260
Researcher(s)
  degrees of freedom of, 580
  flexibility of, 601
Residual deviance, 203–205
Residual error, in MMR, 112
Residualized change approach, in longitudinal data analysis, 255–257
Residual method factor approach, in LST models, 310
Residual plots, 66–67
Residuals, 55, 204
  in EDA, 53
  in LST models, 299
  method factors defined as, 308
Residuals, structured, 255
Resiliency, 337–338
Resistance, 53, 54
Respect for people's rights and privacy, 598
Response habituation, 252
Response probabilities, 412, 413
Response ratios, 145
Results trending, 582
Retention of research data, 571
Retention of subjects, in longitudinal data analysis, 250–251
Retraction of articles, 613
Retraction Watch, 599
Reusability of data, 563, 571
Reuse of one's own research, 606
Richman, E. H., 82
Richter scale, 59
Right-censoring, in event history analysis, 271
Rights, J. D., 236
"Right-Sizing Statistical Models for Longitudinal Data" (Wood), 253
Rindskopf, David, 201–218
Ripley, B. D., 217
Risk difference (Δ), 139–141
Risk of relapse, 139–140
Risk periods, in event history analysis, 271, 275
Risk ratio (θ), 129, 139–142, 544
RMSEA (root mean square error of approximation), 387, 399
Robbins, N. B., 81
Robinson, W. S., 221
Robust methods
  of analysis, 186
  for bad data and inadequate models, 17–18
Robustness
  in multiple regression framework, 188
  of tests in ANOVA, 180
Robustness of test, to violations of assumptions, in ANOVA, 180

634

Robustness testing, 257
Robust regression, 103, 195
Robust regression methods, in multiple regression framework, 188
Robust statistics, as field, 195
Robust variance estimation, in meta-analysis, 551
Robyn, D. L., 77
Rodríguez, Germán, 217
Rofecoxib, 585
Rohwer, G., 278
Role clarity, 524
Role of time, in archival data, 484
Roles, in SRM, 459–460
Ronk, F. R., 155
Roommate examples, 451–454, 458–459
Root-mean-square average, 173
Root mean square error of approximation (RMSEA), 387, 399
Root nodes, 431
Rosenthal, R., 145, 175, 177n3, 186
Rosnow, R. L., 175, 177n3, 186
Ross, M. W., 603
Rotating plots, in EDA, 58
Rothkopf, E. Z., 84
Round-robin + block designs, in SRM, 454
Round-robin designs, 453, 458
Rousseeuw, P. J., 11
Rousselet, Guillaume A., 5–25
Rubin, D. B., 28, 42, 216, 262
Rubin's rules, 39
Ruiz, 157
Rules of thumb, 386
Ruscio, J., 19
Russell, J. A., 491

S (programming language), 217
Saavedra, L. M., 156, 160
Salthouse, 252
Sample-specific norms, 159
Sampling distributions, 7
Sampling error, 172, 178, 192
SAOM (stochastic actor-oriented longitudinal model), 511, 513–515, 528
SAS (software), 106, 393
    for dyadic data analysis, 477
    in event history analysis, 281
    for generalized linear models, 216
    for Johnson-Neyman technique, 118
    in MLM, 236, 241
    in SRM, 462

SAT. *See* Scholastic Aptitude Test example
Satisfaction-intention-turnover mediation model, 521
Saturated correlates, 37, 39
Savalei, Victoria, 318
Scalable Vector Graphics (SVG), 106
Scalar invariance, 261
Scale reduction factor, 41
Scaling of outcome variables, for LGC modeling, 318
Scaling of time, in LGC modeling, 323
Scatterplots, 104
    with bordered boxplots, 95
    in EDA, 55, 58, 61
Schafer, D. W., 218
Scheffé method, for error correction, 184
Schermelleh-Engel, K., 310
Schizophrenia, 157
Schmiege, S., 422
Schmitt, M., 297
Scholastic Aptitude Test (SAT) example, 129–130, 132, 135–136, 138
Scholer, A. A., 516
Schreiber, J. B., 580
Schrodt, P., 456
Schwarz, J. C., 256
Schwarz, N., 582
Schwarz, S. F., 151
Science (journal), 579
Scientific Data, 571
Scott, D. W., 91, 92, 95
Scree, 386, 391
SE (standard error), 393
SEC filings, 489
Secondary data, 482–483
Second-order growth models, in LST, 306
Segal, M. R., 445
Selection bias, 487
Selection effects, in event history analysis, 291
Selection models, 45
Self-accuracy, in SRM, 457
Self-awareness study, 12
Self-disclosed misconduct, 582
Self-esteem and social anxiety example, 193
Self-other agreement, in SRM, 457
Self-ratings, in SRM, 453
SEM. *See* Standard error of measurement; structural equation modeling
SEM (structural equation modeling) trees, 445–446
Sequential interactions, in SRM, 458–459

Sequential specification, 40
Sex differences, social support, and depression example, 116–118
Sexual partners examples, 13, 15, 89, 93–94, 97–98, 182
SF-36 Health Survey, 159
SHARKing (secretly HARKing), 582–583
Sharp error representation, 103
"Short reports," 607
Significance testing, necessity of, 587. *See also* Alpha
Silberzahn, R., 590–591
Silverman, B. W., 92
Similarity, in graphics, 80
Simmons, J. P., 580, 601, 608
Simple main effects, 177
Simple main effects, regions of significance for, 190–191
Simple random sampling, for EDA, 105
Simple regression module, 45
Simple slopes, in MMR, 112
Simple slopes plots, in MMR, 121–123
Simultaneous errors, in MLM, 222
Simultaneous interactions, in SRM, 458–459
Singer, B., 445
Singer, J. D., 217, 286, 291
Single degree of freedom contrasts, 178
Single-measure latent growth modeling, 320–324
Single-trait models, in LST models, 301–302
Single-trait-multistate models, in LST models, 302–304, 307
Singular value decomposition, 105
Skewed distributions, 12–13
Skewness, 60, 180, 181
Skrondal, A., 216
Sleep and exercise example, 115–116, 119–121
Slope
    differences in, formal tests of, 194
    inferences about, 20
Small multiples, in graphics, 86
Smartphone data, in archival research, 493
Smith, H., 195
Smith, J. W., 439
Smoker example, 15–16
Smoothers, 22–23, 95, 194
SNA. *See* Social network analysis
Snowball sampling design, 511
Social cognition, 515
Social contagion effects, 521

Social interactions, in SNA, 504
Social media, in archival research, 489, 490, 492
Social network analysis, 501–537
   basic, 508–510
   complex observable systems and massive online behavior, 520–521
   concepts and methodological foundations, 502–507
   exponential random-graph model, 512–513
   network goal analysis, 516–520
   network perception research, 515–516
   quadratic assignment procedure, 511–512
   stochastic actor-oriented model, 513–515
Social networks
   role behaviors in, 516
   structural measures in, 509
   visualization of, 508
Social roles, in SNA, 504
Social support and depression in females examples, 116–117
Social validity, 150
Soft misconduct, 580
Software
   for data collection and storage, 506, 566
   for dyadic data analysis, 477
   for FMI estimation, 43
   for GLMs, 212, 216–217
   for graphics, 106–107
   for histograms, 91
   for latent differential equation modeling, 343
   for LCA/LPA, 417, 424
   for LGC modeling, 319
   for MLM, 240
   for publication bias, 554
   and p values, 178
   and scatterplots, 58
   for SNA, 516
   specification of, in missing data reporting, 47
Soliz, J., 456
Sonquist, John, 429–432, 446
SOREMO (software), 458, 462
Sorenson, D., 82
Sorting, in graphics, 84–85
Spatial lag models, in SNA, 524
Spearman, C., 379
Specific latent state variables, 310

Spence, I., 77, 81
"Spike and slab prior," 404
Spikes, 95
Spirit consumption example, 91, 95
Spline knots, 194
Spline regressions, 194
Splines, 126, 319
Splitting variables, 445
SPLOM (scatterplot matrix), 58, 85, 99–100
Splus (software), 216, 217
Spreadsheets, for data collection, 566
Springs methods, 101
SPSS (software), 49n7, 83, 106
   for dyadic data analysis, 477
   in event history analysis, 281
   for Johnson-Neyman technique, 118
   in MLM, 241
   in SRM, 462
SPSS/PASW (software), 216
Squared multiple correlation, 171
SRM (social relations model), 451–464
   data structures for, 453–455
   development of SRM study, 456–462
   variances in, 455–456
SRM study development
   analysis considerations in, 461–462
   answerable research questions in, 456–457
   measurement considerations in, 461–462
   procedural considerations in, 458–461
Stability-maintenance processes, in longitudinal data analysis, 254
Stack Overflow, 494
Stamos, A., 488
Stan (software), 217
Standard error of measurement (SEM), 151–154
   for model-hacking, 588
   in psychology research, 580
Standard error(s) (SEs), 393
   of the difference, 159
   of estimate, in ANOVA, 170–171, 174
   pooling of, 42
Standardization, of multilevel modeling (MLM), 235
Standardized indexes of effect size, 185
Standardized mean difference, 132, 541–543. See also d, computation of; Hedges' g
   effect sizes and, 135–139
Standard practice, 62

Stanford University, 432
Stanley, C., 494
Stapel, Diederik, 599
Stark, Tobias, 501–537
Starting values, 34
Stata (software), 417, 477
   for generalized linear models, 216
   for LCA/LPA, 424
   in MLM, 241
State change, in LST models, 297
States
   in event history analysis, 270–271
   in LGC modeling, 332
Statistica (software), 216
Statistical inference, in SNA, 514–515
Statistically reliable change, 152–153
Statistical records, 486–487
Statistical significance, 147
Statistical tests, 385
Statistics, Bayesian. See Bayesian statistics
Statistics, in effect-size estimation, 130
Steers, R. M., 521
Steiger, J. H., 387
Stem-and-leaf displays, in EDA, 57–58
Sterba, S. K., 236, 585
Stevens, S. S., 79
Steyer, Rolf, 297–316
Stigler, S., 77
Stimulus-response paradigm, 150
Stochastic actor-oriented longitudinal model (SAOM), 511, 513–515, 528
Stochastic actor-oriented model, in SNA, 513–515
Stopping criteria, 433, 439, 445
Strauss, Chris L., 351–376
Stripe plot, 93
Stroop test, 60
Structural equation modeling (SEM), 32, 195
   in dyadic data analysis, 465, 467–469, 476–477
   dynamic, 333
   in generalized linear models, 216
   in growth modeling, 351
   in LC models, 414
   in longitudinal data analysis, 257
   trees, 445–446
Structural equation modeling (SEM), in longitudinal data analysis, 251
Structural invariance, 261
Structured residuals, 255
Studentized residuals, 64
Student math success example, 231

Students in classes example, 222–223, 225
Student's t distribution, 17–18
Study-level documentation, 567–568
Study protocols, 567–568
Study time example, 215
Subjective probability, 175
Subject-specific effects, and unobserved heterogeneity, 291
Substantive model-compatible multiple imputation, 40
Success ratio, 544
Supplementary online materials, 607–608
Supportive resistance arcs, 517
Surrogate measure validation, in archival research, 495
Surrogate variables, 445
Survey programs, 487–488
Survival
    analysis, 215, 217
    function, in event history analysis, 276–277, 279
    models, 215, 269
    times, 145
SVG (Scalable Vector Graphics), 106
Switching regression, in dyadic data analysis, 472
Symmetric bootstrap-t method, 17
Symptom Checklist-90, 154
Synergistic effects, of variables, 115
Synergistic interactions, in MMR, 113
Syntaxes for data conversion, in event history analysis, 292–295
Synthesized variables, 356
SYSTAT (software), 83, 86, 92, 93, 106
Systematic reviews, 539–540
System negation arcs, 517
System reactance arcs, 517
System support arcs, 517

T (total number of iterations), 41
Tableau (software), 106
Target
    effects, in SRM, 453, 460
    sample sizes, 587
    variance, 455
Tarlov, A. R., 151
Task feedback, 517
Tasks per minute, 60
Tau-equivalence, 237
t distribution, 178
Tekle, Fetene B., 269–295
Temple, J., 157
Temporal associations, in dyadic data analysis, 468, 475

Temporal design validity, 258
Terminal nodes, 431
Testing to a foregone conclusion, 581
Test-retest stability, 252
Tett, R. P., 522
Texting example, 451–453
THARKing (transparently HARKing), 582–583
Theil-Sen regression estimator, 21–22
Thermoregulation example, 331
Thielmann, D., 311
Third graders, behavior of, example, 210–212
Thomas, J., 140
Thompson, J. S., 398
Thompson, R., 216
3-dimensionality, in graphics, 82–83
Three dimensional plots, in MMR, 120–121
Three-distribution models, 155
Three-level growth models, 361–367
    bivariate, in USMA cadet example, 370–371
    conditional univariate, 363–364
    inclusion of predictors, 365–366
    multivariate, 364–367
    unconditional univariate, 361–363
    univariate, in USMA cadet example, 368–369
Three-variable data, graphic displays for, 97–99
Thurston, L. L., 379, 380, 383, 388, 391, 404, 405, 411
Thurstone, T. G., 379, 391
Thurstone's criteria for simple structures, 388–389
TICs (time-invariant covariates), 354–355
Ties
    and DTSMs (discrete-time survival models), 278
    in SNA, 503, 510
Time
    to an event, 215
    discrete vs. continuous, 272
    measurement, in LGC modeling, 319
    per task, 60
    sampling interval misspecification, 343
Time-delay embedding, 342–343
Time-invariant covariates (TICs), 354–355
Time paths, 351
Time series data, 95, 487
Time-specific values, 356

Time-varying covariates (TVCs), 269, 288, 355–356
Time-varying effects models, 125–126
Timing of assessments, 259
Tingey, R., 155, 160
Tisak, J., 311, 403
Tisak, M. S., 311
TLI (Tucker-Lewis index), 387, 393, 399
Tofighi, D., 229
Toothaker, L. E., 183
TOP (Transparency and Openness Promotion) Guidelines, 608–609
Total number of iterations (T), 41
Trace plots, 41
Traditional statistics vs. exploratory data analysis, 54–55
Trail Making test, 60
Traits, in LGC modeling, 332
Trait-state error models, 311
Trait-state models, in LGC modeling, 332
Trait-state occasion (TSO) models, 332
Transactive goal system, 516
Transformation(s)
    in graphics, 83
    logit, 202–203
    strategies, in ANOVA, 181
Transition probabilities, in LCA/LPA, 423
Transparency and openness, 589
    in archival research, 485
    in research data management and sharing, 602–604
Transparency and Openness Promotion (TOP) Guidelines, 608–609
Transparency of research process, 602–604
t ratios, 174, 514
Treatment effect, 174
    effect sizes vs., 129–130
    effect size vs., 129–130
Treatment response benchmarks, 158
Treatment termination, 158
Treemap, 93–94
Tree of Life Project, 101
Trees, conditional inference, 441
Trellis plot, 86–87
Triangular bivariate distribution, 99–100
Trimmed means
    in ANOVA, 182–183
    in multiple regression framework, 188
Trivedi, T. J., 217

Truax, P., 151–156
True positive, 9
True score variables, method factors defined as difference in, 308–309
Trust, 367–373
Tsao, F., 65n4
TSO (trait-state occasion) models, 332
t tests, 180–182, 257
Tucker, L. R., 387, 389
Tucker-Lewis index (TLI), 387, 393, 399
Tufte, Edward, 77, 81–82, 86, 88, 100
Tukey, J. W., 9, 12, 18, 53, 57, 63, 65n4, 66–68, 93, 194
Tukey HSD method, 179
Tuma, N. B., 271
Turnover example, 521–525
Turnover network contagion, 522–523
Turrisi, R., 189, 190
Tutz, G., 217
TVCs (time-varying covariates), 355–356
Tversky, Amos, 54
Tversky, B., 81
t weighting, 103
Twitter data, in archival research, 492, 494
Twitter users, 484
Two continuous variables, effect-size indexes based on, 143–144
Two-level growth models, 352–361
 conditional two-level univariate, 354–356
 inclusion of predictors, 359–360
 two-level multivariate, 356–361
 unconditional two-level univariate, 352–354
Two-variable data, graphic displays for, 93–97
Two-variable relations, in EDA, 58
TX variable, in LGC modeling, 323, 329
Type I errors, 10
 in ANOVA, 180–181
 in bootstrap methods, 17
 and heteroscedasticity, 16
 in hypothesis testing, 9–10
 and meta-analyses, 546
 and meta-regression, 554–555
 and omnibus F tests, 175
Type II errors, 50, 144, 150, 444
 in ANOVA, 180, 183
 in multiple regression, 191, 193
"Type III errors," 318
Types of change, in longitudinal data analysis, 254

UCINET VI, 512, 516
ULS (unweighted least squares), 384–385
Ulysses (Joyce), 102
UMAP, 105
Uncentered predictors, in MLM, 229
Uncertainty, in graphic displays of data, 102–103
Unchanged (patient category), 153
Unconditional distributions, 46
Unconditional models, in MLM, 228
Underextraction of factors, in EFA, 390
Unfolding model of voluntary turnover, 521–522
Univariate approaches, to latent variable modeling of continuous growth, 329
Univariate normal density function, 32
Univariate normal likelihood, 33
Univariate tests, 251
University of British Columbia, 101
University of California at Berkeley, 101, 432
University of Chicago, 487
University of Michigan, 429, 570
University of Texas at Austin, 101
Unpublished studies and meta-analysis, 553
Unstandardized indexes of effect size, 185
Unsupervised learning algorithms, 54
Unweighted least squares (ULS), 384–385
Usability of data, 567
USA Today, 82, 489
U.S. Bureau of Labor and Statistics, 488
U.S. Census, 486
U.S. Census, 1930, 221
U.S. Census Bureau, 487
U.S. Census data, 484
USMA (US Military Academy) cadets example, 367–371

Vaccination status, 511
Valentine, Jeffrey C., 539–559
Validity, external, 150
Validity studies for distribution-based strategies, 155
Value-trimming of data, 12, 16
Van Aert, R. C. M., 590
Van Assen, M. A. L. M., 590
Van Zomeren, B. C., 11
Variability among the column means, in SRM, 455
Variable fastest-moving approach, in SRM, 461
Variable importance metrics, 435–436
Variable models, continuous latent, 411
Variables, continuous. *See* Continuous variables
Variables, continuous moderator, 190–191
Variables, reporting in manuscripts, 608
Variable transformations, 194
Variance, between-person, 259
Variance, constant, 59–60
Variance, within-person, 259
Variance homogeneity, violations of
 in ANOVA, 180–181
 in multiple regression framework, 187
Varimax, 389
Vautier, S., 310
Vector files, 106
Vega-lite toolkit, 106
Veldkamp, C. L. S., 590
Velleman, Paul F., 53–73, 77
Venables, W. N., 217
Venn diagrams, 101
Venneuler (statistical method), 101
Venn/Euler diagrams, 101–102
Vennmaker (software), 506
Verbal records, 488–490
Vergés, 248
Vermunt, Jeroen K., 269–295
Vertex-edge graphs, 101
Vertices, in SNA, 502
Violations of model assumptions
 in ANOVA, 180–181
 in multiple regressions, 186–187
Vioxx (rofecoxib), 585
Visser, P. S., 510
Visual data, 490–492
Visual displays, of simple slopes plots, 121–122
Visual illusions, in graphics, 83
Visualization, of SNA, 502

Wagner, David T., 481–500
Wainer, H., 77
Wang, Liying, 411–427
Wang, Wei, 501–537
Ware, C., 81
Wasserman, R., 579
Wasserstein, R. L., 587
Waves of measurement
 for LGC modeling, 318
 in LGC modeling, 323
Web applications, for Johnson-Neyman technique, 118
Web scraping algorithms, 490
Wechsler Intelligence Scale for Children (WISC), 189–190
Wedderburn, R. W. M., 201, 217

Weibull distributions, 215
Weighted analyses, of MLM, 235
WEIRD (Western, educated, from industrialized, rich, democratic countries) people, 481–485
Welch's method for critical value determination, 17
West, B. T., 32
West, S. G., 232–233
Westaby, James D., 501–537
Westbrook, D., 155
Westfall, P. H., 180, 183
West Point. See USMA (US Military Academy) cadets example
"Which Came First: The Readiness of the Change?" (Collins), 255
Whitford, H. J., 180
Whole-networks, in SNA, 503, 505
"Why Most Published Research Findings Are False" (Ioannidis), 600
Wicherts, J. M., 585, 589, 590
Wickham, Hadley, 106
Widaman, Keith F., 379–410

Wikipedia, 489
Wilcox, Rand R., 5–25, 171, 180, 182, 183, 186, 188, 194, 195
Wilcoxon-Mann-Whitney test, 19
Wilkinson, Leland, 63, 77–110
Willett, J. B., 217, 286, 291
William of Occam, 61. See also Occam's razor
Williams, D. A., 218
Willoughby, M. T., 255
Wilson, D. B., 145
Wilson, D. E., 539
WinBUGS/OpenBUGS (software), 217
Windle, M., 310
Windows Metafiles (WMF), 106
Wind roses, 101
Winsorizing of data, 12
Winsor's principle, in EDA, 58
WISC (Wechsler Intelligence Scale for Children), 189–190
Within-group data relationships, 220–221
  in MLM, 226
  in SRM, 454

Within-group variation, 148, 158
WMF (Windows Metafiles), 106
Wolf, M. M., 150
Wood, 253
Woods, N., 520
Word clouds, 101–102
Working-memory chunking capability, 83
Wright, P. M., 582, 583

Yamaguchi, K., 271, 291
Young, S. S., 180
Yuen, K. K., 16, 18

Zautra, A., 311, 332
Zero-centered predictors, in MLM, 229
Zero events, in studies, 143
Zero-intercept model, in MLM, 234
Zhang, H., 445
Ziliak, S. T., 585
z-scores, squared, 32–33
Z value, in log-linear models, 205